BURGER'S MEDICINAL CHEMISTRY, DRUG DISCOVERY AND DEVELOPMENT

BURGER'S MEDICINAL CHEMISTRY, DRUG DISCOVERY AND DEVELOPMENT

BURGER'S MEDICINAL CHEMISTRY, DRUG DISCOVERY AND DEVELOPMENT

Seventh Edition

Volume 7: Antiinfectives

Edited by

Donald J. Abraham
Virginia Commonwealth University

David P. Rotella
Wyeth Research

Burger's Medicinal Chemistry, Drug Discovery and Development
is available Online in full color at
http://mrw.interscience.wiley.com/emrw/9780471266945/home/

A JOHN WILEY & SONS, INC., PUBLICATION

Published by John Wiley & Sons, Inc., Hoboken, New Jersey
Published simultaneously in Canada

For general information on our other products and services or for technical support, please contact our Customer Care Department within the United States at (800) 762-2974, outside the United States at (317) 572-3993 or fax (317) 572-4002.

Wiley also publishes its books in a variety of electronic formats. Some content that appears in print may not be available in electronic formats. For more information about Wiley products, visit our web site at www.wiley.com.

Library of Congress Cataloging-in-Publication Data:

Abraham, Donald J., 1936-
  Burger's medicinal chemistry, drug discovery, and development/Donald
J. Abraham, David P. Rotella. – 7th ed.
      p. ; cm.
  Other title: Medicinal chemistry, drug discovery, and development
  Rev. ed. of: Burger's medicinal chemistry and drug discovery. 6th ed. /
edited by Donald J. Abraham. c2003.
    Includes bibliographical references and index.
    ISBN 978-0-470-27815-4 (cloth)
1. Pharmaceutical chemistry. 2. Drug development.   I. Rotella, David P.
II. Burger, Alfred, 1905-2000. III. Burger's medicinal chemistry and drug
discovery. IV. Title. V. Title: Medicinal chemistry, drug discovery, and
development.
    [DNLM: 1. Chemistry, Pharmaceutical–methods. 2. Biopharmaceutics–
methods. 3. Drug Compounding–methods. QV 744 A105b 2010]
    RS403.B8 2010
    615'.19–dc22   2010010779

Printed in Singapore

10   9   8   7   6   5   4   3   2   1

CONTENTS

PREFACE

The seventh edition of Burger's Medicinal Chemistry resulted from a collaboration established between John Wiley & Sons, the editorial board, authors, and coeditors over the last 3 years. The editorial board for the seventh edition provided important advice to the editors on topics and contributors. Wiley staff effectively handled the complex tasks of manuscript production and editing and effectively tracked the process from beginning to end. Authors provided well-written, comprehensive summaries of their topics and responded to editorial requests in a timely manner. This edition, with 8 volumes and 116 chapters, like the previous editions, is a reflection of the expanding complexity of medicinal chemistry and associated disciplines. Separate volumes have been added on anti-infectives, cancer, and the process of drug development. In addition, the coeditors elected to expand coverage of cardiovascular and metabolic disorders, aspects of CNS-related medicinal chemistry, and computational drug discovery. This provided the opportunity to delve into many subjects in greater detail and resulted in specific chapters on important subjects such as biologics and protein drug discovery, HIV, new diabetes drug targets, amyloid-based targets for treatment of Alzheimer's disease, high-throughput and other screening methods, and the key role played by metabolism and other pharmacokinetic properties in drug development.

The following individuals merit special thanks for their contributions to this complex endeavor: Surlan Alexander of John Wiley & Sons for her organizational skills and attention to detail, Sanchari Sil of Thomson Digital for processing the galley proofs, Jonathan Mason of Lundbeck, Andrea Mozzarelli of the University of Parma, Alex Tropsha of the University of North Carolina, John Block of Oregon State University, Paul Reider of Princeton University, William (Rick) Ewing of Bristol-Myers Squibb, William Hagmann of Merck, John Primeau and Rob Bradbury of AstraZeneca, Bryan Norman of Eli Lilly, Al Robichaud of Wyeth, and John Lowe for their input on topics and potential authors. The many reviewers for these chapters deserve special thanks for the constructive comments they provided to authors. Finally, we must express gratitude to our lovely, devoted wives, Nancy and Mary Beth, for their tolerance as we spent time with this task, rather than with them.

As coeditors, we sincerely hope that this edition meets the high expectations of the scientific community. We assembled this edition with the guiding vision of its namesake in mind and would like to dedicate it to Professor H.C. Brown and Professor Donald T. Witiak. Don collaborated with Dr. Witiak in the early days of his research in sickle cell drug discovery. Professor Witiak was Dave's doctoral advisor at Ohio State University and provided essential guidance to a young scientist. Professor Brown, whose love for chemistry infected all organic graduate students at Purdue University, arranged for Don to become a medicinal chemist by securing a postdoctoral position for him with Professor Alfred Burger.

It has been a real pleasure to work with all concerned to assemble an outstanding and up-to-date edition in this series.

Donald J. Abraham
David P. Rotella

March 2010

CONTRIBUTORS

Courtney C. Aldrich, University of Minnesota, Minneapolis, MN

Nitya Anand, Central Drug Research Institute, Lucknow, India

David D. Anderson, Purdue University, West Lafayette, IN

Helena I. Boshoff, National Institute of Allergy and Infectious Diseases, Bethesda, MD

Zapf Christoph, Wyeth, Pearl River, NY

Erik De Clercq, Rega Institute for Medical Research, K.U. Leuven, Leuven, Belgium

Jed F. Fisher, The University of Notre Dame, Notre Dame, IN

Arun K. Ghosh, Purdue University, West Lafayette, IN

W. Armand Guiguemde, St Jude Children's Research Hospital, Memphis, TN

Brian A. Johns, GlaxoSmithKline Research & Development, Research Triangle Park, NC

Bloom Jonathan, Wyeth, Pearl River, NY

R. Kiplin Guy, St Jude Children's Research Hospital, Memphis, TN

Antonin Holý, IOCB & Gilead Sciences Joint Research Center, Praha, Czech Republic

Levin Jeremy, Wyeth, Pearl River, NY

Flint Michael, Wyeth, Pearl River, NY

Lester A. Mitscher, Kansas University, Lawrence, KS

Hiroaki Mitsuya, Kumamoto University, Kumamoto, Japan; National Cancer Institute, Bethesda, MD

Shahriar Mobashery, The University of Notre Dame, Notre Dame, IN

William A. Remers, AmpliMed Corporation, Tucson, AZ

Rory P. Remmel, University of Minnesota, Minneapolis, MN

David C. Smithson, St Jude Children's Research Hospital, Memphis, TN

Jayaram R. Tagat, Schering-Plough Research Institute, Kenilworth, NJ

Sebastian A. Testero, The University of Notre Dame, Notre Dame, IN

Patrick M. Woster, Wayne State University, Detroit, MI

THE FDA APPROVED HIV-1 PROTEASE INHIBITORS FOR TREATMENT OF HIV/AIDS

Arun K. Ghosh[1]
David D. Anderson[1]
Hiroaki Mitsuya[2, 3]
[1]Departments of Chemistry and Medicinal Chemistry, Purdue University, West Lafayette, IN
[2]Department of Hematology and Infectious Diseases, Experimental Retrovirology Section, Kumamoto University School of Medicine, Kumamoto, Japan
[3] HIV and AIDS Malignancy Branch, National Cancer Institute, Bethesda, MD

1. INTRODUCTION

Human immunodeficiency virus (HIV) infection and the resulting acquired immunodeficiency syndrome (AIDS) are a global epidemic impacting the lives of millions of people. First reported in 1981, the joint United Nations Program on HIV/AIDS (UNAIDS) now estimates (2008 report) that 33 million people are currently living with the disease with an annual mortality rate of 2 million people. In addition, the virus infected 2.7 million new individuals during the course of the year [1]. Despite these grim statistics, extensive progress has been made in combating the disease as demonstrated by the increase in life expectancy for those with access to therapy. While no treatment currently exists to completely eradicate the virus from an infected individual, the development of multiple therapeutics targeting various steps of the HIV life cycle have helped transform this deadly ailment into a more manageable chronic infection.

Anti-HIV drug development has been driven in part by the extensive biological characterization of HIV and its life cycle. HIV is classified as a lentivirus belonging to the *retroviridae* family. Its ribonucleic acid (RNA) genome consists of three genes *gag*, *pol*, and *env*. The *pol* gene encodes for three viral enzymes—reverse transcriptase, integrase, and aspartyl protease that play vital roles in viral replication. Multiple genetic variations of the

virus exist that are classified into two major subtypes, HIV-1, and HIV-2, with the most common strains of the virus belonging to the HIV-1 subtype. Initial antiretroviral therapies, known as nucleoside reverse transcriptase inhibitors (NRTIs), targeted the reverse transcriptase enzyme and inhibited transcription of single-stranded viral RNA to double-stranded viral deoxyribonucleic acid (DNA) (see Volume 7 Chapters 4). In the early 1990s, potent inhibitors of the HIV aspartyl protease were developed and shown to provide significant clinical benefits especially when used together with reverse transcriptase inhibitors. This led to the advent of highly active antiretroviral therapies (HAART) that use combinations of antiretroviral drugs to effectively manage the disease. Today, multiple treatment regimens exist and new therapies targeting novel HIV targets have been developed that include inhibitors of the integrase enzyme, viral attachment and membrane fusion (see Volume 7 Chapter 3). Despite these many advances, problems with multidrug viral resistance remain an issue [2,3]. In addition, drug toxicity, drug–drug interactions and the problems of drug resistance warrant the need for improved therapies to be developed [4].

In this chapter, we will briefly review the biology associated with the HIV protease enzyme and how that has translated into the development of potent HIV protease inhibitors (PIs). Next, we will review the ten currently available U.S. Food and Drug Administration (FDA) approved PIs in terms of their development from lead discovery to candidate selection and their clinical performance. We will conclude with a brief discussion of new PI candidates recently under clinical evaluation or currently in preclinical development.

2. BIOLOGY

2.1. Structure and Function of HIV Protease

HIV protease (PR) belongs to a class of enzymes termed aspartyl proteases that use aspartic acid residues to catalyze the hydrolysis of polypeptide bonds. It was the first HIV protein to be characterized structurally and has been found to share many common features with other aspartyl proteases including renin, pepsin, cathespin D, and gastrin [5–7]. The protein is translated as a *gag-pol* fusion product that results from a ribosomal frameshift [8]. A subsequent autocatalytic event releases the protease from the *gag-pol* precursor protein [9]. Structurally, the enzyme exists as a homodimer consisting of two identical polyprotein chains that are 99 amino acids in length. Each monomer contains a flexible "flap" region consisting of two antiparallel β-strands connected by a β-turn that project over the active site and can participate in binding of substrates. The active site is defined by two Asp-Thr-Gly motifs that assist in the nucleophilic attack of water onto the scissile amide bond of viable polypeptide substrates (see Fig. 1). A tetrahedral intermediate is formed that breaks down to two smaller peptide fragments thereby effectively cleaving the polypeptide substrate. HIV PR catalyzes the cleavage of the p55 (*gag*) and p160 (*gag-pol*) polyproteins at nine different cleavage sites (see Table 1) forming various structural proteins p7, p9 (nucleocapsid), p17 (matrix), p24 (capsid) and enzyme products, reverse transcriptase, integrase, and aspartyl protease [10]. The processing of these proteins is a critical step of the HIV life cycle and makes the protease an attractive drug target.

2.2. Design of Inhibitors

HIV PIs are designed to prevent the enzyme from cleaving *gag* or *gag-pol* viral polyproteins resulting in the buildup of immature viral

Table 1. HIV-1 Protease Processing Sites [13]

Cleavage Site	Amino Acid Residues
P2/NC	-Ala-Thr-Ile-**Met/Met**-Gln-Arg-Gly-
CA/p2	-Ala-Arg-Val-**Leu/Ala**-Glu-Ala-Met-
RT/IN	-Arg-Lys-Val-**Leu/Phe**-Leu-Asp-Gly-
NC/p1	-Arg-Gln-Ala-**Asn/Phe**-Leu-Gly-Lys-
RT internal	-Alu-Glu-Thr-**Phe/Tyr**-Val-Asp-Gly-
p1/p6	-Pro-Gly-Asn-**Phe/Leu**-Gln-Ser-Arg-
TF/PR	-Ser-Phe-Asn-**Phe/Pro**-Gln-Ile-Thr-
PR/RT	-Thr-Leu-Asn-**Phe/Pro**-Gln-Ile-Thr-
MA/CA	-Ser-Gln-Asn-**Tyr/Pro**-Ile-Val-Gln-

particles and effectively halting viral replication. Before proceeding further into the design aspects of these molecules, it is important to point out the nomenclature commonly used to describe the relative position of the inhibitor's structural features with respect to the areas of the enzyme to which they bind. Shown in Fig. 2 is an example substrate in the enzyme active site with its scissile amide bond denoted by the wavy red line. Adjacent to this scissile bond are the P_1 and P_1' ligands (blue) of the substrate that extend into the S_1 and S_1' sites (magenta) of the enzyme, respectively. As you move further away from the center point, the labels increase numerically. For the HIV PR, the center point is marked by the location of the catalytic aspartic residues Asp25/Asp25' while the center point of inhibitors is indicated by the functional group mimicking the scissile amide bond of the natural substrate.

A variety of strategies have been implemented in the past toward the design of inhibitors against HIV PR. The earliest approach was to use substrate-based inhibitors that incorpo-

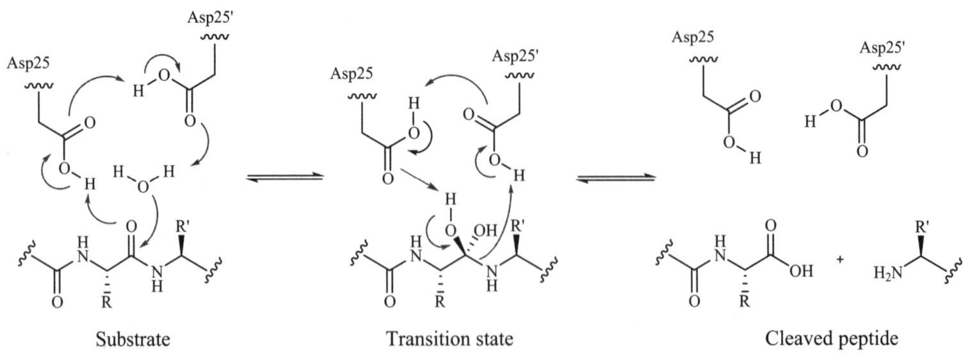

Figure 1. HIV protease peptide cleavage mechanism [11,12]. (This figure is available in full color at http://mrw.interscience.wiley.com/emrw/9780471266945/home.)

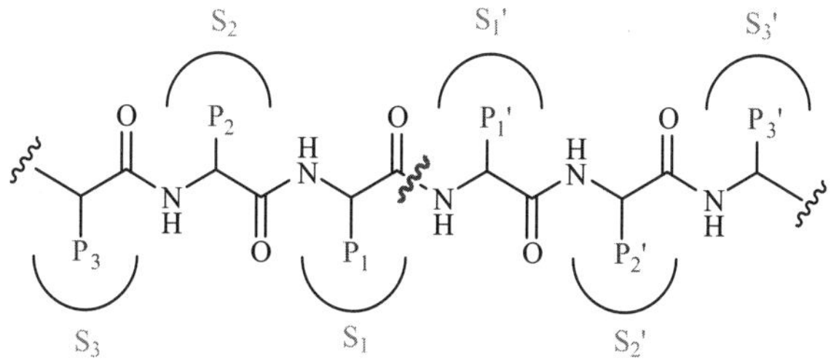

Figure 2. Standard nomenclature for HIV protease binding sites and substrate ligands [14,15]. (This figure is available in full color at http://mrw.interscience.wiley.com/emrw/9780471266945/home.)

rated a noncleavable, transition-state isostere (see Fig. 3) into the molecule in place of the natural substrate's scissile peptide bond. Previous work completed in the search for inhibitors of human renin, a related aspartyl protease, laid the groundwork for these discovery efforts. Saquinavir (SQV), which mimics the Phe-Pro cleavage site, is an example of a successful inhibitor developed from these strategies [16]. Shortly thereafter, it was realized that the HIV PR contained a C_2-axis of symmetry and this element of symmetry could be incorporated into the design of novel inhibitors. Although unsymmetrical itself, ritonavir (RTV) emerged from a development program that initiated with the design of symmetrical inhibitors. A third approach that has become increasing popular is structure-based design made possible by the many advances in crystallography techniques. More than 200 crystal structures of HIV protease/inhibitor complexes currently reside in the Protein Data Bank (PDB). Insights from these structures have played critical roles in the development of many inhibitors, such as nelfinavir (NFV), amprenavir (APV), and indinavir (IDV).

Modern day design efforts retain many elements of these initial strategies, but have incorporated new tools to address the failures of currently available therapies, such as poor bioavailability. A variety of assays are now performed to screen candidates for desirable pharmacokinetic properties. These studies seek to improve drug bioavailability by identifying potent inhibitors that are readily absorbed into the blood plasma, exhibit low serum protein binding, and are not rapidly metabolized by liver enzymes. Another significant challenge in the design of PIs is the occurrence of multidrug resistant viral

strains. Recent efforts to combat this problem have designed inhibitors that interact primarily with the protease's backbone atoms. These atoms are less likely to change during the course of viral mutation making the development of resistance less likely. In addition to this idea, drug candidates are now screened for their ability to treat resistant viral strains. The final selection criteria of darunavir (DRV), for example, included an assay that identified inhibitors with broad-spectrum antiviral activity.

3. FIRST-GENERATION INHIBITORS

Multiple reviews have been written on the discovery and clinical relevance of first-generation inhibitors. For additional information, see Refs [11,18,19].

3.1. Saquinavir Mesylate (Invirase)

3.1.1. General Information Saquinavir (also known as Ro 31-8959) mesylate (see Fig. 4) was the first HIV PI to reach the market, receiving FDA approval on December 6 1995. Developed and marketed by Hoffmann–La Roche, the story of its discovery is a classical example of structure based drug design. In its original formulation (Invirase hard gel), SQV suffered from poor bioavailability. Administration with food and boosting with RTV were found to effectively enhance plasma concentrations. The drug was later (November 7, 1997) reformulated as a soft-gel capsule (Fortovase) in an effort to increase bioavailability; however, both hard and soft-gel forms were replaced in 2005 by Invirase 500 tablets, intended to significantly reduce patient pill burden [20]. References [11,21–24]

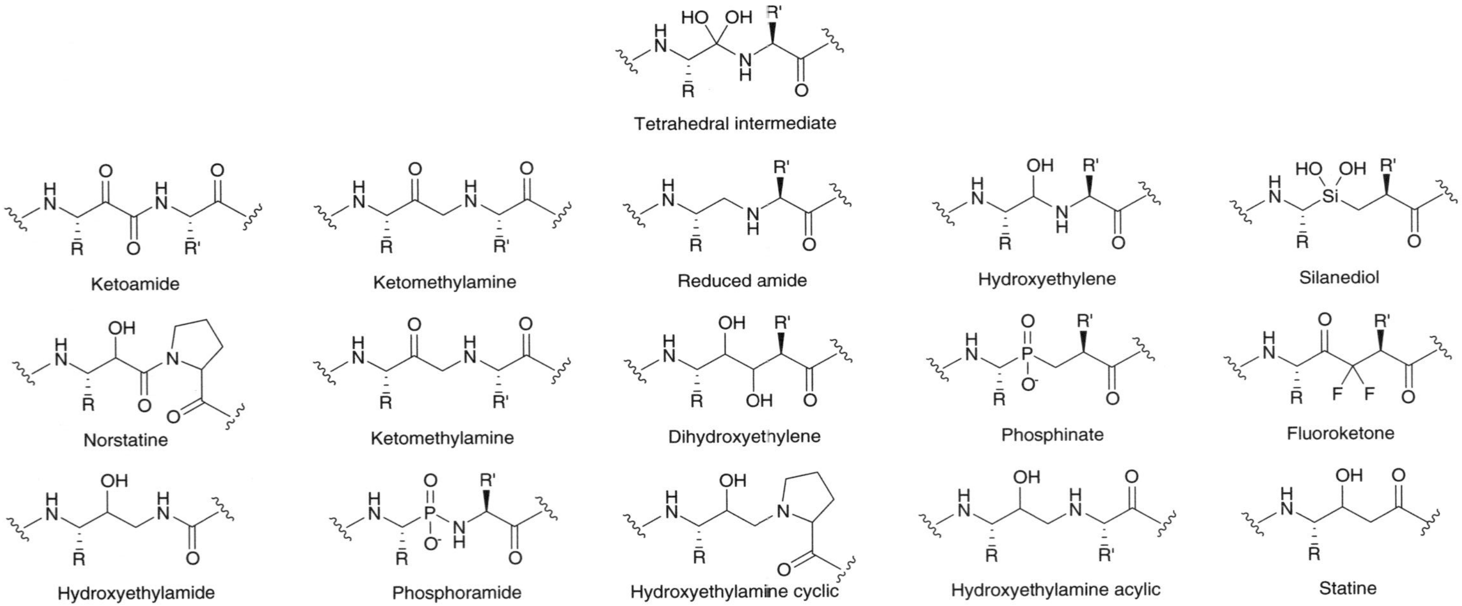

Figure 3. Common transition-state isosteres [11,17].

4

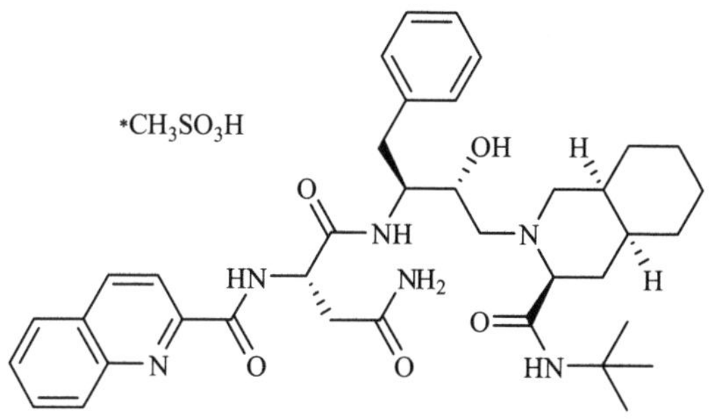

Figure 4. Chemical structure of saquinavir mesylate.

provide additional details of its discovery and pharmacological profile.

3.1.2. Drug Optimization By 1985, the HIV PR had been identified as an enzyme essential to the viral replication cycle and was quickly recognized as an attractive new drug target [25]. Prior to initiating drug development efforts; however, an assay to determine enzyme inhibition was required. Scientists at Roche designed a simple colorimetric assay that measured the cleavage of a simple hep-

tapeptide, Succ.Val.Ser.Gln.Asn.Phe.Pro.Ile. NH^{t}Bu, which was designed to be a small synthetic substrate for HIV PR. Following cleavage at the Phe-Pro linkage, the N-terminal proline would react with isatin producing a compound with a deep blue color with a measurable wavelength at 599 nm [26]. This assay proved to be simple, specific, and quantitative allowing the rapid evaluation of potential inhibitors.

Having developed an assay amenable to high-throughput screening, researchers turned their attention to the development of a lead compound. It was proposed that designing compounds that behaved as transition-state mimetics would be good inhibitors. A variety of isosteres intending to mimic the transition-state were explored (see Table 2) based on the Asn.Phe.Pro cleavage sequence of the *pol* polyprotein. (*R*)-Hydroxyethylamine was found to provide the best activity. Following this discovery, the polypeptide chain was systematically lengthened in both directions (see Table 3). Shortening to a dipeptide significantly reduced activity as did expansion of

Table 2. Transition-State Mimetic Screening [11,16,22]

Compound	Structure	TS Mimetic	IC$_{50}$ (μM)
1	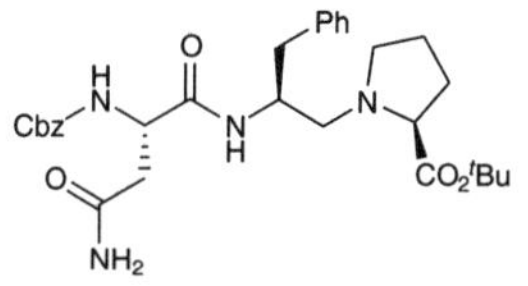	Reduced amide	50
2	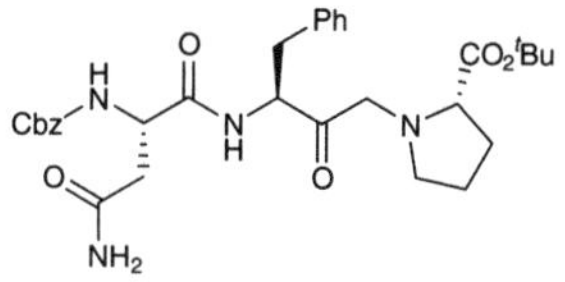	Ketomethylamine	0.87
3	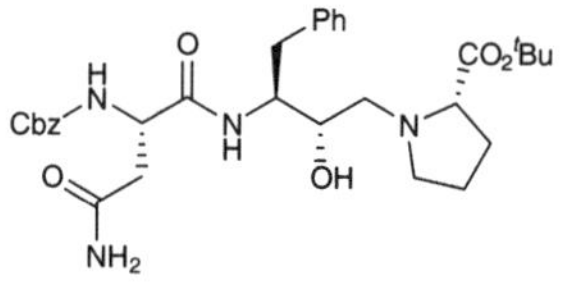	Hydroxyethylamine (*S*)	0.3
4	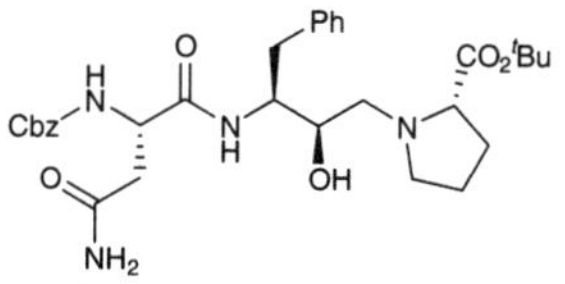	Hydroxyethylamine (*R*)	0.14

Table 3. Correlation of Inhibitor Size to Potency [11,16,22]

Compound	Structure	IC$_{50}$ (μM) (R/S)
5	Cbz.PhΨ[CH(OH)CH$_2$N]Pro.O^{t}Bu	6.5/30
6	Cbz.Asn.PhΨ[CH(OH)CH$_2$N]Pro.O^{t}Bu	0.14/0.30
7	Cbz.Leu.Asn.PhΨ[CH(OH)CH$_2$N]Pro.O^{t}Bu	0.60/1.10
8	Cbz.Asn.PhΨ[CH(OH)CH$_2$N]Pro.Ile.NH^{i}Bu	0.13/2.40
9	Cbz.Leu.Asn.PhΨ[CH(OH)CH$_2$N]Pro.Ile.NH^{i}Bu	0.75/10.0

the N-terminal end. A tripeptide sequence (Asn.Phe.Pro) was chosen for additional development.

Subsequent lead modifications explored the effect of replacing the N-terminal benzyl carbamate (Cbz) group, altering the proline residue, and modification of the Asn side chain (see Tables 4 and 5). Replacement of the Cbz with nonaromatic groups significantly reduced activity; however, installation of a

Table 4. Effect of Modifying End Functionalities on Potency [16]

Compound	Structure	IC$_{50}$ (nM)		EC$_{50}$ (nM)
		HIV-1	HIV-2	HIV-1
10		210	330	400
11		52	50	130
12		23	—	110
13		2	10	17
14		<0.4	<0.8	2

Table 5. Effect of Modifying Asparagine Residue [16]

Compound	Structure	IC$_{50}$ (nM)		EC$_{50}$ (nM)
		HIV-1	HIV-2	HIV-1
15	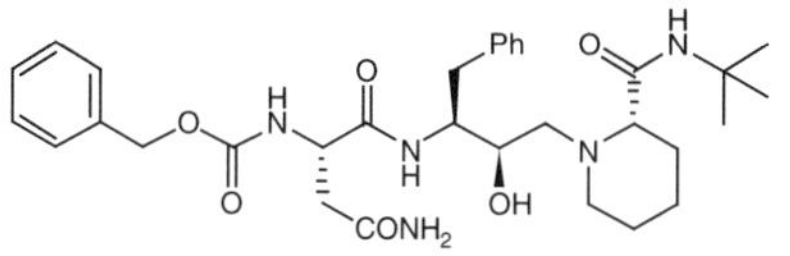	18	—	—
16	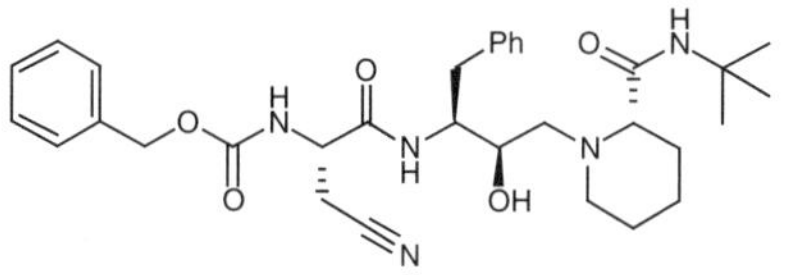	23	—	—
17	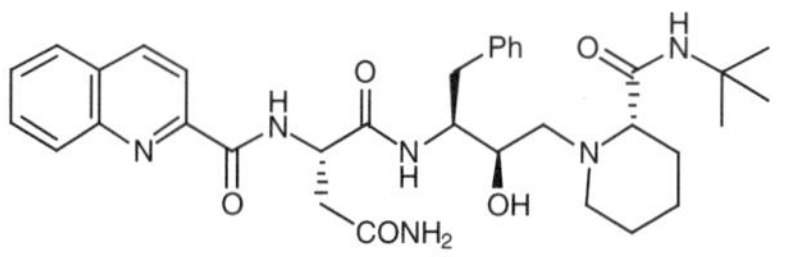	2	10	17
18	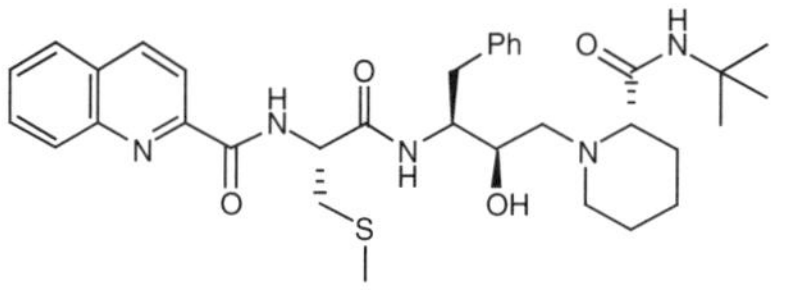	12	15	13

β-naphthoyl increased potency that was further improved through the addition of a quinoline carbonyl. At the other end of the compound, the size of the proline ring was found to greatly influence activity. Reducing the ring to a four-membered system almost completely abolished activity while expansion to a six-membered ring improved enzyme potency by 10-fold. Investigations into fused bicyclic systems led to the discovery of S,S, S-decahydroisoquinoline carboxylic acid, which was the most active ligand. Attempts to replace the asparagine moiety with other functional groups did not significantly improve potency.

3.1.3. Binding Interactions

X-ray crystal structure analysis of SQV complexed with HIV PR has provided valuable insight into the binding interactions between this inhibitor and enzyme (see Fig. 5). SQV's large hydrophobic groups fill the enzyme's lipophilic pockets (S$_3$, S$_1$, S$_1'$ and to a lesser extent S$_2$ and S$_2'$) forming numerous van der Waals interactions with adjacent amino acid residues. A total of seven hydrogen bonds occur between SQV and the protease with four occurring directly between the substrate and enzyme while three hydrogen bonds are mediated by water molecules. This extensive network of substrate-enzyme interactions is responsible for the remarkable potency of SQV against HIV PR [27].

3.1.4. Pharmacokinetics

Values of select pharmacokinetic parameters of SQV have been provided in Table 6. A significant problem with SQV is its low bioavailability resulting from limited absorption into the body and extensive first pass metabolism [28]. Administration within 2 h of consuming a meal is recommended as a means to increase absorption. Metabolism of SQV was found to be mediated primarily by CYP3A resulting in a number of mono- and di-hydroxylated products (see Fig. 6) with reduced viral activity [29]. As a result, coadministration with RTV, a potent inhibitor of CYP3A, effectively

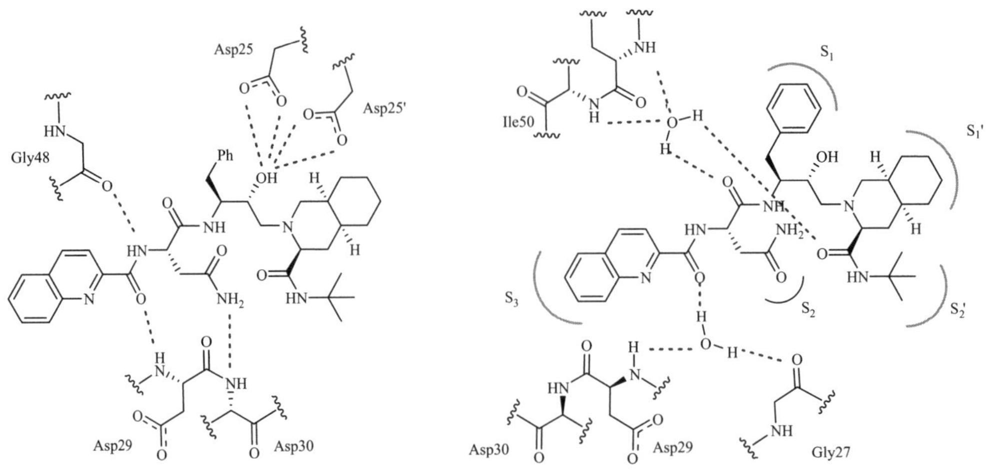

Figure 5. Binding interactions between SQV and HIV PR [27]. (This figure is available in full color at http://mrw.interscience.wiley.com/emrw/9780471266945/home.)

increases plasma concentrations [30]. In the plasma, SQV is highly bound to plasma proteins (98%). SQV clears rapidly from the body with a mean residence time of 7 h. ^{14}C-labeling studies demonstrated the primary route of excretion was through the feces (88%) with low levels observed in the urine (1%).

3.1.5. Efficacy and Tolerability   Due in part to its status as the first HIV PI to market, the efficacy of SQV was established based on clinical endpoints [32]. A number of subsequent studies have occurred evaluating the effects of SQV reformulations and comparing SQV against other PIs as they have been developed. For example, the CHEESE and MaxCmin1 studies compared SQV to IDV and demonstrated similar efficacy with or without RTV boosting [33,34]. The GEMINI and MaxCmin2 studies compared SQV to the second-generation PI lopinavir (LPV) and suggested some degree of inferiority [35,36]. In general, SQV has been found to be reasonably well tolerated

in patients with the most common adverse events reported during clinical trials including diarrhea, fatigue, headache, abdominal pain, nausea, and rash [23]. A number of side effects common to PIs occur during treatment with SQV including lipodystrophy.

3.1.6. Resistance Profile   There are two signature amino acid substitutions associated with the development of viral resistance to SQV, G84V, and L90M [31]. Found on the flap region of the protease, the mutation at G84V typically occurs first and results in reduced susceptibility due to unfavorable steric interactions with SQV [11]. A single mutation at G84V or L90M results in an 8- or 3- loss in SQV activity, respectively [31]. Viral strains containing both substitutions have a 20-fold decrease in susceptibility [11]. Interestingly, these mutations are beneficial in that they result in an abnormal processing of the HIV polyprotein, thereby, hindering viral replication. A number of secondary mutations

Table 6. Select Pharmacokinetic Parameters of Various SQV Formulations [31]

Regimen	AUC$_{24}$ (mcg h/mL)	C$_{min}$ (mcg/mL)
Invirase 600 mg tid	2.6	0.08
Saquinavir soft gel capsules 1200 mg tid	21.7	0.2
Invirase/RTV 400/100 mg bid	32.0	0.5
Invirase/RTV 1000/100 mg bid	29.2	0.4
Saquinavir soft gel capsules/RTV 1000/100 mg bid	38.2	0.4

AUC$_{24}$: area under the concentration curve at 24 h; C$_{min}$: minimum concentration; tid: three times a day; bid: twice a day.

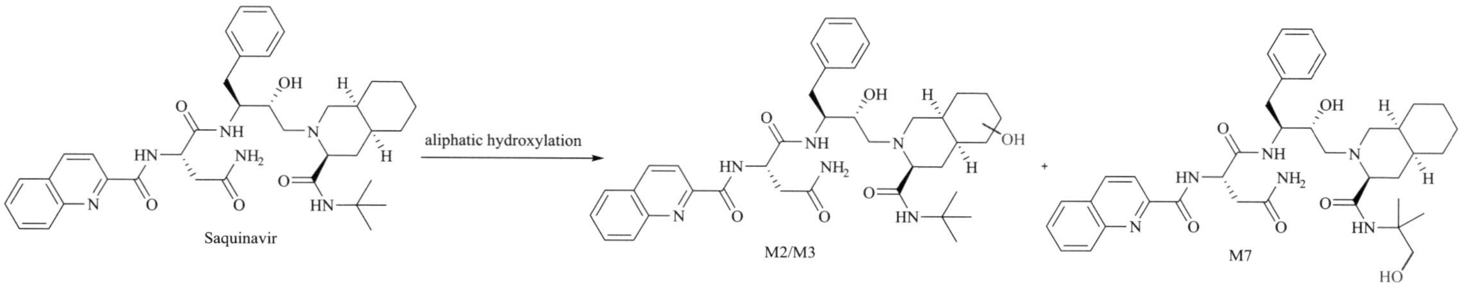

Figure 6. Major metabolites of SQV [29]. (This figure is available in full color at http://mrw.interscience.wiley.com/emrw/9780471266945/home.)

9

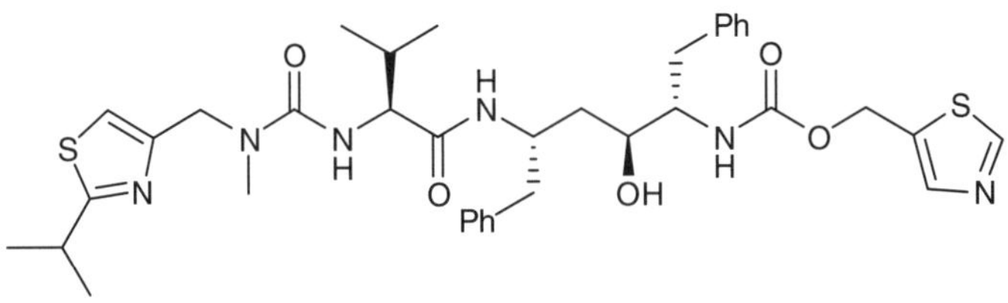

Figure 7. Chemical structure of ritonavir.

contributing additional resistance to SQV have been identified in patients treated with Invirase including L10I/R/V, I54V, A71V/T, G73S, V77I, V82A, and I84V [31]. In general, viral strains possessing greater numbers of mutations display higher levels of resistance to SQV. These viral mutations have also shown variable degrees of cross-resistance toward other PIs.

3.2. Ritonavir (Norvir)

3.2.1. General Information Ritonvavir (RTV also known as ABT-538) (see Fig. 7) was the second HIV PI to market, receiving FDA approval on March 1 1996. Developed and marketed by Abbott Laboratories under the trade name Norvir, the drug was designed as a symmetry-based PI that takes advantage of the HIV PR's C_2-axis of symmetry. In addition to being a potent HIV PI, RTV strongly inhibits cytochrome P450 3A4 isozyme, reducing its metabolic activity. As a result, RTV is commonly used in combination with other PIs that are susceptible to rapid metabolic degradation as a way to increase or "boost" the PIs bioavailability. The drug is currently available as a 100 mg capsule or 80 mg/mL oral suspension. However, due to poor patient tolerability, the use of RTV as a PI is limited. Currently, the drug is primarily used at lower doses to boost other PIs. References [11,37–42] include additional details into the discovery and clinical properties of RTV.

3.2.2. Drug Optimization The discovery of RTV began with the realization that as a dimer of two identical polyprotein strands, the HIV PR contained a C_2-axis of symmetry that could be exploited by symmetrically designed inhibitors. Reference [43] provides a detailed review of early attempts to use this concept in PI design. With respect to RTV, the symmetry

element led Abbott Laboratories to design two compounds, A-75925 and A-74704, that contained symmetrical elements centered around a mono-ol or di-ol core (see Fig. 8) [44]. While potent against HIV PR, both compounds suffered from poor solubility that hindered the bioavailability of the drugs. Detailed crystallography studies revealed that when bound to HIV PR, the phenyl groups of these molecules were exposed to the solvent and could be modified to improve pharmacokinetic properties. They were replaced with pyridyl groups leading to A-77003, which displayed improved solubility. However, preliminary *in vivo* studies indicated the drug was rapidly eliminated from the body making it difficult to maintain adequate plasma concentrations. Removal of a central hydroxyl group and reoptimization led to A-80987, which unfortunately also demonstrated rapid clearance [45]. Metabolic studies on A-80987 indicated the primary metabolic pathway was oxidation of the pyridyl amine. As a result, the groups were replaced with the more stable thiazole functionality leading to the discovery of RTV. RTV demonstrated superior pharmacokinetic properties while retaining potency, establishing it as a potential drug candidate. It was subsequently advanced successfully through clinical phase studies. The result of an extensive SAR study on RTV's core structure that includes more than 180 various analogs has been provided by Ref. [46].

3.2.3. Pharmacokinetics Values of select pharmacokinetic parameters of RTV have been provided in Table 7. RTV is readily absorbed into the body when administered orally with relatively small changes in pharmacokinetics observed when taken with food [39,47]. In the plasma, RTV is highly bound (98–99%) to plasma proteins having a high affinity for both α1-acid glycoprotein and albumin [47].

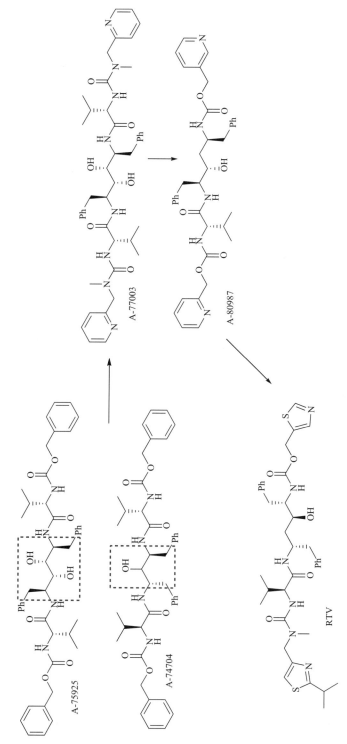

Figure 8. Discovery of RTV [38]. (This figure is available in full color at http://mrw.interscience.wiley.com/emrw/9780471266945/home.)

11

Table 7. Select Pharmacokinetic Properties of RTV [47]

Regimen	C_{max} (mcg/mL)	C_{min} (mcg/mL)	$T_{1/2}$ (h)	CL/F (L/hr)
RTV 600 mg bid	11.2	3.7	3-5	6.0

C_{max}: maximum plasma concentration; C_{min}: minimum plasma concentration; $T_{1/2}$: elimination half-life; CL/F: apparent clearance; bid: twice a day.

The drug is metabolized by CYP3A and CYP2D6 isozymes producing a variety of metabolites (see Fig. 9), five of which have been observed in human urine and feces [47]. Interestingly, the major metabolite, M2, maintains similar antiviral activity as RTV although its concentration in the plasma is relatively low [47]. ^{14}C-RTV studies demonstrated the drug is eliminated primarily in the feces (86.4%) with a lesser amount found in the urine (11.3%). Unchanged ^{14}C-RTV accounted for 33.8% and 3.5% of the observed radioactivity, respectively. RTV is a potent inhibitor of CYP3A, indicating a high potential for drug–drug interactions to occur. This property of RTV has been exploited in HIV therapy in a process termed " boosting" where coadministration of low levels of RTV are used to reduce the metabolism of other coadministered PIs thereby increasing their plasma levels and serum half-life.

3.2.4. Efficacy and Tolerability Similar to SQV, RTV's efficacy toward HIV was established based on clinical endpoints. During Study 247, treatment with RTV as a monotherapy was associated with significant decreases in patient's plasma HIV RNA and appreciable increases in their CD4+ cell counts [47]. Similar results were observed in study 245, which evaluated the usefulness of RTV combination therapy with zidovudine [47]. Treatment with RTV as a monotherapy has been poorly tolerated due in part to adverse events related to gastrointestinal problems and perioral paresthesias [37,50]. Further problems have included neurological adverse events, elevation of triglycerides, and spontaneous bleeding in patients with hemophilia [37,50]

3.2.5. Resistance Profile HIV isolates that developed reduced susceptibility to RTV in cell culture contained amino acid mutations at M46I, A71V, V82F, and V84I [47]. Isolates obtained from patients treated with RTV accumulated mutations at V82A/F, I54V, A71V/T, and I36L [47]. Primary mutations at V82 are specific to RTV and associated with the development of drug resistance. Variable levels of cross-resistance to other PIs have been observed [47].

3.3. Indinavir (Crixivan)

3.3.1. General Information Indinavir (also known as MK-639 and L-735,524) sulfate (see Fig. 10) was the third HIV PI to market, receiving FDA approval on March 13, 1996. Sold by Merck under the trade name Crixivan, the discovery of the drug originated from a high-throughput screening of renin inhibitors that eventually incorporated elements of SQV's basic structure. The drug is currently available as a capsule for oral administration in a variety of strengths (100, 200, 333, and 400 mg). Current day use of IDV has been limited due to the occurrence of multiple undesirable side effects. A number of reviews have been written on IDV describing both its discovery and clinical impact [11,51,52].

3.3.2. Drug Optimization The HIV PR is classified as an aspartic acid protease because it uses aspartic residues to catalyze the cleavage of peptide substrates. Knowing this, researchers at Merck theorized that small-molecule inhibitors of other aspartic acid proteases may also inhibit HIV PR and serve as lead compounds. They began a high-throughput screening program using a library of compounds from a recent renin inhibitor program. From this work, L-364,505 was identified as a lead as it exhibited a high degree of potency toward HIV PR (HIV $IC_{50} = 1$ nM). Development efforts were initiated to reduce molecular size, eliminate the molecule's renin activity ($IC_{50} = 73$ nM), and improve its poor cellular activity ($CIC_{95} > 100 \mu M$). This led to the discovery of L-687,908 (HIV $IC_{50} < 0.3$ nM, renin $IC_{50} > 10,000$ nM, and $CIC_{95} = 12$ nM) that met the predescribed goals, but was not orally available likely due to its high peptidic

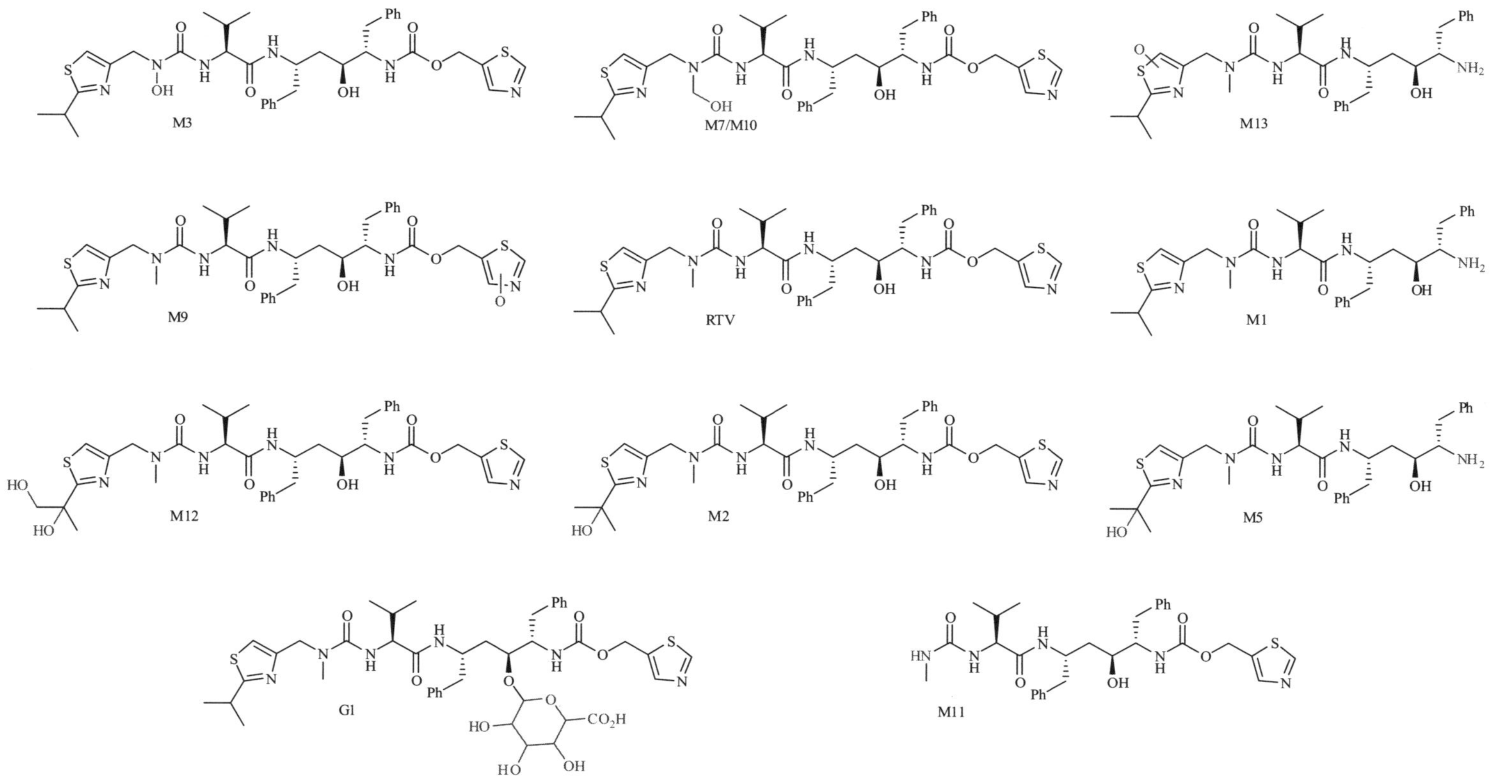

Figure 9. Proposed metabolites of RTV [48,49].

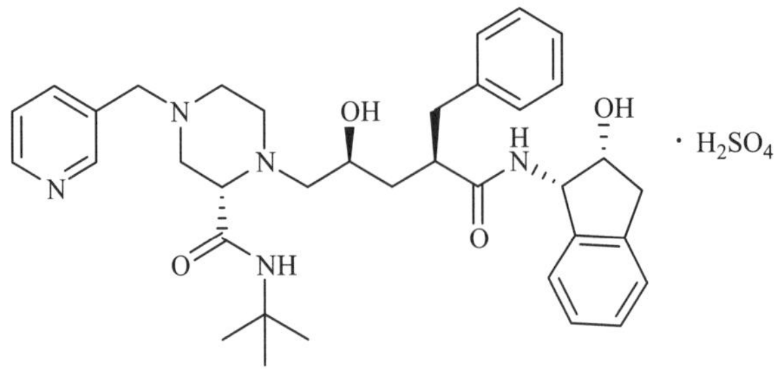

Figure 10. Chemical structure of indinavir sulfate.

nature and poor solubility. Later work, focused on improving these pharmacokinetic properties led to L-689,502 (see Fig. 11), which incorporated a solubilizing group at the 4-position of the phenyl ring located at the P_1/P_1' site. This location was chosen based on modeling studies that indicated functionality at this location would occupy space outside of the enzyme cavity. It is interesting to note that recent PI candidates from GlaxoSmithKline and Gilead Sciences (brecanavir and GS-8374, respectively) are analogs of DRV that incorporate additional functional groups at this same position. The discovery of L-689,502 was significant because it was one of the first potent PIs ($IC_{50} = 0.45$ nM, $CIC_{50} = 12$ nM) that displayed oral bioavailability (5% in dogs). Unfortunately, preliminary safety studies revealed problems with the drug in terms of hepatotoxicity [53].

While these development efforts were underway at Merck, Hoffmann–La Roche published results from work on their promising lead candidate, SQV. Researchers at Merck quickly realized that the decahydroisoquinoline group of SQV contained an amine that might be useful in improving the solubility and oral bioavailability of their compound. As a result, a chimeric compound was synthesized (see Fig. 12) that incorporated features of both SQV and L-685,434. Further, structure–activity relationship studies occurred with the intent of replacing the decahydroisoquinoline group. A substituted piperazine ring was found to be a suitable replacement (see Table 8). In addition to improving activity, this group contained an additional amine that could improve solubility and could be easily functionalized allowing the rapid evaluation of additional analogs. Subsequent analogs

(see Table 9) quickly revealed that a large hydrophobic group was needed at this position to fill the lipophilic S_3 domain of the enzyme and maintain potency. Certain compounds, like the 8-quinolinylsulfonyl analog exhibited subnanomolar potency, but had very little bioavailability. Incorporation of fluorines or amines onto a phenylmethyl ligand had little effect on the potency or cellular activity but significantly enhanced solubility and oral bioavailability. This discovery led to the development of IDV, which was successfully advanced through clinical studies.

3.3.3. Binding Interactions The interactions governing binding of IDV to HIV PR are distinct from those observed with other PIs (see page, 19, Fig. 13). Crystal structure data indicate the existence of 96 van der Waals contacts occurring for the major conformation of the drug [58]. The large hydrophobic groups of IDV fill the empty lipophilic regions of the protease structure (S_1, S_1', S_2' and S_3 subsites). IDV forms eight hydrogen bonds directly to atoms of the protease while another five hydrogen bonds can be found mediated by water molecules [58]. Hydrogen bonding to the Arg8' side chain atoms are a unique attribute of IDV binding.

3.3.4. Pharmacokinetics Values of select pharmacokinetic parameters of IDV have been provided in Table 10. IDV is rapidly absorbed upon administration when patients have not recently consumed any food [59]. Meals high in fat, calories, and protein have a negative effect on IDV's pharmacokinetic profile significantly decreasing the area under the plasma drug concentration–time curve (AUC) (77%) and the maximum plasma concentration of the drug

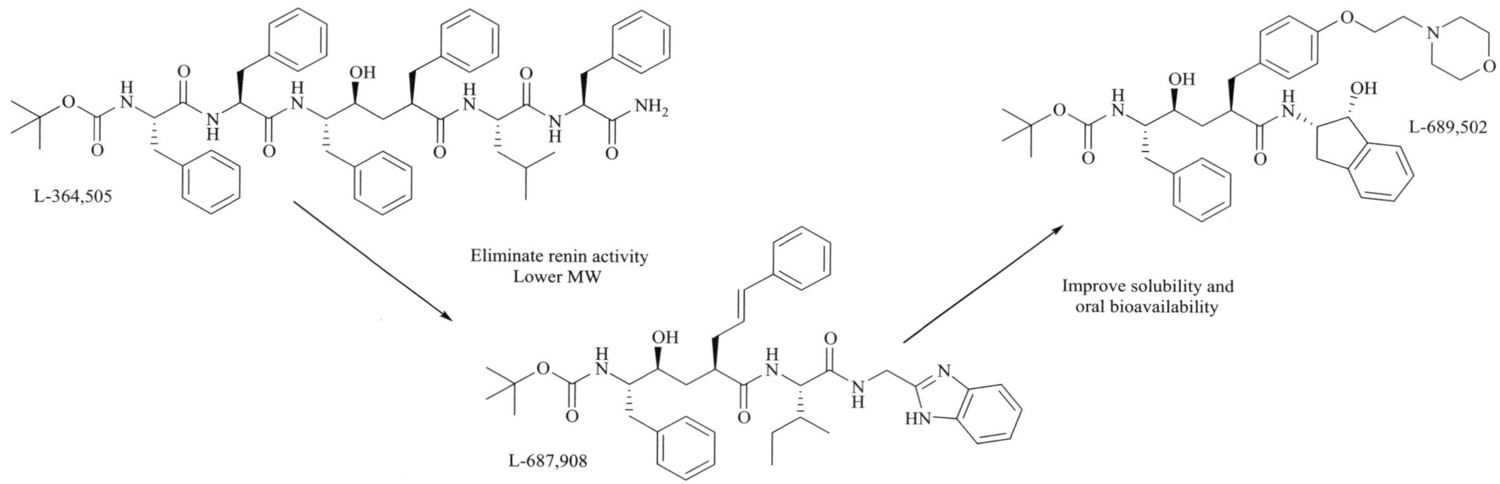

Figure 11. Discovery of L-689502—an important lead [11,52,54–57].

L-689,502

L-687,908

L-364,505

Improve solubility and
oral bioavailability

Eliminate renin activity
Lower MW

15

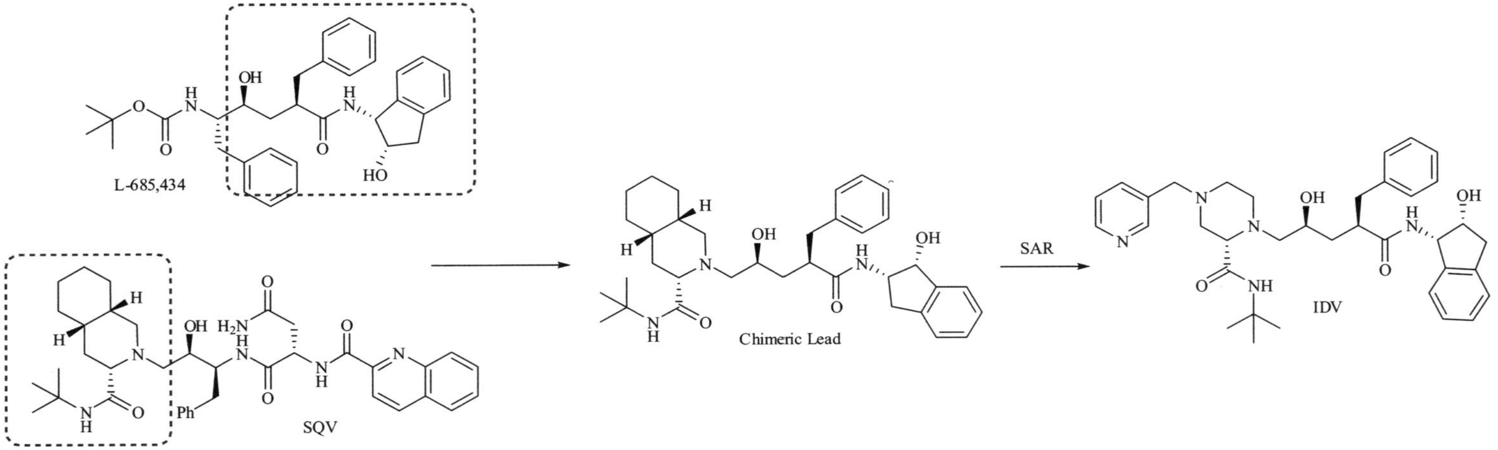

Figure 12. Discovery of IDV [11,52,54–57]. (This figure is available in full color at http://mrw.interscience.wiley.com/emrw/9780471266945/home.)

16

Table 8. Effect of P_1/P_3 Ligands on Protease Inhibition [57]

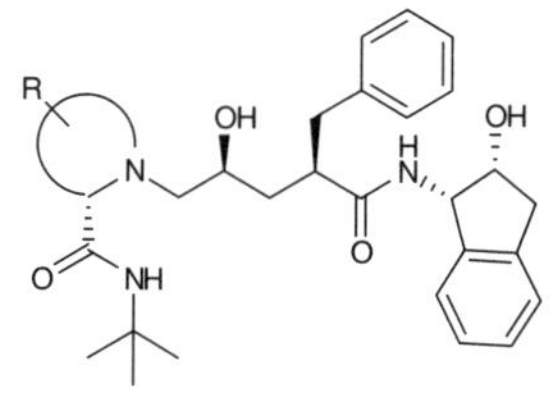

Compound	R	IC_{50} (nM)	CIC_{95} (nM)	Compound	R	IC_{50} (nM)	CIC_{95} (nM)
19	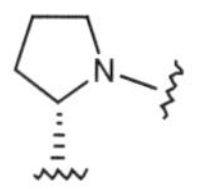	347	1500	21	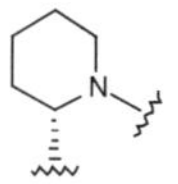	80	—
20	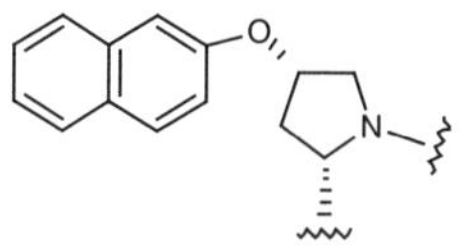	15	>400	22	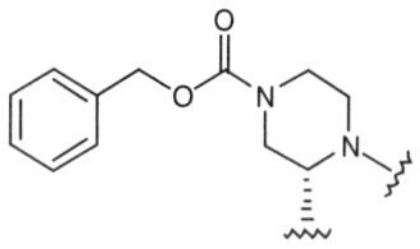	0.35	100
				23	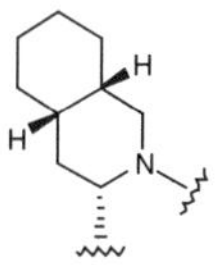	7.8	400

(C_{max}) (84%) [59]. However, coadministration of IDV with RTV significantly reduces this effect from food thereby eliminating the need for meal restrictions during dosing [60]. In the plasma, approximately 60% of IDV is found bound to plasma proteins [59]. Interestingly, IDV has been found in the cerebral spinal fluid (CSF) in concentrations ranging from 2–6% of plasma concentrations [61]. This attribute distinguishes IDV from earlier PIs like NPV, SQV, and RTV whose CSF concentrations were less than 0.5% [62]. Metabolism of IDV occurs primarily by CYP3A4 resulting in the formation of six different oxidative metabolites and one glucuronide conjugate (see Fig. 14) [52,59,63]. The major metabolites, M5 and M6, result from selective N-dealkyation and aliphatic hydroxylation of IDV. Similar to other PIs, IDV is a known inhibitor of CYP3A4 and may be a weak inhibitor of CYP2D6; therefore, interactions with other drugs interacting with these isoforms are

likely. ^{14}C-IDV studies found the majority of IDV and its related metabolites excreted in the feces (83%), although, significant levels (19%) were found in the urine as well [59,63]. Unchanged drug accounted for 35% and 10.4% of observed radioactivity in the feces and urine, respectively [59,63].

3.3.5. Efficacy and Tolerability IDV has been involved in multiple clinical phase trials that have demonstrated the drug's efficacy in treating HIV. Initial studies (ACTG 320, Study 019, Study 028, and Study 035) evaluated the drugs usefulness in relation to nucleoside reverse transcriptase inhibitors [59, 64–66]. In general, coadministration of IDV with NRTIs was more effective then treatment with only NRTIs. Later reports (CHEESE study and MaxCmin1 trial) confirmed the efficacy of IDV was comparable to treatment with SQV [32,33]. Recent studies have focused on boosting IDV with RTV to

Table 9. Optimizing Pharmacokinetic Properties [57]

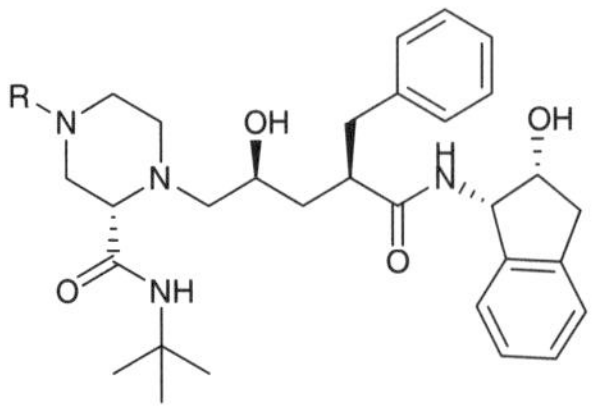

Compound	R	IC_{50} (nM)	CIC_{95} (nM)	C_{max} (µM)	Sol, pH 7.4/5.2 (mg/mL)	$\log P$
24	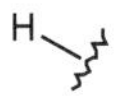	38	3000	—	—	—
25	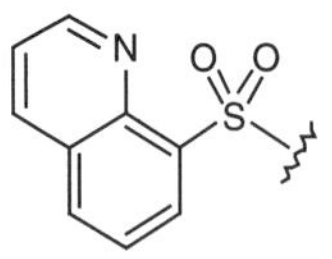	0.013	12.5–50	<0.10	<0.001	3.70
26	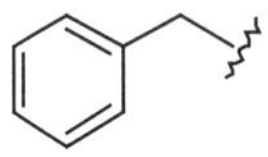	0.30	50	—	—	—
27	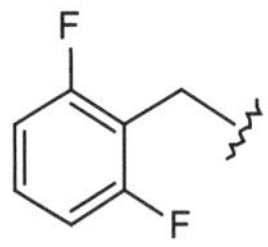	0.31	25–50	0.73	0.001/0.03	3.69
28	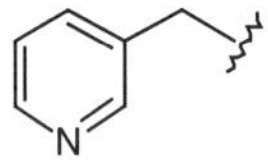	0.56	50.4	11.4	0.07/0.69	2.92

lower dosing concentrations and thereby minimize observed problems with toxicity [18].

Multiple adverse events have been associated with IDV treatment. Pooled results from clinical trial studies indicated approximately 9% of patients receiving IDV-experienced nephrolithiasis with flank pain [51]. Laboratory results from approximately 10% of patients indicated hyperbilirubinemia, which was not associated with hepatic damage [51]. Multiple reports have linked IDV to the development of urolithiasis, a condition that likely occurs due to IDV's high urinary excretion and poor solubility at physiological pH [67,68]. Other conditions specific to IDV include adhesive capsulitis, hair loss, lipodystrophy, and rheumatological complications [51,69]. IDV appears to possess retinoid-like properties in that it has been linked to ingrown toenails and paronychia of the toes and fingers [70]. Many other adverse events have been reported as well, although; direct correlation to IDV administration remains controversial [51]. It has been observed that the severity of these adverse events can be reduced by lowering the dose of IDV and thus toxicity through boosting with RTV. Despite this, the large number of side effects associated with IDV has limited its role in modern-treatment regimens.

3.3.6. Resistance Profile Unlike many other PIs, IDV is unique in that a single point mutation to the HIV genome is insufficient in substantially reducing drug susceptibility [71].

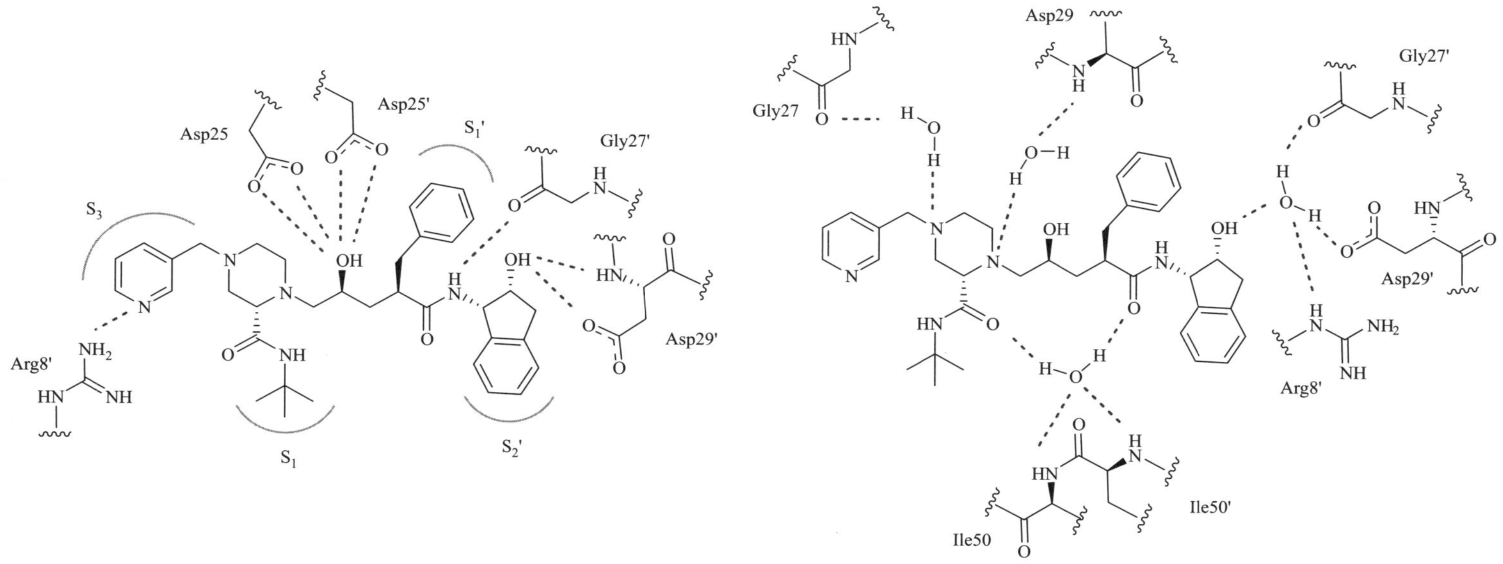

Figure 13. Binding interactions between HIV PR and IDV [58]. (This figure is available in full color at http://mrw.interscience.wiley.com/emrw/9780471266945/home.)

19

Table 10. Select Pharmacokinetic Properties of IDV Administration [59]

Regimen	AUC (mcg·h/mL)	C_{max} (mcg/mL)	T_{max} (h)	$T_{1/2}$ (h)
Crixivan 800 mg tid	30.7	12.6	0.8	1.8

AUC: area under the plasma concentration–time curve; T_{max}: time to C_{max}; $T_{1/2}$: elimination half-life; C_{max}: maximum plasma concentration; tid: three times a day.

Instead, viral strains resistant to IDV have typically accumulated multiple (more than three) mutations. Genotypic analysis of HIV isolates displaying reduced susceptibility to IDV obtained from patients treated with the drug have identified 11 amino acid substitutions associated with IDV resistance: L10I/V/R, K20I/M/R, L24I, I54A/V, L63P, I64V, A71T/V, V82A/F/T, I84V, and L90M [59]. In addition, two primary mutations, M46I/L and V82A/T/F have been associated with IDV [3]. Extensive cross-resistance has been observed between IDV and other PIs. An analysis of 29 HIV isolates displaying reduced susceptibility to IDV indicated 63% and 81% of the viral strains were also resistant to SQV and APV, respectively [3]. Similar observations of cross-resistance occurring between IDV and other early PIs have been reported [51,72].

3.4. Nelfinavir Mesylate (Viracept)

3.4.1. General Information Nelfinavir (NFV also known as AG1343) mesylate (see Fig. 15) was developed through a collaboration between Agouron Pharmaceuticals and Eli Lilly and Company. It received FDA approval on March 14, 1997 and is currently sold under the trade name Viracept by Agouron Pharmaceuticals. The drug is currently available as an orally administered tablet in strengths of 250 or 625 mg [73]. Recent studies indicate NFV may be useful in treating other disorders such as cancer based on its ability to induce cell death mechanisms [74,75]. Ref. [11] includes additional information surrounding its discovery while Ref. [76] discusses its clinical relevance in further detail.

3.4.2. Drug Optimization The development of NFV occurred through a collaborative effort between Agouron Pharmaceuticals and Eli Lilly and Company during the 1990s. SQV had already been identified and served as the initial template upon which structural modifications would be made. The initial strategy was to improve upon the pharmacokinetic properties of SQV by reducing molecular weight and peptidic nature through modifications at three separate locations of SQV (see Fig. 16). Focusing on the perhydroisoquinoline system, initial SAR studies led to the incorporation of an *ortho*-substituted benzamide (LY289612) [77]. While this group was eventually replaced by the original perhydroisoquinoline ligand, it was used extensively during SAR studies that made modifications at other locations. Later development efforts were focused on replacement of the arginine moiety of SQV. Extensive SAR work (see Table 11) led to the identification of a potent inhibitor (AG1254) that contained a novel 2-methyl-3-hydroxy-benzamide group at the P_2 position [78,79]. In addition, thioaryl groups were found to be suitable replacements for the phenyl ligand at the P_1 position (see Table 12) [80,81]. Final modifications aimed at improving aqueous solubility and antiviral activity led to the discovery of NFV, which was successfully advanced through clinical studies [80].

3.4.3. Binding Interactions Due in part to structural similarities, NFV possesses similar binding interactions with HIV PR as SQV (see Fig. 17). The dodecahydroisoquinoline ring system occupies the hydrophobic region of the S_1' subsite while the *tert*-butylcarboxamide fills the S_2' subsite. Other hydrophobic interactions include the S-phenyl group and 2-methyl-3-hydroxy-benzamide that occupy the S_1 and S_2 subsites, respectively. Common to many other PIs, the central hydroxyl group forms hydrogen bonds with the catalytic residues, Asp25 and Asp25', while the two carbonyl groups are involved in water mediated hydrogen bonding to Ile50 and Ile50' on the flap region of the enzyme. In addition, the nitrogen of NFV's backbone amide hydrogen bonds with the carbonyl of Gly27. The hydroxyl group of the 2-methyl-3-hydroxy-benzamide moiety distinct to NFV's structure is involved in hydrogen bonding with the carbonyl of Asp30 [82].

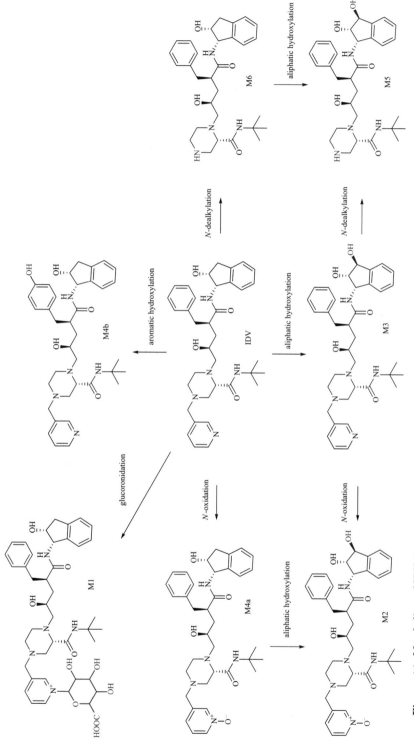

Figure 14. Metabolites of IDV [52,63]. (This figure is available in full color at http://mrw.interscience.wiley.com/emrw/9780471266945/home.)

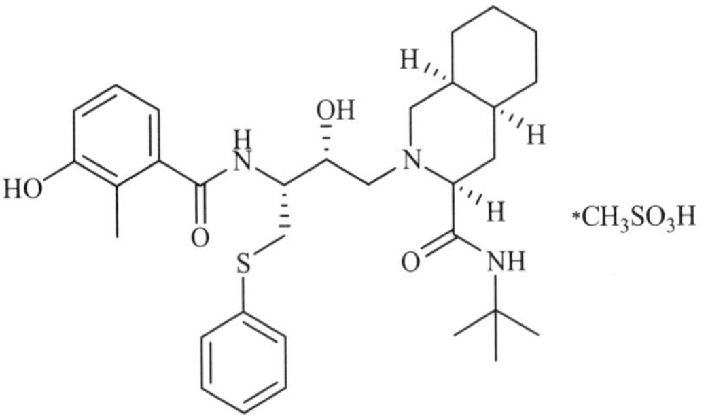

Figure 15. Chemical structure of nelfinavir mesylate.

3.4.4. Pharmacokinetics Values of select pharmacokinetic parameters of NFV have been provided in Table 13. It is recommended that NFV be administered orally with food as meals high in calories or fat have been shown to increase NFV exposure while decreasing pharmacokinetic variance [73]. Once absorbed, NFV undergoes extensive first-pass metabolism resulting in the formation of one major (M8) and several smaller metabolites (see Fig. 18) [73,83]. Cytochrome P-450 enzymes CYP3A and CYP2C19 are the primary isozymes responsible for NFV metabolism [73]. Interestingly, M8 has been shown to retain antiviral activity *in vitro* that is comparable to NFV [73]. In the plasma, both NFV and M8 are highly bound to serum proteins (>98%) and the volume of distribution for NFV was 2–7 L/kg suggesting adequate tissue penetration [73,76]. ^{14}C-NFV studies indicate the primary route of elimination of the drug is through the feces (87%) with only low levels detected in the urine (1–2%) [73]. Oxidative metabolites accounted for the majority of radioactivity in the feces (78%) while low levels of unchanged ^{14}C-NFV were also detected (22%) [73]. In addition to NFV's metabolic susceptibility, it is an inhibitor of CYP3A suggesting the potential for interactions with other drugs [76].

3.4.5. Efficacy and Tolerability A number of studies have demonstrated the efficacy of NFV in combination with other antiretroviral drugs. During study 511, 61% of patients receiving NFV (750 mg three times a day (tid)) with zidovudine (200 mg tid) and lamivudine (150 mg twice a day (bid)) saw viral loads drop below 50 copies/mL at 48 weeks as compared to <10% of patients in the control group [50,73]. Comparable results were observed during the Avanti 3 study [73]. In study 364, NFV was shown to be inferior to treatment with efavirenz; however, coadministration of the drugs with two other nonnucleoside reverse transcriptase inhibitors (NNRTIs) was the most effective treatment regimen [50,73]. Study 542 established that dosing with 1250 mg NFV bid was equally effective as dosing 750 mg NFV tid [50,73]. Subsequent studies have indicated that boosting with RTV is ineffective in increasing the plasma concentration of NFV [50]. In general, treatment with NFV is reasonably well tolerated except for the side effect of diarrhea, which is commonly reported [50,76].

3.4.6. Resistance Profile The primary mutation D30N is unique to NFV resulting in a reduction in drug susceptibility. Another primary mutation associated with NFV is L90M although this substitution occurs less frequently and is commonly associated with several other PIs [85,86]. In terms of secondary mutations, substitutions at amino acid locations 10, 35, 36, 46, 71, 77, and 88 are associated with NFV therapy whereas substitutions at 48, 82, and 84 are not commonly observed despite their exposure to other PI treatments [73,86]. Cross-resistance has been observed between NFV and other PIs. Most patient derived HIV isolates that demonstrate reduced susceptibility (>2.5-fold) to APV, IDV, LPV, or SQV are also cross-resistant to NFV [73]. However, HIV isolates resistant to NFV that contain the D30N mutation typically retain susceptibility (>2.5-fold) to APV, IDV, LPV, and SQV [73].

3.5. Amprenavir (Agenerase)

3.5.1. General Information Amprenavir (APV also known as 141W94, VX-478, and KVX-478) (see Fig. 19, page 28) was approved by the FDA for the treatment of HIV on April 15, 1999. The drug was developed by Vertex Pharmaceuticals who set out to develop a potent PI that was less peptidic in nature and smaller in size than the currently available drugs. APV is currently marketed under the trade names Agenerase and Prozei by GlaxoSmithKline

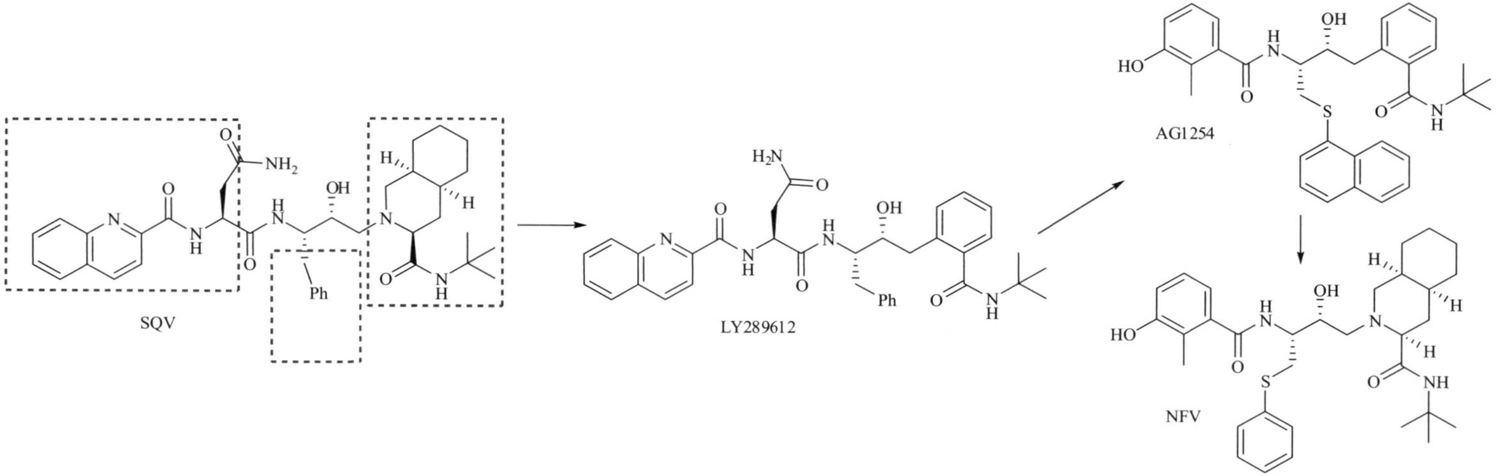

Figure 16. Development of NFV [11]. (This figure is available in full color at http://mrw.interscience.wiley.com/emrw/9780471266945/home.)

23

Table 11. Evaluating Arginine Replacements [79]

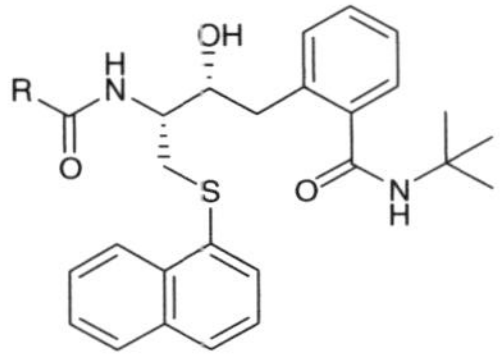

Compound	R	K_i (nM)	IC_{50} (µM)
29	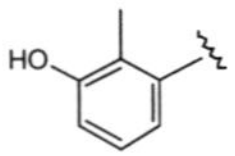	3	0.97 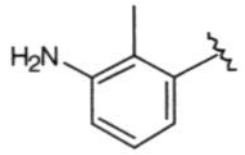 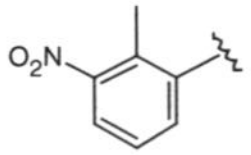
30		500	NA
31		15	NA
32		49	5
33		17	1.3
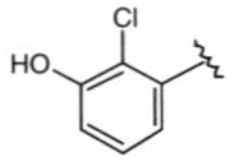 34	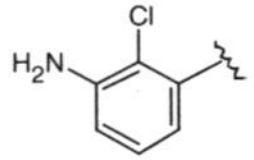	16	1.5
35	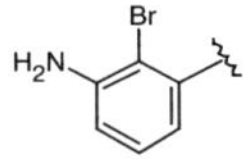	33	1.6
36		540	>50
37		5	0.46

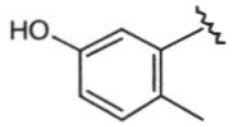

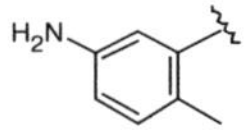

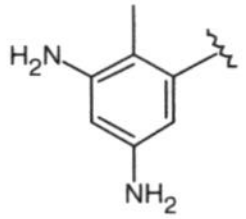

Table 12. Exploration of P$_1$ Ligands [80]

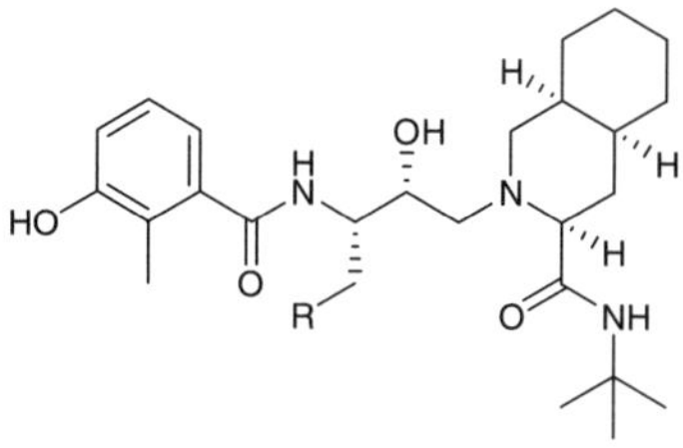

Compound	R	K_i (nM)	ED$_{50}$ (nM)	
38	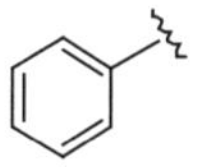	21	33	Mesylate salt
39	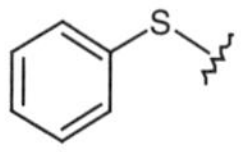	2.0	14	Mesylate salt
40	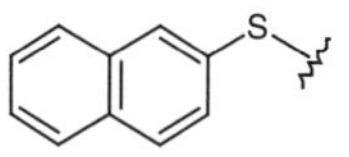	98	100	Free base

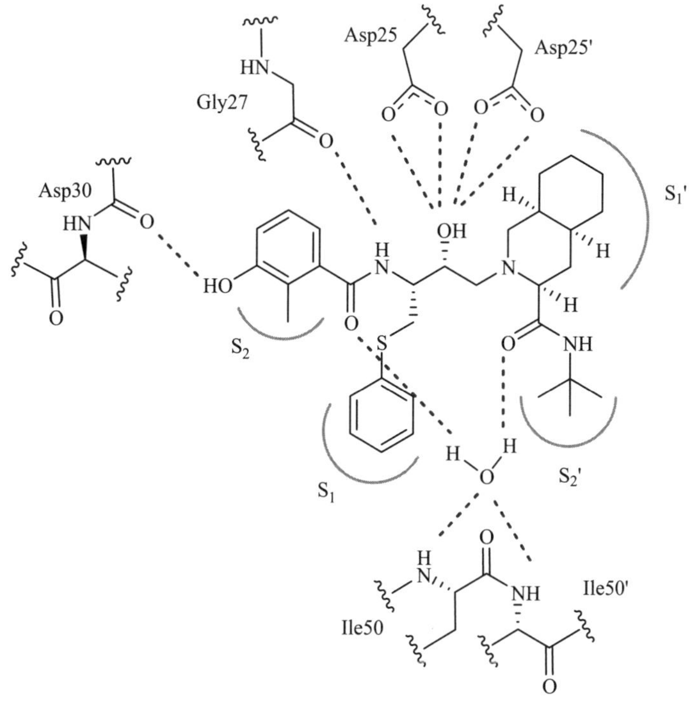

Figure 17. Binding interactions of HIV PR with NFV [82]. (This figure is available in full color at http://mrw. interscience.wiley.com/emrw/9780471266945/home.)

Table 13. Select Pharmacokinetic Parameters of NFV [73,76]

Regimen	C_{max} (mcg/mL)	T_{max} (h)	$T_{1/2}$ (h)	AUC_{24} (mcg·h/mL)	$C_{trough-morning}$ (mcg/mL)	$C_{trough-evening}$ (mcg/mL)	CL/F (L/h/kg)
1250 mg bid	4.0	3	3.7–5.3	52.8	2.2	0.7	0.72
750 mg tid	3.0	—	—	43.6	1.4	1.0	—

AUC_{24}: area under the plasma concentration–time curve at 24 h; T_{max}: time to C_{max}; $T_{1/2}$: elimination half-life; CL/F: apparent clearance; C_{max}: maximum plasma concentration; tid: three times a day; bid: twice a day; $C_{trough-morning}$: minimum morning plasma concentration; $C_{trough-evening}$: minimum evening plasma concentration.

and Kissei Pharmaceutical, respectively. It is currently available as a 50 mg tablet or 15 mg/mL oral suspension [87]. Treatment with APV has been replaced for the most part with Fosamprenavir (FPV), a prodrug form of APV that increases its bioavailability. Refs [11,88–90] include further information pertaining to APV's discovery and clinical success.

3.5.2. Drug Optimization The design of APV began with setting a number of goals intended to improve upon the faults of earlier PIs. A primary goal was to reduce the size of the drug as previous PIs all had molecular weights in excess of 600 Da. To do so, they decided to limit hydrophobic interactions and focus on making hydrogen bonding interactions to protease backbone atoms. It was realized that S_1 and S_2 sites were critical for substrate recognition and specificity from other aspartyl proteases; however, hydrophobic interactions at S_3 and S_4 were deemed unnecessary. A second goal was to improve upon the drugs' pharmacokinetic properties by utilizing nonionizable functional groups and appropriately balancing lipophilicity to allow central nervous system (CNS) penetration and oral bioavailability. While reviewing the binding interactions of earlier PIs, it was observed that the nitrogen at the P_1' location was not critical for binding; however, the corresponding carbonyl was significant due to a water-mediated hydrogen-bonding interaction with the Ile flap residues. A desire to remove this amide group and thereby reduce the peptidic nature of the molecule led to the incorporation of a *N,N*-dialkyl sulfonamide unit. It was envisioned that this functional group would maintain the critical flap binding while offering an easily accessible synthetic route. Shifting focus to the other end of the molecule, it was quickly

realized from computational studies that simple alkyl carbamates could serve as potent lead structures (see Table 14). The use of (*S*)-tetrahydrofuryloxycarbonyl at this position was attractive due to its small size, ease of synthesis, and previously demonstrated successes by Ghosh et al. [91]. Further improvements to binding were realized by replacing cyclopentane with an isobutyl group. Subsequent modifications were made to the phenyl ring linked to the sulfonamide as a means to improve the pharmacokinetic profile (see Table 15). This resulted in the discovery of APV, which was successfully advanced through clinical trials [11].

3.5.3. Binding Interactions APV exhibits multiple binding interactions with the HIV PR (see Fig. 20). Favorable hydrophobic interactions occur from the filling of the S_1 and S_1' sites by the phenyl and isopropyl moieties. Seven hydrogen-bonding interactions occur directly between APV and the protease while a water-mediated hydrogen bond occurs between APV and the flap residues Ile50 and Ile50'. Interestingly, the nitrogen from the carbamate does not hydrogen bond with Gly27 as observed with other inhibitors [92]. A distinguishing feature of APV from other first-generation inhibitors is the hydrogen-bonding interactions occurring between the tetrahedron ring of APV and the nitrogen backbone atoms on Asp29 and Asp30 of the protease. Another distinctive characteristic of APV binding was revealed by thermodynamic studies that showed APV binding to HIV PR was driven by both enthalpy and entropy terms, whereas only entropy drives the binding of the other first-generation inhibitors [93,94]. In addition to binding at the catalytic site, recent studies suggest APV along with DRV bind at a second site located on the surface of the flexible flap

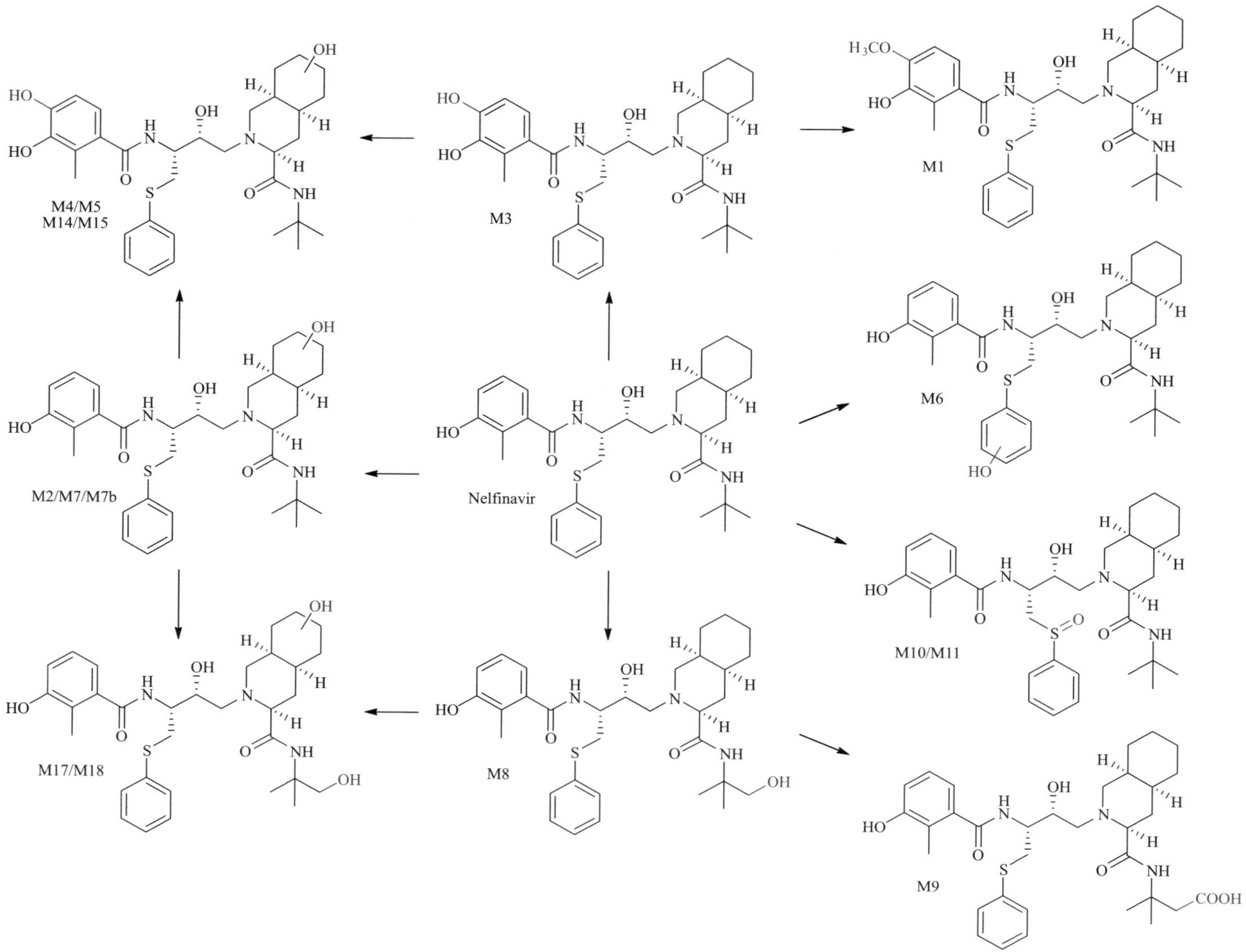

Figure 18. Metabolite profile of NFV [84]. (This figure is available in full color at http://mrw.interscience.wiley.com/emrw/9780471266945/home.)

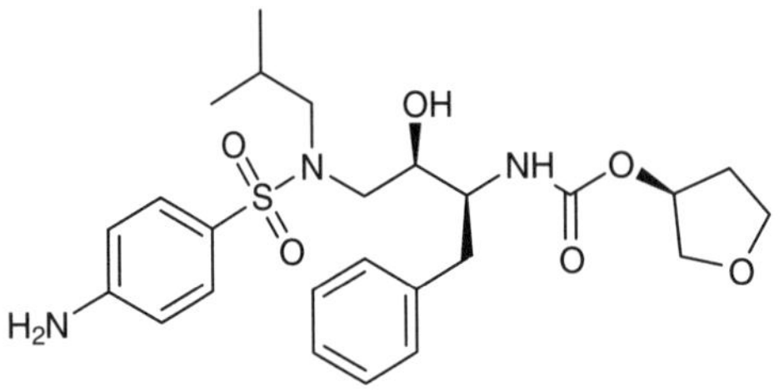

Figure 19. Chemical structure of amprenavir.

Table 14. Exploration of P$_2$ Ligands [11]

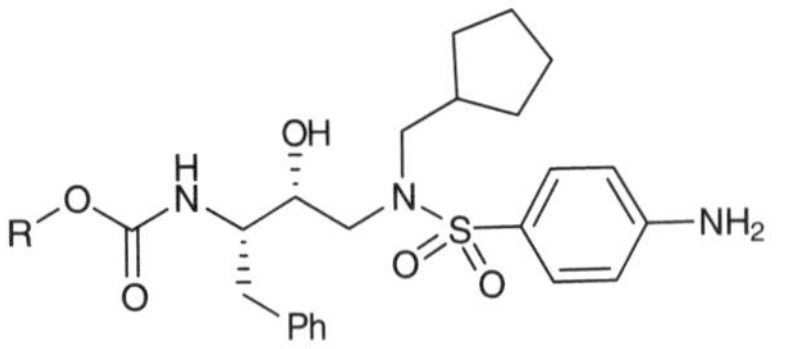

Compound	R	K_i (Calculated)
41	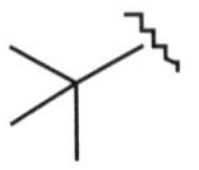	0.3
42	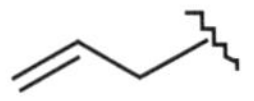	0.1
43	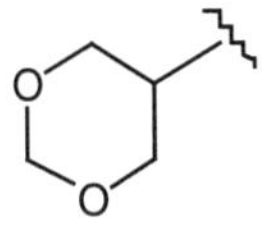	<0.1
44	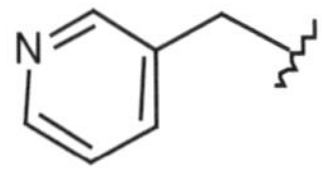	<0.1
45	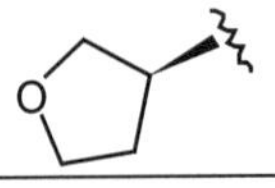	<0.1

Table 15. Optimizing Pharmacokinetic Properties [11]

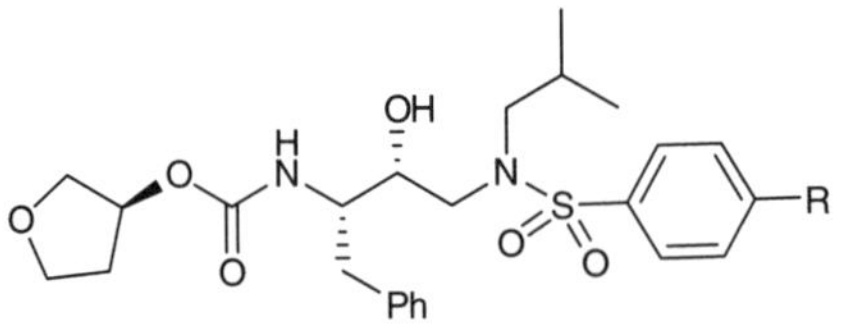

Compound	R	Aq. Solubility (µg/mL)	K_i (nM)	IC$_{90}$ (nM)	C_{max} (nM)
46	—OCH$_3$	1	0.16	50	360
47	—NH—CHCH$_3$	46	1.3	190	424
48	—NH$_2$	190	0.6	47	190

region of the protease [95]. This unique property along with APV's other characteristic binding interactions contributes to the molecule's high potency and unique resistance profile.

3.5.4. Pharmacokinetics Values of select pharmacokinetic parameters of APV have been provided in Table 16. When administered orally, APV is absorbed rapidly into the blood plasma ($T_{max} \sim 1$–2 h) where it is highly bound to serum proteins (90%) having a particular high binding affinity for α_1-acid glycoproteins [87]. Dosing may occur with or without food; however, APV taken with a high-fat meal has been shown to decrease absorption of the drug into the body [87]. While in circulation, APV is extensively metabolized by CYP3A4 forming two main metabolites that result from the oxidation of the tetrahydrofuran and *p*-aniline sulfonate groups (see Fig. 21) [87,96]. ^{14}C-labeling studies indicated the main route of APV elimination is through the feces (75%) with a lesser amount excreted in the urine (14%) [96]. Metabolites of APV accounted for 94% of the radioactivity in the feces with minimal amounts of unchanged APV detected [96]. APV is a known substrate of P-glycoprotein, which may account for its inability to effectively penetrate into the CNS [90]. In addition, APV is a weak inhibitor of CYP3A4 suggesting the potential for drug–drug interactions exist [88].

3.5.5. Efficacy and Tolerability A variety of studies have been conducted to demonstrate the efficacy of APV. In PROAB3001, 53% of therapy-naïve patients receiving APV (1200 mg bid) with lamivudine (150 mg bid)

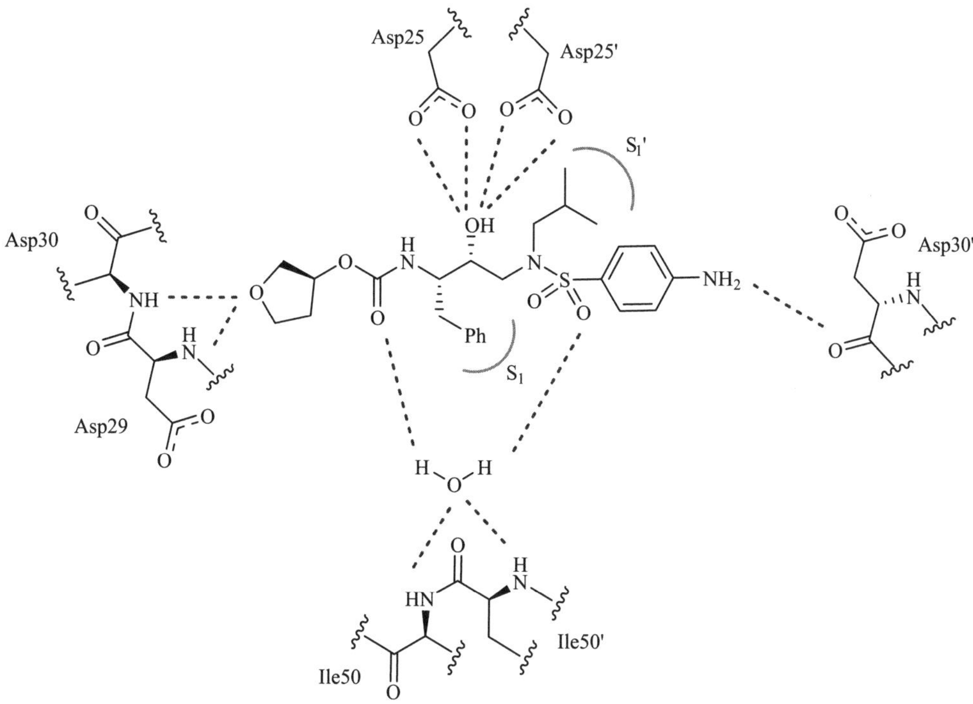

Figure 20. Proposed binding interactions between APV and HIV PR [92,94]. (This figure is available in full color at http://mrw.interscience.wiley.com/emrw/9780471266945/home.)

and zidovudine (300 mg bid) achieved HIV plasma RNA levels below 400 copies/mL in comparison to 11% of therapy-naïve patients receiving only lamivudine and zidovudine [87]. Study PROAB3006 showed APV to be less effective than IDV in NRTI-experienced patients in terms of decreasing plasma viral load and increasing CD4 + cell counts [87]. The use of RTV to boost APV has been shown to be an effective treatment regimen for antiretroviral treatment-experienced patients [89]. In general, administration of APV is reasonably well tolerated with the most common adverse events reported during clinical studies including nausea, vomiting, diarrhea, abdominal pain, and skin rash [87].

3.5.6. Resistance Profile The amino acid substitution I50V is the signature mutation associated with APV resistance [97]. While alternate pathways to APV resistance exist such as I54L/M, I84V, or V32I + I47V, the I50V substitution was not observed with past PIs and was found to significantly reduce viral susceptibility to APV [97]. The secondary mutations M46I/L and I47V commonly occur after I50V and serve to enhance viral resistance to APV [97]. Cross-resistance to other PIs has been observed but occurs to a lesser extent with many of the earlier PIs; however, cross-resistance to RTV is more significant [97].

Table 16. Select Pharmacokinetic Properties of APV [87]

Regimen	C_{max} (mcg/mL)	T_{max} (h)	AUC_{12} (mcg·h/mL)	C_{min} (mcg/mL)	CL/F (mL/min/kg)	V_z/F (L)
Agenerase 1200 mg bid	7.66	1.0	17.7	0.32	19.5	430

AUC_{12}: area under the plasma concentration–time curve at 12 h; T_{max}: time to C_{max}; V_z/F: apparent volume of distribution; C_{max}: maximum plasma concentration; C_{min}: minimum plasma concentration; CL/F: apparent clearance; bid: twice a day.

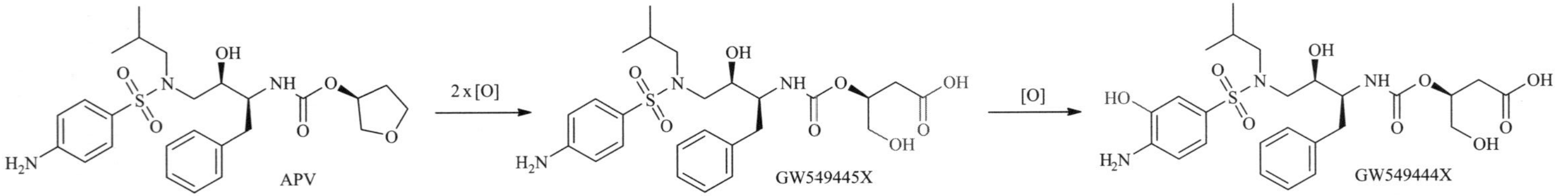

Figure 21. Major metabolites of APV [87]. (This figure is available in full color at http://mrw.interscience.wiley.com/emrw/9780471266945/home.)

4. SECOND-GENERATION INHIBITORS

4.1. Lopinavir and Ritonavir (Kaletra)

4.1.1. General Information Lopinavir (also known as ABT-378) (see Fig. 22) is a unique HIV PI in that it is coformulated with RTV, which is marketed under the trade name Kaletra. Developed by Abbott Laboratories, the drug was the first second-generation HIV PI to become commercially available having received FDA approval on September 15, 2000. LPV was developed from efforts to improve upon RTV by identifying compounds with improved pharmacokinetic properties and higher antiviral activity. Kaletra is currently available as an oral suspension or tablet in a variety of strengths. Reviews [11,37,38] provide additional details of the drug's development and clinical properties.

4.1.2. Drug Optimization The progression of RTV through advanced clinical studies led to three key observations that impacted the development of LPV. First, viral mutations with resistance to RTV were identified, which appeared to accumulate amino acid substitutions during the course of RTV therapy. It was theorized that these mutations developed due to incomplete suppression of viral activity occurring between dosing intervals when RTV plasma concentrations were insufficient. To combat this problem, future drug molecules should have enhanced potency and maintain higher plasma concentrations. It was further noted that RTV resistance was associated with the primary mutation V82A/F/T, which resulted in the loss of a key hydrophobic interaction leading to decreased drug susceptibility. This led to the idea of removing the P_3 ligand from RTV as a means to identify potent compounds that would not rely on this interaction and hence maintain potency against the mutants. As shown in Table 17, this initially led to a decrease in potency; however,

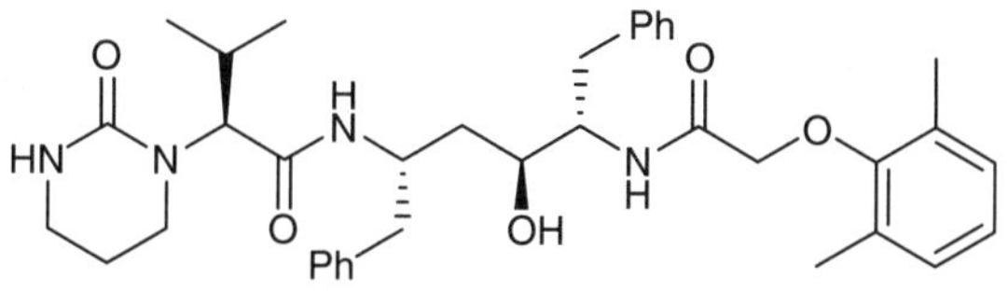

Figure 22. Chemical structure of lopinavir.

Table 17. Effect of Truncating P_3 Ligand of RTV [98]

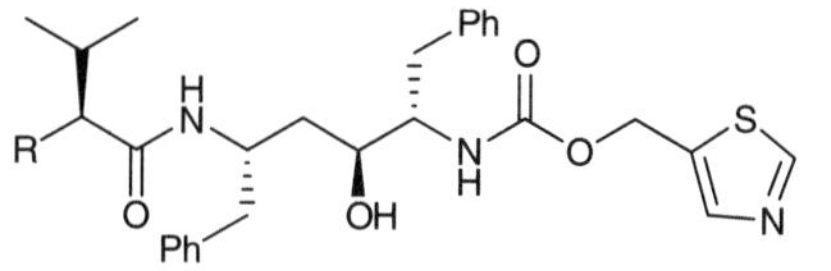

Compound	R	%Inhibition @ 0.5 nM	EC_{50} (µM) 0% HS	EC_{50} (µM) 50% HS
49	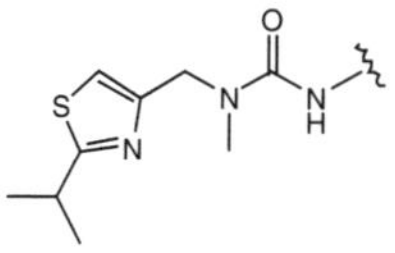	79	0.06	1.04
50	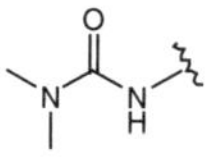	49	1.8	4.2
51	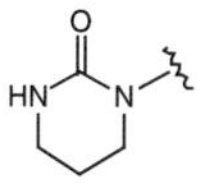	79	0.15	0.64

cyclization of the terminal urea restored much of the activity and further modifications on the other end of the molecule (see Table 18) led to very potent compounds. A second observation made during RTV clinical trials was the high degree to which RTV was bound to serum proteins, which greatly affected the drugs *in vivo* potency. As a result, an assay that determined drug EC_{50} in the presence of either 0% or 50% human serum was used to identify compounds with *in vivo* potencies less sensitive to human serum protein binding. The third finding from the RTV studies was that RTV was a potent inhibitor of the CYP3A isozymes, a property that resulted from the direct binding of RTV's 5-thiazolyl group to the CYP heme iron atom. As such, it was realized that RTV could be used to inhibit the metabolism of drug molecules thereby increasing their plasma concentrations and serum half-life. New drug candidates were subsequently screened for their pharmacokinetic properties in animals evaluated when administered by themselves or with a low level dose of RTV. From these concepts, LPV emerged as a highly potent drug candidate that had impressive pharmacokinetic properties when dosed with RTV and maintained antiviral activity in the presence of human serum proteins and V82 mutations.

4.1.3. Binding Interactions

X-ray crystallography studies have provided insights into the binding interactions between LPV and HIV PR (see Fig. 23). LPV contains four hydrophobic side chains that fill the enzyme's lipophillic subsites S_1, S_2, S_1', S_2' [100]. Interactions common to many other PIs include hydrogen bonding of the hydroxyl group to the catalytic residues Asp25/Asp25' and water-mediated hydrogen bonding of the carbonyl moieties to Ile50/Ile50' on the flap region [100]. The cyclic urea, an important feature to LPV's structure, is involved in hydrogen-bonding interactions with the backbone amine of Asp29 and its side chain [100]. This group lacks van der Waals interactions with V82, a distinction from the isopropylthiazolylmethyl urea moiety of RTV, allowing LPV to maintain potency against many RTV resistant mutants [100].

4.1.4. Pharmacokinetics

Values of select pharmacokinetic parameters of LPV have been provided in Table 19. LPV, when administered orally, is rapidly absorbed into the bloodstream. Dosing with food has been shown to increase the drugs bioavailability and reduce pharmacokinetic variability [101]. In the plasma, LPV is highly bound to serum proteins (98–99%) having a high affinity for α1-acid glycoprotein and slightly lower affinity for albumin [101]. LPV is extensively metabolized to a variety of metabolites (see Fig. 24) by CYP3A4 and CYP3A5 isozymes with M1, M3, and M4 representing the major metabolic pathways [101,102]. As a result, LPV has been formulated with RTV, a potent inhibitor of CYP3A, to slow down the metabolism of LPV and increase its concentration in the plasma. ^{14}C-LPV studies have shown the primary route of LPV elimination is through the feces (82.6%) with a lesser amount found in the urine (10.4%) [101]. Only low levels of unchanged ^{14}C-LPV were found in the urine (2.2%) and feces (19.8%) with the remaining radioactivity attributed to the various metabolites [101].

4.1.5. Efficacy and Tolerability

LPV/r has been involved in a number of clinical studies that have demonstrated its efficacy against HIV. In a comparative study (Study 863) of LPV/r (400/100 mg bid) to NFV (750 mg tid) in antiretroviral treatment-naïve patients also receiving lamivudine and stavudine, administration of LPV/r resulted in a higher percentage of patients demonstrating virologic response at 48 weeks (see Table 20) [101]. Additional clinical trials have shown that once-a-day LPV/r treatment (800/200 mg) is as effective as twice-a-day (400/100 mg) treatment in antiretroviral treatment-naïve patients; however, once–a-day dosing is not recommended for antiretroviral treatment-experienced patients [101]. In antiretroviral treatment-experienced patients receiving a background regimen of NFV and NRTIs, Study 888 compared LPV/r (400/100 mg bid) to an investigator selected PI. A higher percentage of patients receiving LPV/r (57%) demonstrated virologic response at 48 weeks in terms of suppressed HIV plasma RNA concentrations (<400 copies/mL) than pa-

Table 18. Modification of P′₂ Ligand to Enhance Potency [98,99]

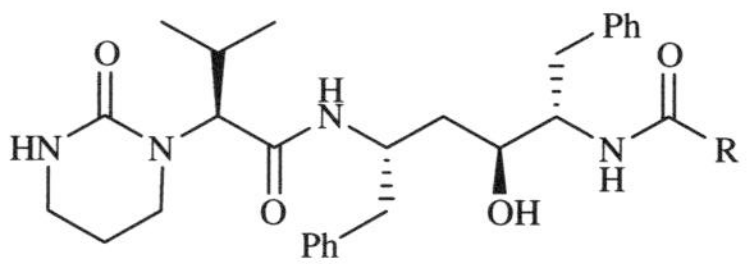

Compound	R	%Inhibition @ 0.5 nM	EC_{50} (µM) 0% HS	EC_{50} (µM) 50% HS	Compound	R	%Inhibition @ 0.5 nM	EC_{50} (µM) 50% HS
52	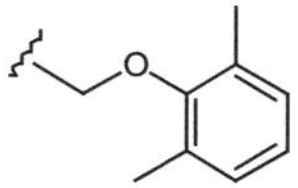	93	0.017	0.10	**58**	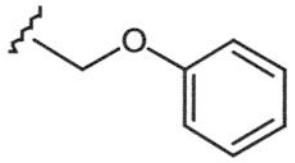	67	1.3
53	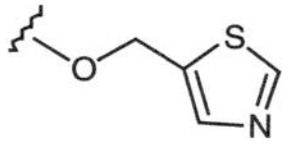	79	0.15	0.64	**59**	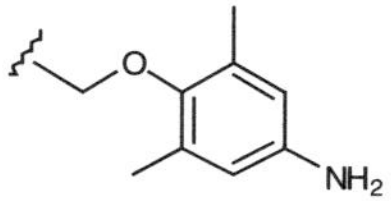	86	16
54	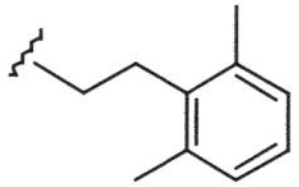	70	—	2.6	**60**	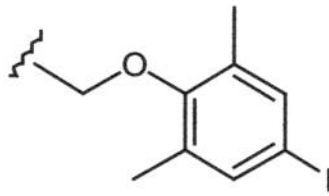	90	0.49
55	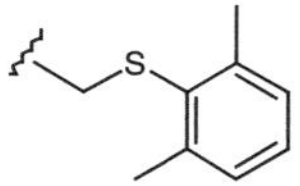	55	—	4.1	**61**	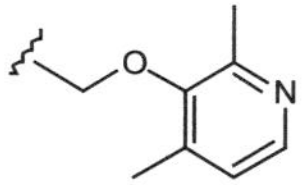	75	0.77
56	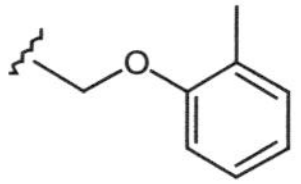	84	—	0.43	**62**	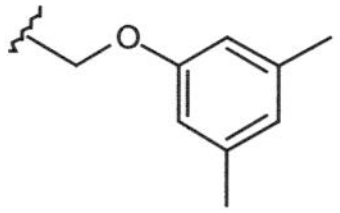	37	38
57	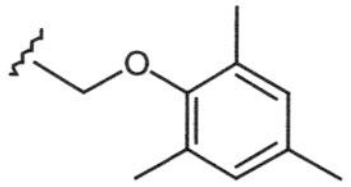	85	—	0.39	**63**	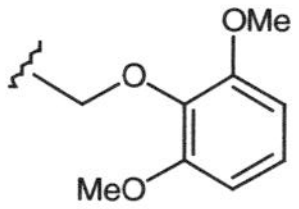	38	14

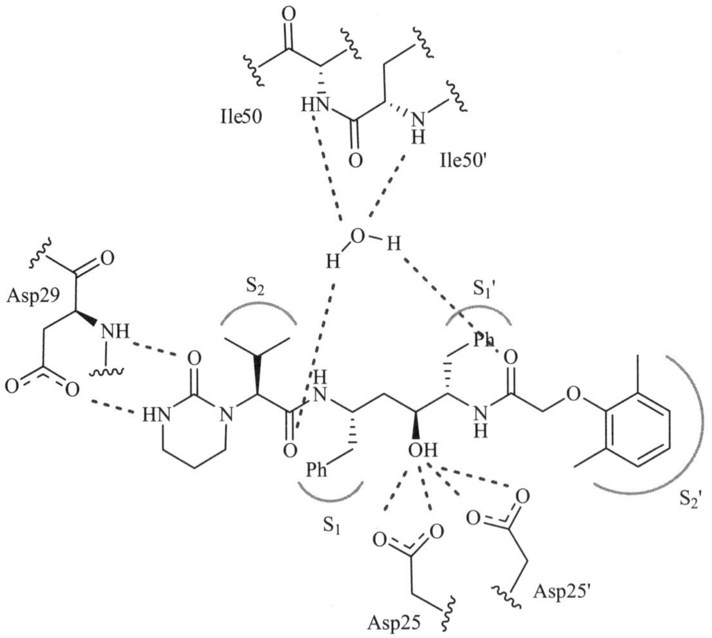

Figure 23. Proposed binding interactions of LPV with HIV PR [100]. (This figure is available in full color at http://mrw.interscience.wiley.com/emrw/9780471266945/home.)

tients receiving comparative PIs (33%) (see Table 20) [101].

Overall LPV/r was generally well tolerated during clinical trials with the most common adverse events including diarrhea, nausea, and vomiting and rare occurrence of serious adverse events [101]. Reports of diarrhea were more frequent in once-a-day dosing regimens [101]. Similar to other PIs, laboratory abnormalities included hypertriglyceridemia and hypercholesterolemia in <39% of patients while elevated levels of aspartate transaminase (AST) and alanine transaminase (ALT) were observed in <10% of patients [101].

4.1.6. Resistance Profile In antiretroviral treatment-naïve patients, no pattern of pri-mary mutations has yet been associated with reduced susceptibility to LPV/r [101]. During clinical testing in antiretroviral treatment-experienced patients, a decrease in virologic response was observed in patients possessing three or more of the following mutations at baseline: L10F/I/R/V, K20/M/N/R, L24I, L33F, M36I, I47V, G48V, I54L/T/V, V82A/C/F/S/T, and I84V [101]. Pooled clinical trial results indicate mutations at M46I/L, I54V, and V82A were the most frequent to develop in antiretroviral treatment-experienced patients receiving LPV/r therapy [104]. Cross-resistance with other PIs has occurred to varying degrees [101]. HIV viral isolates from antiretroviral treatment-experienced patients displaying reduced susceptibility (>4-fold) to NFV and

Table 19. Select Pharmacokinetic Properties of LPV [101,103]

Regimen	AUC_{12} (mcg h/mL)	C_{max} (mcg/mL)	C_{min} (mcg/mL)	T_{max} (h)	CL/F (L/h)
LPV/r 400/100 mg bid	92.6	9.8	5.5	4.4	6.0
LPV/r 800/200 mg qd	82.5	10.9	2.5	6.6	—

AUC_{12}: area under the concentration curve at 12 h; C_{min}: minimum concentration; C_{max}: maximum plasma concentration; CL/F: apparent clearance; bid: twice a day; qd: once a day.

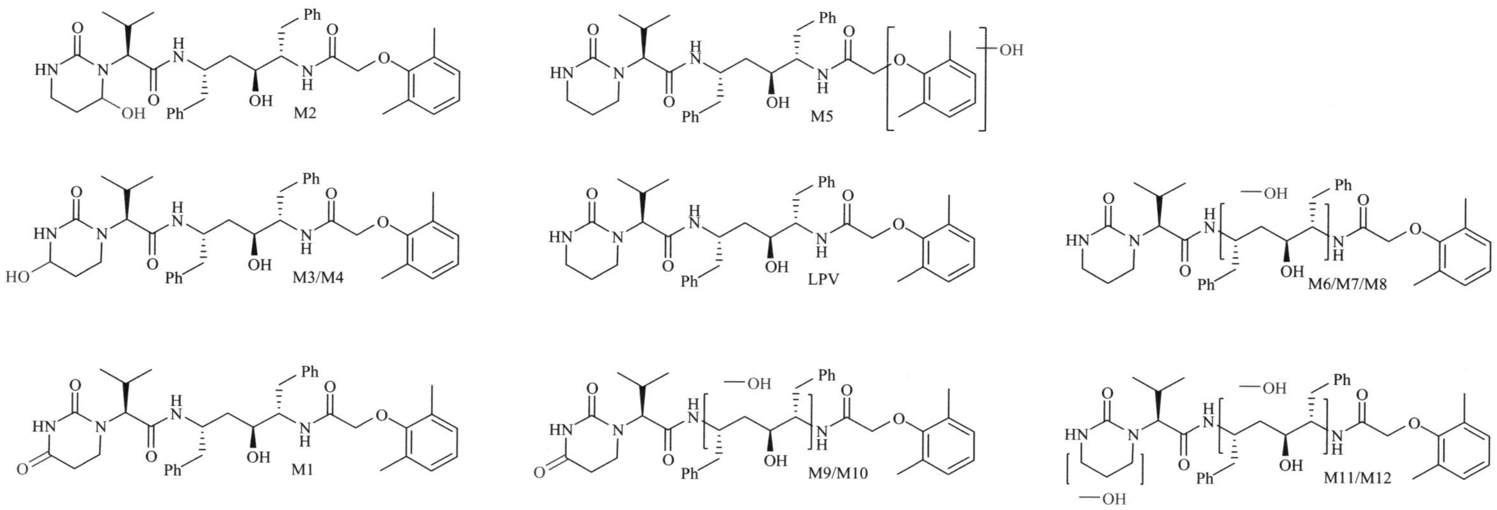

Figure 24. Proposed metabolites of LPV [102]. (This figure is available in full color at http://mrw.interscience.wiley.com/emrw/9780471266945/home.)

35

Table 20. Select Results from LPV/r Clinical Studies [100]

Clinical Study	Study 863		Study 418		Study 888	
Treatment regimen	LPV/r bid 400/100 mg	NFV tid 750 mg	LPV/r qd 800/200 mg	LPV/r bid 400/100 mg	LPV/r bid 400/100 mg	CPI
Background regimen	D4T/3TC		TFR/FTC		NFV/NRTI—	
Baseline statistics						
Number of patients	326	327	115	75	148	140
Patient type	Naïve		Naïve		Experienced	
Baseline CD4+ (cells/L)	259		260		322	
Baseline viral load ($\log_{10}$ copies/mL)	4.9		4.8		4.1	
Efficacy results						
Viral suppression (%):						
<400 (copies/mL)	75	62	—	—	57	33
<50 (copies/mL)	67	52	71	65	—	—
CD4+ increase (cells/L)[a]	207	195	185	196	111	112
Virologic failure	9	25	7	17	24	41

[a]Median value. ATV: atazanavir; r: ritonavir; LPV: lopinavir; EFV: efavirenz; NFV: nelfinavir; SQV: saquinavir; TFR: tenofovir; FTC: emtricitabine; 3TC: lamivudine; ZDV: zidovudine; D4T: stavudine; NRTI: nucleoside reverse transcriptase inhibitor; bid: twice a day; tid: three times a day; qd: once a day.

SQV maintained susceptibility to LPV; however, isolates with reduced susceptibility to IDV and RTV were also resistant to LPV [101].

4.2. Atazanavir Sulfate (Reyataz)

4.2.1. General Information Atazanavir (ATV also known as BMS-232632) sulfate (see Fig. 25) was developed by Bristol-Myers Squibb and is currently marketed under the brand name Reyataz. Approved by the FDA on June 20, 2003, this PI has the advantage of offering a once-a-day dosing regimen and possesses a unique side effect and resistance profile. ATV is an effective treatment for naïve HIV patients; however, its efficacy in antiretroviral treatment-experienced patients is less apparent. It is available in 100, 150, 200, and 300 mg capsules [105–107].

4.2.2. Drug Optimization The development of ATV focused on structure–activity relationships of protease inhibitors that incorporated a hydroxyethyl hydrazine aza-peptide isostere (see Fig. 26). This transition-state mimic offered several advantages over other isosteres including the elimination of a chiral center by replacement of the carbon bearing P_1' substi-

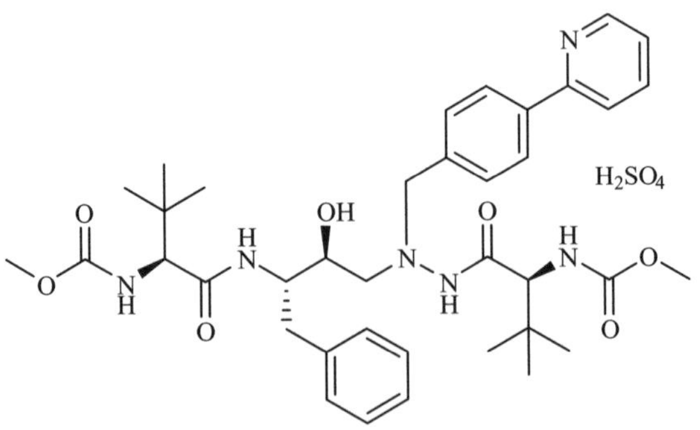

Figure 25. Chemical structure of atazanavir sulfate.

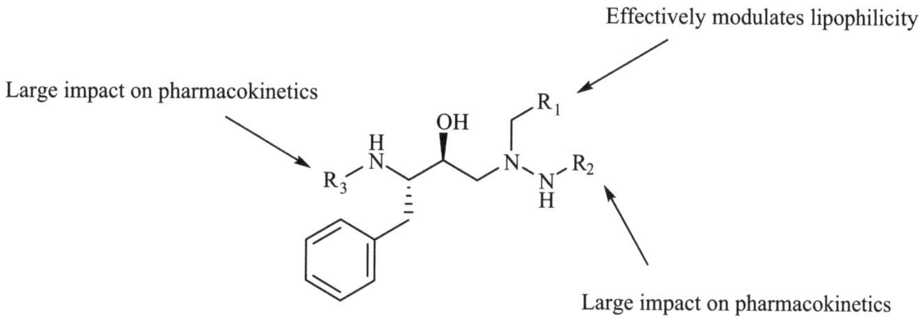

Figure 26. Structure of the hydroxyethyl hydrazine aza-peptide isostere [108,109].

tuent and access to a broad range of substituents by simple acylation chemistry. Initial optimization studies were based on X-ray crystal data of an aza-peptide inhibitor in complex with HIV PR [108]. Variations of R_1 (see Fig. 26) were shown to be largely tolerated in terms of antiviral activity and proved to be an effective site for modulating lipophilicity. Substitutions at R_2 and R_3 (see Fig. 26) were primarily acyl or carbamate residues based on valine or asparagine. Interestingly, small changes made at these locations greatly influenced the pharmacokinetic profile of the inhibitor. Unfortunately, the inhibitors evaluated during this study had either high-antiviral activity or good oral bioavailability, but did not possess both of these properties [109]. As a result, further SAR

work was completed in hopes of incorporating both of these features into a single inhibitor (see Tables 21 and 22). Further examination of the X-ray crystal data suggested that larger groups could be tolerated at R_1. This led to the discovery of a series of molecules that showed similar antiviral activity as SQV and had excellent oral bioavailability. After further characterization, ATV was selected from this group and advanced through clinical trials [110].

4.2.3. Binding Interactions The X-ray crystal structure of ATV in complex with two variants of the HIV PR has provided insight into the binding of ATV in the active site (see Fig. 27). Unlike many protease inhibitors, ATV bind-

Table 21. Effect of Modifying R_3 and R_2 [110]

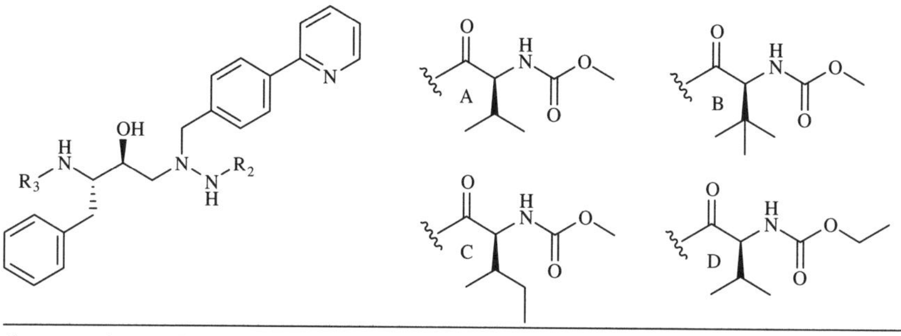

Compound	R_3	R_2	IC_{50} (nM)	ED_{50} (nM)	ED_{90} (nM)	c_{30} (μM)	c_{90} (μM)
64	A	A	29	7.4	30	2.7	2.2
65	A	B	20	2	10	13.8	12.7
66	B	A	31	2.6	10	15.3	13.3
67	B	B	26	1.4	3	21.8	31.8
68	C	A	28	2.8	10	0.4	0.3
69	A	D	34	5.4	30	0.5	0.2

Table 22. Effect of Modifying R_1 [110]

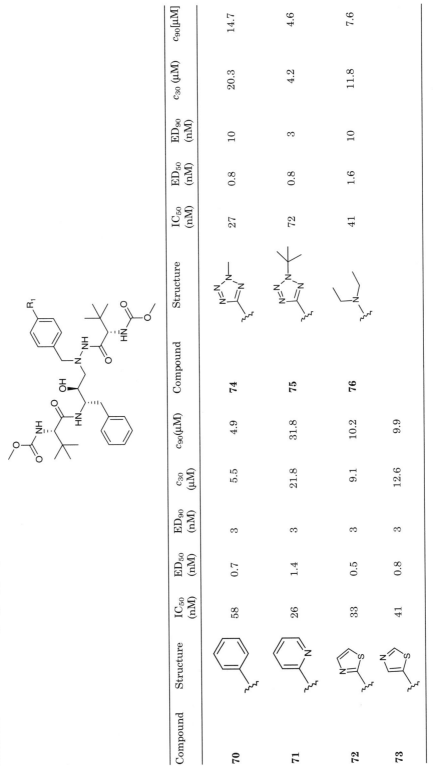

Compound	Structure	IC_{50} (nM)	ED_{50} (nM)	ED_{90} (nM)	c_{30} (µM)	c_{90} (µM)
70	(phenyl)	58	0.7	3	5.5	4.9
71	(pyridine)	26	1.4	3	21.8	31.8
72	(thiazole)	33	0.5	3	9.1	10.2
73	(thiazole)	41	0.8	3	12.6	9.9
74	(methyltriazole)	27	0.8	10	20.3	14.7
75	(tert-butyltriazole)	72	0.8	3	4.2	4.6
76	(diethylamino)	41	1.6	10	11.8	7.6

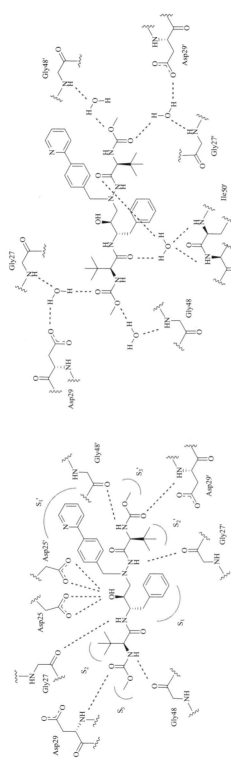

Figure 27. Proposed interactions of ATV with HIV PR [111]. (This figure is available in full color at http://mrw.interscience.wiley.com/emrw/9780471266945/home.)

ing incorporates multiple hydrogen-bond interactions directly to the main-chain atoms of the protease (shown on the left side of Fig. 27 excluding the interaction of the central hydroxyl with Asp25). As a result of these backbone interactions, mutations at these residues would not be expected to affect ATV's antiviral activity. Other factors affecting ATV's binding affinity include hydrophobic interactions of the phenyl, 2-phenylpyridiyl, t-butyl and methyl carbamate groups as well as multiple water-mediated hydrogen bonds (shown on the right side of Fig. 27).

4.2.4. Pharmacokinetics

Values of select pharmacokinetic parameters of ATV have been provided in Table 23. Upon oral administration, ATV is rapidly absorbed into the body. When taken with food, significant increases in bioavailability and a reduction of pharmacokinetic variability were observed [112]. ATV has a high affinity for plasma proteins binding to both α1-acid glycoprotein and albumin (89% and 86%, respectively) [112]. ATV can be extensively metabolized by CYP3A forming monooxygenated and deoxygenated metabolites displaying decreased antiviral activity. A number of other minor metabolites formed from glucuronidation, hydrolysis, N-dealkylation, and oxygenation with dehydrogenation have also been reported [112]. As a result, coadministration with RTV is required to maintain adequate plasma concentrations. ATV is a competitive inhibitor of CYP3A and UGT1A1 and a weak inhibitor of CYP2C8, therefore caution

should be taken to prevent possible drug–drug interactions from occurring [112]. Radiolabelled ^{14}C-ATV studies indicate the drug is primarily eliminated via the biliary pathway with 79% excreted in the feces and only 13% excreted in the urine [112]. Of the material eliminated from the body, 20% (feces) and 7% (urine) were unchanged drug [112].

4.2.5. Efficacy and Tolerability

Results of clinical studies with ATV (see Table 24) have clearly demonstrated the drug's usefulness in antiretroviral treatment-naïve patients. In one study (AI424-138 open label, randomized, multicenter), ATV dosed with RTV (100/100 mg once every day (qd)) was compared to LPV with RTV (400/100 mg qd). Patients were administered a background regiment of tenofovir and emtricitabine (300/200 mg qd). Patients receiving ATV responded in a similar fashion as those in the LPV group. A second study performed with treatment-naïve patients (AI424-008 randomized, multicenter, blinded to dose of ATV), evaluated ATV without RTV taken once-a-day at two separate dosages (400 mg or 600 mg qd) against NFV (1250 mg bid). Participants were administered a background regimen of stavudine and lamivudine (40/150 mg bid). ATV was as effective as NFV even at the lower dosage.

The effectiveness of ATV in antiretroviral treatment-experienced patients has been less definitive. In one study (AI424-034, randomized, double blind, multicenter), ATV (400 mg qd) was compared to the nucleoside reverse transcriptase inhibitor efavirenz (600 mg qd)

Table 23. Select Pharmacokinetic Data for ATV [112]

Patients	C_{min} (mcg/mL)	C_{max} (mcg/mL)	T_{half} (h)	T_{max} (h)	AUC (mcg·h/mL)	Dosage
Healthy ($n = 14$)	0.2 ± 0.2	5.4 ± 1.4	7.9	2.5	29.3 ± 8.3	ATV 400 mg qd
HIV infected ($n = 13$)	0.3 ± 0.3^a	3.2 ± 2.2	6.5	2.0	22.3 ± 20.2	ATV 400 mg qd
Healthy ($n = 28$)	14.4 ± 0.8	6.5 ± 2.0	18.1^b	2.7	61.4 ± 22.9	ATV/r 300/100 mg qd
HIV infected ($n = 10$)	0.9 ± 0.8	5.2 ± 3.0	8.6	3.0	53.8 ± 35.3	ATV/r 300/100 mg qd
At least 6–13 ($n = 17$)	0.5 ± 0.1	4.5 ± 0.0	—	—	42.5 ± 0.0	ATV/r 205/100 mg/m^2
At least 13–18 ($n = 10$)	1.1 ± 0.1	3.7 ± 0.0	—	—	45.0 ± 0.0	ATV/r 205/100 mg/m^2

$^a n = 12.$ $^b n = 26.$
Adult results reported as mean $\pm$ standard deviation.
Pediatric results reported as geometric mean (CV%).
I_{max}: maximum plasma concentration; T_{half}: plasma elimination half-life; AUC: area under the plasma concentration curve h; C_{min}: minimum plasma concentration; T_{max} = time to C_{max}; qd: once a day.

Table 24. Select Results from ATV Clinical Studies at 48 Weeks [112]

Clinical Study	AI424-138		AI424-034		AI424-008		AI424-045		
Treatment regimen	ATV/r qd 300/100 mg	LPV/r bid 400/100 mg	ATV qd 400 mg	EFV qd 600 mg	ATV qd 400 mg	NFV bid 1250 mg	ATV/r qd 300/100 mg	LPV/r bid 400/100 mg	ATV/SQV qd 200/1200 mg
Background regimen	TFR/FTC 300/200 mg qd		3TC/ZDV 150/300 mg bid		3TC/D4T 150/40 mg bid			TDF + NRTI	
Baseline statistics									
Number of patients	441	437	405	405	181	91	119	118	115
Patient type	Naïve		Experienced		Naïve		Experienced		
Baseline CD4+ (cells/L)	204	200	321		295		338		
Baseline viral load ($\log_{10}$ copies/mL)	4.94		4.8		4.7		4.4		
Efficacy results									
Viral suppression (%):									
<400 (copies/mL)	—	—	67	62	67	59	55	57	38
<50 (copies/mL)	78	77	32	37	33	38	38	45	26
CD4+ increase (cells/L)[a]	191	200	176	160	234	211	116	123	72
Virologic failure	12	12	20	21	24	27	—	—	—

[a]Median time on therapy was 48 weeks unless otherwise denoted by parenthesis.

ATV: atazanavir; r: ritonavir; LPV: lopinavir; EFV: efavirenz; NFV: nelfinavir; SQV: saquinavir; TFR: tenofovir; FTC: emtricitabine; 3TC: lamivudine; ZDV: zidovudine; D4T: stavudine; NRTI: nucleoside reverse transcriptase inhibitor; ULN: upper limit of normal bid: twice a day; qd: once a day.

with patients receiving a background regimen of lamivudine and zidovudine (150/300 mg bid). After 48 weeks of therapy, ATV was found to be comparable to efavirenz. A second study in treatment-experienced patients (AI424-045 randomized, multicenter), evaluated the effectiveness of ATV with RTV (300/100 qd) and ATV dosed with SQV (400/1200 qd) to LPV with RTV (400/100 bid) with patients receiving tenofovir and one NRTI as a background regimen. ATV, when dosed with RTV was comparable in efficacy to LPV with RTV; however, ATV with SQV was found inadequate. A third clinical trial (AI424-043, randomized, open label, multicenter), compared ATV without RTV (400 mg qd) to LPV with RTV (400/100 bid) in patients receiving a two NRTIs as a background regimen. The study concluded ATV without RTV was inferior to LPV with RTV in treatment-experienced patients.

During these clinical studies, ATV was relatively well tolerated and demonstrated a unique safety profile as compared to other PIs. The most common adverse reactions ($\geq$2%) observed in treatment-naïve patients receiving ATV were nausea, jaundice/sclera icterus, and rash while the most common in treatment-experienced patients were jaundice/sclera and myalgia. Additional adverse reactions reported included headache, abdominal pain, vomiting, insomnia, peripheral neurological symptoms, dizziness, diarrhea, depression, and fever [112]. Cardiac conduction abnormalities, rash (~20% patients), immune reconstitution syndrome, fat redistribution, and new onset of diabetes mellitus/hyperglycemia were also observed. Reversible hyperbilirubinemia occurred in patients receiving ATV due to increased levels of bilirubin from inhibition of UDP-glucuronosyl transferase (UGT). Hemophilia and hepatoxicity are of concern when taking ATV and are commonly associated with protease inhibitors. In addition, during post-market analysis, nephrolithiasis and the development of kidney stones has been reported [113,114]. Interestingly, the lipid levels of many treatment-experienced patients receiving ATV were shown to normalize during treatment [115,116]. The safety profile of ATV in pediatric patients has been investigated and found to be comparable to that observed in adults.

4.2.6. Resistance Profile The development of viral resistance to ATV has been observed in cell culture and clinical trial studies. Substitutions including I50L, N88S, I84V, A71V, and M46I were found to contribute to ATV resistance in HIV isolates from cell culture studies [112] with I50L representing the signature mutation for ATV resistance [117]. Substitution at I50L made viruses more susceptible to other PIs in cell culture and negatively affected their growth rates [112,117]. During clinical studies, I50L frequently appeared in isolates from treatment-naïve patients taking 400 mg ATV qd that experienced virologic failure in addition to other mutations including A71V, V321, L33F, G73S, V82A, I85V, and N88S [112]. From the isolates of treatment-experienced patients experiencing virologic failure, V32I, L33F/V/I, E35D/G, M46I/L, I50L, F53L/V, I54V, A71V/T/I, G73S/T/C, V82A/T/L, I85V, and L89V/Q/M/T mutations were commonly identified with E34K/A/Q, G48V, I84V, N88S/D/T, and L90M occurring less frequently (<10% isolates) [112]. Cross-resistance was observed between ATV and other PIs with >90% of the isolates resistant to ATV showing cross-resistance to IDV, LPV, NFV, RTV, and SQV and 80% demonstrating cross-resistance to APV [112]. Furthermore, isolates with resistance to a large number of PIs show an increased tendency to be cross-resistant to ATV [118–120].

4.3. Fosamprenavir Calcium (Lexiva or Telzir)

4.3.1. General Information Fosamprenavir calcium (see Fig. 28) is a prodrug of APV,

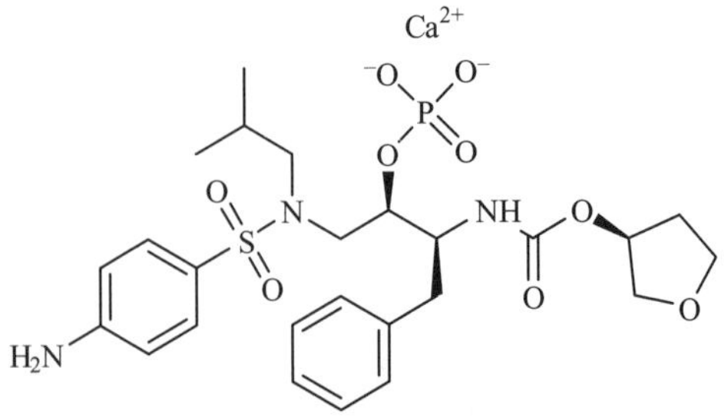

Figure 28. Chemical structure of fosamprenavir calcium.

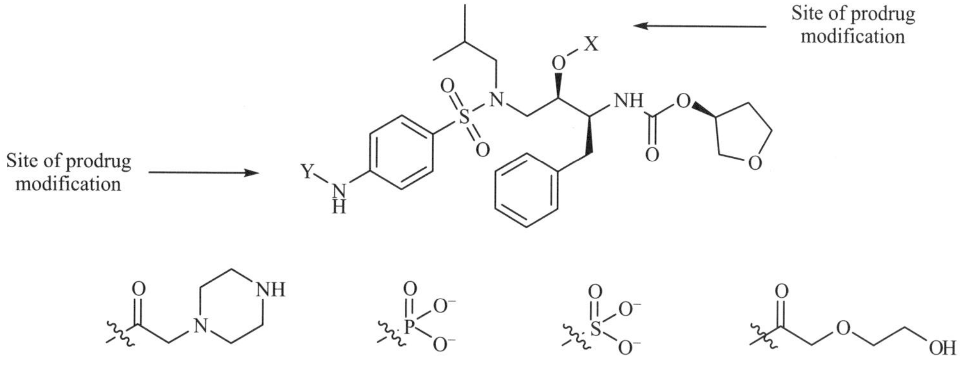

Figure 29. Representative APV prodrugs [127].

marketed under the trade names Lexiva or Telzir. Developed by GlaxoSmithKline, FPV was approved for the treatment of HIV infection by the FDA [121] on October 20, 2003. The main advantage of this treatment is a significant reduction in pill burden as compared to APV. This was achieved by increasing the bioavailability of the drug through the use of a phosphate ester prodrug group. As a result of decreased pill burden, patient adherence is more likely to occur corresponding to a more effective HIV treatment. FPV retains many of the attributes of APV including administration without food restrictions, a similar metabolic profile, and a unique resistance profile as compared to other PIs. It is available as a 700 mg tablet or 50 mg/mL oral suspension and may be dosed with or without RTV [122].

4.3.2. Drug Optimization Some of the problems plaguing first-generation protease inhibitors include large pill burdens, inconvenient dosing requirements, and restrictions on food intake. These factors can have a negative impact on patient compliance leading to sub-

optimal treatment and the development of viral resistance [123–125]. In this context, the focus during the development of FPV was in decreasing the pill burden associated with APV (eight large soft-gel capsules taken twice a day). To accomplish this goal, researchers envisioned using a prodrug (see Volume 4 Chapter 2) of AVP to remedy its low bioavailability by enhancing the drug's solubility and increasing its absorption into the intestinal tissue. Approximately 100 prodrugs of APV were synthesized that incorporated various ester, amide, sulfate, and phosphate groups into the APV scaffold (see Fig. 29) [126,127]. These groups would be easily hydrolyzed or enzymatically cleaved *in vivo* releasing the active moiety, APV, into the circulation. From this set of prodrugs, preclinical testing in rats and dogs identified two compounds (see Fig. 30) with improved solubility and comparable systemic APV exposure to that of clinical APV [128]. The phosphate ester, GW3908, was selected for clinical evaluation based on its superior physical properties making it more amenable to drug development [128]. The cal-

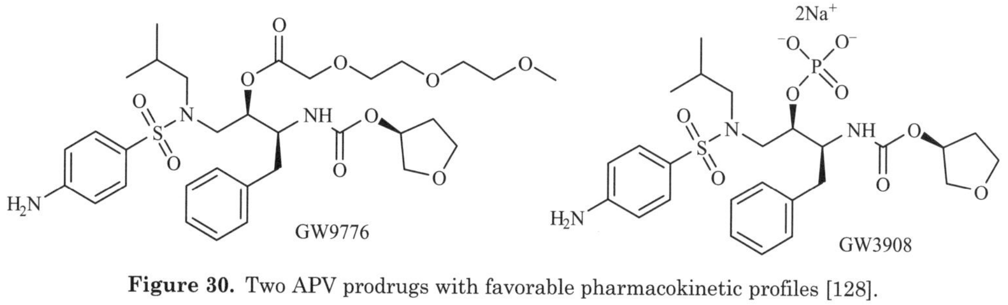

Figure 30. Two APV prodrugs with favorable pharmacokinetic profiles [128].

Table 25. Pharmacokinetic Parameters of Agenerase Compared to Lexiva [87,122]

Regimen	C_{max} (mcg/mL)	T_{max}[a] (h)	AUC_{24} (mcg·h/mL)	C_{min} (mcg/mL)
Agenerase 1200 mg bid	7.66	1.0	35.4	0.32
Lexiva 1400 mg bid	4.82	1.3	33.0	0.35
Lexiva 1400 mg qd + ritonavir 200 mg qd	7.24	2.1	69.4	1.45
Lexiva 1400 mg qd + ritonavir 100 mg qd	7.93	1.5	66.4	0.86
Lexiva 700 mg bid + ritonavir 100 mg bid	6.08	1.5	79.2	2.12

[a]Median value.

C_{max}: maximum concentration; T_{max}: time to I_{max}; AUC_{24}: area under the concentration curve at 24 h; C_{min}: minimum concentration.

cium salt form, GW433908, was examined in Phase I clinical studies and found to be bioequivalent to APV in terms of AUC, C_{max}, and half-life [129]. It was successfully advanced through late phase clinical studies and became the FDA approved drug known as FPV.

4.3.3. Pharmacokinetics

Values of select pharmacokinetic parameters of FPV have been provided in Table 25. FPV is administered orally and is absorbed in the intestinal tract where it is rapidly converted by phosphatase enzymes to the active moiety, APV [129,130]. APV is the primary substance absorbed into circulation with minimal levels of FPV gaining entry [129]. As a result, APV was the primary moiety measured during pharmacokinetic studies on FPV [129]. It was found that APV from the administration of FPV has a similar pharmacokinetic profile to that of APV in capsule [87,122]. FPV is metabolized by CYP3A4 to the same metabolites as APV, which are rapidly removed from the body by excretion in the urine and feces. This metabolism can be inhibited by coadministration of RTV resulting in a "boosting" effect and an increase in systemic exposure and activity of FPV [131]. In addition to the metabolism interaction, CYP3A4 is both inhibited and may be induced by FPV resulting in a potential for various drug interactions to occur. As a result, caution is necessary when using FPV with other drugs that interact strongly with CYP3A4, especially those with a limited therapeutic index. Similar to APV, FPV does not require a restriction on food intake during administration adding another patient benefit to this treatment option [122].

4.3.4. Efficacy and Tolerability

FPV has been evaluated in two clinical trials, NEAT and SOLO, involving antiretroviral treatment-naïve patients and in a single trial, CONTEXT, with patients that are therapy experienced. In the NEAT study, FPV (1400 mg bid) was evaluated against NFV (1250 mg bid) in HIV infected patients that also received abacavir (300 mg bid) and lamivudine (150 mg bid) [132]. After 48 weeks, the results of the study (see Table 26) demonstrated FPV was efficacious as seen by its ability to decrease viral load and increase CD4+ cell count. Some indicators (viral load <400 copies/mL) suggested FPV may be more effective than NFV. In the SOLO study, RTV-boosted FPV (1400/200 mg FPV/RTV qd) was evaluated against NFV treatment (1250 mg bid) in HIV infected patients also receiving abacavir (300 mg bid) and lamivudine (150 mg bid) [131]. After 48 weeks, the two patient groups showed comparable percentages of patients with viral loads <400 copies/mL (see Table 26). The study demonstrated a once-daily dosing of FPV in antiretroviral treatment-naïve patients was an effective treatment regimen. In the CONTEXT study, RTV-boosted FPV (1400/200 mg FPV/RTV qd or 700/100 mg FPV/RTV bid) was evaluated in treatment-experienced patients against RTV-boosted LPV (400/100 mg LPV/RTV) [133]. All patient groups in this study were coadministered two NRTIs that were selected based on resistance testing. The results (see Table 26) suggested once-daily FPV/RTV administration was insufficient for the treatment of antiretroviral-experienced patients and twice-daily dosing was required.

Table 26. Select Clinical Trial Results of FPV in HIV-Infected Patients [122,131–133]

Clinical Trial	Neat (APV30001)		Solo (APV30002)		Context (APV30003)	
Patient type	Antiretroviral-naïve		Antiretroviral-naïve		Antiretroviral-experienced	
Coadministration	300/150 mg ABC/3TR bid		300/150 mg ABC/3TR bid		2 NRTIs	
Patients	166	83	322	327	315	
Baseline CD4+ (cells/L)^a	214	212	166	177	263	
Baseline viral load (log$_{10}$ copies/mL)^a	4.82	4.85	4.8	4.8	4.1	
Patient group	1400 mg FPV bid	1250 mg NFV bid	1400/200 mg FPV/RTV qd	1250 mg NFV bid	700/100 mg FPV/RTV bid	400/100 mg LPV/RTV bid
Viral suppression (%):						
<400 (copies/mL)	66	52	69	68	58	61
<50 (copies/mL)	57	42	58	55	46	50
CD4+ increase (cells/L)^a	201	216	203	207	81	91
Virologic failure (%)	19	32	6	16	29	27

^{a}Median value.
ABC: abacavir; 3TR: lamivudine; bid: twice a day; qd: once a day; NFV: nelfinavir.

The safety of FPV was established throughout the course of these clinical studies. The most common adverse effects reported during these studies were diarrhea, nausea, vomiting, headache, and rash [131–133]. Because FPV contains a sulfonamide, caution is recommended with patients having known sulfonamide allergies. FPV has not been evaluated in children, however, safety and efficacy of Agenerase was established in two pediatric studies with the most common adverse effects being nausea, vomiting, diarrhea, and rash [134,135].

4.3.5. Resistance Profile APV, the active form of FPV, has a distinct resistance profile as compared to earlier protease inhibitors. Genotypic and phenotypic studies have indicated minimal cross-resistance to several other protease inhibitors *in vitro* [136]. Efforts to discover clinically significant mutations arising from APV treatment identified four key protease mutations: I50V, I54L/M, V32I I47V, and I84V with the I50V mutant exhibiting the most resistance to APV [137]. Resistance occurring during FPV treatment was detected in viral isolates from 5 of 29 patients with virological failure during the NEAT study [132]. These mutations included I54L/M, V32I + I47V, and M46I. Resistance data from the SOLO trial found no resistant mutations in 84% of patients at the first failure timepoint [131,138]. In addition, no primary

or secondary protease mutations were found in the patient group receiving FPV/RTV as compared to 50% of the patients treated with NFV [131]. Furthermore, the development of NRTI mutations was statistically lower ($p < 0.0001$) in the FVP/RTV group (13%) as compared to the NFV patients (57%) [131]. It is suggested that the observed differences are the result of a higher genetic barrier due to elevated drug exposure levels obtained with the RTV-boosted FPV treatment.

4.4. Tipranavir (Aptivus)

4.4.1. General Information Tipranavir (TPV) (see Fig. 31) is a novel nonpeptidic protease inhibitor, marketed under the trade name Aptivus by Boehringer Ingelheim. Approved by the FDA [120] on June 22, 2005, its discovery resulted from extensive optimization of a lead compound identified through a

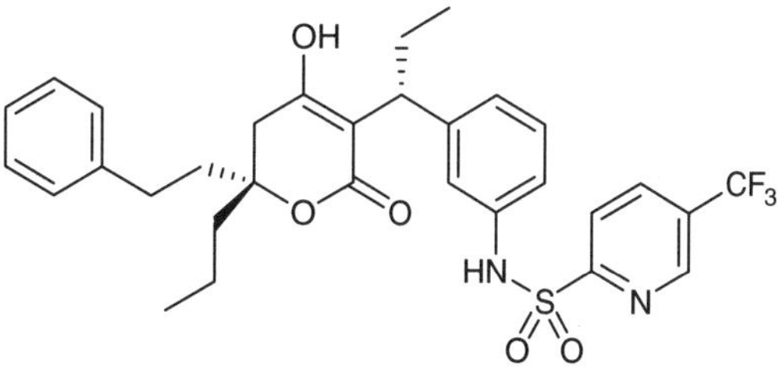

Figure 31. Chemical structure of tipranavir.

compound library screen. TPV boasts a distinct chemical structure compared to other PIs that is responsible for a unique binding to the HIV PR. This is likely the reason why TPV was shown to be an effective treatment for combating HIV in highly experienced antiretroviral treatment patients where other PIs have failed. Despite its success in combating resistant HIV mutants, TPV suffers from a number of undesirable properties. It has been linked to hepatotoxicity, hypertriglyceridemia, lipodystrophy, and an increased risk of intracranial hemorrhage. In addition, TPV is a substrate of cP450 and when administered with RTV will inhibit cP450 activity, induce glucuronidase, and induce P-glycoprotein, resulting in an increased potential for drug–drug interactions. TPV is currently available as a 250 mg tablet or 100 mg/mL oral suspension and is coadministered with RTV [139–143].

4.4.2. Drug Optimization

The development of TPV began with the discovery of phenprocoumon (see Fig. 32) as a lead nonpeptide HIV inhibitor from a broad screening of a Pharmacia and Upjohn compound library [144]. Subsequent structural modifications revealed that replacement of the 4-hydroxycoumarin ring with a 4-hydroxypyrone and incorporation of substituted sulfonamides at the *meta* position of the phenyl side chain (see Fig. 33) resulted in improvements in enzymatic and antiviral activity [144–148]. Further enhancements in activity were achieved through extensive SAR studies that focused on modifying the C6 and C3α alkyl substituents and by variation of the sulfonamide group (see Tables 27–29)[148,149]. These studies revealed the C6 site could be readily substituted with many simple alkyl groups with little effect on enzymatic activity (see Table 27). Similarly, substituting simple alkyl groups at C3α had a minimal impact on activity; however, deleting the side chain significantly reduced activity (see Table 28). Variation of the sulfonamide group showed a preference for aryl substituents over alkyl groups with further improvements realized by the addition of various moieties to the ring system (see Table 29). A careful examination of the effect of stereochemistry on enzymatic and antiviral activity demonstrated a strong preference for the R-configuration at C3α and a weaker dependence for R at C6 (see Table 30).

4.4.3. Binding Interactions

The crystal structure of TPV bound to HIV PR has provided valuable insights into its binding with the viral enzyme [149]. The data show the dihydropyrone ring centered in the active site with the lactone oxygen forming hydrogen bonds (3.1 Å) to the NH groups of Ile50/Ile50′ of the flap region and the 4-hydroxyl group hydrogen bonding (2.8 and 2.5 Å) to the catalytic residues Asp25/Asp25′. Binding is enhanced by a number of hydrophobic interactions with the C6 alkyl groups extending into the S_1' and S_2' sites effectively filling the enzymatic pocket and the C3α projecting into the S_1 and S_2 sites in a similar fashion. Additional interactions occur with the sulfonamide group including hydrogen bonds to Asp30 and a nearby bound water molecule and a hydrophobic interaction of the trifluoromethylpyridyl group that fills the nearby S_3 subsite. The unique binding interactions (see Fig. 34) to the HIV PR result from TPV's distinct chemical structure and are responsible for its unique resistance profile.

4.4.4. Pharmacokinetics

Values of select pharmacokinetic parameters of TPV have been provided in Table 31. TPV is administered orally, twice daily with RTV (500/200 mg TPV/r bid), which is required to obtain sufficient plasma levels of the drug [143]. Once absorbed, TPV is highly bound to plasma proteins (>99.9%), binding to both α1-acid glycoprotein and human serum albumin [143]. It is metabolized primarily by CYP3A to a hydroxyl metabolite and is also a target of glucuronidation (see Fig. 35) [143,150]. The majority of TPV (56%) is excreted from the body between 24 and 96 h after dosing with the feces as the primary route of exit [143]. Radiolabelled ^{14}C studies showed unchanged TPV as the major contributor to radioactivity in the feces (79.9% of fecal radioactivity) with the hydroxyl metabolite as the most abundant metabolite (4.9% of fecal radioactivity) [143]. The glucuronide metabolite of TPV was the most abundant metabolite in the urine (11.0% of urine radioactivity) [143]. At the recommended dosing (500/200 mg TPV/r bid), TPV

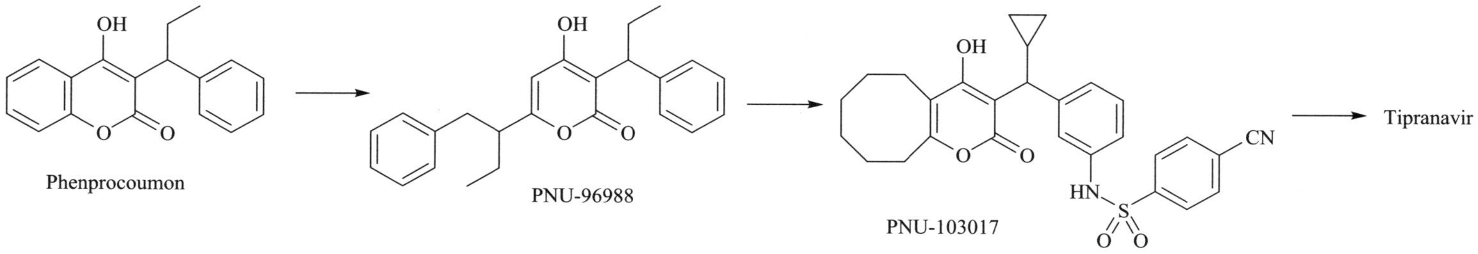

Figure 32. The discovery of TPV [149].

Phenprocoumon

PNU-96988

PNU-103017

Tipranavir

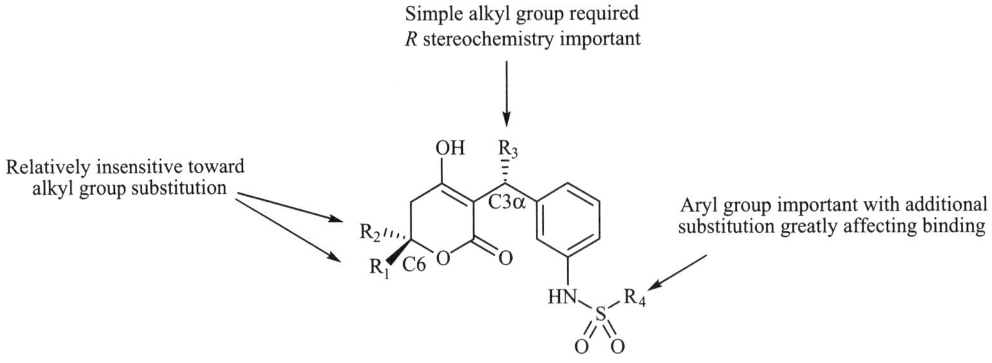

Figure 33. Sites of structural modifications explored during TPV SAR [148,149].

has an approximate elimination half-life of 6 h (see Table 31) [143].

Significant interactions exist between TPV and cP450, glucuronidase, and the broad specificity human ABC-transporter P-glycoprotein, causing concern for interactions with other drug molecules. TPV is a substrate of CYP3A and when administered with RTV

Table 27. TPV SAR—C6 variation [149]

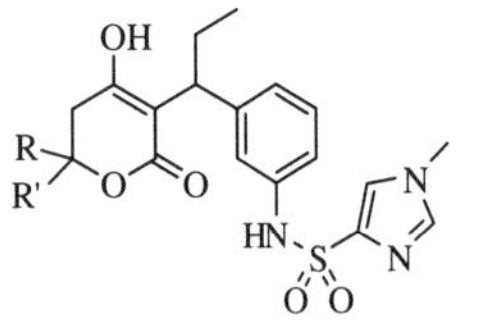

Compound	R,R′	K_i (nM)	IC_{50} (μM)	IC_{90} (μM)
77		1.8	0.8	2.0
78		2.6	1.0	<3
79		1.7	1.8	2.9
80		23	NA	NA
81		1.2	0.5	0.9

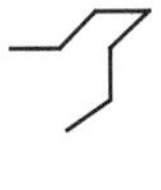

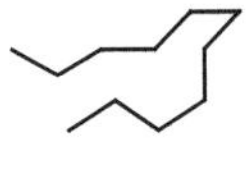

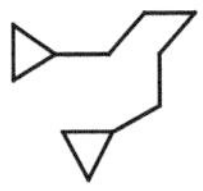

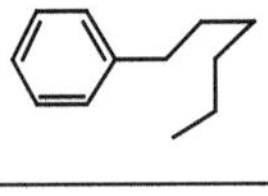

causes the inhibition of CYP1A2, CYP2C9, CYP2C19, CYP2D6, and CYP3A. In addition, the joint drug administration results in the induction of glucuronidase and P-glycoprotein. As a result, the potential for drug–drug interactions is increased when using TPV/r in combination with other drugs that are substrates, inducers, or inhibitors of these systems [143,151,152].

4.4.5. Efficacy and Tolerability The efficacy of TPV was evaluated in two randomized, open-label, multinational, controlled, Phase III trials (RESIST1 and RESIST2 also called 1182.12 and 1182.48). The studies focused on patients that were antiretroviral treatment-experienced requiring they had previously been treated with at least two PI-based regimens and were currently failing a PI-based regimen at the start of the study [143]. In addition, patients had to have protease gene

Table 28. TPV SAR—C3α-Variation [149]

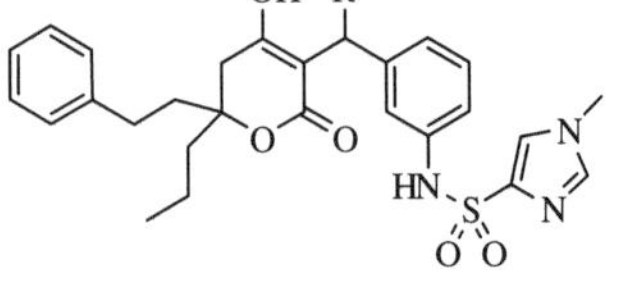

Compound	R	K_i (nM)	IC_{50} (μM)	IC_{90} (μM)
82	Ethyl	1.2	0.5	0.9
83	*cyclo*Propyl	0.71	<1	~1
84	*tert*-Butyl	1.2	0.15	0.69
85	H	13	0% @ 1 μM	

Table 29. TPV—SAR Sulfonamide Variation [148,149]

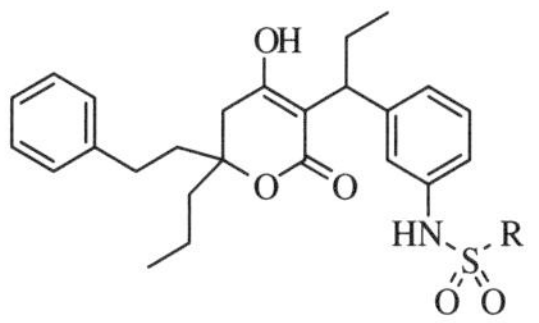

Compound	R	K_i (nM)	IC_{50} (µM)	IC_{90} (µM)
86	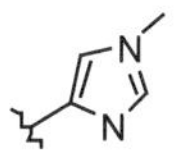	1.2	0.5	0.9
87	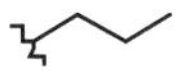	>1 µM	NA	NA
88	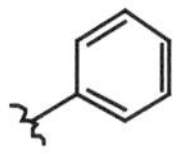	17	1.6	7.3
89	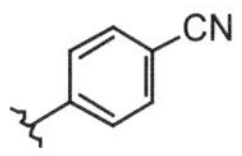	8.2	1.1	4.2
90	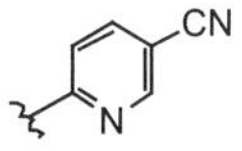	0.10	0.13	0.47

mutations at 30N, 46I, 46L, 48V, 50V, 82A, 82F, 82L, 82T, 84V, or 90M and less than two mutations at 33, 82, 84, or 90 [143]; 3324 patients were screened for the study and 1509 were found to meet the aforementioned conditions [153]. The patients were treated with either TPV/r (500/200 mg bid) with an optimized background regimen (OBR) or, as a control group, with a RTV boosted comparator protease inhibitor (CPI) (LPV, APV, SQV, or INV) with an OBR [143]. The treatment for a subset of each group included the administration of enfuvirtide, an HIV fusion inhibitor (see Volume 7 Chapter 3) [143]. Combined outcomes from the two studies (see Table 32) demonstrated the efficacy of TPV with significantly better results observed with coadministration of enfuvirtide. Patients receiving TPV/r treatment showed higher increases in CD4 + levels than the CPI control group (23 versus 4 without enfuvirtide and 89 versus 18 with enfuvirtide) and a higher percentage of patients achieved a reduced viral load below 400 copies/mL (30.3 versus 13.6 without enfuvirtide and 52.4 versus 19.6 with enfuvirtide). Interestingly, in addition to its therapeutic value against HIV, recent data suggest TPV may also be beneficial in treating various pathogenic fungi [154–156].

Table 30. TPV SAR—Stereochemical Variation [148]

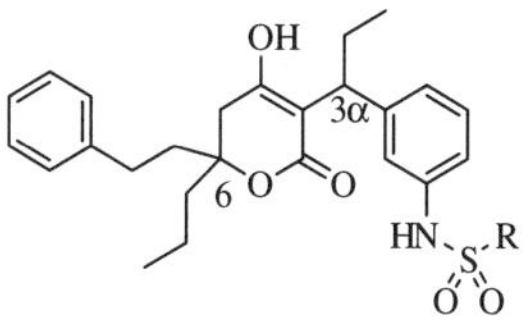

Compound	R	$3\alpha,6$	K_i (nM)	IC_{50} (µM)	IC_{90} (µM)
91		R,S	0.04	0.11	0.89
92	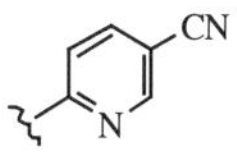	R,R	0.007	0.04	0.26
93		S,S	0.12	>>1	>>1
94		S,R	0.10	0.49	1.0
95		R,S	0.018	0.14	0.84
96	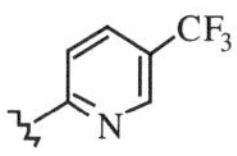	R,R	0.008	0.03	0.10
97		S,S	0.22	1.7	3.0
98		S,R	0.032	0.41	1.8

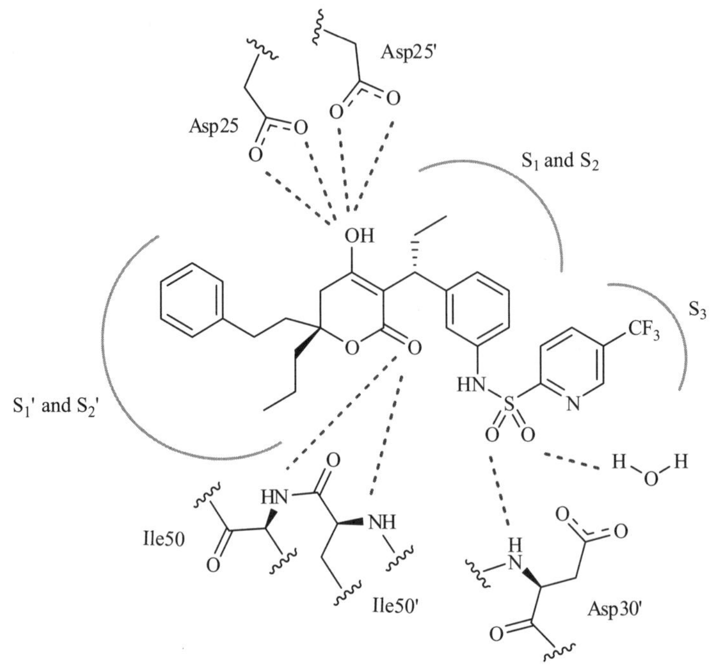

Figure 34. TPV interactions with HIV PR [149]. (This figure is available in full color at http://mrw. interscience.wiley.com/emrw/9780471266945/home.)

Table 31. Select Pharmacokinetic Parameters of TPV [143]

Patients	$C_{Ptrough}$ (mcg/mL)	C_{max} (mcg/mL)	T_{max} (h)	AUC_{0-12} h (mcg h/mL)	CL (L/h)	V_d (L)
Female ($n = 14$)	41.6 ± 24.3	94.8 ± 22.8	5.5	851 ± 309	1.15	7.7
Males ($n = 106$)	35.6 ± 16.7	77.6 ± 16.6	6.0	710 ± 207	1.27	10.2
From 2 to <6 years ($n = 12$)	59.6 ± 23.6	135 ± 44	8.1	1190 ± 332	0.34^a	4.0
From 6 to <12 years ($n = 8$)	66.3 ± 12.5	151 ± 32	7.1	1354 ± 256	0.45^a	4.7
From 12 to 18 years ($n = 6$)	53.3 ± 32.4	138 ± 52	5.2	1194 ± 517	0.99^a	5.3

^{a}CL/F.
Dosing regimen: adults = 500/200 mg TPV/r bid; pediatric = 375/150 mg/m^2 TPV/r.
Results reported as mean ± standard deviation.
C_{max}: maximum concentration; T_{max}: time to C_{max}; AUC_{0-12}: area under the concentration curve at 12 h; $C_{Ptrough}$: trough plasma concentration; CL: apparent total body clearance; V_d: apparent volume of distribution.

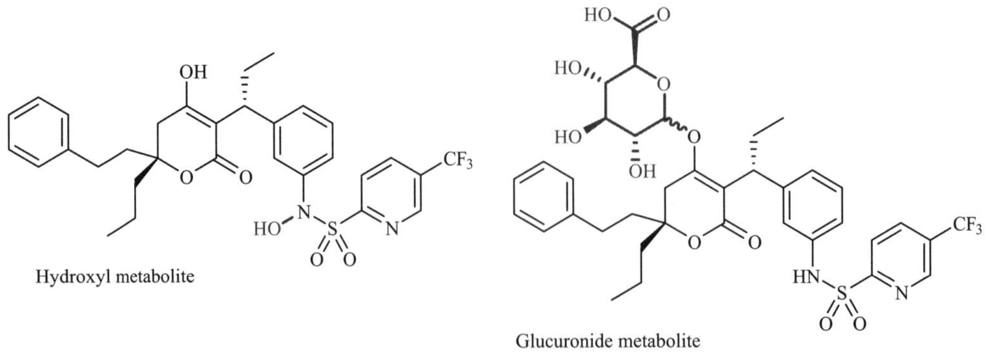

Hydroxyl metabolite

Glucuronide metabolite

Figure 35. TPV metabolites [150]. (This figure is available in full color at http://mrw.interscience.wiley.com/emrw/9780471266945/home.)

Table 32. Select Results from 48-Week Clinical Studies (Pooled Studies RESIST 1 and 2) [11,143,153]

Treatment Regimen	TPV/r 500/200 mg bid + OBR		CPI/r bid + OBR	
Baseline statistics				
Total enrolled/treated	755/746		754/737	
Completed 48-week visit	486		192	
Number of prior ART[a]	12		12	
Number of PGM[a]	16		16	
Used enfuvirtide	169		135	
Baseline CD4+ (cells/L)[a]	162		162	
Baseline viral load (log$_{10}$ copies/mL)[a]	4.8		4.8	
Efficacy Results	No Enfuvirtide	With Enfuvirtide	No Enfuvirtide	With Enfuvirtide
Viral suppression (%):				
<400 (copies/mL)	30.3	52.4	13.6	19.6
<50 (copies/mL)	22.7	37.3	10.2	14.4
CD4+ increase (cells/L)[a]	23	89	4	18
Virologic failure (%)	55.1		77.3	

[a]Median value.

OBR: optimized background regimen; CPI/r: comparator protease inhibitor/r; ART: antiretroviral drugs; PGM: protease gene mutations; bid: twice a day.

The safety of TPV administration was assessed during the RESIST clinical trials. Common adverse events included diarrhea, nausea, vomiting, pyrexia, headache, and fatigue [143]. One of the most serious adverse events recorded during the studies was hepatotoxicity, which has been a concern throughout the drug's development. Grade 3 or 4 liver abnormalities were observed during Phase I studies in 6% of subjects [143] while Phase II studies established that increases in ALT, a measure of liver damage, were TPV dose dependent [157]. Another serious adverse effect recorded during RESIST was hypertriglyceridemia with more patients reporting grade 3 or 4 lipid abnormalities receiving TPV/r then those with CPI/r (20.8% and 11.2%, respectively) [158]. Since receiving FDA approval, further observations of elevated plasma lipid levels leading to pancreatis have been reported in patients administered TPV/r [159]. A related condition that has been linked to TPV/r is lipodystrophy, which is commonly associated with HIV PI therapy [160–162]. In addition to these safety concerns, TPV may be linked to an increased risk of bleeding and intracranial hemorrhage [143]. Initial studies suggest bleeding may result from an inhibitory effect of TPV on platelet aggregation and thromboxane B2 formation [163–166].

4.4.6. Resistance Profile Compared to other PIs, TPV possesses a unique resistance profile, enabling it to retain efficacy in many treatment-experienced patients. HIV isolates from cell cultures having reduced susceptibility to TPV were shown to develop 10 specific mutations over time: L33F, I84V, K45I, I13V, V32I, V82L, M36I, A71V, L10F, and I54V/T [143]. During Phase II and Phase III clinical studies, substitutions at L33V/I/F, V82T, and I84V were observed in isolates from more than 20% of patients experiencing virologic failure while mutations at L10V/I/S, I13V, E35D/G/N, I47V, I54V/A/M, K55R, V82L, and L89V/M were identified from isolates in more than 10% of these patients [143]. Comparison of HIV genotypes in clinical trial patients at baseline and after treatment identified 16 codons that are associated with reduced TPV susceptibility: L10V, I13V, K20M/R/V, L33F, E35G, M36I, K43T, M46L, I47V, I54A/M/V, Q58E, H69K, T74P, V82L/T, N83D, and I84V [143,167]. From this data, multiple algorithms have been developed to predict TPV susceptibility [168,169]; however, the FDA associates more than five of eight mutations (I13, V32, M36, I47, Q58, D60, V82, and I84) with an enhanced probability of TPV treatment failure [170]. Cross-resistance between TPV and other PIs has been associated with substitutions at 84V, 89V, 54M, 47V, and 74P, whereas, other common PI mutations (24I, 48V, 50V, 54S, 54T, and 82A) do not significantly affect susceptibility to TPV [171]. In addition, 90% of HIV isolates examined during clinical trials that were resistant to other PIs, maintained susceptibly toward TPV (less than fourfold decrease observed) [143].

4.5. Darunavir (Prezista)

4.5.1. General Information Darunavir (also known as TMC114) (see Fig. 36) is a potent HIV PI with a broad-spectrum of activity against many resistant viral strains. Darunavir incorporated a (R)-(hydroxyethyl)-sulfonamide isostere and a stereochemically defined *bis*-tetrahydrofuran (*bis*-THF) as the P2-ligand. The Ghosh research group first described this HIV PI in 1998 [172]. DRV was further developed by Tibotec, Inc. who received approval from the FDA on June 23 2006 to market the drug under the brand name Prezista®. Initially designed to reduce the size, complexity, and peptidic nature of first-generation PIs, DRV contains a novel bis-tetrahydrofuranylurethane ligand that was inspired by nature. This structural feature forms multiple interactions with the protease backbone atoms thereby limiting is vulnerability to mutations. DRV was shown to maintain activity against viral strains resistant to other PIs. It is an effective treatment for antiretroviral-experienced patients that do not respond well to other PI treatments. Due to

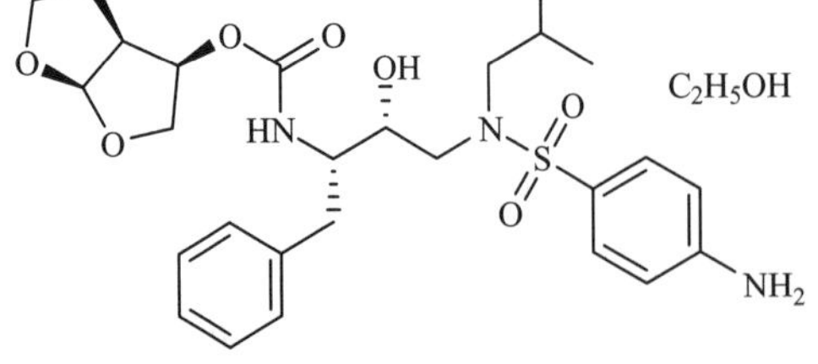

metabolism by CYP3A, coadministration with RTV significantly improved oral bioavailability in humans. Some common side effects related to traditional PIs have been linked to DRV; however, evidence now indicates DRV is unique in that it does not inhibit ZMPSTE24 (related to lipodystrophy). DRV is currently available as a 300, 400, or 600 mg tablet. Refs [173–177] provide additional details of its discovery and pharmacological profile.

4.5.2. Drug Optimization The original idea leading to the development of DRV was to further optimize first-generation PIs by reducing molecular weight, decreasing structural complexity, and eliminating peptide bonds while maintaining potency across a broad-spectrum of viral mutants (see Fig. 37). Initial efforts focused on optimizing the structure of SQV with an emphasis on the P2 ligand, which contained multiple peptide bonds. To find a suitable isostere, investigators turned to nature and began exploring the use of conformationally restrained cyclic ethers, a common functionality found in many natural products [178–180]. Through a careful analysis of the X-ray structure of the SQV-protease complex, these groups were envisioned to be a suitable replacement for the asparagine ligand of SQV. Initial inhibitors incorporating a 3(S)-tetrahydrofuran had only moderate potency (see Table 33) toward HIV PR [181]. Crystal structure analysis of these inhibitors indicated the oxygen atom from the tetrahedron ring was involved in weak interactions with the nitrogens of Asp29 and Asp30, located on the protease backbone structure. Further structure modification aimed at optimizing these interactions led to the development of an inhibitor incorporating a bis-tetrahydrofuranyl urethane (bis-THF) moiety that possessed remarkable potency (see Table 33) [182].

Subsequent investigations were made that incorporated cyclic ether and cyclic sulfone functionalities into (R)-hydroxyethylsulfonamide based inhibitors (see Table 34) [172]. Once again, inhibitors containing the bis-THF group were shown to be exceedingly potent and UIC94003 (TMC-126) was identified as a lead candidate [183]. Unfortunately, TMC-126 was found to possess poor pharmacoki-

Figure 36. Chemical structure of darunavir ethanolate.

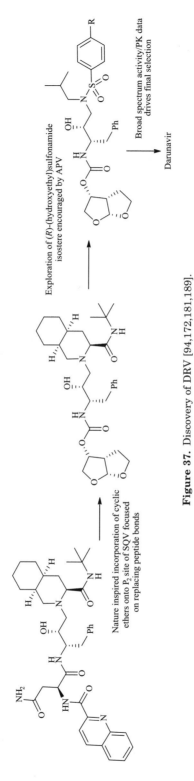

Figure 37. Discovery of DRV [94,172,181,189].

Table 33. SQV with Cyclic Ether P_2 Ligands [181,184]

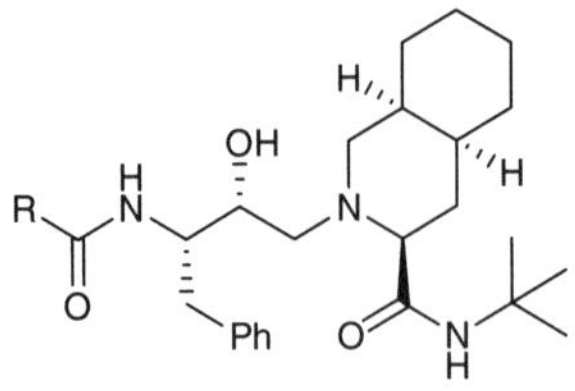

Compound	R	IC$_{50}$ (nM)	Compound	R	IC$_{50}$ (nM)
99	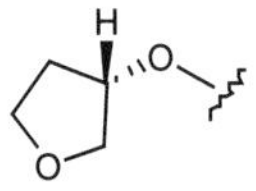	132	**102**	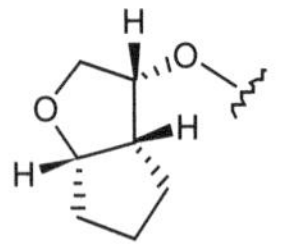	190
100	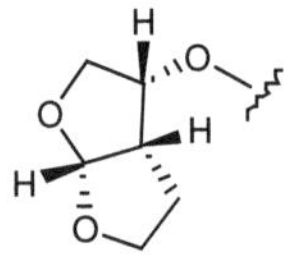	6.4	**103**	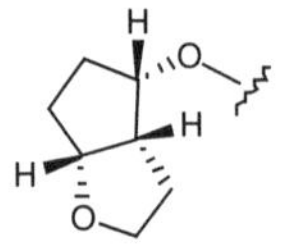	17
101	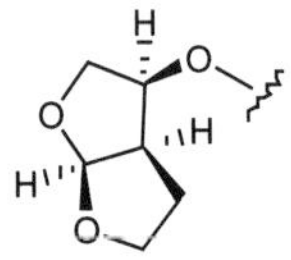	1.8			

Table 34. Evaluation of Cyclic Ether and Sulfone Groups [172]

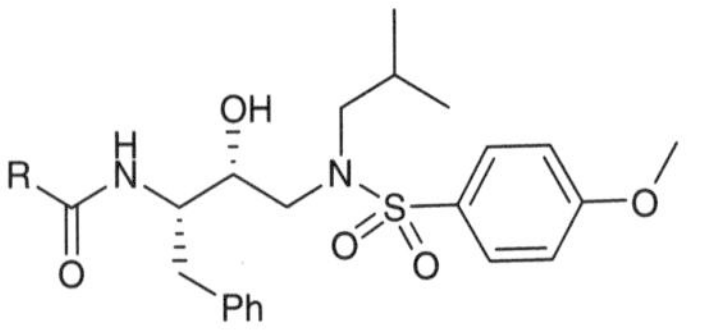

Compound	R	K_i (nM)	ID$_{50}$(nM)	Compound	R	K_i (nM)	ID$_{50}$ (nM)
104	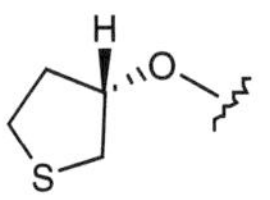	2.5	47	**107**	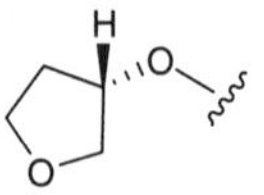	1.5	12
105	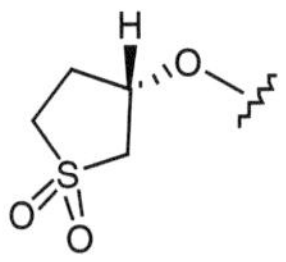	1.2	19	**108**	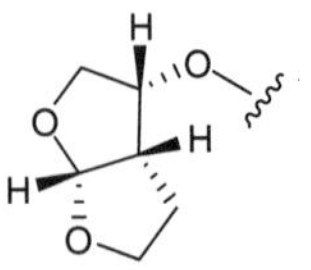 (TMC-126)	1.1	1.4
106	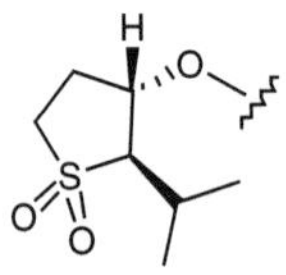	1.4	18	**109**	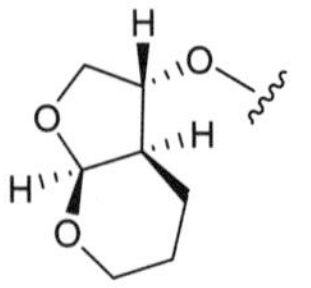	2.2	4.5

Table 35. Optimizing for Broad Specificity and Pharmacokinetic Properties [94]

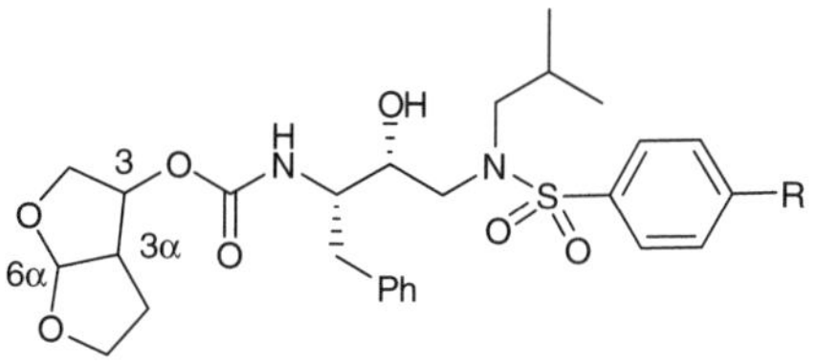

Compound	R	3,3α,6α	Wild-Type pEC_{50}	Mutant Average pEC_{50}	Difference
110	4-NH_2	R,S,R	8.39	8.29	0.10
111	4-NH_2	S,R,S	7.97	7.51	0.46
112	4-NH_2	R,R,S	6.51	—	—
113	4-NH_2	S,S,R	6.62	6.01	0.61
114	4-OCH_3	R,S,R	9.23	8.35	0.88
115	3-NH_2	R,S,R	8.36	7.37	0.99
116	3,4-OCH_2O—	R,S,R	9.21	8.19	1.02
117	4-OH	R,S,R	8.2	8.06	0.14
118	4-CN	R,S,R	8.28	7.01	1.27
119	4-CH_2NH_2	R,S,R	8.15	8.11	0.04
120	4-NO_2	R,S,R	8.61	7.67	0.94
121	4-I	R,S,R	8.82	8.06	0.76
122	4-$COCH_3$	R,S,R	8.71	7.86	0.85
123	4-CH_3	Racemate	8.28	7.22	1.06
124	4-H	Racemate	8.56	7.17	1.39
APV	—	—	7.43	6.49	0.94

netic properties and was on average 10-fold less sensitive against PI-resistant strains. To improve upon the pharmacokinetic profile and identify an inhibitor with a broader spectrum of activity, substitutions were made to the aromatic ring of the benzensulfonamide group (Table 35). Interestingly, some groups (p-CN, p-CH_3, and m-NH_2) had little effect on antiviral activity while electron-withdrawing substituents (p-nitro, p-acetyl, and p-iodo) increased activity against PI-resistant viruses without influencing the potency against the wild-type virus. Small electron-donating groups with the ability to form hydrogen bonds (p-OCH_3 and —OCH_2O—) increased activity toward WT viruses but exhibited a significant potency against the mutant strains. Small, polar groups capable of hydrogen bonding and accepting (p-NH_2, p-OH, p-CH_2NH_2) demonstrated comparable potency toward wild-type and mutant strains classifying them as broad-spectrum inhibitors. Of these compounds, the inhibitor containing p-NH_2 (TMC114 or DRV) displayed the most

promising pharmacokinetic properties and was selected for clinical development [94,185].

4.5.3. Binding Interactions The potency of DRV toward wild-type HIV PR is significantly greater than other approved inhibitors. Crystal structure analysis of DRV complexed with the enzyme attributes the increase in potency to strong interactions between the bis-tetrahydrofuranylurethane group of DRV with Asp29 and Asp30 of the enzyme although other differences can also be found (compare Fig. 38 to Fig. 20) [95,186]. Interestingly, the binding of both compounds is distinct from other protease inhibitors in that APV and DRV are predominantly located within the substrate envelope [95,187]. This feature is likely responsible in part for the unique resistance profiles these drugs possess.

Subsequent X-ray analysis of DRV complexed with HIV PR mutants has revealed a second binding site for DRV on one of the flexible flaps located on the surface of the protease (see Fig. 39) [95,186,188]. Binding

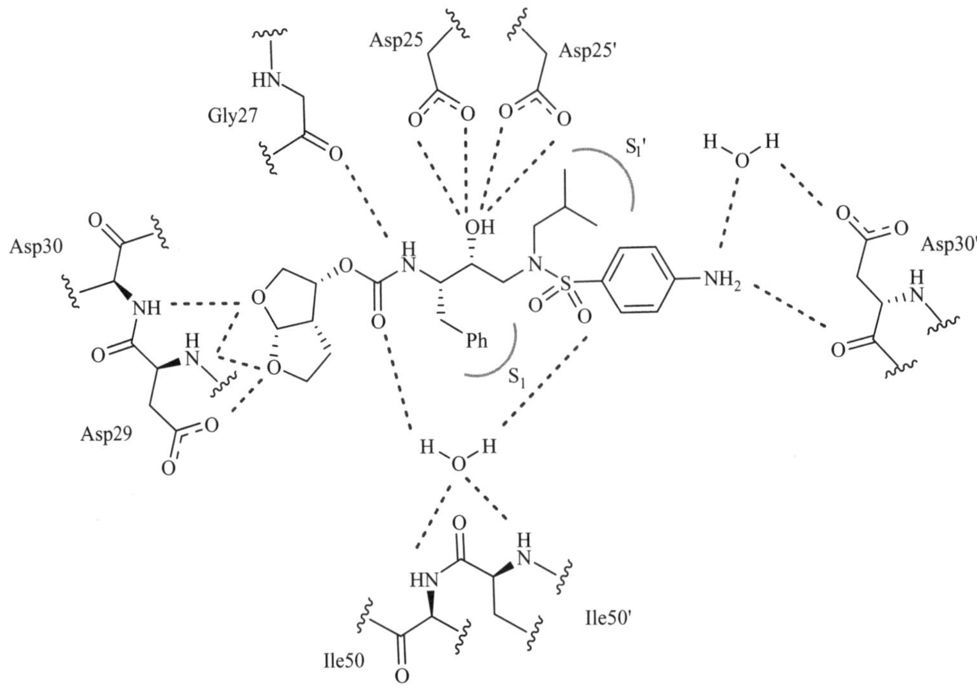

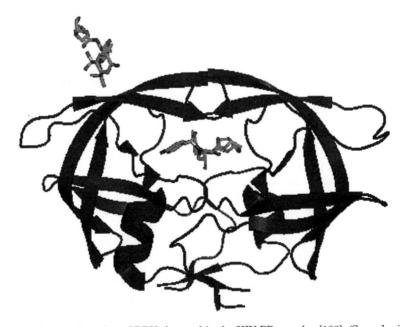

Figure 38. Binding interactions between DRV and HIV PR [186]. (This figure is available in full color at http://mrw.interscience.wiley.com/emrw/9780471266945/home.)

Figure 39. Two binding sites of DRV observed in the HIV PR complex [188]. (See color insert.)

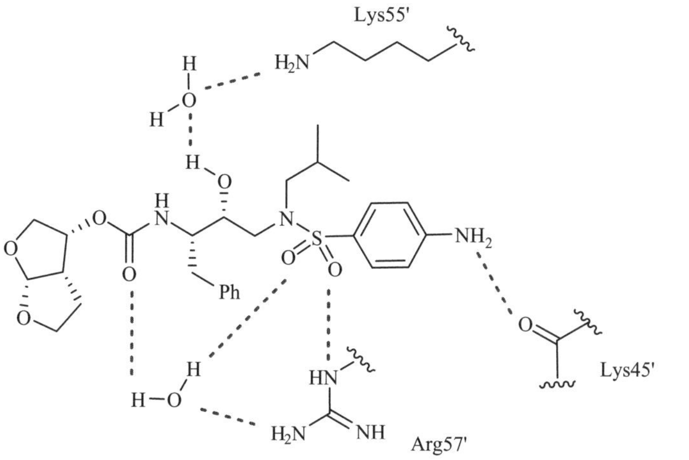

Figure 40. Binding interactions between DRV and HIV PR in the flap site [188].

at this site (see Fig. 40) may relate to an allosteric interaction that could contribute to the inhibition of HIV PR and therefore be partially responsible for DRV's enhanced potency. Furthermore, kinetic studies performed with DRV and APV have revealed a mixed-type competitive-uncompetitive inhibition against HIV PR in contrast to other PIs like SQV that operate purely by competitive inhibition [188]. Interestingly, two distinct diastereomers of DRV related by inversion of the sulfonamide nitrogen were found to bind at the two different sites. At the flap site, this nitrogen assumes an S-configuration while the R-configuration is found binding in the catalytic site [95].

4.5.4. Pharmacokinetics Values of select pharmacokinetic parameters of DRV have been provided in Table 36. DRV/r is orally bioavailable and should be taken with food as this has been found to increase C_{max} and AUC levels by 30% [189]. In the plasma, DRV is highly protein bound (95%) with a strong pre-ference for α1-acid glycoprotein and, to a lesser extent, albumin [189,190]. DRV is readily metabolized by CYP3A resulting in three major metabolites of DRV (see Fig. 41) that occur from carbamate hydrolysis (M19), aromatic hydroxylation (M29), and aliphatic hydroxylation (M23) [190,191]. Each of these metabolites has reduced activity for wild-type HIV virus [189]. To inhibit these metabolic pathways and maintain adequate plasma concentrations of DRV, RTV is coadministered. Coadministration of these drugs results in the inhibition of CYP3A, CYP2D6, and the P-glycoprotein transporter, thereby, providing a potential means for interactions with other drugs [189]. Radiolabelled ^{14}C-DRV experiments demonstrated the majority of DRV was excreted as its unchanged form (48.9%) with the main route of excretion occurring through the feces (79.5%) with a lesser amount found in the urine (13.9%) [189].

4.5.5. Efficacy and Tolerability The efficacy of DRV against HIV was demonstrated in two

Table 36. Select Pharmacokinetic Properties of Prezista [189]

Regimen	T_{max} (h)	AUC$_{24}$ (mcg·h/mL)	C_0 h (mcg/mL)
DRV/r 800/100 mg qd	—	93 ± 27	2.3 ± 1.2
DRV/r 600/100 mg bid (Phase III Study)	2.5–4	117 ± 34	3.5 ± 1.4
DRV/r 600/100 mg bid (Phase II studies)		125 ± 32	3.6 ± 1.2

T_{max}: time to C_{max}; AUC$_{24}$: area under the concentration curve at 12 h times 2; bid: twice a day; qd: once a day.

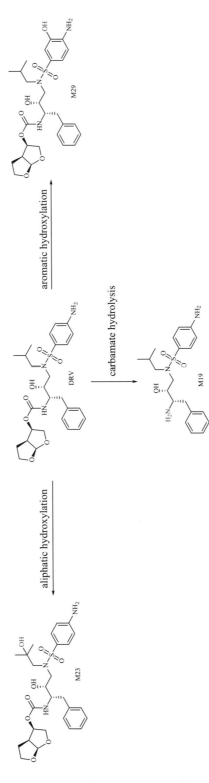

Figure 41. Three major metabolites of DRV [190,191]. (This figure is available in full color at http://mrw.interscience.wiley.com/emrw/9780471266945/home.)

Table 37. Select Results from DRV Clinical Studies [189]

Clinical Study	TMC114-C211 (48 weeks)		TMC114-C214 (48 weeks)		TMC114-C213 and TMC114-C202 (Pooled Analysis— 96 Weeks)	
Treatment regimen	DRV/r qd 800/100 mg	LPV/r qd 800/200 mg	DRV/r bid 600/100 mg	LPV/r bid 400/100 mg	DRV/r bid 600/100 mg	CPI
Background regimen	TFR/FTC 300/200 mg qd	OBR		OBR		OBR
Baseline statistics						
Number of patients	343	346	298	297	131	124
Patient type	Naïve		Experienced		Experienced	
Baseline CD4+ (cells/L)	228	218	235	230	153	163
Baseline viral load (log$_{10}$ copies/mL)	4.86	4.84	4.33	4.28	4.61	4.49
Efficacy results						
Viral suppression (%):						
<400 (copies/mL)	87.8	85.3	77	67	55.0	14.5
<50 (copies/mL)	84	78	71	60	39	9
CD4+ increase (cells/L)	137	141	88	81	103	17
Virologic failure	6	10	11	21	29	80

OBR: optimized background regimen; CPI: comparator PI selected by investigator; DRV: darunavir; r: ritonavir; LPV: lopinavir; TFR: tenofovir; FTC: emtricitabine; bid: twice a day; qd: once a day.

48-week, randomized, controlled, open-label Phase III clinical trials (TMC114-C211 and TMC114-C214 also called POWER 1 and POWER 2) and is further supported by data from two 96-week Phase IIb clinical trials (TMC114-C213 and TMC114-C202 also called ARTEMIS and TITAN). In TMC114-C211, treatment of antiretroviral treatment-naïve patients with DRV/r (800/100 mg qd) was shown to be comparable in terms of efficacy to treatment with LPV/r (800/200 mg) (see Table 37). The second Phase III trial, TMC114-C214, compared DRV/r (600/100 mg bid) to LPV/r (400/100 mg bid) in treatment-experienced patients. Patients receiving DRV/r were more likely to demonstrate a virologic response then those receiving LPV/r. A pooled analysis of the Phase IIb clinical trial results established treatment with DRV/r (600/100 mg bid) as a superior dosing regimen over comparative protease inhibitors in antiretroviral treatment-experienced patients [96].

In general, administration of DRV/r was well tolerated in patients during clinical development. The most common adverse effects (≥5%) reported were diarrhea, nausea, headache, and abdominal pain [189]. Hepatotoxi-city was reported in 0.5% of patients ($n=3063$) receiving DRV/r and rashes developed in 10.3% of subjects [189]. Due to the presence of a sulfonamide in DRV's chemical structure, the potential exists for an allergic reaction to DRV [189]. Hemophilia, immune reconstitution syndrome, new onset diabetes mellitus, hyperglycemia, and lipodystrophy have been reported by patients receiving PI therapy and may therefore arise from DRV/r treatment although no direct linkage has been made [189]. Recent studies have shown that PIs are capable of inhibiting ZMPSTE24 resulting in an accumulation of farnesyl-prelamin A, possibly explaining observed effects of lipodystrophy [162]. On the contrary, DRV does not inhibit ZMPSTE24 and, therefore, may not cause fat redistribution making DRV a potentially attractive treatment option [192,193].

4.5.6. Resistance Profile Preclinical studies demonstrated the effectiveness of DRV in treating HIV strains resistant to other PIs [183,193]. DRV maintained significant activity against HIV$_{NL4-3}$ variants with selected resistance to SQV, IDV, RTV, or APV (see Table 38) [185]. Retaining efficacy

Table 38. Activity of DRV Against PI Resistant HIV Isolates in MT-4 [184,185]

Virus	Substitutions	IC$_{50}$ (μM) SQV	APV	IDV	NFV	RTV	DRV
HIV-1$_{NL4-3}$	Wild Type	0.009	0.027	0.011	0.020	0.018	0.003
HIV-1$_{SQV5}$ μM	L10I, G84V, I54V, L90M	>1	0.17	>1	0.30	>1	0.005
HIV-1$_{APV5}$ μM	L10F, V32I, M46I, I54M, A71V, I84V	0.02	>1	0.31	0.21	>1	0.22
HIV-1$_{IDV5}$ μM	L10F, L24I, M46I, L63P, A71V, G73S, V82T	0.015	0.33	>1	0.74	>1	0.029
HIV-1$_{NFV5}$ μM	L10F, D30N, K45I, A71V, T74S	0.031	0.093	0.28	>1	0.09	0.003
HIV-1$_{RTV5}$ μM	M46I, V82, I84V	0.013	0.61	0.31	0.24	>1	0.025

against the APV resistant strain was particularly exciting as DRV and APV share many common structural features. In addition, DRV maintained potent activity against a variety of clinical HIV variants isolated from antiretroviral-experienced patients that were no longer responsive to existing PI-treatment regimens (see Table 39) [184,185]. Clinical studies later confirmed DRV was effective for treating multi-PI resistant HIV strains.

Despite DRVs apparent broad spectrum of antiviral activity, viral strains resistant to DRV have developed and been identified. In HIV isolates, obtained from cell cultures of wild-type HIV and having a 21–88-fold reduced susceptibility toward DRV, two to four amino acid substitutions at S37D, R41E/T, K55Q, H69Q, K70E, T74S, V77I, or I85V were commonly found [189]. When cell cultures of HIV strains known to possess multiple PI resistance were used, HIV isolates exhibited 50–641-fold reduced susceptibility toward DRV and 22 different mutations were observed (L10F, V11I, I13V, I15V, G16E, L23I, V32I, L33F, S37N, M46I, I47V, I50V, F53L, L63P, A71V, G73S, L76V, V82I, I84V, T91A/S, and Q92R) [189]. In the Phase III study TMC114-C214, isolates from patients experiencing virologic failure while receiving DRV/r commonly contained mutations at V32I, I47V, I54L, T74P, and L76V that were associated with a 44–607-fold decrease in susceptibility to DRV [186,188]. Unfortunately, viruses that have developed resistance to DRV are typically also resistant to the other PIs, although, the extent of cross-resistance to

TPV appears to be limited [186,187]. Overall, 11 mutations are now thought to be specific to DRV resistance including major mutations I50V, I54M, L76V, and I84V and minor mutations V11I, V32I, L33F, I47V, I54L, G73S, and L89V [191,194].

5. NEXT-GENERATION INHIBITORS

Despite the recent approval of multiple second-generation PIs, considerable work remains in the development of HIV PIs. Problems with drug toxicity and the development of viral resistance to current treatments demonstrate the need for novel PIs with unique ADMET properties and broad ranging efficacy. In addition, the next generation of PIs must demonstrate superiority over current treatments and be easy to administer (orally bioavailable/once-a-day dosing) as convenient dosing regimens leads to increase treatment compliance. Unfortunately, these requirements along with intense competition between pharmaceutical companies have set incredibly high standards on new PIs. In addition, other factors such as stringent clinical trial requirements, difficulties in recruiting treatment-experienced trial volunteers, and a growing sentiment that federal funding for HIV research should be reduced are making new drugs more difficult to develop [195–197]. As a result, many new PIs that have begun clinical investigation have seen their development halted (Fig. 42) and relatively few can be found in preclinical status (Table 40) [50,198,199]. Similarly, the

Table 39. Activity of Various PIs Against HIV Clinical Isolates in PHA-PBMC [184,185]

Virus	Additional Information	Substitutions[a]	IC$_{50}$ (μM)						
			AZT	SQV	APV	IDV	NFV	RTV	DRV
HIV-1$_{ERS104pre}$	Wild-type X4	L63P	0.004	0.010	0.023	0.018	0.019	0.027	0.003
HIV-1$_{MOKW}$	Wild-type X5	Lacks PI-resistant substitutions	0.016	0.010	0.011	0.018	0.033	0.032	0.003
HIV-1$_{TM}$	MDR X4	L10I, K14R, R41K, M46L, I54V, L63P, A71V, V82A, L90M, and I93L	0.73	0.23	0.39	>1	0.54	>1	0.004
HIV-1$_{MM}$	MDR R5	L10I, K43T, M46L, I54V, L63P, A71V, V82A, L90M, and Q92K	0.37	0.30	0.34	>1	>1	>1	0.02
HIV-1$_{JSL}$	MDR R5	L10I, L24I, L33F, E35D, M36I, N37S, M46L, I54V, R57K, I62V, L63P, A71V, G73S, and V82A	0.08	0.35	0.75	>1	>1	>1	0.029
HIV-1$_A$	MDR X4	L10I, I15V, E35D, N37E, K45R, I54V, L63P, A71V, V82T, L90M, I93L, and C95F	—	0.14	0.16	>1	0.36	>1	0.004
HIV-1$_B$	MDR X4	L10I, K14R, L33I, M36I, M46I, F53I, K55R, I62V, L63P, A71V, G73S, V82A, L90M, and I93	—	0.31	0.34	>1	>1	>1	0.013
HIV-1$_C$	MDR X4	L10I, I15V, K20R, L24I, M36I, M46L, I54V, I62V, L63P, K70O, and V82A	—	0.037	0.28	>1	0.44	>1	0.003
HIV-1$_G$	MDR X4	L10I, V11I, T12E, I15V, L19I, R41K, M46L, L63P, A71T, V82A, and L90M	—	0.029	0.25	0.39	0.32	0.44	0.004

[a]Relative to the consensus type B sequence from the Los Alamos database.

61

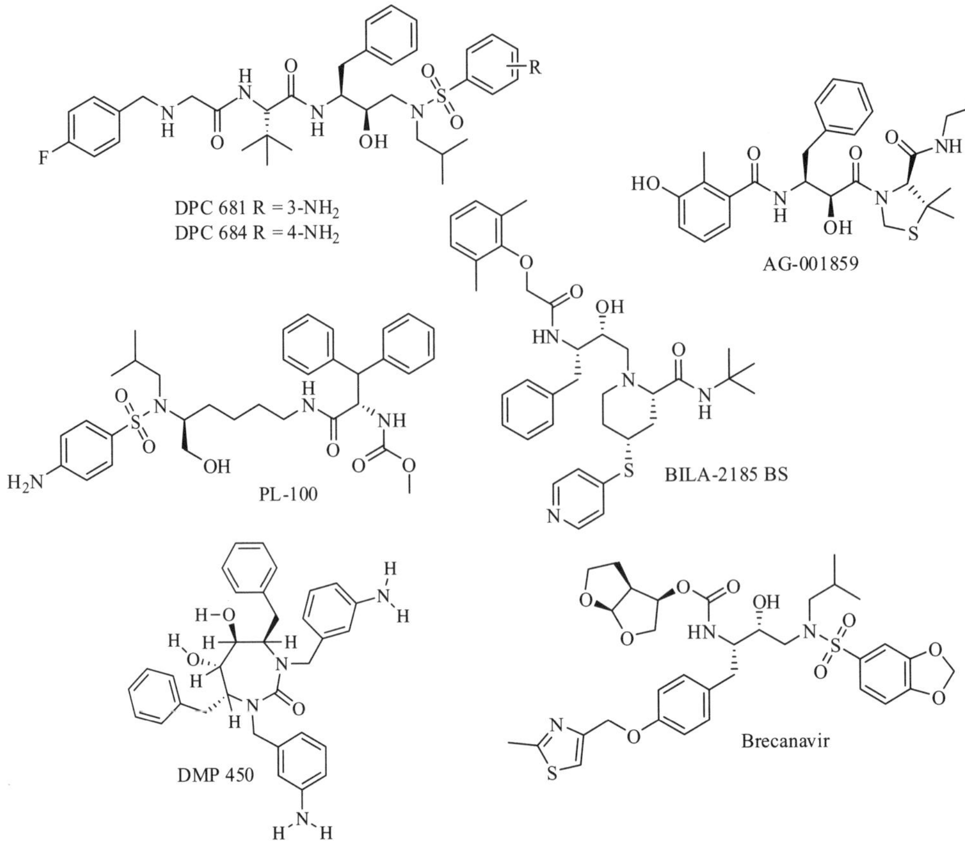

DPC 681 R = 3-NH$_2$
DPC 684 R = 4-NH$_2$

AG-001859

PL-100

BILA-2185 BS

DMP 450

Brecanavir

Figure 42. Chemical structures of PIs no longer in development.

Table 40. Recent PIs Under Development

Protease Inhibitor	Company	Comments	Status	Reference(s)
BILA-2185 BS	Boehringer Ingel-heim, Inc.	Caused reductions in heart rates and blood pressure	Halted	[198]
Mozenavir (DMP-450)	DuPont/Triangle Pharmaceuticals/ Gilead Sciences	Cyclic urea similar to BMS-232632 No advantage over other PIs	Halted 2002	[207,208]
PL-100(MK-8122)	Ambrilla Biophar-ma, Inc./Merck & Co, Inc.	Pending evaluation of other prodrugs/ formulations	On Hold Jul 2008	[209]
Brecanavir (GW640385/VX-385)	GlaxoSmithKline	Lack of viable oral formulation	Halted Dec 2006	[210]
DPC 681	Bristol-Myers Squibb	Cardiotoxicity issues	Halted	[50,211]
DPC 684		Narrow therapeutic range		

(continued)

Table 40. (*Continued*)

Protease Inhibitor	Company	Comments	Status	Reference(s)
AG-001859	Pfizer/Agouron	Not reported in Pfizer pipeline	Halted	[212,213]
SPI-256	Sequoia Pharmaceuticals	First in human data favorable	Phase I	[205]
SPI-390		Novel escape pathway	Preclinical	[206]
SPI-457				
SM-309515	Sumitomo Pharmaceuticals	SAR published	Preclinical	[214]
P-1946	Pharmacor	Lysine derivative Resistance profile published	Preclinical	[215]
GRL-02031	NCI/Kumamoto University/University Illinois at Chicago	Potent against multi PI resistant virus	Preclinical	[216]
UIC-94-003	NCI/Kumamoto University/University Illinois at Chicago	Potent against multi PI resistant virus	Preclinical	[217]
GS-8374	Gilead Sciences	Novel diethyl-phosphonate in P_1-position	Preclinical	[201–204]

FDA currently reports no HIV PIs in investigational drug status [200].

However, the outlook for new PIs is not entirely grim and innovative compounds incorporating novel functionalities are being discovered (see Fig. 42). For example, GS-8374 is a unique HIV PI currently under development by Gilead Sciences [201]. It shares many structural features with DRV and contains a diethyl-phosphonate motif

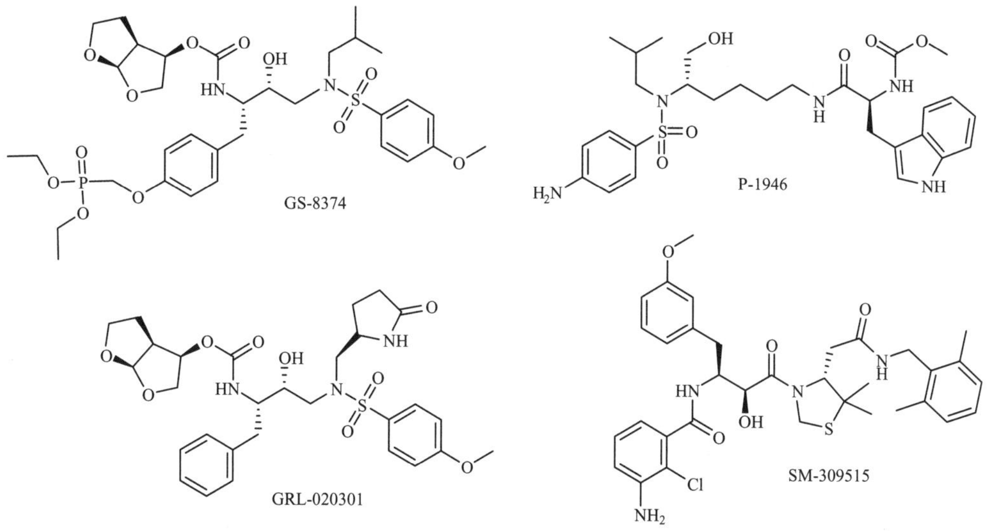

Figure 43. Chemical structures of PIs currently under investigation [201–204,214–216].

located in the P1 position. In contrast to other PIs, GS-8374 maintains potency against a number of resistant HIV strains and may therefore become a viable option for antiretroviral-experienced patients [202–204]. Showing a similarly favorable resistance profile, SPI-256 is currently being developed at Sequoia Pharmaceuticals, which recently reported favorable results for the drug in initial human studies [205]. In addition, the company has two other compounds, SPI-390 and SPI-457, currently in preclinical development that have exhibited novel escape pathways [206]. These drugs offer new hopes for treatment-experienced patients with the potential to combat the most resistant viral strains.

REFERENCES

1. UNAIDS Report on the global HIV/AIDS epidemic 2008. Available at http//wwwunaidsorg/en/KnowledgeCentre/HIVData/GlobalReport/2008/2008_Global_report.asp. Accessed 2008 Oct 30.

2. Condra J. Resistance to HIV protease inhibitors. Haemophilia 1998;4(4):610–615.

3. Hirsch M, Conway B, D'Aquila R, Johnson V, Brun-Vezinet F, Clotet B, Demeter L, Hammer S, Jacobsen D, Kuritzkes D, Loveday C, Mellors J, Vella S, Richman D. Antiretroviral drug resistance testing in adults with HIV infection: implications for clinical management. JAMA 1998;279(24):1984–1991.

4. Malaty L, Kuper J. Drug interactions of HIV protease inhibitors. Drug Saf 1999;20: 147–169.

5. Von der Helm K. Retroviral proteases: structure, function and inhibition from a non-anticipated viral enzyme to the target of a most promising HIV therapy. Biol Chem 1996;377(12):765–774.

6. Navia M, Fitzgerald P, McKeever B, Leu C, Heimbach J, Herber W, Sial I, Darke P, Springer J. Three-dimensional structure of aspartyl protease from human immunodeficiency virus HIV-1. Nature 1989;337(6208):615–620.

7. Wlodawer A, Miller M, Jaskolski M, Sathyanarayana B, Baldwin E, Weber I, Selk L, Clawson L, Schneider J, Kent B. Conserved folding in retroviral proteases: crystal structure of a synthetic HIV-1 protease. Science 1989 Aug;245(4918):616–621.

8. Jacks T, Power M, Masiarz F, Luciw P, Barr P, Varmus H. Characterization of ribosomal fra-meshifting in HIV-1 *gag-pol* expression. Nature 1988;331(6153):280–283.

9. Debouck D, Gorniak J, Strikler J, Meek T, Metcalf B, Rosenberg M. Human immunodeficiency virus protease expressed in *Escherichia coli* exhibits autoprocessing and specific maturation of the gag precursor. Proc Natl Acad Sci USA 1987;84 (24):8903–8906.

10. Patick A, Potts K. Protease inhibitors as antiviral agents. Clin Microbiol Rev 1998;11 (4):614–627.

11. Ogden R, Flexner C, editors. Protease Inhibitors in AIDS Therapy. New York: Marcel Dekker, Inc; 2001.

12. Leung D, Abbentante G, Fairlie D. Protease inhibitors: current status and future prospects. J Med Chem 2000;43(3):305–341.

13. Debouck C. The HIV-1 protease as a therapeutic target for AIDS. AIDS Res Hum Retroviruses 1992;8(2):153–164.

14. Schechter I, Berger A. On the size of the active site in proteases I. Papain. Biochem Biophys Res Comun 1967;27(2):157–162.

15. Mitsuya H, Maeda K, Das D, Ghosh A. Development of protease inhibitors and the fight with drug-resistant HIV-1 variants. Adv Pharmacol 2008;56:169–197.

16. Roberts N, Martin J, Kinchington D, Broadhurst A, Craig J, Duncan I, Galpin S, Handa B, Kay J, Krohn A, Lambert R, Merrett J, Mills J, Parkes K, Redshaw S, Ritchie A, Taylor D, Thomas G, Machin P. Rational design of peptide-based HIV proteinase inhibitors. Science 1990;248(4953):358–361.

17. Brik A, Wong C. HIV-1 protease: mechanism and drug discovery. Org Biomol Chem 2003;1 (1):5–14.

18. Randolph J, DeGoey D. Peptidomimetic inhibitors of HIV protease. Curr Top Med Chem 2004;4(10):1079–1095.

19. Hoetelmans R, Meenhorst P, Mulder J, Burger D, Koks C, Beijnen J. Clinical pharmacology of HIV protease inhibitors: focus on saquinavir, indinavir, and ritonavir. Pharm. World Sci 1997;19(4):159–175.

20. Letter from Roche announcing the discontinuation of Fortovase. Available at http://www.i-base.info/htb/v6/htb6-4/Roche.html. Accessed 2008 Dec 8.

21. King F. The identification of the HIV protease inhibitor saquinavir. In: King F, editor. Medicinal Chemistry. Royal Society of Chemistry; 2002. p 397–406.

22. Redshaw S, Roberts N, Thomas G. The road to fortovase. A history of saquinavir, the first human immunodeficiency virus protease inhibitor. In: Helm K, Korant B, Cheronis J, editors. Proteases as Targets for Therapy. Springer; 2000. pp. 3–21.

23. Vella S, Floridia M. Saquinavir clinical pharmacology and efficacy. Clin Pharmacokinet 1998;34(3):189–201.

24. Plosker G, Scott L. Saquinavir a review of its use in boosted regimens for treating HIV infection. Drugs 2003;63(12):1299–1324.

25. Kramer R, Schaber M, Skalka A, Ganguly K, Wong-Staal F, Reddy E. HTLV-III *gag* protein is processed in yeast cells by the virus *pol*-protease. Science 1986;231(4746):1580–1584.

26. Broadhurst A, Roberts N, Ritchie A, Handa B, Kay C. Assay of HIV-1 proteinase: a colorimetric method using small peptide substrates. Anal Biochem 1991;193(2):280–286.

27. Tie Y, Kovalevsky A, Boross P, Wang Y, Ghosh A, Tozser J, Harrison R, Weber I. Atomic resolution crystal structures of HIV-1 protease and mutants V82A and I84V with saquinavir. Proteins 2007;67(1):232–242.

28. Williams P, Muihead G, Madigan M, Mitchell A, Shaw T. Disposition and bioavailability of the HIV proteinase inhibitor, Ro 31-8959, after single doeses in healthy volunteers. Br J Clin Pharmacol 1992;34:155P–156P.

29. Fitzsimmons M, Collins J. Selective biotransformation of the human immunodeficiency virus protease inhibitor saquinavir by human small-intestinal cytochrome P4503A4; potential contribution to high first-pass metabolism. Drug Metab Dispos 1997;25(2):256–266.

30. Merry C, Barry M, Mulcahy R, Ryan M, Heavey J, Tija J, Gibbons S, Breckenridge A, Back D. Saquinavir pharmacokinetics alone and in combination with ritonavir in HIV-infected patients. AIDS 1997;11(4):F29–F33.

31. Package label information for Invirase (saquinavir). Available at http://www.fda.gov/cder/foi/label/2007/020628s025,021785s004lbl.pdf. Accessed 2008 Dec 8.

32. Stellbrink HJ, Hawkins DA, Clumeck N, Cooper D, Myers R, Delfraissy J, Gill M, Ramirez-Ronda C, Vella S. Randomised, multicentre phase III study of saquinavir plus zidovudine plus zalcitabine in previously untreated or minimally pretreated HIV-infected patients. Clin Drug Invest 2000;20(5):295–307.

33. Cohen Stuart JW, Schuurman R, Burger DM, Koopmans P, Sprenger H, Juttmann J, Richter C, Meenhorst P, Hoetelmans R, Kroon F, Bravenboer B, Hamann D, Boucher C, Borleffs J. Randomized trial comparing saquinavir soft gelatin capsules versus indinavir as part of triple therapy (CHEESE study). AIDS 1999;13(7):F53–F58.

34. Dragstedt UB, Gerstoft J, Pedersen C, Peters B, Duran A, Obel N, Castagna A, Cahn P, Clumeck N, Bruun J, Benetucci J, Hill A, Cassetti I, Vernazza P, Youle M, Fox Z, Lundgren J. Randomised trial to evaluate indinavir/ritonavir versus saquinavir/ritonavir in human HIV type-1 infected patients: the MaxCmin1 trial. J. Inf Dis 2003;188(5):635–642.

35. Slim J, Avihingsanon A, Ruxrungtham K, Schutz M, Walmsley S, Saquinavir/r bid vs lopinavir/r bid plus emtricitabine/tenofovir qd in ARV-naive HIV-infected patients: the GEMINI study. Program and abstracts of the 8th International Congress on Drug Therapy in HIV Infection. Oral presentation PL2. 5. 2006.

36. Dragsted U, Gerstoft J, Youle M, Fox Z, Losso M, Benetucci J, Jayaweera D, Rieger A, Bruun J, Castagna A, Gazzard B, Walmsley S, Hill A, Lundgren J. A randomized trial to evaluate lopinavir/ritonavir versus saquinavir/ritonavir in HIV-1-infected patients: the MaxCmin2 trial. Antivir Ther 2005;10(6):735–743.

37. Lea A, Faulds D, Ritonavir Drugs 1996;52(4):541–546.

38. Kempf D. Ritonavir and lopinavir/ritonavir. In: Taylor J, Triggle D, editors. Comprehensive Medicinal Chemistry II. Elsevier; 2006. p 187–197.

39. Hsu A, Granneman G, Bertz R. Ritonavir clinical pharmacokinetics and interactions with other anti-HIV agents. Clin Pharmacokinet 1998;35(4):275–291.

40. Cooper C, Heeswijk R, Gallicano K, Cameron D. A review of low-dose ritonavir in protease inhibitor combination therapy. Clin Infect Dis 2003;36(12):1585–1592.

41. Foisy M, Yakiwchuk E, Hughes C. Induction effects of ritonavir: implications for drug interactions. Ann Pharmacother 2008 Jul;427:1048–1059.

42. Kempf D, Marsh K, Denissen J, McDonald E, Vasavanonda S, Flentge C, Green B, Fino L, Park C, Kong X, Wideburg N, Saldivar A, Ruiz L, Kati W, Sham H, Robins T, Stewart K, Hsu A, Plattner J, Leonard J, Norbeck D. ABT-538 is a potent inhibitor of human immunodeficiency virus protease and has high oral bioavailability in humans. Proc Natl Acad Sci USA 1995;92(7):2484–2488.

43. Kempf D. Design of symmetry-based, peptidomimetic inhibitors of human immunodeficiency virus protease. Meth Enzymol 1994; 241:334–354.

44. Kempf D, Norbeck D, Codacovi L, Wang X, Kohlbrenner W, Wideburg N, Paul D, Knigge M, Vasavanonda S, Craig-Kennard A, Saldivar A, Rosenbrook W, Clement J, Plattner J, Erickson J, J Med Chem 1990;33(10):2687–2689.

45. Kempf D, Marsh K, Codacovi F, Bryant P, Craig-Kennard A, Sham H, Zhao C, Vasavanonda S, Kohlbrenner W, Wideburg N, Saldivar A, Green B, Herrin T, Norbeck D. Design of orally bioavailable, symmetry-based inhibitors of HIV protease. Bioorg Med Chem 1994;2(9):847–858.

46. Kempf D, Sham H, Marsh K, Flentge C, Betebenner D, Green B, McDonald E, Vasavanonda S, Saldivar A, Wideburg N, Kati W, Ruiz L, Zhao C, Fino L, Patterson J, Molla A, Plattner J, Norbeck D. Discovery of ritonavir, a potent inhibitor of HIV protease with high oral bioavailability and clinical efficacy. J Med Chem 1998;41:602–617.

47. Package label information for Norvir (ritonavir). Available at http://www.fda.gov/cder/foi/label/2008/020945s022,020659s042lbl.pdf. Accessed 2008 Dec 22.

48. Denissen J, Grabowski B, Johnson M, Buko A, Kempf D, Thomas S, Surber B. Metabolism and disposition of the HIV-1 protease inhibitor ritonavir (ABT-538) in rats, dogs, and humans. Drug Metab Dispos 1997;25(4):489–501.

49. Kumar G, Rodrigues D, Buko A, Denissen J. Cytochrome P450-mediated metabolism of the HIV-1 protease inhibitor ritonavir (ABT-538) in human liver microsomes. J Pharmacol Exp Ther 1996;277(1):423–431.

50. HIV medicine 2007 report. Available at http://www.hivmedicine.com/hivmedicine2007.pdf. Accessed 2008 Dec 2.

51. Plosker G, Noble S. Indinavir a review of its use in the management of HIV infection. Drugs 1999;58(6):1165–1203.

52. Lin J. Role of pharmacokinetics in the discovery and development of indinavir. Adv Drug Deliv Rev 1999;39(1–3):33–49.

53. Lin J, Chen I, King J. Dose-dependent toxicokinetics of L-689,502, a potent human immunodeficiency virus protease inhibitor, in rats and dogs. Pharmacol Exp Ther 1992;263 (1):105–111.

54. Vacca J, Guare J, DeSolms S, Sanders W, Giuliani E, Young S, Darke P, Sigal I, Schleif W, Quintero J, Emini E, Anderson P, Huff J. L-687, 908 a potent hydroxyethylene containing HIV protease inhibitor. J Med Chem 1991;34 (3):1225–1228.

55. Lyle T, Wiscount C, Guare J, Thompson W, Anderson P, Darke P, Zugay J, Emini E, Schleif W, Quintero J, Dixon R, Sigal I, Huff J. Benzocycloalkyl amines as novel C-termini for HIV protease inhibitors. J Med Chem 1991;34 (3):1228–1230.

56. Thompson W, Fitzgerald P, Holloway M, Emini E, Darke P, McKeever B, Schleif W, Quintero J, Zugay J, Tucker T, Schwering J, Homnick C, Nunberg J, Springer J, Huff J. Synthesis and antiviral activity of a series of HIV-1 protease inhibitors with functionality tethered to the P1 or P1′ phenyl design. J Med Chem 1992;35(10):1685–1701.

57. Dorsey B, Levin R, McDaniel S, Vacca J, Guare J, Darke P, Zugay J, Emini E, Schleif W, Quintero J, Lin J, Chen I, Holloway M, Fitzgerald P, Axel M, Ostovic D, Anderson P, Huff J. L-735, 524: the design of a potent and orally bioaviable HIV protease inhibitor. J Med Chem 1994;37(21):3443–3451.

58. Mahalingam B, Wang Y, Boross P, Tozser J, Louis J, Harrison R, Weber I. Crystal structures of HIV protease V82A and L90M mutants reveal changes in the indinavir-binding site. Eur J Biochem 2004;271(8):1516–1524.

59. Package label information for Crixivan (indinavir). Available at http://www.fda.gov/cder/foi/label/2008/020685s066lbl.pdf. Accessed 2008 Dec 9.

60. Hsu A, Heath-Chiozzi M, Ashbrenner E, et al. Evaluation of ritonavir/indinavir bid regimens—400 mg of indinavir in combination with 200, 300 or 400 mg or ritonavir in healthy volunteers. AIDS 1998;12(Suppl 4):S28.

61. Brinkman K, Kroon F, Hugen P, Burger D. Therapeutic concentrations of Indinavir in cerebrospinal fluid of HIV-1 infected patients. AIDS 1998;12(5):537.

62. Kravcik S, Gallicano K, Roth V, Cassol S, Hawley-Foss N, Badley A, Cameron D. Cerebrospinal fluid HIV RNA and drug levels with combination ritonavir and saquinavir. J Acquir Immune Defic Syndr 1999;21(5):371–375.

63. Balani S, Woolf E, Hoagland V, Sturgill M, Deutsch P, Yeh K, Lin J. Disposition of indinavir, a potent HIV-1 protease inhibitor, after an oral dose in humans. Drug Metab Dispos 1996;24(12):1389–1394.

64. Hammer S, Squires K, Hughes M, Grimes J, Demeter L, Currier J, Eron J, Feinberg J, Balfour H, Deyton L, Chodakewitz J, Fischl

M. A controlled trial of two nucleoside analogues plus indinavir in persons with human immunodeficiency virus infection and CD4 cell counts of 200 per cubic millimeter or less. N Engl J Med 1997;337(11):725–733.

65. Gulick R, Mellors J, Havlir D, Eron J, Gonzalez C, McMahon D, Jonas L, Meibohm A, Holder D, Schleif W, Condra J, Emini E, Isaacs R, Chodakewitz J, Richman D. Simultaneous vs sequential initation of therapy with indinavir, zidovudine, and lamivudine for HIV-1 infection: 100-week follow-up. JAMA 1998;280(1):35–41.

66. Gulick R, Mellors J, Havlir D, Eron J, Gonzalez C, McMahon D, Richman D, Valentine F, Jonas L, Meibohm A, Emini E, Chodakewitz J. Treatment with indinavir, zidovudine, and lamivudine in adults with human immunodeficiency virus infection and prior antiretroviral therapy. N Engl J Med 1997;337(11):779–781.

67. Wu DS, Stoller ML. Indinavir urolithiasis. Curr Opin Urol 2000;10(6):557–561.

68. Fernandez J, Robles J, Regojo J, Lopez J, Sanchez D, Arocena J, Rosell D, Zudaire J, Berian J. Renal lithiasis due to indinavir. Rev Med Univ Navarra 2002;46(3):28–32.

69. Florence E, Schrooten W, Verdonck K, Dreezen C, Colebunders R. Rheumatological complications associated with the use of indinavir and other protease inhibitors. Ann Rheum Dis 2002;61(1):82–84.

70. Garcia-Silva J, Almagro M, Pena-Penabad C, Fonseca E. Indinavir-induced retinoid-like effects incidence, clinical features and management. Drug Saf 2002;25(14):993–1003.

71. Condra J, Holder D, Schleif W, Blahy O, Danovich R, Gabryelski D, Graham D, Laird J, Quintero J, Rhodes A, Robbins H, Roth E, Shivaprakash M, Yang T, Chodakewitz J, Deutsch P, Leavitt R, Massari F, Mellors J, Squires R, Steigbigel R, Teppler H, Emini E. Genetic correlates of *in vivo* viral resistance to indinavir, a human immunodeficiency virus types 1 protease inhibitor. J Virol 1996;70 (12):8270–8276.

72. Condra J, Schleif W, Blahy O, Gabryeiski L, Graham D, Quintero J, Rhodes A, Robbins H, roth E, Shivaprakash M, Titus D, Yang T, Teppier H, Squires K, Deutsch P, Emini E. *In vivo* emergence of HIV-1 variants resistant to multiple protease inhibitors. Nature 2002;374(6522):569–571.

73. Package label information for Viracept (nelfinavir). Available at http://www.fda.gov/cder/foi/label/2008/020778s029,020779s050, 021503s011lbl. pdf. Accessed 2008 Dec 20.

74. Kast R, Foley K, Focosi D. Doxorubicin cardiomyopathy via TLR-2 stimulation: potential for prevention using current anti-retroviral inhibitors such as ritonavir and nelfinavir. Hematol Oncol 2007;25(2):96–97.

75. Gills J, LoPiccolo J, Dennis P. Nelfinavir a new anti-cancer drug with pleotropic effects and many paths to autophagy. Autophagy 2008;4 (1):107–109.

76. Perry C, Frampton J, McCormack P, Asif M, Siddiqui A, Cvetkovic R. Nelfinavir a review of its use in the management of HIV infection. Drugs 2005;65(15):2209–2244.

77. Kaldor S, Hammond M, Dressman B, Fritz J, Crowell T, Hermann R. New dipeptide isosteres useful for the inhibition of HIV-1 protease. Bioorg Med Chem Lett 1994;4(11):1385–1390.

78. Kaldor S, Dressman B, Hammond M, Appelt K, Burgess J, Lubbehusen P, Muesing M, Hatch S, Wiskerchen M, Baxter A. Isophthalic acid derivatives: amino acid surrogates for the inhibition of HIV-1 protease. Bioorg Med Chem Lett 1995;5(7):721–726.

79. Kalish V, Tatlock J, Davies J, Kaldor S, Dressman B, Reich S, Pino M, Nyugen D, Appelt K, Musick L, Wu B. Structure-based drug design of nonpeptidic P_2 substituents for HIV-1 protease inhibitors. Bioorg Med Chem Lett 1995;5 (7):727–732.

80. Kaldor S, Kalish V, Davies J, Shetty B, Fritz J, Appelt K, Burgess J, Campanale K, Chirgadze N, Clawson D, Dressman B, Hatch S, Khalil D, Kosa M, Lubbenhusen P, Muesing M, Patick A, Reich Si Su K, Tatlock J. Viracept (nelfinavir mesylate, AG1343): a potent, orally bioavailable inhibitor of HIV-1 protease. J Med Chem 1997;40(24):3979–3985.

81. Kaldor S, Appelt K, Fritz J, Hammond M, Crowell T, Baxter A, Hatch S, Wiskerchen M, Muesing M. A systematic study of P_1_P_3 spanning sidechains for the inhibition of HIV-1 protease. Bioorg Med Chem Lett 1995;5 (7):715–720.

82. Kaldor S, Kalish V, Davies J, Shetty B, Fritz J, Appelt K, Burgess J, Campanle K, Chirgadze N, Clawson D, Dressman B, Hatch S, Khalil D, Kosa M, Lubbehusen P, Muesing M, Patick A, Reich S, Su K, Tatlock J. Viracept (Nelfinavir Mesylate, AG1343): a potent, orally bioavailable inhibitor of HIV-1 protease. J Med Chem 1997;40(24):3979–3985.

83. Zhang K, Wu E, Patick A, Kerr B, Zorbas M, Lankford A, Kobayashi T, Maeda Y, Shetty B, Webber S. Circulating metabolites of the human immunodeficiency virus protease inhibi-

tor nelfinavir in humans: structural identification, levels in plasma, and antiviral activities. Antimicrob Agents Chemother 2001;45 (4):1086–1093.

84. Nelfinavir approval review package. Available at http://www.fda.gov/cder/foi/nda/97/020778 ap.pdf. Accessed 2008 Dec 20.

85. Kemper C, Witt M, Keiser P, Dube M, Forthal D, Leibowitz M, Smith D, Rigby A, Hellmann N, Lie Y, Leedom J, Richman D, McCutchan J, Haubrich R. Sequencing of protease inhibitor therapy: insights from an analysis of HIV phenotypic resistance in patients failing protease inhibitors. AIDS 2001;15(5):609–615.

86. Hirsch M, Brun-Vezinet F, D'Aquila R, Hammer S, Johnson V, Kuritzkes D, Loveday C, Mellors J, Clotet B, Conway B, Demeter L, Vella S, Jacobsen D, Richman D. Antiretroviral drug resistance testing in adult HIV-1 infection: recommendations of an International AIDS Society-USA panel. JAMA 2000;283 (10):2417–2426.

87. Package label information for Agenerase (amprenavir). Available at http://www.fda.gov/cder/foi/ label/2005/021007s017lbl.pdf. Accessed 2008 Nov 14.

88. Adkins J, Faulds D, Amprenavir Drugs 1998; 55(6):837–842.

89. Arvieux C, Tribut O. Amprenavir or Fosamprenavir plus ritonavir in HIV infection pharmacology, efficacy and tolerability profile. Drugs 2005;65(5):633–659.

90. Fung H, Kirschenbaum H, Hameed R. Amprenavir: a new human immunodeficiency virus type 1 protease inhibitor. Clin Ther 2000;22 (5):549–572.

91. Ghosh A, Thompson W, McKee S, Duong T, Lyle T, Chen J, Darke P, Zugay J, Emini E, Schleif W, Juff J, Anderson P. 3-Tetrahydrofuran and pyran urethanes as high-affinity P2-ligands for HIV-1 protease inhibitors. J Med Chem 1993;36(2):292–294.

92. Kim E, Baker C, Dwyer M, Murcko M, Rao B, Tung R, Navia M. Crystal structure of HIV-1 protease in complex with VX-478, a potent and orally bioavailable inhibitor of the enzyme. J Am Chem Soc 1995;117(3):1181–1182.

93. Todd M, Luque I, Velazquez-Campoy A, Freire E. Thermodynamic basis of resistance to HIV-1 protease inhibition: calorimetric analysis of the V82F/I84V active site resistant mutant. Biochemistry 2000;39(39):11876–11883.

94. Surleraux D, Tahri A, Verschueren W, Pille G, de Kock H, Jonckers T, Peeters A, De Meyer S, Azijn H, Pauwels R, de Bethune M, King N,

Prabu-Jeyabalan M, Schiffer C, Wigerinck P. Discovery and selection of TMC114, a next generation HIV-1 protease inhibitor. J Med Chem 2005;48(6):1813–1822.

95. Kovalevsky A, Liu F, Leshchenko S, Louis J, Harrison R, Weber I. Ultra-high resolution crystal structure of HIV-1 protease mutant reveals two binding sites for clinical inhibitor TMC114. J Mol Biol 2006;363 (1):161–173.

96. Sadler B, Chittick G, Polk R, Slain D, Kerkering T, Studenberg S, Lou Y, Moore K, Woolley J, Stein D. Metabolic disposition and pharmacokinetics of [^{14}C]-amprenavir, a human immunodeficiency virus type 1 (HIV-1) protease inhibitor, administered as a single oral dose to healthy male subjects. J Clin Pharmacol 2001;41(4):386–396.

97. Tisdale M, Myers R, Randall S, Maguire M, Ait-Khaled M, Elston R, Snowden W. Resistance to the HIV protease inhibitor amprenavir *in vitro* and in clinical studies a review. Clin Drug Invest 2000;20(4):267–285.

98. Sham H, Kempf D, Molla A, Marsh K, Kumar G, Chen C, Kati W, Stewart K, Lal R, Hsu A, Betebenner D, Korneyeva M, Vasavanonda S, McDonald E, Saldivar A, Wideburg N, Chen X, Niu P, Park C, Jayanti V, Grabowski B, Granneman G, Sun E, Japour A, Leonard J, Plattner J, Norbeck D. ABT-378, a highly potent inhibitor of the human immunodeficiency virus protease. Antimicrob Agents Chemother 1998;42(12):3218–3224.

99. Sham H, Betebenner D, Chen X, Saldivar A, Vasavanonda S, Kempf D, Plattner J, Norbeck D. Synthesis and structure–activity relationships of a novel series of HIV-1 protease inhibitors encompassing ABT-378 (lopinavir). Bioorg Med Chem Lett 2002;12: 1185–1187.

100. Stoll V, Qin W, Stewart K, Jakob C, Park C, Walter K, Simmer R, Helfrich R, Bussiere D, Kao J, Kempf D, Sham H, Norbeck D. X-ray crystallographic structure of ABT-378 (lopinavir) bound to HIV-1 protease. Bioorg Med Chem 2002;10(8):2803–2806.

101. Package label information for Kaletra (lopinavir/ritonavir). Available at http://www.fda.gov/ cder/foi/label/2007/021226s022lbl.pdf. Accessed 2008 Dec 22.

102. Kumar G, Jayanti V, Lee R, Whittern D, Uchic J, Thomas S, Johnson P, Grabowski B, Sham H, Betebenner D, Kempf D, Denissen J. *In vitro* metabolism of the HIV-1 protease inhibitor ABT-378: species comparison and meta-

bolite identification. Drug Metab Dispos 1999;27(1):86–91.

103. Oldfield V, Plosker G. Lopinavir/ritonavir a review of its use in the management of HIV infection. Drugs 2006;66(9):1275–1299.

104. Mo H, King M, King K, Molla A, Brun S, Kempf D. Selection of resistance in protease inhibitor-experienced, human immunodeficiency virus type 1-infected subjects failing lopinavir- and ritonavir-based therapy: mutation patterns and baseline correlates. J Virol 2005;79 (6):3329–3338.

105. Busti J, Hall R, Margolis D. Atazanavir for the treatment of human immunodeficiency virus infection. Pharmacotherapy 2004;24 (12):1732–1747.

106. Harrison T, Scott L. Atazanvir a review of its use in the management of HIV infection. Drugs 2005;65(16):2309–2336.

107. Tiec C, Barrail A, Goujard C, Taburet A. Clinical pharmacokinetics and summary of efficacy and tolerability of atazanavir. Clin Pharmacokinet 2005;44(10):1035–1050.

108. Priestel J, Fassler A, Rosel J, Tintelnot-Blomley M, Strop P, Grutter M. Comparative analysis of the X-ray structures of HIV-1 and HIV-2 proteases in complex with CGP 53820 a novel pseudosymmetric inhibitor. Structure 1995;3 (4):381–389.

109. Fassler A, Guido B, Capraro H, Cozens R, Mestan J, Poncioni B, Rosel J, Tintelnot-Blomley M, Lang M. Aza-peptide analogs as potent human immunodeficiency virus type-1 protease inhibitors with oral bioavailability. J Med Chem 1996;39(16):3203–3216.

110. Bold G, Fassler A, Capraro H, Cozens R, Klimkait T, Lazdins J, Mestan J, Poncioni B, Rosel J, Stover D, Tintelnot-Blomley M, Acemoglu F, Beck W, Boss E, Eschbach M, Hurlimann T, Masso El Roussel S, Ucci-Stoll K, Wyss D, Lang M. New aza-dipeptide analogues as potent and orally absorbed HIV-1 protease inhibitors: candidates for clinical development. J Med Chem 1998;41 (18):3387–3401.

111. Klei H, Kish K, Lin P, Guo Q, Friborg J, Rose R, Zhang Y, Goldfarb V, Langley D, Wittekind M, Sheriff S. X-ray crystal structures of human immunodeficiency virus type 1 protease mutants complexed with atazanavir. J Virol 2007;81(17):9525–9535.

112. Package label information for Reyataz (atazanavir sulfate). Available at http://www.fda.gov/cder/foi/label/2008/021567s017lbl.pdf. Accessed 2008 Nov 26.

113. Chan-Tack K, Truffa M, Struble K, Birnkrant D. Atazanavir-associated nephrolithiasis: cases from the US Food and Drug Administration's adverse event reporting system. AIDS 2007;21(9):1215–1218.

114. Chang H, Pella P. Atazanavir Urolithiasis. New Engl J Med 2006;355(20):2158–2159.

115. Wood R, Phanuphak P, Cahn P, Pokrovskiy V, Rozenbaum W, Pantaleo G, Sension M, Murphy R, Mancini M, Kelleher T, Giordano M. Long-term efficacy and safety of atazanavir with stavudine and lamivudine in patients previously treated with nelfinavir or atazanavir. J Acquir Immune Defic Syndr 2004;36 (2):684–692.

116. Haerter G, Manfras B, Mueller M, Kern P, Trein A. Regression of lipodystrophy in HIV-infected patients under therapy with the new protease inhibitor atazanavir. AIDS 2004;18 (6):952–955.

117. Colonno R, Rose R, McLaren C, Thiry A, Parkin N, Friborg J. Identification of I50L as the signature atazanavir (ATV)-reistance mutation in treatment-naïve HIV-1 infected patients receiving ATV-containing regimens. J Infect Dis 2004;189(10):1802–1810.

118. Colonno R, Thiry A, Limoli K, Parkin N. Activites of atazanavir (BMS-232632) against a large panel of human immunodeficiency virus type 1 clinical isolates resistant to one or more approved protease inhibitors. Antimicrob Agents Chemother 2003;47(4):1324–1333.

119. Schnell T, Schmidt B, Moschik G, Thein G, Paatz C, Korn K, Walter H. Distinct cross-resistance profiles of the new protease inhibitors amprenavir, lopinavir, and atazanavir in a panel of clinical samples. AIDS 2003;17 (8):1258–1261.

120. Gong Y, Robinson B, Rose R, Deminie C, Spicer T, Stock D, Colonno R, Lin P. In vitro resistance profile of the human immunodeficiency virus type 1 protease inhibitor BMS-232632. Antimicrob Agents Chemother 2000;44 (0):2319–2326.

121. FDA list of protease inhibitors used in the treatment of HIV aids. Available at http://www.fda.gov/oashi/aids/virals.html. Accessed 2008 Nov 13.

122. Package label information for Lexiva (fosamprenavir). Available at http://www.fda.gov/cder/foi/label/2008/021548s017,022116s001lbl.pdf. Accessed 2008 Nov 14.

123. Barlett J, Demasi R, Quinn J, Moxham C, Rousseau F. Overview on the effectiveness of triple combination therapy in antiretroviral-

naïve HIV-1 infected adults. AIDS 2001;15 (11):1369–1377.

124. Stone V. Strategies for optimizing adherence to highly active antiretroviral therapy: lessons from research and clinical practice. Clin Infect Dis 2001;33(6):865–872.

125. Sethi A, Celentano D, Gange S, Moore R, Gallant J. Association between adherence to antiretroviral therapy and human immunodeficiency virus drug resistance. Clin Inf Dis 2003;37(8):1112–1118.

126. Spaltenstein A, Baker C, Gray-Nunez Y, Kaldor I, Kazmierski W, Reynolds D, Tung R, Wheelan P, Furfine E. Highly polar, water soluble prodrugs of the HIV protease inhibitor amprenavir. A new approach toward a more compact dosing regimen. Antiviral Res 2000;46(1):A37.

127. Spaltenstein A, Kazmierski W, Miller J, Samano V. Discovery of next generation inhibitors of HIV protease. Curr Top Med Chem 2005;5(16):1589–1607.

128. Furfine E, Baker C, Hale M, Reynolds D, Salisbury J, Searle A, Studenberg S, Todd D, Tung R, Spaltenstein A. Preclinical pharmacology and pharmacokinetics of GW433908, a water-soluble prodrug of the human immunodeficiency virus protease inhibitor amprenavir. Antimicrob Agents Chemother 2004;48 (3):791–798.

129. Falcoz C, Jenkins J, Bye C, et al. Pharmacokinetics of GW433908, a prodrug of amprenavir, in healthy male volunteers. J Clin Pharmacol 2002;42(8):887–898.

130. Wood R, Arasteh K, Stellbrink H, et al. Six-week randomized controlled trial to compare the tolerabilities, pharmacokinetics, and antiviral activities of GW433908 and amprenavir in human immunodeficiency virus type 1-infected patients. Antimicrob Agents Chemother 2004;48(1):116–123.

131. Gathe J, Ive P, Wood R, et al. SOLO: 48-week efficacy and safety comparison of once-daily Fosamprenavir/ritonavir versus twice-daily nelfinavir in naïve HIV-1-infected patients. AIDS 2004;18(11):1529–1537.

132. Rodriguez-French A, Boghossian J, Gray G, Nadler J, Quinones A, Sepulveda G, Millard J, Wannamaker P. The NEAT study: a 48-week open-label study to compare the antiviral efficacy and safety of GW433908 versus nelfinavir in antiretroviral therapy-naive HIV-1 infected patients. J Acquir Immune Defic Syndr 2004;35(1):22–32.

133. DeJesus E, LaMarca A, Sension M, Beltran C, Yeni P. The context study: efficacy and safety of GW433908/RTV in protease inhibitor experienced subjects with virological failure (24 week results). The Tenth Conference on Retroviruses and Opportunistic Infections; 2003. Abstract 178.

134. Church J, Rathore M, Rubio T, et al. Phase III study of amprenavir in protease-inhibitor naïve and experienced HIV-infected children and adolescents. The Seventh Conference on Retroviruses and Opportunistic Infections; 2000. Abstract 693.

135. Blanche S, Fetter A, Cox H, Yeo J, Randall S, Snowden W. A phase II study of amprenavir in antiretroviral-experienced children with HIV infection. The Seventh Conference on Retroviruses and Opportunistic Infections; 2000. Abstract 695.

136. Noble S, Goa K. Amprenavir: a review of its clinical potential in patients with HIV infection. Drugs 2000;60(6):1383–1410.

137. Maguire M, Shortino D, Klein A, Harris W, Manohitharajah V, Tisdale M, Elston R, Yeo J, Randall S, Xu F, Parker H, May J, Snowden W. Emergence of resistance to protease inhibitor amprenavir in human immunodeficiency virus type 1 infected patients: selection of four alternative viral protease genotypes and influence of viral susceptibility to coadministered reverse transcriptase nucleoside inhibitors. Antimicrob Agents Chemother 2002;46(3):731–738.

138. MacManus S, Yates P, Elston R, White S, Richards N, Snowden W. GW433908/ritonavir once daily in antiretroviral therapy-naïve HIV infected patients: absence of protease resistance at 48 weeks. AIDS 2004;18(4):651–655.

139. King J, Acosta E. Tipranavir a novel nonpeptidic protease inhibitor of HIV. Clin Pharmacokinet 2006;45(7):665–682.

140. Dong B, Mocohoba J. Tipranavir: a protease inhibitor for HIV salvage therapy. Ann Pharmacother 2006;40(7–8):1311–1321.

141. Luna B, Townsend M. Tipranavir: the first nonpeptidic protease inhibitor for the treatment of protease resistance. Clin Ther 2007;29 (11):2309–2318.

142. Temesgen Z, Feinberg J. Tipranavir: a new option for the treatment of drug-resistant HIV infection. Clin Infect Dis 2007;45(6):761–769.

143. Aptivus label information. Available at http://www.fda.gov/cder/foi/label/2008/021814s005, 022292lbl.pdf. Accessed 2008 Nov 24.

144. Thaisrivongs S, Tomich P, Watenpaugh K, Chong K, Howe W, Yang C, Strohbach J, Turner S, McGrath J, Bohanon M, Lynn J, Mulichak A, Spinelli P, Hinshaw R, Pagano P, Moon J,

Ruwart M, Wilkinson K, Rush B, Zipp G, Dalga R, Schwended F, Howard G, Padbury G, Toth L, Zhao Z, Koeplinger K, Kakuk T, Cole S, Zaya R, Piper R, Jeffrey P. Structure-based design of HIV protease inhibitors: 4-hydroxycoumarins and 4-hydroxy-2-pyronens as nonpeptidic inhibitors. J Med Chem 1994;37(20): 3200–3204.

145. Skulnick H, Johnson P, Howe W, Tomich P, Chong K, Watenpaugh K, Janakiraman M, Dolak L, McGrath J, Lynn J, Horng M, Hinshaw R, Zipp G, Ruwart M, Schwende F, Zhong W, Padbury G, Dalga R, Shiou L, Possert P, Rush B, Wilkinson K, Howard G, Toth L, Williams M, Kakuk T, Cole S, Zaya R, Thaisrivongs S, Aristoff A. Structure-based design of sulfonamide substituted nonpeptidic HIV protease inhibitors. J Med Chem 1995;38(26):4968–4971.

146. Thaisrivongs S, Watenpaugh K, Howe W, Tomich P, Dolak L, Chong K, Tomich C, Tomasselli A, Turner S, Strohbach J, Mulichak A, Janakiraman M, Moon J, Lynn J, Horng M, Hinshaw R, Curry K, Rothrock D. Structure-based design of novel HIV protease inhibitors: carboxamide-containing 4-hydroxycoumarins and 4-hydroxy-2-pyrones as potent nonpeptidic inhibitors. J Med Chem 1995;38 (18):3624–3637.

147. Thaisrivongs S, Romero D, Tommasi R, Janakiraman M, Strohbach J, Turner S, Biles C, Morge R, Johnson P, Aristoff P, Tomich P, Lynn J, Horng M, Chong K, Hinshaw R, Howe W, Finzel B, Watenpaugh K. Structure-based design of HIV protease inhibitors: 5 6-dihydro-4-hydroxy-2-pyrones as effective, nonpeptidic inhibitors. J Med Chem 1996;39(23):4630–4642.

148. Thaisrivongs S, Skulnick H, Turner S, Strohbach J, Tommasi R, Johnson P, Aristoff P, Judge T, Gammill R, Morris J, Romines K, Chrusciel R, Hinshaw R, Chong K, Tarpley W, Poppe S, Slade D, Lynn J, Horng M, Tomich P, Seest E, Dolak L, Howe W, Howard G, Schwende F, Toth L, Padbury G, Wilson G, Shiou L, Zipp G, Wilkinson K, Rush B, Ruwart M, Koeplinger K, Zhao Z, Cole S, Zaya R, Kauk T, Janakiraman M, Watenpaugh K. Structure-based design of HIV protease inhibitors: sulfonamide-containing 5 6-dihdrox-4-hydroxy-2-pyrones as nonpeptidic inhibitors. J Med Chem 1996;39(22):4349–4353.

149. Turner S, Strohbach J, Tommasi R, Aristoff P, Johnson P, Skulnick H, Dolak L, Seest E, Tomich P, Bohanon M, Horng M, Lynn J, Chong K, Hinshaw R, Watenpaugh K, Janakiraman M, Thaisrivongs S, Tipranavir (PNU-140690): a potent, orally bioavailable nonpep-tidic HIV protease inhibitor of the 5 6-dihydro-4-hydroxy-2-pyrone sulfonamide class. J Med Chem 1998;41(18):3467–3476.

150. Latli B, Hrapchak M, Easter JA, Stolle WT, Grozinger K, Krishnamurthy D, Senanayake CH. Synthesis of [^{14}C]- and [^{13}C$_6$]-labeled tipranavir and its potential hydroxyl metabolite and the glucuronide conjugate. J Labelled Compd Radiopharm 2008;51(8):314–320.

151. Vourvahis M, Kashuba A. Mechanisms of pharmacokinetic and pharmacodynamic drug interactions associated with ritonavir-enhanced tipranavir. Pharmacotherapy 2007; 27(6):888–909.

152. Boffito M, Maitland D, Pozniak A. Practical perspectives on the use of tipranavir in combination with other medications: lessons learned from pharmacokinetic studies. J Clin Pharmacol 2006;46(2):130–139.

153. Hicks C, Cahn P, Cooper D, Walmsley S, Katlama C, Clotet B, Lazzarin A, Johnson M, Neubacher D, Mayers D, Valdez H. Durable efficacy of tipranavir-ritonavir in combination with an optimized background regimen of antiretroviral drugs for treatment-experienced HIV-1 infected patients at 48 weeks in the Randomized Evaluation of Strategic Intervention in multi-drug resistant patients with Tipranavir (RESIST) studies: an analysis of combined data from two randomized open-label trials. Lancet 2006;368(9534):466–475.

154. Cenci E, Francisci D, Belfiori B, Pierucci S, Baldelli F, Bistoni F, Vecchiarelli A. Tipranavir exhibits different effects on opportunistic pathogenic fungi. J Infect 2008;56(1):58–64.

155. Francesca M, Elisa T, Valerio A, Marcus G, Marcel K, Alessandro T, Benedetti F, Cargnel A, Chiara A. The non-peptidic HIV protease inhibitor tipranavir and two synthetic peptidomimetics (TS98 and TS102) modulate Pneumocystis carinii growth and proteasome activity of HEL299 cell line. J Eukaryot Microbiol 2006;53(Suppl 1):S144–S146.

156. Chiara A, Paola V, Regazzi M, Mazza F, Valerio A, Tronconi E, Maruzzi M, Antonietta C. Detection of HIV protease inhibitors in alveolar epithelial lining fluid: relevance for modulation of pneumocystis infection in the course of HAART. J Eukaryot Microbiol 2006;53 (Suppl 1):S140–S141.

157. Kohlbrenner V, Gathe J, Pierone G, et al. Tipranavir/ritonavir (TPV/r) demonstrates potent efficacy in multiple protease inhibitor (PI)-experienced patients at 24 weeks. 9th European AIDS Conference; 2003, Abstract 72/2.

158. Cooper D, Hicks C, Cahn P, et al. 24-Week RESIST study analysis: the efficacy of tipranvir/ritonavir (TPV/r) is superior to lopinavir/ritonavir (LPV/r), and the TPV/r treatment response is enhanced by inclusion of genotypically active antiretrovirals in the optimized background regimen (OBR). 12th Conference on Retroviruses and Opportunistic Infections; 2005. Abstract 560.

159. Chapman S, Woolley I, Visvanathan K, Korman T. Acute pancreatitis caused by tipranavir/ritonavir-induced hypertriglyceridaemia. AIDS 2007;21(4):532–533.

160. Coffinier C, Hudon S, Farber E, Chang S, Hrycyna C, Young S, Fong L. HIV protease inhibitors block the zinc metalloproteinase ZMPSTE24 and lead to an accumulation of prelamin A in cells. PNA 2007;104 (33):13432–13473.

161. Chen D, Misra A, Garg A. Clinical review 153: lipodystrophy in human immunodeficiency virus-infected patients. J Clin Endocrinol Metab 2002;87(11):4845–4856.

162. Hudon S, Coffinier C, Michaelis S, Fong L, Young S, Hrycyna C. HIV-protease inhibitors block the enzymatic activity of purified Ste24p. Biochem Biophys Res Commun 2008;374 (2):365–368.

163. Graff J, von Hentig N, Kuczka K, Carlo A, Gute P, Klauke S, Babacan E, Sebastian H. Significant effects of tipranavir on platelet aggregation and thromboxane B_2 formation *in vitro* and *in vivo*. J Antimicrob Chemo 2008;61(2):394–399.

164. Arbuthnot C, Wilde J. Increased risk of bleeding with the use of tipranavir boosted with ritonavir in haemophilic patients. Haemophilia 2008;14(1):140–141.

165. Chrysos G, Gerakari S, Stasini F, Kokkoris S, Kourousis D, Velegraki A. Intracranial haemorrhage possible related to tipranavir in an HIV-1 patient with cryptococcal meningitis. J Infect 2008;57(1):85–87.

166. Justice A, Zingmond D, Gordon K, Fultz S, Goulet J, King J, Bravata D, Valdez H, Kraft M, Mattocks K. Drug toxicity, HIV progression, or comorbidity of aging: does tipranavir use increase the risk of intracranial hemorrhage?. Clin Infect Dis 2008;47(9):1226–1230.

167. Baxter J, Schapiro J, Boucher C, Kohlbrenner V, Hall D, Scherer J, Mayers D. Genotypic changes in human immunodeficiency virus type 1 protease associated with reduced susceptibility and virologic response to the protease inhibitor tipranavir. J Virol 2006;80 (21):10794–801.

168. Parkin N, Chappey C,Protease mutations associated with higher or lower than expected tipranavir susceptibility based on the TPV mutation score. 13th Conference on Retroviruses and Opportunistic Infections; 2006. Abstract 637.

169. Van der Borght K, Winters B, Van Craenenbroeck E, Braido V, Bacheler L, Kohlbrenner V, Hall D, Villacian J,Correlation of resistance algorithms for tipranavir susceptibility with response to tipranavir containing regimens in the RESIST trials. 5th European HIV drug resistance workshop; 2007; Available at http//wwwnataporg/ Accessed 2008 Dec 3.

170. Naeger L, Struble K. Food and Drug Administration analysis of tipranavir clinical resistance in HIV-1 infected treatment-experienced patients. AIDS 2007;21(2):179–185.

171. Scherer J, Kohlbrenner V, Hall D, Baxter J, Schapiro J, Boucher C, 2007. Mutations associated with cross-resistance to tipranavir in patients previously treated with two or more protease inhibitors. 5th European HIV Drug Resistance Workshop. Abstract 100.

172. Ghosh A, Kincaid J, Cho W, Walters D, Krishnan K, Hussain K, Koo Y, Cho H, Rudall Cl Holland L, Buthod J. Potent HIV protease inhibitors incorporating high-affinity P_2-ligands and (*R*)-(hydroxyethylamino)sulfonamide isostere. Bioorg Med Chem Lett 1998;8 (6):687–690.

173. Rittweger M, Arasteh K. Clinical pharmacokinetics of darunavir. Clin Pharmacokinet 2007;46(9):739–756.

174. Ge-Fei H, Yang G. Progress in the new generation nonpeptide sulfonamide anti-HIV protease inhibitor darunavir. Youji Huaxue 2008;28(9):1545–1552.

175. Fenton C, Perry C. Darunavir in the treatment of HIV-1 infection. Drugs 2007;67(18): 2791–2801.

176. McCoy C. Darunavir: a nonpeptidic antiretroviral protease inhibitor. Clin Ther 2007;29 (8):1559–1576.

177. Busse K, Penzak S. Darunavir: a second-generation protease inhibitor. Am J Health-Syst Pharm 2007;64(15):1593–1602.

178. Clark M, Mohandas N, Shohet S. Hydration of sickle cells using the sodium ionophore monensin. J Clin Invest 1982;70(5): 1074–1080.

179. Nakanishi K. Terpene trilactones from Gingko biloba: from ancient times to the 21st century. Bioorg Med Chem 2005;13(17):4987–5000.

180. Ghosh A, Dawson Z, Mitsuya H, Darunavir a conceptually new HIV-1 protease inhibitor for the treatment of drug-resistant HIV. Bioorg Med Chem 2007;15(24):7576–7580.

181. Ghosh A, Thompson W, Fitzgerald P, Culberson J, Axel M, McKee S, Huff J, Anderson P. Structure-based design of HIV-1 protease inhibitors: replacement of two amides and a 10π-aromatic system by a fused bis-tetrahydrofuran. J Med Chem 1994;37(16):2506–2508.

182. Ghosh A, Chapsal B, Weber I, Mitsuya H. Design of HIV protease inhibitors targeting protein backbone: an effective strategy for combating drug resistance. Acc Chem Res 2008;41 (1):78–86.

183. Yoshimura K. Kato R, Kavlick MF, Nguyen A, Maroun V, Maeda K, Hussain KA, Ghosh AK, Gulnik SV, Erickson JW, Mitsuya H. A potent human immunodeficiency virus type 1 protease inhibitor, UIC-94003 (TMC-126), and selection of a novel (A28S) mutation in the protease active site. J. Virol. 2002,76, 1349–1358.

184. Ghosh A, Sridhar P, Kumaragurubaran N, Koh Y, Weber I, Mitsuya H. Bis-tetrahydrofuran: a privileged ligand for darunavir and a new generation of HIV protease inhibitors that combat drug resistance. ChemMedChem 2006;1(9):939–950.

185. Koh Y, Nakata H, Maeda K, Ogata H, Bilcer G, Devasamudram T, Kincaid J, Boross P, Wang Y, Tie Y, Volarath P, Gaddis L, Harrison R, Weber I, Ghosh A, Mitsuya H. Novel bis-tetrahydrofuranylurethane-containing nonpeptidic protease inhibitor (PI) UIV-94017 (TMC114) with potent activity against multi-PI-resistant human immunodeficiency virus *in vitro*. Antimicrob Agents Chemother 2003;47(10):3123–3129.

186. Tie Y, Boross PI, Wang YF, Gaddis L, Hussain AK, Leshchenko S, Ghosh AK, Louis JM, Harrison RW, Weber IT. High resolution crystal structures of HIV-protease with a potent nonpeptide inhibitor (UIC-94017) active against multi-drug-resistant clinical strains. J. Mol. Biol. 2004,338,341–352.

187. King N, Prabu-Jeyabalan M, Nalivaika E, Wigerinck P, de Bethune M, Schiffer C. Structural and thermodynamic basis for the binding of TMC114 a next-generation human immunodeficiency virus type 1 protease inhibitor. J Virol 2004;78(21):12012–12021.

188. Kovalevsky A, Ghosh A, Weber I. Solution kinetics measurements suggest HIV-1 protease has two binding sites for darunavir and amprenavir. J Med Chem 2008;51 (20):6599–6603.

189. Package label information for Prezista (darunavir). Available at http://www.fda.gov/cder/ 2008 Dec 3.

190. Sekar V, Spinosa-Guzman S, Lefebvre E, Hoetelmans R.Clinical pharmacology of TMC114: a new HIV protease inhibitor. 16th International AIDS Conference; 2006. Poster No. TUPE0083.

191. Prezista pharmacology review. Available at http://www.fda.gov/cder/foi/nda/2006/ 021976s000_Sprycel_PharmR.pdf. Accessed 2008 Dec 7.

192. Coffinier C, Hudon S, Lee R, Farber E, Nobumori C, Miner J, Andres D, Spielmann H, Hrycyna C, Fong L, Young S. A potent HIV protease inhibitor, darunavir, does not inhibit ZMPSTE24 or lead to an accumulation of farnesyl-prelamin A in cells. J Biol Chem 2008;283(15):9797–9804.

193. Storch C, Theile D, Lindenmaier H, Haefeli W, Weiss J. Comparison of the inhibitory activity of anti-HIV drugs on P-glycoprotein. Biochem Pharmacol 2007;73(10):1573–1581.

194. Mitsuya Y, Liu T, Rhee So, Fessel J, Shafer R. Prevalence of darunavir resistance-associated mutations: patterns of occurrence and association with past treatment. J Infect Dis 2007;196 (8):1177–1179.

195. Kresge K. Drug pipelines may flourish, but not for HIV. HIV AIDS Treatment Insider. 2004;5 (7):1–8.

196. 2008 HIV drug pipeline report. Available at http://napwa.org.au/pl/2008/09/aids-2008-is-the-hiv-drug-pipeline-drying-up. Accessed 2008 Dec 2.

197. England R. The writing is on the wall for UNAIDS. Br Med J 2008;336(7652):1072.

198. Rusconi S, Vigano O. New HIV protease inhibitors for drug-resistant viruses. Therapy 2006;3(1):79–88.

199. Stellbrink H. Antiviral drugs in the treatment of aids: what is in the pipeline? Eur J Med Res 2007;12(9):483–495.

200. FDA investigational drugs. Available at http:// aidsinfo.nih.gov/DrugsNew/SearchResults. aspx?MenuItem=Drugs&DrugName=& DrugClass=All&DrugType=Investigational %20Drugs. Accessed 2008 Dec 2.

201. 14th Annual Conference on Retroviruses and Opportunistic Infections Coverage Report. Available at http://www.hivandhepatitis.com/

2007icr/croi/docs/040307_a.html. Accessed 2008 Dec 2.

202. Cihlar T, Gong-Xin H, Xiahong L, Chen J, Hatada M, Swaminathan S, McDermott M, Yang Z, Mulato A, Chen X, Leavitt S, Stray K, Lee W. Suppression of HIV-1 protease inhibitor resistance by phosphonate-mediated solvent anchoring. J Mol Biol 2006;363 (3):635–647.

203. Callebaut C, Stray K, Tsai L, Xu L, He G, Mulato A. Priskich T. Parkin N. Lee W. Cihlar T. *In vitro* antiretroviral activity, toxicity and resistance profile of GS-8374 a novel phosphonate-containing HIV protease inhibitor. 14th Conference on Retroviruses and Opportunistic Infections; 2007. Poster No. 491.

204. Callebaut C, Yan Q, Koster J, Tsai L, Cihlar T, Hruz P. GS-8374, a novel HIV protease inhibitor, does not alter peripheral glucose disposal in a healthy rodent model system. 15th Conference on Retroviruses and Opportunistic Infections; 2008. Poster No 732.

205. Press release from Sequoia Pharmaceuticals. Available at http://www.sequoiapharmaceuticals.com/news_press/news_press.html. Accessed 2008 Dec 2.

206. Conference report on SPI-390 and SPI-457. Available at http://www.natap.org/2007/ResisWksp/ResisWksp_45.htm. Accessed 2008 Dec 2.

207. Online review of DMP-450. Available at http://www.aidsmap.com/cms1032487.asp. Accessed 2008 Dec 2.

208. Online review of DMP-450. Available at http://www.aidsmeds.com/drugs/DMP-450.htm. Accessed 2008 Dec 2.

209. News update for PL-100. Available at http://www.natap.org/2008/newsUpdates/081508_01.htm. Accessed 2008 Dec 2.

210. GlaxoSmithKline Statement to HIV Patient Community. Available at http://img.thebody.com/press/2006/brecanavir_end.pdf. Accessed 2008 Dec 2.

211. Kaltenbach R, Trainor G, Getman D, Harris G, Garber S, Cordova B, Bacheler L, Jeffrey S, Logue K, Cawood P, Klabe R, Diamond S, Davies M, Saye J, Jona J, Erickson-Viitanen S. DPC 681 and DPC 684: potent, selective inhibitors of human immunodeficiency virus protease active against clinically relevant mutant variants. Antimicrob Agents Chemother 2001;45(11):3021–3028.

212. Pfizer 2008 drug pipeline report. Available at http://media.pfizer.com/files/research/pipeline/2008_0930/pipeline_2008_0930.pdf. Accessed 2008 Dec 2.

213. Hammond J, Graham J, Blair W, Patick A. *In vitro* selection and characterization of HIV with reduced sensitivity to AG-001859. 12th Conference on Retroviruses and Opportunistic Infections 2005. Poster No 561.

214. Mimoto T, Nojima S, Terashima K, Takaku H, Shintani M, Hayashi H. Structure–activity relationships of novel HIV-1 protease inhibitors containing the 3-amino-2-chlorobenzoyl-allophenylnorstatine structure. Bioorg Med Chem 2008;16(3):1299–1308.

215. Sevigny G, Stranix B, Tian B, Dubois A, Sauve G, Petropoulos C, Lie Y, Hellmann N, Conway B, Yelle J. Antiviral activity and cross-resistance profile of P-1946, a novel human immunodeficiency virus type 1 protease inhibitor. Antiviral Res 2006;70(2):17–20.

216. Koh Y, Das D, Leschenko S, Nakata H, Ogata-Aoki H, Amano M, Nakayama M, Ghosh A, Mitsuya H.GRL-02031: a novel nonpeptidic protease inhibitor (PI) containing a stereochemically defined fused cyclopentanyltetrahydrofuran (Cp-THF) potent against multi-PI-resistante HIV-1 *in vitro*. Antimicrob Agents Chemother Available online 27 Oct 2008. DOI: 10. 1128/AAC. 00689-08.

217. Ghosh A, Pretzer E, Cho H, Hussain K, Cho W, Walters D, Duzgunes N, 1999. Antiviral activity of UIC-94-003, a novel inhibitor of the human immunodeficiency virus type 1 protease. Intersci Conf Antimicrob Agents Chemother Abstract 928.

HIV INTEGRASE

BRIAN A. JOHNS

Department of Medicinal Chemistry, Infectious Diseases Center for Excellence in Drug Discovery, GlaxoSmithKline Research & Development, Research Triangle Park, NC

1. INTRODUCTION

Human immunodificiency virus type 1 (HIV-1) is the causative agent of acquired immune deficiency syndrome (AIDS). According to UNAIDS estimates for 2007, more than 33 million people globally were living with the virus that causes AIDS. These estimates include 2.5 million individuals that became newly infected with HIV and tragically 2.1 million have perished during 2007 alone [1]. These numbers unfortunately solidify HIV/AIDS as a major epidemic threatening entire nations and populations of people. The ascension of HIV/AIDS into a major epidemic is remarkable and a hallmark that is typically reserved for an infectious agent as it is a relatively new disease state with the realization of its existence coming only in the past 25 or so years. The virus infection of humans most certainly predates this timeline by several decades, but was not noted until the first report of AIDS related symptoms appeared in the CDC's June 5 1981 *Morbidity and Mortality Weekly Report* (*MMWR*) where five patients displayed *Pneumocystis carinii* pneumonia, a disease typically limited to only severely immunosuppressed patients [2–5]. The rarity of this disease in previously healthy individuals with no underlying clinically apparent immunodeficiency and their proximity and homosexual lifestyle provided the first obvious evidence of an infectious agent transmitted through sexual contact. At this point, the causative agent was not clear only the epidemiological relationship. The virus was, however, identified and characterized by Montagnier and Gallo in 1983 [6–12]. What was first termed human T-lymphotropic retrovirus III (HTLV-III) by Gallo and lymphadenopathy-associated virus (LAV) by Montagnier turned out to be the same virus that soon turned to be known as HIV-1 [13–15].

The discovery of the HIV virus was disclosed at a now infamous press conference by Gallo and the Secretary of the U.S. Department of Health and Human Services at the time, Margaret Heckler, who also suggested that within 2 years a vaccine would be in place. Unfortunately, now 25 years after the virus was identified and 24 years after Ms. Heckler's announcement, there is no vaccine and much of the vaccine work during that period has resulted in disappointment. The alternative quickly became apparent that there would be a need for chemotherapeutics to combat this newly identified human pathogen.

Nearly as soon as the virus was identified, work began worldwide to identify potential treatments for patients that were without options for the extremely lethal disease. Early efforts focused on any and every target that could be hypothesized to impact the virus from initial infectivity, fusion, entry, replication, maturation, egress, etc., but arguably the most logical place to begin was the virally encoded enzymatic targets of reverse transcriptase (RT), protease (PR), and integrase (IN). The philosophy to target the viral enzymatic machinery is twofold. First, these protein targets are enzymes, hence the catalytic biochemical processes appeared (are) to be essential for viral replication. Thus, if a drug can be found, it will stand an excellent chance of being efficacious. Secondly, if selectivity for the viral target can be achieved this will minimize mechanistically related side effects from inhibition of nonvirally encoded targets that the host may require for other functions. Taken further in the case of IN, there is no human homolog and thus the attainment of the desired selectivity should be more facile than for RT or PR targets.

Unfortunately, these advantages did not necessarily make IN more amenable to drug discovery when compared to its counterpart virally encoded enzymes RT and PR.

Significant progress was made very quickly against RT resulting in the discovery of AZT (zidovudine), a nucleoside reverse transcriptase inhibitor (NRTI) [16,17]. While AZT immediately began prolonging lives, it was quickly apparent that a single drug from a single class was not going to suffice and AZT alone was only a stop gap. It should be noted that the timelines that are commonly inferred for the period from target selection to launch of a small-molecule drug are typically 10–15 years. The entire timeline for AZT was from discovery in a plaque reduction assay in November 1984 to launch in March 1987 was barely 28 months. The pace at which AZT was brought to patients emphasizes the desperation of the situation in the mid-1980s. While several more NRTIs were developed in between the launch of AZT and the mid-1990s, it was the development of additional classes of antiretroviral small molecules in particular the HIV protease inhibitors (PI) that began to give patients hope of long-term survival through highly active antiretroviral therapy (HAART) that became available in 1996 [18]. The first nonnucleoside reverse transcriptase inhibitors (NNRTI) became available soon thereafter and have additionally impacted HAART chemotherapy [19].

Meanwhile, progress against HIV IN, the enzyme that integrates double-stranded viral DNA into host chromosomal DNA was very much lagging that of the other two viral enzymes. There were numerous reasons for the slower progress such as the protein properties, limited or misleading early structural information and reports of early inhibitors resulting from assay systems that were not physiologically relevant. Fortunately, advances over the past decade have facilitated the development of early generation IN inhibitors and eventually culminated in the approval of the first licensed drug, raltegravir [20]. This chapter discusses how HIV IN is involved in HIV replication, aspects of the protein structure and biochemistry, a detailed mechanism of the integration process at the molecular level, pharmacophore-based inhibitor design and progress medicinal chemistry efforts have made to date on key series with a short section at the end on future directions for the field.

2. HIV AND THE RETROVIRAL REPLICATION CYCLE

HIV is from the lentivirus genus and retroviridae family. The classification as a retrovirus results from the fact that HIV carries its genetic information in the form of RNA, which is transcribed to DNA during the replication cycle that is "reverse" of the normal flow of genetic information from DNA to RNA during transcription. Retroviruses are also unique in that they integrate their double-stranded DNA into host chromosomal DNA, thus leaving the infected cell with a lifelong copy of the viral genome annealed into its genetic code. The infected cells can exist in a latent state for long periods and upon reactivation begin producing new virions and unless the cell with integrated viral DNA undergoes some form of cell death, the potential for viral production remains indefinitely.

The viral particle consists of a capsid surrounded by the virion envelope (Fig. 1). Two copies of the genomic length RNA are contained within the capsid core of the viral particle. The RNA sequences are approximately 9 kb in length and are packaged along with the enzymes RT, IN, and PR as well as additional viral proteins such as the major capsid protein (p24) and nucleocapsid protein p7/p9. In the case of IN, there are approximately 40–100 copies of the protein included in a typical infectious viral particle. The viral envelope consists of a lipid bilayer membrane and the envelope precursor protein gp160. Cellular proteases cleave gp160 into the outer membrane protein gp120 and the transmembrane protein gp41. The HIV-1 genome encodes nine open reading frames, three of which encode the *gag*, *pol*, and *env* (5'-gag-pol-env-3'). Six additional accessory genes (Vif, Vpr, Nef, Tat, Rev, and Vpu) are also encoded by the virus. Within the three major gene segments (*gag*, *pol*, and *env*), the proteins that are made are initially in the form a polyproteins and later proteolysed into the individual proteins and including the three viral enzymes reverse transcriptase, integrase and protease [21]. The *gag* gene encodes viral proteins p17, p24, and p7/p9 while the *pol* gene encodes RT, IN, and PR.

It is important to take a moment and discuss how the IN enzyme fits into the overall HIV replication scheme. It was mentioned above that this protein has enzymatic activity that provides for integrating viral and host DNA sequences and thus is crucial to the flow of genetic information during the replication

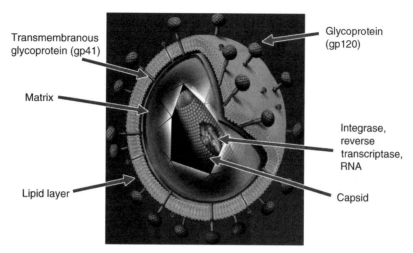

Figure 1. HIV virion structure. (This figure is available in full color at http://mrw.interscience.wiley.com/emrw/9780471266945/home.)

cycle. The integration event is essential for production of new virus. For the purpose of this discussion, the replication cycle is greatly simplified and primarily focused on the viral nucleic acid journey. The infectious virion interacts with the host T-cell membrane receptor molecule CD4 via the viral GP120 surface protein (Fig. 2). Binding of the gp120 and CD4 receptor causes a conformational change in the gp120 opening up a site to interact with a chemokine receptors generally either CCR5 or CXCR4. Binding of the coreceptor causes the gp41 to undergo a conformational change that results in fusion of the viral and cell membranes and entry into the cell. The viral capsid then is uncoated and the viral RNA is released into the cell along with copies of RT and IN that were packaged into the infecting virion along with other viral proteins. The genomic single-stranded RNA is then reverse transcribed via an RNA dependent DNA polymerization process by reverse transcriptase

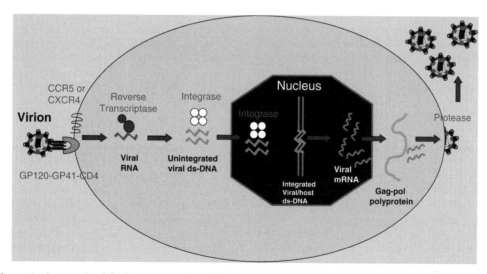

Figure 2. An oversimplified representation of the HIV-1 retroviral replication cycle. (This figure is available in full color at http://mrw.interscience.wiley.com/emrw/9780471266945/home.)

(RT) to form a heteroduplex RNA/DNA oligo-nucleotide. The RNA strand is subsequently degraded via the ribonuclease (RNAse H) active site within the RT heterodimer. The remaining single strand of DNA serves as template for the DNA dependent DNA polymerization to form double-stranded viral DNA.

At this point in the HIV life cycle, the viral DNA undergoes integration whereby the viral DNA is incorporated into the host chromosomal DNA sequence. A more detailed mechanistic explanation of this process is presented below. The replication cycle continues following integration as the cell transcribes DNA into RNA that not only produces mRNA for protein synthesis but also the required copies of HIV genomic RNA that are packaged into the new virions upon egress. The viral protein that is made is a polyprotein initially that along with two copies of the viral RNA is incorporated into a newly forming viral capsid and buds from the cell to form new viral particles. Subsequent to viral egress, HIV protease cleaves the polyprotein into new copies of the viral proteins thus completing the process at least for this simple view of the viral life cycle.

3. INTEGRASE AND THE INTEGRATION PROCESS

The IN protein is derived from proteolytic cleavage of the carboxy-terminal portion of the viral *gag-pol* polyprotein and it is transported into the host cell as part of capsid structure of the virion. IN alone can catalyze integration *in vitro*, however, the *in vivo* process in a whole cell environment is significantly more complex and only partially understood. Numerous cellular proteins and cofactors along with nucleic acid are involved, however, for the purpose of drug discovery the biochemical steps are well understood and have allowed for inhibitor design and optimization. Overall the process of integration involves several discreet steps, but two of these are catalyzed by IN where bond breaking and bond forming reactions are occurring biochemically [22]. Upon entry into the cell and reverse transcription, the resultant viral ds-DNA is associated with IN. The first step in

the sequence occurs in the cytoplasm where the two long terminal repeat (LTR) segments of the viral DNA are modified on their respective 3' termini. A terminal GT dinucleotide is removed by enzymatic catalysis where water is the nucleophile that attacks the phosphodiester bond in a step termed 3' processing. Integrase remains intact with the viral DNA after the 3' processing event within the pre-integration complex (PIC) which then enters the cell nucleus through a nuclear pore in an ATP driven process [23,24]. Preintegration complexes are large nucleoprotein structures containing both viral and host proteins along with viral nucleic acid and after many years of study still are not well characterized. Once in the nucleus, IN coordinates with the host cell chromosomal DNA, and the recessed 3' ends of the viral DNA nick the host nucleic acid strands 5 bp apart in a process called strand transfer. Once the DNA nicking event has occurred, the remaining base pair extensions are removed and the strands are ligated by host cell repair enzymes [25–27] and the proviral DNA is fully integrated into the chromatin (Fig. 3).

Since integration is a unique step required of the virus and not the host for replication, IN is an attractive drug target due to an inherent selectivity benefit since there is no human homolog [28]. HIV IN is a 32 kDa protein consisting of a 288 amino acid primary sequence [29–34] that was first reported to be cloned and expressed in 1990 by Fyfe and Sherman at Wellcome Research Laboratories [35]. The protein consists of three domains: The N-terminal domain consisting of amino acids 1–50 has an HHCC zinc finger binding motif shown to promote multimerization to tetrameric structure that is believed to be the active form of the enzyme [36–40]. The C-terminal domain consisting of amino acids 213–288 binds DNA nonspecifically [41,42]. The catalytic core domain consisting of residues 51–212 contains a highly conserved triad of DD(35)E carboxylate residues at positions Asp64, Asp116, and Glu152. The carboxylate motif that creates the active site within the IN protein is commonly found in polynucleotidyl transferases. Substitution of any of these residues completely renders the enzymatic reactivity of the protein inactive [43–45]. The

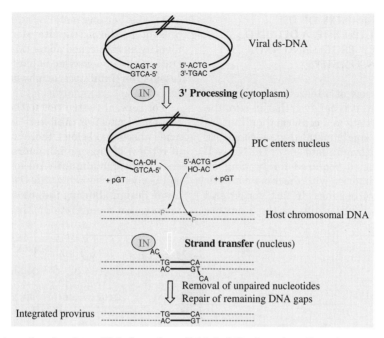

CAGT-3'   5'-ACTG
GTCA-5'   3'-TGAC

Viral ds-DNA

IN   3' **Processing** (cytoplasm)

CA-OH   5'-ACTG
GTCA-5'   HO-AC
+ pGT   + pGT

PIC enters nucleus

P----------P

Host chromosomal DNA

IN
AC

Strand transfer (nucleus)

TG——CA
AC——GT
CA

Removal of unpaired nucleotides
Repair of remaining DNA gaps

Integrated provirus   TG——CA
AC——GT

Figure 3. Integration chemistry. (This figure is available in full color at http://mrw.interscience.wiley.com/emrw/9780471266945/home.)

catalytic core domain is also involved in binding the viral DNA ends [46,47].

Key to understanding the IN biochemistry is the presence of two Mg^{2+} metal ions in the active site [48,49]. The aforementioned DD(35)E catalytic triad coordinates two magnesium ions and is key to the stabilization of the phosphodiester cleavage and bond formation reactions that are catalyzed during the integration sequence. There was some early discrepancy as to whether the active site metals were magnesium or manganese, but it has been shown that the metal cofactors for HIV IN are in fact divalent magnesium ions [50–53].

The core domain alone can carry out the reverse of integration (i.e., disintegration), but both 3' processing and strand transfer require the N- and C-terminal domains [54–59]. Significant efforts have been put forth to obtain structural information on the catalytic core as well as the terminal domains and various combinations of several constructs. A key aspect of much of this work is a F185K mutation to improve solubility and handling properties of the protein constructs [60]. Much of the structural work to date has been complicated by the inability to crystallize full length IN and none of the work has successfully cocrystallized IN with viral nucleic acid. Additionally, the *in vivo* situation is believed to involve a tetrameric IN complex with both viral and host DNA [61].

Several groups have used the existing structural information for computational approaches to model the various IN complexes with or without nucleic acid [62–66]. These types of approaches are always a valuable tool to the medicinal chemist in helping to optimize and design inhibitors, however, significant uncertainty remains with this work involving IN due to the complex nature of the protein and its substrates. One particularly difficult region of the protein has been a flexible loop near the catalytic active site consisting of residues 139–148. Several key mutations in this region have given rise to laboratory and clinical resistance. The limited structural information and perceived flexibility in this portion of the protein has hindered the design of inhibitors to circumvent the effects of these mutations.

4. THE BIOCHEMISTRY OF THE INTEGRASE ACTIVE SITE. A DETAILED LOOK AT THE 3′ PROCESSING AND STRAND TRANSFER STEPS

A molecular view of integration is shown in Fig. 4. Initially, it is believed that *in vitro* the *apo*-enzyme exists in a conformation that involves only a single metal (Fig. 4, Stage A). Early crystallography data shows Glu152 well out of the region required for binding an Mg^{2+} in coordination with the other catalytic triad aspartate residues. In fact, for several years, there was uncertainty in the literature as to whether one metal or two metals were present in the active site along with their identity as mentioned above (Mn or Mg). This state of the *apo*-enzyme is likely either inaccessible for inhibitors or physiologically not relevant.

For several years prior to the discovery of two-metal chelator inhibitors such as diketo acids (discussed below), there were a number of reports of enzyme inhibitors that did not show corresponding antiviral activity in whole cell assays. Presumably, this was an artifact of assay design allowing the inhibitor to bind a nonrelevant conformation of the protein in the

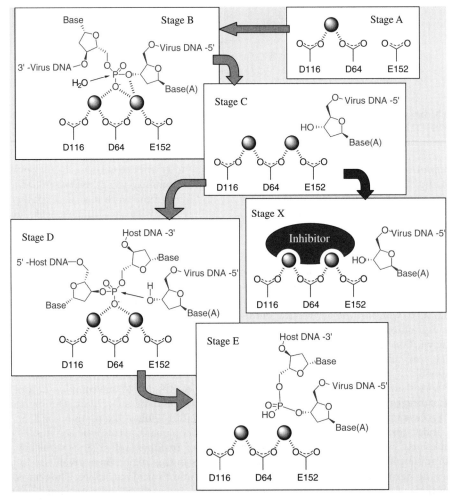

Figure 4. Molecular level view of viral/host DNA integration and inhibition by metal chelators. Reprinted from Ref. [88] with permission from Elsevier. (This figure is available in full color at http://mrw.interscience. wiley.com/emrw/9780471266945/home.)

absence of nucleic acid or creating a situation in the absence of DNA that is not sufficiently accessible in the *in vivo* situation. It was not until the assays were developed to include a DNA/enzyme preincubation step that biochemical results started to translate into antiviral activities. Upon coordination of the viral DNA LTR, the negatively charged phosphate backbone of the DNA likely can supply the second metal and the catalytically active two-metal containing core is then intact and can coordinate to a phosphodiester bridge of the viral nucleic acid (Stage B). In this view, the metal atoms coordinate to the triad of enzyme carboxylates and serve to stabilize a negative charge of the transition state during phosphate hydrolysis [67]. Water serves as the nucleophile to attack the phosphodiester linkage and a hydrolysis proceeds by stabilization of the metal centers present in the active site resulting in a cleavage of the terminal dinucleotide to give a recessed 3' hydroxyl group as shown in Stage C. As the sequence proceeds to Stage D, host DNA coordinates to the now open active site and the remaining 3' hydroxyl group of the viral DNA serves as an activated nucleophile through metal coordination and attacks the host phosphodiester bridge effectively nicking the cellular DNA and proceeding to the final stage shown in Stage E. This process happens to both termini of the viral strands as a result of the tetrameric (or more accurately, dimer of dimers) integrase complex being tethered to the two LTR regions of the viral DNA. The nicking of the two host strands occurs with a 5 bp separation resulting in both strands being ligated to the respective strands of the viral nucleic acid. All that remains for completion of the integration is gap repair by host mechanisms.

5. THE DISCOVERY OF THE DIKETO ACIDS AND ELABORATION OF THE TWO-METAL CHELATION PHARMACOPHORE

Strand transfer is the second chemical step of DNA integration catalyzed by IN. It is this step that has been most amenable to inhibition by a class of compounds known as two-metal binders (Fig. 4, Stage X). By binding to the open form of the active site during the

opportune time while post 3' processing, the metals are not involved in coordination of a phosphodiester from the viral DNA and prior to the complexation of host DNA, this class of inhibitors has been successful in stopping the productive ligation of the viral and host DNA during the strand transfer event. The cartoon showing an inhibitor binding to the active site magnesium ions requires further elaboration as a simple metal chelation motif is not sufficient for enzyme inhibition. A more comprehensive representation of the basic two-metal binding pharmacophore is represented in Fig. 5a. This consists of a planar heteroatom two-metal chelation region that binds to a pair of divalent magnesium metal centers held in place by a triad of aminoacid carboxylate residues (Asp116/Asp64/Glu152), a flexible linker and a hydrophobic aromatic substituent.

It took nearly a decade from when the first purified IN protein was reported to elucidate this basic pharmacophore. Researchers at Merck [69–71] and Shionogi [72,73] nearly simultaneously disclosed in the patent literature the first inhibitors of the IN enzyme that also displayed activity in whole cell replication assays. The original structures were identified through a random screening effort of more than 250,000 compounds resulting in a distinct pharmacophore containing the diketo acid moiety [74,75]. The key to identification of robust inhibitors of the strand transfer event and hence activity that would translate into cellular inhibition, was to develop an assay that uncoupled assembly from catalysis that also helped to explain much of the data in the literature that showed apparent biochemical inhibition but no antiviral activity [76]. The original leads from that screen are shown in Table 1. While the structures 1–4 differ in the aromatic portion and its substitution, they all contain the metal binding motif known as the diketo acid (DKA). Compounds 1–3 show submicromolar activity against the biochemical assay using recombinant IN enzyme and also similar potency against the isolated preintegration complex. In addition, they display activity in a whole-cell assay in the micromolar range. The disparity from enzyme and PIC assays to cellular assays is not surprising and a hint to one of the major problems with the diketo acids in that they are generally not

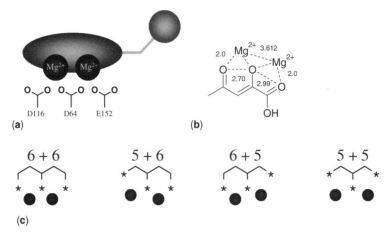

Figure 5. (a) Two-metal chelator pharmacaphore; (b) Chelation region interatom distance model; (c) Metal-heteroatom chelation model templates [68]. (This figure is available in full color at http://mrw.interscience. wiley.com/emrw/9780471266945/home.)

sufficiently permeable to make acceptable drug candidates. Work to optimize the diketo acid series was reported subsequently and it was demonstrated that for an optimized derivative (**5**) that antiviral potency could be significantly improved to the 100 nM level [77]. Further evidence of their antiviral mechanism was conferred through resistance data both via loss of activity resulting from point mutations and from the ability to raise resistance via mutations in the IN protein through passaging studies.

From the SAR data acquired during the diketo acid investigations, a model of the metal coordinating region was established (Fig. 5b) [78]. Taking this a step further, several permutations on the chelation model theme can be conceived whereby the ring formed between the Lewis basic coordinating groups and the positively charged metal centers consist of a five- or six-membered chelate. The four major model systems are depicted in Fig. 5c. The 6 + 5 and 5 + 6 models are interesting as they give a hint toward a potential symmetry element of the metal binding motif that will be further elaborated below. This element is also potentially present in the 6 + 6 and 5 + 5 models when the noncentral coordinating groups represented by the asterisks are differing groups. A final point that needs to be made about the chelation model and inhibitor design is the apparent requirement for the central Lewis basic group to be

able to donate a lone pair to each metal. Taken in its simplest form, this requires two lone pairs and in practice all inhibitors known to date have a means to adopt a full negative charge in this position to make the dual coordination to two electropositive metal centers possible. It is also interesting that other metal containing nucleic acid processing enzymes, while not closely related to integrase homology do utilize a similar phosphodiester cleavage mechanism and have been inhibited to varying levels of success by related two-metal binding scaffolds. Examples of these are HIV RNase H [79–82], influenza endonuclease [83] and the HCV NS5B RNA-dependent RNA polymerase [84–86].

One perceived liability early on was the carboxylic acid contained in the diketo acid structure. Researchers at Shionogi & Co. Ltd utilized a heterocyclic isostere of the carboxylic acid group to examine additional analogs that utilize the diketone moiety as part of the metal coordinating motif [87,88]. Their work centered around the use of a triazole or tetrazole primarily as the acid isostere. One noteworthy early example in amongst this series was 5-CITEP (**7**) (Table 2) [89]. An X-ray crystal structure of 5-CITEP bound to the catalytic core domain was reported. The inhibitor is bound at the active site of the construct and makes several contacts with amino acid residues that are known to be involved with resistance with this type of inhibitor.

Table 1. Activity of Original Diketo Acid Derivatives

Compound	Structure	IN ST[a]	HIV-1PIC[b]	AV[c]
(1) L-731,988	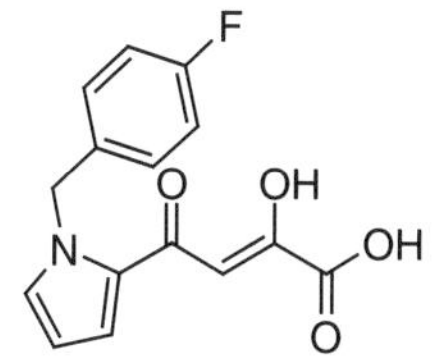	0.05	0.08	1.0
(2) L-708,906	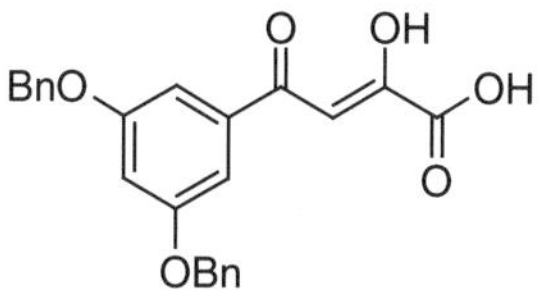	0.10	0.15	2.0
(3) L-731,927	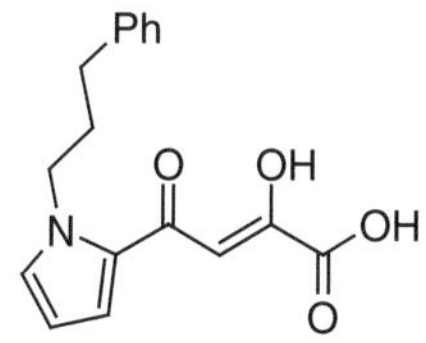	0.50	0.40	15
(4) L-731,942	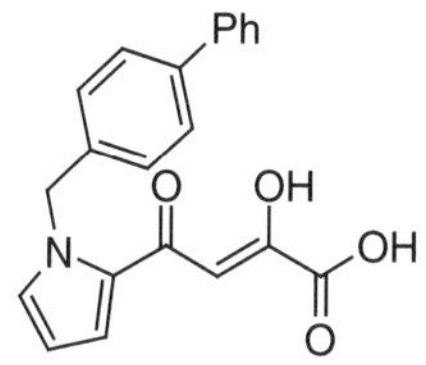	7.50	>100	>50
(5)	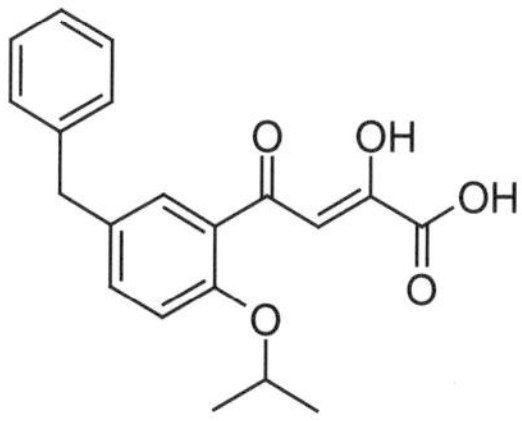	<0.10	—	0.10

[a] Recombinant IN strand transfer IC$_{50}$ (μM).
[b] Preintegration complex IC$_{50}$ (μM).
[c] Antiviral single cycle assay for HIV-1 infectivity IC$_{50}$ (μM).

However, there are some limitations to the use of this data for inhibitor design in that there are no metals present in the binding mode and no viral DNA. These are two highly relevant components to the binding of these types of molecules and raise questions as to how this structure can be used [90]. The final compound in Table 2 is S-1360 (8). This compound was the first integrase inhibitor to enter into clinical trials [91]. However, as is typical of many of the DKA derivatives, S-1360 has significant in vitro metabolism that was found to correlate well with in vivo clinical exposures and it was not fully developed [92].

The DKAs were instrumental in establishing interest in the two-metal coordination motif and the field quickly expanded through modifications of the DKA structure. One such alternative to the aryl ketone portion of the DKAs was replacement with an amido group that served as a link to the requisite benzyl substituent. Researchers at Bristol-Myers

Table 2. Comparison of Diketo Acid to Acid Isostere Containing Diketo Inhibitors

Compound	Structure	Strand Transfer MWPA-Mn	MTT Cellular AV
(6)	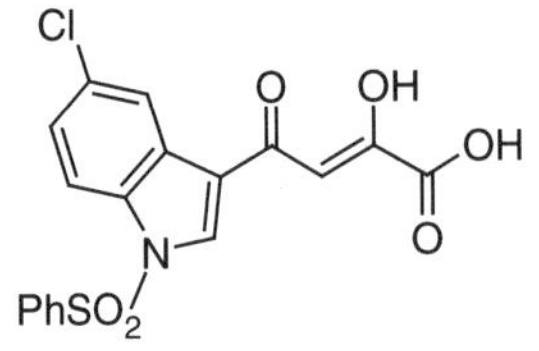	0.018	60
(7) 5-CITEP	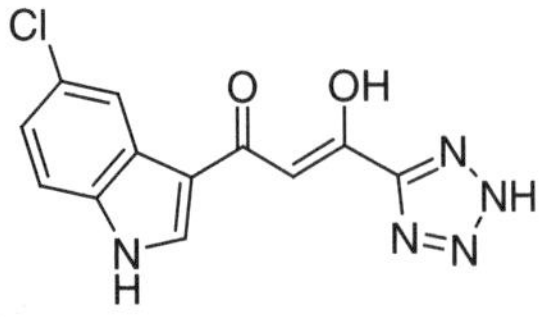	8.6	>35
(8) S-1360	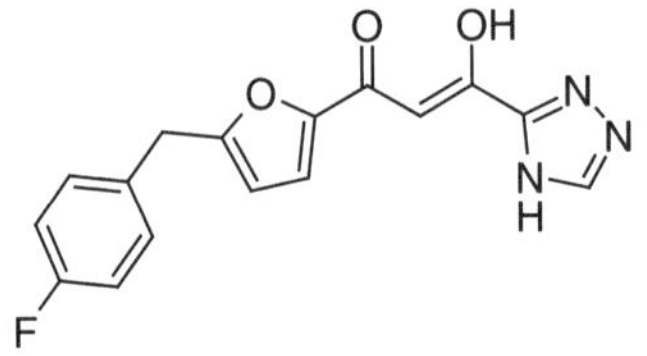	0.02	0.2

IC_{50} values are reported in micromolar.

Squibb presented extensive modification of the amide keto acid structure providing analogs such as acid **9** [93,94] and a related prodrug **10** containing a similar metal binding sequence but with an N-alkoxy-N-alkyl amide (Fig. 6) [95–97]. In addition to the amide/acid mixed compounds the BMS team also ventured into diamide compounds like **11** and a related series of anilide-ketoacids [98] and triketoacids [99]. The acyl sulfonamide group tethered to the metal coordinating core is also characteristic of many of their analogs. Taking the above structures to the next step involved cyclization to give structures like pyrrolidinone **12** [100]. Related hydroxy-pyrrolidinones have been exploited by Shionogi where the 2,5-disubstituted furyl system is used to scaffold the benzyl moiety in compound **13** in a similar fashion to S-1360 (**8**) [101]. Shionogi has expanded on this concept by replacing the keto carbonyl with a heterocycle and further distances the metal coordinating template from the original DKA structures as in compound **14**. Early work also focused on maintaining the keto acid terminus but replacing the remote carbonyl with other coordinating functionality including pyridine and pyrimi-

dyl groups as in compound **15** [102] and was subsequently extended to isosteric acid replacements such as in **16** [103].

The DKAs and their modified counterparts mentioned above greatly advanced the field as the first IN inhibitors and provided encouraging preclinical data but for the most part lacked sufficient potency when protein binding and pharmacokinetic properties were taken into account to make good drug candidates. It was again researchers from Merck who were the first to publish data in a series of patent applications in 2002 that showed that a complete isosteric replacement could be found to replace the DKA moiety with a now more drug-like heterocyclic core template of naphthyridines [104–108]. A mapping of the pharmacophore elements from the diketo acid to the naphthyridine is shown in Fig. 7.

Initial work in this area was a measured step away from the original work whereby the lipophilic aromatic region was taken directly from DKA **5**. In this case, a naphthyridine-phenyl ketone containing a m-arylmethyl substituent on the phenyl ring provided the metal binding and aromatic regions respectively in compound **17** (Table 3). Modest potency

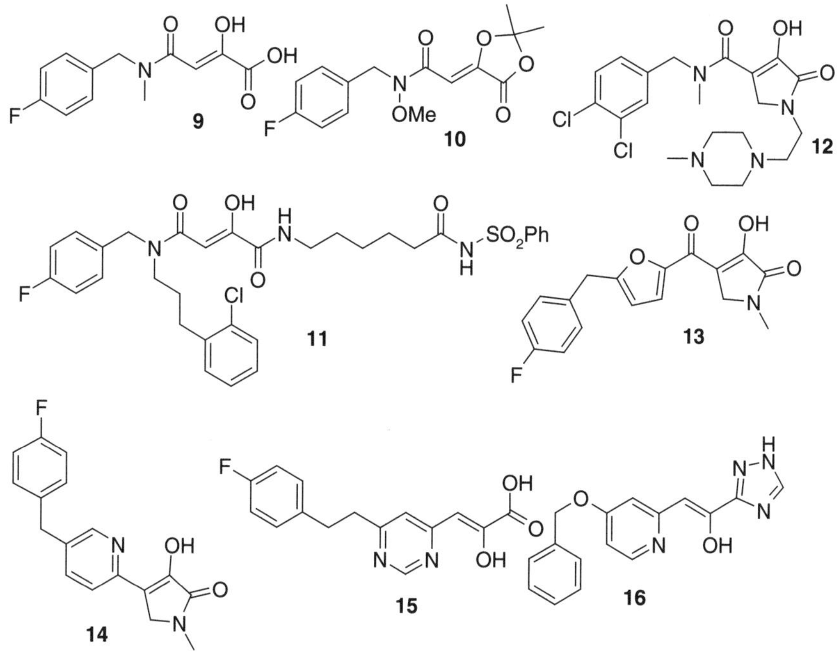

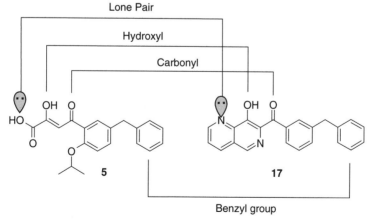

Figure 6. Further modifications of first-generation integrase two-metal binding inhibitors based on the diketo acid-like pharmacophore. (This figure is available in full color at http://mrw.interscience.wiley.com/emrw/9780471266945/home.)

against the enzyme and cellular assays was observed with some separation from cytotoxicity [109]. Compared to the corresponding 8-hydroxyquinoline **18**, the naphthyridine imparts a ninefold improvement in enzyme potency and is significantly less toxic. It is proposed that the naphthyridine nitrogen at position 6 of the ring system serves to remove a significant aryl–aryl repulsion resulting in **17** being able to adopt a more planar conformation with less energy cost. It was also noted that the alternative 8-hydroxyquinoline **19** that also is able to adopt a more planar arrangement than **18** is nonetheless still significantly more toxic

Figure 7. Mapping of the diketo acid pharmacophore the a naphthyridine heterocyclic replacement. (This figure is available in full color at http://mrw.interscience.wiley.com/emrw/9780471266945/home.)

Table 3. Naphthyridine Integrase Inhibitors

Compound	Structure	IN ST[a]	AV[b]	Cytotox[c]
18	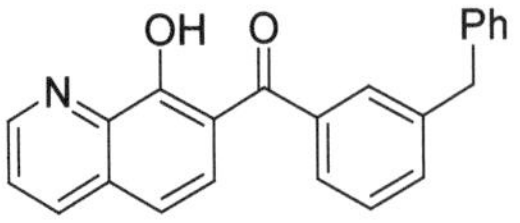	0.37	5.00	1.25
17		0.04	6.20	12.5
19	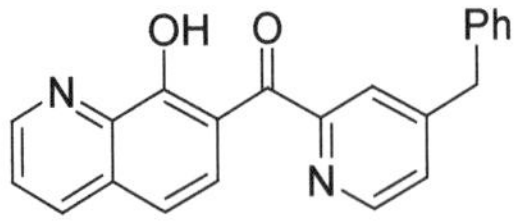	0.05	2.50	2.50
20	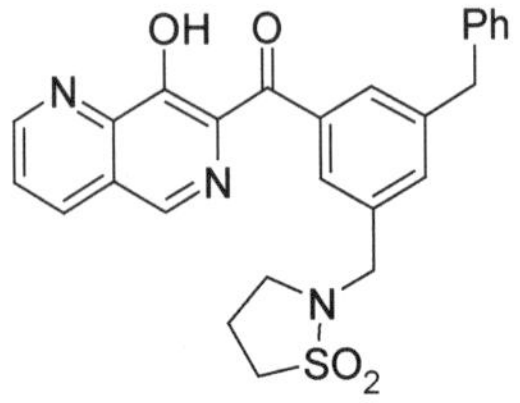	0.01	0.39	>12.5
21 (L-870,810)	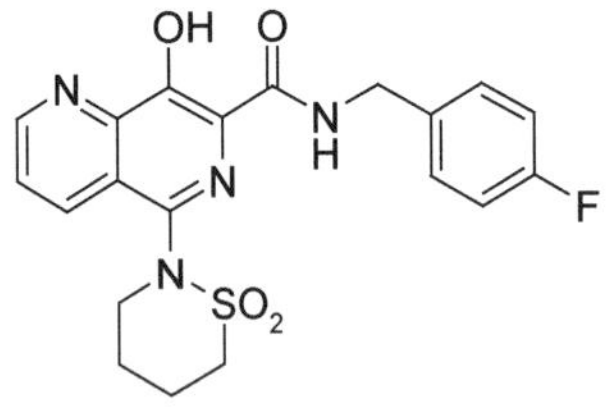	0.01	0.015	NR
22	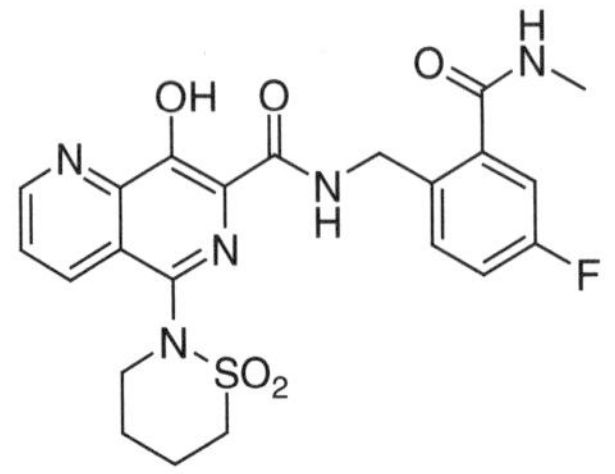	0.01	0.016[d]	NR

[a] Recombinant IN strand transfer IC_{50} (μM).
[b] Antiviral activity IC_{95} (μM).
[c] Cytotoxicity (μM).
[d] Reported as an IC_{50}.
NR: not reported.

than the naphthyridine. The authors suggest that the weaker affinity for metal coordination of the naphthyridine compared to the 8-hydroxyquinoline is the reason for the improved level of cell toxicity. Naphthyridine 20 showed further improvement in activity showing now an improvement over the corresponding DKA and no cytotoxicity to the limits measured. In addition, it showed cross-resistance to integrase mutations that confer resistance to the DKA's suggesting a similar binding mode. Furthermore, naphthyridine 20 showed encouraging *in vivo* exposure when administered to rats both IV and orally.

The naphthyridine scaffold was further elaborated to improve its properties and a series of benzyl amide derivatives served to advance the SAR understanding and resulted in the first nondiketo acid to advance into the clinic [110–112]. The analog L-870,810 (**21**) was the first integrase inhibitor to show viral load reduction in HIV infected patients. The further substituted amido analog **22** was shown to have an improved *in vitro* profile with a less than threefold shift in the presence of human serum proteins while maintaining an favorable pharmacokinetic profile in rats, dogs, and monkeys [113]. A closely related analog, L-870,812 (**23**) was reported to show viral suppression of SHIV infected rhesus macaques providing further early evidence of the efficacy of inhibition of the integration step in the viral replication cycle [114]. A final noteworthy point is that it has been reported that the naphthyridine series while mechanistically identical to the diketo acids were found to show a differing mutation pattern upon viral passaging and also were necessarily susceptible to resistance mutations that confer loss of activity with the diketo acids. This data suggests minimally differences in their binding modes and possibly multiple binding sites for mechanistically similar pharmacophores [115].

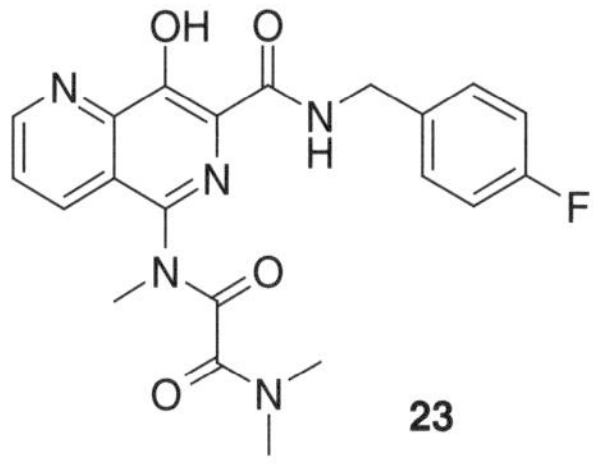

23

An alternative metal chelation motif was discovered by our group at GlaxoSmithKline wherein the benzyl amide that had evolved in the naphthyridine work from the Merck group was replaced with a series of five-membered heterocycles (Table 4) [116]. It was found that the use of either a triazole or isomeric oxadiazoles imparted potent enzyme activity clearly showing the amide isosteres ability to participate in the two-metal binding pharmacophore. The C5 protio derivatives **24–26**

(Table 4) also were submicromolar in an antiviral assay with robust separation of their activity from cytotoxicity. Further substitution similar to L-870,810 where a C5 sultam group is installed resulted in a marked improvement of both enzyme and cellular activities. In the case of the 1,3,4-oxadiazole **28**, an antiviral activity of 13 nM was observed.

As mentioned above, a planar arrangement of the metal binding motif is requisite for good inhibitory activity and the N-6 of the 1,6-naphthyridine ring system in the Merck and GSK series has shown to be key to improvement in activity. Other means of accomplishing the coplanarity while maintaining the naphthyl-like 6,6-aromatic system have also been explored and one noteworthy example is the naphthyridinone ring system as shown in compound **29** [117]. Since this scaffold has only appeared thus far in patent format, little detail about SAR and potency has appeared, however, the generic description of the enzymatic and cellular potency suggest the naphthyridinone benzyl amide scaffold represented by **29** is a potent and acceptable replacement for the related naphthyridine structures like L-870,810.

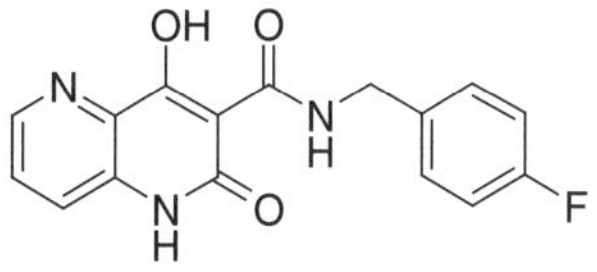

29

The next series that will be described also consists of the naphthyridinone core, however, the comparison to the above structure **29** gives rise to a subtle but very interesting feature that many of the two-metal binding IN inhibitors offer. Since the core template is generally planar and the phenolate-like central coordinating group is flanked on each side by another Lewis basic group there is a binding symmetry about the metal chelation motif. This is depicted in cartoon format in Fig. 8. If the necessary lipophilic benzyl group can be appropriately placed on the opposite end of the planar metal coordination template, the scaffold can effectively be reversed end for end and bind 180° about the magnesium ions. This can allow for an entirely new SAR and

Table 4. Heterocycle-Substituted Naphthyridine Integrase Inhibitors

Compound	Structure	IN ST[a]	PHIV[b]	TI[c]
24	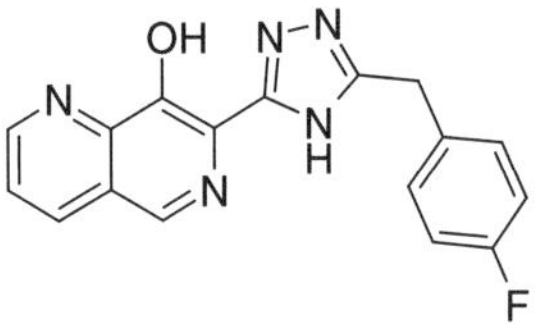	0.13	0.32	>4
25	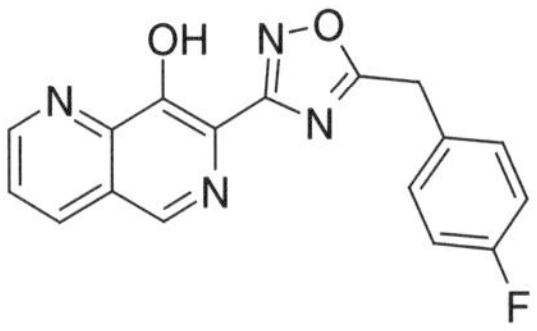	0.13	0.22	114
26	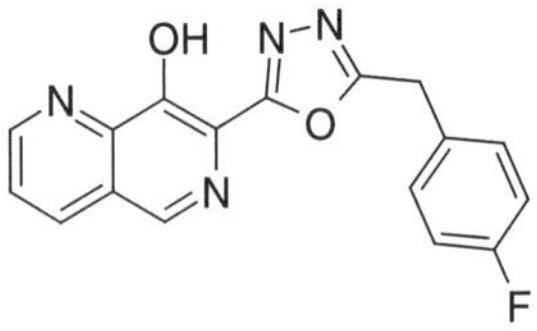	0.042	0.13	>270
27	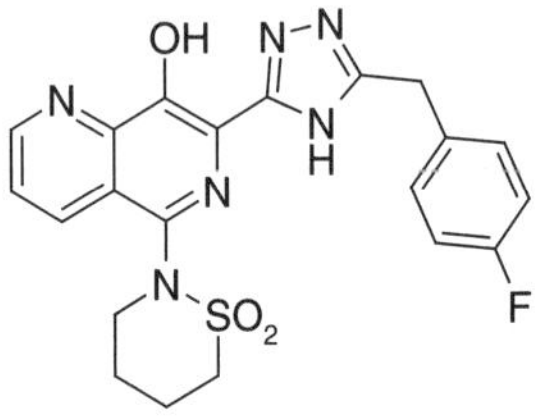	0.011	0.24	>104
28	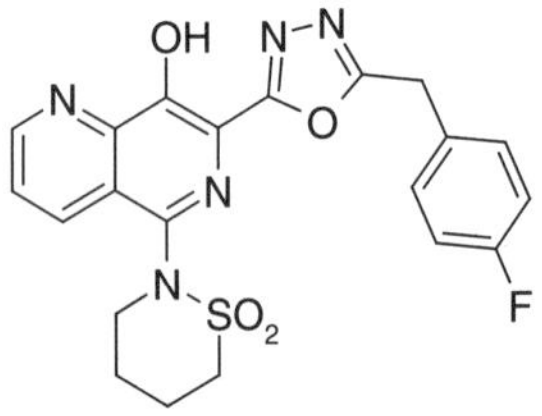	0.002	0.013	198

[a] Recombinant IN strand transfer IC_{50} (μM).
[b] Pseudo-typed HIV antiviral assay IC_{50} (μM).
[c] Therapeutic index.

substitution possibilities and if in fact the case as demonstrated by work from our laboratories that examined the naphthyridinone series exemplified by compound **30** (Table 5) [118,119]. As can be seen with the relatively undecorated substitution pattern of **30**, the series is very potent against both the recombinant enzyme and the cellular system. However, this N1 protio analog is quite highly protein bound as is evident in the protein adjusted antiviral value. A minor change to the methoxyethyl amido group in **31** results in a fourfold decrease in protein shift as would be expected from a less lipophilic substitution. Interestingly, the ester **32** shows only a small decrease in enzyme potency but a significant loss of antiviral activity [120]. Further introduction of polar groups such as the acetamide in **33** further reduced protein shift values and finally the derivative **34** is the clinical candidate S/GSK364735 [121]. This compound was advanced into clinical trials and showed

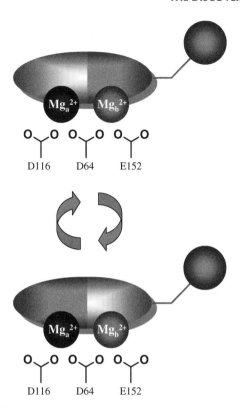

Figure 8. Pseudo-symmetry of two-metal binding integrase inhibitors. (This figure is available in full color at http://mrw.interscience.wiley.com/emrw/9780471266945/home.)

significant viral load reduction but was terminated due to concerns about a limited safety margin from preclinical studies [122–124]]. The resistance profile of **34** has also been extensively studied and shown to be consistent with the mechanism of being an active site strand transfer inhibitor [125,126]. While much of the data shows cross-resistance between **34** and other clinical IN inhibitors, there are differences in susceptibility to some of the amino acid changes and much of the field is driven today by a concern about resistance to this new class of antivirals and the primary focus is to find new compounds that can address these concerns.

In a further modification of the azanaphthyl systems, researchers at Gilead have taken the step to cyclize the amide and aromatic core ring system to ensure a coplanar arrangement resulting in a series of tricyclic lactams. In this work one of their parent ex-

amples **35** (Table 6) was sub-100 nM in an MT-4 cell assay [127]. Introducing an additional nitrogen in the pyrazinyl example **36** reduced activity and reduction to the fused piperazine **37** nearly obliterates all activity. Imide derivative **38** shows little loss of activity compared to the corresponding lactam (**35**) at the enzyme level, however, in the cellular assay a loss of two orders of magnitude is observed. It is proposed that low solubility may be responsible for the decreased cellular activity [128]. The tertiary amide **39**, however, was found to have a substantial increase in potency and even in the presence of added human serum albumin delivered an IC_{50} of 88 nM [129]. The C5-aza analog **40** was similarly potent but showed a lesser shift in the presence of serum proteins with an IC_{50} of 11 nM [130]. Compound **40** is also known as GS-9160 and was taken into phase 1 clinical trials. In preclinical pharmacokinetic studies, it showed low clearance in both rats and dogs (0.28 and 0.4 L/h/kg, respectively) and a modest to good half-life of 1 h in rats and 5 h in dogs. However, the compound was terminated after phase 1 due to an insufficient human PK profile to support once daily dosing [131]. Additional SAR work is reported on a related series of phthalimide derivatives from workers at Tibotec [132]. The SAR is largely confirmatory of the work already discussed, however, does appear to be a broader examination of the pyrazinyl substitution as well as some additional substituents on the benzyl moiety.

Probably the most noteworthy series to date in this area would have to be the dihydroxypyrimidine and pyrimidinone series that have led to the discovery of raltegravir. Raltegravir (**41**) is the first FDA-approved integrase inhibitor and has been extremely well received both by the patients and by the marketplace in general. Much has been written about raltegravir but the medicinal chemistry story is well compiled by Rowley in a recent review of the joint Merck and IRBM research teams [133]. The initial lead for the program came interestingly enough from another antiviral program targeting HCV NS5b polymerase [134,135]. Work to improve on the drug-like properties of meconic acid **42** (Fig. 9) led the team to look at the dihydroxypyrimidine series represented by acid **43**. In the case

Table 5. Naphthyridinone Integrase Inhibitors

Compound	Structure	IN ST[a]	PHIV[b]	PA-PHIV[c]
30	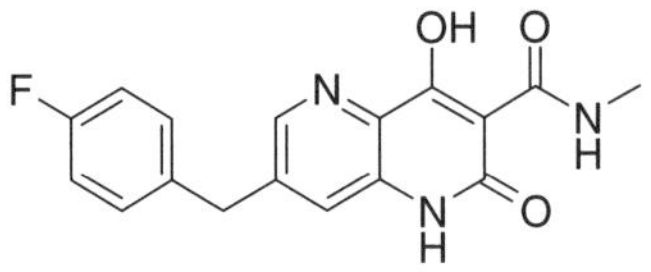	0.006	0.003	0.12
31	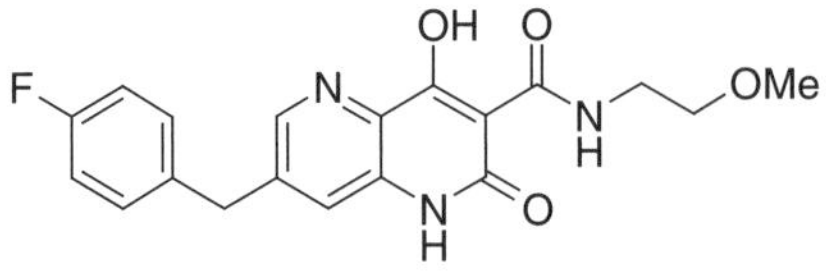	0.005	0.005	0.036
32	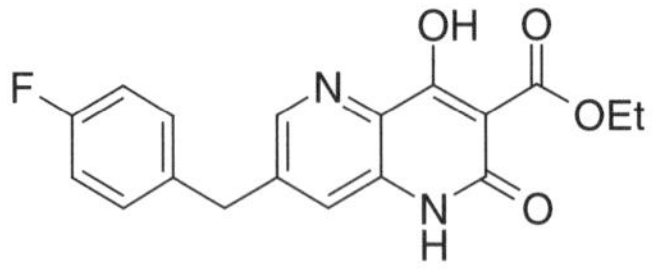	0.013	1198	ND
33	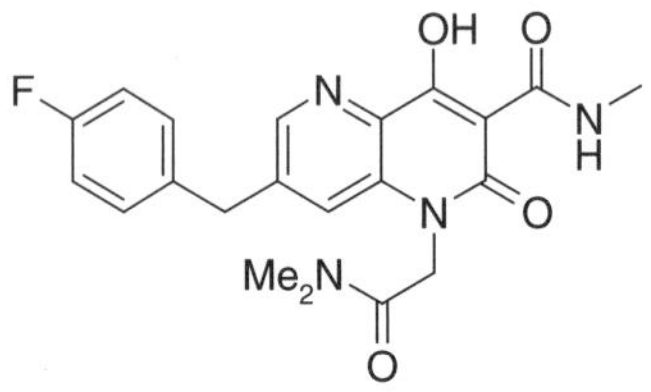	0.009	0.006	23
34 S/GSK364735	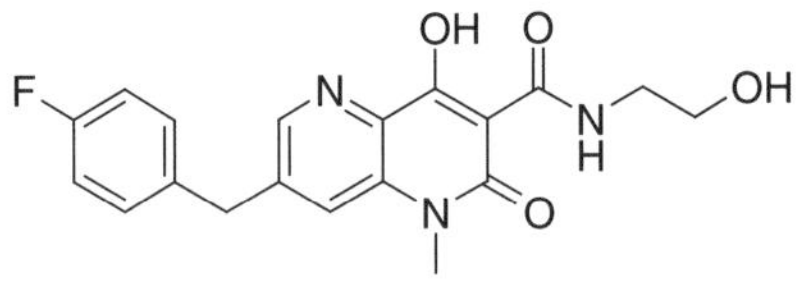	0.008	0.002	20

[a] Recombinant IN strand transfer IC_{50} (μM).

[b] Pseudo-typed HIV antiviral assay IC_{50} (μM).

[c] Protein adjusted pseudo-typed HIV antiviral assay with 40 mg/mL HSA.

ND: not determined.

of the acid-diol, low cell penetration led them to make modifications and benzyl amide **44** was found to have potent IN activity (85 nM) against the strand transfer reaction that was found during a cross-screening between the programs [136].

After extensive SAR investigations, the IRBM and Merck team found that much like many of the above series the minimal pharmacophore requirements were the metal binding motif and the lipophilic flexible side chain and that the remainder of the scaffold could be modified to optimize secondary properties such as protein binding and the simultaneous effects on PK properties. Starting with the 2-thiophene-substituted analog **44** (Table 7)

with no antiviral activity, they were able to find that modification of the related 2-benzyl derivative **45** to an analog containing a basic amine **46** conferred good potency in the cell-based assay. Removal of the lipophilic aromatic group and cyclization of the C2 substituent led to the 2-piperidinyl analog **47** that now showed not only good antiviral activity at low serum levels but also had only a modest shift in the presence of high serum. They made a point to spend significant efforts to find an optimal protein binding profile so as to retain potent activity with only a modest shift in activity in the presence of human serum, but not to create clearance liabilities from having too much free drug. This double-edged sword

Table 6. Tricyclic Quinoline Lactam Integrase Inhibitors

Compound	Structure	IN ST[a]	MT-4[b]	Cytotox[c]
35	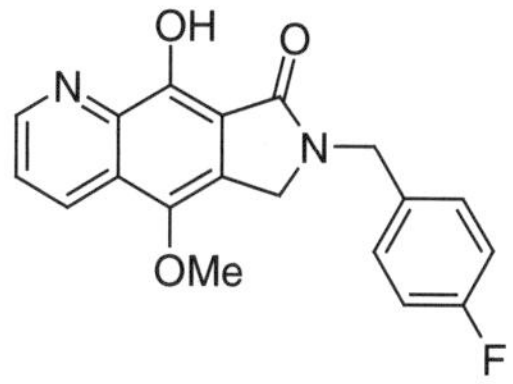	0.05	0.089	5.1
36	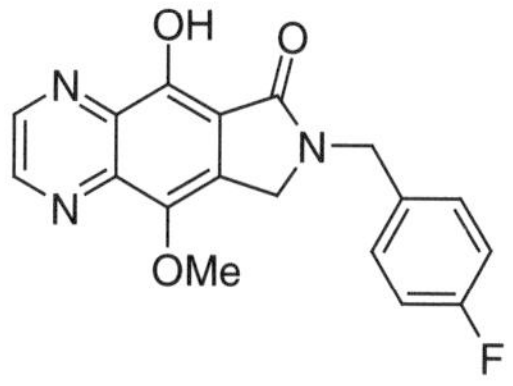	0.21	3.55	87
37	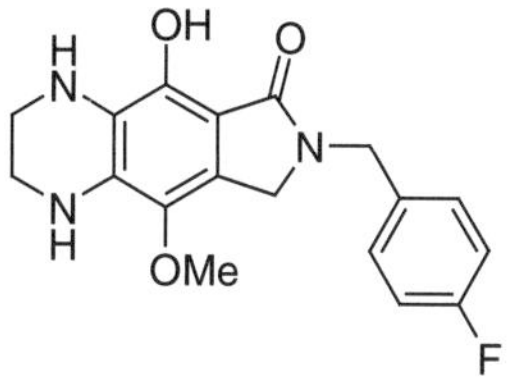	24	>10	25
38	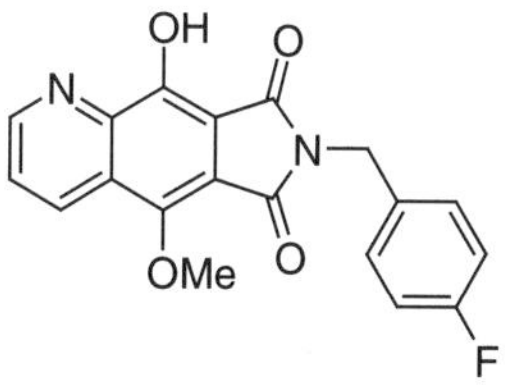	0.080	7.5	19
39	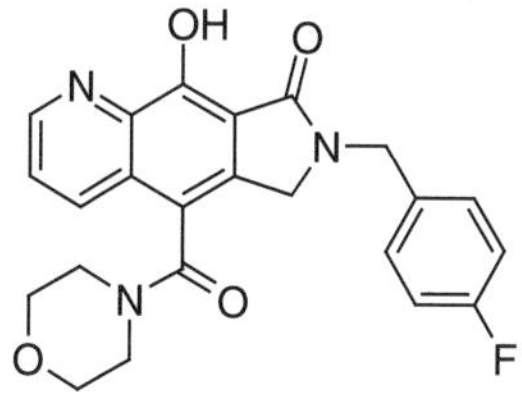	0.036	0.003	4
40 GS-9160	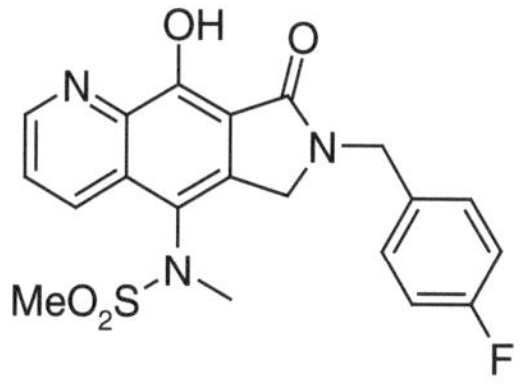	0.028	0.002	NR

[a] Recombinant IN strand transfer IC_{50} (μM).
[b] MT-4 antiviral assay IC_{50} (μM).
[c] Cytotoxicity in the MT-4 cells CC_{50} (μM).
NR: not reported.

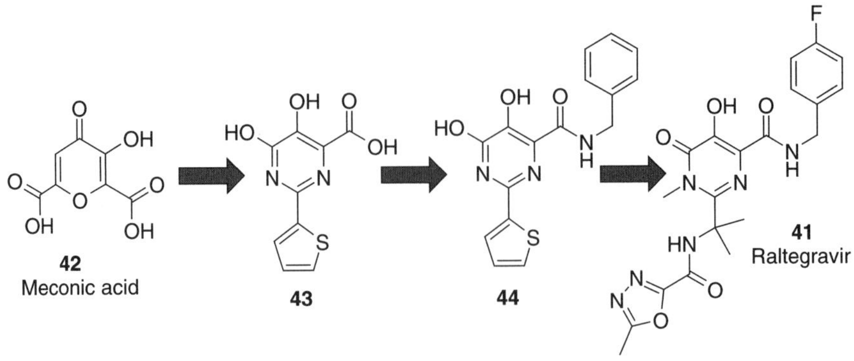

Figure 9. Lead progression from meconic acid (**42**) to raltegravir (**41**). (This figure is available in full color at http://mrw.interscience.wiley.com/emrw/9780471266945/home.)

is one that all groups working in this area have faced extensively. It was this quest for balance that led their efforts to the *N*-methyl pyrimidinone series represented by **48** that while not as potent as its dihydroxy counterpart **47** did show a higher free fraction and improved PK profile. A conscious decision was made to attempt to optimize the potency in the pyrimidinone scaffold that had inherently better PK and protein binding properties rather than try to optimize PK in the more potent dihydroxy series.

Turning their attention to the *N*-methylpyrimidinones they investigated a series of substituted 2-aminomethyl derivatives represented by **49** (Table 8) that were highly potent in the dihydroxypyrimidine series. However, many of the basic amine-substituted compounds in the pyrimidinone scaffold were more than 1 μM in the cell assays and did not have any improvement when close analogs were examined. It was noted from their previous work in the naphthyridine series whereby L-870,810 and L-870,812 were developed that neither had a basic amine, thus they began to examine acylating the aminomethyl derivatives [137]. The amide **50** was evaluated along with several additional analogs and appeared to have an excellent potency profile both at low and at high serum concentrations. Additionally, several small heterocycles were used to mimic the oxamoyl group in **50** one of which was the 1,3,4-oxadiazole that ultimately became raltegravir **41**. Both **50** and **41** were taken into humans and it is reported that the resistance properties of **41** were at

least part of the reason for its selection for full development. As with many of these classes, the primary route of metabolism for **41** is via glucuronidation by primarily UGT1A1. Little interaction with the CYP450s is observed and it is not an inhibitor of the UGT1A1 so drug--drug interactions are not a big problem with raltegravir. The free fraction in rat, dog, rhesus monkey, and human are 27, 29, 15, and 17%, respectively, showing a significant amount of drug is available for target interaction. It appears that this also is partially the reason for a modest half-life in humans and resulting in a twice daily dose of 400 mg [138–142]. Extensive SAR investigations on this and related series have been published [143–150].

There is a second compound well advanced in clinical trials being developed jointly by Japan Tobacco and Gilead Sciences. It is a quinolone structure and was originally known as JTK-303 and upon licensing by Gilead it was termed GS-9137 that became elvitegravir upon generic naming. Elvitegravir (**51**) was derived from the quinolone antibiotics that do not show IN activity [151,152].

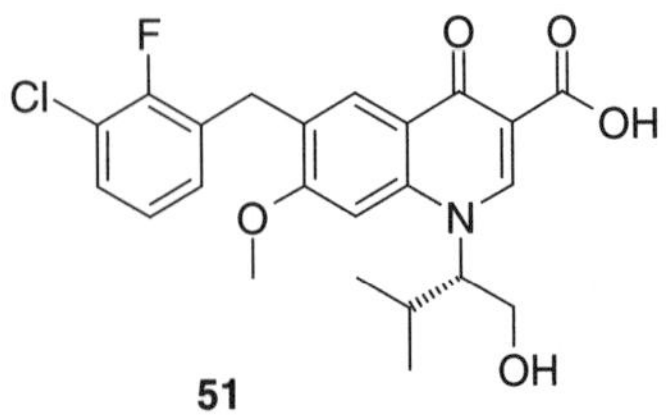

51
Elvitegravir

Table 7. Dihydroxypyrimidine SAR

Compound	Structure	IN ST[a]	CIC$_{95}$[b]	PA-CIC$_{95}$[c]
44	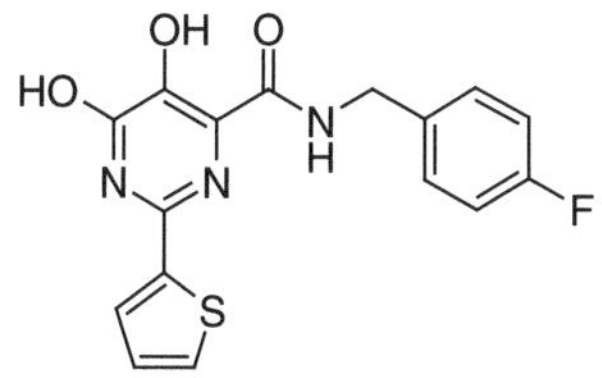	0.085	>10	ND
45	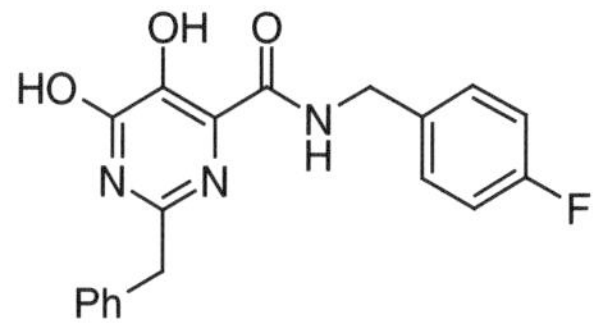	0.05	5.8	>10
46	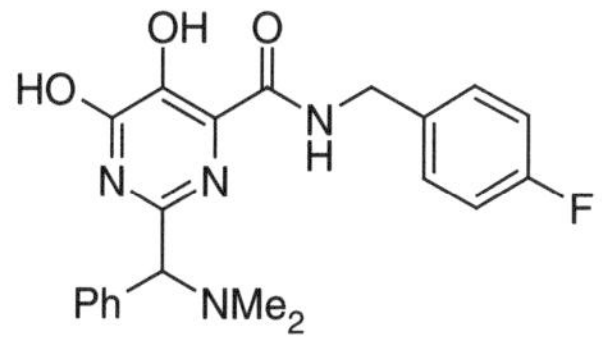	0.2	0.30	>10
47	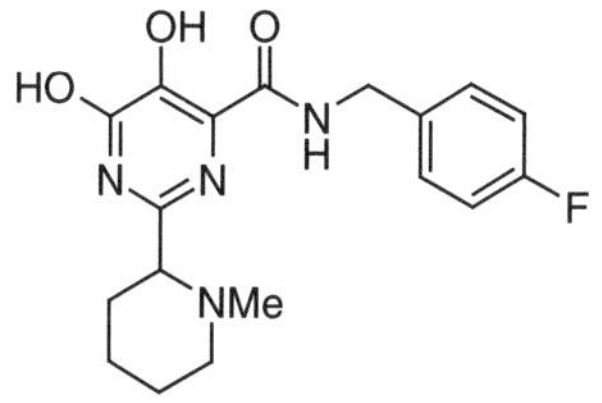	0.20	0.15	0.40
48	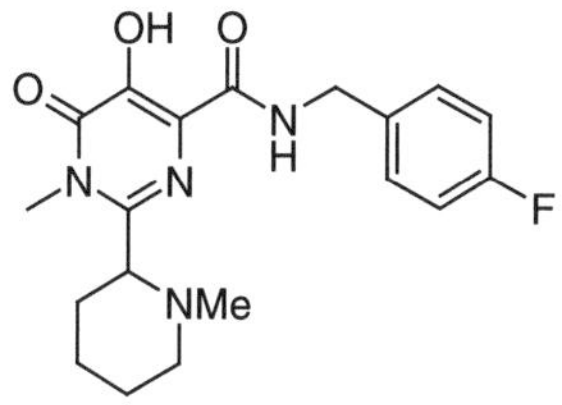	0.21	0.84	1.10

[a] Recombinant IN strand transfer IC$_{50}$ (μM).
[b] Spread multicycle cell-based antiviral assay IC$_{95}$ (μM).
[c] Spread multicycle cell-based antiviral assay IC$_{95}$ with 50% normal human serum (μM).
ND: not determined.

In their original design, the Japan Tobacco workers attempted to incorporate three chelator substituents that are reminiscent of the diketo acid motif since they presumed all three Lewis basic groups would be necessary for binding. However, the designed structure compound **52** did not show inhibitory activity but rather a precursor derivative **53** did show an IC$_{50}$ of 1.6 μM in the strand transfer assay. Further modification to introduce the 2-F,3-Cl aryl substitution pattern led to a remarkable increase in potency for compound **54**. Substitution on the quinolone nitrogen again improved potency to give **55** that was now sub-100 nM

Table 8. *N*-Methyl Pyrimidinone SAR

Compound	Structure	IN ST[a]	CIC$_{95}$[b]	PA-CIC$_{95}$[c]
48	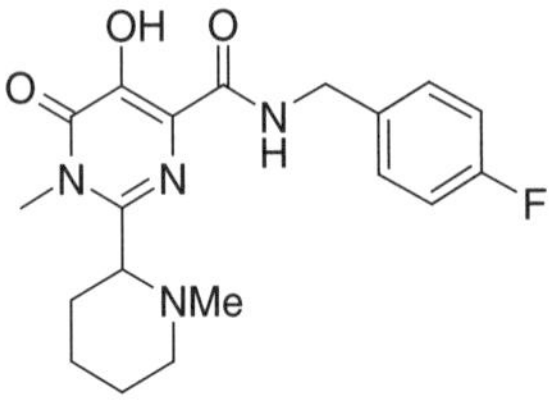	0.21	0.84	1.10
49	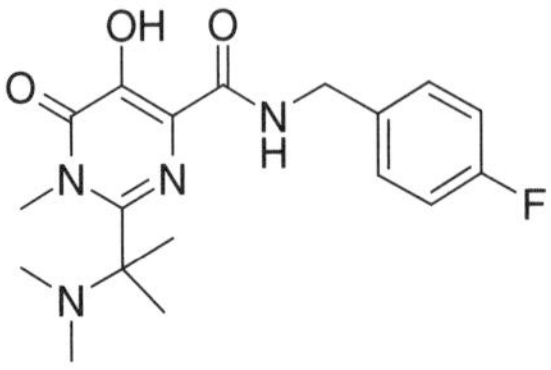	0.23	>1	>1
50	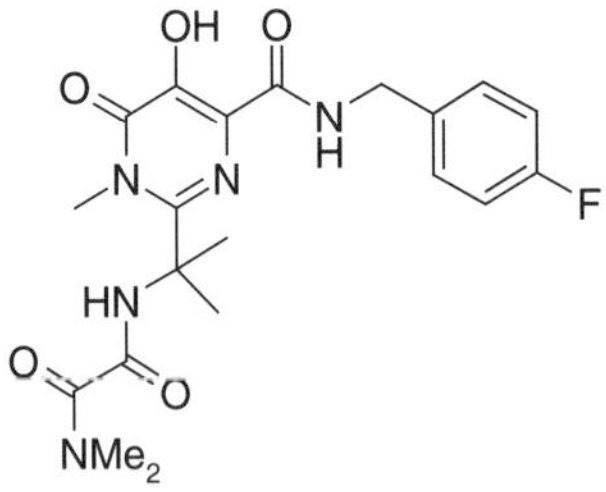	0.01	0.045	0.074
41 Raltegravir	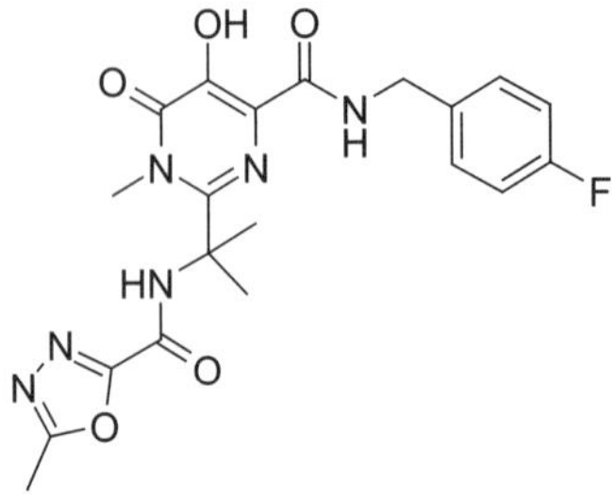	0.015	0.019	0.031

[a] Recombinant IN strand transfer IC$_{50}$ (µM).
[b] Spread multicycle cell-based antiviral assay IC$_{95}$ (µM).
[c] Spread multicycle cell-based antiviral assay IC$_{95}$ with 50% normal human serum (µM).

activity in the MT-4 cell assay. The 7-methoxy substituent in **56** served to improve activity further and finally modification of the nitrogen substituent from hydroxyethyl to a valinol derived substituent in **57** further increased the cell-based activity. Combining the valinol group, the haloaryl substitution and the 7-methoxy group appear to all contribute to improved potency and resulted in **51** that became

elvitegravir now with an MT-4 activity less than 1 nM.

At first glance, it would appear these structure do not contain a two-metal chelation motif, however, it seems plausible that the carboxylate in deprotonated form can both mimic the phenolate like group in many of the above structures as well as one of the outside coordinating groups and effectively coordinate as a

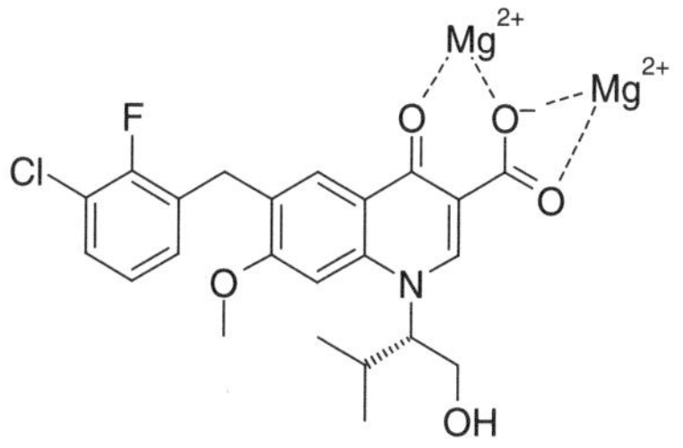

Figure 10. A proposed model for two-metal chelation for the quinolone carboxylic acid moiety.

bidentate ligand (Fig. 10). This has not been shown in the literature but does seem to be a reasonable explanation of what otherwise seems to be a novel aspect to the pharmacophore model. It has been shown that elvitegravir is mechanistically identical to the other classes of strand transfer inhibitors and shows cross-resistance with DKA and raltegravir derived mutations [153–156]. In addition, passage studies show similar mutations arise from elvitegravir selective pressure consistent with the two-metal chelator binding motif (Fig. 10).

Elvitegravir has progressed through proof of concept studies and has recently begun phase 3 clinical trials. It has moderate bioavailability in preclinical species (between 29% and 34%), low clearance (0.5 and 1.0 L/h/kg), and a good half-life of 2.3 and 5.2 h in rats and dogs, respectively [156]. It is primarily metabolized via CYP450 oxidation and shows a marked increase in human exposure with ritonavir boosting. The drug is currently being investigated for once daily dosing with ritonavir boosting at a dose of a few hundred milligrams [158–160].

There are many series that are beyond the scope of this chapter where the goal was to give an overview of the field and discuss the major series within the area that have impacted scaffold design and general SAR of the two-metal binding pharmacophore. Many of these series are only published in patent applications. Much of that work has been reviewed elsewhere [161]. The field now has turned from finding first-generation potent, orally bioavailable and safe drugs to treat IN inhibitor-naïve patients to finding compounds that can address existing resistance from treatment experienced patient or improve upon raltegravir and elvitegravir in time to resistance and durability. In addition, a major area of focus is on patient compliance with their dosing regimens. One way to improve upon the adherence to taking every dose on schedule is to deliver drugs that only require once daily dosing and consist of a single pill with multiple agents. In order to accomplish this, lower doses are required and an excellent pharmacokinetics is a must. It is with this in mind that the last area discussed is focused on compounds that have been reported to have the potential for improved activity against IN mutations that confer resistance to the existing drugs.

From examination of the literature from conference presentations, a few exciting compound profiles have emerged. It is unclear what the development status of these series are, but they minimally serve to demonstrate that very potent inhibition can be attained against some of the resistance mutations that render the current drugs raltegravir and elvitegravir essentially useless. In the case of the first three examples in Table 10, they arise from a series of fused pyrazole analogs. Derivative **58** (Table 10) is only of marginal activity with significant falloff against the panel of mutants. However, small changes to introduce an pyridazine ring, additional halogenation of the benzyl and a chiral nonracemic methyl substituent render compounds **59** (MK-2048) and **60** significantly more potent against wild-type virus as well as exceptional against this panel of mutants [162]. A second series exemplified by **61** (MK-0536) has also shown a very good retention of antiviral activity against a same panel of mutants [163–164].

Table 9. Quinolone Carboxylic Acid SAR

Compound	Structure	IN ST[a]	MT-4[b]	Cytotox[c]
52	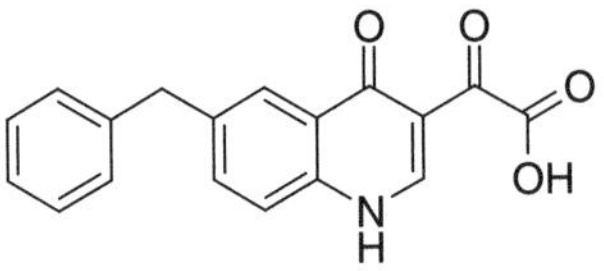	NR	NR	NR
53	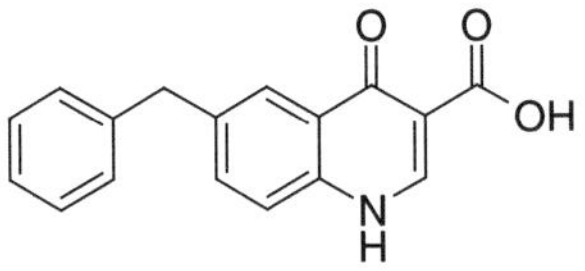	1.6	>30	>30
54	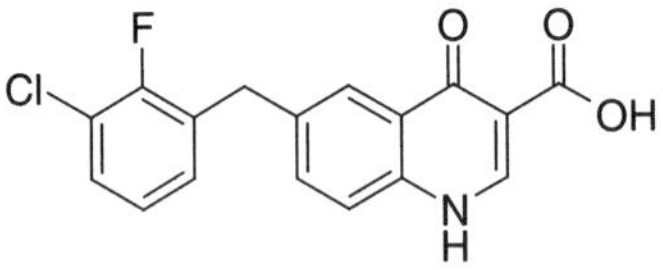	0.043	0.80	>12
55	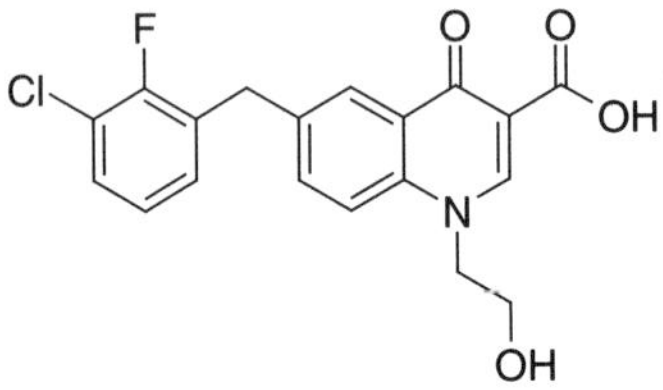	0.024	0.076	>15
56	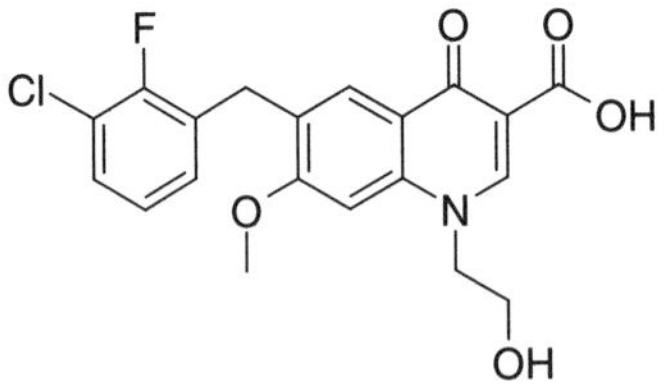	0.009	0.017	5.3
57	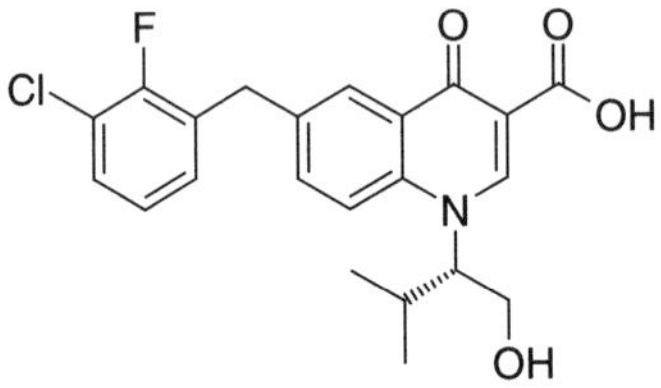	0.008	0.007	14
51 Elvitegravir	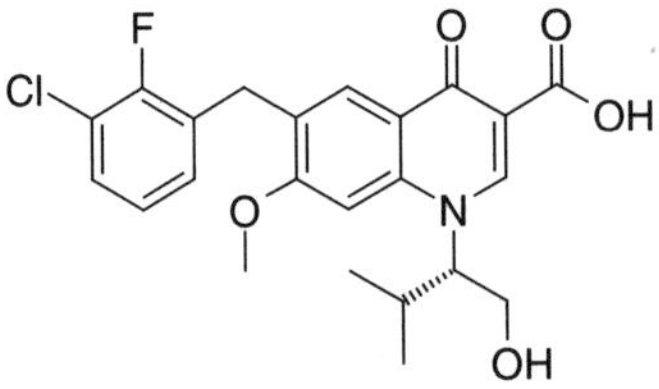	0.007	0.0009	4

[a] Recombinant IN strand transfer IC_{50} (μM).
[b] MT-4 antiviral assay IC_{50} (μM).
[c] Cytotoxicity in the MT-4 cells CC_{50} (μM).
  NR: not reported.

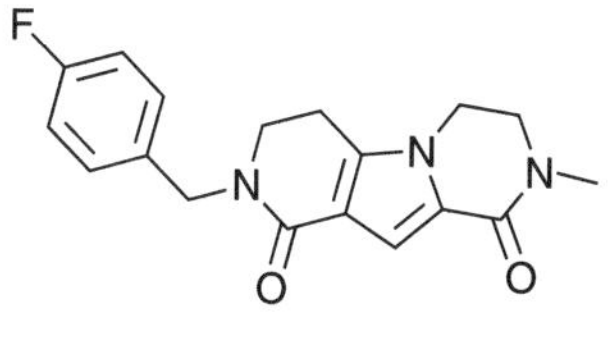

58

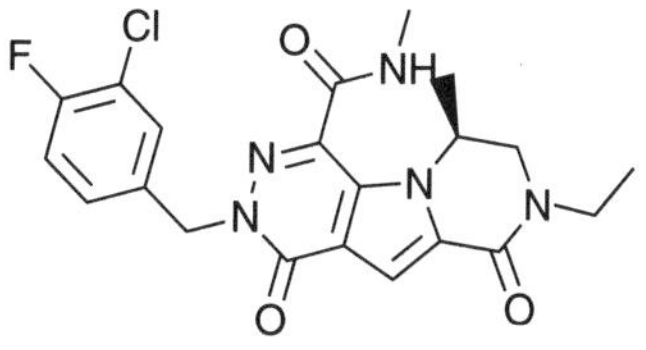

59

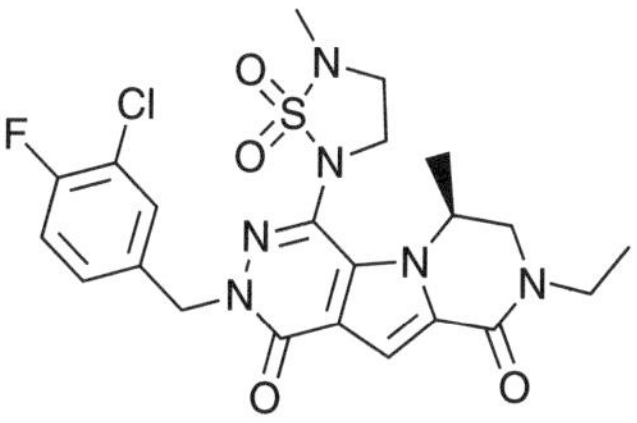

60

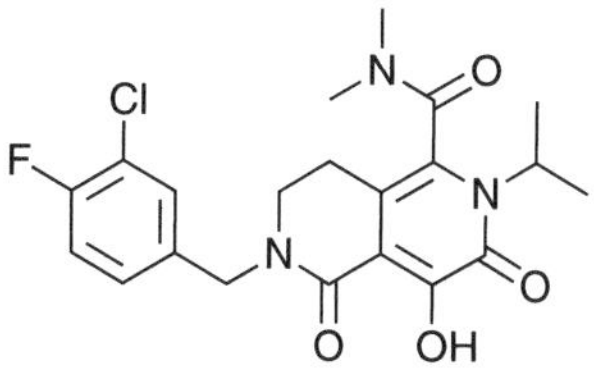

61

Table 10. Potential Next-Generation Integrase Inhibitor Potencies Against IN Mutants

Compound	Wt CIC$_{95}$[a]	T66I/S153Y[b]	N155S[b]	Q148K[b]	E138A/G140A/Q148K[b]	F121Y[b]
58	0.15	22x	76x	31	90x	20x
59 MK-2048	0.009	1x	2x	2x	16x	1x
60	0.0008	1x	1x	1x	1x	1x
61 MK-0536	0.04	1x	3x	1x	118x	1x

[a] Spread multicycle cell-based antiviral assay IC$_{95}$ (μM).

[b] Reported at fold resistance.

6. CONCLUSIONS

It should be clear that the field of HIV-1 IN inhibitors has expanded immensely over the past decade. It should not be surprising that once a foothold was established with respect to the two-metal binding pharmacophore that the teams of medicinal chemists that appear in the associated references were exceptional at delivering preclinical leads, clinical candidates, and ultimately efficacious drugs to the clinic. At the time of drafting this chapter, the first generation of inhibitors consisting of raltegravir and soon to come elvitegravir are making their mark as first in class drugs. However, resistance problems are sure to plague this mechanism as it has with the inhibitors of reverse transcriptase and protease. Fortunately, the field appears to be well developed to deliver improved next-generation compounds that address resistance either directly or possibly in addition to potency against mutants by compounds that are amenable to lower doses on a more optimal once daily regimen. Time will tell as to how successful the dedicated teams that work in this area will be but clearly the science is exciting and fruitful for both the chemists and most importantly the patients who desperately seek new treatment options that are safe, tolerable, and efficacious.

ACKNOWLEDGMENTS

I would like to thank Mary St. Clair for allowing the use of several figures in the introductory section. It is a great privilege to work alongside someone such as Marty that has been a legend in the field of HIV drug discovery since its inception in the early 1980s. Additionally, I would like to thank Takashi Kawasuji and Ryuichi Kiyama of Shionogi & Co. Ltd for generously providing Figs 4 and 5. I also would like to thank Dr. Emile Velthuisen for critical review of this manuscript.

REFERENCES

1. United Nations Program on HIV/AIDS (UN-AIDS). AIDS epidemic update 2007. Available at www.UNAIDS.org. Dec 2007.

2. Gottlieb MS, Schanker HM, Fan PT, Saxon A, Weisman JD. Pneumocystis pneumonia—Los Angeles. Morbid Mort Weekly Rep 1981;30:1–3.

3. Gottlieb MS, Schroff R, Schanker HM, Weisman JD, Fan PT, Wolf RA, Saxon A. *Pneumocystis carinii* pneumonia and mucosal candidiasis in previously healthy homosexual men: evidence of a new acquired cellular immunodeficiency. N Engl J Med 1981;305:1425–1431.

4. Masur H, Michelis MA, Greene JB, Onorato I, Stouwe RA, Holzman RS, Wormser G, Brettman L, Lange M, Murray HW, Cunninghan-Rundles S. An outbreak of community-acquired *Pneumocystis carinii* pneumonia: initial manifestation of cellular immune dysfunction. N Engl J Med 1981;305:1431–1438.

5. Siegal FP, Lopez C, Hammer GS, Brown AE, Kornfield SJ, Gold J, Hassett J, Hirschman SZ, Cunningham-Rundles C, Adelsberg BR. Severe acquired immunodeficiency in male homosexuals, manifested by chronic perianal ulcerative herpes simplex lesions. N Engl J Med 1981;305:1439–1444.

6. Barre-Sinoussi F, Chermann JC, Rey F, Nugeyre MT, Chamaret S, Gruest J, Dauguet C, Axler-Blin C, Vezinet-Brun F, Rouzioux C, Rozenbaum W, Montagnier L. Isolation of a T-lymphotropic retrovirus from a patient at risk for acquired immune deficiency syndrome (AIDS). Science 1983;220:868–871.

7. Gallo RC, Sarin PS, Gelmann EP, Robert-Guroff M, Richardson E, Kalyanaraman VS, Mann D, Sidhu GD, Stahl RE, Zolla-Pazner S, Leibowitch J, Popovic M. Isolation of human T-cell leukemia virus in acquired immune deficiency syndrome (AIDS). Science 1983;220:865–867.

8. Gelmann EP, Popovic M, Blayney D, Masur H, Sidhu G, Stahl RE, Gallo RC. Proviral DNA of a retrovirus, human T-cell leukemia virus, in two patients with AIDS. Science 1983;220:862–865.

9. Popovic M, Sarngadharan MG, Read E, Gallo RC. Detection, isolation, and continuous production of cytopathic retroviruses (HTLV-III) from patients with AIDS and pre-AIDS. Science 1984;224:497–500.

10. Gallo RC, Salahuddin SZ, Popovic M, Shearer GM, Kaplan M, Haynes BF, Palker TJ, Redfield R, Oleske J, Safai B. Frequent detection and isolation of cytopathic retroviruses (HTLV-III) from patients with AIDS and at risk for AIDS. Science 1984;224:500–503.

11. Schupbach J, Popovic M, Gilden RV, Gonda MA, Sarngadharan MG, Gallo RC. Serological analysis of a subgroup of human T-lymphotropic retroviruses (HTLV-III) associated with AIDS. Science 1984;224:503–505.

12. Sarngadharan MG, Popovic M, Bruch L, Schupbach J, Gallo RC. Antibodies reactive with human T-lymphotropic retroviruses (HTLV-III) in the serum of patients with AIDS. Science 1984;224:506–508.

13. Montagnier L. A history of HIV discovery. Science 2002;298:1727–1728.

14. Gallo RC. The early years of HIV/AIDS. Science 2002;298:1728–1729.

15. Ratner L, Gallo RC, Wong-Staal F. HTLC-III, LAV, ARV are variants of same AIDS virus. Nature 1985;313:636–637.

16. St. Clair MH, Richards CA, Spector T, Weinhold KJ, Miller WH, Langlois AJ, Furman PA. 3′-Azido-3′-deoxythymidine triphosphate as an inhibitor and substrate of purified human immunodeficiency virus reverse transcriptase. Antimicrob Agents Chemother 1987;31: 1972–1977.

17. Mitsuya H, Weinhold KJ, Furman PA, St. Claire MH Lerhman SN, Gallo RC, Bolognesi D, Barry DW, Broder S. 3′-Azido-3′-deoxythymidine (BW A509U): an antiviral agent that inhibits the infectivity and cytopathic effect of human T-lymphotrophic virus type III/lymphadenopathy-associated virus *in vitro*. Proc Natl Acad Sci USA 1985;82:7096–7100.

18. Walensky RP, Paltiel AD, Losina E, Mercincavage LM, Schackman BR, Sax PE, Weinstein MC, Freedberg KA. The survival benefits of AIDS treatment in the United States. J Infect Dis 2006;194:11–19.

19. De Clercq E. The design of drugs for HIV and HCV. Nature Rev Drug Discov 2007;6: 1001–1018.

20. Deeks SG, Kar S, Gubernick SI, Kirkpatrick P. Raltegravir. Nature Rev Drug Discov 2008;7: 117–118.

21. Frankel AD, Young JAT. HIV-1: fifteen proteins and an RNA. Annu Rev Biochem 1998;67:1–25.

22. Bushman FD, Craigie R. Activities of human immunodeficiency virus (HIV) integration pro-

tein *in vitro*: specific cleavage and integration of HIV DNA. Proc Natl Acad Sci USA 1991;88:1339–1343.

23. Zeinalipour-Loizidou E, Nicolaou C, Nicolaides A, Kostrikis LG. HIV-1 integrase: from biology to chemotherapeutics. Curr HIV Res 2007;5:365–388.

24. Pommier Y, Pilon AA, Bajaj K, Mazumder A, Neamati N. HIV-1 integrase as a target for antiviral drugs. Antiviral Chem Chemother 1997;8:463–483.

25. Acel A, Udashkin BE, Wainberg MA, Faust EA. Efficient gap repain catalyzed *in vitro* by an intrinsic DNA polymerase activity of human immunodeficiency type 1 integrase. J Virol 1998;72:2062–2071.

26. Daniel R, Greger JG, Katz RA, Taganov KD, Wu X, Kappes JC, Skalka AM. Evidence that stable retroviral transduction and cell survival following DNA integration depend on components of the nonhomologous end joining repair pathway. J Virol 2004;78:8753–8581.

27. Yoder KE, Bushman FD. Repair of gaps in retroviral DNA integration intermediates. J Virol 2000;74:11191–11200.

28. LeFemina RL, Schneider CL, Robbins HL, Callahan PL, LeGrow K, Roth E, Schleif WA, Emini EA. Requirement of active human immunodeficiency virus type 1 integrase enzyme for productive infection of human T-lymphoid cells. J Virol 1992;66:7414–7419.

29. Engelman A, Bushman RD, Craigie R. Identification of discrete functional domains of HIV-1 integrase and their organization within an active multimeric complex. EMBO J 1993;12:3269–3275.

30. Hindmarsh P, Leis J. Retroviral DNA Integration. Microbiol Mol Biol Rev 1999;63:836–843.

31. Engelman A, Craigie R. Identification of conserved amino-acid residues critical for human immunodeficiency virus type 1 integrase function *in vitro*. J Virol 1992;66:6361–6369.

32. Mumm SR, Grandgenett DP. Defining nucleic acid-binding properties of avian retrovirus integrase by deletion analysis. J Virol 1991;65:1160–1167.

33. Van Gent DC, Oude Groenegar AM, Plasterk RHA. Identification of amino acids in HIV-2 integrase involved in site-specific hydrolysis and alcoholysis of viral DNA termini. Nucleic Acids Res 1993;21:3373–3377.

34. Katzman M, Sudol M. Mapping domains of retroviral integrase responsible for viral DNA specificity and target site selection by analysis of chimeras between human immunodefi-

ciency virus type 1 and visna virus integrases. J Virol 1995;69:5687–5696.

35. Sherman PA, Fyfe JA. Human immunodeficiency virus integration protein expressed in *Escherichia coli* possesses selective DNA cleaving activity. Proc Natl Acad Sci USA 1990;87:5119–5123.

36. Deprez E, Tauc P, Leh H, Mouscadet J-F, Auclair C, Brochon J-C. Oligomeric states of the HIV-1 integrase as measured by time-resolved fluorescence anisotropy. Biochemistry 2000;39:9275–9284.

37. Lee SP, Xiao J, Knutson JR, Lewis MS, Han MK. Zn^{2+} promotes the self-association of human immunodeficiency virus type-1 integrase *in vitro*. Biochemistry 1997;36:173–180.

38. Asante-Appiah E, Skalka AM. HIV-1 Integrase: structural organization, conformational changes, and catalysis. Adv Virus Res 1999;52:351–369.

39. Lee SP, Han MK. Zinc stimulates Mg^{2+}-dependent 3′-processing activity of human immunodeficiency virus type-1 integrase *in vitro*. Biochemistry 1996;35:3837–3844.

40. Zheng R, Jenkins TM, Craigie R. Zinc folds the N-terminal domain of HIV-1 integrase, promotes mulitmerization, and enhances catalytic activity. Proc Natl Acad Sci USA 1996;93:13659–13664.

41. Cannon PM, Byles ED, Kingsman SM, Kingsman AJ. Conserved sequences in the carboxy terminus of integrase that are essential for human immunodeficiency virus type 1 replication. J Virol 1996;70:651–657.

42. Lutzke RA, Vink C, Plasterk RH. Characterization of the minimal DNA-binding domain of the HIV integrase protein. Nucleic Acids Res 1994;22:4125–4131.

43. Drelich M, Wilhelm R, Mous J. Identification of amino acid residues critical for endonuclease and integration activities of HIV-1 IN protein *in vitro*. Virology 1992;188:459–468.

44. Kulosky J, Jones KS, Katz RA, Mack JPG, Skalka AM. Residues critical for retroviral integrative recombination in a region that is highly conserved among retroviral/retrotransposon integrases and bacterial insertion sequence transposases. Mol Cell Biol 1992;12:2331–2338.

45. Leavitt AD, Shiue L, varmust HE. Site-directed mutagenesis of HIV-1 integrase demonstrates differential effects on integrase functions *in vitro*. J Biol Chem 1993;268: 2113–3119.

46. Esposito D, Craigie R. Sequence specificity of viral end DNA binding by HIV-1 integrase

reveals critical regions for protein–DNA interaction. EMBO J 1998;17:5832–5843.

47. Gerton JL, Ohgi S, Olsen M, Derisi J, Brown PO. Effects of mutations in residues near the active site of human immunodeficiency virus type 1 integrase on specific enzyme–substrate interactions. J Virol 1998;72:5046–5055.

48. Kiyama R, Kawasuji T. Inhibitor for enzyme having two divalent metal ions as active centers. WO01/95905, 2001. *Chem Abstr***2001**;*136*: 53570.

49. Grobler JA, Stillmock K, Hu B, Witmer M, Felock P, Espeseth AS, Wolfe A, Egbertson M, Bourgeois M, melamed J, Wai JS, Young S, Vacca J, Hazuda DJ. Diketo acid inhibitor mechanism and HIV-1 integrase: implications for metal binding in the active site of phophotransferase enzymes. Proc Natl Acad Sci USA 2002;99:6661–6666.

50. Asante-Appiah E, Skalka AM. A metal induced conformational change and activation of HIV-1 integrase. J Biol Chem 1997;272:16196–16205.

51. Cowan J. Metal activation of enzymes in nucleic acid biochemistry. Chem Rev 1998;98: 1067–1087.

52. Pemberton IK, Buckle M, Buc H. The metal ion-induced cooperative binding of HIV-1 integrase to DNA exhibits a marked preference for Mn(II) rather than Mg(II). J Biol Chem 1996;271:1498–1506.

53. Wang LD, Liu C-L, Chen W-Z, Wang C-X. Constructing HIV-1 integrase tetramer and exploring influences of metal ions on forming integrase–DNA complex. Biochem Biophys Res Commun 2005;337:313–319.

54. Mazmumder, Engelman A, Craigie R, Fesen M, Pommier Y. Intermolecular disintegration and intramolecular strand transfer activities of wild-type and mutant HIV-1 integrase. Nucleic Acids Res 1994;22:1037–1043.

55. Bushman FD, Engelman A, Palmer I, Wingfield P, Craigie R. Domains of the integrase protein of human immunodeficiency virus type 1 responsible for polynucleotidyl transfer and zinc binding. Proc Natl Acad Sci USA 1993;90:3428–3432.

56. Jonsson CB, donzella GA, Gaucan E, Smith CM, Roth MJ. Functional domains of moloney murine leukemia virus integrase defined by mutation and complementation analysis. J Virol 1996;70:64585–4597.

57. Vink C, Groeneger A, Plasterk RHA. Identificatio of the catalytic and DNA-binding region of the human immunodeficiency virus type 1 integrase protein. Nucleic Acids Res 1993;21: 1419–1425.

58. Schauer M, Billich A. The N-terminal region of HIV1 integrase is required for integration activity, but not for DNA binding. Biochem Biophys Res Commun 1992;185:874–880.

59. Kulkosky J, Katz RA, Merkel G, Skalka AM. Activities and substrate specificity of the evolutionarily conserved central domain of retroviral integrase. Virology 1995;206:448–456.

60. Jenkins TM, Hickman AB, Dyda F, Ghirlando R, Davies DR, Craigie R. Catalytic domain of human immunodeficiency virus type 1 integrase: identification of a soluble mutant by systematic replacement of hydrophobic residues. Proc Natl Acad Sci USA 1995;92:6057–6061.

61. Chiu TK, Davies DR. Structure and function of HIV-1 integrase. Curr Top Med Chem 2004;4: 965–977.

62. Keseru GM, Kolossvary I. Fully flexible low-mode docking: application to induced fit in HIV integrase. J Am Chem Soc 2001;123: 12708–12709.

63. Dayam R, Neamati N. Active site binding modes of the beta-diketoacids: a multi-active site approach in HIV-1 integrase inhibitor design. Bioorg Med Chem 2004;12:6371–6381.

64. Schames JR, Henchman RH, Siegel JS, Sotriffer CA, Ni H, McCammon JA. Discovery of a novel binding trench in HIV integrase. J Med Chem 2004;47:1879–1881.

65. Savarino A. *In-silico* docking of HIV-1 integrase inhibitors reveals a novel drug type acting on an enzyme/DNA reaction intermediate. Retrovirology 2007;4:21.

66. Chen X, Tsiang M, Yu F, Hung M, Jones GS, Zeynalzadegan A, Qi X, Jin H, Kim CU, Swaminathan S, Chen JM. Modeling analysis, and validation of a novel HIV integrase structure provide insights into the binding models of potent integrase inhibitors. J Mol Biol 2008;380:504–519.

67. De Vivo M, Dal Peraro M, Klein ML. Phosphodiester cleavage in ribonuclease H occurs via an associative two-metal-aided catalytic mechanism. J Am Chem Soc 2008;130: 10955–10962.

68. The chelation model templates shown in Fig. 5c originate from an unpublished personal communication from Ryuichi Kiyama of Shionogi & Co. Ltd, Osaka, Japan. Presented herein with permission from Dr. Kiyama.

69. Selnick HG, Hazuda DJ, Egbertson M, Guare Jr, JP, Wai JS, Young SD, Clark DL, Medina JC. HIV integrase inhibitors. WO99/62513, 1999;Chem Abstr 1999;132:22866.

70. Young SD, Wai JS, Embrey MW, Fisher TE. HIV integrase inhibitors. WO99/62897, 1999; Chem Abstr1999;132:12255.

71. Young SD, Egbertson M, Payne LS, Wai JS, Fisher TE, Guare Jr, JP, Embrey MW, Tran L, Zhuang L, Vacca JP, Langford M, Melamed J, Clark DL, Medina JC, Jaen J. HIV integrase inhibitors. WO99/62520, 1999;Chem Abstr 1999;132:22755.

72. Fujishita T, Yoshinaga T. Indole derivatives with antiviral activity. WO99/50245, 1999; Chem Abstr 1999;131:271806.

73. Fujishita T, Yoshinaga T, Sato A. Aromatic heterocycle compounds having HIV integrase inhibiting activities. WO00/39086, 2000;Chem Abstr 2000;133:89529.

74. Hazuda D, Felock PJ, Hastings JC, Pramanik B, Wolfe AL. Discovery and analysis of inhibitors of the human immunodeficiency integrase. Drug Des Discov 1997;15:17–24.

75. Hazuda DJ, Felock P, Witmer M, Wolfe A, Stillmock K, Grobler JA, Espeseth A, Gabryelski L, Schleif W, Blau C, Miller MD. Inhibitors of strand transfer that prevent integration and inhibit HIV-1 replication in cells. Science 2000;287:646–650.

76. Hazuda DJ, Felock PJ, Hastings JC, Pramanik B, Wolfe AL. Differential divalent cation requirements uncoupled the assembly and catalytic reactions of human immunodeficiency virus type 1 integrase. J Virol 1997;71: 7005–7011.

77. Wai JS, Egbertson MS, Payne LS, Fisher TE, Embrey MW, Tran LO, Melamed JY, Langford HM, Guare Jr, JP, Zhuang L, Grey VE, Vacca JP, Holloway MK, Naylor-Olsen AM, Hazuda DJ, Felock PJ, Wolfe AL, Stillmock KA, Schleif WA, Gabryelski LJ, Young SD. 4-Aryl-2,4-dioxobutanoic acid inhibitors of HIV-1 integrase and viral replication in cells. J Med Chem 2000;43:4923–4926.

78. Grobler, J. A.; Stillmock, K.; Hu, B.; Witmer, M.; Felock, P.; Espeseth, A. S.; Wolfe, A.; Egbertson, M.; Bourgeois, M.; melamed, J.; Wai, J. S.; Young, S.; Vacca, J.; Hazuda, D. J. Diketo acid inhibitor mechanism and HIV-1 integrase: Implications for metal binding in the active site of phophotransferase enzymes. Proc. Natl. Acad. Sci. USA. 2002 99, 6661–6666.

79. Shaw-Reid CA, Munshi V, Graham P, Wolfe A, Witmer M, Danzeisen R, Olsen DB, Carroll SS, Embrey M, Wai JS, Miller MD, Cole JL, Hazuda DJ. Inhibition of HIV-1 ribonuclease H by a novel diketo acid, 4-[5-(benzoylamino)thien-2-yl]-2,4-dioxobutanoic acid. J Biol Chem 2003;278:2777–2780.

80. Klumpp K, Mirzadegan T. Recent progress in the design of small molecule inhibitors of HIV RNase H. Curr Pharm Des 2006;12: 1909–1922.

81. Hang JQ, Rajendran S, Yang Y, Li Y, In PWK, Overton H, Parkes KEB, Cammack N, Martin JA, Klumpp K. Activity of the isolated HIV RNase H domain and specific inhibition by *N*-hydroxyimides. Biochem Biophys Res Commun 2004;317:321–329.

82. Klumpp K, Hang JQ, Rajendran S, Yang Y, Derosier A, In PWK, Overton H, Parkes KEB, Cammack N, Martin JA. Two-metal ion mechanism of RNA cleavage by HIV RNase H and mechanism-based design of selective HIV RNase H inhibitors. Nucleic Acids Res 2003;31:6852–6859.

83. Parkes KEB, Ermert P, Faessler J, Ives J, Martin JA, Merrett JH, Obrecht D, Williams G, Klumpp K. Use of a pharmacophore model To discover a new class of influenza endonuclease inhibitors. J Med Chem 2003;46:1153–1164.

84. Summa V, Petrocchi A, Pace P, Matassa VG, De Francesco R, Altamura S, Tomei L, Koch U, Neuner P. Discovery of α,γ-diketo acids as potent selective and reversible inhibitors of hepatitis C virus NS5b RNA-dependent RNA polymerase. J Med Chem 2004;47:14–17.

85. Pace P, Nizi E, Pacini B, Pesci S, Matassa V, De Francesco R, Altamura S, Summa V. The monoethyl ester of meconic acid is an active site inhibitor of HCV NS5B RNA-dependent RNA polymerase. Bioorg Med Chem Lett 2004;14:3257–3261.

86. Summa V, Petrocchi A, Matassa VG, Taliani M, Laufer R, De Francesco R, Altamura S, Pace P. HCV NS5b RNA-dependent RNA polymerase inhibitors: from α,γ-diketoacids to 4,5-dihydroxypyrimidine- or 3-methyl-5-hydroxypyrimidinonecarboxylic acids. Design and synthesis. J Med Chem 2004;47:5336–5339.

87. Kawasuji T, Yoshinaga T, Sato A, Yodo M, Fujiwara T, Kiyama R. A platform for designing HIV integrase inhibitors. Part 1. 2-Hydroxy-3-heteroaryl acrylic acid derivatives as novel HIV integrase inhibitor and modeling of hydrophilic and hydrophobic pharmacophores. Bioorg Med Chem 2006;14:8430–8445.

88. Kawasuji T, Fuji M, Yoshinaga T, Sato A, Fujiwara T, Kiyama R. A platform for designing HIV integrase inhibitors. Part 2. A two-metal binding model as a potential mechanism of HIV integrase inhibitors. Bioorg Med Chem 2006;14:8420–8429.

89. Goldgur Y, Craigie R, Cohen GH, Fujiwara T, Yoshinaga T, Fujishita T, Sugimoto H, Endo T, Murai H, Davies DR. Structure of the HIV-1 integrase catalytic domain complexed with an inhibitor: a platform for antiviral drug

design. Proc Natl Acad Sci USA 1999;96: 13040–13043.

90. Hazuda DJ, Young SD. Inhibitors of human immunodeficiency virus integration. Adv Antiviral Drug Des 2004;4:63–77.

91. Garvey EP. Unexploited viral and host targets for the treatment of human immunodeficiency virus type 1 infection. Curr Drug Targets Infect Dis 2001;1:107–123.

92. Resemond MJC, St. John-Williams L, Yamaguchi T, Fujishita T, Walsh JS. Enzymology of a carbonyl reduction clearance pathway for the HIV integrase inhibitor S-1360: role of human liver cytosolic aldo-keto reductases. Chem Biol Interact 2004;147:129–139.

93. Walker MA, Johnson TD, Meanwell NA, Banville J.HIV integrase inhibitors. WO01/96283, 2001;Chem Abstr 2001;136:53533.

94. Walker MA, Johnson T, Naidu BN, Banville J, Remillard R, Plamondon S, Martel A, Li C, Torri A, Samanta H, Lin Z, Dicker I, Krystal M, Meanwell NA. Benzyl amide-ketoacid inhibitors of HIV-integrase. Bioorg Med Chem Lett 2007;17:4886–4890.

95. Walker MA, Gulgeze HB, Banville J, Remillard R, Corson D. Acyl sulfonamides as inhibitors of HIV integrase. WO04/103278, 2004; Chem Abstr 2004;142:23099.

96. Krystal M, Deminie CA, Bollini S, Terry BJ. Methods of treating HIV infection. US2006/0058286, 2006. Chem Abstr 2006;144:305114.

97. Nugent WA, Zhu K, Simpson JH, Delaney EJ. Process for the preparation of Z-5-carboxymethylene-1,3-dioxolan-4-ones. US2006/0047129, 2006. Chem Abstr 2006;144:274257.

98. Walker MA, Johnson T, Ma Z, Zhang Y, Banville J, Remillard R, Plamondon S, Pendri A, Wong H, Smith D, Torri A, Samanta H, Lin Z, Deminie C, Terry B, Krystal M, Meanwell N. Exploration of the diketoacid integrase inhibitor chemotype leading to the discovery of the anilide-ketoacids chemotype. Bioorg Med Chem Lett 16; 2006;5818–5821.

99. Walker MA, Johnson T, Ma Z, Banville J, Remillard R, Kim O, Zhang Y, Staab A, Wong H, Torri A, Samanta H, Lin Z, Deminie C, Terry B, Krystal M, Meanwell N. Triketoacid inhibitors of HIV-integrase: a new chemotype useful for probing the integrase pharmacophore. Bioorg Med Chem Lett 2006;16: 2920–2924.

100. Walker MA, Ma Z, Naidu BN, Sorenson ME, Pendri A, Banville J, Plamondon S, Remillard R. HIV integrase inhibitors. WO04/004657, 2004;Chem Abstr 2004;*140*:111271.

101. Kiyama R, Kanda Y, Tada Y, Fujishita T, Kawasuji T, Takechi S, Fuji M. Antiviral agent. WO03/916275, 2003;Chem Abstr 2003; 138:204936.

102. Kawasuji T, Fuji M, Yoshinaga T, Sato A, Fujiwara T, Kiyama R. 3-Hydroxy-1,5-dihydro-pyrrol-2-one derivatives as advanced inhibitors of HIV integrase. Bioorg Med Chem Lett 2007;17:5487–5492.

103. Kawasuji T, Yoshinaga T. Integrase inhibitors containing aromatic heterocycle derivatives. WO01/17968, 2001;Chem Abstr 2001;134: 237486.

104. Anthony NJ, Gomez RP, Bennett JJ, Young SD, Egbertson M, Wai JS.Aza- and polyaza-naphthalenyl-carboxamides useful as HIV integrase inhibitors. WO02/30426, 2002;Chem Abstr 2002;136:325438.

105. Anthony NJ, Gomez RP, Young SD, Egbertson M, Wai JS, Zhuang L, Embrey M, Tran L, Melamed JY, Langford HM, Guare JP, Fisher TE, Jolly SM, Kuo MS, Perlow DS, Bennett JJ, Funk TW. Aza- and polyaza-naphthalenyl-carboxamides useful as HIV integrase inhibitors. WO02/30930, 2002;Chem Abstr 2002;136:325531.

106. Anthony NJ, Gomez RP, Young SD, Egbertson M, Wai JS, Zhuang L, Embrey M, Tran L, Melamed JY, Langford HM, Guare JP, Fisher TE, Jolly SM, Kuo MS, Perlow DS, Bennett JJ, Funk TW.Aza- and polyaza-naphthalenyl-carboxamides useful as HIV integrase inhibitors. WO02/30931, 2002;Chem Abstr 2002;136: 309919.

107. Zhuang L, Wai JS, Payne LS, Young SD, Fisher TE, Embrey M, Guare JP. Aza- and polyaza-naphthalenyl ketones useful as HIV integrase inhibitors. WO02/36734, 2002;Chem Abstr 2002;136:386029.

108. Anthony NJ, Gomez RP, Bennett JJ, Young SD. Aza- and polyaza-naphthalenyl-carboxamides useful as HIV integrase inhibitors. WO02/055079, 2002;Chem Abstr 2002;137: 109214.

109. Zhuang L, Wai JS, Embrey MW, Fisher TE, Egbertson MS, Payne LS, Guare JP, Jr, Vacca JP, Hazuda DJ, Felock PJ, Wolfe AL, Stillmock KA, Witmer MV, Moyer G, Schleif WA, Gabryelski LJ, Leonard YM, Lynch JJ, Jr, Michelson SR, Young SD. Design and Synthesis of 8-hydroxy-[1,6]naphthyridines as novel inhibitors of HIV-1 integrase *in vitro* and in infected cells. J Med Chem 2003;46:453–456.

110. Embrey MW, Wai JS, Funk TW, Homnick CF, Perlow DS, Young SD, Vacca JP, Hazuda DJ,

Felock PJ, Stillmock KA, Witmer MV, Moyer G, Schleif WA, Gabryelski LJ, Jin L, Chen I-W, Ellis JD, Wong BK, Lin JH, Leonard YM, Tsou NN, Zhuang L. A series of 5-(5,6)-dihydrouracil substituted 8-hydroxy-[1,6]naphthyridine-7-carboxylic acid 4-fluorobenzylamide inhibitors of HIV-1 integrase and viral replication in cells. Bioorg Med Chem Lett 2005;15: 4550–4554.

111. Guare JP, Wai JS, Gomez RP, Anthony NJ, Jolly SM, Cortes AR, Vacca JP, Felock PJ, Stillmock KA, Schleif WA, Moyer G, Gabryelski LJ, Jin L, Chen I-Wu, Hazuda DJ, Young SD. A series of 5-aminosubstituted 4-fluorobenzyl-8-hydroxy-[1,6]naphthyridine-7-carboxamide HIV-1 integrase inhibitors. Bioorg Med Chem Lett 2006;16:2900–2904.

112. Melamed JY, Egbertson MS, Varga S, Vacca JP, Moyer G, Gabryelski L, Felock PJ, Stillmock KA, Witmer MV, Schleif W, Hazuda DJ, Leonard Y, Jin L, Ellis JD, Young SD. Synthesis of 5-(1-H or 1-alkyl-5-oxopyrrolidin-3-yl)-8-hydroxy-[1,6]-naphthyridine-7-carboxamide inhibitors of HIV-1 integrase. Bioorg Med Chem Lett 2008;18:5307–5310.

113. Egbertson Melissa S, Moritz H Marie, Melamed Jeffrey Y, Han Wei, Perlow Debra S, Kuo Michelle S, Embrey Mark Vacca Joseph P, Zrada Matthew M, Cortes Amanda R, Wallace Audrey, Leonard Yvonne, Hazuda Daria J, Miller Michael D, Felock Peter J, Stillmock Kara A, Witmer Marc, V, Schleif William, Gabryelski Lori J, Moyer Gregory, Ellis Joan D, Jin Lixia, Xu Wei, Braun Matthew P, Kassahun Kellem, Tsou Nancy N, Young Steven D. A potent and orally active HIV-1 integrase inhibitor. Bioorg Med Chem Lett 2007;17: 1392–1398.

114. Hazuda DJ, Young SD, Guare JP, Anthony NJ, Gomez RP, Wai JS, Vacca JP, Handt L, Motzel SL, Klein HJ, Dornadula G, Danovich RM, Witmer MV, Wilson KAA, Tussey L, Schleif WA, Gabryelski LS, Jin L, Miller MD, Casimiro DR, Emini EA, Shiver JW. Integrase inhibitors and cellular immunity suppress retroviral replication in rhesus macaques. Science 2004;305:528–532.

115. Hazuda DJ, Anthony NJ, Gomez RP, Jolly SM, Wai JS, Zhuang L, Fisher TE, Embrey M, Guare JP, Jr, Egbertson MS, Vacca JP, Huff JR, Felock PJ, Witmer MV, Stillmock KA, Danovich R, Grobler J, Miller MD, Espeseth AS, Jin L, Chen I-W, Lin JH, Kassahun K, Ellis JD, Wong BK, Xu W, Pearson PG, Schleif WA, Cortese R, Emini E, Summa V, Holloway MK, Young SD. A naphthyridine carboxamide provides evidence for discordant resistance be-

tween mechanistically identical inhibitors of HIV-1 integrase. Proc Natl Acad Sci USA 2004;101:11233–11238.

116. Johns BA. Naphthyridine integrase inhibitors. WO04/101512, 2004;Chem Abstr 2004;142: 6507.

117. Egbertson M, Melamed JY, Langford HM, Young SD. Preparation of hydroxynaphthyridinone carboxamides useful as HIV integrase inhibitors. WO03/062204, 2003;Chem Abstr 2002;139:133554.

118. Johns BA, Boros EE, Kawasuji T, Koble CS, Kurose N, Murai H, Sherrill RG, Weatherhead JG. HIV integrase inhibitors. WO05/077050, 2005;Chem Abstr 2002;143:248371.

119. Johns BA. Naphthyridinone (NTD) integrase inhibitors: discovery of the clinical candidate S/GSK364735. 235th National Meeting of the American Chemical Society, HIV Integrase Inhibitor Symposium; 2008 April 6–10; New Orleans, LA. Abstract MEDI-004.

120. Boros EE, Edwards CE, Foster SA, Fuji M, Fujiwara T, Garvey EP, Golden PL, Hazen RJ, Jeffrey JL, Johns BA, Kawasuji T, Kiyama R, Koble CS, Kurose N, Miller WH, Mote AL, Murai H, Sato A, Thompson JB, Woodward MC, Yoshinaga T. Synthesis and antiviral activity of 7-benzyl-4-hydroxy-1,5-naphthyridin-2(1H)-one HIV integrase inhibitors. J. Med. Chem. 2009;52:2754–2761.

121. Garvey EP, Johns BA, Gartland M, Foster SA, Miller WH, Ferris RG, Hazen RJ, Underwood MR, Boros EE, Thompson JB, Weatherhead JG, Koble CS, Allen SH, Schaller LT, Sherrill RG, Yoshinaga T, Kobayashi M, Wakasa-Morimoto C, Miki S, Nakahara K, Noshi T, Sato A, Fujiwara T. The naphthyridinone GSK364735 is a novel, potent human immunodeficiency virus integrase inhibitor and antiretroviral. Antimicrob Agents Chemother 2008;52: 901–908.

122. Reddy Sunila Y, Min Sherene S, Borland Julie, Song Ivy, Lin Jiang, Palleja Sandra, Symonds William T. Safety and pharmacokinetics of GSK364735, a human immunodeficiency virus type 1 integrase inhibitor, following single and repeated administration in healthy adult subjects. Antimicrob Agents Chemother 2007;51: 4284–4289.

123. Golden PL, Piscitelli S, Min S, Reddy S, Johns B, Garvey E, Ferris R, Hazen R, Edwards C, Woodward M, Yoshinaga T, Sato A, Iwashita S, Kadono K, Ohkawa T, Masuda K, Horie K, Fujiwara T, Palleja S. In vitro antiviral potency and preclinical pharmakokinetics of GSK364735 predict clinical efficacy in a phase 2a study. 47th Interscience Conference on

Antimicrobial Agents and Chemotherapy (ICAAC); 2007 September 17–20; Chicago, IL. H-1047.

124. Garvey E, Johns B, Foster S, Miller W, Ferris R, Hazen R, Underwood M, Boros E, Thompson J, Weatherhead J, Koble C, Allen S, Schaller L, Sherrill R, Yoshinaga T, Noshi T, Sato A. The naphthyridinone GSK364735 is a potent HIV integrase inhibitor and antiretroviral. 47th Interscience Conference on Antimicrobial Agents and Chemotherapy (ICAAC); 2007 September 17–20; Chicago, IL. 2007. H-1048.

125. Kobayashi M, Nakahara K, Seki T, Miki S, Kawauchi S, Suyama A, Wakasa-Morimoto C, Kodama M, Endoh T, Osugi E, Matsushita Y, Murai H, Fujishita T, Yoshinaga T, Garvey E, Foster S, Underwood M, Johns B, Sato A, Fujiwara T. Selection of diverse and clinically relevant integrase inhibitor-resistant human immunodeficiency virus type 1 mutants. Antiviral Res 2008;80:213–222.

126. Yoshinaga T, Nakahara K, Kobayashi M, Miki S, Noshi T, Sato A, Garvey E, Foster S, Underwood M, Johns B, Fujiwara T. Resistance profile of the integrase inhibitor S/GSK364735. 15th Conference of Retroviruses and Opportunistic Infections (CROI); 2008 February 3–6; Boston, MA; Session 136. Abstract 860.

127. Metobo SE, Jin H, Tsiang M, Kim CU. Design, synthesis, and biological evaluation of novel tricyclic HIV-1 integrase inhibitors by modification of its pyridine ring. Bioorg Med Chem Lett 2006;16:3985–3988.

128. Fardis M, Jin H, Jabri S, Cai RZ, Mish M, Tsiang M, Kim CU. Effect of substitution on novel tricyclic HIV-1 integrase inhibitors. Bioorg Med Chem Lett 2006;16:4031–4035.

129. Jin H, Cai RZ, Schacherer L, Jabri S, Tsiang M, Fardis M, Chen X, Chen JM, Kim CU. Design, synthesis, and SAR studies of novel and highly active tri-cyclic HIV integrase inhibitors. Bioorg Med Chem Lett 2006;16:3989–3992.

130. Jin H, Wright M, Pastor R, Mish M, Metobo S, Jabri S, Lansdown R, Cai R, Pyun P, Tsiang M, Chen X, Kim CU. Tricyclic HIV integrase inhibitors: potent and orally bioavailable C5-aza analogs. Bioorg Med Chem Lett 2008;18: 1388–1391.

131. Jin H, Wright M, Matobo S, Mish M, Jabri S, Lansdown R, Fardis M, Cai R, Pyun P, Pastor R, Schacherer L, Tsiang M, Chen X, Chen J, Kim CU. Tricyclic HIV-1 integrase inhibitors: SAR studies and preclinical evaluations. 235th National Meeting of the American Chemical Society, HIV Integrase Inhbitor Symposium;

New Orleans, LA; 2008 April 6–10. Abstract MEDI-003.

132. Verschueren WG, Dierynck I, Amssoms KIE, Hu L, Boonants PMJG, Pille GME, Daeyaert FFD, Hertogs K, Surleraux DLNG, Wigerinck PBTP. Design and optimization of tricyclic phthalimide analogues as novel inhibitors of HIV-1 integrase. J Med Chem 2005;48: 1930–1940.

133. Rowley M. The discovery of raltegravir, an integrase inhibitor for the treatment of HIV infection. Prog Med Chem 2008;46:1–28.

134. Pace P, Nizi E, Pacini B, Pesci S, Matassa V, De Francesco R, Altamura S, Summa V. The monoethyl ester of meconic acid is an active site inhibitor of HCV NS5B RNA-dependent RNA polymerase. Bioorg Med Chem Lett 2004;14:3257–3261.

135. Koch U, Attenni B, Malancona S, Colarusso S, Conte I, Di Filippo M, Harper S, Pacini B, Giomini C, Thomas S, Incitti I, Tomei L, De Francesco R, Altamura S, Matassa VG, Narjes F. 2-(2-Thienyl)-5,6-dihydroxy-4-carboxypyrimidines as inhibitors of the hepatitis C virus NS5B polymerase: discovery, SAR, modeling, and mutagenesis. J Med Chem 2006;49: 1693–1705.

136. Summa V, Petrocchi A, Matassa VG, Gardelli C, Muraglia E, Rowley M, Paz OG, Laufer R, Monteagudo E, Pace P. 4,5-Dihydroxypyrimidine carboxamides and N-alkyl-5-hydroxypyrimidinone carboxamides are potent, selective HIV integrase inhibitors with good pharmacokinetic profiles in preclinical species. J Med Chem 2006;49:6646–6649.

137. Summa V, Petrocchi A, Bonelli F, Crescenzi B, Donghi M, Ferrara M, Fiore F, Gardelli C, Gonzalez Paz O, Hazuda DJ, Jones P, Kinzel O, Laufer R, Monteagudo E, Muraglia E, Nizi E, Orvieto F, Pace P, Pescatore G, Scarpelli R, Stillmock K, Witmer MV, Rowley M. Discovery of raltegravir, a potent, selective orally bioavailable HIV-integrase inhibitor for the treatment of HIV-AIDS infection. J Med Chem 2008;51:5843–5855.

138. Iwamoto M, Wenning LA, Petry AS, Laethem M, De Smet M, Kost JT, Merschman SA, Strohmaier KM, Ramael S, Lasseter KC, Stone JA, Gottesdiener KM, Wagner JA. Safety, tolerability, and pharmacokinetics of raltegravir after single and multiple doses in healthy subjects. Clin Pharm Therapeut 2008;83:293–299.

139. Croxtall JD, Lyseng-Williamson KA, Perry CM. Raltegravir. Drugs 2008;68:131–138.

140. Markowitz M, Morales-Ramirez JO, Nguyen B-Y, Kovacs CM, Steigbigel RT, Cooper DA,

Liporace R, Schwartz R, Isaacs R, Gilde LR, Wenning L, Zhao J, Teppler H. Antiretroviral activity, pharmacokinetics, and tolerability of MK-0518, a novel inhibitor of HIV-1 integrase, dosed as monotherapy for 10 days in treatment-naive HIV-1-infected individuals. J Acquir Immune Defic Syndr 2006;43:509–515.

141. Deeks SG, Kar S, Gubernickj SI, Kirkpatrick P. Raltegravir Nat Rev 2008;7:117–118.

142. Anker M, Corales RB. Raltegravir (MK-0518): a novel integrase inhibitor for the treatment of HIV infection. Expert Opin Investig Drugs 2008;17:97–103.

143. Pace P, Rowley M. Integrase inhibitors for the treatment of HIV infection. Curr Opin Drug Discov Dev 2008;11:471–479.

144. Petrocchi A, Koch U, Matassa VG, Pacini B, Stillmock KA, Summa V. From dihydroxypyrimidine carboxylic acids to carboxamide HIV-1 integrase inhibitors: SAR around the amide moiety. Bioorg Med Chem Lett 2007;17: 350–353.

145. Pace P, Di Francesco ME, Gardelli C, Harper S, Muraglia E, Nizi E, Orvieto F, Petrocchi A, Poma M, Rowley M, Scarpelli R, Laufer R, Gonzalez P, Odalys M, Edith BF, Hazuda D, Stillmock KA, Summa V. Dihydroxypyrimidine-4-carboxamides as novel potent and selective HIV integrase inhibitors. J Med Chem 2007;50:2225–2239.

146. Gardelli C, Nizi E, Muraglia E, Crescenzi B, Ferrara M, Orvieto F, Pace P, Pescatore G, Poma M, del Rosario Rico Ferreira M, Scarpelli R, Homnick CF, Ikemoto N, Alfieri A, Verdirame M, Bonelli F, Gonzalez Paz O, Taliani M, Monteagudo E, Pesci S, Laufer R, Felock P, Stillmock KA, Hazuda D, Rowley M, Summa V. Discovery and synthesis of HIV integrase inhibitors: development of potent and orally bioavailable N-methyl pyrimidones. J Med Chem 2007;50:4953–4975.

147. Muraglia E, Kinzel O, Gardelli C, Crescenzi B, Donghi M, Ferrara M, Nizi E, Orvieto F, Pescatore G, Laufer R, Gonzalez-Paz O, Di Marco A, Fiore F, Monteagudo E, Fonsi M, Felock PJ, Rowley M, Summa V. Design and synthesis of bicyclic pyrimidinones as potent and orally bioavailable HIV-1 integrase inhibitors. J Med Chem 2008;51:861–874.

148. Kinzel OD, Monteagudo E, Muraglia E, Orvieto F, Pescatore G, Ferreira MdRR, Rowley M, Summa V. The synthesis of tetrahydropyridopyrimidones as a new scaffold for HIV-1 integrase inhibitors. Tetrahedron Lett 2007;48: 6552–6555.

149. Di Francesco ME, Pace P, Fiore F, Naimo F, Bonelli F, Rowley M, Summa V. Development of 2-t-butyl-N-methyl pyrimidones as potent inhibitors of HIV integrase. Bioorg Med Chem Lett 2008;18:2709–2713.

150. Ferrara M, Crescenzi B, Donghi M, Muraglia E, Nizi E, Pesci S, Summa V, Gardelli C. Synthesis of a hexahydropyrimido[1,2-a]azepine-2-carboxamide derivative useful as an HIV integrase inhibitor. Tetrahedron Lett 2007;48:8379–8382.

151. Sato M, Motomura T, Aramaki H, Matsuda T, Yamashita M, Ito Y, Kawakami H, Matsuzaki Y, Watanabe W, Yamataka K, Ikeda S, Kodama E, Matsuoka M, Shinkai H. Novel HIV-1 integrase inhibitors derived from quinolone antibiotics. J Med Chem 2006;49:1506–1508.

152. Kirschberg T, Parrish J. Metal chelators as antiviral agents. Curr Opin Drug Discov Dev 2007;10:460–472.

153. Goethals O, Clayton R, Van Ginderen M, Vereycken I, Wagemans E, Geluykens P, Dockx K, Strijbos R, Smits V, Vos A, Meersseman G, Jochmans D, Vermeire K, Schols D, Hallenberger S, Hertogs K. Resistance mutations in human immunodeficiency virus type 1 integrase selected with elvitegravir confer reduced susceptibility to a wide range of integrase inhibitors. J Virol 2008;82:10366–10374.

154. Shimura K, Kodama E, Sakagami Y, Matsuzaki Y, Watanabe W, Yamataka K, Watanabe Y, Ohata Y, Doi S, Sato M, Kano M, Ikeda S, Matsuoka M. Broad antiretroviral activity and resistance profile of the novel human immunodeficiency virus integrase inhibitor elvitegravir (JTK-303/GS-9137). J Virol 2008;82: 764–774.

155. Marinello J, Marchand C, Mott BT, Bain A, Thomas CJ, Pommier Y. Comparison of raltegravir and elvitegravir on HIV-1 integrase catalytic reactions and on a series of drug-resistant integrase mutants. Biochemistry 2008;47:9345–9354.

156. Hombrouck A, Voet A, Van Remoortel B, Desadeleer C, De Maeyer M, Debyser Z, Witvrouw M. Mutations in human immunodeficiency virus type 1 integrase confer resistance to the naphthyridine L-870810 and cross-resistance to the clinical trial drug GS-9137. Antimicrob Agents Chemother 2008;52: 2069–2078.

157. Sorbera LA, Serradell N. GS-9137: anti-HIV agent HIV integrase inhibitor. Drugs Fut 2006;31:310–313.

158. DeJesus E, Berger D, Markowitz M, Cohen C, Hawkins T, Ruane P, Elion R, Farthing C,

Zhong L, Cheng AK, McColl D, Kearney BP. Antiviral activity, pharmacokinetics, and dose response of the HIV-1 integrase inhibitor GS-9137 (JTK-303) in treatment-naive and treatment-experienced patients. J Acquir Immune Defic Syndr 2006;43:1–5.

159. Rmanathan S, Shen G, Cheng A, Kearney BP. Pharmacokinetics of emtricitabine, tenofovir, and GS-9137 following coadministration of emtricitabine/tenofovir disoproxil fumarate and ritonavir-boosted GS-9137. J Acquir Immune Defic Syndr 2007;45:274–279.

160. Ramanathan S, Shen G, Hinkle J, Enejosa J, Kearney BP. Pharmacokinetics of coadministered ritonavir-boosted elvitegravir and zidovudine, didanosine, stavudine, or abacavir. J Acquir Immune Defic Syndr 2007;46:160–166.

161. Johns BA, Svolto AC. Advances in two-metal chelation inhibitors of HIV integrase. Expert Opin Ther Patents 2008;18:1225–1237.

162. Wai J, Fisher T, Embrey M, Egbertson M, Vacca J, Hazuda D, Miller M, Witmer M, Gabryelski L, Lyle T. Next generation inhibitors of HIV-1 integrase strand transfer: structural diversity and resistance profiles. 14th Conference on Retroviruses and Opportunistic Infections, Los Angeles, CA. 2007 February 25–28. Abstract 87.

163. Han W, Egbertson M, Wai J, Perlow DS, Payne LS, Vacca J, Hazuda D, Miller M, Felock PJ, Stillmock K, Witmer MV, Gabryelski LJ, Schleif WA, Ellis J, Anari MR, Lyle TA. A potential second generation HIV-1 integrase strand transfer inhibitor with a high genetic barrier to mutation. 235th National Meeting of the American Chemical Society, HIV Integrase Inhbitor Symposium; New Orleans, LA; 2008 April 6–10. Abstract MEDI-005.

164. Perlow DS, Egbertson M, Wai J, Payne LS, Han W, Martyr CD, Obligado VE, Hoffman KL, Vacca J, Hazuda DJ, Felock PJ, Stillmock KA, Schleif WA, Gabryelski L, Anari MR, Ellis J, Witmer MV, Miller M, Tsou NN, Biba M, Welch CJ, Lyle TA. Discovery and synthesis of a potent long-acting inhibitor of HIV integrase. 235th National Meeting of the American Chemical Society, HIV Integrase Inhbitor Symposium; 2008 April 6–10; New Orleans, LA; Abstract MEDI-055.

CCR5 ANTAGONISTS: SMALL-MOLECULE INHIBITORS FOR BLOCKING HIV-1 ENTRY

JAYARAM R. TAGAT
Chemical Research Department,
Schering-Plough Research Institute,
Kenilworth, NJ

1. INTRODUCTION

Nearly three decades after its initial discovery, the human immunodeficiency virus (HIV-1), which after infecting its host, eventually causes the spectrum of disease symptoms collectively known as acquired immune deficiency syndrome (AIDS), remains a major public health issue worldwide, especially in the developing countries [1]. Great strides have been made in reducing the morbidity associated with HIV-1 infection by treating infected individuals with highly active antiretroviral therapy (HAART), a combination of drugs targeting one or more steps in the viral life cycle [2,3]. However, noncompliance to treatment due to side effects and difficult dosing regimens has resulted in many patients failing to achieve sustained suppression of viral replication, which in turn has led to the emergence of drug-resistant strains of HIV-1 [4–7]. Therefore, there continues to be a need for the discovery of novel agents with more tolerable side effects as well as agents directed toward novels targets in the sequence of steps involved in HIV-1 proliferation.

Over the past decade, new classes of drugs known as HIV entry inhibitors have gained prominence due to their ability to protect target cells from HIV infection [8,9]. The key steps involved in the HIV entry process include recognition of cell surface receptors by the virus, viral attachment to target receptors on the cell surface, fusion of the viral and cell membranes, and viral entry into the cell. It has been well established that the HIV envelope protein comprises the gp41 transmembrane glycoprotein, which is noncovalently associated with the gp120 attachment protein. The first step in the HIV-entry process is the recognition and attachment of gp120 to the primary receptor (CD4) on the surface of

T cells and macrophages. This target engagement causes a stabilizing conformational change in gp120, exposing the binding sites for a secondary coreceptor on the cell surface. The chemokine coreceptors, CCR5 and CXCR4, which are expressed on macrophages and T cells, were identified during the late 1990s as being essential for the entry of HIV into cells [10]. The coreceptor binding of HIV results in a second conformational change, this time in the gp41 glycoprotein, which exposes a fusion peptide that is inserted into the cell membrane. This event draws the viral and cellular membranes closer together, facilitating their mutual fusion. Inhibitors of each of these steps have been discovered [11] and proof-of-concept studies have demonstrated efficacy for some of these agents (Fig. 1).

This chapter will focus on the discovery and development of CCR5 antagonists that inhibit the entry of HIV-1 into the CD4 target immune system cells. As this topic has been extensively reviewed [12–21], rather than comprehensively describing numerous agents, we will focus on case histories of the first six small-molecule CCR5 antagonists, five of which entered the clinic and one has been approved for human therapy thus far. On the basis of published data, each case will be discussed from a preclinical point of view, starting with initial hit and lead discovery through lead optimization and the nomination of a clinical candidate. In our opinion, each case depicts a fascinating story of structure–activity relationship (SAR) studies and illustrates the effect of structural modification on pharmacokinetics, the frustration of running into road blocks in the form of unexpected off-target effects, the thrill of overcoming those issues through cross-functional collaboration, and the gratification that comes with eventual success in identifying a useful clinical agent.

2. BACKGROUND

The initial excitement in the discovery of the HIV coreceptors CCR5 and CXCR4 as new targets for therapeutic intervention was tempered with caution given that these receptors are expressed on the surface of immune system cells. While mutations are less likely to

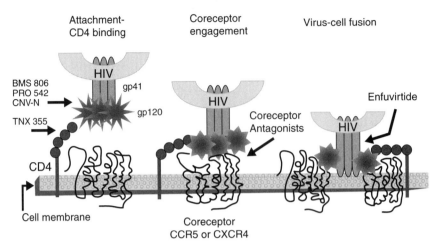

Figure 1. Steps in the HIV-1 entry process and agents that inhibit the viral entry. Reprinted from Ref. [11]. © 2008, Elsevier, Inc. (This figure is available in full color at http://mrw.interscience.wiley.com/emrw/ 9780471266945/home.)

occur in host-cell receptors than in the virus, blocking a receptor on macrophages and T cells might adversely affect the immune system. An early indication that coreceptor blockade was feasible came from the *in vitro* inhibition of HIV replication by synthetic and recombinant forms of their endogenous ligands, RANTES (regulated upon activation, normal T cell expressed and secreted), macrophage inflammatory protein (MIP)-1α, and MIP-1β [22–24]. The most compelling evidence came from a study by Liu et al. reporting that a 32-base-pair deletion in the CCR5 gene (Δ-32 homozygous genotype) was strongly protective against HIV infection despite repeated exposures [25]. A larger study also reported that individuals who expressed only one of the two alleles for CCR5, and thus were heterozygous for CCR5, showed significantly slower disease progression than individuals who expressed both alleles for the CCR5 gene [25,26]. Importantly, the lack of functional CCR5 did not result in any apparent immunologic defects in these individuals. Together, these findings provided an impetus for this nascent field of research by indicating that blockade of this coreceptor with small molecules would have few mechanism-based side effects and would inhibit HIV from infecting human immune system cells.

The presence of CCR5 and CXCR4 confer "viral tropism" with respect to HIV-1. CCR5 is the coreceptor preferred by R5 tropic HIV-1

strains and CXCR4 is the coreceptor preferred by X4 tropic HIV-1 strains. Dual tropic (R5/X4) viruses also exist. R5 tropic viruses are preferentially transmitted during the early years of the HIV-1 infection and X4 viruses emerge in about 50% of patients as the disease progresses [27]. However, in a majority of cases, many patients succumb to the R5 virus without a change in tropism to the X4 form [28]. Currently, tropism screening is required prior to prescribing maraviroc and for all clinical trials.

At the molecular level, CCR5 is a member of the G-protein-coupled receptor (GPCR) superfamily of receptor proteins. The GPCRs are membrane-spanning polypeptides that typically contain seven loops and mediate various intracellular events when triggered by extracellular ligands. As key mediators of signaling cascades, GPCRs have been very popular as targets for drug design since they were first identified [29]. Moreover, the availability of drug-like molecules and their fragments has enabled the rapid screening of compound libraries and the identification of potential novel leads. Thus, the design of CCR5 inhibitors has attracted widespread interest from many research groups.

The following six case histories were selected for discussion based on the availability of full details of discovery efforts leading to each clinical compound (Fig. 2). Although many other CCR5 antagonists based on some

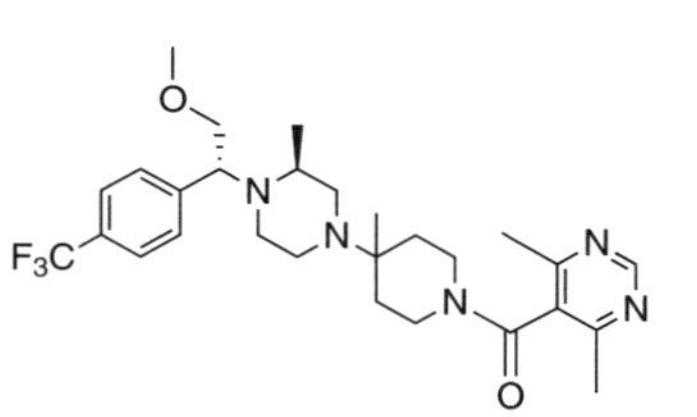

Figure 2. Diverse structures of CCR5 antagonists.

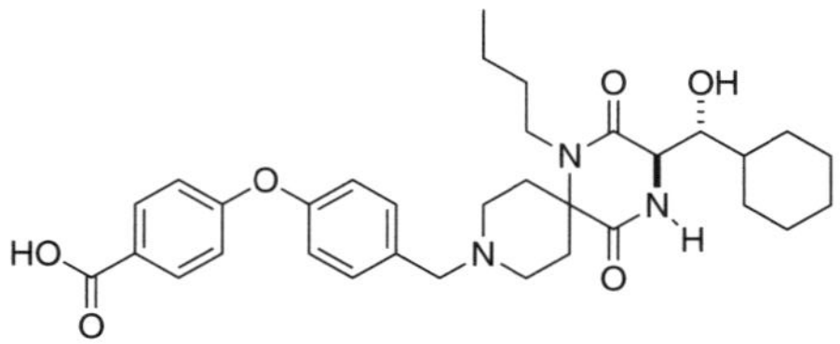

125 (ONO-4128; GW-873140; Aplaviroc)

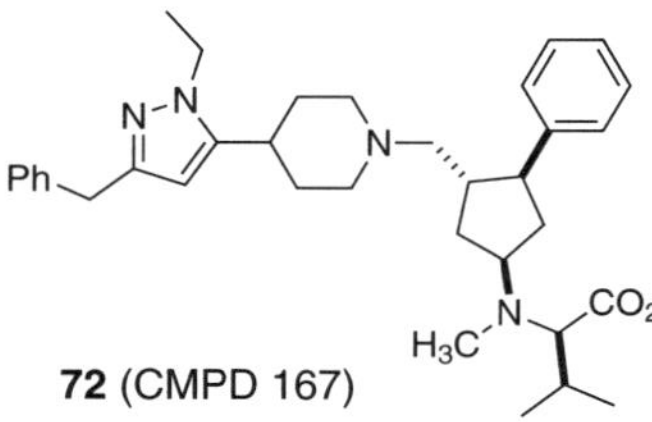

117 (TAK-220)

60 (UK-427,857/Maraviroc)

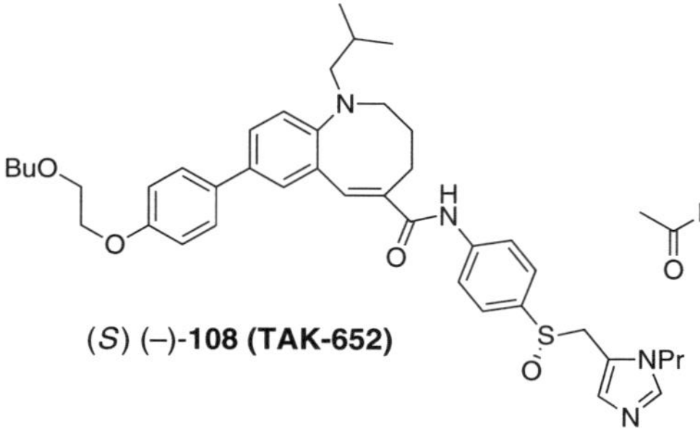

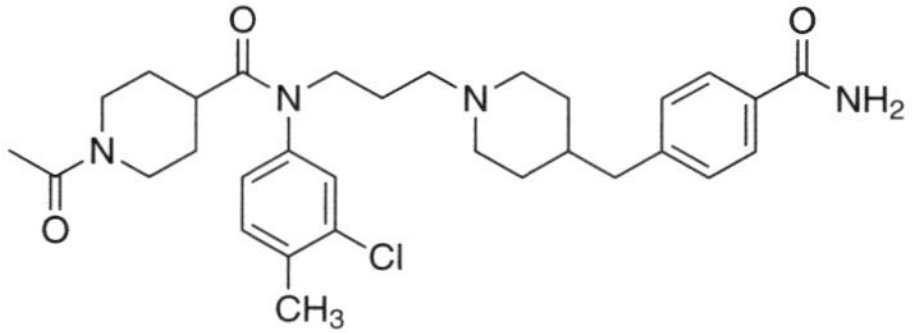

(S) (−)-108 (TAK-652)

33 (SCH-417690/SCH-D/Vicriviroc)

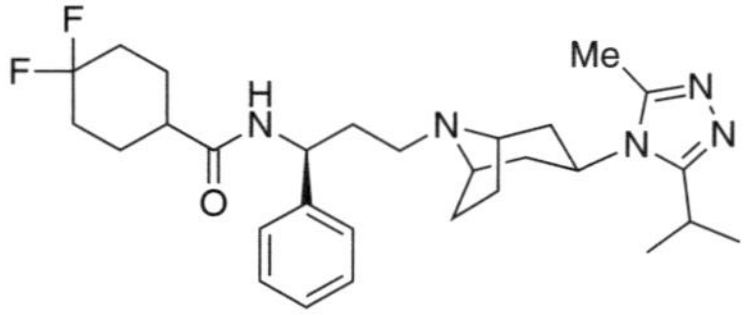

72 (CMPD 167)

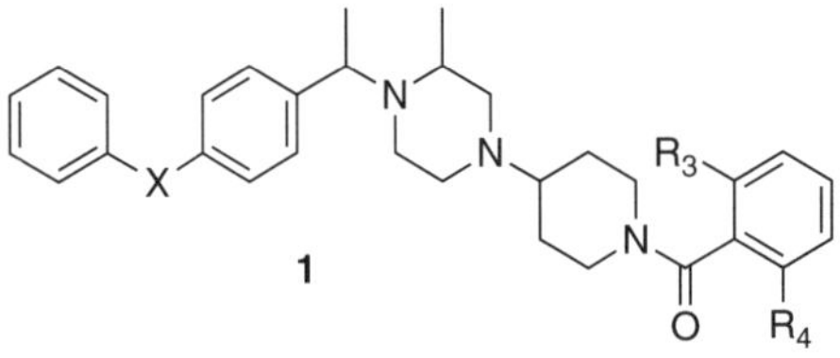

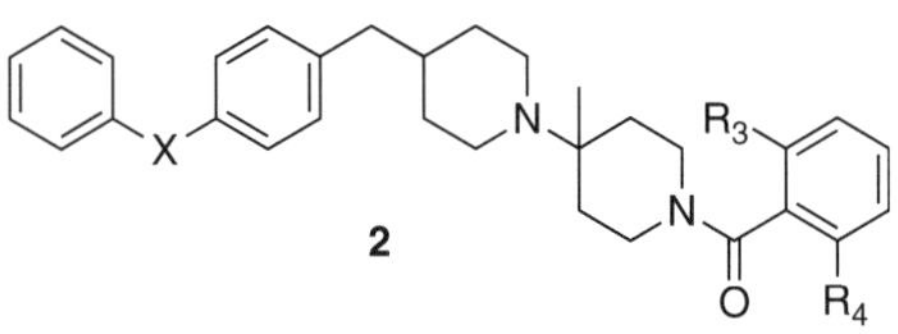

Figure 3. Two families of CCR5 antagonists from high-throughput screening.

of these structures and some hybrid structures have been reported (see Ref. [21], for a list), their details have not yet been fully disclosed. CCR5 antagonists may also have applications other than as anti-HIV agents, such as in the treatment of autoimmune diseases, but these uses are beyond the scope of this chapter.

3. PIPERAZINE AND PIPERIDINE-BASED CCR5 ANTAGONISTS (Schering-Plough)

The first orally bioavailable CCR5 antagonist to show proof of concept by decreasing viral load through the inhibition of HIV-1 entry was SCH-351125 (SCH-C, **25**). The discovery of this compound at Schering-Plough started with the high-throughput screening of their compound collection. Several chemotypes, representing various GPCR antagonist families, were found to inhibit CCR5-RANTES binding. However, only two series of compounds from the piperazino-piperidine- (**1**) and piperidino-piperidine- (**2**) based muscarinic antagonists showed activity in antiviral assays at subcytotoxic levels. Interestingly, the SAR trend, developed in parallel, showed that similar structural features were required at the two

ends of the molecules **1** and **2** (Fig. 3), whereas the structural requirements in the center of the molecule were quite distinct [30–39].

In the piperazino-piperidine series, initial hits included compounds such as **3** and **4** that were potent antagonists of the muscarinic M2 receptor and weak binders of CCR5 (Fig. 4). The 2(R)-methyl piperazine moiety was essential for potent binding in the muscarinic antagonists whereas 2(S)-methyl piperazine afforded improved affinity for CCR5. Similarly, changing the *ortho*-substituted benzamide group, which is required for potent M2 binding, to 2,6-disubstituted benzamide tweaked the selectivity further in favor of CCR5 over the M2 receptor.

The early lead compound **5** that embodied these key structural features also showed good activity in the mechanistic cell-based entry assay ($IC_{50} = 2$ nM) (Fig. 5). Further, compound **5** inhibited HIV growth in peripheral blood mononuclear cells (PBMCs) with an IC_{50} of 8 nM. It was also shown to be a functional antagonist of the CCR5 receptor.

So as to determine the minimum structural features necessary for CCR5 binding, the left-hand side of the lead compound **5** was truncated to furnish **7**, readily accessible from the common intermediate **6** in the synthetic

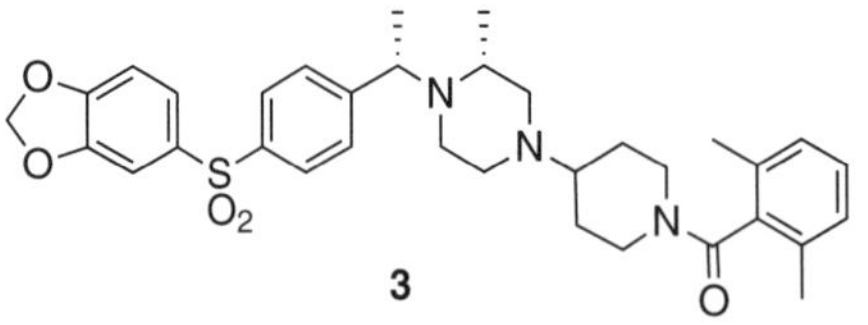

IC$_{50}$ (RANTES) = 440 nM

K_i (M2) = 0.8 nM

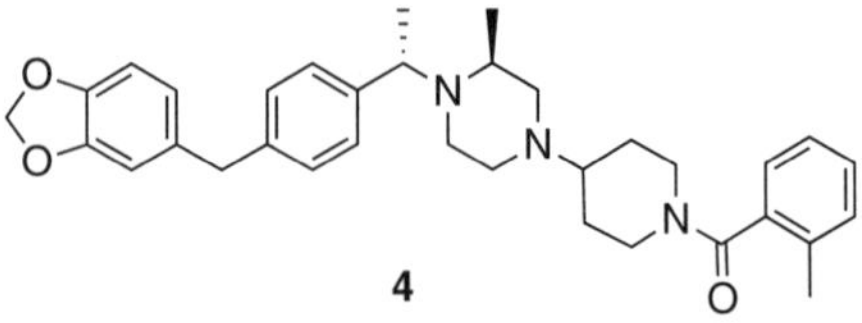

IC$_{50}$ (RANTES) = 90 nM

K_i (M2) = 35 nM

Figure 4. Initial hits in the piperazino-piperidine series.

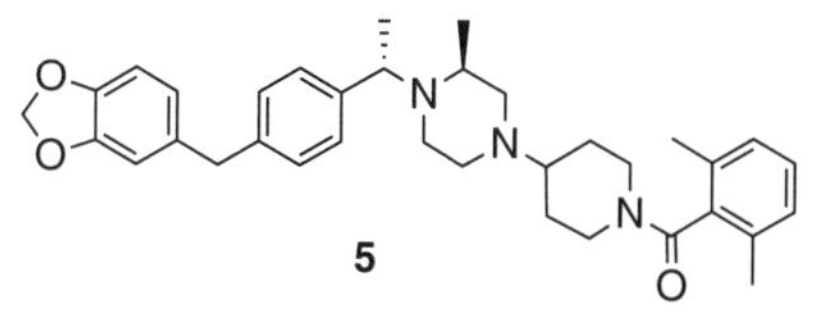

| Compound | Binding K_i (nM) | | Entry | PBMC |
	CCR5	M2	IC$_{50}$ (nM)	IC$_{50}$ (nM)
3	14	760	2	8

Functional antagonist: Ca Flux/GTP-γS assays.

Figure 5. Improving CCR5 affinity.

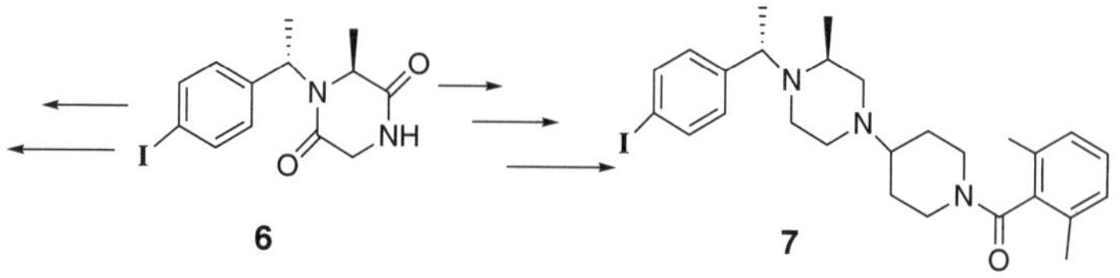

CCR5 binding, K_i = 15 nM
M2 binding, K_i = 1450 nM
HIV entry, EC$_{50}$ = 4 nM

Scheme 1. Discovery of a new lead (**7**).

sequence leading to **5** (Scheme 1). The new lead **7** maintained the binding and functional potency similar to **5** but showed a remarkable improvement in the CCR5/M2 selectivity (100-fold for **7** versus 50-fold for **5**).

Further probing of minimum requirements for CCR5 affinity showed that the parent piperazino-piperidine **8** is only a weak inhibitor (K_i = 440 nM). The introduction of the 2(S)-methyl group on the piperazine ring (**10**) improves the potency 15-fold, and this is further improved to 30-fold in the new lead **7** (S,S-diastereomer), which also has a benzylic methyl group. Introduction of a quaternary methyl group at the ring junction between the two heterocyclic rings resulted in compound **12** with excellent potency and selectivity (Table 1). The R/S diastereomer of compound **12** was eightfold less active whereas the R/R and the S/R diastereomers had little affinity for CCR5.

When the iodo-substituent in compound **7** was moved from the *para*-position to the *ortho* or *meta*-positions, the activity was diminished; the iodo-substituent also served as a functional handle to introduce a variety of other substituents. The phenyl ring bearing electron-withdrawing groups such as CF$_3$ and SO$_2$CH$_3$ was introduced at the start of an alternative synthetic sequence (Scheme 2). Medium-sized groups were preferred as the *para*-substituent on the left-side phenyl ring (I ~ CF$_3$ > Br > Cl > CN > Ph > SO$_2$CH$_3$ >> H).

The trifluoromethyl group conferred desirable pharmacokinetic properties to the CCR5 pharmacophore, and compound **15** showed modest blood plasma level (area under the curve (AUC)) when dosed orally in rat. The plasma levels resulting from oral administration were found to improve with the polarity of the amide moiety on the right side (Table 2). Thus, by changing the lipophilic benzamide **15** to the anthranilamide **17** or the salicylamide

Table 1. Methylation Patterns Determine CCR5 Affinity

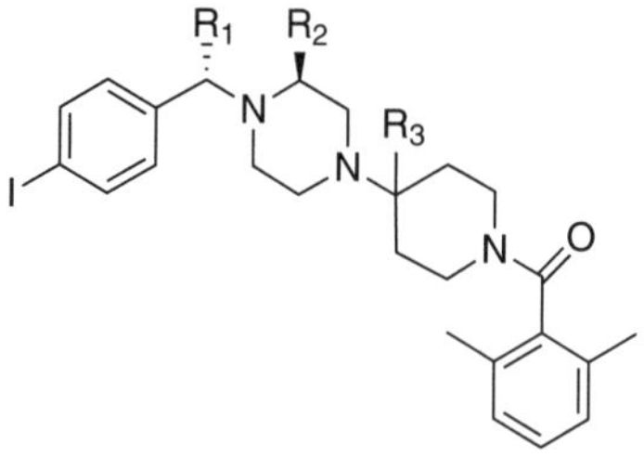

Compound	R$_1$	R$_2$	R$_3$	K_i (nM)	EC$_{50}$ (nM)*
8	H	H	H	440	N.D.
9	H	H	CH$_3$	62	N.D.
10	H	CH$_3$	H	30	N.D.
7	CH$_3$	CH$_3$	H	15	4
11	H	CH$_3$	CH$_3$	8	2.7
12	CH$_3$	CH$_3$	CH$_3$	4	1

Entry data is for JrFl strain of HIV-1.
N.D: not determined.

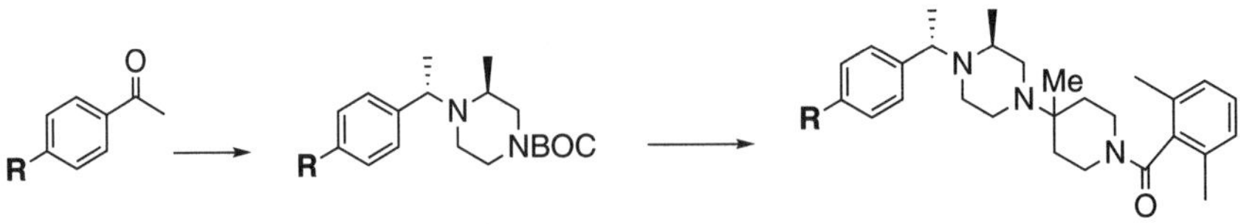

Compound	R	CCR5 Binding K_i (nM)	HIV Entry EC_{50} (nM)
15	CF_3	11	1
16	SO_2CH_3	9	3

Scheme 2. Enantio-selective synthesis from acetophenones.

18, the AUC values were improved by two- to threefold. However, the potency in the entry assay also seemed to diminish as the amide polarity increased (Table 2).

When the phenyl ring of the right side amide moiety was changed to a pyridine ring, a significant improvement in oral exposure resulted without a concomitant decrease in functional activity. The nicotinamide 19 had excellent potency in the CCR5 binding and the functional entry assays, low affinity for the muscarinic receptors and a fourfold increase in the AUC (rat) over the benzamide derivative 15. In mice, the nicotinamide resulted in modest oral exposure compared to in rats and was found to undergo rapid first-pass metabolism to the nicotinamide N-oxide 20, which was the major circulating metabolite in

mouse. Synthetically prepared nicotinamide N-oxide 20 had slightly reduced potency compared to the nicotinamide 19 but showed excellent oral bioavailability in rat (Table 3).

The muscarinic M1 receptors are prevalent in the gastrointestinal (GI) tract and the M2 receptors are widely distributed in the brain and heart tissue. During preliminary safety evaluations, when the compound 20 was administered orally to rats, side effects related to heart rate and GI function and were noticed at doses of 10 mg/kg. As a consequence, compound 20 could not be progressed further.

One of the initial hits in the piperidino-piperidine series was compound 21, which was

Table 2. Effect of Varying the Amide on Oral Exposure in Rat

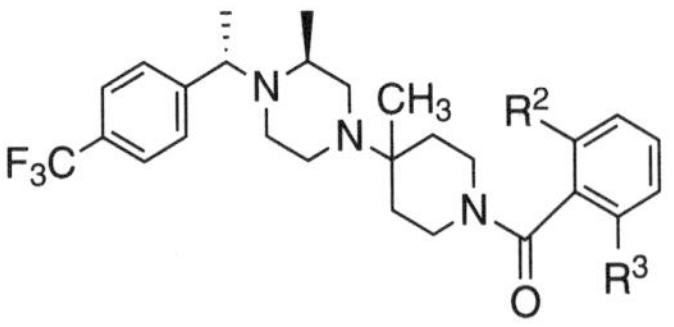

Compound	R_2	R_3	CCR5 Data K_i (nM)	EC_{50} (nM)	Rapid Rat PK[a] AUC (ng.hr·ml)
15	CH_3	CH_3	1	0.4	922
17	Cl	NH_2	5	1.2	1872
18	CH_3	OH	5	3.2	2540

[a] Dose = 10 mpk, p.o.

Table 3. Nicotinamide and its N-oxide

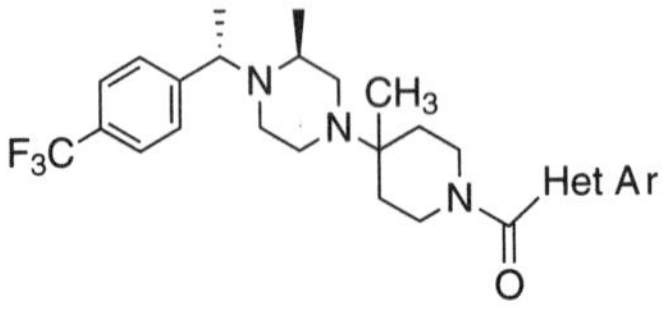

Compound	HetAr	M2 K_i (nM)	CCR5 Data K_i (nM)	EC_{50} (nM)	Rapid Rat PK[a] AUC (ng hr·ml)
19	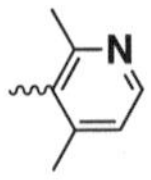	2500	2.3	0.5	3.905
20	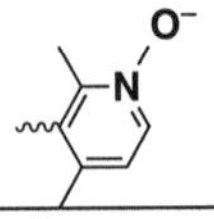	250	7.2	3.2	9,243

[a] Dose = 10 mpk, p.o.

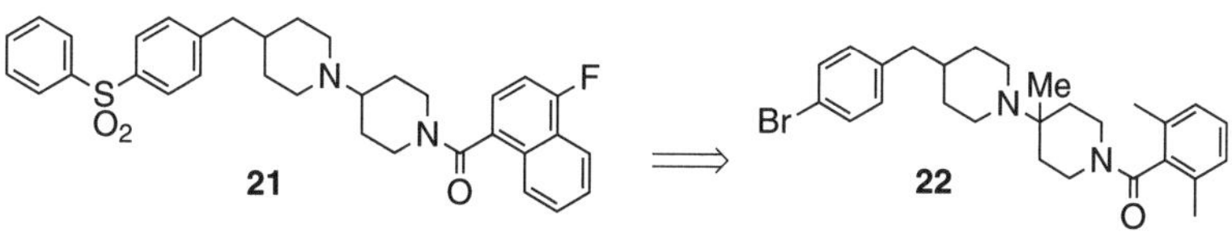

Figure 6. Discovery of the early lead (**22**) in the piperidino-piperidine series.

a potent M2 antagonist with weak CCR5 activity. Replacing the large *para*-substituent on the left side with a small group (preferably Br), installing the *ipso*-methyl group at the junction between the piperidine rings and capping the terminal amine with 2,6-dimethyl benzamide on the right side resulted in the early lead **22** with increased affinity for the CCR5 receptor (Fig. 6).

The linker (**X**) between the left side phenyl ring and the central piperidine was the key to further improving the potency of the early lead **22**. Changing the methylene linker to heteroatoms (O, N) improved binding without affecting functional potency. However, the oximes derived from the ketone linker improved both K_i and EC_{50} (entry assay) values (Table 4). In particular, the Z-oxime was an order of magnitude more potent than the E-oxime.

Table 4. Importance of the Linker in the Piperidino-Piperidine Series

X	K_i (nM)
CH$_2$	66
CO	55
O	29
NH	7
C=NOMe (E/Z)	11
C=NOMe (E)	25
C=NOMe (Z)	2

Gratifyingly, use of more polar amides again improved pharmacokinetic parameters when the piperidino-piperidines were orally administered to rodents and higher animals (Table 5). The combination of the Z-ethoxime as the linker with nicotinamide N-oxide as the capping amide group on the right side gave compound **25** (SCH-351125, SCH-C) with a high level of potency, CCR5/M2 selectivity, and oral bioavailability in rat and monkey. This compound inhibited a geographically diverse panel of HIV isolates with a mean $IC_{90} = 40$ nM, showed efficacy in the severe combined immune deficiency (*SCID*)-*hu* disease model in mouse, and demonstrated a synergistic effect when combined with reverse transcriptase and HIV protease inhibitors. SCH-351125 (SCH-C, **25**) had minimal affinity for the muscarinic receptors, and no pharmacological safety issues were observed. In clinical trials, SCH-351125 was well tolerated up to doses of 200 mg (bid, p.o.) and demonstrated dose-proportional reduction of HIV viral loads in treatment-naïve patients. However, QT_c prolongation was observed at higher doses causing further studies with this compound to be discontinued. The observation of QT_c prolongation in clinical studies was thought to be due to the binding of **25** to the hERG channel. Thus, reducing the hERG liability became one of the primary goals of the backup program.

The novel nicotinamide and its N-oxide, which give **25** its superior pharmacokinetic properties, also pose a unique structural problem. Being unsymmetrical tertiary amides, they exist as four rotational isomers observable on high-performance liquid chromatography (HPLC) (Scheme 3). Two of these rotamers are due to the slow rotation about the NCO

Table 5. Discovery of the Proof of Concept Compound (25, SCH-351125, SCH-C)

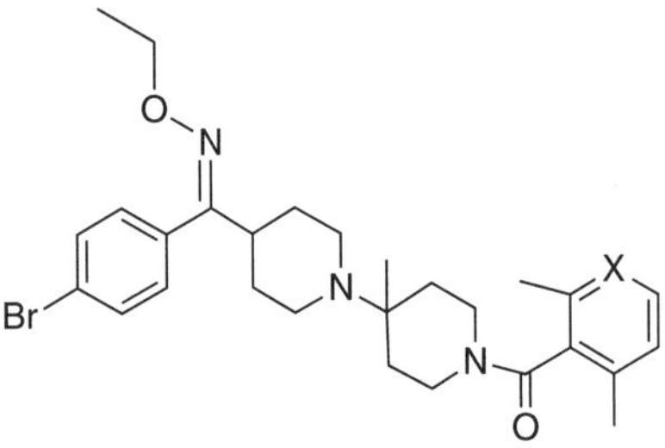

Compound	X	Binding, K_i (nM)		Rat PK
		CCR5	M2	$AUC_{0-6h}{}^a$
23	CH	2	>1000	1400
24	N	1	>1000	2100
25	N^+O^-	2	>1200	6500

^{a} Dose = 10 mg/kg. AUC = ng/mL · hr.

bond that is commonly found in many tertiary amides and is of no consequence. However, the second set of rotamers arises due to hindered rotation about the bond connecting the carbonyl group to the heteroaryl ring and generates a pair of atropisomers. In order to develop compound **25** (SCH-351125/SCH-C), all four rotamers were isolated by HPLC at low temperature, characterized with the RANTES binding assay, and were shown to equilibrate under physiological conditions to an equal mixture of all four isomers.

The main goals of the backup program were to reduce or eliminate the number of rotamers, minimize QT_c prolongation due to hERG binding, and improve the receptor selectivity (CCR5/M2) while maintaining the desirable functional potency and oral bioavailability observed with the first-generation compounds. For structural diversity, focus was directed to the piperazino-piperidine series. Since the high-energy rotamers (from bond rotation b in Scheme 3) stem from the unsymmetrical nature of the nicotinamide moiety, two types of symmetrical heteroaryl amides were developed. While the isonicotinamide **26** was a potent inhibitor of HIV entry and showed good oral exposure in rat, it showed only 10- to 12-fold selectivity for CCR5 over the M2 receptor. By contrast, the pyrimidine carboxamide **27** had matching potency in the HIV entry assay and similar oral exposure in rat with a 150-fold CCR5/M2 selectivity (Table 6).

Despite its improved CCR5/M2 selectivity ratio, compound **27** also showed some GI side effects at the 30 mg/kg dose during early safety studies in rats, and it was necessary to improve receptor selectivity further.

The structural similarities between compounds **20** and **25** and the parallel nature of their SAR, with the exception of higher receptor selectivity for **25**, indicated that the central portion of **25** was the origin of receptor selectivity. Changing the methyl group on the piperazine ring to an ethyl group resulted in diminished affinity for CCR5; thus, attention was centered on the benzylic site.

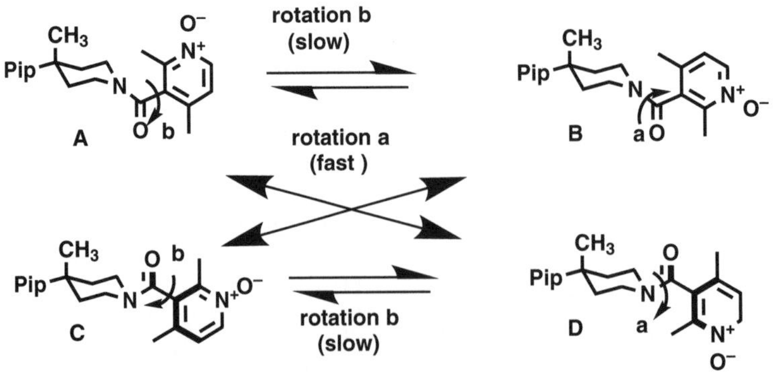

Scheme 3. Rotational isomers (rotamers) of compounds **20** and **25**.

Table 6. Symmetrical Heteroaryl Amides

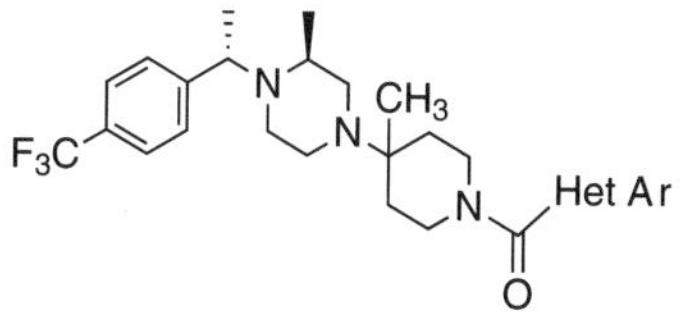

Compound	HetAr	M2	CCR5 Data		Rat PK[a]
		K_i (nM)	K_i (nM)	EC$_{50}$ (nM)	AUC (ng·hr/mL)
26	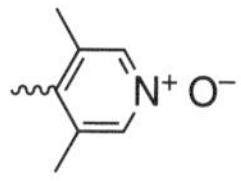	255	18	0.9	6,760
27	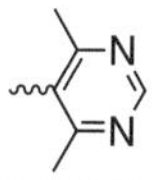	456	3	0.5	6210

[a] Dose = 10 mpk, p.o.

As the size of the benzylic methyl group was increased sequentially to ethyl, propyl, and benzyl groups, the receptor selectivity improved greatly. However, the increased lipophilicity of the molecule with the larger benzylic substituent also resulted in a decrease in the level of oral exposure observed in rat pharmacokinetics. The propyl derivative 29 had the optimal combination of excellent potency against a diverse panel of HIV isolates, a high level of CCR5/M1–M3 receptor selectivity, and good oral bioavailability in rat and cynomolgus monkey (Table 7). It neither inhibited nor induced cytochrome p450 enzymes but was >99% protein bound. It also showed 90% inhibition of the hERG channel at 10 μM and formed an acyl glucuronide metabolite via oxidation of the propyl side chain.

To block oxidation of the propyl side chain, the side chain was replaced by cyclopropyl methyl (31), trifluoromethyl (32), and meth-

Table 7. Larger Benzylic Substituent Improves CCR5/Muscarinic Receptor Selectivity

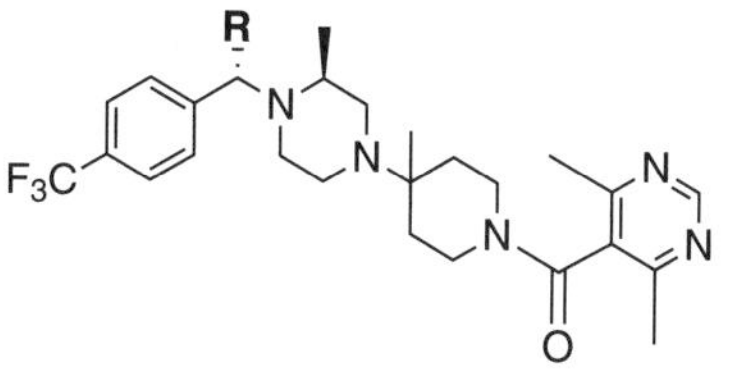

Compound	R	Bindings, K_i (nM)			EC$_{50}$ (nM)[a]	Rat PK[b]
		CCR5	M1	M2	Yu-2	AUC$_{0-6h}$
27	Methyl	2.8	575	456	0.5	6210
28	Ethyl	5.2	3900	4750	0.35	7310
29	Propyl	1.1	6075	4760	0.18	4600
30	Benzyl	1.4	>3900	>5700	0.13	2030

[a] HIV entry inhibition
[b] AUC = ng/mL·hr. Dose = 10 mg/kg

Table 8. Discovery of Vicriviroc (33, SCH-417690/SCH-D)

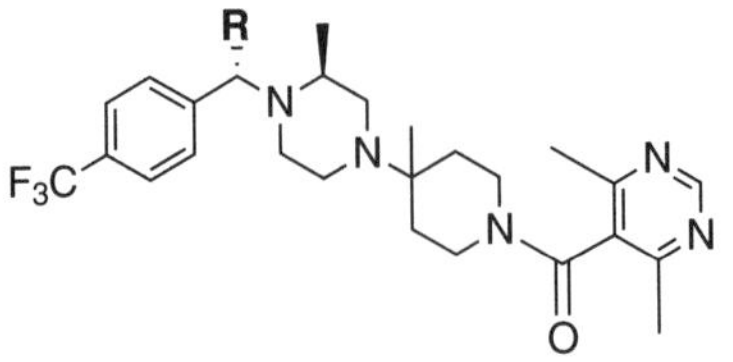

Compound	R	Bindings, K_i (nM)			EC$_{50}$ (nM)^a	Rat PK^b
		CCR5	M1	M2	Yu-2	AUC$_{0-6h}$
31	cyc-PrCH$_2$	1.6	1894	3512	0.8	5900
32	CF$_3$CH$_2$CH$_2$	ND	>3700	>6700	1.4	4600
33	CH$_3$OCH$_2$	2.5	6075	4760	0.45	6900

^{a} HIV entry inhibition.
^{b} AUC = ng/mL·hr.
Dose = 10 mg/kg.

oxy methyl (**33**) groups, respectively (Table 8). The cyclopropyl methyl derivative **31** had excellent potency in the HIV entry and proliferation (PBMC) assays and good oral exposure in rat. However, this compound potently inhibited hERG (>90% at 10 μM). Trifluoromethyl analog **32** was excluded from further study due to a similarly high level of hERG inhibition and reduced potency in the cell-based HIV entry and PBMC assays. The methoxymethyl analog **33** had the best receptor selectivity (M2/CCR5 > 5000) and excellent oral bioavailability (100% in rat and 89% in monkey). In a geographically diverse panel of HIV isolates, compound **33** had an IC$_{90}$ of 4 nM, an order of magnitude higher than the first-generation compound **25**. While the propyl, cyclopropyl methyl, and trifluoromethyl analogs were all highly (99%) protein bound and also inhibited hERG, compound **33** was only 84% protein bound. Importantly, it had reduced affinity for the hERG channel (IC$_{50}$ = 6 μM) compared to the oximino-piperidine compound **25** (hERG IC$_{50}$ = 1 μM).

Initial toxicology studies showed no unexpected safety concerns with compound **33** (SCH-417690, SCH-D, vicriviroc) and the compound entered clinical trials. It was well tolerated up to doses of 200 mg bid and showed dose-proportional reduction of HIV viral titers in treatment-naïve patients. This agent is currently in phase III clinical trials.

4. TROPANE-BASED CCR5 ANTAGONISTS (Pfizer)

At Pfizer [40–42], high-throughput screening produced a number of hits, and those that were not compliant with Lipinski's Rule of Five were discarded. Application of the next filter of ligand efficiency, a measure of heavy atom contribution to binding, helped normalize the binding affinities and molecular weights. On the basis of these criteria, compound **34** (MIP-1β IC$_{50}$ = 400 nM) was chosen for the hit-to-lead effort. The initial goals of the program were to identify a CCR5 antagonist that inhibited HIV entry into cells with an IC$_{90}$ comparable to that of HIV protease inhibitors, with good selectivity for CCR5 over related targets, acceptable pharmacokinetics, and minimal inhibition of cytochrome p450 enzymes. However, compound **34** was completely lacking in antiviral activity and potently inhibited Cyp 2D6 (IC$_{50}$ = 40 nM); the latter effect was thought to be due to the pyridine nitrogen in **34**. The benzimidazole **35** (Fig. 7), made to address the Cyp issue, showed stronger affinity for CCR5 (MIP-1β IC$_{50}$ = 4 nM) and weaker off-target activity (2D6 IC$_{50}$ = 710 nM), albeit antiviral effects were still lacking.

The high lipophilicity wrought by the benzhydryl group was reduced by introducing an amide linker resulting in the benzamide **36**

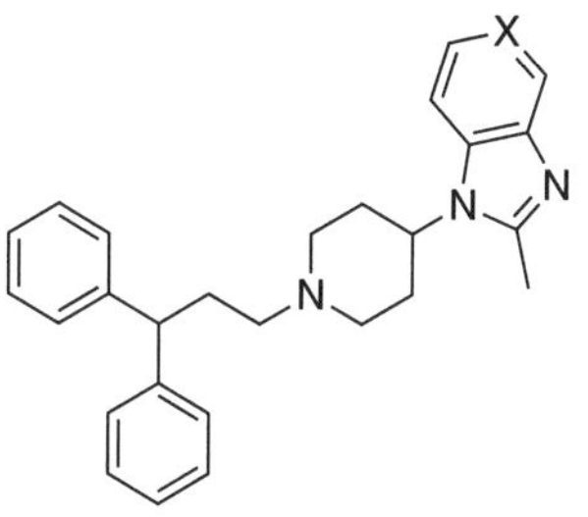

Compound	X	IC$_{50}$ (MIP-1b)	IC$_{50}$ (Cyp-2D6)
34	N	400 nM*	40 nM
35	CH	4 nM*	710 nM

* No antiviral activity (HIV Bal/PM-1 cells).

Figure 7. Minimizing Cyp 2D6 liability in CCR5 hits.

(Table 9). Although slightly less potent than **35**, compound **36** (MIP-1β IC$_{50}$ = 45 nM) showed promising levels of antiviral activity (HIV-Bal-PM-1 cells: IC$_{90}$ = 210 nM). A parallel synthesis approach was used to further investigate the SAR of the amide moiety. As shown in Table 9, replacing the benzamide with polar groups such as the picolinamide **37** or the urea **38** reduced the CCR5 affinity by at least an order of magnitude, indicating that lipophilic groups would produce greater antiviral activity. The acetamide **39** was too small and the phenyl acetamide **40** was too bulky. Mid-sized isopropyl amide was equipotent to **36** in its binding affinity but had slightly

Table 9. Lipophilic Amides Have Antiviral Activity

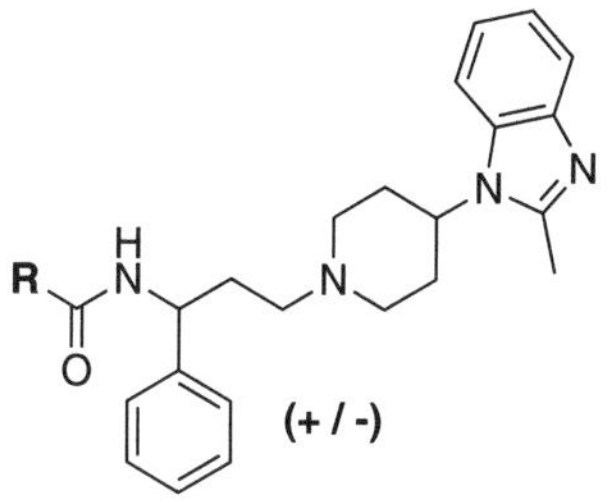

(+ / -)

Compound	R	IC$_{50}$ (MIP-1b)	IC$_{50}$ (Bal/PM-1)
36	Ph	45	210
37	2-Pyridyl	820	9250
38	Me$_2$N	430	>10,000
39	CH$_3$	270	7110
40	PhCH$_2$	100	740
41	i-Pr	50	700
42	cyc-Butyl	40	75

IC$_{50}$ values in nanomolar concentrations (nM).

diminished antiviral activity. The cyclobutyl amide **42** was the optimal compound, with a MIP-1β IC$_{50}$ of 40 nM and an IC$_{90}$ for HIV-Bal/PM-1 of 75 nM.

A homochiral synthesis of the two enantiomers of the benzamide established that activity was associated with the (S)-enantiomer (**43**). The (R)-enantiomer had much reduced CCR5 affinity (MIP-1β IC$_{50}$ = 580 nM) and no measurable antiviral activity (Bal/PM-1 IC$_{50}$ > 10 μM). Similarly, the (S)-enantiomer (**44**) of the cyclobutyl amide was obtained by enantio-selective synthesis and shown to possess an adequate level of antiviral activity (Fig. 8).

Compound **44** still showed Cyp 2D6 inhibition. Modeling studies suggested that this was due to the interaction of the basic piperidine nitrogen with a key residue Asp301 in the enzyme active site. The SAR strategy then was to diminish this particular interaction between the piperidine nitrogen and the Asp301 in Cyp 2D6 via the creation of target structures in which the piperidine nitrogen was sterically encumbered. While 2,6-dimethyl piperidine (**45**) had moderate antiviral activity, the tropane-based inhibitors **46** and **47** were both highly potent inhibitors of HIV entry and replication and were devoid of Cyp 2D6 inhibition (Fig. 9).

Proton nuclear magnetic resonance (NMR) analysis combined with molecular modeling demonstrated that the benzimidazole forces the endo-substituted bridged piperidine (**47**) into a boat conformation, allowing its structure to overlap with the exo-substituted tropane scaffold (**46**), thus accounting for their similar levels of activity.

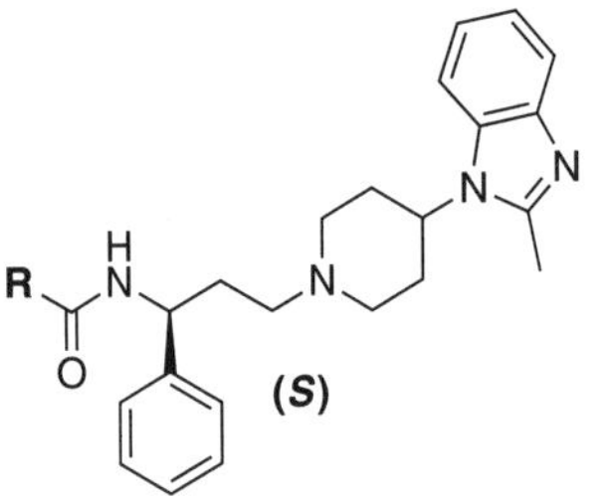

Compound	R	IC$_{50}$ (MIP-1b)	IC$_{50}$ (Bal/PM-1)
43	Ph	13	190
44	cyc-Butyl	20	73

IC$_{50}$ values in nanomolar concentrations (nM).

Figure 8. Activity resides in the (S)-enantiomer of the amide.

The endo-isomer **47** also showed potent antiviral activity against a range of primary origin CCR5-tropic HIV isolates in peripheral blood lymphocytes with IC$_{50}$ values ranging from 1–10 nM. However, compound **47** could not be progressed further as it showed 99% inhibition of the hERG channel at 1 μM, indicating the potential for safety issues with prolongation of the QT$_c$ interval. Docking of this molecule in a homology model of the hERG channel suggested that replacing the cyclobutyl ring in the carboxamide with more polar groups might minimize hERG binding by reducing hydrophobic interactions (Table 10).

The azetidine acetamide **48** did indeed reduce the hERG channel affinity without compromising antiviral potency. However, this compound had low cell permeability as per Caco-2 data and was predicted that the compound would have poor oral bioavailability *in vivo*. The calculated polar surface area (PSA) was then used to design compounds with improved cell permeability, with the expectation that compounds with PSA values of less than 80 Å^2 would have acceptable cell permeability. This approach led to the synth-

esis of tetrahydropyranyl amide (**51**), which demonstrated high antiviral potency, showed a lower level of hERG inhibition, and a higher level of cell permeability. Further profiling of **51** showed this compound to be a highly selective CCR5 receptor antagonist, with a wide therapeutic window between its on target inhibition of HIV entry into PBMCs and low cytotoxicity. The only unfavorable aspect of this compound pertained to its pharmacokinetic parameters: the oral bioavailability for **51** was <10% in dog due to extensive first-pass metabolism, and it was predicted that this characteristic would be similar in humans.

The next strategy was to balance the lipophilicity (as measured by the calculated log octanol/water partition coefficient, $c\log p$) of the lead template **47** by focusing on the right side of the molecule to achieve both cell permeability and metabolic stability. Replacing the benzimidazole with smaller heteroaryl rings containing three heteroatoms reduced $c\log p$ by more than one log unit. The 1,2,4-triazole, appropriately substituted with alkyl groups to modulate its polarity, emerged as being the optimal group to use on the right

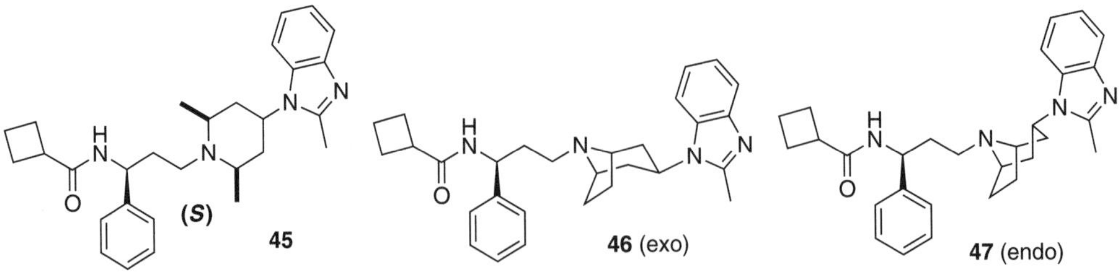

IC$_{50}$ (MIP-1b) = 8 nM
IC$_{50}$ (Bal/PM-1) = 53 nM

IC$_{50}$ (MIP-1b) = 2 nM
IC$_{50}$ (Bal/PM-1) = 13 nM

IC$_{50}$ (MIP-1b) = 6 nM
IC$_{50}$ (Bal/PM-1) = 3 nM

Figure 9. Sterically encumbered piperidine cores.

Table 10. Polar Amides Reduce hERG Binding

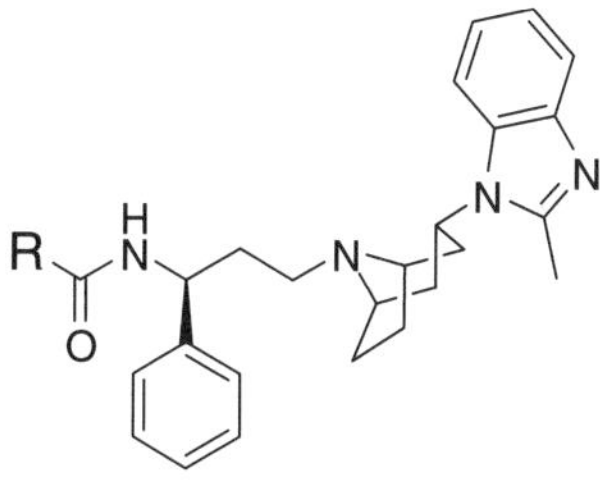

Compound	R	IC$_{90}$ (nM)^a	hERG^b	Caco-2 (cm/s)^c	PSA (Å^2)
47		3	80% (300 nM)	Not tested	45
48	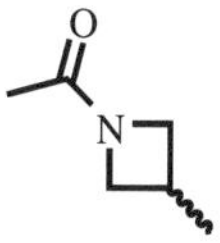	1	0% (300 nM)	$<1 \times 10^{-6}$	77
49	NCCH$_2^-$	3	10% (300 nM)	11×10^{-6}	115
50	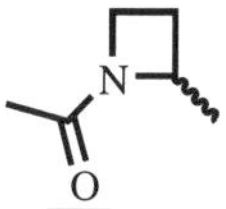	3	16% (1 nM)	7×10^{-6}	62
51		0.6	0% (100 nM)	23×10^{-6}	59

^{a} The concentration required to inhibit the replication of HIV (Bal) into PM-1 cells by 90%.
^{b} Percent inhibition of ^{3}H-dofetilide binding to hERG stably expressed on HEK-293 cells at different concentrations.
^{c} Apical to basal flux rate of compound through a monolayer of Caco-2 cells at 25 μM (pH 7.4).

side. The triazole derivatives of exo- and the endo-tropanes, **52–55** (Fig. 10), had similar antiviral potency. But the *in vitro* parameters predictive of better pharmacokinetics, such as human liver microsomal stability ($T_{1/2} = 55$ min) and cell permeability as measured by Caco-2 ($4.5 \times 10_{-6}$ cm/sec) and PSA (76 Å) data, were in favor of the exo-isomer **53**. Accordingly, **53** showed acceptable absorption (80%) and oral bioavailability (43%) in dog. Unfortunately, study of this compound had to be discontinued because of predicted QT$_c$ prolongation (hERG = 30% inhibition at 300 nM) at therapeutic concentrations.

Larger substituents on the triazole ring resulted in diminished antiviral potency. The 1,3,4-triazole analog (**56**) with its smaller dipole moment (3 Debye) showed a sixfold increase in cell permeability (Caco-2 AP → BL:

30×10^{-6} cm/s compared to the 1,2,4-triazole **53** (dipole moment = 6.1 Debye). However, the antiviral potency of **56** was threefold lower than that of **53** while the hERG binding was stronger (65% inhibition at 300 nM). As predicted, replacing the 1,2,4-triazole with an imidazole (**57**) improved antiviral potency but reduced microsomal stability (Table 11).

Once the central and right sides of the triazolyl tropane CCR5 antagonist had been fully optimized, attention was turned again to the left side of the exo-isomer **53**. The homologous cyclopentyl derivative **58** had increased antiviral potency and cell permeability but reduced mirosomal stability ($T_{1/2} = 21$ min for **58** versus $T_{1/2} = 55$ min for **53**). Oxidation of the cyclopentyl ring in **58** was identified as the major route of microsomal metabolism. Given these encouraging data, variations of

Exo-Series

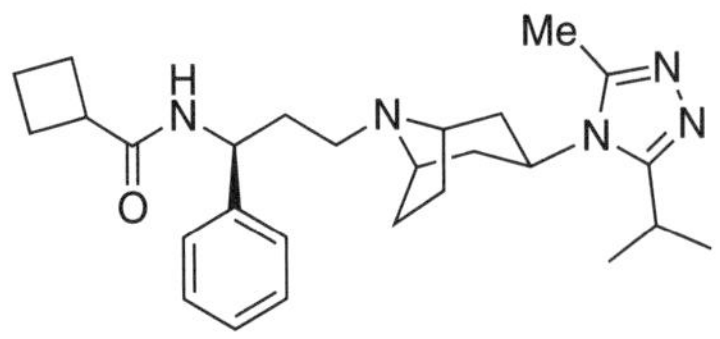

Endo-Series

Compound	R	IC_{90} (nM)*
52	Me	13
53	i-Pr	8

* HIV (Bal)/PM-1 cells.

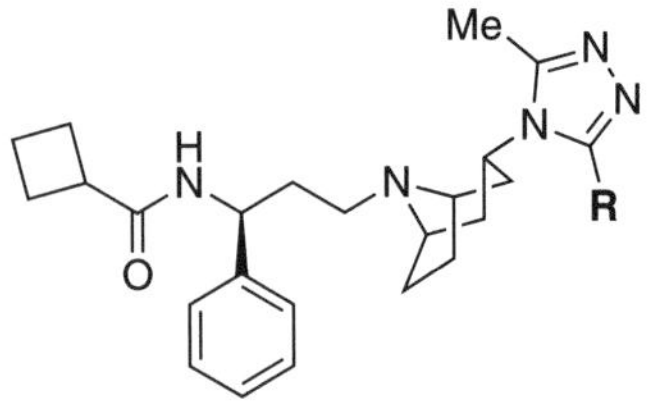

Compound	R	IC_{90} (nM)*
54	Me	6
55	i-Pr	101

* HIV (Bal)/PM-1 cells.

Figure 10. Triazole group is optimal on the right side.

the amide moiety in **54** were explored via parallel synthesis. The 4,4-difluorocyclcohexyl amide **60** demonstrated the optimal combination of antiviral potency, microsomal stability, and absence of hERG channel affinity, whereas the isosteric tetrahydropyranyl amide **59** was significantly less potent (Table 12).

Based on its early promising activity, compound **60** (UK-427,857; maraviroc) progressed to full-scale, preclinical profiling. In the PBMC assay, compound **60** exhibited broad-spectrum antiviral potency against primary origin, CCR5-tropic HIV isolates with a geometric mean $IC_{90} = 2$ nM ($n = 44$). The compound was also highly selective and showed no significant activity against a panel of pharmacologically relevant targets, including many chemokines, specifically CCR2, which is closely related to CCR5. Notably, UK-427,857 showed no significant inhibition of the major isoforms of the cytochrome p450 liver enzymes ($IC_{50} > 50\,\mu M$ for Cyp 1A2, 2C9, 3A4, and 2D6), indicating that the compound would be

Table 11. Variation of the Triazole Substituent

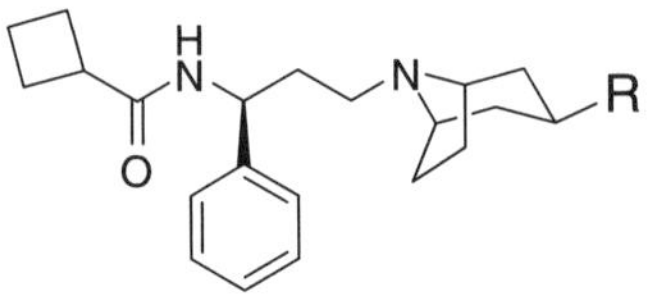

Compound	R	IC_{90} (nM)	hERG	Caco-2 (cm/s)	HLM (min)^a
56	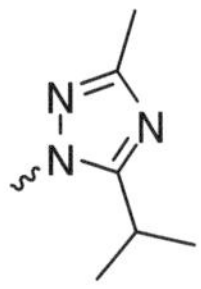	29	65% (300 nM)	30×10^{-6}	56
57	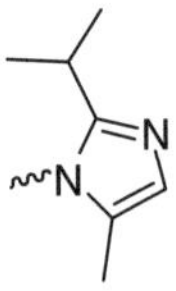	1	85% (300 nM)	Not determined	13

^{a} Half-life (*in vitro*) after incubation with human liver microsomes (HLMs).

Table 12. Discovery of Maraviroc (60)

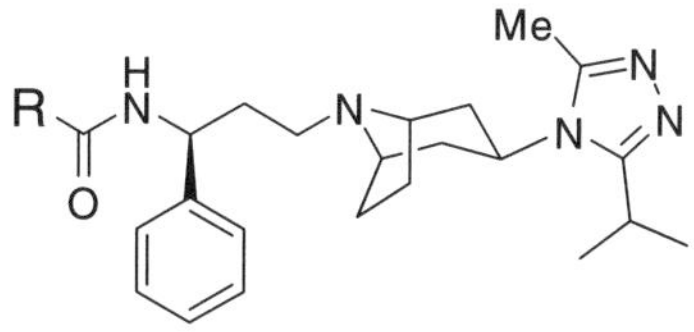

Compound	R	IC$_{90}$ (nM)	hERG	Caco-2 (cm/s)	HLM (min)^a
58	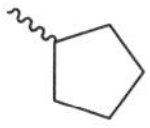 (cyclopentyl)	1.6	<30% Inhibition (300 nM)	5.6×10^{-6}	21
59	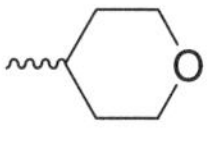 (tetrahydropyran)	125	0% Inhibition (300 nM)	N.D.	N.D.
60	 (4,4-difluorocyclohexyl)	1	0% Inhibition (300 nM)^b	$>6 \times 10^{-6}$	51

Human liver microsomes ($T_{1/2}$). N.D.: not determined.
^{a} hERG affinity for compound **60**: 19% inhibition at 10 µM.

expected to have minimal impact on the metabolism of coadministered drugs.

In terms of pharmacokinetics, in rat (dose: 1 mg/kg, i.v. and 10 mg/kg, p.o), UK-427,857 had an AUC = 12.4 ng·h/mL; a half-life ($T_{1/2}$) = 0.9 h; a clearance rate (Cl) = 74 mL/min/kg; and a bioavailability (F) = 6%. In dog (dose of 1 m/kg, i.v. and p.o.), compound **60** showed an AUC = 335 ng·h/mL; $T_{1/2}$ = 2.3 h; Cl = 21 mL/min/kg; and F = 42%. Compound **60** also was characterized by relatively low plasma protein binding (rat = 51%; dog = 64%). Kinetic studies showed that the binding of this compound to CCR5 is noncompetitive (with the chemokine ligands and HIV) and it has a long off-rate from the receptor ($T_{1/2}$ > 8 h).

On the strength of the above preclinical data, UK-427,857 (maraviroc) (**60**) was advanced into clinical study, in which it was found to be safe and well tolerated up to 600 mg (multiple dose) and 900 mg (single dose). A slow absorption profile, food effects, and a long terminal $T_{1/2}$ (17 h) were also reported. Most importantly, at the optimal dosing regimen of 100 mg bid (p.o.), maraviroc was maintained in concentrations greater than the trough IC$_{90}$ value for several hours, resulting in impressive efficacy (mean 1.42 log$_{10}$ reduction in viral load) following 10 days of monotherapy. In 2007, maraviroc (**60**, Selzentry®) became the first U.S. Food and Drug Administration (FDA)-approved CCR5 antagonist used to treat HIV infection in experienced patients; recently, it was also approved for use in naïve patients. In 2008, Pfizer disclosed a second-generation analog of **60**, featuring an imidazo-piperidine right side (UK-232,798), that had similar potency but improved PK profile suitable for once daily dosing.

5. TRI-SUBSTITUTED PYRROLIDINES AS CCR5 ANTAGONISTS (Merck)

A series of publications from research groups at Merck [42] have described the development of acyclic and cyclic scaffolds with CCR5 antagonistic activity. The acyclic series was based on the 2-aryl-1,4-diamino butane platform and is represented by the screening hit **61**. This compound had an IC$_{50}$ = 40 nM in the CCR5/MIP-1α binding assay but had weak antiviral activity (HIV/Yu-2-PBMC IC$_{95}$ = 12 µM). Early SAR studies around this scaffold indicated that the 2(S)-phenyl enantiomer was 24-fold more active than the 2(R)-phenyl isomer, and that activity was optimal when the benzene sulfonamide was positioned on the right side. It was found that the spirocyclic ring at the 4-position of the piperidine could be replaced with a simple phenyl ring (**62**) or an N-alkyl carbamate group (**63**). While these changes generated new templates with potent

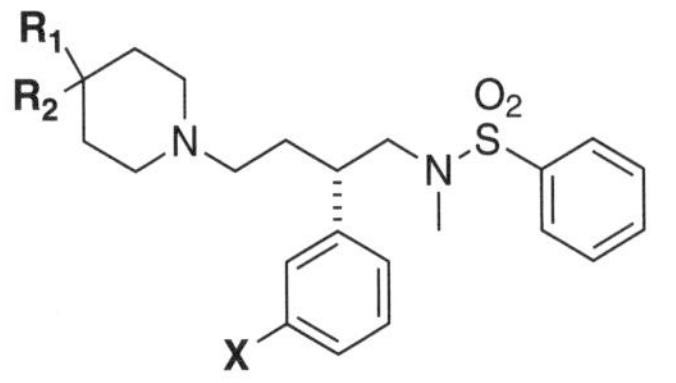

Compound	R_1	R_2	X	IC_{50} (nM)*
61	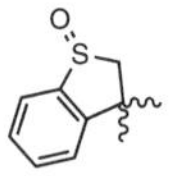 (thiophene-fused bicyclic, S=O)	–	Cl	40
62	Ph	H	Cl	30
63	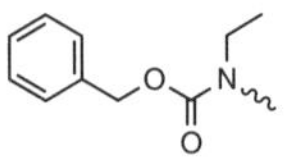 (benzyl carbamate ethyl-N)	H	H	20

* CCR5-MIP-1α binding assay

Figure 11. Butane 1,4-diamine scaffolds as hits with CCR5 affinity.

CCR5 binding affinity, the antiviral potency was still weak (PBMC: $IC_{95} > 10 \,\mu M$) (Fig. 11).

Compound **64** combining a 4-nitrobenzyl carbamate and an *N*-allyl group on the left side was the first to show an improved antiviral activity (HIV Bal/PBMC: $IC_{95} = 400$ nM). Antiviral activity was further increased by installing a quaternary methyl group adjacent to the 2(*S*)-phenyl ring (**65**) which substantially improved antiviral potency ($IC_{95} = 13 \,nM$) (Fig. 12).

Compound **65** had an excellent selectivity profile against other chemokines and GPCRs. In rats, it had modest oral bioavailability (29%) and a reasonably long half-life ($T_{1/2} = 2 \,h$). In dogs, despite the long plasma half-life ($T_{1/2} = 10 \,h$), the compound had poor oral bioavailability ($F < 1\%$). The poor oral availability was thought to be due to the presence of the *N*-methyl sulfonamide group. Creative, isosteric replacements of the right-side group led again to new compounds with potent CCR5 affinity but modest antiviral activity.

Rational drug design via locking of the active conformation led to the development of

a novel 1,3,4-tri-substituted pyrrolidine scaffold exemplified by compound **66** (Fig. 13). Notably, the 3,4-*trans* derivative was significantly more active than the 3,4-*cis* isomer; absolute stereochemistry was also important, with the 3(*S*), 4(*S*) configuration demonstrating increased antiviral activity.

With respect to the two groups at the 3- and 4-positions in the *trans*-pyrrolidine, the SAR trends were similar to the acyclic series, with the two groups shown for compound **65** being optimal. However, a wider range of substituents was tolerated at the pyrrolidine nitrogen in contrast to the requirement of an aryl sulfonamide in the acyclic series. Optimization at this site led to the 2-chloro benzamide group embedded in structure **66**. Compound **66** is a potent CCR5 antagonist ($IC_{50} < 1 \,nM$) and inhibited HIV (Bal) entry in a HeLa-cell-based reporter gene assay and inhibited the replication of live HIV (Yu-2) in PBMC with an $IC_{95} = 31 \,nM$. Additionally, this compound showed good oral bioavailability ($F = 39\%$) and a $T_{1/2} = 1.2 \,h$ in rat. Observation of off-target GPCR activ-

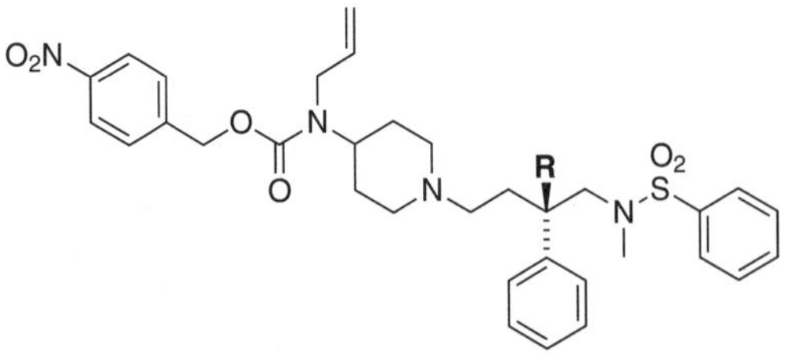

		Binding potency	Antiviral potency
Compound	R	IC_{50} (nM)^a	IC_{95} (nM)^b
64	H	1	400
65	CH_3	0.1	13

^{a}Inhibition of CCR5-MIP-1a binding.
^{b}Inhibition of HIV (Yu-2) replication in PBMC.

Figure 12. Allyl amino carbamate confers antiviral activity.

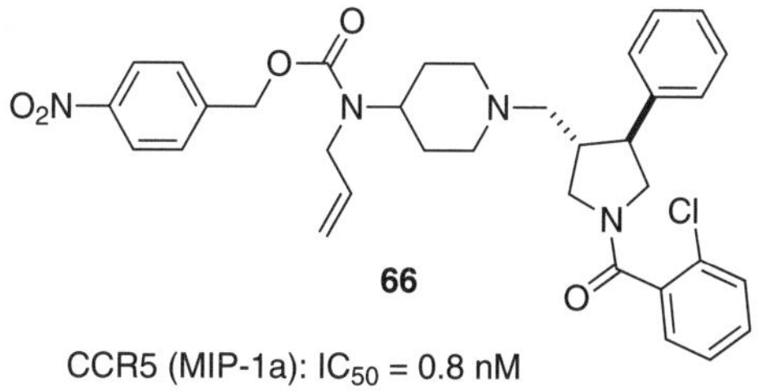

66

CCR5 (MIP-1a): IC$_{50}$ = 0.8 nM

HIV (Yu-2)/PBMC: IC$_{95}$ = 31 nM

Figure 13. Novel 1,3,4-tri-substituted pyrrolidine scaffold.

ities for **66** prompted the search for less basic compounds.

A combinatorial approach to further optimize the N1 and C4 substituents identified

the zwitterionic structures **67** and **68** with subnanomolar affinity for CCR5. Compound **67** was reported to have an IC$_{95}$ = 77 nM in the HIV Yu-2/PBMC assay and an oral bioavailability of 26% in rats, 43% in dogs, and 10% in rhesus monkeys. While compound **68** had improved antiviral activity (PBMC: IC$_{95}$ = 8 nM), its pharmacokinetic behavior was similar to that of **67**. In the amino-acid series, the gem-difluoro derivative **69** had the best combination of antiviral potency and pharmacokinetic parameters (Fig. 14).

The floppy phenyl propyl side chain in structure **67** was constrained in the form of a pyrazole ring resulting in compound **70**, significantly improving antiviral activity (Fig. 15). However, this compound showed very high clearance in the rat (Cl = 64 mL/min/kg),

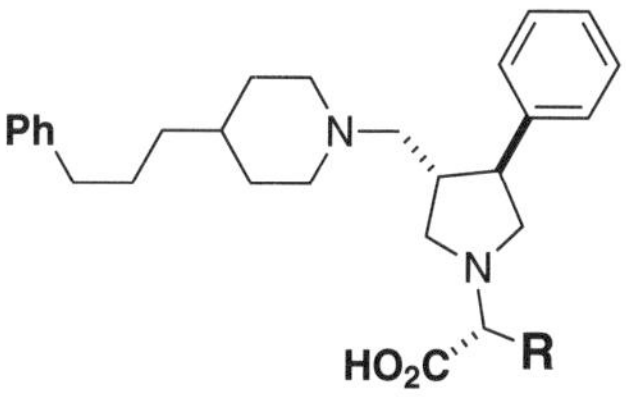

Compound	R	Binding potency IC$_{50}$ (nM)[a]	Antiviral potency IC$_{95}$ (nM)[b]
67	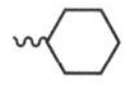	<1	77
68		<1	8

[a]Inhibition of CCR5-MIP-1a binding.
[b]Inhibition of HIV (Yu-2) replication in PBMC.

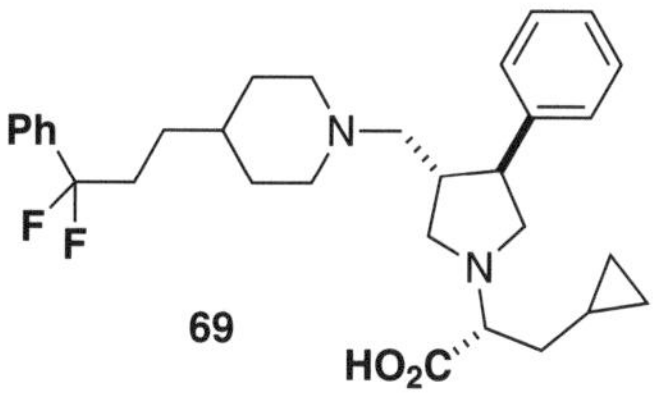

CCR5 (MIP-1a): IC$_{50}$ = 0.06 nM

Entry (HeLa): IC$_{90}$ = 0.4 nM

HIV (Bal)/PBMC: IC$_{95}$ = 8 nM

$T_{1/2}$ = 7.5 h (rat); 2.4 h (dog); 5.6 h (monkey)

69

Figure 14. Amino acid derivatives with improved antiviral activity.

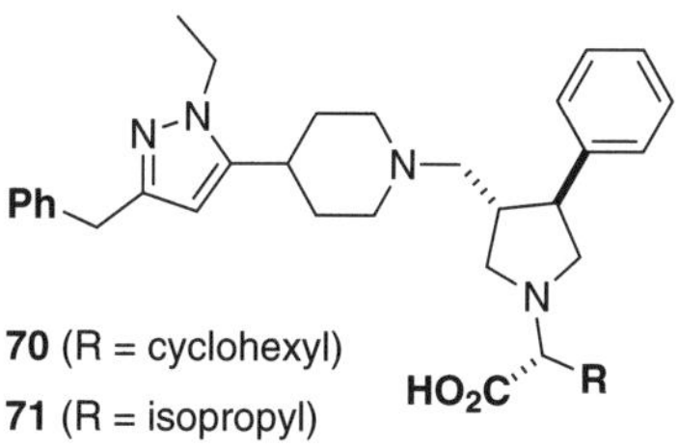

70 (R = cyclohexyl)
71 (R = isopropyl)

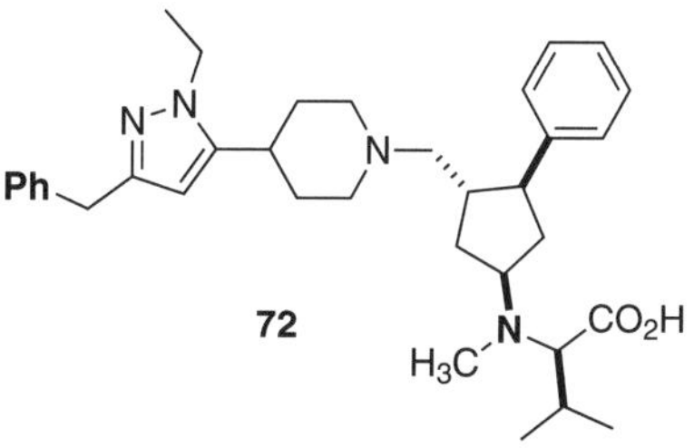

72

Figure 15. Pyrazole as a constraining element on the left side.

which was dramatically reduced by replacing the cyclohexyl ring with a simple isopropyl group as in **71** (Cl = 3.2 mL/min/kg). Efforts to diversify the core template led to an aminocyclopentane core (**72**) with potent antiviral activity (PBMC/HIV Bal: $IC_{95} < 8$ nM). When dosed at 2 mg/kg (i.v.) and 10 mg/kg (p.o.), compound **72** showed good oral bioavailability ($F = 43–66\%$) in rats, dogs, and monkeys. The absorption of this compound is limited by P-glycoprotein (PgP) efflux and it is metabolized rapidly by Cyp 3A4. Coadministration with the HIV protease inhibitor ritonavir inhibits both of these processes and substantially improves the oral exposure to compound **72**.

In an efficacy model study, compound **72** showed significant reduction in viral load in macaques infected with the simian-human immunodeficiency virus (SHIV). In this study, when the compound was applied vaginally to the monkeys prior to the viral challenge, the results seemed encouraging. This observation suggests the potential for prophylactic application of CCR5 antagonists in the form of topical microbicides (see Ref. [11], p 110–111). However, there have been no reports to date of clinical studies with compound **72** or its analogs.

6. CCR5 ANTAGONISTS BUILT AROUND AN ANILIDE CORE (Takeda)

The first CCR5 antagonist to be described in the scientific literature was **TAK-779 (81)** from Takeda Chemical Industries, Ltd. [44]. The initial lead compound **73** (Fig. 16) was discovered from high-throughput screening efforts based on the CCR5-RANTES binding assay ($IC_{50} = 390$ nM). This compound had been synthesized originally as a monocyte

chemo attractant protein (MCP-1) receptor (CCR2b) antagonist. The high level of homology (76%) between the CCR2b and the CCR5 receptors contributed to the cross-reactivity of this lead. The hit-to-lead effort found that while the piperidinium salt in structure **73** can be replaced by salts of pyrrolidine or azepane with similar IC_{50} values, quaternary salts of less basic amines (morpholine, pyridine) had diminished activity.

A variety of polar and nonpolar substituents were tolerated on the left-hand phenyl ring and the structure with a *para*-tolyl group was selected for further optimization. The cinnamyl amide **74** was less active than the dihydronaphthyl amide **73**, underscoring the importance of the ring constraint and the topology of the amide-quaternary salt moiety.

The next step in the lead identification process investigated changes to the core ring system. The benzopyran-based inhibitor **76** was more than twofold less potent than the dihydronaphthalene derivative **75**. Replacing the core dihydronaphthalene ring system (**75**) with the slightly larger [6,7]-fused benzocycloheptane (**77**) greatly increased potency as did the expansion of the benzopyran to the [6,7]-fused benzoxepine (**78**). In each case (Fig. 17), the ring enlargement resulted in an order of magnitude improvement in the affinity of the compound for CCR5. Compounds **77** and **78** were selected for the lead optimization efforts.

The distance of the quaternary amine from the amide moiety appeared to be critical; when the methylene linker connecting the quaternary nitrogen to the phenyl ring was replaced by an ethylene linker, the resulting product **79** was twofold less potent (Fig. 18).

In addition, quaternary salts of branched, bulky amines (Fig. 19) showed a further order of magnitude improvement in the inhibition of the CCR5-RANTES binding interaction.

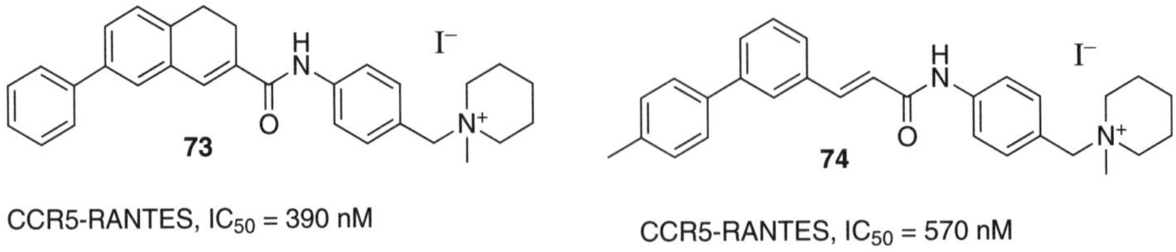

73

CCR5-RANTES, IC_{50} = 390 nM

74

CCR5-RANTES, IC_{50} = 570 nM

Figure 16. Quaternary amine salts as hits for inhibiting CCR5.

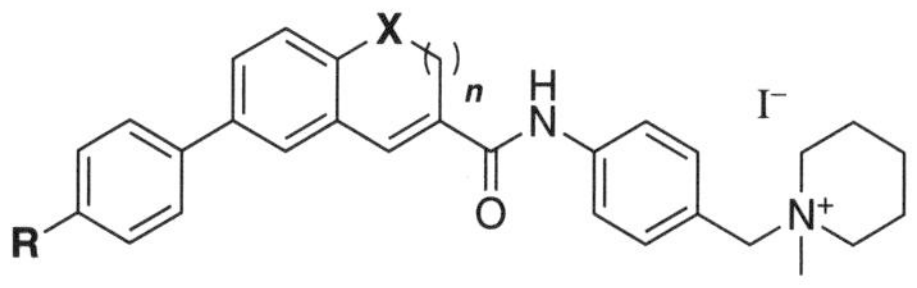

Compound	X	n	IC$_{50}$ (nM)*
75	CH$_2$	1	240
76	O	1	660
77	CH$_2$	2	25
78	O	2	43

R = CH$_3$

* CCR5-RANTES binding assay

Figure 17. Cores with larger rings enhance potency.

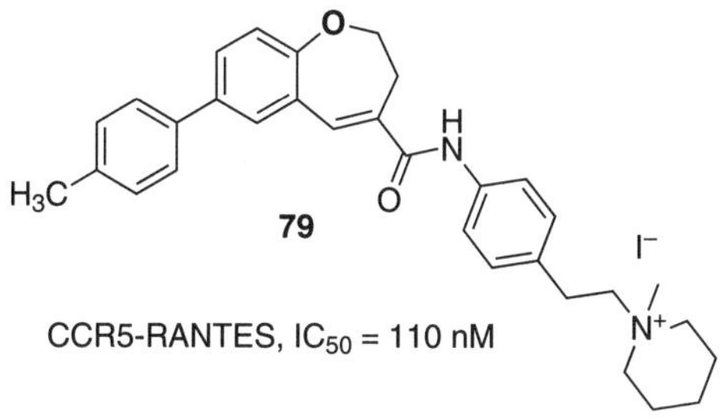

79

CCR5-RANTES, IC$_{50}$ = 110 nM

Figure 18. Importance of the length of the linker on the right side.

Notably, installing the dimethyl tetrahydropyranyl amine salt gave compounds **80** and **81** with single-digit nanomolar IC$_{50}$ values for CCR5 affinity.

Compound **81** (**TAK-779**) had a 20-fold lower affinity for the CCR2b receptor (IC$_{50}$ = 27 nM) but did not bind to other chemokine receptors (CCR1, CCR3, and CCR4). It also inhibited the replication of HIV-1 (Bal strain) in MAGI cells expressing CCR5 on their surface (EC$_{50}$ = 1.2 nM) as well as in PBMCs (EC$_{50}$ = 3.7 nM). It also had low cytotoxicity in these cells.

Based on the above data, **TAK-779 (81)** was selected for clinical evaluation via subcutaneous delivery [45]. However, this candidate was discontinued in the clinic due to the adverse event of irritation around the site of injection. The subsequent strategy was to design CCR5 antagonists based on the **TAK-779 (81)** scaffold but with good oral exposure so that they could compete with other oral therapeutic agents.

The first step was to find a replacement for the quaternary ammonium moiety, as exemplified in structures **80** and **81**, since this group most likely contributed to the poor oral absorption of these compounds. The tertiary amine **82**, which is a precursor to **81**, was nearly three orders of magnitude less potent, but gratifyingly, showed a high level of oral absorption in rats. Having established that the tertiary amine on the right side provided modest oral exposure, attention was turned to the core benzocycloheptane for further modification (Fig. 20).

The 1-benzoxepine analog **83** was nearly twice as potent as **82** but the 1-benzothiepine **84** had similar CCR5 affinity as **82**. However,

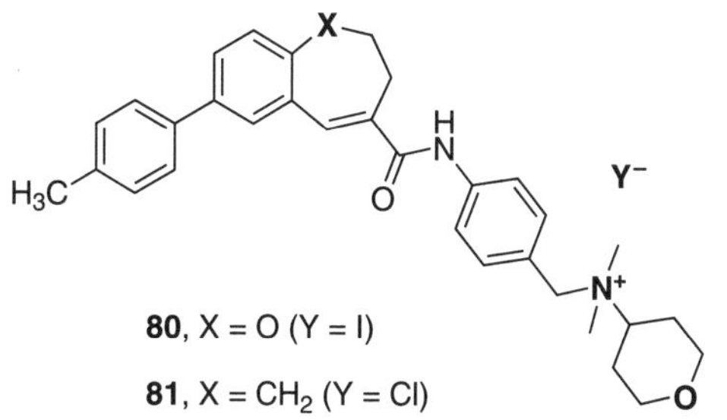

80, X = O (Y = I)

81, X = CH$_2$ (Y = Cl)

Compound	X	IC$_{50}$ (nM)*
80	O	1.4
81	CH$_2$	1.4

* CCR5-RANTES binding assay

Figure 19. Discovery of **TAK-779 (81)**.

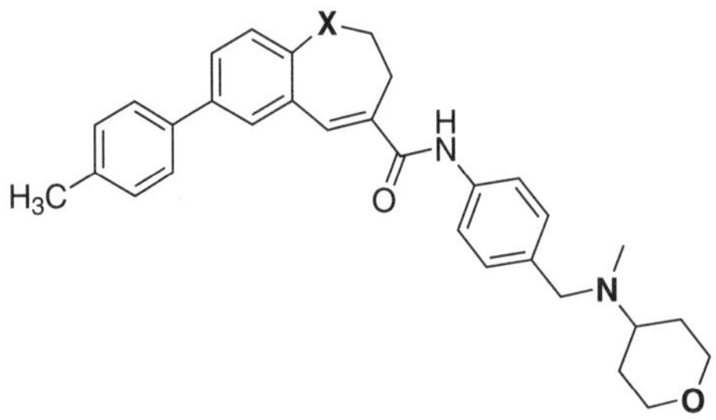

			Rat PK*	
Compound	X	IC$_{50}$ (nM)^a	AUC^b	%F^c
82	CH$_2$	950	1.03	48
83	O	530	ND	ND
84	S	800	ND	ND
85	SO	300	ND	ND
86	SO$_2$	200	1.55	52
87	N-CH$_3$	130	1.56	67

^{a}CCR5-RANTES binding assay.
^{b}AUC = mg.h/mL. ^{c}Oral bioavailability.
*Dose 10 mg/Kg, p.o.

Figure 20. Branched tertiary amines show modest oral exposure in rats.

the more polar sulfoxide (85) and sulfone (86) analogs showed increased affinity for CCR5, and the N-methyl-1-benzazepine (87) had an IC$_{50}$ = 130 nM in the CCR5-RANTES binding assay. Both the sulfone 86 and the 1-benzazepine 87 also showed slight improvements in oral exposure in rat compared to the benzocycloheptane 82 [46].

Replacement of the methyl group on the left side of the 1-benzothiepine-1,1-dioxide (86) with a propoxy group (88) resulted in a sixfold improvement in CCR5 affinity (Fig. 21). Further investigation of the SAR at this site led to the identification of the 2-(butoxy)-ethoxy group (89) as being the optimal replacement for the methyl group at this position to favorably affect potency and oral exposure in rats. The ether group (88) improved oral exposure in rat by an order of magnitude while the bis-ether (89) improved oral exposure by

two orders of magnitude over the initial lead 86 [47]. Both compounds 88 and 89 improved the CCR5 binding potency relative to 86; however, compound 89 only modestly inhibited the membrane fusion between cells expressing HIV-1 envelope and cells expressing CCR5 (EC$_{50}$ = 410 nM).

Improvements in functional potency as measured by the membrane fusion assay were achieved in the N-methyl-1-benzazepine series by replacing the 7-methyl group on the left side in 87 with the 2-(butoxy)-ethoxy group first and then modulating the size and polarity of the N1-substituent (Fig. 22). As the size of the N1-alkyl group was increased from methyl to propyl, isobutyl, and then benzyl, both CCR5 affinities in the RANTES binding assay and potency in the membrane fusion assay improved several folds to single-digit nanomolar values [47]. The reported oral exposures in

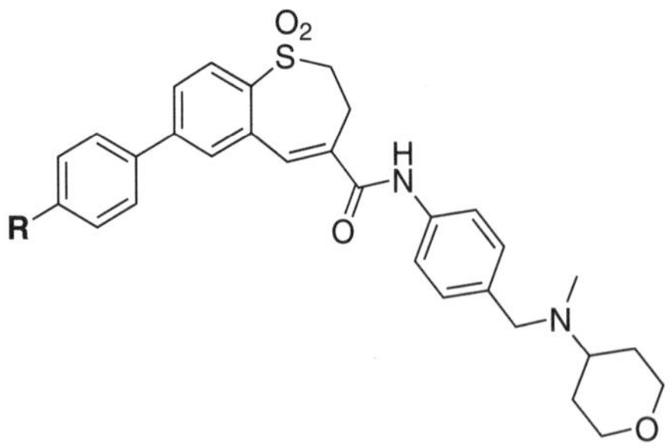

		Binding^a	Fusion^b	Rat PK^c
Compound	R	IC$_{50}$ (nM)	EC$_{50}$ (nM)	AUC
86	CH$_3$	200	ND	1.55
88	PrO	35	ND	130
89	BuO(CH$_2$)$_2$O	27	410	244

^{a}CCR5-RANTES binding assay. ^{b}HIV-CCR5 membrane fusion assay. ^{c}AUC = mg.h/mL. Dose = 10 mg/Kg, p.o.

Figure 21. Effect of a left-side ether substituent on the sulfone core.

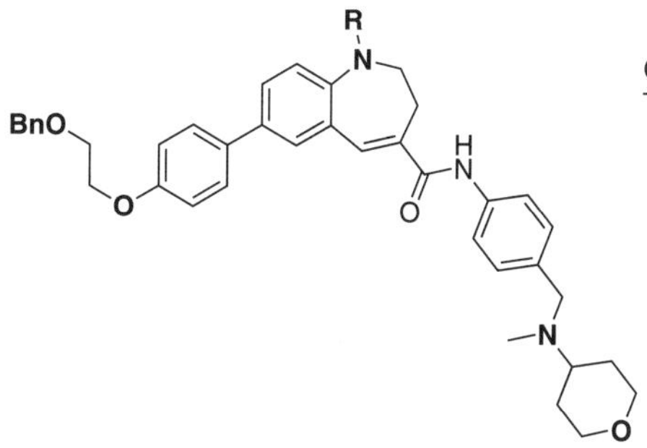

Compound	R	Binding[a] IC$_{50}$ (nM)	Fusion[b] EC$_{50}$ (nM)	Rat PK[c] AUC
90	CH$_3$	21	ND	ND
91	Pr	3.5	54	17.2
92	i-Bu	3.6	1.7	1.03
93	Bn	5.3	5.3	ND
94	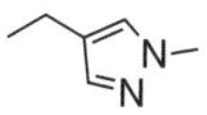	2.7	2.7	8.35

[a]CCR5-RANTES binding assay. [b]HIV-CCR5 membrane. fusion assay. [c]AUC = mg·h/mL. Dose = 10 mg/Kg, p.o.

Figure 22. Effect of *N*-substituent in 1-benzepine series.

rat for compounds **91** and **94** in this series, while significantly lower than those of the sulfone analogs discussed above, were nonetheless sufficient to cover the low EC$_{50}$ values.

In order to improve the oral exposure level in the 1-benzazepine series, SAR study was focused on the right side with the goal of replacing the tertiary amine moiety, a vestige from the **TAK-779** scaffold. This study led to the discovery of the 2-(α-hydroxy benzyl) pyridine *N*-oxide **96** with low nanomolar IC$_{50}$ and EC$_{50}$ values in the primary screens and a 30-fold improvement in oral exposure in rat compared to the corresponding tertiary amine analog **92** (Fig. 23). Notable features of the SAR development included the *S*-stereochemistry of the α-hydroxy group, which had a sixfold higher CCR5 affinity than the *R*-enantiomer, and the importance of the substituent on the right side phenyl ring (R = CF$_3$). Both of these features greatly enhanced the functional potency as measured by the HIV$_{env}$-CCR5 membrane fusion assay [48].

The discovery of **96** prompted the design and synthesis of the isosteric sulfoxide analog **97** (Fig. 24). Although compound **97** was not found to be very potent in the binding assay, introduction of a methylene linker improved the CCR5 affinity, with the linker between the sulfoxide and pyridine ring as in compound **99** being preferred. Further fine-tuning of binding potency was accomplished by replacing the *N*-propyl substituent on the 1-benzazepine with *N*-isobutyl group and by moving the pyridyl nitrogen around the ring. These changes resulted in identification of compound **101** for further SAR studies [49].

Introduction of an additional nitrogen atom in the pyridyl ring to form pyridazine, pyrazine, and pyrimidine rings was detrimental to activity. However, the 5-member heterocyclic rings such as imidazole and triazole generally had a favorable effect on the anilide sulfoxide scaffold with respect to CCR5 affinity (Fig. 25). The 1-propylimidazol-5-yl compound (**104**) showed three times more affinity

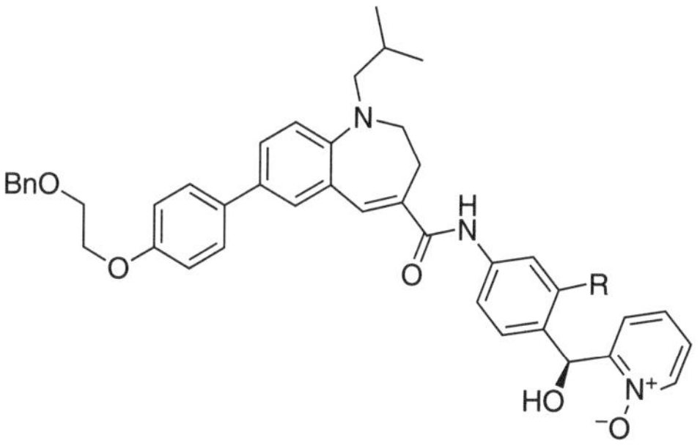

Compound	R	Binding[a] IC$_{50}$ (nM)	Fusion[b] EC$_{50}$ (nM)	Rat PK[c] AUC
95	H	15	4000	ND
96	CF$_3$	7.2	5.4	33.1

[a]CCR5-RANTES binding assay. [b]HIV-CCR5 membrane fusion assay. [c]AUC = mg·h/mL. Dose = 10 mg/Kg, p.o.

Figure 23. Pyridine *N*-oxide enhances functional potency and oral exposure.

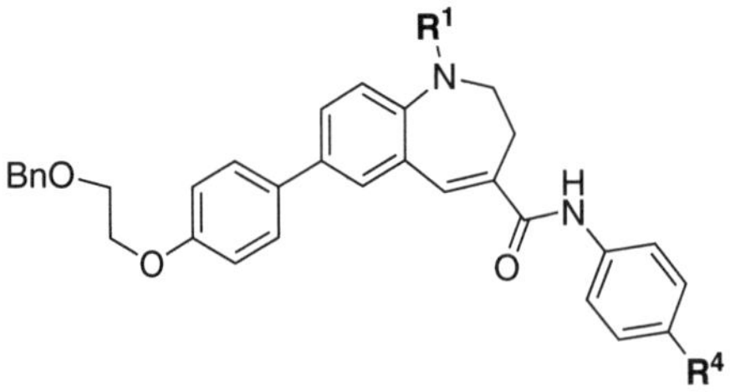

Compound	R^1	R^4	IC_{50} (nM)*
97	Pr	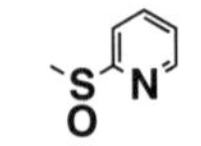	450
98	Pr	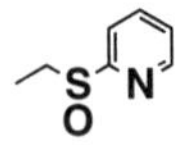	250
99	Pr	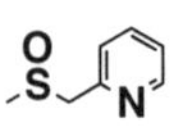	67
100	i-Bu	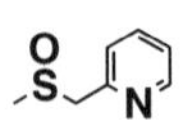	38
101	i-Bu	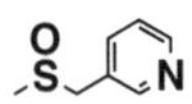	15 ←
102	i-Bu	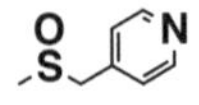	160

* CCR5-RANTES binding assay

Figure 24. Chiral sulfoxides replace benzyl carbinol.

for the target compared to the 1-propylimida-zol-2-yl isomer (**103**). Enantio-selective synthesis of both antipodes of the racemic sulfoxide **104** demonstrated that the (S)-enantiomer **105** is a very potent CCR5 antagonist and inhibitor of HIV_{env}-CCR5 membrane fusion. Surprisingly, the corresponding R-isomer (not shown), which is a weaker CCR5 antagonist, by only threefold, was extremely weak in its inhibition of membrane fusion ($IC_{50} = 6.8$ nM; $EC_{50} = 410$ nM). The 4-propyl-1,2,4-triazole analog **106** also showed potent activity. Again, the activity resided in the (S)-enantiomer of the sulfoxide (**107**), with the R-isomer showing

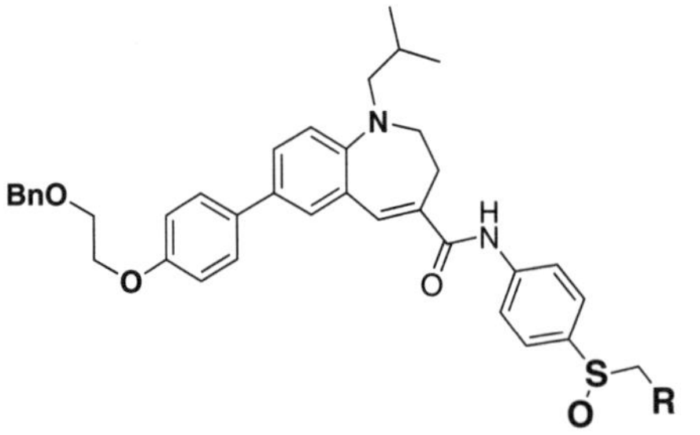

Compound	R	Binding[a] IC_{50} (nM)	Fusion[b] EC_{50} (nM)	Rat PK[c] AUC
103	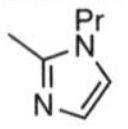	4.3	11	ND
(±)-104	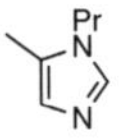	3.6	3.0	ND
(S)-105	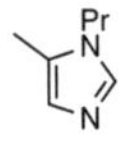	1.9	1.0	14.1
(±)-106	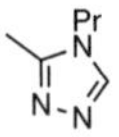	2.6	8.7	ND
(S)-107	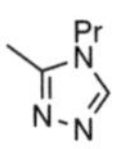	1.5	2.2	1.4

[a]CCR5-RANTES binding assay. [b]HIV-CCR5 membrane fusion assay. [c]AUC = μg·h/mL (dose = 10 mpk).

Figure 25. Five-member heteroaryl rings replace pyridine-N-oxide.

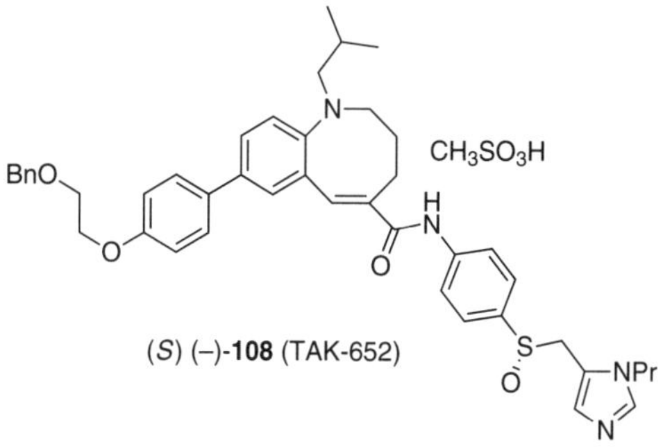

Binding, IC_{50}	Fusion, EC_{50}	HIV Replication, IC_{90}		
3 nM	0.1 nM	Mean = 0.25 nM		
Pharmacokinetics*:		Rat	Dog	Monkey
$AUC_{0-24\,h}$ (ug·h/mL):		2.3	6	0.67
Bioavailability, %F:		10	88	15

*Doses: 1 mpk, i.v.; 3 mpk, p.o.

Figure 26. Clinical candidate with anilide core (**TAK-652**).

only weak activity in the HIV-CCR5 membrane fusion assay. The enantiomeric imidazole (**105**) showed a 10-fold increase in oral exposure over the 1,2,4-triazole analog (**107**) following oral dosing in rats at 10 mg/kg. Replacement of the *N*-isobutyl group in 1-benzazepines **105** and **107** with an *n*-propyl group resulted in a large improvement on oral exposure ($AUC_{0-24\,h} = 75.1$ and $22.4\,\mu g/mL$, respectively) with only a slight decline in the antiviral potency ($EC_{50} = 2.8$ and $7.7\,nM$, respectively) [49].

The final push toward achieving subnanomolar antiviral potency (fusion assay, EC_{50}) took the form of enlarging the [6,7]-fused 1-benzazepine nucleus. A series of [6,8]-, [6,9]-, and [6,10]-fused compounds containing (*S*)-sulfoxide motifs were synthesized and evaluated. From this study, the 1-benzazocine compound (*S*)-(-)-**108** (**TAK-652**) emerged as the development candidate (Fig. 26). This compound had impressive potency in binding and antiviral assays (inhibition of membrane fusion and the replication of diverse HIV

clades in PBMC) [50,51]. It also showed good-to-excellent oral bioavailability in rat, monkey, and dog. Thus, **TAK-652** was selected for evaluation in clinical studies. It has completed a phase I trial.

Concurrently with the development of SAR in the 1-benzazepine series that led to **TAK-652**, the Takeda group also sought other novel leads that could be developed as CCR5 antagonists with oral bioavailability. Another high-throughput screening campaign resulted in compound **109**, which, interestingly, also contained the anilide motif (Fig. 27). Though **109** itself was only modestly active ($IC_{50} \sim 2\,\mu M$) in the CCR5-RANTES binding assay, the hit-to-lead part of the project found that this molecule was amenable to two point modifications. Thus, deletion of the ketone to a simple benzyl group on the right side produced compound **110** with a fourfold improvement in binding potency ($IC_{50} = 480\,nM$). On the left side, replacement of the 5-oxopyrrolidine-3-carboxamide group with other cyclic carboxamide groups identified the piperi-

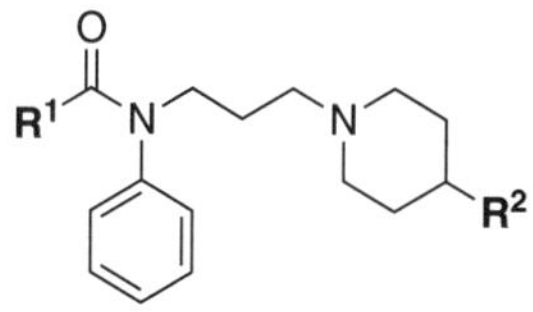

Compound	R^1	R^2	IC_{50} (nM)*
109	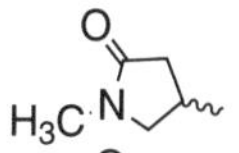	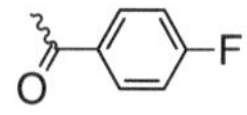	1900
110	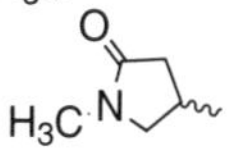	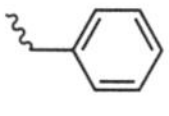	480
111	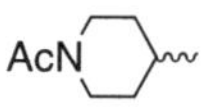	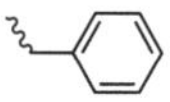	16

*CCR5-RANTES binding assay.

Figure 27. Identifying a novel anilide template that inhibits CCR5 binding.

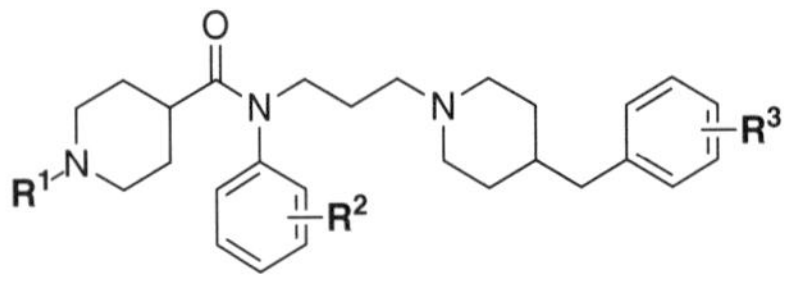

Compound	R^1	R^2	R^3	IC_{50} (nM)[a]	EC_{50} (nM)[b]
111	Ac	H	H	16	72
112	Ac	3,4-DiCl	H	1.9	4.2
113	Ac	3,4-DiCl	F	1.2	3.0
114	Ac	3-Cl,4-Me	H	0.62	0.73
115	Ac	3-Cl,4-Me	F	0.29	0.23
116	Ms	3,4-DiCl	SO_2CH_3	2.2	0.8

[a]CCR5-RANTES binding assay. [b]HIV-CCR5 membrane fusion assay.

Figure 28. Diverse substations are tolerated around the template.

dine-4-carboxamide **111** ($IC_{50} = 16$ nM) as the new lead. The corresponding piperidine-3-carboxamide analog was 40-fold less potent. The 3-carbon chain length, as depicted for **111**, was found to be optimal as the linker for the left and right side groups [52,53].

Lead optimization efforts starting with **111** found that introduction of small hydrophobic substituents (Cl, Me) on the central phenyl ring increased the binding affinity by 10-fold (Fig. 28). Addition of a 4-fluoro substituent on the right side phenyl ring further improved the binding affinity to subnanomolar levels. The antiviral potency as measured by the HIV_{env}-CCR5 membrane fusion assay correlated well with the CCR5 affinity from the RANTES binding assay.

It was found that the 4-fluoro group on the right-side benzyl could be replaced by a variety of polar and nonpolar groups while compounds retained antiviral activity. The piperidine methyl sulfonamide analog **116** had an $EC_{50} = 0.8$ nM in the fusion assay. It also inhibited the replication of HIV-1 (Ba-L strain) in human PBMCs with an EC_{50} value

of 0.59 nM. It was not cytotoxic up to a concentration of 20 µM. When administered orally in beagle dogs at 10 mg/kg, compound **116** had a peak plasma concentration (C_{max}) of 0.57 µg/mL at 4 h. The exposure as measured by AUC_{0-24h} was 8.06 µg · h/mL [55].

However, *in vitro* metabolic studies showed that compounds **115** and **116** are rapidly metabolized when incubated with human hepatic microsomes (only 47% and 62% of compound remained for **115** and **116**, respectively, after 20 min of incubation). A systematic study to decrease the lipophilicity ($c\log p$) of these compounds by introducing polar carboxamides in the right side phenyl ring identified the primary carboxamide **117** as the top compound (Fig. 29). It had a $c\log p$ value of 3.3 compared to $c\log p$ values of 5.0 and 3.9 for compounds **115** and **116**, respectively. After 20 min of incubation with microsomes, 92% of **117** remained unchanged. When tested against a panel of other chemokines, this compound did not inhibit CCR1, CCR2b, CCR3, CCR4, and CCR7, even at a concentration of 10 µM. It is notable that

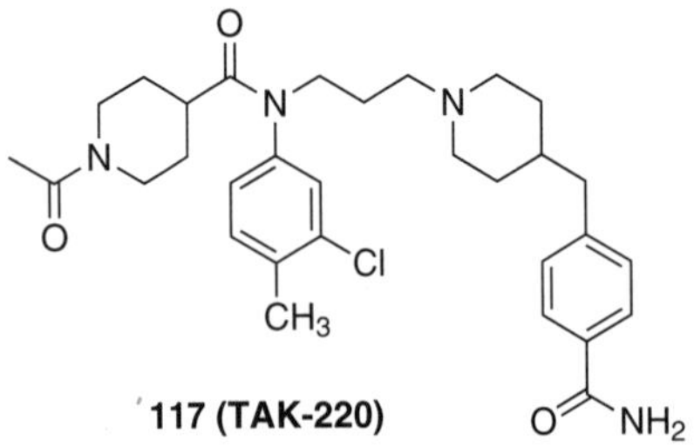

Binding, IC_{50}	Fusion, EC_{50}	HIV Replication, IC_{90}
3.5 nM	0.42 nM	Mean = 13 nM

Monkey PK (1 mpk i.v.; 5 mpk p.o.):

AUC_{0-24h} = 0.54 ug/ml; %F = 29

hu-plasma protein binding ~ 55%

117 (TAK-220)

Figure 29. Third clinical candidate with an anilide core (**TAK-220**).

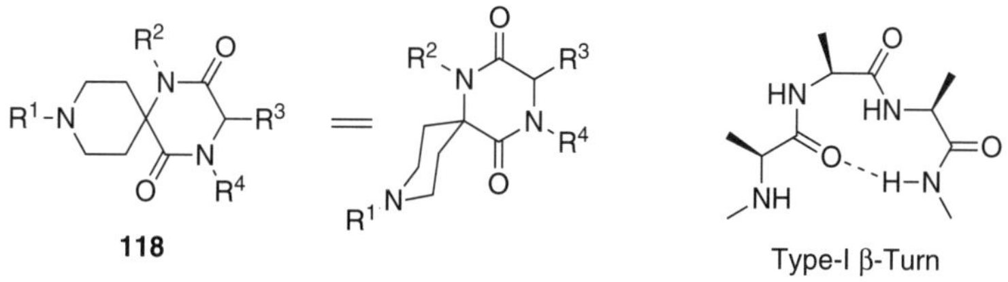

Figure 30. Proposed scaffold for library design.

compound **117** (**TAK-220**) is highly specific for its intended target CCR5 and does not inhibit CCR2b, unlike most compounds from the other series represented by **TAK-770** and **TAK-652**. **TAK-220** was therefore selected as a clinical candidate [55].

7. SPIRO DIKETOPIPERAZINE-BASED CCR5 ANTAGONISTS (Ono/GlaxoSmithKline)

The discovery of the CCR5 antagonists described thus far has followed the traditional track to lead identification through the high-throughput screening of an available compound collection toward a specific target. The research group at Ono Pharmaceuticals took an alternative approach by designing a novel combinatorial library of compounds targeting many chemokine receptors through rapid screening techniques. The hits for each chemokine target were further analyzed to refine their activity for a particular target (CCR5) by preparing more focused sublibraries in an iterative manner. Impressively, this *de novo* design approach has led to the identification of several CCR5 antagonists and eventually led to a clinical candidate [56].

The first step of their rational design process was the observation that the spiropiperidine moiety appears as an element of the pharmacophore in many privileged structures directed at various GPCR families [57].

Secondly, they selected the diketopiperazine as a template for building in diversity due to its potential for 4-point modification, ability to mimic the β-turn of a peptide, and the ease of synthesis (Fig. 30). This rational design was embedded in **118** [58].

The Ugi multiple component reaction (MCR) was used to prepare the spiro-diketo piperazines on the solid phase. Heating N-protected piperidone, various amines, and a diverse panel of N-protected amino acids over an isonitrile resin generated the 4,4-disubstituted piperidine on the solid surface. After the protecting group was removed, heating with acetic acid in toluene at 90°C resulted in cyclization to the spirodiketopiperazine and concomitant cleavage from the resin. Reductive amination of the resin-bound piperidine with a panel of aldehydes was used prior to cyclative cleavage to introduce diverse R_1-groups. When the piperidone protecting group was also BOC, this step was run in the solution phase after cleavage of the free spiropiperidine from the resin (Fig. 31).

The compound library was tested at 30 μM for inhibition of calcium mobilization against several types of human chemokine receptors over expressed on Chinese hamster ovary (CHO) cells stimulated by the corresponding endogenous ligand (for example, hMIP-1α/ CCR5). Compounds that showed >50% inhibition were resynthesized in optically pure form and the activity was confirmed by running do-

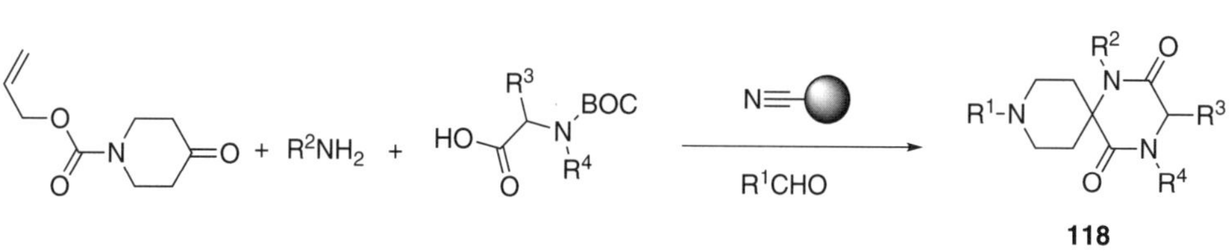

Figure 31. Solid-phase synthesis via Ugi multicomponent reaction.

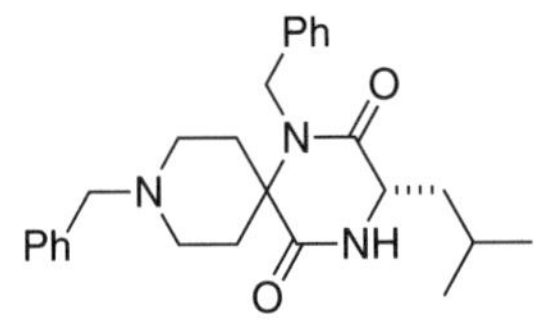

119

hMIP-1a/hCCR5, IC_{50} = 3.2 uM

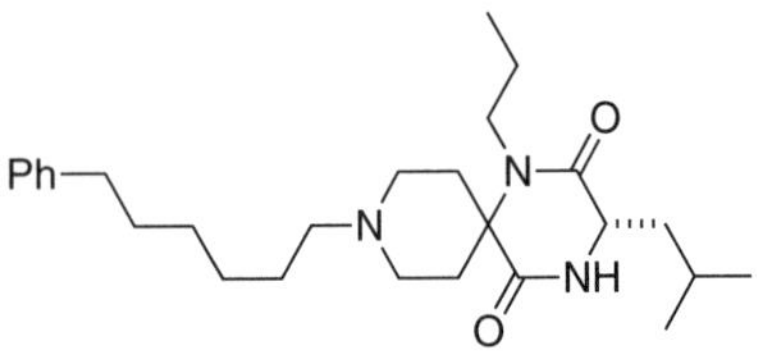

120

hMIP-1a/hCCR5, IC_{50} = 2 uM

Figure 32. New leads identified.

se–response curves in the same assay to determine IC_{50} values.

The hit-to-lead part of the program identified compounds **119** and **120**, which had modest affinity for hCCR5 but were not active at hCCR2, hCCR4, and hCXCR4 receptors. The other antipode was less active in each case (Fig. 32).

With the above two leads as the starting points, focused libraries were prepared to explore the SAR at each diversity site R_1, R_2, and R_3 ($R_4 = H$). From the R_1-library screening, SAR indicated that replacement of the benzyl or 6-phenylhexyl groups with a 4-substituted benzyl group resulted in significant improvement in binding to the target. It was also found that the piperidine nitrogen should be basic in nature given that derivatives, such as amides, sulfonamides, and urea, were less active. At the R_2-position, the n-butyl group was found to be optimal. A cyclohexyl methyl group was equipotent to the isopropyl group at the R_3-site.

After each individual site was optimized, a final library comprising of diverse combina-

tions of the optimal groups at each site was synthesized and tested. As shown by the data for selected examples below from the combination library, compounds such as **121**, **122**, and **123** (Fig. 33) with potent CCR5 affinity in the hMIP-1α/CCR5 binding assay were identified. They were also very selective for CCR5 over the other chemokine receptors (particularly CXCR4) and potently inhibited the replication of both primary and multidrug-resistant HIV-1 strains [59].

However, due to oxidative metabolism in the liver, compounds **121–123** (Fig. 33) showed low oral bioavailability in rodents. Metabolite identification following incubation with liver microsomes for 1.5 h showed that the compounds were hydroxylated in both of their alkyl side chains. Isolation and screening of the metabolites indicated that hydroxylation of the n-butyl side chain at the C3-position rendered the molecule inactive in the Ca mobilization assay. However, the products of microsomal hydroxylation of the proximal carbon on the right side in **122** improved the

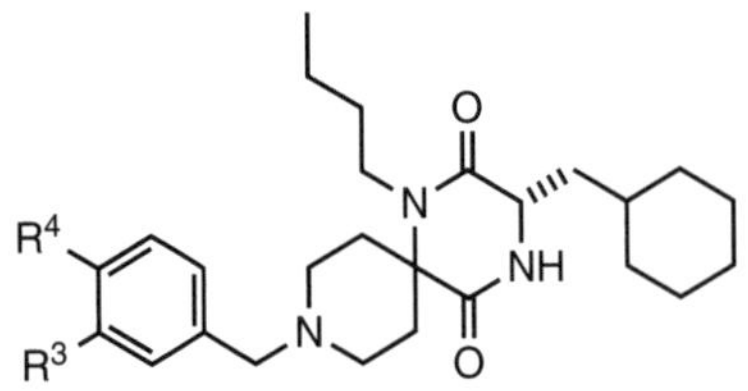

			IC_{50} (uM)	
Compound	R^3	R^4	Ca Flux[a]	MIP-1a[b]
121	H	4-OMe	0.12	0.004
122	H	4-OPh	0.17	0.006
123	$-OCH_2CH_2O-$		0.02	0.002

[a]Ca mobility assay. [b]MIP-1a/CCR5 binding assay

Figure 33. Optimized leads with potent CCR5 inhibitory activity.

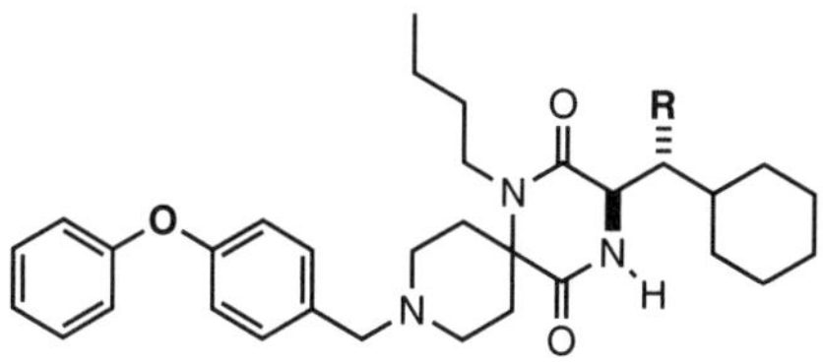

			IC$_{50}$ (nM)	
Compound	R	MIP-1a[a]	CCR5-HIV-1[b]	HIV-Bal[c]
122	H	6.1	31	337
124	OH	1.1	0.6	6.0

[a]MIP-1a/CCR5 binding assay. [b]Inhibition of HIV entry assay
[c]Inhibition of HIV-Bal replication in MAGI cells.

Figure 34. Identification of an active metabolite (**124**).

CCR5 binding potency. Metabolite characterization through synthesis identified compound **124**, as significantly more active than the other three diastereomers. Most notably, compared to the parent compound **122**, the hydroxylated analog **124** was 50 times more potent (Fig. 34) in cell-based assays for inhibiting HIV-1 entry and replication [60].

Further refinement of the left-hand-side phenyl ring led to the development of compound **125** (ONO-4128; GW 873140; aplaviroc; APV) with superior antiviral potency (Fig. 35). In clinical trials, APV was administered orally at a dose of up to 1200 mg once daily and did not show any serious adverse effects. At a dose of 600 mg twice a day for 10 days, APV produced a mean viral load reduction of 1.5 log$_{10}$. Its zwitterionic nature may have contributed to poor cell permeability and limited oral bioavailability. Unfortunately, APV was dropped from clinical development due to the observation of idiosyncratic hepatotoxicity in approximately 1% of the patients [61].

8. BINDING MODE AND MECHANISM OF ACTION OF CCR5 ANTAGONISTS

Since there is no X-ray structure for the membrane bound CCR5 receptor, a homology model of CCR5 was generated based on the crystal structure of bacterial rhodopsin. Site-directed mutagenesis combined with a CCR5 binding/HIV entry assay was used to map the putative binding site of many of the above molecules. Despite their diverse structures, they all appear to bind within a hydrophobic pocket formed by the transmembrane helices H1–H3 near the extracellular surface of the receptor (Fig. 36), whereas the N-terminus and the extracellular loops (E1–E3) are not involved in the binding of these antagonists [62–64].

Mutation of specific residues in the transmembrane domains 1, 2, 3, and 7 reduced the binding of SCH-C (**25**) to CCR5. The mutation of the E283 residue in TM7 to an alanine significantly reduced the binding potency of SCH-C, **TAK-779**, and APV, suggesting that their binding modes overlap at this point.

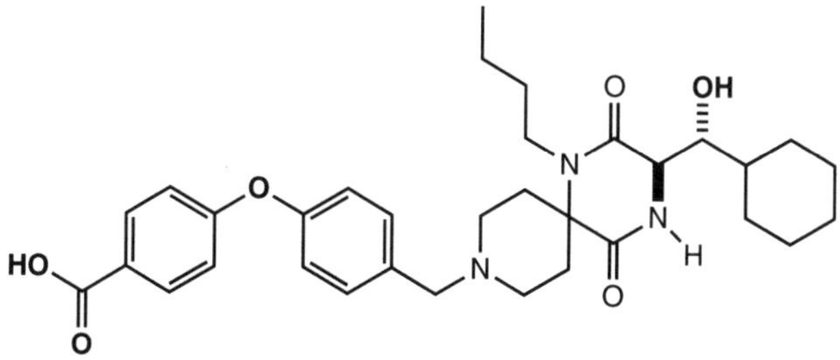

125 (ONO-4128; GW-873140; Aplaviroc)   Anti-HIV1 (Bal), IC$_{50}$ = 0.4 nM

Figure 35. Clinical candidate aplaviroc (APV, **125**)

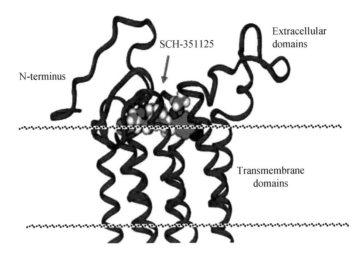

Figure 36. Binding mode of CCR5 antagonists. Reprinted from Ref. [11]. © 2008, Elsevier, Inc. (See color insert.)

However, some of the other mutations affected the binding potency of only one of these three compounds. Taken together, these studies show that while the binding sites of these small molecules overlap, they are not identical. This suggests a high barrier to the development of resistance, as it would require multiple mutations. Though resistance to CCR5 antagonists *in vitro* can be generated following numerous passages, these mutations tend to be strain specific and the resistance is compound specific [65–68]. However, reports on cross-resistance have been inconsistent so far.

Mechanistically, small-molecule CCR5 inhibitors are functional antagonists that can inhibit receptor internalization induced by chemokine agonists. Since they bind deep inside an allosteric cavity formed by the extracellular loops, they are unlikely to compete with gp120 for CCR5 binding. The small-molecule CCR5 antagonists described herein seem to inhibit HIV infection by stabilizing a conformation of CCR5 receptor that is unfavorable for gp120 binding.

SUMMARY

The six case histories of diverse CCR5 antagonists described herein serve as prime examples of the process of modern drug discovery. Many of the techniques used today in the pharmaceutical industry were established during the era when these compounds were identified. For example, the following methods have all become common practice in the past decade: development of parallel and combinatorial synthetic methods to prepare small- and medium-sized libraries of compounds and their rapid screening; the screening of low-molecular-weight compound fragments to identify new leads for further optimization; realization of the value of in house privileged structures for generating leads for new programs; the refinement of binding, chemotaxis and reporter gene assays for lead optimization; the development of rapid pharmacokinetic determination whereby pooled samples of plasma taken shortly after the dosing of two animals can be used to predict oral exposure levels for a new compound; and use of metabolite identification techniques to generate new lead compounds with improved oral exposure. In addition, adverse events, such as the formation of acyl glucuronide and QT_c prolongation, have prompted studies to better understand the causes underlying these adverse effects and have resulted in efforts to correct them. Screening compounds for hERG channel binding activity in order to identify the potential for QT_c prolongation in the clinic is now part of every drug discovery paradigm. Homology models have been developed to understand the similarities and subtle differences in the binding modes of these diverse structures and how resistance might result from a decrease in binding ability; such an understanding might help overcome issues of resistance. As shown for maraviroc and vicriviroc, designing compounds with improved selectivity for the desired target and minimizing off-target binding can improve the side effect profile of compounds. Maraviroc (Selzentry) has been approved by the FDA and other regulatory agencies for clinical use as an anti-HIV agent. It is hoped that others from the above short list would soon follow.

This chapter is dedicated to the scientists behind these great discoveries at various organizations, whose creativity, hard work, motivation, and perseverance in the face of setbacks has advanced our understanding of the treatment of HIV/AIDS and hopefully will improve outcomes for patients suffering from this devastating condition.

ACKNOWLEDGMENTS

I thank Dr. Julie Strizki (Schering Plough Research Institute) for many discussions on CCR5 antagonists and for providing Figs 1 and 36. Thanks are also due to Dr. David Rotella (Wyeth-Pfizer) for the invitation to write this chapter.

REFERENCES

1. World Health Organization. AIDS epidemic update, December 2005: UNAIDS/03.39E. Available at www.who.int/hiv/epi-update 2005_en.pdf. Accessed 2009 May 21.

2. Richman DD. HIV chemotherapy. Nature 2001; 410(6831): 995–1001.

3. Fauci AS. HIV and AIDS: 20 years of science. Nat Med 2003;9(7): 839–843.

4. Carr A. Toxicity of antiretroviral therapy and implications for drug development. Nat Rev Drug Discov 2003;2(8): 624–634.

5. Duran S, Savès M, Spire B, Cailleton V, Sobel A, Carrieri P, Salmon D, Moatti JP, Leport C, APROCO Study Group. Failure to maintain long-term adherence to highly active antiretroviral therapy: the role of lipodystrophy. AIDS 2001;15(18): 2441–2444.

6. Fumero E, Podzamczer D. New patterns of HIV-1 resistance during HAART. Clin Microbiol Infect 2003;9(11): 1077–1084.

7. Ickovics JR, Meade CS. Adherence to HAART among patients with HIV: breakthroughs and barriers. AIDS Care. 2002;14(3): 309–318.

8. LaBonte J, Lebbos J, Kirkpatrick P, Enfuvirtide. Nat Rev Drug Discov 2003;2(5): 345–346.

9. Esté JA. Virus entry as a target for anti-HIV intervention. Curr Med Chem 2003;10(17): 1617–1632.

10. Berger EA, Murphy PM, Farber JM. Chemokine receptors as HIV-1 coreceptors: roles in viral entry, tropism, and disease. Annu Rev Immunol 1999;17:657–700.

11. Strizki J, Targeting HIV attachment and entry for therapy. Adv Pharmacol 2008;56:93–120.

12. Kazmierski W, Bifulco N, Yang H, Boone L, DeAnda F, Watson C, Kenakin T. Recent progress in discovery of small-molecule CCR5 chemokine receptor ligands as HIV-1 inhibitors. Bioorg Med Chem 2003;11(13): 2663–2676.

13. Maeda K, Nakata H, Ogata H, Koh Y, Miyakawa T, Mitsuya H. The current status of, and challenges in, the development of CCR5 inhibitors as therapeutics for HIV-1 infection. Curr Opin Pharmacol 2004;4(5): 447–452.

14. Barber CG. CCR5 antagonists for the treatment of HIV. Curr Opin Investig Drugs 2004;5(8): 851–861.

15. Rusconi S, Scozzafava A, Mastrolorenzo A, Supuran CT. New advances in HIV entry inhibitors development. Curr Drug Targets Infect Disord 2004;4(4): 339–355.

16. Barbaro G, Scozzafava A, Mastrolorenzo A, Supuran CT. Highly active antiretroviral therapy: current state of the art, new agents and their pharmacological interactions useful for improving therapeutic outcome. Curr Pharm Des 2005;11(14): 1805–1843.

17. Duan M, Feldman PL, Gudmundsson KS, Jenkinson S, Kazmierski WM, Kenakin TP, Peckham JP, Piscitelli SC. Recent progress in the discovery of new CCR5 and CXCR4 chemokine receptor antagonists as inhibitors of HIV-1 entry. Part 2. Curr Med Chem Anti-infective agents 4(2): 2005; 133–152.

18. Westby M, van der Ryst E. CCR5 antagonists: host-targeted antivirals for the treatment of HIV infection. Antivir Chem Chemother 2005;16(6): 339–354.

19. Lyle TA, Miller MD. New developments in HIV therapeutics. In: Annette MD, editor. Annual Reports of Medicinal Chemistry. Vol. 40:

Kidlington, Oxford: Academic Press; 2005; 293–300.

20. Palani A, Tagat JR. Discovery and development of small-molecule chemokine coreceptor CCR5 antagonists. J Med Chem 2006;49(10): 2851–2857.

21. Kazmierski WM, Gudmundsson KS, Piscitelli SC. Small molecule CCR5 and CXCR4-Based viral entry inhibitors for anti-HIV therapy currently in development. In: Annette MD, editor. Annual Reports of Medicinal Chemistry Vol. 42:Kidlington, Oxford: Academic Press; 2007; 301–320.

22. Cocchi F, DeVico AL, Garzino-Demo A, Arya SK, Gallo RC, Lusso P. Identification of RANTES, MIP-1 alpha, and MIP-1 beta as the major HIV-suppressive factors produced by CD8+ T cells. Science 1995;270(5243): 1811–1815.

23. Alkhatib G, Combadiere C, Broder CC, Feng Y, Kennedy PE, Murphy PM, Berger EA. CC CKR5: a RANTES, MIP-1alpha, MIP-1beta receptor as a fusion cofactor for macrophage-tropic HIV-1. Science 1996;272(5270): 1955–1958.

24. Simmons G, Clapham PR, Picard L, Offord RE, Rosenkilde MM, Schwartz TW, Buser R, Wells TN, Proudfoot AE. Potent inhibition of HIV-1 infectivity in macrophages and lymphocytes by a novel CCR5 antagonist. Science 1997;276 (5310): 276–279.

25. Liu R, Paxton WA, Choe S, Ceradini D, Martin SR, Horuk R, MacDonald ME, Stuhlmann H, Koup RA, Landau NR. Homozygous defect in HIV-1 coreceptor accounts for resistance of some multiply-exposed individuals to HIV-1 infection. Cell 1996;86(3): 367–377.

26. Dean M, Carrington M, Winkler C, Huttley GA, Smith MW, Allikmets R, Goedert JJ, Buchbinder SP, Vittinghoff E, Gomperts E, Donfield S, Vlahov D, Kaslow R, Saah A, Rinaldo C, Detels R, O'Brien SJ. Genetic restriction of HIV-1 infection and progression to AIDS by a deletion allele of the CKR5 structural gene. Hemophilia Growth and Development Study, Multicenter AIDS Cohort Study, Multicenter Hemophilia Cohort Study, San Francisco City Cohort, ALIVE Study. Science 1996;273(5283): 1856–1862.

27. Connor RI, Sheridan KE, Ceradini D, Choe S, Landau NR. Change in coreceptor use correlates with disease progression in HIV-1-infected individuals. J Exp Med 1997;185(4): 621–628.

28. de Roda Husman AM, Schuitemaker H. Chemokine receptors and the clinical course of HIV-1 infection. Trends Microbiol 1998;6(6): 244–249.

29. Schlyer S, Horuk R. I want a new drug: G-protein-coupled receptors in drug development. Drug Discov Today 2006;11(11–12): 481–493.

30. Palani A, Shapiro S, Clader JW, Greenlee WJ, Cox K, Strizki J, Endres M, Baroudy BM. Discovery of 4-[(Z)-(4-bromophenyl)-(ethoxyimino) methyl]-1'-[(2,4-dimethyl-3-pyridinyl)carbonyl]-4'-methyl-1,4'-bipiperidine N-oxide (SCH 351125): an orally bioavailable human CCR5 antagonist for the treatment of HIV infection. J Med Chem 2001;44(21): 3339–3342.

31. Strizki JM, Xu S, Wagner NE, Wojcik L, Liu J, Hou Y, Endres M, Palani A, Shapiro S, Clader JW, Greenlee WJ, Tagat JR, McCombie S, Cox K, Fawzi AB, Chou CC, Pugliese-Sivo C, Davies L, Moreno ME, Ho DD, Trkola A, Stoddart CA, Moore JP, Reyes GR, Baroudy BM. SCH-C (SCH 351125), an orally bioavailable, small molecule antagonist of the chemokine receptor CCR5, is a potent inhibitor of HIV-1 infection *in vitro* and *in vivo*. Proc Natl Acad Sci USA 2001;98(22): 12718–12723.

32. Reynes J, Rouzier R, Kanouni T, Baillat V, Baroudy B, Keung A, Hogan C, Markowitz M, Laughlin M. SCH-C: safety and antiviral effects of a CCR5 receptor antagonist in HIV-1 infected subjects. Proceedings of the 9th Conference on Retroviruses and Opportunistic Infections, Seattle, WA. February 24–28, 2002; Abstract 1.

33. Palani A, Shapiro S, Clader JW, Greenlee WJ, Vice S, McCombie S, Cox K, Strizki J, Baroudy BM. Oximino-piperidino-piperidine-based CCR5 antagonists. Part 2. Synthesis, SAR and biological evaluation of symmetrical heteroaryl carboxamides. Bioorg Med Chem Lett 2003;13(4): 709–712.

34. Tagat JR, McCombie SW, Steensma RW, Lin S, Nazareno DV, Baroudy B, Vantuno N, Xu S, Liu J. Piperazine-based CCR5 antagonists as HIV-1 inhibitors. I. 2(S)-methyl piperazine as a key pharmacophore element. Bioorg Med Chem Lett 2001;11(16): 2143–2146.

35. Tagat JR, Steensma RW, McCombie SW, Nazareno DV, Lin SI, Neustadt BR, Cox K, Xu S, Wojcik L, Murray MG, Vantuno N, Baroudy BM, Strizki JM. Piperazine-based CCR5 antagonists as HIV-1 inhibitors. II. Discovery of 1-[(2,4-dimethyl-3-pyridinyl)carbonyl]-4-methyl-4-[3(S)-methyl-4-[1(S)-[4-(trifluoromethyl)phenyl]ethyl]-1-piperazinyl]-piperidine N1-oxide (Sch-350634), an orally bioavailable, potent CCR5 antagonist. J Med Chem 2001; 44 (21):3343–3346.

36. McCombie SW, Tagat JR, Vice SF, Lin SI, Steensma R, Palani A, Neustadt BR, Baroudy BM, Strizki JM, Endres M, Cox K, Dan N, Chou CC. Piperazine-based CCR5 antagonists as HIV-1 inhibitors. III. Synthesis, antiviral and pharmacokinetic profiles of symmetrical het-

eroaryl carboxamides. Bioorg Med Chem Lett 2003;13(3): 567–571.

37. Tagat JR, McCombie SW, Nazareno D, Labroli MA, Xiao Y, Steensma RW, Strizki JM, Baroudy BM, Cox K, Lachowicz J, Varty G, Watkins R. Piperazine-based CCR5 antagonists as HIV-1 inhibitors. IV. Discovery of 1-[(4,6-dimethyl-5-pyrimidinyl)carbonyl]-4-[4-[2-methoxy-1(R)-4-(trifluoromethyl)phenyl]ethyl-3(S)-methyl-1-piperazinyl]-4-methylpiperidine (Sch-417690/Sch-D), a potent, highly selective, and orally bioavailable CCR5 antagonist. J Med Chem 2004;47(10): 2405–2408.

38. Strizki JM, Tremblay C, Xu S, Wojcik L, Wagner N, Gonsiorek W, Hipkin RW, Chou CC, Pugliese-Sivo C, Xiao Y, Tagat JR, Cox K, Priestley T, Sorota S, Huang W, Hirsch M, Reyes GR, Baroudy BM. Discovery and characterization of vicriviroc (SCH 417690), a CCR5 antagonist with potent activity against human immunodeficiency virus type 1. Antimicrob Agents Chemother 2005;49(12): 4911–4919.

39. Schurmann D, Rouzier R, Nougarede R, Reynes J, Fatkenheuer G, Raffi F, Michelet C, Tarral A, Hoffmann C, Kiunke J, Sprenger H, vanLier J, Sansone A, Jackson M, Laughlin M. SCH D: antiviral activity of a CCR5 receptor antagonist. Proceedings of the 11th Conference on Retroviruses and Opportunistic Infections, Seattle, WA. February 8–11, 2004; Abstract 140LB.

40. Wood A, Armour D. The discovery of the CCR5 receptor antagonist, UK-427,857, a new agent for the treatment of HIV infection and AIDS. Prog Med Chem 2005;43:239–271.

41. Price DA, Armour D, de Groot M, Leishman D, Napier C, Perros M, Stammen BL, Wood A. Overcoming hERG affinity in the discovery of the CCR5 antagonist maraviroc. Bioorg Med Chem Lett 2006;16(17): 4633–4637.

42. Pozniak Al Fatkenheuer G, Johnson M, Hoepelman I, Rockstroh J, Goebel F, Abel S, James I, Rosario M, Medhurst C, Sullivan J, Youle M, Van Der Ryst E. Effect of short-term monotherapy with UK-427,857 on viral load in HIV-infected patients. Proceedings of the 43rd Interscience Conference on Antimicrobial Agents and Chemotherapy (ICAAC), Chicago, IL September 14–17, 2003; Abstract H-443.

43. Mills SG, DeMartino JA. Chemokine receptor-directed agents as novel anti-HIV-1 therapies. Curr Top Med Chem 2004;4(10): 1017–1033.

44. Baba M, Nishimura O, Kanzaki N, Okamoto M, Sawada H, Iizawa Y, Shiraishi M, Aramaki Y, Okonogi K, Ogawa Y, Meguro K, Fujino M. A small-molecule, nonpeptide CCR5 antagonist with highly potent and selective anti-HIV-1 activity. Proc Natl Acad Sci USA 1999;96(10): 5698–5703.

45. Shiraishi M, Aramaki Y, Seto M, Imoto H, Nishikawa Y, Kanzaki N, Okamoto M, Sawada H, Nishimura O, Baba M, Fujino M. Discovery of novel, potent, and selective small-molecule CCR5 antagonists as anti-HIV-1 agents: synthesis and biological evaluation of anilide derivatives with a quaternary ammonium moiety. J Med Chem 2000;43(10): 2049–2063.

46. Aramaki Y, Seto M, Okawa T, Oda T, Kanzaki N, Shiraishi M. Synthesis of 1-benzothiepine and 1-benzazepine derivatives as orally active CCR5 antagonists. Chem Pharm Bull 2004; 52 (2):254–258.

47. Seto M, Aramaki Y, Okawa T, Miyamoto N, Aikawa K, Kanzaki N, Niwa S, Iizawa Y, Baba M, Shiraishi M. Orally active CCR5 antagonists as anti-HIV-1 agents: synthesis and biological activity of 1-benzothiepine 1,1-dioxide and 1-benzazepine derivatives containing a tertiary amine moiety. Chem Pharm Bull 2004;52(5): 577–590.

48. Seto M, Aramaki Y, Imoto H, Aikawa K, Oda T, Kanzaki N, Iizawa Y, Baba M, Shiraishi M. Orally active CCR5 antagonists as anti-HIV-1 agents. Part 2. Synthesis and biological activities of anilide derivatives containing a pyridine N-oxide moiety. Chem Pharm Bull 2004;52(7): 818–829.

49. Seto M, Miyamoto N, Aikawa K, Aramaki Y, Kanzaki N, Iizawa Y, Baba M, Shiraishi M. Orally active CCR5 antagonists as anti-HIV-1 agents. Part 3. Synthesis and biological activities of 1-benzazepine derivatives containing a sulfoxide moiety. Bioorg Med Chem 2005;13(2): 363–386.

50. Baba M, Takashima K, Miyake H, Kanzaki N, Teshima K, Wang X, Shiraishi M, Iizawa Y. TAK-652 inhibits CCR5-mediated human immunodeficiency virus type 1 infection *in vitro* and has favorable pharmacokinetics in humans. Antimicrob Agents Chemother 2005;49(11): 4584–4591.

51. Seto M, Aikawa K, Miyamoto N, Aramaki Y, Kanzaki N, Takashima K, Kuze Y, Iizawa Y, Baba M, Shiraishi M. Highly potent and orally active CCR5 antagonists as anti-HIV-1 agents: synthesis and biological activities of 1-benzazocine derivatives containing a sulfoxide moiety. J Med Chem 2006;49(6): 2037–2048.

52. Imamura S, Ishihara Y, Hattori T, Kurasawa O, Matsushita Y, Sugihara Y, Kanzaki N, Iizawa Y, Baba M, Hashiguchi S. CCR5 antagonists as anti-HIV-1 agents. 1. Synthesis and biological

evaluation of 5-oxopyrrolidine-3-carboxamide derivatives. Chem Pharm Bull 2004;52(1): 63–73.

53. Imamura S, Kurasawa O, Nara Y, Ichikawa T, Nishikawa Y, Iida T, Hashiguchi S, Kanzaki N, Iizawa Y, Baba M, Sugihara Y. CCR5 antagonists as anti-HIV-1 agents. Part 2. Synthesis and biological evaluation of N-[3-(4-benzylpiperidin-1-yl)propyl]-N,N'-diphenylureas. Bioorg Med Chem 2004;12(9): 2295–2306.

54. Imamura S, Nishikawa Y, Ichikawa T, Hattori T, Matsushita Y, Hashiguchi S, Kanzaki N, Iizawa Y, Baba M, Sugihara Y. CCR5 antagonists as anti-HIV-1 agents. Part 3. Synthesis and biological evaluation of piperidine-4-carboxamide derivatives. Bioorg Med Chem 2005;13(2): 397–416.

55. Imamura S, Ichikawa T, Nishikawa Y, Kanzaki N, Takashima K, Niwa S, Iizawa Y, Baba M, Sugihara Y. Discovery of a piperidine-4-carboxamide CCR5 antagonist (TAK-220) with highly potent anti-HIV-1 activity. J Med Chem 2006; 49(9): 2784–2793.

56. Maeda K, Yoshimura K, Shibayama S, Habashita H, Tada H, Sagawa K, Miyakawa T, Aoki M, Fukushima D, Mitsuya H. Novel low molecular weight spirodiketopiperazine derivatives potently inhibit R5 HIV-1 infection through their antagonistic effects on CCR5. J Biol Chem 2001;276(37): 35194–35200.

57. Patchett AA, Nargund RP. Privileged structures: an update. Ann Rep Med Chem 2000; 35:289–298.

58. Fischer PM. Diketopiperazines in peptide and combinatorial chemistry. J Pept Sci 2003;9(1): 9–35.

59. Habashita H, Kokubo M, Hamano S, Hamanaka N, Toda M, Shibayama S, Tada H, Sagawa K, Fukushima D, Maeda K, Mitsuya H. Design, synthesis, and biological evaluation of the combinatorial library with a new spirodiketopiperazine scaffold. Discovery of novel potent and selective low-molecular-weight CCR5 antagonists. J Med Chem 2006;49(14): 4140–4152.

60. Nishizawa R, Nishiyama T, Hisaichi K, Matsunaga N, Minamoto C, Habashita H, Takaoka Y, Toda M, Shibayama S, Tada H, Sagawa K, Fukushima D, Maeda K, Mitsuya H. Spirodiketopiperazine-based CCR5 antagonists: lead optimization from biologically active metabolite. Bioorg Med Chem Lett 2007;17(3): 727–731.

61. Steel HM. Special presentation on aplaviroc-related hepatotoxicity. Program and abstracts of the European AIDS Clinical Society 10th European AIDS Conference, Dublin, Ireland. November 17–20, 2005; Special presentation.

62. Seibert C, Sakmar TP. Small-molecule antagonists of CCR5 and CXCR4: a promising new class of anti-HIV-1 drugs. Curr Pharm Des 2004;10(17): 2041–2062.

63. Seibert C, Ying W, Gavrilov S, Tsamis F, Kuhmann SE, Palani A, Tagat JR, Clader JW, McCombie SW, Baroudy BM, Smith SO, Dragic T, Moore JP, Sakmar TP. Interaction of small molecule inhibitors of HIV-1 entry with CCR5. Virology 2006;349(1): 41–54.

64. Maeda K, Das D, Ogata-Aoki H, Nakata H, Miyakawa T, Tojo Y, Norman R, Takaoka Y, Ding J, Arnold GF, Arnold E, Mitsuya H. Structural and molecular interactions of CCR5 inhibitors with CCR5. J Biol Chem 2006;281(18): 12688–12698.

65. Trkola A, Kuhmann SE, Strizki JM, Maxwell E, Ketas T, Morgan T, Pugach P, Xu S, Wojcik L, Tagat J, Palani A, Shapiro S, Clader JW, McCombie S, Reyes GR, Baroudy BM, Moore JP. HIV-1 escape from a small molecule, CCR5-specific entry inhibitor does not involve CXCR4 use. Proc Natl Acad Sci USA 2002;99(1): 395–400.

66. Baba M, Miyake H, Wang X, Okamoto M, Takashima K. Isolation and characterization of human immunodeficiency virus type 1 resistant to the small-molecule CCR5 antagonist TAK-652. Antimicrob Agents Chemother 2007;51(2): 707–715.

67. Marozsan AJ, Kuhmann SE, Morgan T, Herrera C, Rivera-Troche E, Xu S, Baroudy BM, Strizki J, Moore JP. Generation and properties of a human immunodeficiency virus type 1 isolate resistant to the small molecule CCR5 inhibitor, SCH-417690 (SCH-D). Virology 2005;338(1): 182–199.

68. Westby M, Smith-Burchnell C, Mori J, Lewis M, Mosley M, Stockdale M, Dorr P, Ciaramella G, Perros M. Reduced maximal inhibition in phenotypic susceptibility assays indicates that viral strains resistant to the CCR5 antagonist maraviroc utilize inhibitor-bound receptor for entry. J Virol 2007;81(5): 2359–2371.

HIV REVERSE TRANSCRIPTASE INHIBITORS

Erik De Clercq

Rega Institute for Medical Research,
K.U. Leuven, Leuven, Belgium

1. INTRODUCTION

The first antiviral compound ever shown to be active *in vitro* against HIV (human immunodeficiency virus) (originally referred to as HTLV-III (human lymphotropic virus type III) and LAV-1 (lymphadenopathy-associated virus type 1)) was suramin [1]; suramin was also the first antiviral found to be effective *in vivo* in the treatment of HIV infections [2]. Suramin was explored as a potential strategy for the therapy of AIDS because it has been recognized as a potent inhibitor of the reverse transcriptase (RT) associated with a number of animal retroviruses [3]. Later, it became evident that suramin primarily acts against HIV infections as an inhibitor of virus adsorption rather than an RT inhibitor [4].

Incidentally, the polyoxometalate HPA-23 was also reported to be effective against HIV infection in 1985 [5] based on its RT-inhibitory activity, although HPA-23, akin to suramin, and many other polyoxometalates, were later shown to primarily act as inhibitors of virus adsorption [6]. Thus, the first HIV inhibitors ever reported to exhibit anti-HIV activity presumably because they interfered with RT, could not be considered as genuine RT inhibitors but nevertheless they paved the way for the discovery of an almost uncountable array of RT inhibitors which would be later divided into nucleoside RT inhibitors (NRTIs), nucleotide RT inhibitors (NtRTIs), and nonnucleoside RT inhibitors (NNRTIs) and which, as of today, represent about half of the 25 compounds that have been officially approved for the treatment of HIV infections.

Even before suramin or HPA-23 had ever a chance to be fully explored for their potential in the treatment of HIV infections, azidothymidine (AZT, zidovudine) came along in 1985 [7] as a novel anti-HIV agent targeted at the HIV RT [8], and following AZT several other $2',3'$-dideoxynucleoside (ddN) analogs, that is, ddI (didanosine) and ddC (dideoxycytidine) were recognized in 1986 as effective NRTIs [9], and were later marketed as anti-HIV drugs.

The discovery of AZT as an anti-HIV agent ignited the search for new ddN analogs, soon culminating in 1986 in the discovery of d4C ($2',3'$-dideoxy-$2',3'$-didehydrocytidine) [10] which was not further developed, and d4T ($2',3'$-dideoxy-$2',3'$-didehydrothymidine [11], which was efficiently developed into an anti-HIV drug (stavudine). The anti-HIV activity of d4T as originally demonstrated by Baba et al. [11] was confirmed by Hamamoto et al. [12] and Lin et al. [13], and d4T (stavudine) became, following AZT, ddI and ddC, the fourth NRTI to be launched for the treatment of HIV infections.

As the numbers five, six, and seven of the NRTIs presently approved for the treatment of HIV infections, emerged lamivudine (3TC), originally discovered as $2'$-deoxy-$3'$-thiacytidine (BCH-189) by the late Bernard Belleau in 1989 [14], abacavir, originally described by the late Susan Daluge and her coworkers at Glaxo Wellcome in the 1990s [15] and emtricitabine ((−)FTC), also originally described in the 1990s by Schinazi and his colleagues [16–18].

The first NtRTI to be mentioned for its antiretroviral activity was PMEA [adefovir, 9-(2-phosphonylmethoxyethyl)adenine] in 1986, in a paper that primarily dealt with the broad-spectrum anti-DNA virus activity of (S)-HPMPA [(S)-9-(3-hydroxy-2-phosphonylmethoxypropyl)adenine] [19]. The *in vitro* and *in vivo* antiretroviral properties of PMEA were further documented by Pauwels et al. [20] and Balzarini et al. [21]. While adefovir was originally developed as a potential anti-HIV agent, it was eventually superseded for this purpose by tenofovir [(R)-9-(2-phosphonylmethoxypropyl)adenine, (R)-PMPA] that was first described as an antiretroviral agent in 1993 [22]. Tenofovir in its oral prodrug form tenofovir disoproxil fumarate (TDF) has become the cornerstone in the treatment of HIV infections: it is now available in three formulations, as such, in combination with the NRTI emtricitabine, and in combination with emtricitabine and the NNRTI efavirenz [23].

The first NNRTIs to be identified long before the name itself (NNRTI) was coined, were the HEPT (1-[2-(hydroxyethoxy)methyl]-6-(phenylthio)thymine) and TIBO (tetrahydro-imidazo[4,5,1-*jk*][1,4]-benzodiazepin-2(1*H*)-one and -thione) derivatives. The HEPT derivatives were first mentioned as antiretroviral agents by Baba et al. [24] and Miyasaka et al. [25], shortly followed by the TIBO derivatives in 1990 [26]. Although the HEPT and TIBO derivatives were discovered independently from one another, it soon became clear that they were apparently interacting in a similar fashion, that is as allosteric inhibitors of HIV-1 RT (for HEPT: see Baba et al. [27,28]; for TIBO: see Debyser et al. [29]). In fact, with a little imagination, HEPT and TIBO could be seen as overlapping structures [30]. While HEPT and TIBO themselves were not commercialized, several of these congeners, that is, nevirapine, delavirdine, efavirenz, and etravirine were formally licensed for clinical use (and others, i.e., rilpivirine, may follow in the near future), and all these compounds, while, structurally different, share common conformational features that make them to specifically fit into a "niche" or hydrophobic pocket within the HIV-1 RT. This pocket is located at a short distance (approximately 15 Å) from the catalytic site, which explains why the NNRTIs when occupying this niche are capable of disturbing the normal functioning (i.e., DNA polymerization process) of the HIV-1 RT.

2. THE TARGET: REVERSE TRANSCRIPTASE

The retroviral reverse transcriptase (RT) is a multifunctional enzyme that catalyzes the conversion of the single-stranded viral RNA genome to double-stranded DNA apt to be integrated into the host genome. The RT first uses viral RNA as the template to synthesize minus-strand DNA, thus resulting in a DNA. RNA hybrid, which is then cleaved by RNAase H (H for hybrid) to produce short RNA fragments hybridized to nascent DNA. Specific RNA fragments, known as the polypurine tracts (PPTs) serve as primers for the synthesis of plus-strand DNA from the minus-strand DNA template. The RT requires strand displacement during both minus- and plus-strand DNA synthesis [31].

Although X-ray crystallography has clearly contributed to our understanding of RT-containing nucleoprotein complexes, it provides a static picture, revealing few details on the motion (dynamics) of the enzyme. Recent developments of site-specific footprinting and application of single molecule spectroscopy have allowed us to follow individual steps in the RT process with significantly greater precision [32].

HIV-1 reverse transcriptase can simultaneously engage its DNA/RNA substrate at both DNA polymerase and RNAse H active sites. This concept [33] is inconsistent with models postulating that the substrate toggles between both active sites such that the primer 3'-terminus is disengaged from the polymerase active site when the template is in contact with the RNAse H active site.

Using single-molecule fluorescence resonance energy transfer to probe the interaction between RT and nucleic acid substrates in real time, RT was observed to slide on nucleic acid duplexes, rapidly shuttling ("sliding") between opposite termini of the duplex. Upon reaching the DNA 3'-terminus, RT spontaneously flips into a polymerization orientation. These long-range translocation activities facilitate multiple stages of the RT, including DNA polymerization and strand displacement [34]: single-molecule fluorescence resonance energy transfer (FRCT) experiments showed that RT has a remarkable ability to slide on nucleic acid duplexes, rapidly shuttling between the two ends and flipping into the polymerase-competent binding mode when needed [35]. Structural features of RT [36,37] and its molecular interactions with substrates and inhibitors have been elucidated through extensive crystallographic studies [38]. HIV RT is an asymmetric heterodimer composed of p66 and p51 subunits: the p66 subunit has enzymatic activity (polymerase and RNAse H), whereas the p51 subunit only plays a structural role [35].

Since the HIV RT plays an essential role in HIV replication, it has been considered a primary target for antiretroviral drug development, and three classes of RT inhibitors (RTIs) have been recognized for the treatment of HIV-1 infections: nucleoside RTIs (NRTIs), nucleotide RTIs (NtRTIs), and nonnucleoside RTIs (NNRTIs). All of the RTI mutations included in the most widely used resistance tables, such as that from the International AIDS Society USA expert panel [39], map to the DNA polymerase domain of HIV-1 RT, but dismiss mutations in the RNAse H domain of RT, despite the fact that these domains contain key residues essential for RT structure–function [40].

3. NUCLEOSIDE REVERSE TRANSCRIPTASE INHIBITORS

There are at present seven nucleoside reverse transcriptase inhibitors (NRTIs) that have been formally approved for clinical use against HIV infections: zidovudine (AZT, Retrovir®) (1), didanosine (ddI, Videx®) (2), zalcitabine (ddC, Hivid®) (3), stavudine (d4T, Zerit®) (4), lamivudine (3TC, Epivir®) (5), abacavir (ABC, Ziagen®) (6), and emtricitabine ((−)FTC, Emtriva®) (7). Lamivudine (3TC) is also marketed in a fixed-dose combination with zidovudine (AZT) under the trade name Combivir®), and with abacavir (ABC) under the trade name Epzicom®, and with both zidovudine (AZT) and abacavir (ABC) under the trade name Trizivir®. Emtricitabine ((−)FTC) is also marketed in a fixed-dose combination with TDF under the trade name Truvada®, and in combination with both TDF and efavirenz under the trade name Atripla® [23].

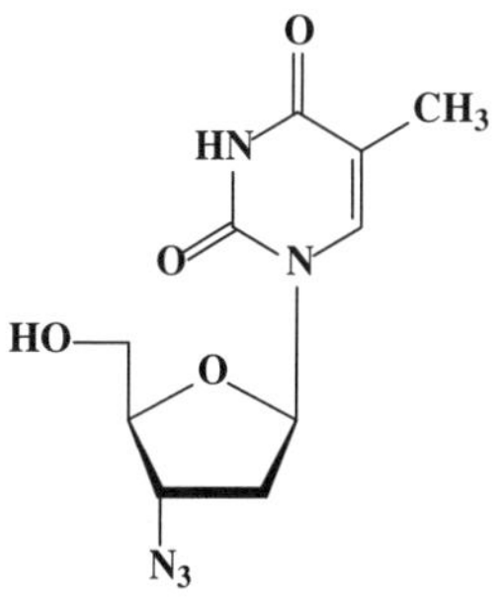

1
Zidovudine
3′-Azido-2′,3′-dideoxythymidine,
azidothymidine (AZT)
Retrovir®

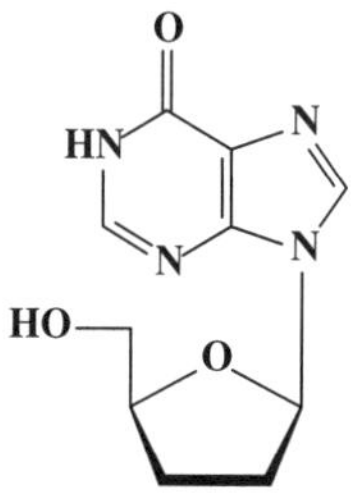

2
Didanosine
2′,3′-Dideoxyinosine (ddI)
Videx®, Videx® EC

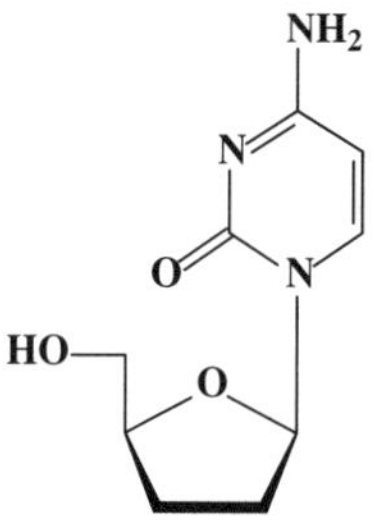

3
Zalcitabine
2′,3′-Dideoxycytidine (ddC)
Hivid®

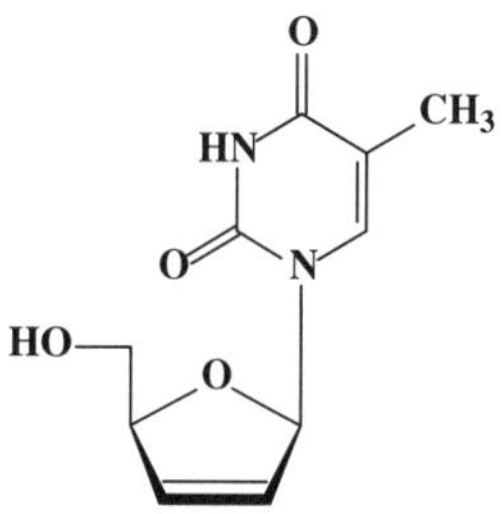

4
Stavudine
2′,3′-Didehydro-2′,3′-dideoxythymidine
(d4T)
Zerit®

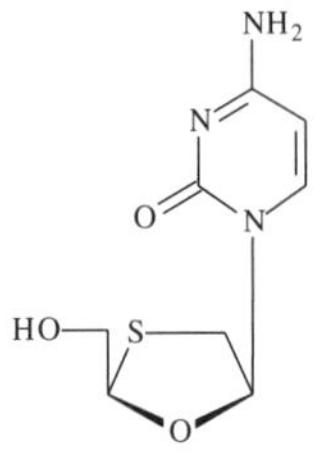

5
Lamivudine
2',3'-Dideoxy-3'-thiacytidine
3TC
Epivir®

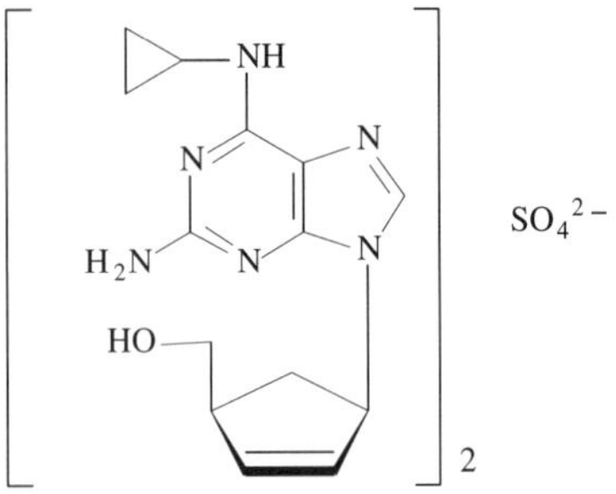

6
Abacavir
ABC
(1*S*,4*R*)-4-[2-amino-6-(cyclopropylamino)-9*H*-
purin-9-yl]-
2-cyclopentene-1-methanol   sulfate (salt) (2:1)
Ziagen®

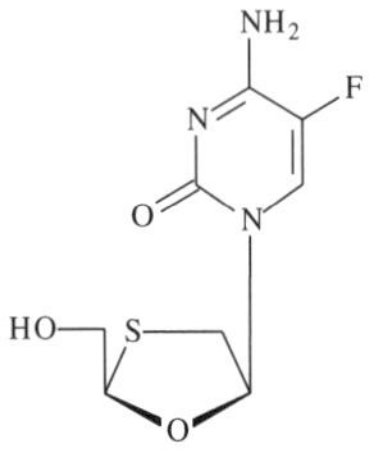

7
(-)-FTC
Emtricitabine
(-)-β-L-3'-thia -2',3'-dideoxy -5-fluorocytidine
Emtriva®

All the NRTIs are assumed to act in a similar fashion: following phosphorylation to the active 5'-triphosphate form [AZT → AZT-MP → AZT-DP → AZT-TP;   ddI → ddI-MP → succinoddA-MP → ddA-MP → ddA-DP → ddA-TP; ddC → ddC-MP → ddC-DP → ddC-TP; d4T → d4T-MP → d4T-DP → d4T-TP;   3TC → 3TC-MP → 3TC-DP → 3TC-TP; ABC → ABC-MP → carbovir(CBV)-MP → CBV-DP → CBV-TP; (−)FTC → (−)FTC-MP → (−)FTC-DP → (−)FTC-TP]. These active metabolites interact as competitive inhibitors/alternative substrates with respect to the natural substrates (dATP, dCTP, dTTP, or dGTP) in the RT (RNA-dependent DNA polymerization) reaction. When incorporated into the DNA chain they act as obligatory chain terminators.

Under (pre)clinical development are (or have been) [41] the following NRTIs: Racivir®, racemic (±)FTC (**8**) or FdOTC [which corresponds to 5-fluoro-substituted (±)-2'-deoxy-3'-oxa-4'-thiocytidine ((±)dOTC, BCH-10652)], apricitabine ((−)dOTC, AVX-754, previously called SPD-754) (**9**), dexelvucitabine (Reverset™, RVT, DPC-817, β-D-Fd4C) (**10**), elvucitabine (ACH-126443, β-L-Fd4C) (**11**), alovudine (MIV-310, FddThd, FLT) (**12**), [FLG (3'-fluoro-2',3'-dideoxyguanosine)prodrug MIV-210] (**13**), amdoxovir (DAPD, diaminopurine dioxolane) (**14**), 1-(β-D-dioxolane)thymine (DOT) (**15**), 4'-ethynyl-2-fluoro-2'-deoxyadenosine (EFdA) (**16**), and 4'-ethynyl-2',3'-dideoxy-2',3'-didehydrothymidine (Ed4T) (**17**).

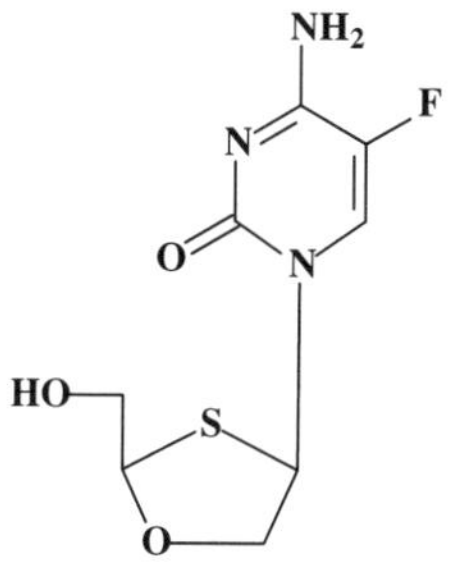

8
Racemic (±)FTC (FdOTC)
Racivir®

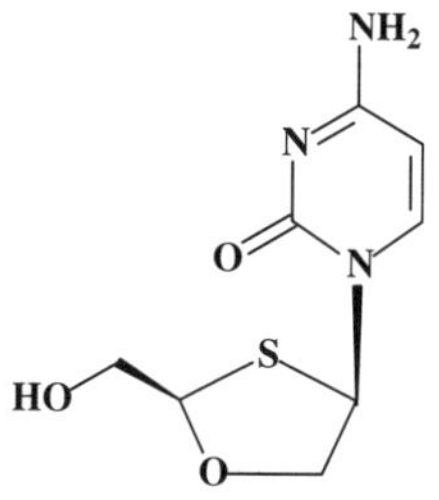

9
AVX-754 ((-)-dOTC)
SPD-754
Apricitabine

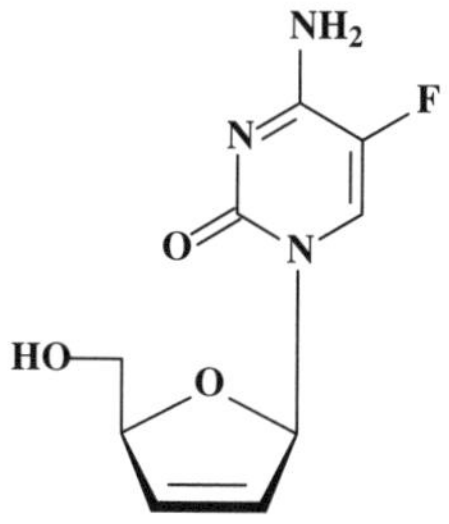

10
DPC-817 (β-D-Fd4C)
Dexelvucitabine
Reverset™

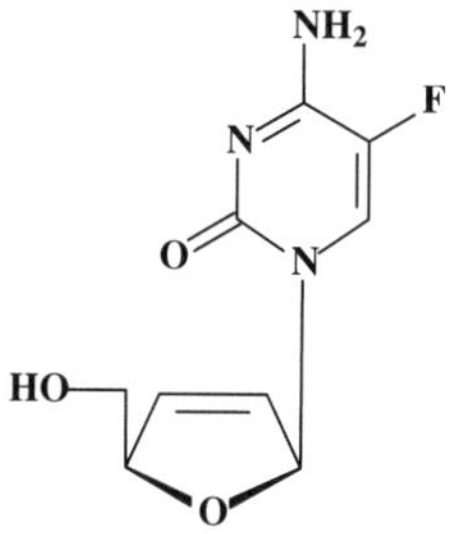

11
ACH-126443 (β-L-Fd4C)
Elvucitabine

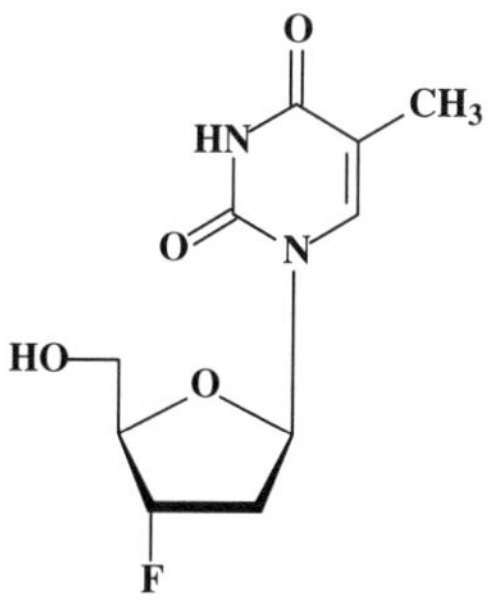

12
MIV-310 (FddThd, FLT)
Alovudine

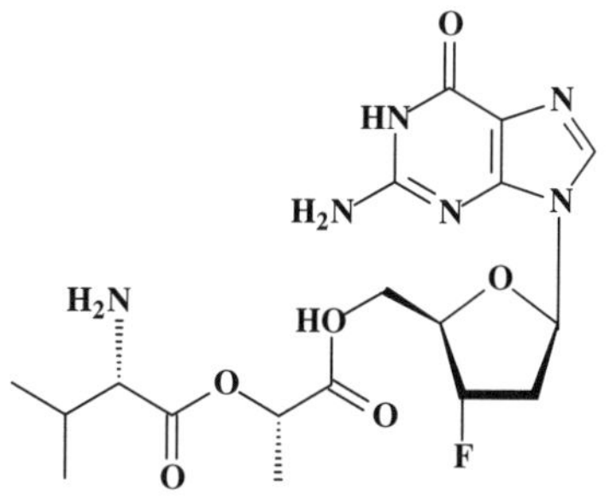

13
MIV-210
[FLG (3′-fluoro-2′,3′-dideoxyguanosine)
prodrug]

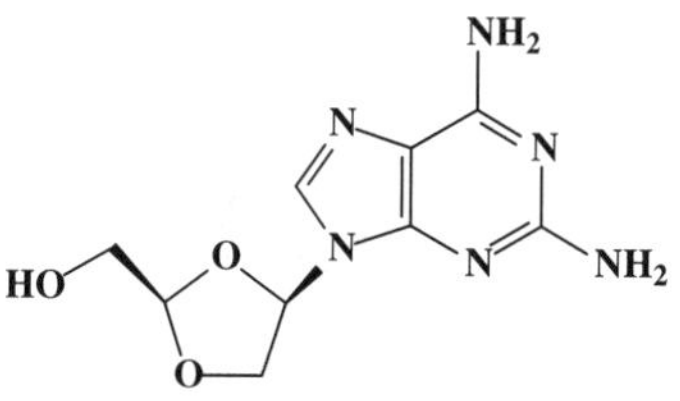

14
Diaminopurine dioxolane (DAPD)
Amdoxovir

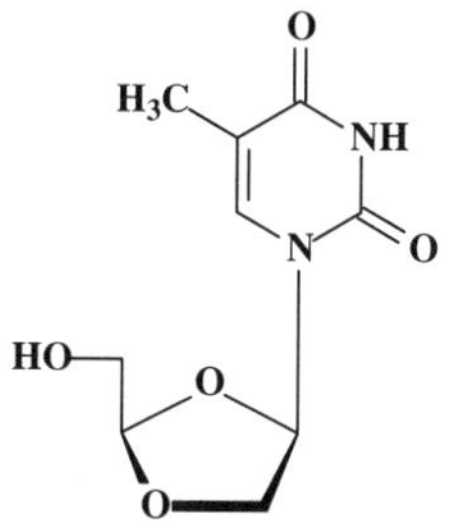

15
1-(β-D-dioxolane)thymine
DOT

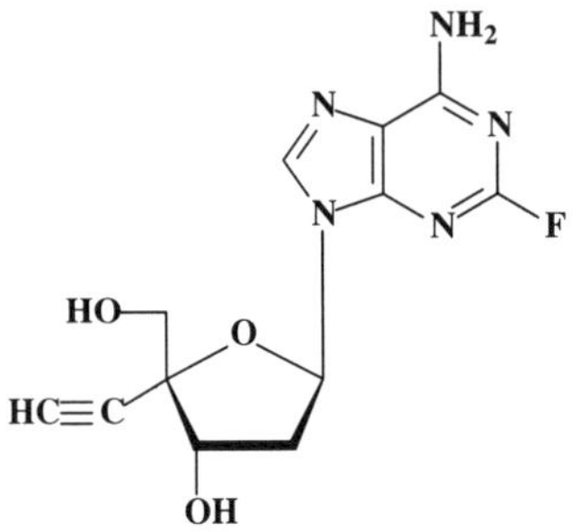

16
EFdA

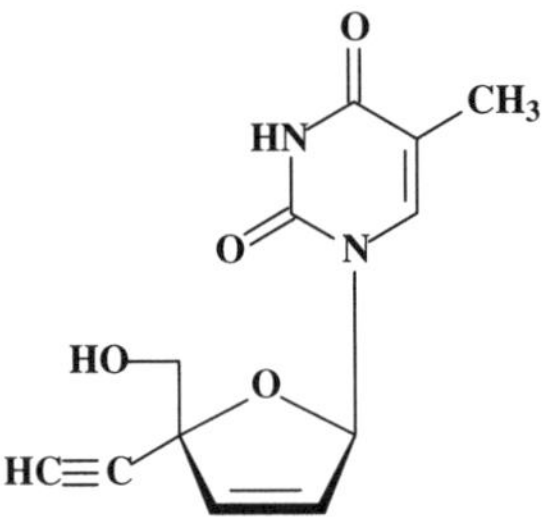

17
Ed4T

These compounds have been further investigated because, in general, they should be more effective against HIV strains that are resistant to the established NRTIs [42,43]. BCH-10652 ((±)dOTC) proved effective against lamivudine-resistant HIV-1 in Scid-hu Thy/Liv mice [44]. The (−)enantiomer of dOTC (AVX-754) [45] is active against HIV strains harboring the M184V and multiple thymidine analog mutations (TAMs). Similarly, β-D-Fd4C (RVT) retains activity against HIV isolates carrying mutations in the RT gene that confer resistance to 3TC or AZT [46]; however, RVT seems less potent against multi-NRTI-resistant viruses, particularly those carrying the Q151M mutation, and by itself, RVT selects for the K65R mutation [47].

AVX-754 (apricitabine) has a low propensity to select for resistance [48], and may be recommended for the treatment of HIV infection that is refractory to existing NRTIs [49]. Phase I clinical (pharmacokinetic) studies with apricitabine have been initiated [50,51]. Single-dose as well as multiple-dose pharmacokinetic studies have also been started with elvucitabine, in combination with ritonavir or lopinavir–ritonavir [52,53].

Amdoxovir (DAPD) is converted intracellularly by adenosine deaminase to dioxolane guanine (DXG), which is then further phosphorylated (intracellularly) to its active metabolite DXG 5'-triphosphate [54]. DXG 5'-triphosphate (TP) acts as an alternative substrate/inhibitor of the HIV-1 reverse transcriptase [55]. Intracellular DXG-TP levels have been demonstrated in peripheral blood mononuclear cells from HIV-infected patients receiving oral DAPD (500 mg bid) [56]. DAPD/DXG has proven effective against HIV-1 mutants resistant to zidovudine (M41L, D67N,

K70R, T215Y, and K219Q) and lamivudine (M184V) [54]. Also, drug-resistant HIV-1 isolates (including multidrug resistance variants with the 69 double codon insertion SS or SG) from patients where standard nucleoside therapy failed, remained susceptible to DXG; resistance to DXG was observed only for recombinant isolates carrying the K65R and Q151M double mutation [57].

Amdoxovir effected a small but significant decrease in viral load ($0.37 \log_{10}$ units) in patients with virus strains ranging a median of six NRTI mutations [58,59]. Lens opacities originally reported in a pilot trial (in monkeys) did not appear to be an issue in larger studies (in HIV-infected patients) [60].

DOT [1-(β-D-dioxolane)thymine], which, like DAPD, represents a dioxolane derivative [61] was found to be effective against various clinically relevant NRTI-resistant HIV strains containing the K65R, L74V, M184V, T215Y, T215Y and M184V, M41L, D67N, K70R and T215Y, and T69SSG, L1210W, V108I and T215D mutations, proving that DOT is more resilient to the mutations (TAMs, M184V, and K65R) that are commonly found in viruses isolated from subjects failing multinucleoside drug therapy [62].

Other NRTIs warranting further consideration for development are 4'-ethynyl-2-fluoro-2'-deoxyadenosine (EFdA), which represents a potent anti-HIV-1 agent with the possibility of once- or twice-a-day dosing [63], and 4'-ethynyl-2',3'-dideoxy-2',3'-didehydrothymidine (Ed4T), which is also predicted to require less frequent dosing (and better compliance) than d4T (stavudine) [64]. Compounds such as EFdA and Ed4T may be assumed to be metabolized in a similar fashion as the other NRTIs, that is, to be phosphorylated to their 5′-triphosphate form, upon which their 5′-triphosphates may act as chain terminators, although for EFdA chain termination should, in view of the presence of a 3′-hydroxyl group, be nonobligatory and attributable to a conformational change due to the neighboring ethynyl group.

In contrast with the 2′,3′-dideoxynucleosides (ddNs), their bioisosteric analogs, 2′,3′-dideoxy-4′-selenonucleosides (4′-seleno-ddNs) did not show anti-HIV activity, although the 4′-seleno-ddNs adopted the same C2′-endo/C3′-exo (South) conformation as the anti-HIV active ddNs [65]. D-carba T, however, a carbocyclic thymidine with a 3′-hydroxyl on the pseudo-

sugar (**18**), which, when incorporated into DNA would allow further chain elongation, was found effective against HIV replication [66].

D-carba T should, in principle, be active against NRTI-resistant HIV-1 variants that efficiently excise the NRTIs (or ddNs such as AZT) from the 3′-terminal end. Likewise, the 3′-azido-2′,3′-dideoxyribopurine nucleosides, that is, 3′-azido-2′,3′-dideoxyadenosine (**19**) and 3′-azido-2′,3′-dideoxyguanosine (**20**), a class of compounds already described more than 20 years [67], retain activity against viruses containing K65R, L74V or M184V, or multiple thymidine analog mutations (D67N/K70R/T215F/K219Q) [68].

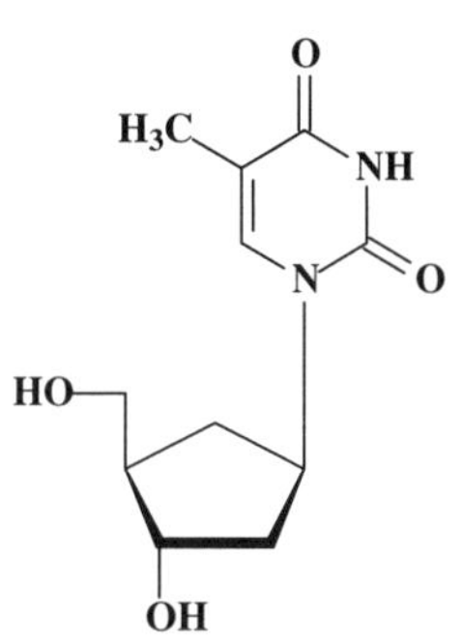

18
D-Carba-T

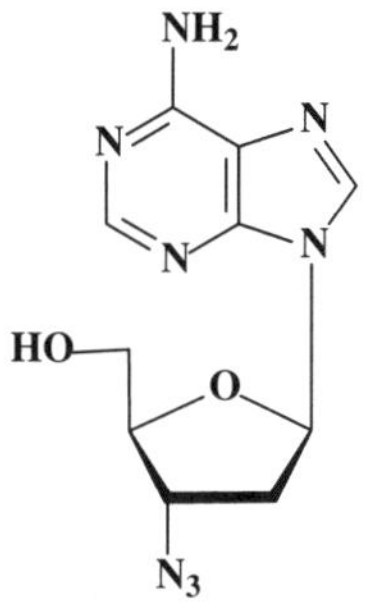

19
3′-Azido-2′,3′-dideoxyadenosine
3′-Azido-ddA

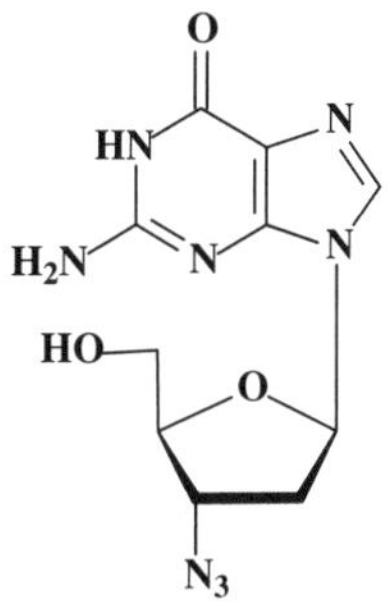

20
3′-Azido-2′,3′-dideoxyguanosine
3′-Azido-ddG

Inefficient cellular phosphorylation of the NRTIs to their active 5′-triphosphate (NTP) forms is one of the limitations for their use in HIV therapy: this problem can be overcome by the direct binding of the NRTI 5′-triphosphates onto magnetic nanoparticles: for AZT 5′-triphosphate this nanoformulation was shown to suppress HIV-1 replication in peripheral blood mononuclear cells [69].

4. NUCLEOTIDE REVERSE TRANSCRIPTASE INHIBITORS

Nucleotide reverse transcriptase inhibitors (NtRTIs) should be clearly discerned from the NRTIs in that they are analogs of the nucleoside monophosphates ("nucleotides"), whether this nucleoside is an acyclic nucleoside as in adefovir (PMEA) (**21**) or adefovir dipivoxil (**22**) or tenofovir [(R)-PMPA] (**23**) or tenofovir disoproxil fumarate (**24**) or a cyclic nucleoside as in PMDTA (or PMDTT), or GS-9148 (see below).

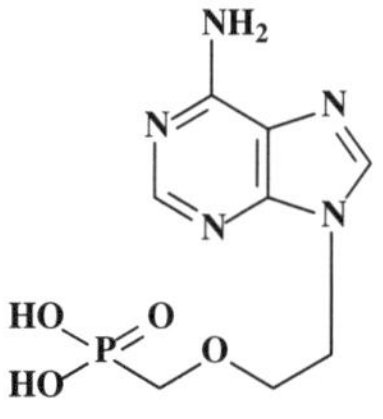

21
Adefovir
PMEA

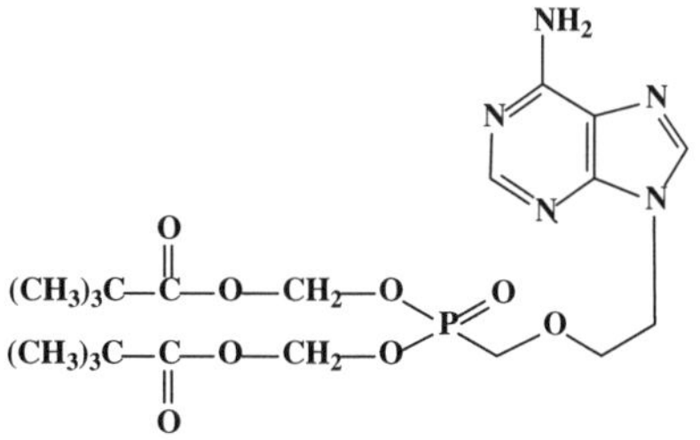

22
Adefovir dipivoxil

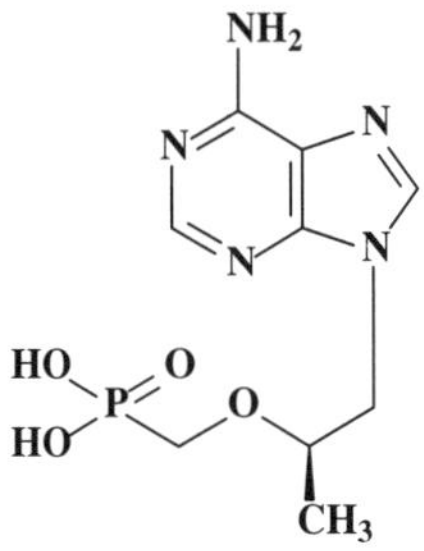

23
Tenofovir
(*R*)-9-(2-phosphonylmethoxypropyl)adenine
PMPA

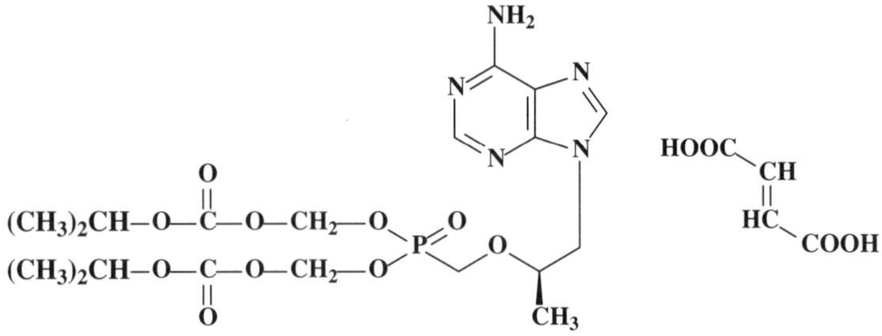

24
Tenofovir disoproxil fumarate
TDF

Based on the same "phosphonate" concept as present in adefovir and tenofovir [70–72] several new acyclic nucleoside phosphonates were constructed, that is, 5-substituted 2, 4-diamino-6-[2-(phosphonomethoxy)ethoxy]-pyrimidines [PMEO-DAPy (**25**) and (*R*)-PMPO-DAPy (**26**)], one of the most promising of these new NtRTIs being PMEO-5-Me-DAPy (**27**), which should deserve further (pre)clinical investigation as candidate anti-HIV drugs [73,74]. Also, according to the observations of Hostetler et al. [75], the alkoxyalkyl (hexadecyloxopropyl and octadecyloxyethyl) esters of (*S*)-HPMPA (**28**) (i.e., HDP-HPMPA (**29**) and ODE-HPMPA (**30**)) should be further pursued for their potential impact as anti-HIV agents. Furthermore, the hexadecyloxypropyl-9-(*R*)-[2-phosphonomethoxy)propyl]adenine, CMX157 (HDP-PMPA) (**31**) has been reported to be an orally bioavailable alternative to TDF for the treatment of HIV-1 (as well as HBV) infections [76].

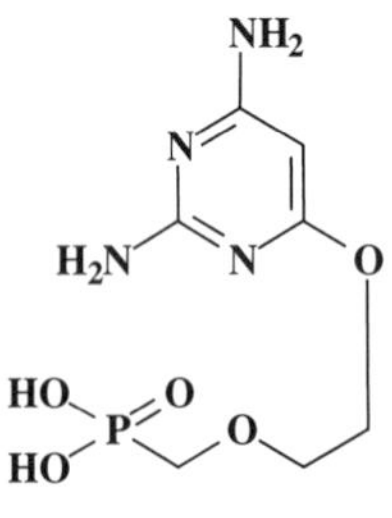

25
PMEO-DAPy

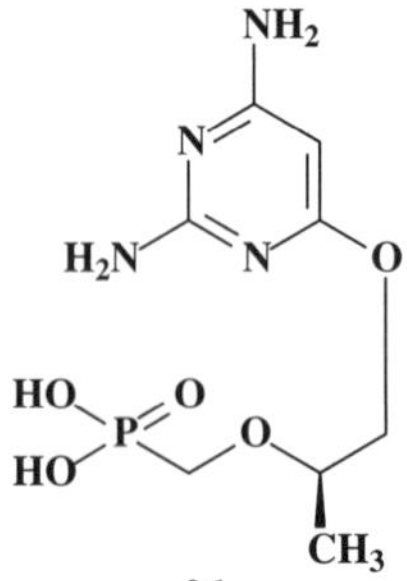

26
(*R*)-PMPO-DAPy

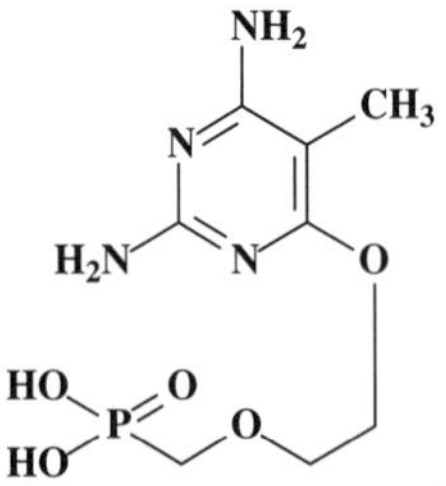

27
PMEO-5-Me-DAPy

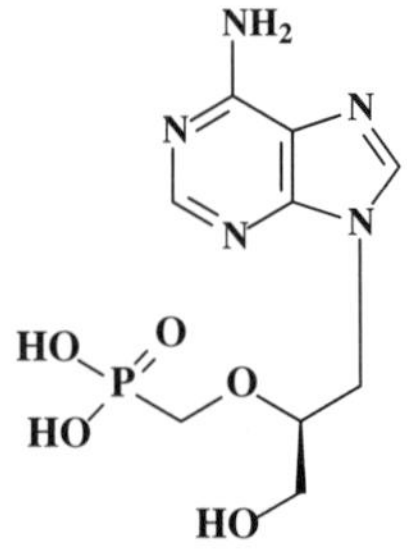

28
HPMPA

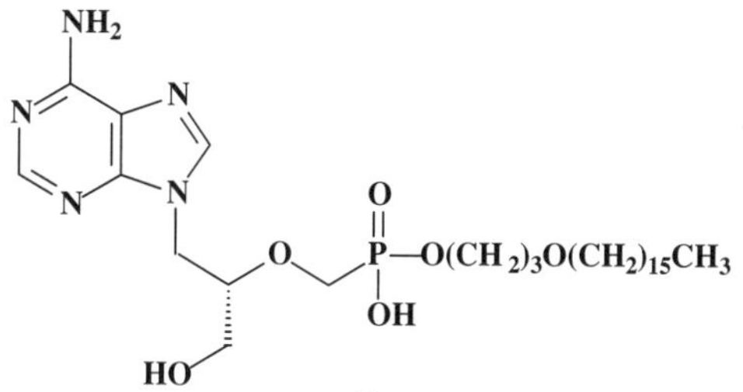

29

HDP-HPMPA

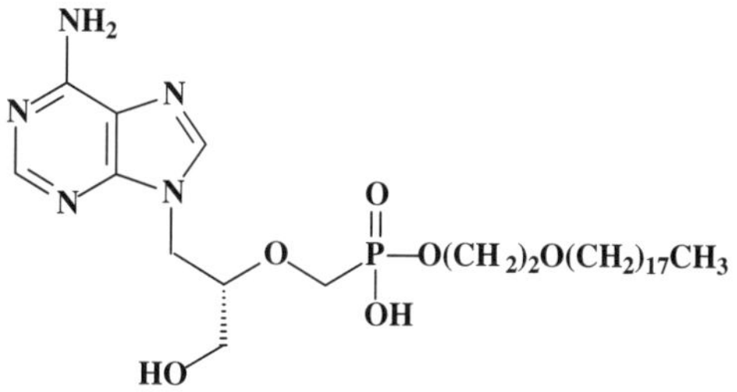

30

ODE-HPMPA

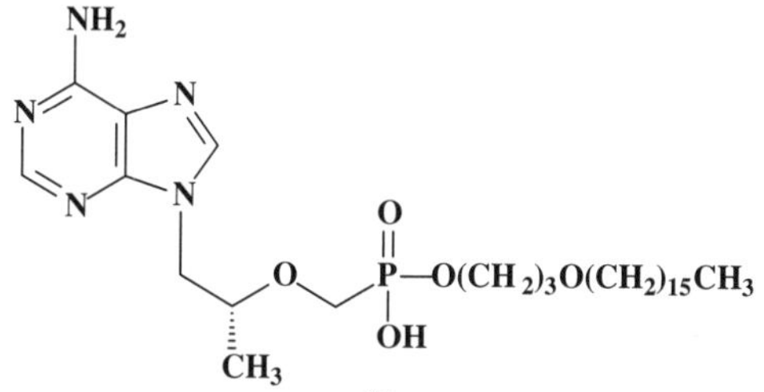

31

CMX157

HDP-PMPA

Initial attempts by Piet Herdewijn and his colleagues to discover antivirally active nucleoside phosphonates starting from furanose skeleton were not successful [77], but when the phosphonate was attached to a 2-deoxythreosyl entity, as in PMDTA (**32**) and PMDTT (**33**), the latter turned into selective anti-HIV agents [78]. Unfortunately, the synthesis of these 2-deoxythreosyl phosphonate nucleosides has proven to be more cumbersome than originally thought, and, hence, paucity of material has hampered a thorough evaluation of the biological properties, and eventual therapeutic potential, of this class of compounds.

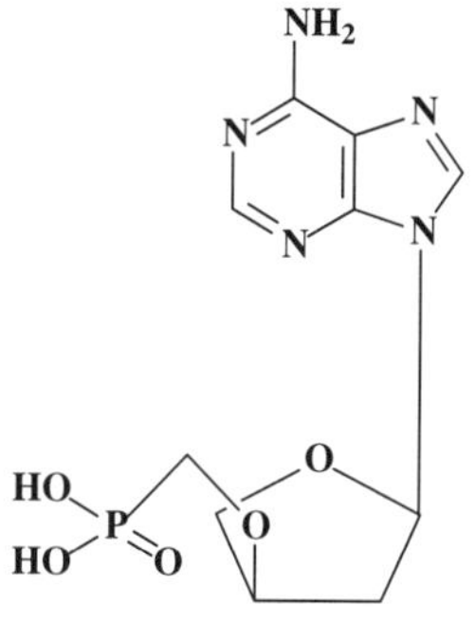

32

PMDTA

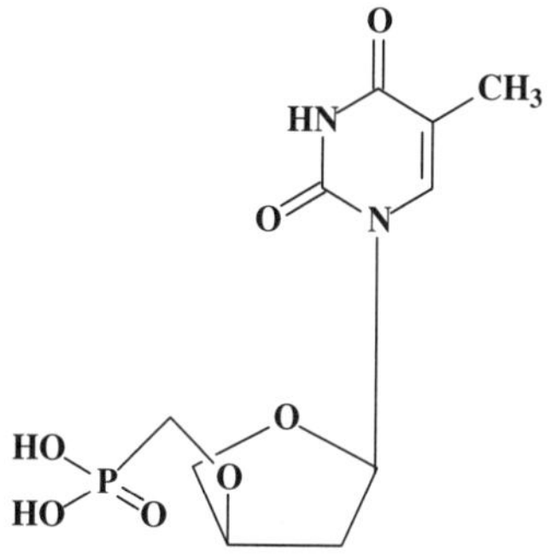

33

PMDTT

Recently, a novel NtRTI, 5-(6-aminopurin-9-yl)-4-fluoro-2,5-dihydrofuran-2-yloxymethyl) phosphonic acid (GS-9148) (**34**), was described, which retained activity against NRTI-resistant variants containing the K65R, L74V, or M184V RT mutations [79]. The orally bioavailable ethylalaninyl phosphonoamidate prodrug thereof, GS-9131 (**35**) [79], once it has been taken by the cells, is readily hydrolyzed to GS-9148, which is then further phosphorylated to its active diphosphate metabolite [80]. GS-9148, akin to GS-7340 (**36**), the isopropylalaninyl monoamidate phenyl monoester prodrug of tenofovir [81], directs phosphonoamidate prodrugs principally to lymphoid tissue where HIV replication takes place [81]. In comparison with the acyclic nucleotides cidofovir, adefovir, and tenofovir, GS-9148 showed 60- to 100-fold lower efficiency of transport by the

human renal organic anion transporter type 1 (ROAT1), indicating that GS-9148 has a lower potential for renal accumulation and nephrotoxicity [82].

Recently, 4'-modified carbocyclic nucleoside phosphonate derivatives, such as (1*S*,4*R*)-4-(6-amino-9*H*-purin-9-yl)-1-ethynyl-cyclopent-2-enyloxy)methylphosphonic acid [4'-ethynyl-cpAP (**37**)] have been described, with an EC$_{50}$ 16 μM, within twofold of GS-9148, and within fivefold of tenofovir (PMPA) [83].

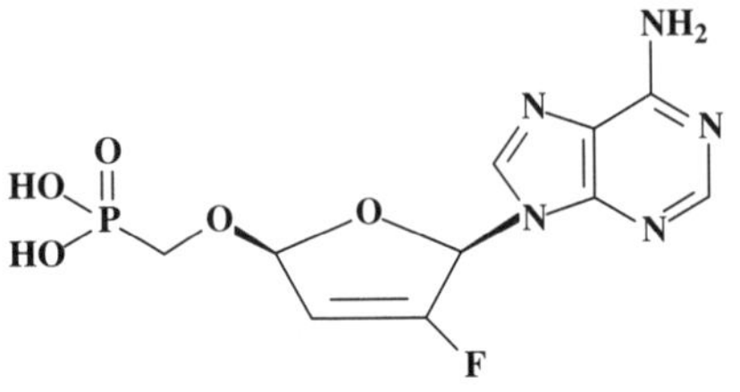

34
GS-9148

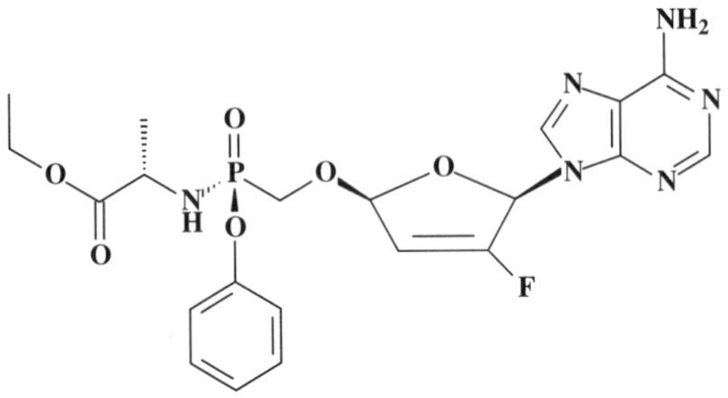

35
GS-9131

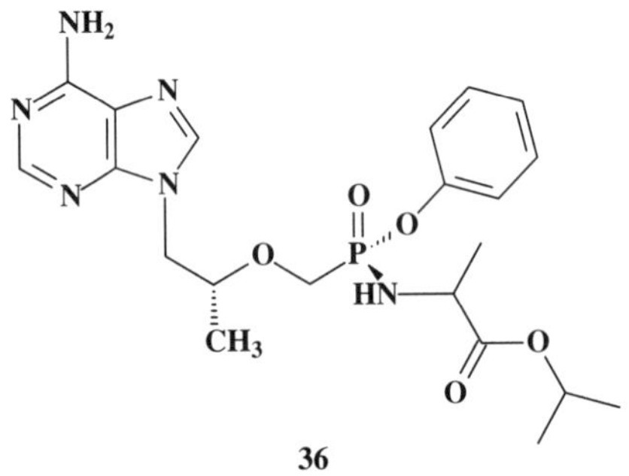

36
GS-7340

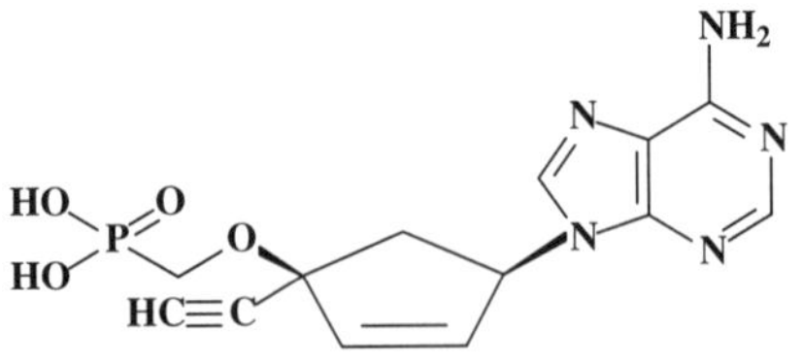

37
4'-Ethynyl-cpAP

5. NONNUCLEOSIDE REVERSE TRANSCRIPTASE INHIBITORS

Following the HEPT (**38**) and TIBO (**39**) "leads," more than 30 structurally different classes of compounds have been identified as nonnucleoside reverse transcriptase inhibitors (NNRTIs) [84], that is, compounds that specifically inhibit the replication of HIV-1 by interacting with a specific, allosteric (nonsub-

strate binding) site of the reverse transcriptase [30]. Furthest developed (but eventually not licensed for clinical use) was the HEPT derivative MKC-442 (emivirine, Coactinon®) (**40**). At present, four NNRTIs are formally licensed for clinical use in the treatment of HIV infections: nevirapine (Viramune®) (**41**), delavirdine (Rescriptor®) (**42**), efavirenz (Sustiva® and Stocrin®) (**43**), and etravirine (Intelence®) (**44**).

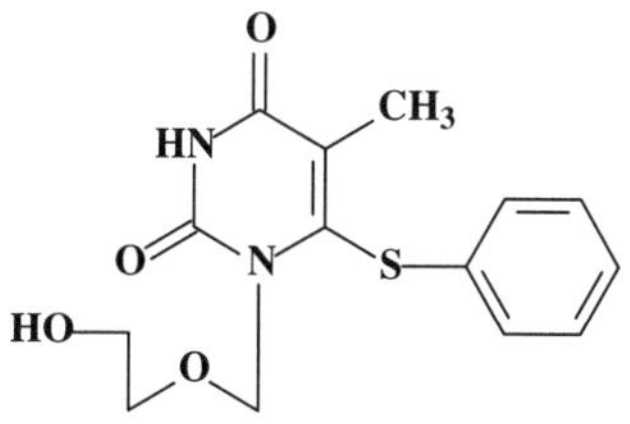

38
HEPT

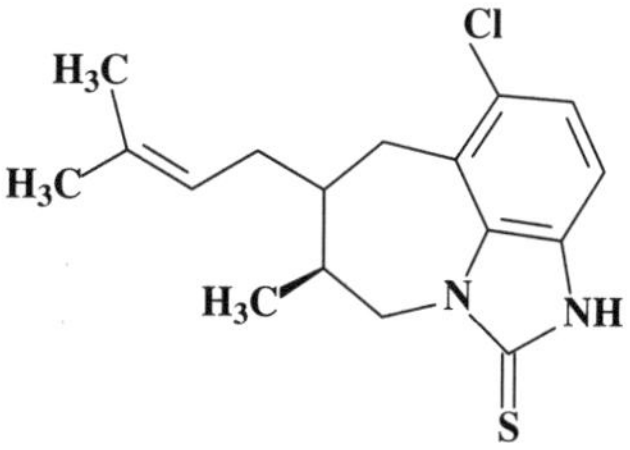

39
8-Chloro-TIBO
R86183
Tivirapine

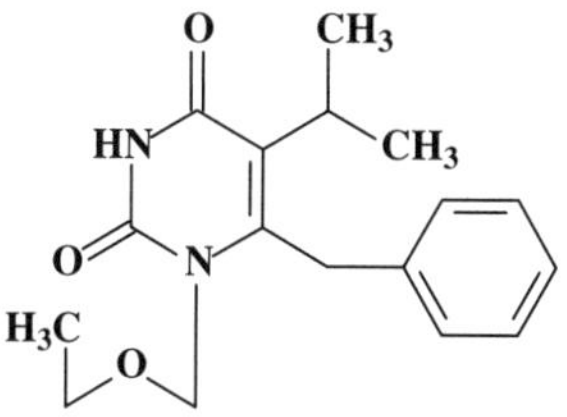

40
Emivirine
MKC-442
Coactinon®

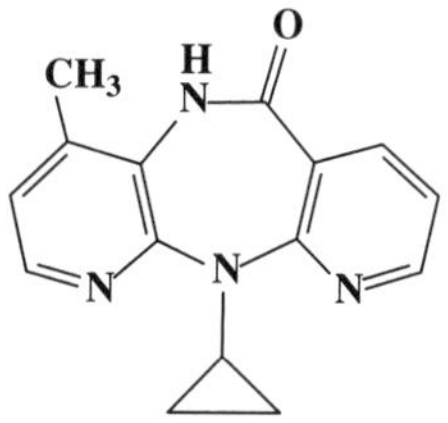

41
Nevirapine
Viramune®

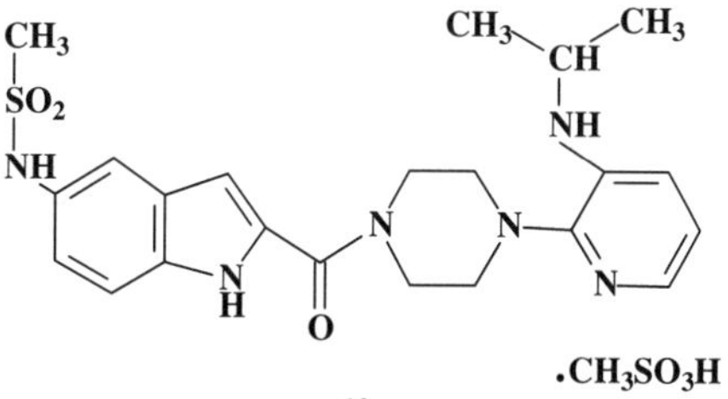

42
Delavirdine
Rescriptor®

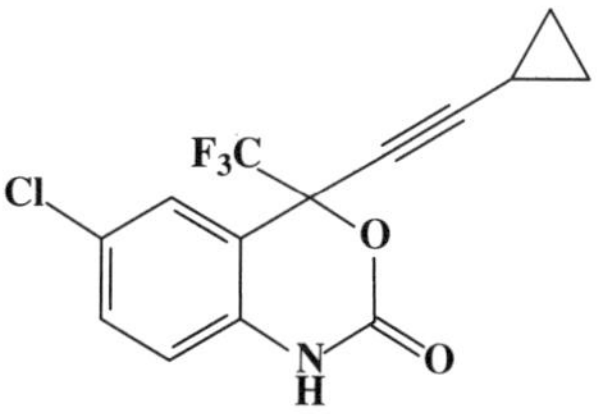

43
Efavirenz
Sustiva®, Stocrin®

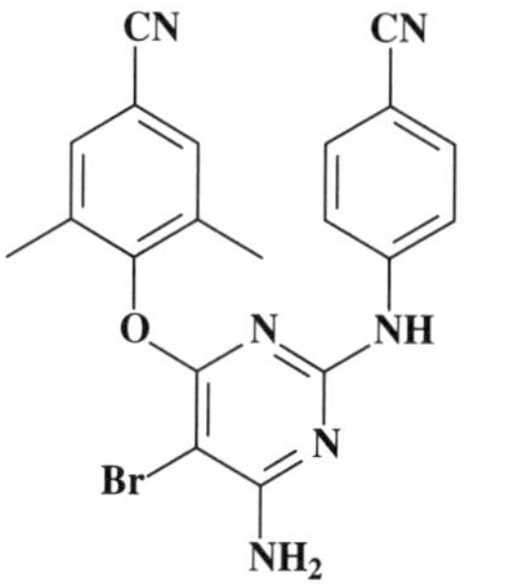

44
Etravirine (TMC-125, R-165335)
Intelence®

Etravirine (TMC 125) represents the most recent, and the 25th, anti-HIV drug to be approved for clinical use. Etravirine displays a high genetic barrier to the development of resistance [85]. In an initial screen for activity against a panel of 25 viruses carrying single and double RT amino acid substitutions associated with NNRTI resistance, the EC_{50} of etravirine was <5 nM for 19 viruses, including those that contained the double mutations K101E + K103N and K103N + Y181C [86]. The efficacy and safety of etravirine in the treatment of HIV-1-infected patients have been well demonstrated [87,88]. From a clinical viewpoint, etravirine offers, when combined with darunavir ("boosted" by ritonavir) interesting perspectives for the treatment of HIV infections [89–91]. (Likewise, nevirapine could be considered for combination therapy with darunavir in HIV-infected patients [92]).

Etravirine has been quoted as "the first NNRTI that has been developed to be effective against HIV-1 resistant to other NNRTIs" [93]. However, because of its effect on the cytochrome P450 system, it may lead to important drug interactions [93]. Etravirine is effective when used as part of an optimized HAART regimen in NNRTI treatment-experienced adult patients with HIV [94].

The thiocarboxanilide UC-781 (45) has been recognized as a retrovirucidal agent that is capable of reducing the infectivity of HIV-1

virions [95], and, therefore, seems to be an excellent candidate microbicide (virucide), for example, when formulated in replens gel [96], for topical application to prevent sexual transmission of HIV. Similarly, a series of diaryltriazines and diarylpyrimidines, such as dapivirine (TMC-120, R147681) (46) seem to be promising candidates as microbicides as they are able to completely block HIV infection at a concentration of 10–100 nM [97]. Yet, two other NNRTIs, MIV-170 and IQP0528, yield great promise as anti-HIV microbicides, MIV-170 (47) because of its high potency against HIV-1 mutants that are resistant to other NNRTIs and low risk for resistance development [98,99] and IQP0528 (48) because it is a dual-acting HIV inhibitor targeting both reverse transcription and virus entry into the cells [100].

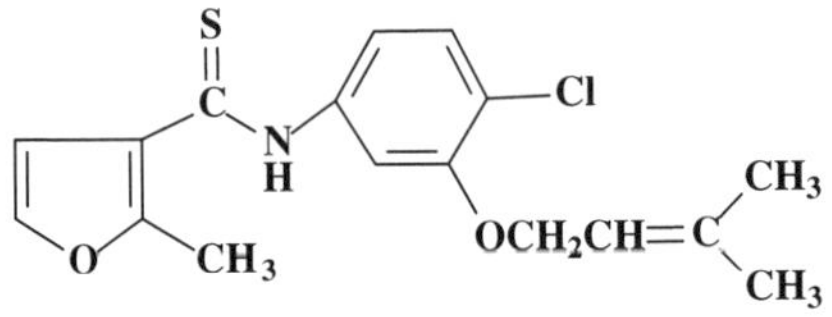

45

Thiocarboxanilide UC-781

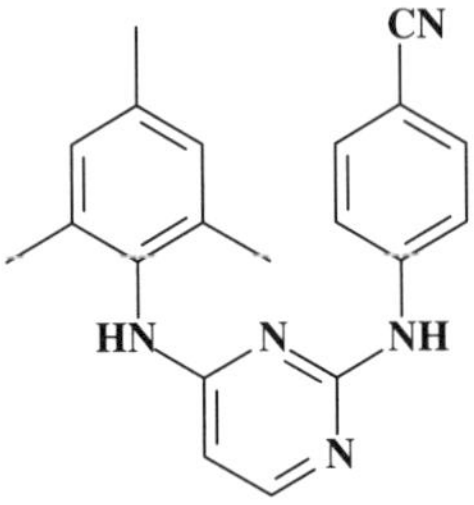

46

Dapivirine (TMC120, R147681)

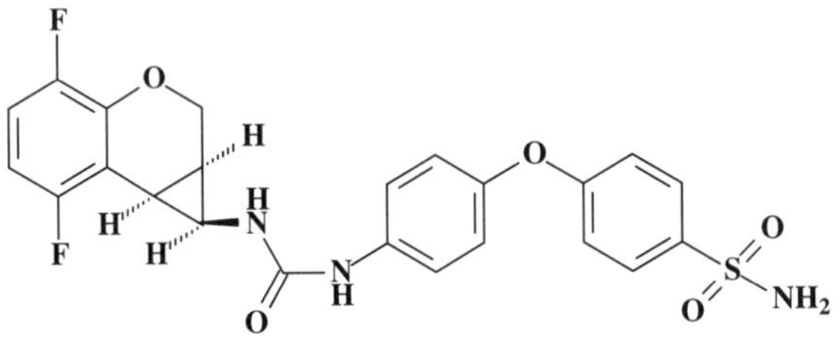

47

MIV-170

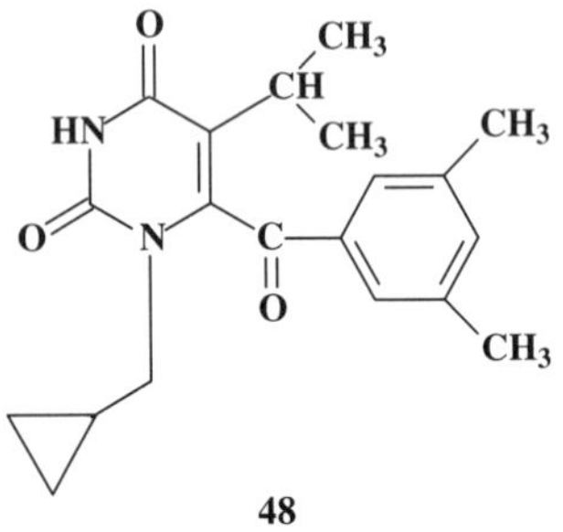

48

IQP0528

A multidisciplinary approach involving medicinal chemistry, virology, crystallography, molecular modeling, analytical chemistry, toxicology, and pharmacology has led to the identification of rilpivirine (R-278474, TMC-278) as a highly promising NNRTI drug candidate with EC_{50} values against wild-type, K103N, and K103N + Y181C mutants

that were comprised within the 0.1–1 nM range [101]. Starting point for the eventual development of rilpivirine (as well as etravirine) was tivirapine (TIBO R86183) (39), which through several rounds of "lead" optimization successively led to loviride (α-APA, R-89439) (49), ITU R-100943 (50), DATA R-106168 (51), DAPY R-147681 (TMC-120) (46), and finally, etravirine (R-165335, TMC-125) (**44**) and rilpivirine (R-278474, TMC-278) (**52**) [101]. Proof-of-principle that rilpivirine is antivirally effective *in vivo* has been provided [102]. Rilpivirine, at a daily dose of 25 mg, is now in international phase III clinical trials for the treatment of therapy-naïve HIV-1-infected subjects [103]. Moreover, ril-

pivirine could be delivered as a long-acting parenteral depot formulation [104]. A long-acting injectable formulation of rilpivirine with 200 nm sized nanoparticles has recently been developed [105]. Also, a powder for reconstituting rilpivirine has been developed that may serve as a starting point for pediatric formulations [106].

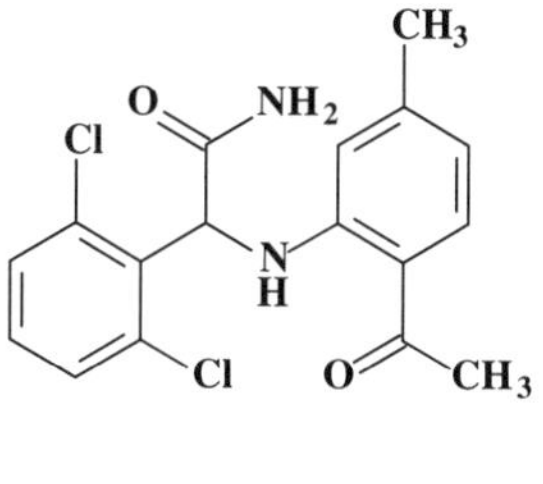

49

α-APA
R89439
Loviride

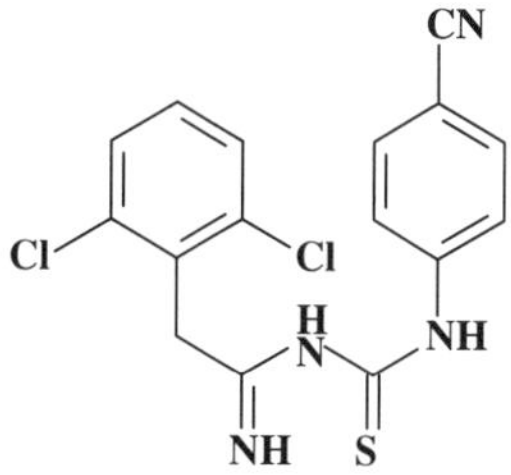

50

ITU R-100943

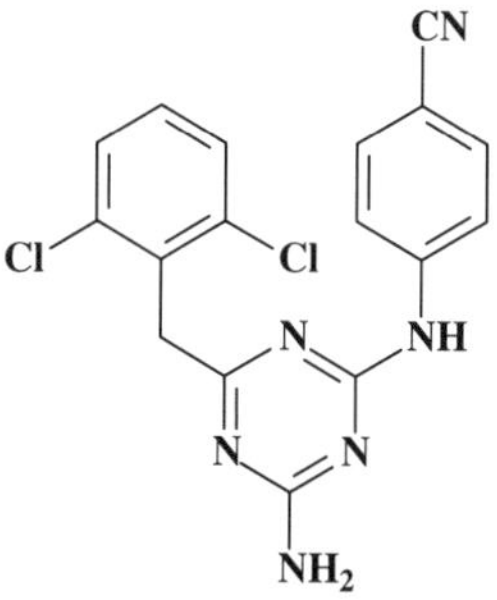

51

DATA R-106168

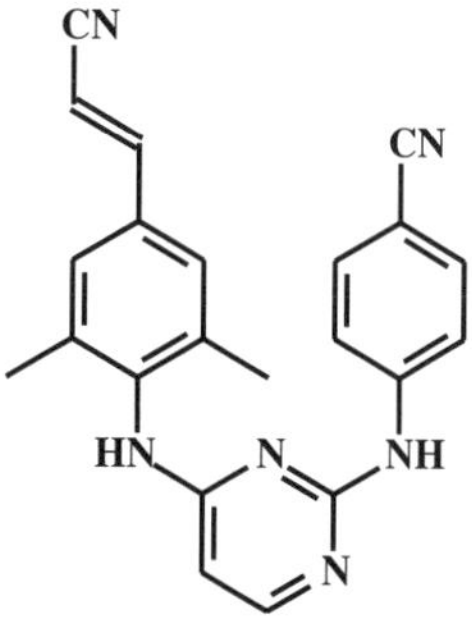

52

Rilpivirine (TMC278, R278474)

In developing new NNRTIs for the treatment of HIV infections, two broad strategies could be envisaged: (i) understanding the mechanism(s) of drug resistance and developing drugs that effectively inhibit mutant viruses and (ii) designing drugs that interact with portions of the viral machinery that are evolutionarily conserved [107]. In the design of new NNRTIs as anti-HIV-1 drugs, conformational flexibility and positional adaptability seem to be prime determinants: torsional flexibility ("wiggling") of the inhibitors can generate numerous conformational variants, and the compactness of the inhibitors permits significant repositioning and reorientation within the pocket

("jiggling"). Exploitation of inhibitor conformational flexibility, such as torsional flexibility about strategically located chemical bonds, may power drug design, especially when hitting a moving (that is, mutating) target [108].

In further attempting at elucidating the mechanism of action of NNRTIs, Ivetac and McCammon [109] came to the conclusion that NNRTIs act as "molecular wedges," their chief effect being to constrain the motion between the "fingers" and "thumb" subdomains of the p66 subunit [109].

In total, 44 mutations (V90I, A98G, L100I, K101E/P/Q, K103H/N/S/T, V106A/I/M, V108I, E138G/K/Q, V179D/E/F/G/I, Y181C/I/V,

Y188C/H/L, V189I, G190A/C/E/Q/S, H221Y, P225H, F227C/L, M230I/L, P236L, K238N/T, and Y318F) have been associated with HIV-1 resistance to NNRTIs [110]. A total of 17 mutations (V90I, A98G, L100I, K101E, K101P, K101H, V106I, E138A, V179D, V179F, V179T, V181C, Y181I, Y181V, G190A, G190S, and M230L) have been linked to etravirine, although at least three must be present simultaneously in order to diminish etravirine susceptibility [111].

More than three-quarters of the HIV-1 strains from patients exposed to nevirapine or efavirenz are still sensitive to etravirine [111]. Yet, recent evidence suggests that NNRTI (i.e., nevirapine)-resistant mutants can be transmitted from mother to child, even without selective drug pressure [112]. However, vertical (from mother-to-child) transmission of nevirapine-resistant HIV can be counteracted or avoided by using HAART [113] or combination of TDF with emtricitabine [114].

Recently, Ehteshami et al. [115] identified a new class of RT inhibitors, such as INDOPY-1 (**53**), that would compete directly with the natural deoxynucleoside triphosphates (dNTPs) and could, therefore, be termed as "nucleotide-competing RT inhibitors (NcRTIs)" [115].

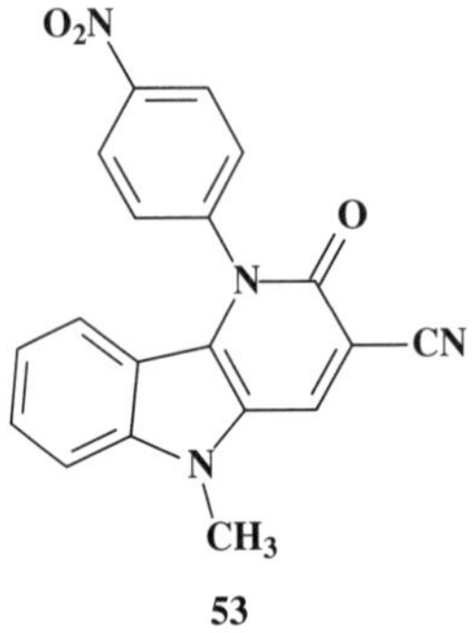

Featuring among these novel NNRTIs (structures not shown) are 1,3-dihydro-2*H*-benzimidazol-2-ones and their sulfones [117], bisphenylbenzimidazoles (BPBIs) [118], 2-alkylsulfanyl-6-benzyl-3,4-dihydropyrimidin-4(3*H*)-ones (*S*-DABOs) [119], diaryltriazine analogs (DATAs) [120,121], 2-(coumarin-4-yloxy)-4,6-(substituted)-*s*-triazine derivatives [122], sulfanyltriazole/tetrazoles [123], 2-(1-aryl-1*H*-imidazol-2-ylthio)acetamide [imidazole thioacetanilide (ITA) derivatives] [124], 1,2,3-selenadiazole thioacetanilides [125], 2-(4-(naphthalen-2-yl)-1,2,3-thiadiazol-5-ylthio)-*N*-acetamides [126], 5-aryloxyimidazole derivatives [127], di-halo-indolylarylsulfones [128], and a variety of acylthiocarbamates [129–131], including *N*-aryl-*O*-(2-phthalimidoethyl)thiocarbamates [132].

One of the most prominent among these compounds is 6-chloro-1-(3,5-dimethylphenylsulfonyl)-1,3-dihydro-2*H*-benzimidazol-2-one (**54**), with an EC$_{50}$ of 0.002 µM, a CC$_{50}$ of 39 µM (selectivity index: 17,846) [117,133,134].

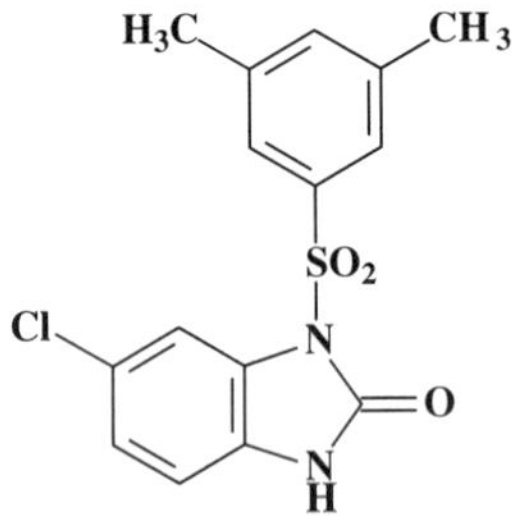

54

Sulfonyl-1,3-dihydrobenzimidazol-2-one

[117]

53

INDOPY-1

6. SEARCH FOR NEW NNRTIS: PRIMARILY INTENDED TO OVERCOME THE RESISTANCE PROBLEM

Predominant among the abundance of NNRTI resistance mutations [110] that may emerge in the HIV-1 RT are K103N and/or Y181C. The (risk for the) emergence of NNRTI resistance mutation has fueled the search for new NNRTIs (for a review, see Ref. [116]).

Of the alkenyldiarylmethanes (ADAMs) that I recently reviewed in Medicinal Research Reviews [135], one of the most promising is the ADAM containing a benzo[*d*]isoxazole group (**55**), exhibiting an EC$_{50}$ of 20 nM (versus HIV-1(III$_B$)) [136]. Improved resilience to resistance mutations (such as K103N and Y181C) has been noted with benzophenone derivatives (such as **56**), probably due to better contacts with the immutable W229, and reduced aromatic stacking interactions with the highly mutable Y181 side chain [137].

Also, new pyrrolobenz(pyrido)oxazepinones, that is, (57) (EC$_{50}$: 0.05 μM) have been synthesized in attempts to overcome the NNRTI resistance problem [138]. With naphthyl-substituted diarylpyrimidines of the general structure 58 EC$_{50}$ values against HIV-1(III$_B$) in the range of 1–5 nM were obtained (the EC$_{50}$ for the K103N + Y181C double mutant still being 0.24 μM or higher) [139].

Similar potency (EC$_{50}$ for wild type in the nanomolar range, and for K103N and Y181C in the 0.1–1 μM range) was noted for a series of indazole derivatives (59) [140]. These compounds make important edge-to-face π-interactions with the immutable W229 residue, while the indazole NH makes a hydrogen bond with the peptide main chain of residue K101.

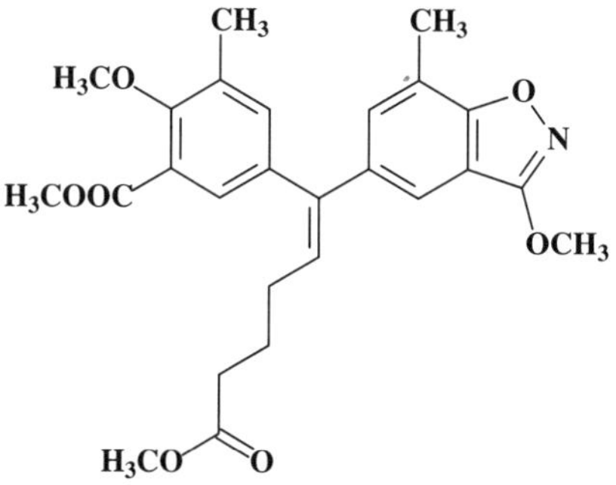

55

ADAM containing a benzo[*d*]isoxazole ring

[136]

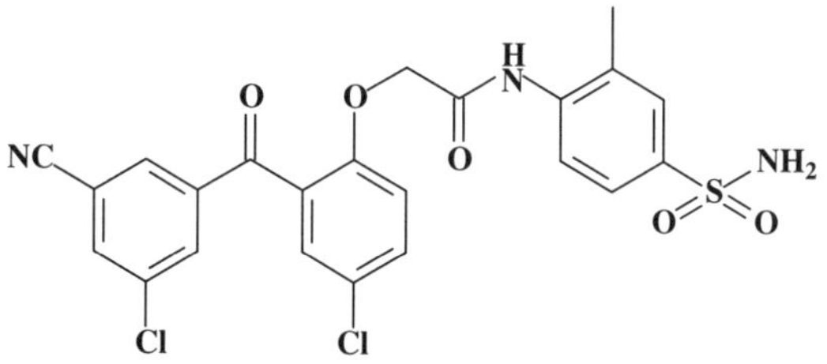

56

Benzophenone

[137]

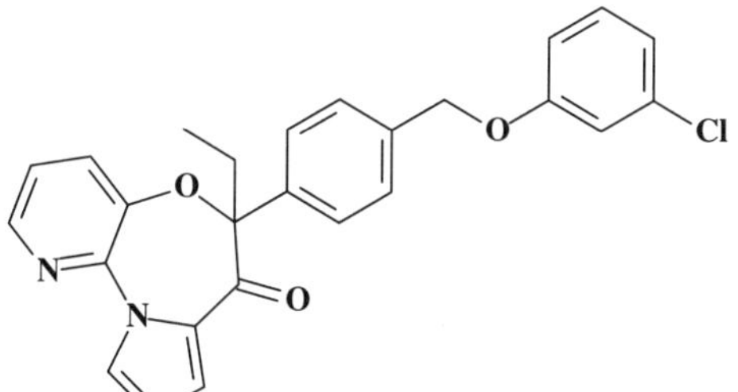

57

Pyrrolobenzo(pyrido) oxazepinone

[138]

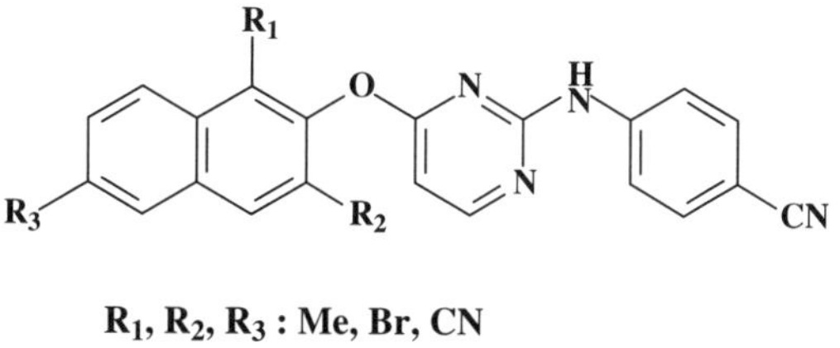

R$_1$, R$_2$, R$_3$: Me, Br, CN

58

Napthylarylpyrimidines

[139]

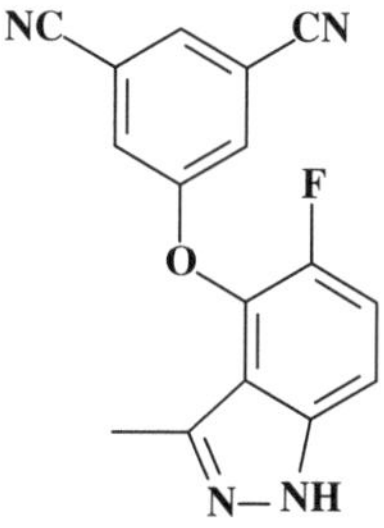

59

Indazole

[140]

For tetrahydroquinolines, such as those shown in **60**, IC_{50} values for both the wild-type and K103N and Y181C mutant reverse transcriptases fall within the 1–10 nM concentration range [141]. Likewise, a series of diphenyl ether compounds, such as the imidazolinone **61**, show IC_{50} and EC_{50} values for both wild-type and mutant polymerase and wild-type and mutant virus replication within the 1–10 nM concentration range [142].

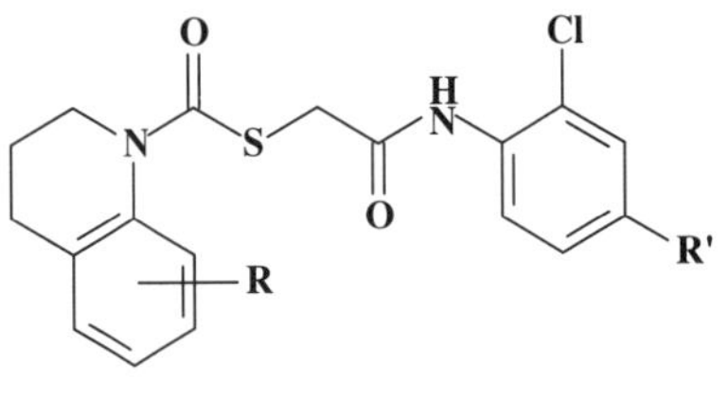

R = Cl
R′ = CONHBn, SO₂CH₃, CONH(CH₂)₃NH₂

60
[141]

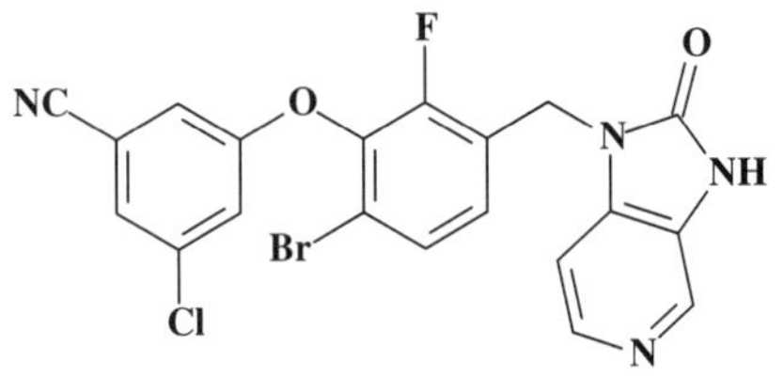

61
Imidazolinone
[142]

Structurally related to the imidazolinone **61** (the only difference being the pyrazolo[3,4-*c*]pyridazine part) are the so-called annulated pyrazoles, that is, **62** [143], which has an EC_{50} of 1 nM for the wild-type and an EC_{50} of 3 nM for the K103N/Y181C mutant.

Structurally reminiscent of rilpivirine (TMC278, R278474) is the diarylpyridine **63**, with an EC_{50} value for wild-type HIV-1 falling below the 1 nM threshold (selectivity index: ~10,000) [144].

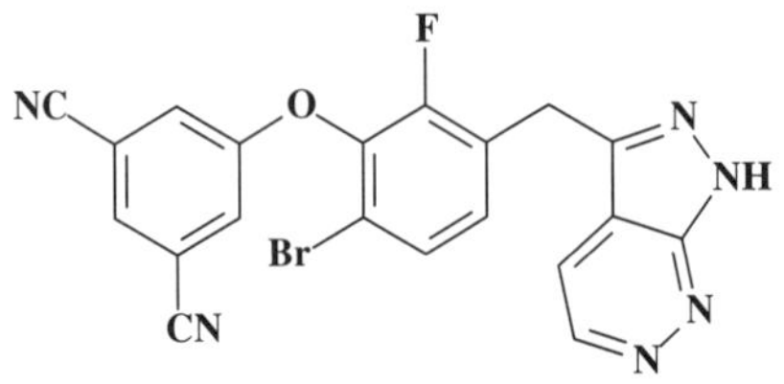

62
Pyrazolo[3,4-*c*]pyridazine
[143]

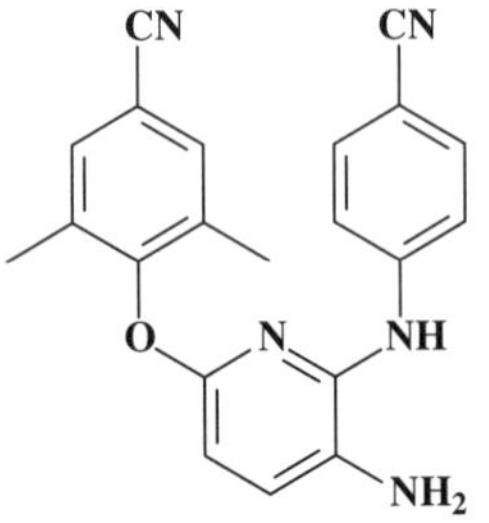

63
Diarylpyridine
[144]

Based on the data reported, the most potent NNRTI, however, with an IC_{50} of 0.2, 0.5 and 0.4 nM for the wild-type, K103N and Y181C RT polymerase, respectively [145], appears to be 3-{5-[(6-amino-1*H*-pyrazolo[3,4-*b*]pyridine-3-yl)methoxy]-2-chlorophenoxy}-5-chloro-benzonitrile (MK-4965) (**64**). It is likely that the ability of this compound to make a direct interaction with the backbone of K103 and to avoid contact with Y181 contributes to its resilience to resistance. In addition to its exquisite potency against wild-type and key mutant viruses, MK-4965 has also been quoted as having excellent oral bioavailability and overall pharmacokinetics [145]. Consequently, MK-4965 has advanced to phase I clinical trials.

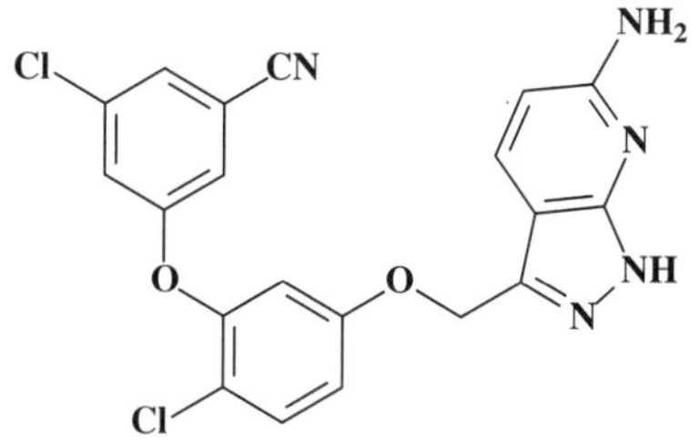

64

MK-4965

[145]

MK-4965 was evaluated against a panel of 15 viruses with NNRTI-resistance-associated mutations: it showed a superior mutant profile to that of efavirenz but not to that of etravirine [146]. The anti-HIV-1 activity was nonantagonistic with each of the 18 FDA-licensed drugs. Taken together, the *in vitro* data gathered with MK-4965 suggested it possesses the desired properties for further development for the treatment of HIV-1 infections [146].

7. CLINICAL POTENTIAL OF CURRENT, NRTI-, NTRTI-, AND NNRTI-BASED CHEMOTHERAPEUTICS

Within 25 years after the discovery of HIV [147,148] 25 compounds have been approved as anti-HIV drugs, half of them (12 compounds) being targeted at the HIV-1 RT: 7 NRTIs (zidovudine, didanosine, zalcitabine, stavudine, lamivudine, abacavir, and emtricitabine), 1 NtRTI (tenofovir), and 4 NNRTIs (nevirapine, delavirdine, efavirenz, and etravirine), and a fifth one, rilpivirine, forthcoming [149].

As a rule, anti-HIV drugs are used in drug combination regimens, so as to (i) diminish the risk of HIV drug resistance development, (ii) obtain a synergistic anti-HIV action, and (iii) limit the individual drug dose levels and their toxic side effects. This synergistic anti-HIV-1 activity has been clearly demonstrated with the triple drug combination of tenofovir, emtricitabine and efavirenz [150]. *In vivo*, that is, treatment-naïve patients with HIV-1 infection, the triple drug combination of teno-

fovir, emtricitabine, and the integrase inhibitor raltegravir proved equally efficacious and safe as the combination of tenofovir, emtricitabine, and efavirenz [151].

Tenofovir disoproxil fumarate, which has recently also been licensed for the treatment of chronic hepatitis B (at the same daily dose of 300 mg as used for the treatment of HIV infections) [152], has become the cornerstone, at a fixed dose (300 mg) in combination with the NRTI emtricitabine (200 mg) and the NNRTI efavirenz (600 mg) [Atripla®], for the treatment of AIDS [23]. (In the future, efavirenz may be replaced by rilpivirine (25 mg) in this fixed-dose combination.) Current treatment guidelines also recommend a TDF-based regimen as the treatment of choice for HIV/HBV coinfections [153].

In view of raising concerns about exhaustion of future antiretroviral drug options [154], Atripla certainly is a standard first-line regimen to be recommended. Other fixed-dose combinations that have been (and are still being) used are Combivir (zidovudine plus lamivudine), Trizivir (zidovudine plus lamivudine plus abacavir) [155], and Truvada (tenofovir disoproxil fumarate plus emtricitabine) [156]. Also, a quadruple NRTI/NtRTI regimen of tenofovir plus zidovudine/lamivudine/abacavir has been considered [157].

Current HIV treatment modalities have shifted towards early antiretroviral drug therapy: in infants, early HIV diagnosis and early antiretroviral drug therapy would reduce early infant mortality by 76% and HIV progression by 75% [158]. Once-daily fixed-dose drug combinations, such as Atripla, possess improved tolerability and convenience compared to earlier antiretroviral drug options, leading to a simplification of antiretroviral therapy [159,160], and this is reflected by an increased regimen durability [161,162].

Depending on the drugs used, vigilance is needed for drug resistance development, as in the case of lamivudine [163], lipodystrophy, as in the case of stavudine [164], and kidney tubular dysfunction, as in the case of tenofovir [165].

While reduced drug susceptibility has been clearly associated with RT mutations such as M184V (lamivudine), L74V (didanosine), L74I (zidovudine plus abacavir) [166],

Y181C (NNRTIs) [167], and K103N [168], the emergence of virus–drug resistance should not necessarily be considered a deleterious effect: for example, the resistance mutation I132M conferring high-level resistance to nevirapine and delavirdine was found to engender hypersensitivity to NRTIs such as lamivudine and NtRTIs such as tenofovir [169], and the lamivudine resistance mutation M184V decreases *in vivo* fitness of the virus, as compared to the wild type [170]. On the other hand, HIV-1 drug resistance mutations may be elicited by certain compounds that are not assumed to possess a specific anti-HIV activity, such as the RT M184V mutation by the anti-HBV agent entecavir [171,172] and the RT V75I mutation by the anti-HSV agent acyclovir [173,174].

One clinical application where (the risk of) emergence of virus–drug resistance may be of lesser importance is topical use of the RT inhibitors. NtRTIs (such as tenofovir) and NNRTIs [such as the thiocarboxanilide UC-781 and dapivirine (TMC120)] have been considered for topical application as vaginal microbicides [95–97], for which there is a clear and urgent need [175,176]. A number of candidate vaginal microbicides have progressed to phase III clinical trials, one of the foremost being the Carraguard®-based microbicides to prevent vaginal HIV infection [177]; these trials should also be extended to colorectal microbicides [178]. Systemic RT inhibitors (i.e., zidovudine, lamivudine, and emtricitabine) may also be useful in postexposure prophylaxis of vaginal transmission [179] as well as mother-to-child transmission of HIV [180].

Of continuous concern associated with the long-term use of RT inhibitors, especially NRTIs and NtRTIs, is their potential toxicity. For didanosine, there is the danger of development of noncirrhotic portal hypertension (NCPH) [181]. Whether loss of bone mineral density (BMD) is linked to antiretroviral therapy has not been established [182], or would not be greater with NNRTI regimens than with protease inhibitor regimens [183]. The use of Combivir (zidovudine plus lamivudine) contributes to limb fat loss (lipoatrophy, lipodystrophy) [184], and this lipoatrophy diminishes when switching away from thymidine NRTIs [185].

Abacavir is notorious for the hypersensitivity it can cause in 5–8% of patients initiating therapy, and this is associated with the pharmacogenetic HLA-B*5701 PGx marker [186]. Of greater concern is that abacavir may lead to an increased risk of cardiovascular disease (myocardial infarction) [187], although the increased risk of myocardial infarction following abacavir therapy has been questioned lately [188].

As mentioned above [189], the NtRTI tenofovir can cause kidney (proximal) tubular dysfunction, as it targets mitochondria of the renal proximal tubules [190,191]. Yet, no clinically relevant renal disease or adverse events were demonstrated in antiretroviral-naïve patients treated with TDF through 144 weeks, pointing to the 3-year renal safety of TDF [192]. Tenofovir may also be expected to be safe when used in combination with other drugs such as tacrolimus [193], and raltegravir [194], as it does not show significant drug interactions with these compounds.

All the toxicity remarks described above concern adults and should not necessarily be extrapolated as such to children. In children, for example, regimens containing zidovudine (AZT) have less toxicity than those containing stavudine (D4T) [195] that favors the use of AZT-containing regimens over that of D4T-containing regimens for first-line therapy in HIV-infected children.

ACKNOWLEDGMENT

I thank Mrs. Christiane Callebaut for her dedicated editorial assistance.

REFERENCES

1. Mitsuya H, Popovic M, Yarchoan R, Matsushita S, Gallo RC, Broder S. Suramin protection of T cells *in vitro* against infectivity and cytopathic effect of HTLV-III. Science 1984;226: 172–174.

2. Broder S, Yarchoan R, Collins JM, Lane HC, Markham PD, Klecker RW, Redfield RR, Mitsuya H, Hoth DF, Gelmann E. Effects of suramin on HTLV-III/LAV infection presenting as Kaposi's sarcoma or AIDS-related complex: clinical pharmacology and suppression of virus replication *in vivo*. Lancet 1985;ii:627–630.

3. De Clercq E. Suramin: a potent inhibitor of the reverse transcriptase of RNA tumor viruses. Cancer Lett 1979;8:9–22.

4. De Clercq E. Suramin in the treatment of AIDS: mechanism of action. Antiviral Res 1987;7:1–10.

5. Rozenbaum W, Dormont D, Spire B, Vilmer E, Gentilini M, Griscelli C, Montagnier L, Barré-Sinoussi F, Chermann JC. Antimoniotungstate (HPA 23) treatment of three patients with AIDS and one with prodrome. Lancet 1985;1:450–451.

6. Yamamoto N, Schols D, De Clercq E, Debyser Z, Pauwels R, Balzarini J, Nakashima H, Baba M, Hosoya M, Snoeck R, Neyts J, Andrei G, Murrer BA, Theobald B, Bossard G, Henson G, Abrams M, Picker D. Mechanism of anti-human immunodeficiency virus action of polyoxometalates, a class of broad-spectrum antiviral agents. Mol Pharmacol 1992;42:1109–1117.

7. Mitsuya H, Weinhold KJ, Furman PA, St Clair MH, Lehrman SN, Gallo RC, Bolognesi D, Barry DW, Broder S. 3'-Azido-3'-deoxythymidine (BW A509U): an antiviral agent that inhibits the infectivity and cytopathic effect of human T-lymphotropic virus type III/lymphadenopathy-associated virus in vitro. Proc Natl Acad Sci USA 1985;82:7096–7100.

8. Furman PA, Fyfe JA, St Clair MH, Weinhold K, Rideout JL, Freeman GA, Lehrman SN, Bolognesi DP, Broder S, Mitsuya H, Barry DW. Phosphorylation of 3'-azido-3'-deoxythymidine and selective interaction of the 5'-triphosphate with human immunodeficiency virus reverse transcriptase. Proc Natl Acad Sci USA 1986;83:8333–8337.

9. Mitsuya H, Broder S. Inhibition of the in vitro infectivity and cytopathic effect of human T-lymphotrophic virus type III/lymphadenopathy-associated virus (HTLV-III/LAV) by 2',3'-dideoxynucleosides. Proc Natl Acad Sci USA 1986;83:1911–1915.

10. Balzarini J, Pauwels R, Herdewijn P, De Clercq E, Cooney DA, Kang G-J, Dalal M, Johns DG, Broder S. Potent and selective anti-HTLV-III/LAV activity of 2',3'-dideoxycytidinene, the 2',3'-unsaturated derivative of 2',3'-dideoxycytidine. Biochem Biophys Res Commun 1986;140:735–742.

11. Baba M, Pauwels R, Herdewijn P, De Clercq E, Desmyter J, Vandeputte M. Both 2',3'-dideoxythymidine and its 2',3'-unsaturated derivative (2',3'-dideoxythymidinene) are potent and selective inhibitors of human immunodeficiency virus replication in vitro. Biochem Biophys Res Commun 1987;142:128–134.

12. Hamamoto Y, Nakashima H, Matsui T, Matsuda A, Ueda T, Yamamoto N. Inhibitory effect of 2',3'-didehydro-2',3'-dideoxynucleosides on infectivity, cytopathic effects, and replication of human immunodeficiency virus. Antimicrob Agents Chemother 1987;31:907–910.

13. Lin TS, Schinazi RF, Prusoff WH. Potent and selective in vitro activity of 3'-deoxythymidin-2'-ene (3'-deoxy-2',3'-didehydrothymidine) against human immunodeficiency virus. Biochem Pharmacol 1987;36:2713–2718.

14. Soudeyns H, Yao XI, Gao Q, Belleau B, Kraus JL, Nguyen-Ba N, Spira B, Wainberg MA. Anti-human immunodeficiency virus type 1 activity and in vitro toxicity of 2'-deoxy-3'-thiacytidine (BCH-189), a novel heterocyclic nucleoside analog. Antimicrob Agents Chemother 1991;35:1386–1390.

15. Daluge SM, Good SS, Faletto MB, Miller WH, St Clair MH, Boone LR, Tisdale M, Parry NR, Reardon JE, Dornsife RE, Averett DR, Krenitsky TA. 1592U89, a novel carbocyclic nucleoside analog with potent, selective anti-human immunodeficiency virus activity. Antimicrob Agents Chemother 1997;41:1082–1093.

16. Schinazi RF, Boudinot FD, Ibrahim SS, Manning C, McClure HM, Liotta DC. Pharmacokinetics and metabolism of racemic 2',3'-dideoxy-5-fluoro-3'-thiacytidine in rhesus monkeys. Antimicrob Agents Chemother 1992;36:2432–2438.

17. Gosselin G, Schinazi RF, Sommadossi J-P, Mathé C, Bergogne M-C, Aubertin A-M, Kirn A, Imbach J-L. Anti-human immunodeficiency virus activities of the beta-L enantiomer of 2',3'-dideoxycytidine and its 5-fluoro derivative in vitro. Antimicrob Agents Chemother 1994;38:1292–1297.

18. Schinazi RF, Gosselin G, Faraj A, Korba BE, Liotta DC, Chu CK, Mathé C, Imbach J-L, Sommadossi J-P. Pure nucleoside enantiomers of beta-2',3'-dideoxycytidine analogs are selective inhibitors of hepatitis B virus in vitro. Antimicrob Agents Chemother 1994;38:2172–2174.

19. De Clercq E, Holý A, Rosenberg I, Sakuma T, Balzarini J, Maudgal PC. A novel selective broad-spectrum anti-DNA virus agent. Nature 1986;323:464–467.

20. Pauwels R, Balzarini J, Schols D, Baba M, Desmyter J, Rosenberg I, Holý A, De Clercq E. Phosphonylmethoxyethyl purine derivatives: a new class of anti-human immunodeficiency virus agents. Antimicrob Agents Chemother 1988;32:1025–1030.

21. Balzarini J, Naesens L, Herdewijn P, Rosenberg I, Holý A, Pauwels R, Baba M, Johns DG, De Clercq E. Marked *in vivo* antiretrovirus activity of 9-(2-phosphonylmethoxyethyl)adenine, a selective anti-human immunodeficiency virus agent. Proc Natl Acad Sci USA 1989;86:332–336.

22. Balzarini J, Holý A, Jindrich J, Naesens L, Snoeck R, Schols D, De Clercq E. Differential antiherpesvirus and antiretrovirus effects of the (S) and (R) enantiomers of acyclic nucleoside phosphonates: potent and selective *in vitro* and *in vivo* antiretrovirus activities of (R)-9-(2-phosphonomethoxypropyl)-2,6-diaminopurine. Antimicrob Agents Chemother 1993;37:332–338.

23. De Clercq E. From adefovir to Atripla™ via tenofovir, Viread™ and Truvada™. Future Virol 2006;1:709–715.

24. Baba M, Tanaka H, De Clercq E, Pauwels R, Balzarini J, Schols D, Nakashima H, Perno C-F, Walker RT, Miyasaka T. Highly specific inhibition of human immunodeficiency virus type 1 by a novel 6-substituted acyclouridine derivative. Biochem Biophys Res Commun 1989;165:1375–1381.

25. Miyasaka T, Tanaka H, Baba M, Hayakawa H, Walker RT, Balzarini J, De Clercq E. A novel lead for specific anti-HIV-1 agents: 1-[(2-hydroxyethoxy)methyl]-6-(phenylthio)thymine. J Med Chem 1989;32:2507–2509.

26. Pauwels R, Andries K, Desmyter J, Schols D, Kukla MJ, Breslin HJ, Raeymaeckers A, Van Gelder J, Woestenborghs R, Heykants J, Schellekens K, Janssen MAC, De Clercq E, Janssen PAJ. Potent and selective inhibition of HIV-1 replication *in vitro* by a novel series of TIBO derivatives. Nature 1990;343:470–474.

27. Baba M, De Clercq E, Tanaka H, Ubasawa M, Takashima H, Sekiya K, Nitta I, Umezu K, Nakashima H, Mori S, Shigeta S, Walker RT, Miyasaka T. Potent and selective inhibition of human immunodeficiency virus type 1 (HIV-1) by 5-ethyl-6-phenylthiouracil derivatives through their interaction with the HIV-1 reverse transcriptase. Proc Natl Acad Sci USA 1991;88:2356–2360.

28. Baba M, De Clercq E, Tanaka H, Ubasawa M, Takashima H, Sekiya K, Nitta I, Umezu K, Walker RT, Mori S, Ito M, Shigeta S, Miyasaka T. Highly potent and selective inhibition of human immunodeficiency virus type 1 by a novel series of 6-substituted acyclouridine derivatives. Mol Pharmacol 1991;39: 805–810.

29. Debyser Z, Pauwels R, Andries K, Desmyter J, Kukla M, Janssen PAJ, De Clercq E. An antiviral target on reverse transcriptase of human immunodeficiency virus type 1 revealed by tetrahydroimidazo-[4,5,1-*jk*][1,4]benzodiazepin-2(1*H*)-one and -thione derivatives. Proc Natl Acad Sci USA 1991;88:1451–1455.

30. De Clercq E. Non-nucleoside reverse transcriptase inhibitors (NNRTIs): past, present and future. Chem Biodivers 2004;1:44–64.

31. Lanciault C, Champoux JJ. Single unpaired nucleotides facilitate HIV-1 reverse transcriptase displacement synthesis through duplex RNA. J Biol Chem 2004;279:32252–32261.

32. Götte M, Rausch JW, Marchand B, Sarafianos S, Le Grice SF. Reverse transcriptase in motion: conformational dynamics of enzyme-substrate interactions. Biochim Biophys Acta 2010;1804:1202–1212.

33. Beilhartz GL, Wendeler M, Baichoo N, Rausch J, Le Grice S, Götte M. HIV-1 reverse transcriptase can simultaneously engage its DNA/RNA substrate at both DNA polymerase and RNase H active sites: implications for RNase H inhibition. J Mol Biol 2009;88: 462–474.

34. Liu S, Abbondanzieri EA, Rausch JW, Le Grice SF, Zhuang X. Slide into action: dynamic shuttling of HIV reverse transcriptase on nucleic acid substrates. Science 2008;322:1092–1097.

35. Sarafianos SG, Arnold E. Biochemistry. RT slides home.... Science 2008;322:1059–1060.

36. Kohlstaedt LA, Wang J, Friedman JM, Rice PA, Steitz TA. Crystal structure at 3.5 Å resolution of HIV-1 reverse transcriptase complexed with an inhibitor. Science 1992;256: 1783–1790.

37. Jacobo-Molina A, Ding J, Nanni RG, Clark AD Jr, Lu X, Tantillo C, Williams RL, Kamer G, Ferris AL, Clark P, Hizi A, Hughes SH, Arnold E. Crystal structure of human immunodeficiency virus type 1 reverse transcriptase complexed with double-stranded DNA at 3.0 Å resolution shows bent DNA. Proc Natl Acad Sci USA 1993;90:6320–6324.

38. Sarafianos SG, Das K, Tantillo C, Clark AD Jr, Ding J, Whitcomb JM, Boyer PL, Hughes SH, Arnold E. Crystal structure of HIV-1 reverse transcriptase in complex with a polypurine tract RNA:DNA. EMBO J 2001;20:1449–1461.

39. Johnson VA, Brun-Vézinet F, Clotet B, Gunthard HF, Kuritzkes DR, Pillay D, Schapiro JM, Richman DD, Update of the drug resistance mutations in HIV-1: spring 2008 Top HIV Med 2008;16:62–68.

40. Brehm JH, Mellors JW, Sluis-Cremer N. Mechanism by which a glutamine to leucine substitution at residue 509 in the ribonuclease H domain of HIV-1 reverse transcriptase confers zidovudine resistance. Biochemistry 2008;47: 14020–14027.

41. Stellbrink HJ. Novel compounds for the treatment of HIV type-1 infection. Antiviral Chem Chemother 2009;19:189–200.

42. De Clercq E. Emerging anti-HIV drugs. Expert Opin Emerg Drugs 2005;10:241–274.

43. De Clercq E. Emerging antiviral drugs. Expert Opin Emerg Drugs 2008;13:393–416.

44. Stoddart CA, Moreno ME, Linquist-Stepps VD, Bare C, Bogan MR, Gobbi A, Buckheit RW Jr, Bedard J, Rando RF, McCune JM. Antiviral activity of 2′-deoxy-3′-oxa-4′-thiocytidine (BCH-10652) against lamivudine-resistant human immunodeficiency virus type 1 in SCID-hu Thy/Liv mice. Antimicrob Agents Chemother 2000;44: 783–786.

45. Mansour TS, Jin H, Wang W, Hooker EU, Ashman C, Cammack N, Salomon H, Belmonte AR, Wainberg MA. Anti-human immunodeficiency virus and anti-hepatitis-B virus activities and toxicities of the enantiomers of 2′-deoxy-3′-oxa-4′-thiocytidine and their 5-fluoro analogues in vitro. J Med Chem 1995;38:1–4.

46. Schinazi RF, Mellors J, Bazmi H, Diamond S, Garber S, Gallagher K, Geleziunas R, Klabe R, Pierce M, Rayner M, Wu JT, Zhang H, Hammond J, Bacheler L, Manion DJ, Otto MJ, Stuyver L, Trainor G, Liotta DC, Erickson-Viitanen S. DPC 817: a cytidine nucleoside analog with activity against zidovudine- and lamivudine-resistant viral variants. Antimicrob Agents Chemother 2002;46: 1394–1401.

47. Geleziunas R, Gallagher K, Zhang H, Bacheler L, Garber S, Wu JT, Shi G, Otto MJ, Schinazi RF, Erickson-Viitanen S. HIV-1 resistance profile of the novel nucleoside reverse transcriptase inhibitor beta-D-2′,3′-dideoxy-2′,3′-didehydro-5-fluorocytidine (Reverset). Antiviral Chem Chemother 2003;14:49–59.

48. Oliveira M, Moisi D, Spira B, Cox S, Brenner BG, Wainberg MA. Apricitabine does not select additional drug resistance mutations in tissue culture in human immunodeficiency virus type 1 variants containing K65R, M184V, or M184V plus thymidine analogue mutations. Antimicrob Agents Chemother 2009;53:1683–1685.

49. Cox S, Southby J. Apricitabine: a novel nucleoside reverse transcriptase inhibitor for the treatment of HIV infection that is refractory

50. Holdich T, Shiveley L, Sawyer J. Pharmacokinetics of single oral doses of apricitabine, a novel deoxycytidine analogue reverse transcriptase inhibitor, in healthy volunteers. Clin Drug Investig 2006;26:279–286.

51. Holdich T, Shiveley LA, Sawyer J. Effect of Lamivudine on the plasma and intracellular pharmacokinetics of apricitabine, a novel nucleoside reverse transcriptase inhibitor, in healthy volunteers. Antimicrob Agents Chemother 2007;51:2943–2947.

52. Colucci P, Pottage JC, Robison H, Turgeon J, Ducharme MP. Effect of a single dose of ritonavir on the pharmacokinetic behavior of elvucitabine, a nucleoside reverse transcriptase inhibitor, administered in healthy volunteers. Antimicrob Agents Chemother 2009;53: 646–650.

53. Colucci P, Pottage JC, Robison H, Turgeon J, Schürmann D, Hoepelman IM, Ducharme MP. Multiple-dose pharmacokinetic behavior of elvucitabine, a nucleoside reverse transcriptase inhibitor, administered over 21 days with lopinavir–ritonavir in human immunodeficiency virus type 1-infected subjects. Antimicrob Agents Chemother 2009;53:662–669.

54. Furman PA, Jeffrey J, Kiefer LL, Feng JY, Anderson KS, Borroto-Esoda K, Hill E, Copeland WC, Chu CK, Sommadossi JP, Liberman I, Schinazi RF, Painter GR. Mechanism of action of 1-beta-D-2,6-diaminopurine dioxolane, a prodrug of the human immunodeficiency virus type 1 inhibitor 1-beta-D-dioxolane guanosine. Antimicrob Agents Chemother 2001;45:158–165.

55. Jeffrey JL, Feng JY, Qi CC, Anderson KS, Furman PA. Dioxolane guanosine 5′-triphosphate, an alternative substrate inhibitor of wild-type and mutant HIV-1 reverse transcriptase. Steady state and pre-steady state kinetic analyses. J Biol Chem 2003;278: 18971–18979.

56. Kewn S, Wang LH, Hoggard PG, Rousseau F, Hart R, MacNeela JP, Khoo SH, Back DJ. Enzymatic assay for measurement of intracellular DXG triphosphate concentrations in peripheral blood mononuclear cells from human immunodeficiency virus type 1-infected patients. Antimicrob Agents Chemother 2003;47:255–261.

57. Mewshaw JP, Myrick FT, Wakefield DA, Hooper BJ, Harris JL, McCreedy B, Borroto-Esoda K. Dioxolane guanosine, the active form of the

prodrug diaminopurine dioxolane, is a potent inhibitor of drug-resistant HIV-1 isolates from patients for whom standard nucleoside therapy fails. J Acquir Immune Defic Syndr 2002;29:11–20.

58. Gripshover BM, Ribaudo H, Santana J, Gerber JG, Campbell TB, Hogg E, Jarocki B, Hammer SM, Kuritzkes DR, A5118 Team. Amdoxovir versus placebo with enfuvirtide plus optimized background therapy for HIV-1-infected subjects failing current therapy (AACTG A5118). Antiviral Ther 2006;11:619–623.

59. Margolis DM, Mukherjee AL, Fletcher CV, Hogg E, Ogata-Arakaki D, Petersen T, Rusin D, Martinez A, Mellors JW. The use of beta-D-2,6-diaminopurine dioxolane with or without mycophenolate mofetil in drug-resistant HIV infection. AIDS 2007;21:2025–2032.

60. Thompson MA, Kessler HA, Eron JJ Jr, Jacobson JM, Adda N, Shen G, Zong J, Harris J, Moxham C, Rousseau FS, DAPD-101 Study Group. Short-term safety and pharmacodynamics of amdoxovir in HIV-infected patients. AIDS 2005;19:1607–1615.

61. Chu CK, Yadav V, Chong YH, Schinazi RF. Anti-HIV activity of (−)-(2R,4R)-1-(2-hydroxymethyl-1,3-dioxolan-4-yl)-thymine against drug-resistant HIV-1 mutants and studies of its molecular mechanism. J Med Chem 2005;48:3949–3952.

62. Lennerstrand J, Chu CK, Schinazi RF. Biochemical studies on the mechanism of human immunodeficiency virus type 1 reverse transcriptase resistance to 1-(beta-D-dioxolane) thymine triphosphate. Antimicrob Agents Chemother 2007;51:2078–2084.

63. Nakata H, Amano M, Koh Y, Kodama E, Yang G, Bailey CM, Kohgo S, Hayakawa H, Matsuoka M, Anderson KS, Cheng YC, Mitsuya H. Activity against human immunodeficiency virus type 1, intracellular metabolism, and effects on human DNA polymerases of 4′-ethynyl-2-fluoro-2′-deoxyadenosine. Antimicrob Agents Chemother 2007;51:2701–2708.

64. Paintsil E, Dutschman GE, Hu R, Grill SP, Lam W, Baba M, Tanaka H, Cheng YC. Intracellular metabolism and persistence of the anti-human immunodeficiency virus activity of 2′,3′-didehydro-3′-deoxy-4′-ethynylthymidine, a novel thymidine analog. Antimicrob Agents Chemother 2007;51: 3870–3879.

65. Jeong LS, Choi YN, Tosh DK, Choi WJ, Kim HO, Choi J. Design and synthesis of novel 2′,3′-dideoxy-4′-selenonucleosides as potential antiviral agents. Bioorg Med Chem 2008;16: 9891–9897.

66. Boyer PL, Vu BC, Ambrose Z, Julias JG, Warnecke S, Liao C, Meier C, Marquez VE, Hughes SH. The nucleoside analogue D-carba T blocks HIV-1 reverse transcription. J Med Chem 2009;52:5356–5364.

67. Herdewijn P, Balzarini J, Baba M, Pauwels R, Van Aerschot A, Janssen G, De Clercq E. Synthesis and anti-HIV activity of different sugar-modified pyrimidine and purine nucleosides. J Med Chem 1988;31:2040–2048.

68. Sluis-Cremer N, Koontz D, Bassit L, Hernandez-Santiago BI, Detorio M, Rapp KL, Amblard F, Bondada L, Grier J, Coats SJ, Schinazi RF, Mellors JW. Anti-human immunodeficiency virus activity, cross-resistance, cytotoxicity, and intracellular pharmacology of the 3′-azido-2′,3′-dideoxypurine nucleosides. Antimicrob Agents Chemother 2009;53: 3715–3719.

69. Saiyed ZM, Gandhi NH, Nair MP. AZT 5′-triphosphate nanoformulation suppresses human immunodeficiency virus type 1 replication in peripheral blood mononuclear cells. J NeuroVirol 2009;15:343–347.

70. De Clercq E, Holý A. Acyclic nucleoside phosphonates: a key class of antiviral drugs. Nat Rev Drug Discov 2005;4:928–940.

71. De Clercq E. Acyclic nucleoside phosphonates: past, present and future. Bridging chemistry to HIV, HBV, HCV, HPV, adeno-, herpes-, and poxvirus infections: the phosphonate bridge. Biochem Pharmacol 2007;73:911–922.

72. De Clercq E. Acyclic nucleoside phosphonates: past, present and future. Bridging chemistry to HIV, HBV, HCV, HPV, adeno-, herpes-, and poxvirus infections: the phosphonate bridge. Antiviral Res 2007;75:1–13.

73. De Clercq E, Andrei G, Balzarini J, Leyssen P, Naesens L, Neyts J, Pannecouque C, Snoeck R, Ying C, Hocková D, Holý A. Antiviral potential of a new generation of acyclic nucleoside phosphonates, the 6-[2-(phosphonomethoxy)alkoxy]-2,4-diaminopyrimidines. Proceedings of the XVIth International Round Table on Nucleosides, Nucleotides and Nucleic Acids, Minneapolis, MN, USA, September 12–16 2004; Nucleosides Nucleotides Nucleic Acids 2005; 24:331–341.

74. Balzarini J, Schols D, Van Laethem K, De Clercq E, Hocková D, Masojidkova M, Holý A. Pronounced in vitro and in vivo antiretroviral activity of 5-substituted 2,4-diamino-6-[2-(phosphonomethoxy)ethoxy] pyrimidines. J Antimicrob Chemother 2007;59:80–86.

75. Hostetler KY, Aldern KA, Wan WB, Ciesla SL, Beadle JR. Alkoxyalkyl esters of (S)-9-[3-hy-

droxy-2-(phosphonomethoxy)propyl]adenine are potent inhibitors of the replication of wild-type and drug-resistant human immunodeficiency virus type 1 *in vitro*. Antimicrob Agents Chemother 2006;50:2857–2859.

76. Painter GR, Almond MR, Trost LC, Lampert BM, Neyts J, De Clercq E, Korba BE, Aldern KA, Beadle JR, Hostetler KY. Evaluation of hexadecyloxypropyl-9-*R*-[2-(Phosphonomethoxy)propyl]-adenine, CMX157, as a potential treatment for human immunodeficiency virus type 1 and hepatitis B virus infections. Antimicrob Agents Chemother 2007;51:3505–3509.

77. Jie L, Van Aerschot A, Balzarini J, Janssen G, Busson R, Hoogmartens J, De Clercq E, Herdewijn P. 5'-*O*-Phosphonomethyl-2',3'-dideoxynucleosides: synthesis and anti-HIV activity. J Med Chem 1990;33:2481–2487.

78. Wu T, Froeyen M, Kempeneers V, Pannecouque C, Wang J, Busson R, De Clercq E, Herdewijn P. Deoxythreosyl phosphonate nucleosides as selective anti-HIV agents. J Am Chem Soc 2005;127:5056–5065.

79. Cihlar T, Ray AS, Boojamra CG, Zhang L, Hui H, Laflamme G, Vela JE, Grant D, Chen J, Myrick F, White KL, Gao Y, Lin KY, Douglas JL, Parkin NT, Carey A, Pakdaman R, Mackman RL. Design and profiling of GS-9148, a novel nucleotide analog active against nucleoside-resistant variants of human immunodeficiency virus type 1, and its orally bioavailable phosphonoamidate prodrug, GS-9131. Antimicrob Agents Chemother 2008;52:655–665.

80. Ray AS, Vela JE, Boojamra CG, Zhang L, Hui H, Callebaut C, Stray K, Lin KY, Gao Y, Mackman RL, Cihlar T. Intracellular metabolism of the nucleotide prodrug GS-9131, a potent anti-human immunodeficiency virus agent. Antimicrob Agents Chemother 2008;52:648–654.

81. Lee WA, He GX, Eisenberg E, Cihlar T, Swaminathan S, Mulato A, Cundy KC. Selective intracellular activation of a novel prodrug of the human immunodeficiency virus reverse transcriptase inhibitor tenofovir leads to preferential distribution and accumulation in lymphatic tissue. Antimicrob Agents Chemother 2005;49:1898–1906.

82. Cihlar T, Laflamme G, Fisher R, Carey AC, Vela JE, Mackman R, Ray AS. Novel nucleotide human immunodeficiency virus reverse transcriptase inhibitor GS-9148 with a low nephrotoxic potential: characterization of renal transport and accumulation. Antimicrob Agents Chemother 2009;53:150–156.

83. Boojamra CG, Parrish JP, Sperandio D, Gao Y, Petrakovsky OV, Lee SK, Markevitch DY, Vela JE, Laflamme G, Chen JM, Ray AS, Barron AC, Sparacino ML, Desai MC, Kim CU, Cihlar T, Mackman RL. Design, synthesis, and anti-HIV activity of 4'-modified carbocyclic nucleoside phosphonate reverse transcriptase inhibitors. Bioorg Med Chem 2009;17:1739–1746.

84. De Clercq E. The role of non-nucleoside reverse transcriptase inhibitors (NNRTIs) in the therapy of HIV-1 infection. Antiviral Res 1998;38:153–179.

85. Vingerhoets J, Azijn H, Fransen E, De Baere I, Smeulders L, Jochmans D, Andries K, Pauwels R, de Béthune MP. TMC125 displays a high genetic barrier to the development of resistance: evidence from *in vitro* selection experiments. J Virol 2005;79:12773–12782.

86. Andries K, Azijn H, Thielemans T, Ludovici D, Kukla M, Heeres J, Janssen P, De Corte B, Vingerhoets J, Pauwels R, de Béthune MP. TMC125, a novel next-generation nonnucleoside reverse transcriptase inhibitor active against nonnucleoside reverse transcriptase inhibitor-resistant human immunodeficiency virus type 1. Antimicrob Agents Chemother 2004;48:4680–4686.

87. Madruga JV, Cahn P, Grinsztejn B, Haubrich R, Lalezari J, Mills A, Pialoux G, Wilkin T, Peeters M, Vingerhoets J, de Smedt G, Leopold L, Trefiglio R, Woodfall B. Efficacy and safety of TMC125 (etravirine) in treatment-experienced HIV-1-infected patients in DUET-1: 24-week results from a randomised, double-blind, placebo-controlled trial. Lancet 2007;370:39–48.

88. Lazzarin A, Campbell T, Clotet B, Johnson M, Katlama C, Moll A, Towner W, Trottier B, Peeters M, Vingerhoets J, de Smedt G, Baeten B, Beets G, Sinha R, Woodfall B. Efficacy and safety of TMC125 (etravirine) in treatment-experienced HIV-1-infected patients in DUET-2: 24-week results from a randomised, double-blind, placebo-controlled trial. Lancet 2007;370:39–48.

89. Boffito M, Winston A, Jackson A, Fletcher C, Pozniak A, Nelson M, Moyle G, Tolowinska I, Hoetelmans R, Miralles D, Gazzard B. Pharmacokinetics and antiretroviral response to darunavir/ritonavir and etravirine combination in patients with high-level viral resistance. AIDS 2007;21:1449–1455.

90. Schöller-Gyüre M, Kakuda TN, Sekar V, Woodfall B, De Smedt G, Lefebvre E, Peeters

M, Hoetelmans RM. Pharmacokinetics of darunavir/ritonavir and TMC125 alone and coadministered in HIV-negative volunteers. Antiviral Ther 2007;12:789–796.

91. Geretti AM. Shifting paradigms: the resistance profile of etravirine. J Antimicrob Chemother 2008;62:643–647.

92. Dailly E, Raffi F, Perré P, Martin J, Deslandes G, Jolliet P. Influence of darunavir coadministration on nevirapine pharmacokinetics in HIV-infected patients: a population approach. HIV Med 2009;10:586–589.

93. Jayaweera DT, Espinoza L, Castro J. Etravirine: the renaissance of non-nucleoside reverse transcriptase inhibitors. Expert Opin Pharmacother 2008;9:3083–3094.

94. Schiller DS, Youssef-Bessler M. Etravirine: a second-generation nonnucleoside reverse transcriptase inhibitor (NNRTI) active against NNRTI-resistant strains of HIV. Clin Ther 2009;31:692–704.

95. Borkow G, Barnard J, Nguyen TM, Belmonte A, Wainberg MA, Parniak MA. Chemical barriers to human immunodeficiency virus type 1 (HIV-1) infection: retrovirucidal activity of UC781, a thiocarboxanilide nonnucleoside inhibitor of HIV-1 reverse transcriptase. J Virol 1997;71:3023–3030.

96. Balzarini J, Naesens L, Verbeken E, Laga M, Van Damme L, Parniak M, Van Mellaert L, Anné J, De Clercq E. Preclinical studies on thiocarboxanilide UC-781 as a virucidal agent. AIDS 1998;12:1129–1138.

97. Van Herrewege Y, Vanham G, Michiels J, Fransen K, Kestens L, Andries K, Janssen P, Lewi P. A series of diaryltriazines and diarylpyrimidines are highly potent nonnucleoside reverse transcriptase inhibitors with possible applications as microbicides. Antimicrob Agents Chemother 2004;48:3684–3689.

98. Elinder M, Danielson H, Unge T, VanHam G, Öberg B. MIV-170, a novel NNRTI exhibiting tight binding to HIV-1 reverse transcriptase (RT). Abstracts of the Twenty-First International Conference on Antiviral Research (ICAR), Montreal, Quebec, Canada, April 13–17 2008. Antiviral Res 2008; 78: A37, no 55.

99. Öberg B, Sahlberg BL, Sahlberg C, Samuelsson B, Wikström K, Vrang L, Zhang H. MIV-170, a novel NNRTI with potent activity against HIV and HIV mutants. Abstracts of the Twenty-First International Conference on Antiviral Research (ICAR), Montreal, Quebec, Canada, April 13–17 2008. Antiviral Res 2008; 78: A51, no 92.

100. Watson KM, Yang L, Buckheit CE, Buckheit RW Jr. Development of the dual-acting pyrimidinedione IQP0528 as a vaginal topical anti-HIV microbicide. Abstracts of the Twenty-First International Conference on Antiviral Research (ICAR), Montreal, Quebec, Canada, April 13–17 2008. Antiviral Res. 2008; 78: A26, no 26.

101. Janssen PA, Lewi PJ, Arnold E, Daeyaert F, de Jonge M, Heeres J, Koymans L, Vinkers M, Guillemont J, Pasquier E, Kukla M, Ludovici D, Andries K, de Béthune MP, Pauwels R, Das K, Clark AD Jr, Frenkel YV, Hughes SH, Medaer B, De Knaep F, Bohets H, De Clerck F, Lampo A, Williams P, Stoffels P. In search of a novel anti-HIV drug: multidisciplinary coordination in the discovery of 4-[[4-[[4-[(1E)-2-cyanoethenyl]-2,6-dimethylphenyl]amino]-2-pyrimidinyl]amino]benzonitrile (R278474, rilpivirine). J Med Chem 2005;48:1901–1909.

102. Goebel F, Yakovlev A, Pozniak AL, Vinogradova E, Boogaerts G, Hoetelmans R, de Béthune MP, Peeters M, Woodfall B. Short-term antiviral activity of TMC278—a novel NNRTI—in treatment-naive HIV-1-infected subjects. AIDS 2006;20:1721–1726.

103. Garvey L, Winston A. Rilpivirine: a novel non-nucleoside reverse transcriptase inhibitor. Expert Opin Investig Drugs 2009;18:1035–1041.

104. van't Klooster G, Verloes R, Baert L, van Velsen F, Bouche MP, Spittaels K, Leempoels J, Williams P, Kraus G, Wigerinck P. Long-acting TMC278, a parenteral depot formulation delivering therapeutic NNRTI concentrations in preclinical and clinical settings. Abstracts of the 15th Conference on Retroviruses and Opportunistic Infections, Boston, MA, USA, February 3–6 2008. no 134.

105. Baert L, van't Klooster G, Dries W, François M, Wouters A, Basstanie E, Iterbeke K, Stappers F, Stevens P, Schueller L, Van Remoortere P, Kraus G, Wigerinck P, Rosier J. Development of a long-acting injectable formulation with nanoparticles of rilpivirine (TMC278) for HIV treatment. Eur J Pharm Biopharm 2009;72:502–508.

106. Van Gyseghem E, Pendela M, Baert L, Rosier J, van't Klooster g De Man H, Bouche MP, Schueller L, Van Remoortere P, Wigerinck P, Adams E, Hoogmartens J, Van den Mooter G. Powder for reconstitution of the anti-HIV-1 drug TMC278: formulation development, stability and animal studies. Eur J Pharm Biopharm 2008;70:853–860.

107. Sarafianos SG, Das K, Hughes SH, Arnold E. Taking aim at a moving target: designing

drugs to inhibit drug-resistant HIV-1 reverse transcriptases. Curr Opin Struct Biol 2004;14: 716–730.

108. Das K, Lewi PJ, Hughes SH, Arnold E. Crystallography and the design of anti-AIDS drugs: conformational flexibility and positional adaptability are important in the design of non-nucleoside HIV-1 reverse transcriptase inhibitors. Prog Biophys Mol Biol 2005;88:209–231.

109. Ivetac A, McCammon JA. Elucidating the inhibition mechanism of HIV-1 non-nucleoside reverse transcriptase inhibitors through multicopy molecular dynamics simulations. J Mol Biol 2009;388:644–658.

110. Tambuyzer L, Azijn H, Rimsky LT, Vingerhoets J, Lecocq P, Kraus G, Picchio G, de Béthune MP. Compilation and prevalence of mutations associated with resistance to non-nucleoside reverse transcriptase inhibitors. Antiviral Ther 2009;14:103–109.

111. Ghosn J, Chaix ML, Delaugerre C. HIV-1 resistance to first- and second-generation non-nucleoside reverse transcriptase inhibitors. AIDS Rev 2009;11:165–173.

112. Machado ES, Afonso AO, Nissley DV, Lemey P, Cunha SM, Oliveira RH, Soares MA. Emergence of primary NNRTI resistance mutations without antiretroviral selective pressure in a HAART-treated child. PLoS One 2009;4:e4806.

113. Lehman DA, Chung MH, Mabuka JM, John-Stewart GC, Kiarie J, Kinuthia J, Overbaugh J. Lower risk of resistance after short-course HAART compared with zidovudine/single-dose nevirapine used for prevention of HIV-1 mother-to-child transmission. J Acquir Immune Defic Syndr 2009;51:522–529.

114. TEmAA ANRS 12109 Study group, Arrivé E, Chaix ML, Nerrienet E, Blanche S, Rouzioux C, Coffie PA, Kruy Leang S, McIntyre J, Avit D, Srey VH, Gray G, N'Dri-Yoman T, Diallo A, Ekouévi DK, Dabis F. Tolerance and viral resistance after single-dose nevirapine with tenofovir and emtricitabine to prevent vertical transmission of HIV-1. AIDS 2009;23: 825–833.

115. Ehteshami M, Scarth BJ, Tchesnokov EP, Dash C, Le Grice SF, Hallenberger S, Jochmans D, Götte M. Mutations M184V and Y115F in HIV-1 reverse transcriptase discriminate against "nucleotide-competing reverse transcriptase inhibitors". J Biol Chem 2008; 283:29904–29911.

116. Prajapati DG, Ramajayam R, Yadav MR, Giridhar R. The search for potent, small molecule NNRTIs: a review. Bioorg Med Chem 2009;17: 5744–5762.

117. Monforte AM, Logoteta P, Ferro S, Luca LD, Iraci N, Maga G, De Clercq E, Pannecouque C, Chimirri A. Design, synthesis, and structure–activity relationships of 1,3-dihydrobenzimidazol-2-one analogues as anti-HIV agents. Bioorg Med Chem 2009;17:5962–5967.

118. Lagos CF, Caballero J, Gonzalez-Nilo FD, David Pessoa-Mahana C, Perez-Acle T. Docking and quantitative structure–activity relationship studies for the bisphenylbenzimidazole family of non-nucleoside inhibitors of HIV-1 reverse transcriptase. Chem Biol Drug Des 2008;72:360–369.

119. Wang YP, Chen FE, De Clercq E, Balzarini J, Pannecouque C. Synthesis and *in vitro* anti-HIV evaluation of a new series of 6-arylmethyl-substituted S-DABOs as potential non-nucleoside HIV-1 reverse transcriptase inhibitors. Eur J Med Chem 2009;44:1016–1023.

120. Xiong YZ, Chen FE, Balzarini J, De Clercq E, Pannecouque C. Non-nucleoside HIV-1 reverse transcriptase inhibitors. Part 13. Synthesis of fluorine-containing diaryltriazine derivatives for *in vitro* anti-HIV evaluation against wild-type strain. Chem Biodivers 2009;6:561–568.

121. Li Z, Han J, Chen HF. Revealing interaction mode between HIV-1 reverse transcriptase and diaryltriazine analog inhibitor. Chem Biol Drug Des 2008;72:350–359.

122. Mahajan DH, Pannecouque C, De Clercq E, Chikhalia KH. Synthesis and studies of new 2-(coumarin-4-yloxy)-4,6-(substituted)-*S*-triazine derivatives as potential anti-HIV agents. Arch Pharm 2009;342:281–290.

123. Zhan P, Li Z, Liu X, De Clercq E. Sulfanyltriazole/tetrazoles: a promising class of HIV-1 NNRTIs. Mini Rev Med Chem 2009;9: 1014–1023.

124. Zhan P, Liu X, Zhu J, Fang Z, Li Z, Pannecouque C, De Clercq E. Synthesis and biological evaluation of imidazole thioacetanilides as novel non-nucleoside HIV-1 reverse transcriptase inhibitors. Bioorg Med Chem 2009;17: 5775–5781.

125. Zhan P, Liu X, Fang Z, Pannecouque C, De Clercq E. 1,2,3-Selenadiazole thioacetanilides: synthesis and anti-HIV activity evaluation. Bioorg Med Chem 2009;17:6374–6379.

126. Zhan P, Liu X, Fang Z, Li Z, Pannecouque C, De Clercq E. Synthesis and anti-HIV activity evaluation of 2-(4-(naphthalen-2-yl)-1,2,3-thiadiazol-5-ylthio)-*N*-acetamides as novel non-nucleoside HIV-1 reverse transcriptase inhibitors. Eur J Med Chem 2009;44: 4648–4653.

127. Jones LH, Allan G, Corbau R, Hay D, Middleton DS, Mowbray CE, Newman SD, Perros M, Randall A, Vuong H, Webster R, Westby M, Williams D. Optimization of 5-aryloxyimidazole non-nucleoside reverse transcriptase inhibitors. ChemMedChem 2008;3: 1756–1762.

128. Samuele A, Kataropoulou A, Viola M, Zanoli S, La Regina G, Piscitelli F, Silvestri R, Maga G. Non-nucleoside HIV-1 reverse transcriptase inhibitors di-halo-indolyl aryl sulfones achieve tight binding to drug-resistant mutants by targeting the enzyme-substrate complex. Antiviral Res 2009;81:47–55.

129. Spallarossa A, Cesarini S, Ranise A, Schenone S, Bruno O, Borassi A, La Colla P, Pezzullo M, Sanna G, Collu G, Secci B, Loddo R. Parallel synthesis, molecular modelling and further structure–activity relationship studies of new acylthiocarbamates as potent non-nucleoside HIV-1 reverse transcriptase inhibitors. Eur J Med Chem 2009;44:2190–2201.

130. Cichero E, Cesarini S, Spallarossa A, Mosti L, Fossa P. Acylthiocarbamates as non-nucleoside HIV-1 reverse transcriptase inhibitors: docking studies and ligand-based CoMFA and CoMSIA analyses. J Mol Model 2009;15: 871–884.

131. Cichero E, Cesarini S, Fossa P, Spallarossa A, Mosti L. Thiocarbamates as non-nucleoside HIV-1 reverse transcriptase inhibitors: docking-based CoMFA and CoMSIA analyses. Eur J Med Chem 2009;44:2059–2070.

132. Spallarossa A, Cesarini S, Ranise A, Bruno O, Schenone S, La Colla P, Collu G, Sanna G, Secci B, Loddo R. Novel modifications in the series of O-(2-phthalimidoethyl)-N-substituted thiocarbamates and their ring-opened congeners as non-nucleoside HIV-1 reverse transcriptase inhibitors. Eur J Med Chem 2009;44:1650–1663.

133. Barreca ML, Rao A, De Luca L, Zappalà M, Monforte AM, Maga G, Pannecouque C, Balzarini J, De Clercq E, Chimirri A, Monforte P. Computational strategies in discovering novel non-nucleoside inhibitors of HIV-1 RT. J Med Chem 2005;48:3433–3437.

134. Monforte AM, Rao A, Logoteta P, Ferro S, De Luca L, Barreca ML, Iraci N, Maga G, De Clercq E, Pannecouque C, Chimirri A. Novel N1-substituted 1,3-dihydro-2H-benzimidazol-2-ones as potent non-nucleoside reverse transcriptase inhibitors. Bioorg Med Chem 2008;16:7429–7435.

135. De Clercq E. The next ten stories on antiviral drug discovery. Part E. Advents, advances and adventures. Med Res Rev 2009, in press.

136. Deng BL, Zhao Y, Hartman TL, Watson K, Buckheit RW Jr, Pannecouque C, De Clercq E, Cushman M. Synthesis of alkenyldiarylmethanes (ADAMs) containing benzo[d]isoxazole and oxazolidin-2-one rings, a new series of potent non-nucleoside HIV-1 reverse transcriptase inhibitors. Eur J Med Chem 2009;44:1210–1214.

137. Ren J, Chamberlain PP, Stamp A, Short SA, Weaver KL, Romines KR, Hazen R, Freeman A, Ferris RG, Andrews CW, Boone L, Chan JH, Stammers DK. Structural basis for the improved drug resistance profile of new generation benzophenone non-nucleoside HIV-1 reverse transcriptase inhibitors. J Med Chem 2008;51:5000–5008.

138. Butini S, Brindisi M, Cosconati S, Marinelli L, Borrelli G, Coccone SS, Ramunno A, Campiani G, Novellino E, Zanoli S, Samuele A, Giorgi G, Bergamini A, Di Mattia M, Lalli S, Galletti B, Gemma S, Maga G. Specific targeting of highly conserved residues in the HIV-1 reverse transcriptase primer grip region. 2. Stereoselective interaction to overcome the effects of drug resistant mutations. J Med Chem 2009;52: 1224–1228.

139. Liang YH, Feng XQ, Zeng ZS, Chen FE, Balzarini J, Pannecouque C, De Clercq E. Design, synthesis, and SAR of naphthyl-substituted diarylpyrimidines as non-nucleoside inhibitors of HIV-1 reverse transcriptase. ChemMedChem 2009;4:1537–1545.

140. Jones LH, Allan G, Barba O, Burt C, Corbau R, Dupont T, Knöchel T, Irving S, Middleton DS, Mowbray CE, Perros M, Ringrose H, Swain NA, Webster R, Westby M, Phillips C. Novel indazole non-nucleoside reverse transcriptase inhibitors using molecular hybridization based on crystallographic overlays. J Med Chem 2009;52:1219–1223.

141. Su DS, Lim JJ, Tinney E, Wan BL, Young MB, Anderson KD, Rudd D, Munshi V, Bahnck C, Felock PJ, Lu M, Lai MT, Touch S, Moyer G, Distefano DJ, Flynn JA, Liang Y, Sanchez R, Prasad S, Yan Y, Perlow-Poehnelt R, Torrent M, Miller M, Vacca JP, Williams TM, Anthony NJ. Substituted tetrahydroquinolines as potent allosteric inhibitors of reverse transcriptase and its key mutants. Bioorg Med Chem Lett 2009;19:5119–5123.

142. Sweeney ZK, Kennedy-Smith JJ, Wu J, Arora N, Billedeau JR, Davidson JP, Fretland J, Hang JQ, Heilek GM, Harris SF, Hirschfeld D, Inbar P, Javanbakht H, Jernelius JA, Jin Q, Li Y, Liang W, Roetz R, Sarma K, Smith M, Stefanidis D, Su G, Suh JM, Villaseñor AG, Welch M,

Zhang FJ, Klumpp K. Diphenyl ether non-nu-cleoside reverse transcriptase inhibitors with excellent potency against resistant mutant viruses and promising pharmacokinetic properties. ChemMedChem 2009;4:88–99.

143. Sweeney ZK, Harris SF, Arora SF, Javanbakht H, Li Y, Fretland J, Davidson JP, Billedeau JR, Gleason SK, Hirschfeld D, Kennedy-Smith JJ, Mirzadegan T, Roetz R, Smith M, Sperry S, Suh JM, Wu J, Tsing S, Villaseñor AG, Paul A, Su G, Heilek G, Hang JQ, Zhou AS, Jernelius JA, Zhang FJ, Klumpp K. Design of annulated pyrazoles as inhibitors of HIV-1 reverse transcriptase. J Med Chem 2008;51:7449–7458.

144. Tian X, Qin B, Lu H, Lai W, Jiang S, Lee KH, Chen CH, Xie L. Discovery of diarylpyridine derivatives as novel non-nucleoside HIV-1 reverse transcriptase inhibitors. Bioorg Med Chem Lett 2009;19:5482–5485.

145. Tucker TJ, Sisko JT, Tynebor RM, Williams TM, Felock PJ, Flynn JA, Lai MT, Liang Y, McGaughey G, Liu M, Miller M, Moyer G, Munshi V, Perlow-Poehnelt R, Prasad S, Reid JC, Sanchez R, Torrent M, Vacca JP, Wan BL, Yan Y. Discovery of 3-{5-[(6-amino-1H-pyrazo-lo[3,4-b]pyridine-3-yl)methoxy]-2-chlorophe-noxy}-5-chlorobenzonitrile (MK-4965): a potent, orally bioavailable HIV-1 non-nucleoside reverse transcriptase inhibitor with improved potency against key mutant viruses. J Med Chem 2008;51:6503–6511.

146. Lai MT, Munshi V, Touch S, Tynebor RM, Tucker TJ, McKenna PM, Williams TM, DiStefano DJ, Hazuda DJ, Miller MD. Antiviral activity of MK-4965, a novel nonnucleoside reverse transcriptase inhibitor. Antimicrob Agents Chemother 2009;53:2424–2431.

147. Popovic M, Sarin PS, Robert-Gurroff M, Kalyanaraman VS, Mann D, Minowada J, Gallo RC. Isolation and transmission of human retrovirus (human T-cell leukemia virus). Science 1983;219:856–859.

148. Barré-Sinoussi F, Chermann JC, Rey F, Nugeyre MT, Chamaret S, Gruest J, Dauguet C, Axler-Blin C, Vézinet-Brun F, Rouzioux C, Rozenbaum W, Montagnier L. Isolation of a T-lymphotropic retrovirus from a patient at risk for acquired immune deficiency syndrome (AIDS). Science 1983;220:868–871.

149. De Clercq E. Anti-HIV drugs: 25 compounds approved within 25 years after the discovery of HIV. Int J Antimicrob Agents 2009;33: 307–320.

150. Feng JY, Ly JK, Myrick F, Goodman D, White KL, Svarovskaia ES, Borroto-Esoda K, Miller MD. The triple combination of tenofovir, emtricitabine and efavirenz shows synergistic anti-HIV-1 activity in vitro: a mechanism of action study. Retrovirology 2009;6:44.

151. Lennox JL, DeJesus E, Lazzarin A, Pollard RB, Madruga JV, Berger DS, Zhao J, Xu X, Williams-Diaz A, Rodgers AJ, Barnard RJ, Miller MD, DiNubile MJ, Nguyen BY, Leavitt R, Sklar P, STARTMRK, investigators. Safety and efficacy of raltegravir-based versus efavirenz-based combination therapy in treatment-naive patients with HIV-1 infection: a multicentre, double-blind randomised controlled trial. Lancet 2009;374:796–806.

152. Marcellin P, Heathcote EJ, Buti M, Gane E, de Man RA, Krastev Z, Germanidis G, Lee SS, Flisiak R, Kaita K, Manns M, Kotzev I, Tchernev K, Buggisch P, Weilert F, Kurdas OO, Shiffman ML, Trinh H, Washington MK, Sorbel J, Anderson J, Snow-Lampart A, Mondou E, Quinn J, Rousseau F. Tenofovir disoproxil fumarate versus adefovir dipivoxil for chronic hepatitis B. N Engl J Med 2008;359: 2442–2455.

153. Matthews GV, Avihingsanon A, Lewin SR, Amin J, Rerknimitr R, Petcharapirat P, Marks P, Sasadeusz J, Cooper DA, Bowden S, Locarnini S, Ruxrungtham K, Dore GJ. A randomized trial of combination hepatitis B therapy in HIV/HBV coinfected antiretroviral naïve individuals in Thailand. Hepatology 2008;48: 1062–1069.

154. Johannessen A, Naman E, Kivuyo SL, Kasubi MJ, Holberg-Petersen M, Matee MI, Gundersen SG, Bruun JN. Virological efficacy and emergence of drug resistance in adults on antiretroviral treatment in rural Tanzania. BMC Infect Dis 2009;9:108.

155. Shey M, Kongnyuy EJ, Shang J, Wiysonge CS. A combination drug of abacavir-lamivudine-zidovudine (Trizivir®) for treating HIV infection and AIDS. The Cochrane Collaboration 2009; p 1–21.

156. Smith KY, Patel P, Fine D, Bellos N, Sloan L, Lackey P, Kumar PN, Sutherland-Phillips DH, Vavro C, Yau L, Wannamaker P, Shaefer MS, HEAT Study Team. Randomized, double-blind, placebo-matched, multicenter trial of abacavir/lamivudine or tenofovir/emtricitabine with lopinavir/ritonavir for initial HIV treatment. AIDS 2009;23:1547–1556.

157. Stephan C, Dauer B, Khaykin P, Stuermer M, Gute P, Klauke S, Staszewski S. Quadruple nucleos(t)ide reverse transcriptase inhibitors-only regimen of tenofovir plus zidovudine/lamivudine/abacavir in heavily pre-treated HIV-1

infected patients: salvage therapy or backbone only?. Curr HIV Res 2009;7:320–326.

158. Violari A, Cotton MF, Gibb DM, Babiker AG, Steyn J, Madhi SA, Jean-Philippe P, McIntyre JA, CHER Study Team. Early antiretroviral therapy and mortality among HIV-infected infants. N Engl J Med 2008;359:2233–2244.

159. Dejesus E, Young B, Morales-Ramirez JO, Sloan L, Ward DJ, Flaherty JF, Ebrahimi R, Maa JF, Reilly K, Ecker J, McColl D, Seekins D, Farajallah A, AI266073 Study Group. Simplification of antiretroviral therapy to a single-tablet regimen consisting of efavirenz, emtricitabine, and tenofovir disoproxil fumarate versus unmodified antiretroviral therapy in virologically suppressed HIV-1-infected patients. J Acquir Immune Defic Syndr 2009;51:163–174.

160. Martínez E, Arranz JA, Podzamczer D, Loncá M, Sanz J, Barragán P, Ribera E, Knobel H, Roca V, Gutiérrez F, Blanco JL, Mallolas J, Llibre JM, Clotet B, Dalmau D, Segura F, Arribas JR, Cosín J, Barrufet P, Casas E, Ferrer E, Curran A, González A, Pich J, Cruceta A, Arnaiz JA, Miró JM, Gatell JM, BICOMBO Study Team. A simplification trial switching from nucleoside reverse transcriptase inhibitors to once-daily fixed-dose abacavir/lamivudine or tenofovir/emtricitabine in HIV-1-infected patients with virological suppression. J Acquir Immune Defic Syndr 2009;51:290–297.

161. Willig JH, Abroms S, Westfall AO, Routman J, Adusumilli S, Varshney M, Allison J, Chatham A, Raper JL, Kaslow RA, Saag MS, Mugavero MJ. Increased regimen durability in the era of once-daily fixed-dose combination antiretroviral therapy. AIDS 2008;22:1951–1960.

162. Annan NT, Nelson M, Mandalia S, Bower M, Gazzard BG, Stebbing J. The nucleoside backbone affects durability of efavirenz- or nevirapine-based highly active antiretroviral therapy in antiretroviral-naive individuals. J Acquir Immune Defic Syndr 2009;51:140–146.

163. Gupta RK, Hill A, Sawyer AW, Cozzi-Lepri A, von Wyl V, Yerly S, Lima VD, Günthard HF, Gilks C, Pillay D. Virological monitoring and resistance to first-line highly active antiretroviral therapy in adults infected with HIV-1 treated under WHO guidelines: a systematic review and meta-analysis. Lancet Infect Dis 2009;9:409–417.

164. Ribera E, Paradiñeiro JC, Curran A, Sauleda S, García-Arumí E, Castella E, Puiggròs C, Crespo M, Feijoo M, Diaz M, Del Saz SV, Planas M,

Sureda D, Falcó V, Ocaña I, Pahissa A. Improvements in subcutaneous fat, lipid profile, and parameters of mitochondrial toxicity in patients with peripheral lipoatrophy when stavudine is switched to tenofovir (LIPOTEST study). HIV Clin Trials 2008;9:407–417.

165. Rodríguez-Nóvoa S, Labarga P, Soriano V, Egan D, Albalater M, Morello J, Cuenca L, González-Pardo G, Khoo S, Back D, Owen A. Predictors of kidney tubular dysfunction in HIV-infected patients treated with tenofovir: a pharmacogenetic study. Clin Infect Dis 2009;48:e108–e116.

166. Wirden M, Lambert-Niclot S, Marcelin AG, Schneider L, Ait-Mohand H, Brunet C, Angleraud F, Amard S, Katlama C, Calvez V. Antiretroviral combinations implicated in emergence of the L74I and L74V resistance mutations in HIV-1-infected patients. AIDS 2009;23:95–99.

167. Nichols SE, Domaoal RA, Thakur VV, Tirado-Rives J, Anderson KS, Jorgensen WL. Discovery of wild-type and Y181C mutant non-nucleoside HIV-1 reverse transcriptase inhibitors using virtual screening with multiple protein structures. J Chem Inf Model 2009;49:1272–1279.

168. Wang B, Dwyer DE, Chew CB, Kol C, He ZP, Joshi H, Steain MC, Cunningham AL, Saksena NK. Sensitive detection of the K103N non-nucleoside reverse transcriptase inhibitor resistance mutation in treatment-naïve HIV-1 infected individuals by rolling circle amplification. J Virol Methods 2009;161:128–135.

169. Ambrose Z, Herman BD, Sheen CW, Zelina S, Moore KL, Tachedjian G, Nissley DV, Sluis-Cremer N. The human immunodeficiency virus type 1 nonnucleoside reverse transcriptase inhibitor resistance mutation I132M confers hypersensitivity to nucleoside analogs. J Virol 2009;83:3826–3833.

170. Paredes R, Sagar M, Marconi VC, Hoh R, Martin JN, Parkin NT, Petropoulos CJ, Deeks SG, Kuritzkes DR. In vivo fitness cost of the M184V mutation in multidrug-resistant human immunodeficiency virus type 1 in the absence of lamivudine. J Virol 2009;83:2038–2043.

171. McMahon MA, Jilek BL, Brennan TP, Shen L, Zhou Y, Wind-Rotolo M, Xing S, Bhat S, Hale B, Hegarty R, Chong CR, Liu JO, Siliciano RF, Thio CL. The HBV drug entecavir: effects on HIV-1 replication and resistance. N Engl J Med 2007;356:2614–2621.

172. Tchesnokov EP, Obikhod A, Schinazi RF, Götte M. Delayed chain termination protects the anti-hepatitis B virus drug entecavir from excision by HIV-1 reverse transcriptase. J Biol Chem 2008;283:34218–34228.

173. McMahon MA, Siliciano JD, Lai J, Liu JO, Stivers JT, Siliciano RF, Kohli RM. The antiherpetic drug acyclovir inhibits HIV replication and selects the V75I reverse transcriptase multidrug resistance mutation. J Biol Chem 2008;283:31289–31293.

174. Tchesnokov EP, Obikhod A, Massud I, Lisco A, Vanpouille C, Brichacek B, Balzarini J, McGuigan C, Derudas M, Margolis L, Schinazi RF, Götte M. Mechanisms associated with HIV-1 resistance to acyclovir by the V75I mutation in reverse transcriptase. J Biol Chem 2009;284:21496–21504.

175. Foss AM, Vickerman PT, Heise L, Watts CH. Shifts in condom use following microbicide introduction: should we be concerned?. AIDS 2003;17:1227–1237.

176. Shattock R, Solomon S. Microbicides: aids to safer sex. Lancet 2004;363:1002–1003.

177. Turville SG, Aravantinou M, Miller T, Kenney J, Teitelbaum A, Hu L, Chudolij A, Zydowsky TM, Piatak M Jr, Bess JW Jr, Lifson JD, Blanchard J, Gettie A, Robbiani M. Efficacy of Carraguard-based microbicides *in vivo* despite variable *in vitro* activity. PLoS One 2008;3:e3162.

178. Herrera C, Cranage M, McGowan I, Anton P, Shattock RJ. Reverse transcriptase inhibitors as potential colorectal microbicides. Antimicrob Agents Chemother 2009;53: 1797–1807.

179. Bourry O, Brochard P, Souquiere S, Makuwa M, Calvo J, Dereudre-Bosquet N, Martinon F, Benech H, Kazanji M, Le Grand R. Prevention of vaginal simian immunodeficiency virus transmission in macaques by postexposure prophylaxis with zidovudine, lamivudine and indinavir. AIDS 2009;23:447–454.

180. Hirt D, Urien S, Rey E, Arrivé E, Ekouévi DK, Coffié P, Leang SK, Lalsab S, Avit D, Nerrienet E, McIntyre J, Blanche S, Dabis F, Tréluyer JM. Population pharmacokinetics of emtricitabine in human immunodeficiency virus type 1-infected pregnant women and their neonates. Antimicrob Agents Chemother 2009;53:1067–1073.

181. Kovari H, Ledergerber B, Peter U, Flepp M, Jost J, Schmid P, Calmy A, Mueller NJ, Muellhaupt B, Weber R, Swiss HIV Cohort Study. Association of noncirrhotic portal hypertension in HIV-infected persons and antiretroviral therapy with didanosine: a nested case–control study. Clin Infect Dis 2009;49:626–635.

182. Brown TT, McComsey GA, King MS, Qaqish RB, Bernstein BM, da Silva BA. Loss of bone mineral density after antiretroviral therapy initiation, independent of antiretroviral regimen. J Acquir Immune Defic Syndr 2009;51: 554–561.

183. Duvivier C, Kolta S, Assoumou L, Ghosn J, Rozenberg S, Murphy RL, Katlama C, Costagliola D, ANRS 121 Hippocampe Study Group. Greater decrease in bone mineral density with protease inhibitor regimens compared with nonnucleoside reverse transcriptase inhibitor regimens in HIV-1 infected naive patients. AIDS 2009;23:817–824.

184. van Vonderen MG, van Agtmael MA, Hassink EA, Milinkovic A, Brinkman K, Geerlings SE, Ristola M, van Eeden A, Danner SA, Reiss P, MEDICLAS Study Group. Zidovudine/lamivudine for HIV-1 infection contributes to limb fat loss. PLoS One 2009;4:e5647.

185. Benn P, Sauret-Jackson V, Cartledge J, Ruff C, Sabin CA, Moyle G, Linney A, Reilly G, Edwards SG. Improvements in cheek volume in lipoatrophic individuals switching away from thymidine nucleoside reverse transcriptase inhibitors. HIV Med 2009;10:351–355.

186. Lai-Goldman M, Faruki H. Abacavir hypersensitivity: a model system for pharmacogenetic test adoption. Genet Med 2008;10:874–878.

187. Strategies for Management of Anti-Retroviral Therapy/INSIGHT, DAD Study Groups. Use of nucleoside reverse transcriptase inhibitors and risk of myocardial infarction in HIV-infected patients. AIDS 2008;22:F17–F24.

188. Brothers CH, Hernandez JE, Cutrell AG, Curtis L, Ait-Khaled M, Bowlin SJ, Hughes SH, Yeo JM, Lapierre DH. Risk of myocardial infarction and abacavir therapy: no increased risk across 52 GlaxoSmithKline-sponsored clinical trials in adult subjects. J Acquir Immune Defic Syndr 2009;51:20–28.

189. Rodríguez-Nóvoa S, Labarga P, Soriano V, Egan D, Albalater M, Morello J, Cuenca L, González-Pardo G, Khoo S, Back D, Owe A. Predictors of kidney tubular dysfunction in HIV-infected patients treated with tenofovir: a pharmacogenetic study. Clin Infect Dis 2009;48:e108–e116.

190. Kohler JJ, Hosseini SH, Hoying-Brandt A, Green E, Johnson DM, Russ R, Tran D, Raper CM, Santoianni R, Lewis W. Tenofovir renal toxicity targets mitochondria of renal proximal tubules. Lab Invest 2009;89:513–519.

191. Lebrecht D, Venhoff AC, Kirschner J, Wiech T, Venhoff N, Walker UA. Mitochondrial tubulopathy in tenofovir disoproxil fumarate-treated rats. J Acquir Immune Defic Syndr 2009;51: 258–263.

192. Gallant JE, Winston JA, DeJesus E, Pozniak AL, Chen SS, Cheng AK, Enejosa JV. The 3-year renal safety of a tenofovir disoproxil fumarate vs. a thymidine analogue-containing regimen in antiretroviral-naive patients. AIDS 2008;22:2155–2163.

193. Chittick GE, Zong J, Begley JA, Alianti JR, Sorbel JJ, Blum MR. Pharmacokinetics of emtricitabine/tenofovir disoproxil fumarate and tacrolimus at steady state when administered alone or in combination. Int J Clin Pharmacol Ther 2008;46:627–636.

194. Wenning LA, Friedman EJ, Kost JT, Breidinger SA, Stek JE, Lasseter KC, Gottesdiener KM, Chen J, Teppler H, Wagner JA, Stone JA, Iwamoto M. Lack of a significant drug interaction between raltegravir and tenofovir. Antimicrob Agents Chemother 2008;52:3253–3258.

195. Van Dyke RB, Wang L, Williams PL, Pediatric AIDS Clinical Trials Group 219C Team. Toxicities associated with dual nucleoside reverse-transcriptase inhibitor regimens in HIV-infected children. J Infect Dis 2008;198: 1599–1608.

RECENT ADVANCES IN HEPATITIS C THERAPIES

BLOOM JONATHAN
ZAPF CHRISTOPH
LEVIN JEREMY
FLINT MICHAEL
Wyeth, Pearl River, NY

1. INTRODUCTION

Based on its prevalence and poor therapeutic options, hepatitis C is arguably one of the most significant infectious diseases in the world today. Although not as well known as HIV/AIDS, hepatitis C virus (HCV), the causative agent of the disease, infects 2–3% of the world's population (about 170 million people) [1], roughly four times that of HIV [2], making it an enormous public health burden [3]. The discovery of HCV in 1989 has spurred an enormous worldwide research effort. While this research has not yet provided an approved HCV drug, we are likely now at the inception of an era of specific and effective treatments or a cure for the disease. This chapter will provide an overview of the biological and medicinal chemistry progress of the past two decades, focusing on promising candidates in clinical trials, as well as notable candidates that have been discontinued.

It is instructive to examine the similarities and differences between HIV and HCV. Unlike HIV, which can be readily transmitted by sexual activity or blood, HCV is predominantly blood borne; infection from sexual contact is much less common. HIV is a retrovirus, a member of the *Retroviridae* family, characterized by the use of reverse transcriptase to catalyze the synthesis of complementary DNA copies of the viral RNA genome within the cell nucleus. The newly formed viral DNA is inserted into the DNA of the host cell via the HIV integrase enzyme, and is incorporated into the host cell genome. HCV is a member of the *Flaviviridae* family [4] that also includes the human pathogens yellow fever, West Nile, and dengue viruses. HCV has no integrase; therefore, the genome of the newly infected cell remains unchanged. Rather, HCV replicates solely within the cytoplasm of the infected host cell. Structurally, the two pathogens have little in common. However, since they both are transmitted by blood, cooccurrence is common. HCV–HIV coinfection is a rapidly growing problem [5,6], presenting a more difficult therapeutic challenge than either infection alone. There is no vaccine available for either disease.

The *sequelae* of the diseases following infection are quite different. Before the advent of effective antiretroviral therapies, the interval between HIV infection and progression to AIDS was about 2 years [7,8]. By contrast, symptomatic, acute HCV infection is uncommon [9,10], although 85% of infected patients will enter a chronic disease state over the course of a 20-year period. Approximately 15–20% of these patients will develop cirrhosis, with 4% progressing to hepatocellular carcinoma and end-stage liver disease [9,11,12]. The long interval between infection and symptomology has resulted in HCV being labeled "the silent killer" [13–15]. HCV infection is the leading cause of liver transplants in Europe and the United States [1].

Although much of HCV inhibitor research has been modeled after the target-based HIV approach, there have been significant differences in outcome. This is best illustrated by comparing the time interval between the initiation of discovery research and the launch of therapies for both diseases. By any measure, HCV progress is lagging behind that of HIV [16]. Both viruses were isolated in the 1980s—HIV in 1983 [17,18] and HCV in 1989 [19]—at which time it was identified as the major cause "non-A non-B hepatitis" (formerly called NANBH). Within 5 years of the discovery of HIV, azidothymidine (AZT, zidovudine), the first small-molecule inhibitor of the virus, was reported [20] and approved shortly thereafter. Although AZT was of limited use, the next two decades of AIDS research would yield more than 20 drugs working by five different mechanisms [21], including inhibition of HIV protease [22], reverse transcriptase [23–25], integrase [26], and cell entry [27]. A 2001 review discusses the rapid progress made during the first two decades of HIV research, noting that AIDS is now viewed as a manageable, chronic disease rather than an automatic death sentence [28].

169

In contrast, two decades after the identification of HCV, no specifically targeted antiviral (STAT-C) therapies are available. A recent review in *Nature* compares and contrasts the challenges and progress of HIV and HCV research [29], illustrating that the use of analogous strategies successfully employed in HIV research have thus far not yielded comparable results in HCV. Other reviews have examined the status of anti-HCV candidates in various stages of discovery, development, or that have been discontinued [30–36].

Current therapies for HCV infection are, at best, suboptimal. The current standard of care is pegylated interferon-α (PEG-IFN-α) [37,38], an inducer of innate immunity, in combination with ribavirin, a broad-spectrum nucleoside antiviral agent that acts synergistically with interferon. The mechanism of action of ribavirin is poorly understood [39–41]. The success rate of this therapy varies, depending on multiple factors including virus genotype and patient ethnicity, with the overall efficacy as measured by sustained viral response (SVR, defined by the absence of detectable virus 6 months following the cessation of treatment) being in 50–60% of patients [42,43]. This therapy is less effective in patients infected with HCV genotype 1 [37,38,44,45], which is the most common variant found in the United States and Northern Europe [46–49]. Only 42–46% of these patients attain SVR [37,38]. Furthermore, patient compliance is a significant issue due to debilitating side effects, including depression, fatigue, flu-like symptoms, gastrointestinal distress, and anemia [50,51]. Discontinuation of therapy due to adverse side effects is fairly common. Studies have shown that dropout rates due to side effects are approximately 10–20% [44,51] and that 45% of patients require reduction of their IFN dose [37,38]. The poor efficacy coupled with the significant side effects of the IFN-ribavirin therapy makes new therapies for HCV a pressing medical need.

The failure to realize new therapies does not imply a lack of progress in the science of HCV. On the contrary, there have been substantial technical advances in the study of the virus, including identification and X-ray crystallography of viral proteins enabling structure-based drug design, development of a cell-based subgenomic replicon assay, and predictive animal models. Use of these technologies has yielded a substantial number of candidate antivirals, some of which have induced remarkable reductions or elimination of viral load in infected patients. Although all of the initial clinical candidates failed for a number of reasons (usually toxicity), these trials have provided proof of concept that an inhibitor of HCV with suitable pharmaceutical properties should work as an anti-HCV agent in humans. In some cases, companies that discontinued one inhibitor have multiple backup candidates, some of which have already entered clinical trials.

This chapter will examine advances in biology, medicinal chemistry, and drug design in the hepatitis C field. Clinical data of selected HCV clinical candidates will be examined, including candidates currently in development and some that have been discontinued. The scope will be limited to small-molecule, specific antiviral inhibitors. Vaccines, immune modulators, and agents that modify cell function will not be reviewed.

2. BIOLOGY OF HCV

2.1. Classification

HCV is an enveloped RNA virus and a member of the *hepacivirus* genus of the family *Flaviviridae* (reviewed in Ref. [52]). Other genera in the *Flaviviridae* include the flaviviruses (such as yellow fever, dengue, and West Nile viruses) and the pestiviruses (classical swine fever and bovine viral diarrhea viruses). HCV has a single-stranded RNA genome, approximately 9.6 kb long that, as with other positive-strand RNA viruses, serves as a messenger RNA. The genome encodes a polyprotein approximately 3000 amino acids in length that is cleaved to give functional viral proteins (Fig. 1). These may be divided into structural and nonstructural proteins. Structural proteins are those that are components of viral particles and include the core protein (also called C or capsid) and two envelope glycoproteins, E1 and E2. The nonstructural proteins include those required for viral replication: p7, NS-2, -3, -4A, -4B, -5A,

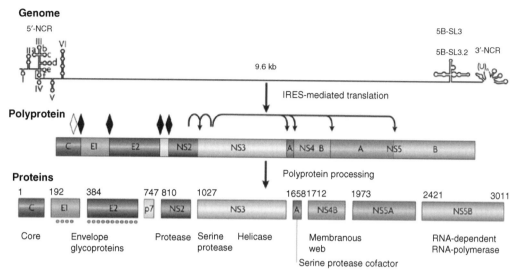

Figure 1. The 9.6 kb positive-strand RNA genome is schematically depicted at the top. Simplified RNA secondary structures in the 5′- and 3′-noncoding regions (NCRs) and the core gene, as well as the NS5B stem-loop 3 *cis*-acting replication element (5B-SL3) are shown. Internal ribosome entry site (IRES)-mediated translation yields a polyprotein precursor that is processed into the mature structural and nonstructural proteins. Amino-acid numbers are shown above each protein (HCV H strain; genotype 1a). Solid diamonds denote cleavage sites of the HCV polyprotein precursor by the endoplasmic reticulum signal peptidase. The open diamond indicates further C-terminal processing of the core protein by signal peptide peptidase. Arrows indicate cleavages by the HCV NS2–3 and NS3–4A proteases. Dots in E1 and E2 indicate the glycosylation of the envelope proteins (4 and 11 N-linked glycans, respectively, in the HCV H strain). Note that polyprotein processing, illustrated here as a separate step for simplicity, occurs co- and posttranslationally [53]. Reproduced with permission by Nature Publishing Group. (This figure is available in full color at http://mrw.interscience.wiley.com/emrw/9780471266945/home.)

and -5B. Flanking the polyprotein are 5′- and 3′-untranslated regions (UTRs) that contain RNA sequences responsible for translation of the viral proteins and are for viral replication. In recent years, considerable progress has been made into understanding the functions of each of the viral proteins, revealing a number of potential targets for therapeutic intervention.

HCV has a high level of sequence diversity. Isolates can be classified into six genotypes that can be subdivided into more than 70 subtypes [54]; at the nucleotide level, genotypes differ by 31–33%, and subtypes between 20% and 25%. An additional level of diversity is apparent in an infected individual, where HCV exists as population of related viral sequences, known as a quasispecies. This level of diversity has implications for the development of resistance to antiviral agents and is discussed further below.

2.2. The Viral Life Cycle and Potential Targets for Intervention

As an obligate intracellular parasite, a virus must cross the plasma membrane of a target cell to access the host factors required to replicate its genome. For HCV, this is a multistage process involving a series of interactions between the viral glycoproteins, E1 and E2, and specific receptor molecules on the cell surface. Several host factors have been identified as receptors, including glycosaminoglycans, CD81, scavenger receptor class B type I and claudin-1, -6, or -9 [55–60]. For recent reviews, see Refs [61,62]. Two lectins, DC-SIGN (dendritic cell-specific intercellular adhesion molecule 3-grabbing nonintegrin) and the related L-SIGN (liver-specific intercellular adhesion molecule 3-grabbing nonintegrin), have also been implicated in the entry process, although these may not function as traditional receptors and rather play roles in the dissemination of HCV particles to other host cells [63,64]. In addition, plasma-derived HCV is frequently associated with low- and very-low-density lipoproteins and the interaction of these particle-associated lipoproteins with lipoprotein receptors may also contribute to entry mechanism (reviewed in Ref. [65]). After binding to receptors on the surface of target cells, the viral particles are thought to be internalized by clathrin-mediated endocytosis and delivered to early endosomes [66,67]. The low pH in these vesicles induces conformational changes in the viral envelope glycoproteins that lead to fusion of the viral and cellular membranes and the release of the viral genome into the cytoplasm [66,68–71]. Agents that interfere with the acidification of the endosomal compartment, such as bafilomycin A1, concanamycin A, or chloroquine, inhibit HCV entry in cell culture [66,70].

While the precise sequence of events during HCV entry has yet to be elucidated, it is apparent that the mechanism is a complex process involving a series of interactions between the virus and the host cell factors. Each of these interactions represents a potential therapeutic target. The successful development of inhibitors of HIV entry, enfuvirtide (Fuzeon, Roche) and maraviroc (Selzentry, Pfizer), suggests that HCV entry may be a tractable target for inhibition.

2.3. Expression of the Viral Proteins

Once the viral genome has been delivered into the cytoplasm, it is translated by host cell ribosomes. Translation of the HCV proteins is mediated by an IRES located in the 5′-UTR (Fig. 1). This highly structured RNA sequence is capable of binding the ribosomal 40S subunit, placing the ribosome in proximity to the initiating AUG codon of the polyprotein. Because it is critical for expression of the viral proteins and its sequence is highly conserved between genotypes, IRES function may be a target for inhibition, possibly by antisense oligonucleotides, ribozymes or an RNAi-based therapy [72].

Once translated, the HCV polyprotein is cleaved in a series of proteolytic events that release the individual viral proteins. Signal peptidase, a host cell protease, releases the core protein, E1, E2, and p7. The junction between NS2 and NS3 is cleaved by the NS2-3 protease, an autocatalytic activity contained within the C–terminus of NS2 and the N-terminus of NS3. The catalytic protease domain of NS2 was crystallized to reveal that it is a dimeric cysteine protease with an active site comprised of residues from both monomers [73]. A serine protease in the N-terminus of NS3 is responsible for cleaving the polyprotein at other junctions. A ribosomal frameshifting event within the core sequence may lead to the production of an additional viral protein, designated F for frame shift. Antibodies to the F protein are detectable in infected patients, indicating that it is made *in vivo*, but its function is currently unknown.

The NS3 serine protease is a member of the chymotrypsin-like serine protease family and, with its cofactor NS4A, is responsible for releasing NS4A, -4B, -5A, and -5B from the polyprotein. This activity is essential for viral replication *in vivo* [74]. Despite its shallow and featureless substrate binding pocket, several NS3 protease inhibitors have been successfully designed and will be discussed in detail in Section 3. In addition to processing the viral polyprotein, the NS3/4A protease has been found to cleave cellular molecules that regulate the host antiviral response [75–77]. This may be a mechanism that HCV uses to evade host cell responses to infection. Inhibitors of NS3/4A may therefore inhibit HCV through two mechanisms: by directly inhibiting viral protein processing and by restoring the normal host antiviral response. Consistent with this, an experimental HCV protease inhibitor and IFN-α showed a synergistic effect on HCV replicon cells [78].

The cofactor for NS3, NS4A is only 54 amino acids long, but is required for full protease activity. The central part of NS4A comprises one strand of the first β-barrel in the chymotrypsin-like fold of NS3. NS4A has a hydrophobic N-terminal region that associates with intracellular membranes and likely causes NS3 to localize to these membranes. NS4A was validated as an antiviral target in a proof-of-concept clinical trial of the NS4A antagonist, ACH-806 (GS-9132) (Achillion/Gilead), though nephrotoxicity precluded further development of this particular compound [79].

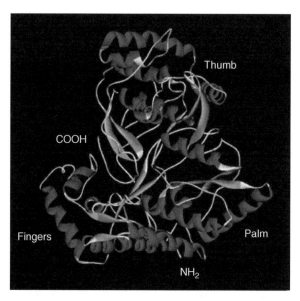

Figure 2. Ribbon representation of the first 570 residues from the amino terminus of HCV nonstructural protein 5B (NS5B), with α-helices and β-strands represented in red and cyan, respectively. The "thumb," "finger," and "palm" subdomains are common to all known polymerases. NH_2 and COOH indicate the positions of the amino and carboxy terminus of the protein, respectively [2]. Reproduced with permission by Nature Publishing Group. (This figure is available in full color at http://mrw.interscience.wiley.com/emrw/9780471266945/home.)

2.4. Replication of the Viral Genome

As with other positive-strand RNA viruses, the replication of the HCV genome occurs in a membrane-associated replication complex, composed of viral proteins, replicating RNA, altered cellular membranes and other host factors. These complexes are located in what has been described as the "membranous web," an assembly of vesicles embedded in a membrane matrix, originally identified by electron microscopy of HCV replicon cells [80]. Replication of the viral genome occurs at these sites, through the copying of the positive-sense genome to a complementary negative-sense intermediate, which is then used as a template for the production of further positive-sense progeny genomes. Progeny RNA may be translated to yield more viral proteins, serve as templates for the production of more negative-strands, or can be packaged into newly synthesized viral particles.

NS5B has RNA-dependent RNA-polymerase (RdRp) activity and plays a key role in the replication of the viral genome. NS5B has the palm, finger and thumb domains typical of polymerases, but does possess an unusual structural feature; its active site is completely encircled through a tight interaction between the thumb and the finger domains (Fig. 2). Other notable features of NS5B include a GTP-binding site and a hydrophobic C-terminal tail that mediates interactions with cellular membranes. Nucleoside inhibitors of NS5B function as competitive substrate analogs that terminate nascent RNA chains, whereas nonnucleoside inhibitors appear to act through allosteric mechanisms that inhibit the initiation of synthesis or elongation of RNA. Inhibitors of NS5B function will be discussed in detail in Section 3.2. NS5B has also been found to interact with cyclophilins. This appears to be essential for replication, as cyclosporine A, which disrupts the interaction, inhibits HCV replication [81,82]. A nonimmunosuppressive derivative of cyclosporine A, Debio 025 (Debiopharm), is currently being developed as a therapeutic for HCV [83,84].

The C-terminal domain of NS3 has helicase activity that unwinds double-stranded nucleic acids. This activity is thought to separate the annealed positive- and negative-sense strands of viral RNA that are formed during replication. Alternatively, the helicase may be necessary to unwind stable secondary structures in viral RNA prior to their use as a template. Whatever its role, the helicase is required for replication *in vivo* [74] and may be a target for therapy, although the development of HCV helicase inhibitors for clinical use has been slow (reviewed in Ref. [85]).

NS4B is a membrane protein containing an N-terminal amphipathic helix and a nucleotide binding motif, that are both required for replication in cell culture [86,87]. NS4B appears to have a central role in inducing the membranous web, as it generates similar structures when expressed alone. NS4B specifically bound to the 3′-end of the negative-sense viral RNA *in vitro* [88], suggesting that it may anchor or orient negative strands in the replication complex.

NS5A is a phosphoprotein that can exist in a hypophosphorylated or hyperphosphorylated form. The phosphorylation status of NS5A may regulate viral RNA replication, as mutations that enhance replication of the HCV replicon often arise in NS5A and decrease the hyperphosphorylated proportion [89]. Kinase inhibitors that decrease the amount of the hyperphosphorylated form actually appear to stimulate replication of a wild-type HCV sequence [90]. NS5A contains an amphipathic α-helix at its N-terminus that promotes membrane association. NS5A has been found to interact with multiple host proteins, including vesicle-associated membrane protein-associated protein A (VAP-A), a geranylgeranylated F box protein (FBL2), TBC Rab-GAP (GTPase-activating protein), and PKR. The role of these interactions in the viral life cycle is unknown. BMS-790042 (Bristol-Meyers Squibb), an inhibitor of NS5A is currently in Phase II trials.

The process by which HCV particles are assembled is poorly understood, though recently some significant advances have been made (reviewed in Ref. [91]). Newly formed particles are thought to bud at intracellular membranes and exit the infected cell via the cellular secretory pathway. The core protein may play a key role in assembly, as it is known to interact with other protein monomers and also the envelope glycoprotein E1 [92–97]. Recent work has confirmed the importance of the core protein for production of infectious virus [98]. The core protein accumulates at lipid droplets in infected cells, suggesting that these cholesterol-rich organelles may be the site of particle assembly [99,100].

The p7 protein is a small, hydrophobic protein that assembles into a membrane-spanning oligomer with ion channel activity [101,102]. This activity is inhibited by amantadine, an anti-influenza drug that blocks the function of the influenza virus ion channel protein, M2. The anti-HCV effect of amantadine has been tested, but remains controversial [103–105]. The p7 protein is not thought to be a structural protein, nor is it essential for RNA replication, but instead, has been speculated to be involved in the early stages of viral particle formation [106].

2.5. Cell Culture Assays for HCV Replication

The understanding of HCV replication was severely hampered for many years by a lack of cell culture systems that support efficient replication. The development of HCV replicons (autonomously replicating RNAs) [89,107] was a significant advance that has greatly facilitated the study of HCV replication. Such replicons typically contain an antibiotic resistance gene (e.g., neomycin phosphotransferase), that, following introduction of the replicon RNA into a population of naïve cells permits the selection of those cells that bear the replicon. Once selected, and if passaged in the presence of the selective agent, the cells can efficiently and stably maintain the replicon RNA. The first replicons were bicistronic and subgenomic, carrying the IRES from encephalomyocarditis virus to direct translation of the HCV proteins from NS3 to NS5B. Later replicons contained the whole HCV polyprotein. Further refinements permitted the introduction of reporter genes, such as luciferase or secreted alkaline phosphatase [108], that reflect replicon abundance and facilitate compound screening campaigns. The HCV replicon has proven invaluable for testing the efficacy of prospective anti-HCV drugs, for studies of synergy between antivirals, for the selection of resistance mutations, and for determinations of mutant fitness (a selection of recent work employing the HCV replicon for antiviral drug discovery includes references [109–113]). As with any *in vitro* model, caution should be taken interpreting results obtained in the replicon system as they may not necessarily hold true *in vivo*, but the replicon system is a hugely important tool for anti-HCV drug discovery.

A major advance permitting the study of HCV entry was the generation of HCV pseudotype particles (HCVpp) [69,114]. These are retroviruses (HIV or murine leukemia virus), which are lacking their own glycoprotein genes but carry a reporter gene, expressed together with the HCV glycoproteins in cultured cells. E1 and E2 are incorporated into particles as they bud from the expressing cells. Subsequent infection with HCVpp is mediated by the HCV glycoproteins and can be detected by expression of the reporter gene in a target cell line [58,68,115–117].

Recently, systems that permit the complete HCV life cycle to occur *in vitro*, allowing the generation of infectious HCV in cell culture (HCVcc), have been developed [118–120]. The HCVcc systems rely on an unusual genotype 2a patient isolate, JFH-1, which exhibits robust replication and infectious virus production in the human hepatoma cell-line, Huh-7.5. Viral mechanisms such as uncoating and assembly may now be studied using HCVcc, and inhibitors targeting these processes may now be tested. It should be noted, however, that the JFH-1 replicase is both derived from genotype 2a and unusual in its ability to produce virus in cell culture. The implications of findings for wild-type genotype 1 HCV should be treated with caution.

Another infectious HCV cell culture system has been described, based on a genotype 1 sequence but bearing multiple mutations that enhance its ability to replicate in cell culture and, in concert, appears to raise the level of viral replication such that infectious viral particles are released [121]. While it does use a genotype 1 sequence, this system is less efficient than the JFH-1-based HCVcc model and the effect of the cell culture adaptive mutations on susceptibility to therapies is unknown.

2.6. Animal Models

Other than man, the common chimpanzee (*Pan troglodytes*) is the only species known to become persistently infected by HCV. Historically, the chimpanzee has played a key role in HCV research, with the first cDNA clone of the viral sequence being derived from chimpanzees inoculated with blood products from humans with non-A, non-B hepatitis. The course of disease in the chimpanzee mirrors that in humans, a persistent infection that leads to liver disease, hence the chimpanzee has been used extensively to study immunological responses to infection that are difficult to examine in humans. Unfortunately, the expense involved in chimpanzee experiments has limited their use in the drug discovery field. Direct inoculation of synthetic HCV RNA into the liver of chimpanzees results in a productive infection [122]. In a seminal study, this method was used to test a series of mutants and demonstrate that the NS2/3 protease, NS3/4A protease, NS3 NTPase and helicase, and the NS5B polymerase activities are all required for infectivity *in vivo* and are therefore potential targets for therapy [89].

For reasons that are unclear, rodents are not susceptible to infection by HCV. Transgenic, immunodeficient *SCID* mice, that overexpress urokinase in their liver, lose their hepatocytes within the first few weeks of their lives. Human hepatocytes can be engrafted into these animals and rescue liver function, and a chronic HCV infection can be initiated by inoculation with serum from an HCV-positive individual [123]. IFN-α and BILN-2061 showed antiviral efficacy in this system [124].

2.7. Antiviral Resistance and Its Implications for Drug Discovery

NS5B is an error-prone enzyme and during replication of the viral RNA wrongly incorporates around one in 10,000 bases. Consequently, sequence variants constantly arise during replication. These variants will compete with existing sequences, undergo selection and, if they survive, contribute to the viral quasispecies. This is one way in which HCV is thought to escape host immune responses, and is likely to present a significant challenge to the design of effective anti-HCV therapies, as resistant variants present in a patient's quasispecies will be rapidly selected upon exposure to drug.

For many small-molecule anti-HCV compounds, resistant mutants can readily be generated in the replicon by selecting for cells able to grow in the presence of the compound of interest and antibiotic selective pressure. Frequently, a single mutation in the target gene is sufficient to significantly reduce susceptibility to inhibition. For example, replicon resistance studies, confirmed in biochemical assays, revealed that a single amino acid change, S282T in the NS5B gene, reduced susceptibility to the HCV polymerase inhibitor NM283 [125,126]. Mutations conferring cross-resistance to protease inhibitors were detected in the replicon; A156V/T mediated reduced susceptibility to both telaprevir and BILN 2061 [127]. Importantly, in patients receiving telaprevir monotherapy, the NS3/4A A156V/T change was frequently correlated with lack of virologic response [128]. Several resistant variants found in telaprevir treated patients were not detected during replicon studies, probably due to higher levels of telaprevir used for selection of resistant replicons [129]. A further use of the replicon is in determining the level of resistance that a mutation conferred to multiple antiviral agents. The A156V/T variant was fully sensitive to inhibition by IFN, providing support for the combination of telaprevir with the current standard of care, a regimen that subsequently exhibited significant antiviral efficacy [130].

Resistance mutations are often associated with deleterious effects on viral fitness where, in the absence of the selecting drug, the mutant has a lower replicative capacity than that of the wild-type sequence [112,113,131]. The effect of mutations on fitness may be measured by transient replication in the replicon, or by testing catalytic efficiency of a mutant enzyme in a biochemical assay.

The experience with the treatment of HIV/AIDS suggests that the development of resistance may be curtailed by combining therapies with different targets. It should be noted that a dually resistant variant bearing resistance mutations for both a protease and a polymerase inhibitors in the same genome, could be isolated in the replicon [113]. Initial strategies for an anti-HCV combination therapy combine a first-generation protease or polymerase inhibitor with the current standard of care. Subsequent combinations will likely include additional drugs. One strategy to prevent the development of resistance is by specifically designing compounds whose resistant mutants are unfit. Such compounds would likely have conserved contact residues, for instance within the active site of a viral enzyme, such that changes at these positions would be predicted to adversely impact the enzyme activity.

3. MEDICINAL CHEMISTRY

3.1. NS3/4A Protease Inhibitors

3.1.1. Ciluprevir (BILN-2061, Boehringer-Ingelheim)
The seminal work in the HCV NS3/4A protease inhibitor field was carried out at Boehringer-Ingelheim. Integrating medicinal chemistry, X-ray crystallography, structure-based drug design, peptide mimetics, and ADMET (absorption, distribution, metabolism, excretion, and toxicity), a hexapeptide substrate fragment was transformed into a potent drug-like molecule—BILN–2061 (Fig. 3) [132,133]. This body of work is arguably among the most impressive efforts in drug discovery, and for many years, experts in the field have regarded BILN-2061 as the "gold standard" for the inhibition of the HCV protease. Although development was ultimately discontinued, it provided the first proof of concept, demonstrating that inhibition of the NS3/4A protease by a small molecule can bring about viral reduction in HCV patients [134].

A large number of compounds were screened at Boehringer-Ingelheim to identify appropriate leads for the inhibition of NS3/4A protease without success. Instead, a peptide-based approach was subsequently applied [133]. The effort advanced significantly when hexapeptide 1 was identified as an inhibitor of NS3/4A (IC$_{50}$ = 77 μM). The potency of this peptide was better than expected, making this compound an attractive starting point for SAR studies. By incorporating various natural and unnatural amino acids into the hexapeptide, it was found that the N-terminal acetamide 3

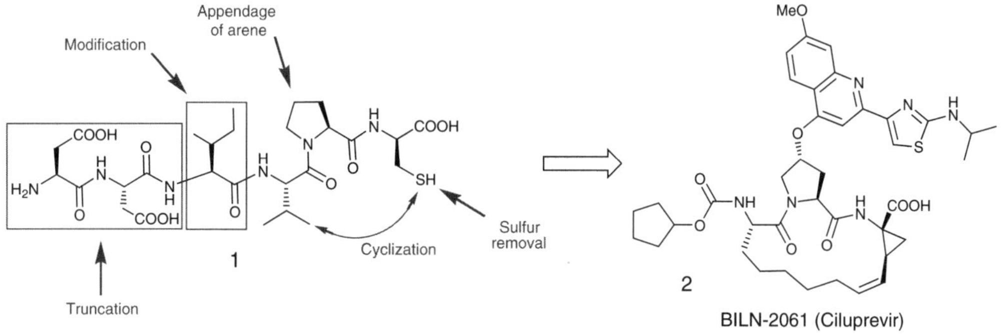

Figure 3. Summary of key modifications applied to hexapeptide **1** leading to BILN-2061 **2**. (This figure is available in full color at http://mrw.interscience.wiley.com/emrw/9780471266945/home.)

is almost 20 times more potent (IC$_{50}$ = 4 µM) than **1** [135]. The undesired C-terminal Cys was replaced by the amino acid norvaline (Nva), moderately reducing the potency of the peptide **4** (IC$_{50}$ = 17 µM) [136]. Analogs that have structural modifications at the C-terminal carboxylic acid were also prepared, but among the reported analogs only **4** possesses the desired selectivity over other proteases while retaining acceptable aqueous solubility. Additional structural modifications within the amino acid side chains were examined,

including appendages on the pyrrolidine ring. Among these compounds, **5** (IC$_{50}$ = 0.027 µM) was found to be a submicromolar inhibitor that is highly selective over other relevant proteases [137].

With the potent aryl-substituted proline analogs **5** and **6** in hand, another attempt was made to derivatize the C-terminal carboxylate. A series of azapeptides was prepared that showed potency in the submicromolar range and promising selectivity over human leukocyte elastase (HLE) [138].

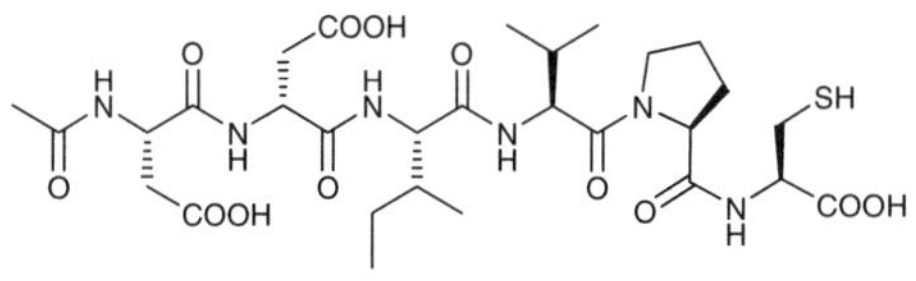

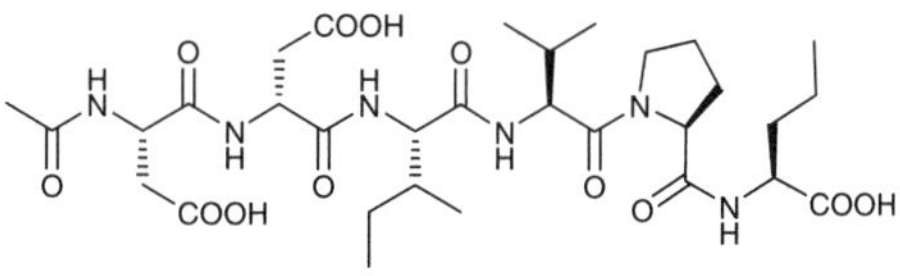

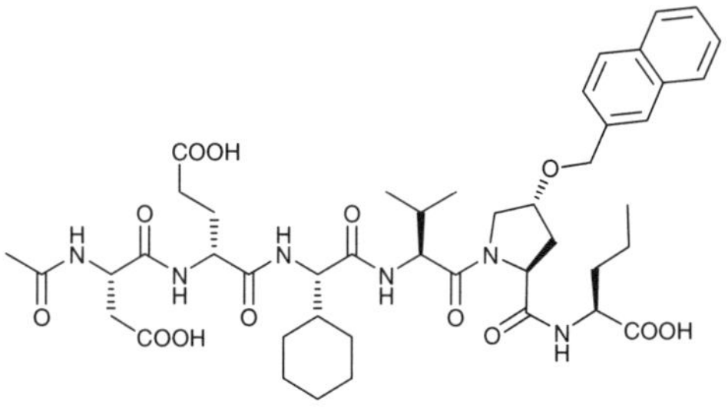

At the time, X-ray crystallographic information of any ligand bound to the NS3/4A protease was not available. To gain more structural insight into the biologically active conformation of the hexapeptides, differential line broadening (DLB) NMR experiments were carried out on several peptides to iden-

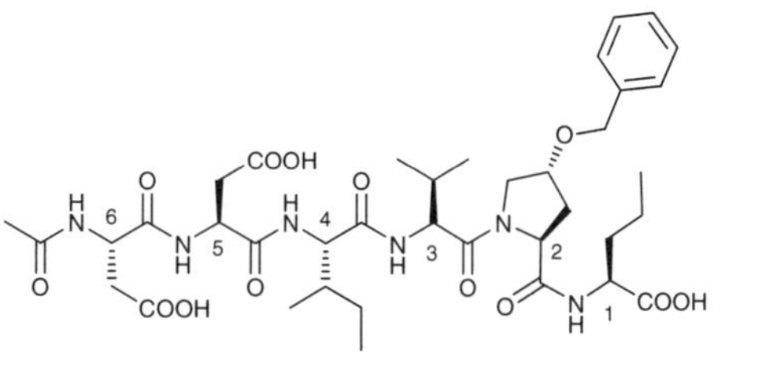

tify the portions of the molecules that are in contact with the protease. When a small quantity of the protease is added to an inhibitor such as **6** (IC$_{50}$ = 7 µM), the atoms that interact directly with the protein experience a broadening of their resonances in the NMR spectrum. These experiments led to the

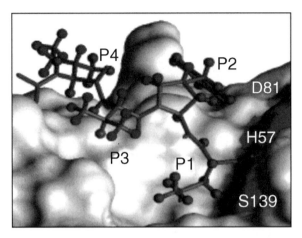

Figure 4. Model of NS3/4A protease with **6**. Hydrogens highlighted in blue indicate resonances for which no broadening perturbations were observed, while hydrogens in red showed significant resonance broadening upon addition of protease. Terminal Ac-Asp-Asp dipeptide is not shown [141]. Reproduced with permissions by Wiley-VCH Verlag GmbH & Co. KGaA and Prof. Youla S. Tsantrizos. (See color insert.)

conclusion that the four C-terminal amino acids and their side chains are crucial for providing the essential interactions with the protease (Fig. 4). Among the six amino acids in **6**, residues 1, 2, and 4 experience the most pronounced line-broadening effect whereas residues 3, 5, and 6 are mostly solvent exposed and are not in direct contact with the protein [139].

To further increase the binding affinity of the inhibitor to the protease it was important to gain insight into the structural difference of the inhibitor bound to the protease versus its conformation in solution. If the substrate had to adopt a conformation in the bound state that was significantly different from in solution, analogs could be designed that would bind conformation. To this end, compound **6** was studied by NOESY and ROESY experiments. These studies revealed that the conformation of the peptide backbone does not change significantly when the compound binds to the protease. However, a substantial difference was noted for the amino acid side chains. It was also apparent that the side chains were much less flexible in the bound conformation.

It is possible to measure the internal flexibility of a compound on the pico- and nanosecond timescale utilizing an NMR technique that is referred to as "^{13}C NMR spin-lattice relaxation." This experiment determines relaxation times T_1 for ^{13}C atoms. Longer T_1

values are usually indicative of increased flexibility. Relaxation times can be measured expeditiously on a qualitative level for ^{13}C atoms bearing hydrogen atoms. Upon binding to a protein, a ligand generally exhibits a reduction in flexibility, leading to a shortened relaxation time T_1. The change of the relaxation time, and thus the change in flexibility upon binding to a protein, is obtained in an experiment that has been coined "transferred $^{13}C T_1$." An increase in rigidity comes at an entropic and energetic cost, and thus there is an opportunity for the design of new analogs with greater activity incorporating less flexible moieties [140].

When compound **6** was studied in the ^{13}C NMR spin-lattice relaxation experiment, it was found that the n-propyl chain of Nva, the phenyl ring appended to proline, and the terminal methyl groups of Ile were the most flexible. After the addition of a substoichiometric amount of protease to the ligand, a transferred $^{13}C T_1$ experiment was conducted, revealing that the γ-CH_3 of Nva and the δ-CH_3 of Ile experience a substantial decrease in flexibility while the isopropyl group of Val remains unaffected by the binding to the protease (Fig. 4) [140].

As mentioned above, early studies on the hexapeptides illustrated that exchanging some amino acids for more optimized building blocks could enhance the potency of the peptide leading to compounds such as **5**. It was postulated that these molecules could be truncated further to reduce molecular weight and improve physical and pharmacokinetic properties. While tetrapeptides such as **7** ($IC_{50} = 0.9\,\mu M$) and **8** ($IC_{50} = 3.5\,\mu M$) were slightly less potent when compared to some of the optimized hexapeptides, they did indicate a way forward. Surprisingly, no DLB was observed for the cyclopropyl ring of a 1-aminocyclopropyl carboxylic acid (ACCA) derivative upon

addition of protease, leading to more SAR work around this C-terminal amino acid [142]. When a vinyl group was attached to the cyclopropyl ring of **8** with the appropriate stereochemistry, an almost sixfold increase in potency was observed for compound **9** ($IC_{50} = 0.6\,\mu M$). The optimization of the aromatic group attached to proline [143], based on a detailed understanding of its conformational requirements, ultimately led to highly potent inhibitors such as **10** ($IC_{50} = 0.013\,\mu M$) [144].

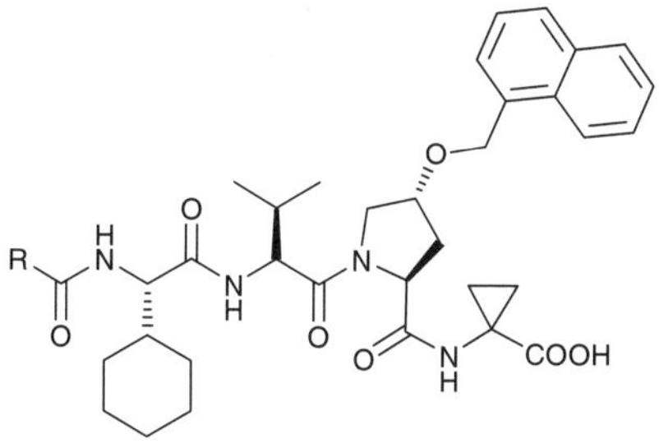

7 R = (CH₂)₃COOH
8 R = CH₃

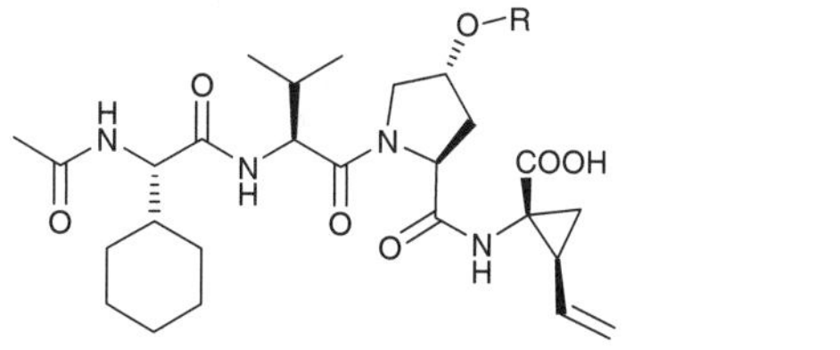

9 R =

10 R =

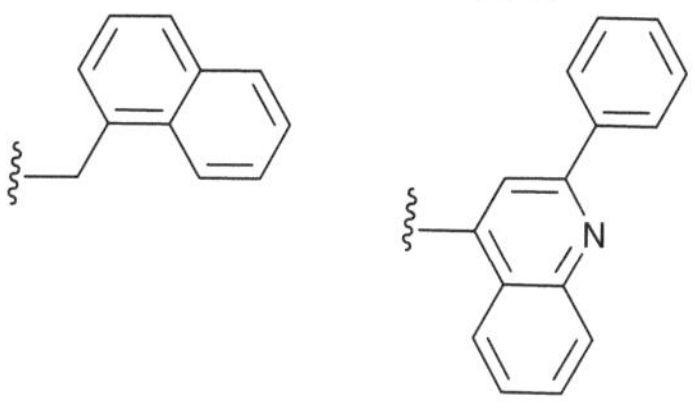

The activity of peptide **10** can be further increased by the introduction of a methoxy-group at position 7 or 8 on the quinoline ring ($IC_{50} = 2$ and $5\,nM$, respectively). In addition, replacement of valine with *tert*-leucine provides peptide **11** with an IC_{50} of $1\,nM$. Tripeptide analogs such as **12** in which the *N*-acyl

cyclohexyl glycine has been replaced with a urethane are slightly less active (IC_{50} values between 20 and 40 nM). Despite their excellent binding affinity, the potency of these tripeptides in a cell-based replicon assay is substantially less, presumably as a result of the linear peptidic nature of the compounds [145].

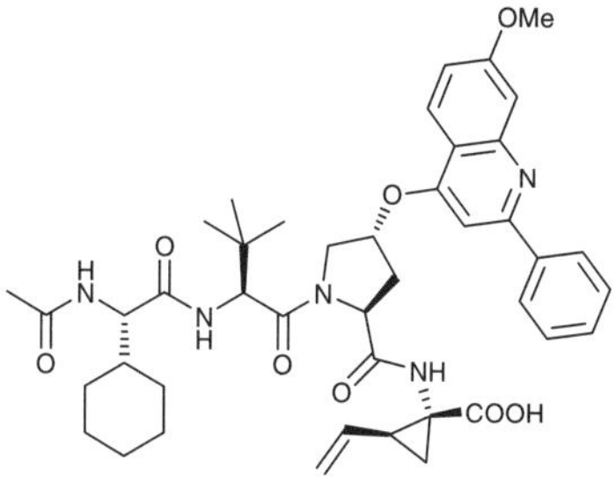

11

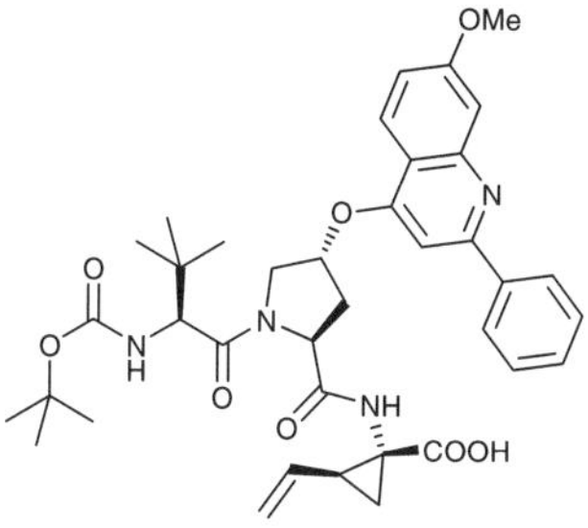

12

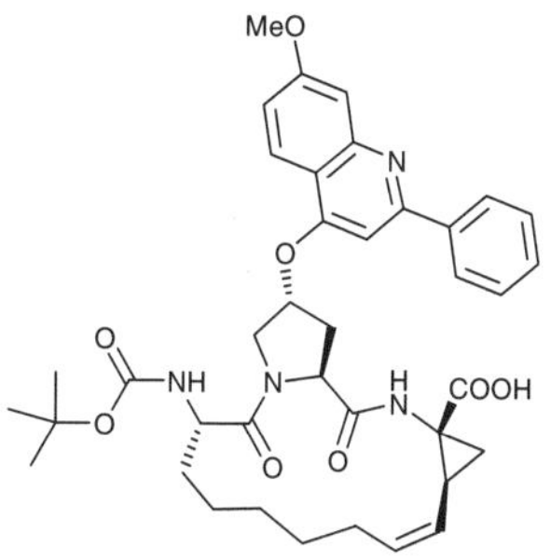

13

To further increase the rigidity of the molecule and to obtain less peptide-like compounds, the linear tripeptides were converted into macrocyclic structures. As can be seen in various literature review articles

[32,34] and later in this chapter, this has been a successful strategy in the design of small-molecule inhibitors NS3/4A. Previous NMR experiments on peptide **6** suggested that the valine side chain rests on top of the solvent

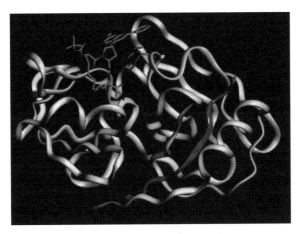

Figure 5. The crystal structure of inhibitor **13** (carbon atoms colored green) complexed to NS3 protease domain (gray ribbon) and NS4A (magenta ribbon) is shown [141]. Reproduced with permissions by Wiley-VCH Verlag GmbH & Co. KGaA and Prof. Youla S. Tsantrizos. (See color insert.)

exposed surface of the protease and in proximity to the side chain of the C-terminal amino acid. It was proposed that linking these groups would reduce the energetic penalty the molecule pays to adopt the conformation required for binding to the protease. Furthermore, it would force the Pro-Val amide bond into an exclusive *trans*-orientation. Among the initial examples, the 15-membered macrocycle **13** stands out as the most active analog $(IC_{50} = 11\,nM,\ EC_{50} = 77\,nM)$, and was the first compound reported by Boehringer-Ingelheim with significant activity in the replicon assay. The contribution of the macrocyclization can be appreciated when comparing **13** with the corresponding ring-opened analog **14** $(IC_{50} = 400\,nM)$, which is about 36 times less active [141]. The stereochemistry of the vinyl group on the cyclopropyl ring is critical for potency, with the 2-position epimer being 80-fold less active.

A cocrystal structure of **13** bound to the protease (Fig. 5) confirmed the structural data inferred from the NMR analysis. As shown, the aromatic moiety attached to the proline occupies a shallow cleft that is solvent exposed. The interactions responsible for the tight binding are attributed to the aromatic system, however, a more detailed understanding remains elusive. The critical nature of this substituent can be underscored by comparing **13** to the truncated macrocycle **15**, which is about 36,000-fold less potent $(IC_{50} = 400\ \mu M)$ [141]. Understandably, both this substituent and the N-terminal capping group were subsequently investigated in much greater detail since both are clearly critical for potency [146].

14   **15**   **16** R = Ac
                                2 R = *i*-Pr

A number of 5-membered ring heterocycles attached to the 2-position of the 7-methoxy-quinoline were reported, with several N-substituted 2-amino-thiazole-4-yl rings being optimal for cell-based activity. As anticipated, the binding affinities of these analogs differed only slightly since this portion of the molecule is solvent exposed. Having established the optimized thiazole substituent, the N-terminal functionality was varied. Urethanes and ureas were reported with cyclopentyl carbamate **16** ($IC_{50} = 2.5$ nM, $EC_{50} = 0.4$ nM) being slightly superior to the cyclobutyl derivative with respect to binding affinity and cell-based activity. A final round of optimization of the aromatic substituent on the quinoline was then carried out. This effort led to the discovery of ciluprevir (**2**) ($IC_{50} = 3.0$ nM) that binds reversibly to the NS3/4A protease ($K_i = 0.30$ nM and 0.66 nM for genotypes 1a and 1b, respectively) and is very selective for this protease over other human proteases [138]. In the replicon assay, BILN-2061 is potent against subtypes 1a and 1b with an EC_{50} of 4 and 3 nM, respectively. Addition of 50% human serum to the assay led to a less than 10-fold reduction in the EC_{50} values, indicating low plasma protein binding. When dosed orally at 20 mg/kg in rats, BILN-2061 showed a C_{max} of 2.5 µM and an $AUC_{0 \rightarrow \infty}$ of 12.5 µM·h. It is 42% bioavailable, has low clearance (13 mL/min/kg) and $t_{1/2}$ of 1.3 h [138].

Ciluprevir was evaluated in healthy volunteers in a double-blind dose-escalating study with placebo controls. The doses ranged from 5 to 2400 mg and only one adverse effect (gastrointestinal irritation) was observed at the highest dose, establishing the maximum tolerated dose (MTD) at 2000 mg. The C_{max} was reached within 2–4 h after dosing, with a mean elimination $t_{1/2}$ of 4 h, and linear PK properties in doses up to 1200 mg. In a twice-daily dosing schedule of 200 mg, a trough plasma concentration of 42 nM was predicted that is 14 times above the cellular EC_{50} of BILN-2061 for genotype 1b.

Subsequently, the compound was administered in a double-blind placebo controlled study in HCV infected patients (genotype 1). The patients received either a 200 mg oral dose of BILN-2061 or placebo, which led to an unprecedented drop of 2–3 $\log_{10}$ units (99–99.9%) in viral count in the treated group. In most patients, the undetectable levels of virus were observed within 48 h posttreatment. After the dosing was discontinued, the viral load rebounded to pretreatment levels within several days while no reduction of viral load was observed in the placebo group (Fig. 6) [134]. Further clinical trials of BILN-2061 had to be discontinued due to unexpected cardiac toxicity in animals [147].

3.1.2. Telaprevir (VX-950, Vertex)

17

Telaprevir

As of mid-2009, telaprevir (**17**) (VX-950, Vertex) is expected to be the first approved STAT-C drug. This putative first-in-class therapy is the result of an intensive, structure-based design program that began more than a decade ago. The detailed chronology of the discovery of telaprevir is not within the scope of this chapter; however, several reviews covering the development of the drug have been published [148–150].

The key features of the Vertex drug discovery program are the application of previously known serine trap technology [151] in combination with peptide replacement techniques leading to several series of potent, acyclic peptidomimetic inhibitors capped with electrophilic functional groups. The resulting analogs are classified as "reversible, covalent" active site inhibitors due to strong interactions between the electrophilic functionality of the molecules with the amino acids forming the protease's catalytic triad. This "transition state inhibitor" approach makes use of the enzyme's ability to stabilize the high-energy tetrahedral intermediate formed when water adds to the scissile amide bond. Other groups have implemented similar strategies for inhibition of substrate-based proteolysis [152–154].

The prototypical electrophilic cap (also known as the warhead), a terminal aldehyde,

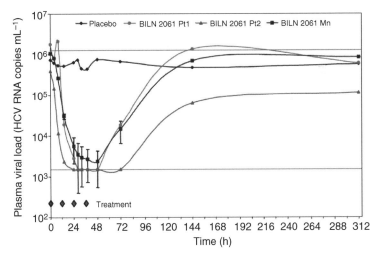

Figure 6. Antiviral efficacy of BILN-2061 in HCV-infected patients. The graphs represent viral load in the plasma of two patients treated with BILN 2061, one placebo and the geometric mean. Diamonds represent time of administration [134]. Reproduced with permission by Nature Publishing Group. (This figure is available in full color at http://mrw.interscience.wiley.com/emrw/9780471266945/home.)

was the basis of a series of moderately potent, tetrapeptide-based inhibitors [155]. Earlier protease inhibitors were larger, more complex and required charged functional groups for potency [154]. Although beneficial for binding potency, the presence of additional amino acid residues gave rise to inhibitors with high mo-

lecular weight and poor pharmacological properties. Exploitation of the electrophilicity of the terminal aldehyde was seen as a way to offset the loss of binding affinity while minimizing the size and eliminating the charge of the inhibitors.

The optimal 10-amino acid length for a substrate-based peptide inhibitor of the NS3/4A protease is unworkable. However, studies have reported reduction of this length to a more manageable 4–6 amino acids [153,156]. Thus, the Vertex group prepared pentapeptide-aldehyde **18** ($K_i = 0.89\,\mu M$) as their starting point [155]. The activity of **18** suggests that addition of the P_1 aldehyde group partially offsets the loss of binding from the deletion of four amino acids. Further removal of the P_5 and P_6 amino acids, followed by

capping the N-terminus with a neutral pyrazine group gave **19a** (Table 1), with only three amide bonds and a far more drug-like scaffold. The loss of potency resulting from this modification is only 15-fold ($K_i = 12\,\mu M$), demonstrating that potency could be regained by the incorporation of a terminal aldehyde and optimization of other regions of the molecule. Indeed, incorporation of the capping aldehyde coupled with variation of the oxygen substituent on the proline ring gave inhibitors that equaled or surpassed the potency of **18** with

Table 1. 4-Hydroxyproline Modifications

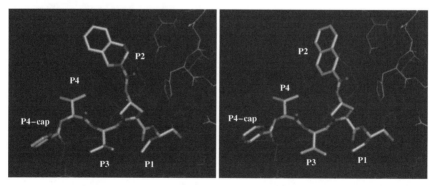

	R	K_i (μM)
19a	Benzyl	12
19b	C(O)-2-Naphthyl	0.40
19c		0.89
19d		7.9

the 2-naphthoyl ester **19b** ($K_i = 400$ nM) the most potent inhibitor reported. It was proposed that the increased binding affinity arose from interactions of the bulky naphthyl group with amino acid residues in the S2 pocket of the protein, where the active site proteolytic triad resides. Interestingly, the replacement of the aldehyde group with other electrophilic functionalities known to inhibit serine and cysteine proteases, such as a trifluoromethyl ketone, α-chloroketone and 1,3,4-oxadiazole [157] did not yield potent NS3/4A inhibitors.

Attempts to replace the hydrolytically unstable proline ester substituents by urethane isosteres were partially successful (Table 1). The tetrahydroisoquinoline (THIQ) analog **19c** has similar activity to **19b**, and an X-ray study of **19b** and **19c** shows they have a virtually identical binding mode (Fig. 7). Simple, monoaromatic urethane derivatives such as **19d** are weak inhibitors. Although instability of the aliphatic aldehyde group precluded development of this series, the study demonstrated that significant truncation of large peptidic substrate-based protease inhibitors can nonetheless afford compounds with good potency and more drug-like structures by the incorporation of an electrophilic cap at P_1.

In an effort to replace the P_1 aldehyde, a series of α-ketoamides was explored [158]. The degree of potency of the ketoamides is significantly affected by the nature of the N-alkyl amide group (Table 2). Thus, the N-benzyl ketoamide **20b** is fourfold more potent than the corresponding aldehyde **20a**. This can be either increased or decreased by the addition of a branching methyl substituent, depending on the stereochemistry of the methyl group. The S-isomer, **20c** is fourfold more potent than **20b**, while the R-isomer **20d** is fourfold less potent. This stereochemical preference is consistent with previously reported data [159].

The crystal structure of **20c** bound to the NS3/4A protease (Fig. 8) rationalizes the potent binding of the ketoamides. Reversible covalent addition of the active site Ser139 side-chain oxygen to the electrophilic ketone carbonyl mimics the high-energy tetrahedral

Figure 7. Binding of **19c** (left) and **19b** to NS3/4A [155]. Reproduced with permission by Elsevier. (See color insert.)

Table 2. SAR of N-Substituted Proline Benzyl Ethers

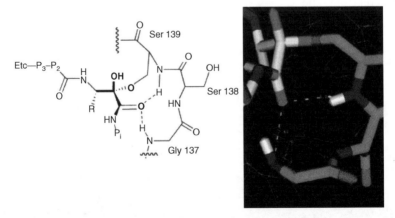

	R	K_i (μM)
20a	CHO	16
20b	(ketoamide, N-CH₂-Ph)	4.0
20c	(ketoamide, N-CH(CH₃)-Ph)	0.92
20d	(ketoamide, N-CH(CH₃)-Ph)	17

intermediate of the substrate's scissile carbon–nitrogen bond. Additional stabilization results from hydrogen bonding interactions between the Ser139 and the Gly137 amide hydrogens and the carbonyl group of the terminal amide. Binding affinity is further enhanced by the size and electrostatic characteristics of the P_2P_3 peptidomimetic scaffold as well as the P_1'-substituent of the terminal amide.

Consistent with the trend in Table 1, compounds in which the benzyl ether was replaced by the THIQ group displayed better inhibition [155]. With the THIQ group held constant, variation of the N-terminal group afforded a series of highly potent ketoamides (Table 3). A diverse group of nitrogen substituents are well tolerated in this position. The S-phenethyl amide **21f** has a K_i of less than 200 nM, fourfold more potent than the corresponding benzyl ether **20c**. Several other amides also inhibited in the 200 nM range (Table 3).

Although potent, compounds containing large, hydrophobic 4-substituted hydroxyproline moieties (Tables 2 and 3) have pharmaceutical property liabilities, including high $c\log p$ values and susceptibility to oxidative metabolism [160]. Modeling suggested that the S_2 pocket of NS3/4A could be filled by a smaller P_2 fragment, such as a simple alkyl group. Furthermore, earlier studies [153] predicted that the relocation of a lipophilic group from the C-4 to the C-3 position of the proline pyrrolidine might be beneficial. Indeed, replacement of the C-4 benzyl ether of **20c** with a C-3 methyl group resulted in only a slight loss

Figure 8. A representation of the covalent interaction between a bound ketoamide inhibitor and the serine active site (left). The X-ray crystal structure of **20c** bound to NS3/4A (right) [158]. Reproduced with permission by Elsevier. (See color insert.)

Table 3. Potent α-Ketoamide-THIQ Analogs

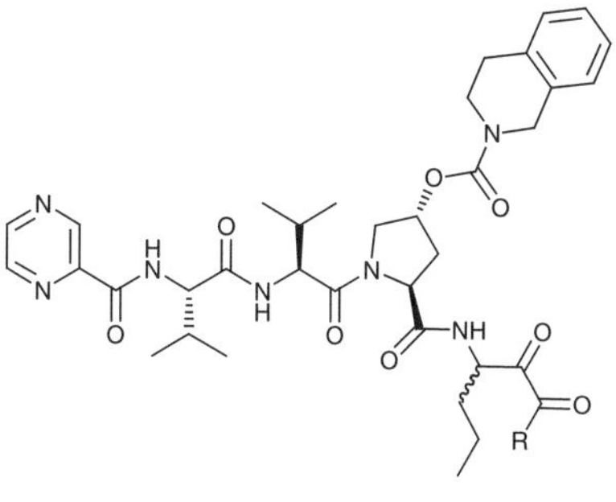

22

	R	
21a	Gly	
21b	Ala	
21c	Naphthyl-Ala	
21d	NHBenzyl	$K_i \sim 200\,nM$
21e	NHcyclopropyl	
21f	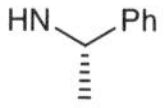 HN⟍⟋Ph	

of potency (0.92 μM versus 1.4 μM). Further improvements in activity were obtained in a collaborative effort with scientists from Lilly [161,162], wherein the C-3 alkyl moiety was held constant, and the P$_3$ and P$_4$ groups were optimized. Replacement of the P$_3$ and P$_4$ valine groups by *tert*-butylglycine and cyclohexylglycine, respectively, gave a very potent series of 3-alkyl substituted proline analogs, **22** [161].

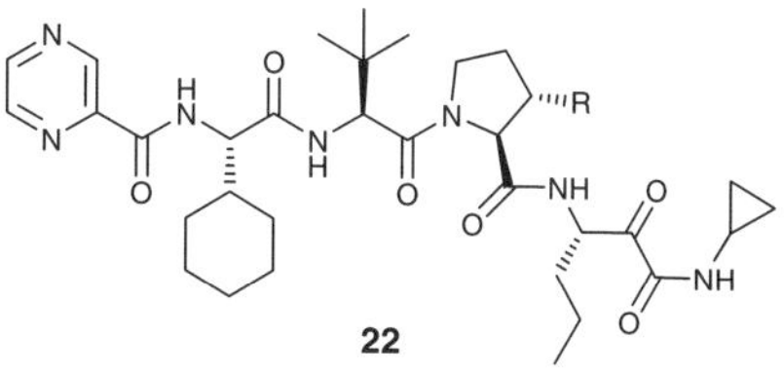

The SAR for this series (**22**, R = 2–6 carbon alkyl group) is flat, with K_i values ranging from 0.09 to 0.46 μM. This suggests that the S$_2$ pocket can accommodate a variety of different-sized lipophilic groups. However, a substituent is required as the unsubstituted proline analog (R = H) is about 10-fold less active. Although the analog where R = Et is not the most potent in this group, it demonstrates superior replicon activity (IC$_{50}$ = 0.45 μM), presumably due to better cellular permeability.

Additional studies from the Lilly group revealed that replacement of the P$_2$ proline moiety with a bicycloproline group [161,162] yielded a series of novel, potent protease inhibitors, some of which are exemplified in Table 4. Substitution of the bicycloproline ring generally results in less active protease inhibitors (**23a–23d**) relative to the unsubstituted analogs **23e–23f**. Two capping amide groups were investigated at the P$_1$-position. Among this group, carboxylic acids **23c** and **23f** are extremely potent against NS3/4A, but have no replicon activity, most likely due to poor cellular permeability arising from the pheny-

Table 4. Bicycloproline Inhibitors

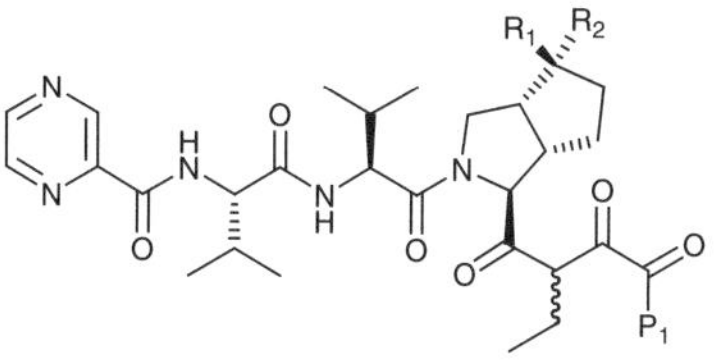

Compound	R$_1$	R$_2$	P$_1$	K_i (μM)	Replicon
23a	F	F	NH-cyclopropyl	0.37	64% @25 μM
23b	F	H	NH-cyclopropyl	0.30	84% @25 μM
23c	F	H	Phe	0.082	−8% @25 μM
23d	H	OCH$_2$OMe	NH-cyclopropyl	0.41	80% @25 μM
23e	H	H	NH-cyclopropyl	0.12	IC$_{50}$ = 7 μM
23f	H	H	Phe	0.068	−88% @25 μM

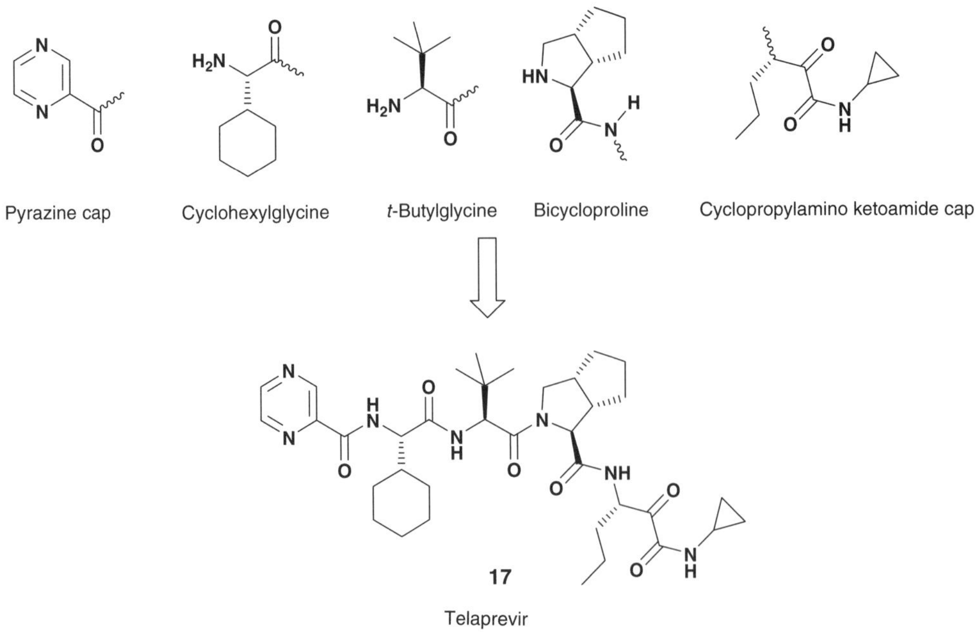

Pyrazine cap   Cyclohexylglycine   *t*-Butylglycine   Bicycloproline   Cyclopropylamino ketoamide cap

17

Telaprevir

Figure 9. Optimized telaprevir fragments.

lalanine carboxyl group. As demonstrated in previous studies, cyclopropylamine confers good potency to the P_1 amide group. Combination of the optimal groups for P_4, P_3, and P_1 (Fig. 9) coupled with the incorporation of the unsubstituted bicycloproline yielded telaprevir, **17** ($K_i = 0.04 \, \mu M$, replicon $IC_{50} = 0.35 \, \mu M$).

Given the advanced clinical status of telaprevir, there is a large volume of published clinical data. Several reviews detail Phases I–III results of the drug, both alone and in combination with standard of care therapy [148,149,163]. Telaprevir was well tolerated in single doses up to 1250 mg in healthy volunteers, as well as in multiple doses in patients with chronic HCV [164]. Doses ranging from 450 to 1250 mg resulted in a remarkable decrease in HCV RNA ranging from $-3.5 \log_{10}$ to $-4.8 \log_{10}$. In combination with PEG-IFN [164], the average drop in RNA was $-5.5 \log_{10}$, with half of the patients having undetectable viral RNA after 2 weeks of therapy. With the addition of ribavirin [165], all patients had undetectable HCV RNA after 28 days of treatment. There are currently at least four Phase III trials ongoing [166–169].

3.1.3. Boceprevir (SCH 503034, Schering-Plough) Schering-Plough also employed a

peptide truncation approach, analogous to that of Boehringer-Ingelheim. After an unproductive screening campaign of several million compounds, they initiated a structure-based discovery effort centered around peptide inhibitor **24**, making use of the previously discussed electrophilic α-ketoamide warhead to covalently interact with Ser139 [151]. Undecapeptide **24** is a potent inhibitor of NS3/4A ($K_i^* = 1.9 \, nM$) suitable to serve as a lead structure for a drug discovery program [170]. Truncating this large peptide and incorporating optimized building blocks eventually resulted in the discovery of SCH 503034, also known as boceprevir (Fig. 10), currently in Phase III clinical trials.

Thus, a series of peptides was prepared in which the C-terminal amino acids of **24** had been truncated and the proline converted to an imidazolidinone [171] in an attempt to make the inhibitors more druglike. The resulting heptapeptide **26** ($K_i^* = 310$ nM) is less active than **24** but still displays considerable activity despite the extent of the molecular weight reduction. To further reduce the molecular weight of **26** while retaining potency, the two N-terminal glutamic acids were removed and a C-terminal carboxylate added in an attempt to target

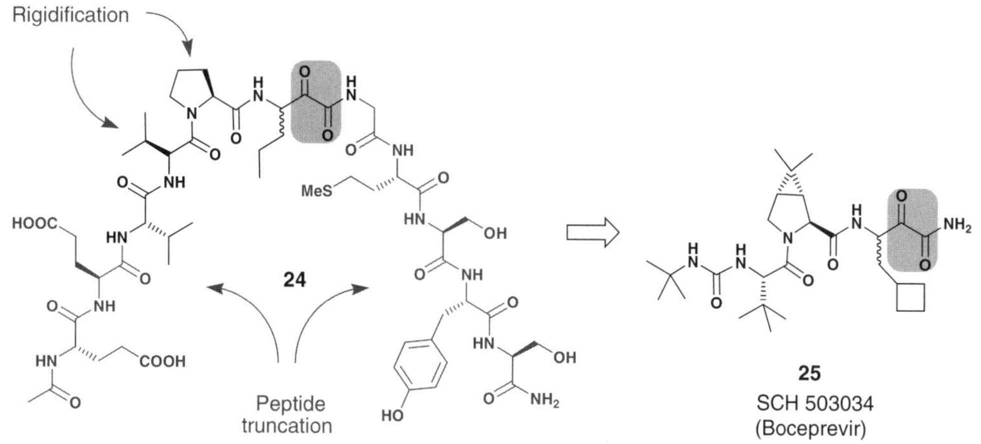

Figure 10. Medicinal Chemistry efforts enabled the discovery of SCH 503034 (**25**) from undecapeptide **24**. (This figure is available in full color at http://mrw.interscience.wiley.com/emrw/9780471266945/home.)

Lys136 in the NS3/4A active site. Although none of the carboxylic acids are potent, the corresponding primary amides were found to be good inhibitors [172]. The *iso*-butylcarbamate N-capped analog **27** ($K_i^* = 66$ nM), in which the imidazolidinone and valine groups were replaced with leucine and cyclohexylglycine, respectively, is about fivefold more active than **26** despite being considerably smaller.

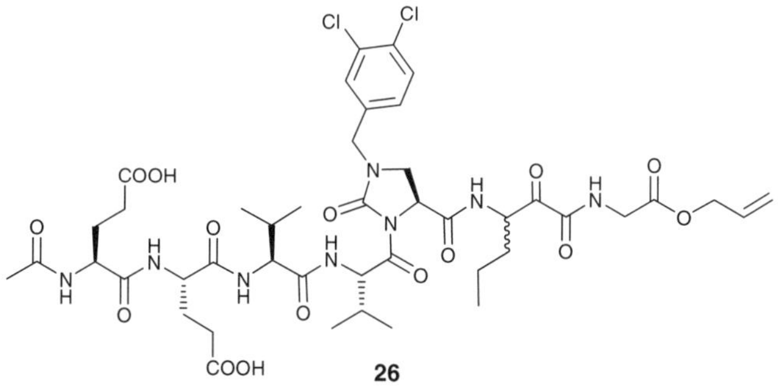

26

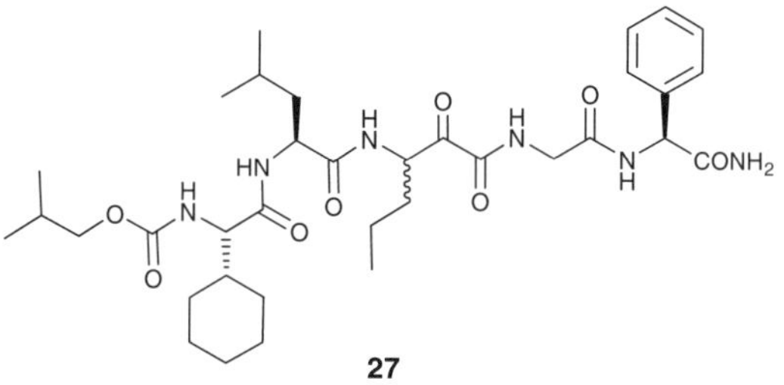

27

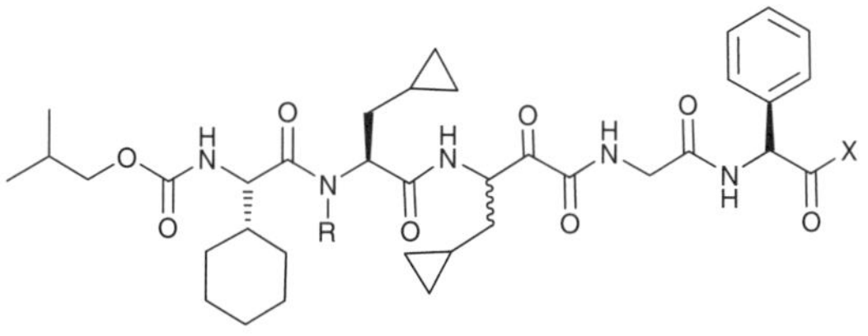

28 R = H, X = OH
29a R = H, X = NMe$_2$
29b R = Me, X = NMe$_2$

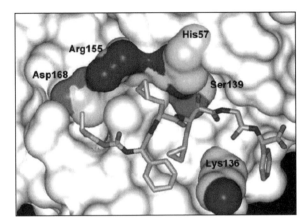

Figure 11. X-ray crystal structure of hexapeptide **28** bound to NS3/4A [173]. Reproduced with permission by Elsevier. (See color insert.)

Having optimized both termini of the hexapeptide scaffold, the central dipeptide unit was examined and hydrophobic dipeptide-based fragments improved binding affinity. The di-cyclopropylalanine analog **28** was the most potent enzyme inhibitor ($K_i^* = 15$ nM) in this series but is essentially inactive in the replicon assay, probably due to the carboxylic acid [173]. Figure 11 shows an X-ray crystal structure of **28** bound to the protease. As can be seen, the compound binds in the anticipated fashion. The electrophilic ketone engages the serine side chain in a covalent interaction while the cyclopropyl and cyclohexyl side chains of the inhibitor form critical hydrophobic interactions with the protein. Another characteristic binding feature of these protease inhibitors is referred to as the "C-clamp." The C-terminal tripeptide sequence encompassing the cyclopropylalanine, glycine, and phenylglycine, adopt a C-shape conformation that wraps around Lys136, thus contributing to the overall binding affinity.

Conversion of **28** into the corresponding dimethylamides **29a** and **29b** provides excellent activity in the binding assay ($K_i^* = 0.050$ and $0.060\,\mu$M, respectively). However, the activities of **29a** and **29b** in the replicon assay are significantly different (EC$_{50} > 5.0$ and $0.95\,\mu$M, respectively). This has been attributed to **29b** being structurally similar to the proline residue found in the native substrate. Therefore, subsequent analogs focused on incorporating proline-derived building blocks at this position [174].

Guided by these X-ray crystallography studies, a series of compounds was prepared in which the leucine residue in **27** was replaced by several proline mimetics and the C-terminus was capped with a dimethylamide group. Many of the analogs in this series showed excellent binding affinity for NS3/4A. It was found that an optically pure 2,2-dimethylcyclopropylproline was optimal in this position, not only for binding but also for cell-based activity. With this optimized amino acid in place, the two flanking amino acids and the N-terminal capping group were explored. This led to the discovery of SCH6 (**30**) containing a *tert*-leucine and cyclopropylalanine [175]. This compound is very active against the enzyme as well as in the replicon assay ($K_i^* = 3.8$ nM, EC$_{90} = 100$ nM) and it shows 1000-fold selectivity over human neutrophil elastase (HNE), a human serine protease closely related to NS3/4A.

30

SCH6

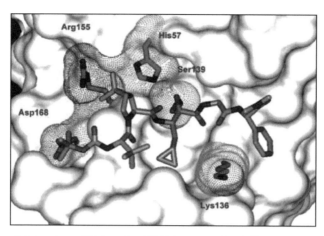

Figure 12. X-ray crystal structure of **30** bound to NS3/4A protease [176]. Reproduced with permission by the American Chemical Society. (See color insert.)

The X-ray crystal structure of **30** bound to NS3/4A (Fig. 12) reveals that the inhibitor binds in the anticipated fashion. Ser139 binds covalently to the ketoamide as expected and the resulting hydroxyl anion engages in a hydrogen bond with His57. Like analog **28** (Fig. 11), **30** also adopts the characteristic "C-clamp" when bound to the protease.

Because of its *in vitro* potency, **30** was chosen for PK studies in rats and monkeys. When administered subcutaneously (10 mg/kg in rat, 1 mg/kg in monkey), **30** had high blood levels and good exposure (AUC = 19.5 and 5.6 μMh), and a C_{max} of 4.37 and 1.6 μM in rat and monkey, respectively [175]. However, when the drug was administered PO the AUC, bioavailability and C_{max} were low, suggesting that the high molecular weight of **30** contributed to its poor PK properties [176], and further optimization was needed.

Since the N-terminal portion of the molecule was already optimized, attempts to reduce molecular weight were focused on truncation of the C-terminus. Modifications of the phenylglycine group showed that the amide NH was not required for binding since analogous terminal esters show similar potency. A large number of analogs with modifications at the C-terminus were synthesized. However, the desired reduction in molecular weight negatively impacted the potency of the analogs. This was resolved with the synthesis of tripeptide **31**, in which the glycyl-phenylala-nyl-dimethylamide moiety was truncated to give the primary α-keto amide. Despite its reduced molecular weight, this compound retained its potency, ($K_i^* = 0.1$ μM) and the expected improvement in PK properties in rat was achieved (AUC = 2.52 μMh following oral administration; dose not reported) [170].

Having established that lower molecular weight compounds terminating with a primary α-keto amide can be potent and orally bioavailable, attention was turned to the norvaline and cyclohexylglycine side-chains of **31** to further optimize activity. Incorporating racemic cyclobutylalanine in place of the norvaline in **31** resulted in a truncated tripeptide analog **32** with greatly improved binding affinity ($K_i^* = 8$ nM) and replicon potency (EC90 = 0.7 μM). Furthermore, **32** is 138-fold selective for HCV over HNE. This compound showed acceptable PK in rat (AUC = 1.5 μMh, $F = 28$%, 10 mg/kg), however, the PK profile in monkey was poor [170].

Several tripeptide analogs of **31** were investigated, in which the cyclohexylalanine was replaced with a *tert*-butyl glycine, and cyclopropylalanine or cyclobutylalanine was substituted for norvaline. The cyclobutylalanine derivative ($K_i^* = 76$ nM, EC90 = 0.8 μM) is slightly less active than the corresponding cyclopropyl derivative ($K_i^* = 57$ nM, EC90 = 0.6 μM) in binding affinity and replicon activity, but it is significantly more selective for HCV over HNE (684-fold versus 112-fold) [170].

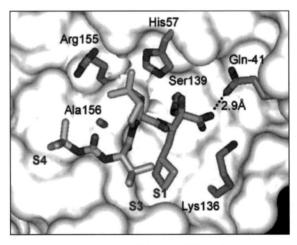

31   **32**   **33** R =

25 R =

The final phase of the discovery of boceprevir was the identification of the optimal capping group for the N-terminus of the tripeptide. A large number of analogs were surveyed in which either racemic cyclopropylalanine or cyclobutylalanine was paired with *tert*-butylglycine while capping the tripeptide at the N-terminus with a variety of carbamates or ureas. While the nature of the carbamate group did not significantly affect the binding affinity of the molecule, the corresponding urea-capped peptides such as **33** and **25** (boceprevir) showed significantly improved potency ($K_i^* = 13$ and $14\,nM$, respectively). The cell-based activity and selectivity of **25** ($EC_{90} = 350\,nM$, HCV/HNE > 2200) was also improved with respect to **32**. An X-ray crystal structure of **25** was obtained (Fig. 13), but cannot rationalize the superiority of the optimized *tert*-butyl urea, *tert*-butyl glycine

and cyclobutylalanine over closely related analogs. As seen before in the X-ray crystal structure of **30**, Ser139 engages the α-ketoamide in a covalent fashion while the primary amide forms a hydrogen bond with Gln41; thus, locking the ligand to the active site of the protease. The crystal structure also demonstrates that the diastereomer with the (S)-configuration at the α-keto amide binds preferentially to the protease. While the two diastereomers of **25** could be separated by HPLC, racemization occurred rapidly in the presence of organic and inorganic bases. Since this rapid equilibration of the stereocenter also occurred under the assay conditions, the diasteromeric mixture was used for biological evaluation [176].

When dosed orally in rat (10 mg/kg), monkey (3 mg/kg) and dog (3 mg/kg), **25** showed an AUC of 1.52, 0.12, and 3.08 μMh, and a

Figure 13. X-ray crystal structure of **25** bound to NS3/4A [170]. Reproduced with permission by the American Chemical Society. (See color insert.)

bioavailability of 26%, 4–11%, and 30%, respectively. Other pharmaceutical properties of **25** (absorption, liver/plasma ratio, and liver exposure) were acceptable and no hERG and CYP inhibition was observed. When replicon cell lines were exposed to a concentration equal to six times the EC_{90} of **25**, a greater than 4-log reduction in viral RNA was detected after 15 days [177].

Boceprevir (**25**) was studied in Phase I clinical trials where it was shown to be well tolerated and efficacious. Subsequently, in a Phase II study in previously untreated HCV patients, boceprevir in combination with peginterferon alfa-2b and ribavirin substantially improved SVR in a 28-week regimen. It nearly doubled the SVR in a 48-week treatment compared to the standard of care. With a 4 week lead-in using peginterferone alfa-2b and ribavirin, the SVR was slightly improved [178]. Boceprevir is currently in Phase III clinical trials [170].

3.1.4. ITMN-191 (R7227, InterMune-Roche)

Boehringer-Ingelheim's progress in the NS3/4A protease area spurred efforts among many pharmaceutical companies to find structurally similar inhibitors, which would hopefully be devoid of any cardiac side effects *in vivo*. InterMune employed a similar peptide-based approach, culminating in the discovery of ITMN-191 (**34**). This 15-membered macrocyclic NS3/4A protease inhibitor displays many structural features related to ciluprevir.

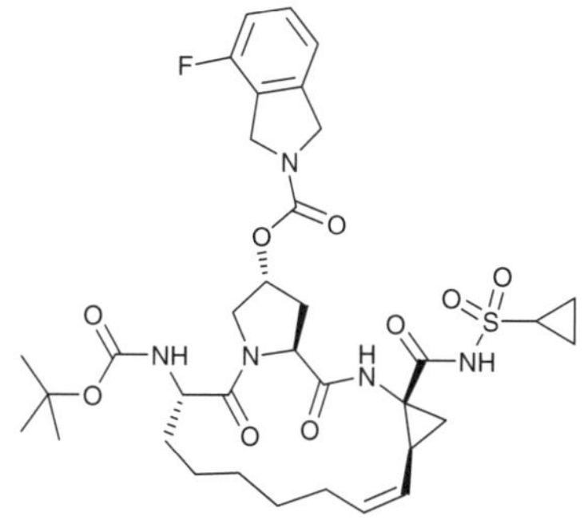

34

ITMN-191

This compound is reported to be highly potent against the genotype 1b protease ($IC_{50} < 0.25$ nM) as well as four relevant mutants (IC_{50} values between 0.4 and 4.5 nM). Furthermore, it is potent against genotypes 1a and 2 (IC_{50} values $= 0.4$ nM), but slightly less potent against genotype 3 ($IC_{50} = 12.4$ nM). Compound **34** also displays excellent potency in the cell-based replicon assay ($EC_{50} = 1.6$ nM, $EC_{90} = 14$ nM) indicating good cell permeability. It is metabolized in human hepatocytes at a moderate rate, and is a weak inhibitor of the cytochrome P450 enzymes. Animal exposure data suggested that **34** would require bid dosing in humans [179].

Biochemical experiments led to the hypothesis that binding of **34** proceeds in a two-step process via an initial reversible complex with NS3/4A, leading to a stable complex with a slow off-rate. When the inhibitor is preincubated with the protease, the IC_{50} is 120 pM. However, without preincubation, the IC_{50} is about sixfold higher (800 pM), supporting a time-dependent binding. Unlike α-ketoamide inhibitors, the complex of ITMN-191 with the protein does not involve formation of a covalent bond [180].

Viral RNA levels, as measured by RT-PCR, were below the limit of detection when replicon cells were treated with **34** at a concentration of 45 nM for 14 days. When rats and primates were dosed orally with **34** bid (dose and duration of treatment not reported), trough liver concentration greatly exceeded this value. In addition, coadministration with pegylated INF-α-2a (2 ng/mL) resulted in a dramatic reduction ($>4.7 \log_{10}$) of the viral load, to levels below the limit of detection. This reduction was also observed in a 14-day regimen using **34** at a concentration of 15 nM, the lowest concentration tested [181].

Subsequently, **34** was studied in the replicon assay in combination with the Roche nucleoside polymerase inhibitors R1626 (**35**) and R7128 (**36**). Viral RNA levels were below the limit of detection after 14 days during which ITMN-191 was dosed at 6 nM (3.3-fold EC_{50}) together with R7128 at 300 nM (0.25-fold EC_{50}). A similar effect was observed when ITMN-191 was dosed at 6 nM together with R1626 at 450 nM (0.25-fold EC_{50}) [182].

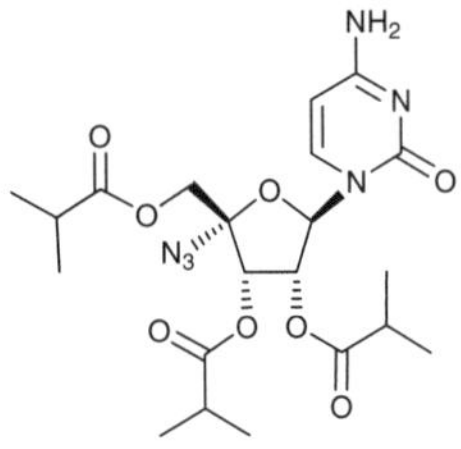

35
R1626

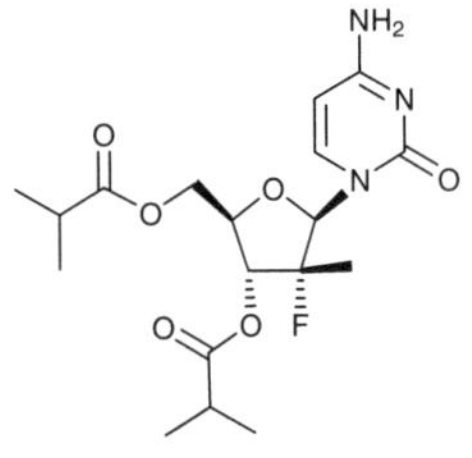

36
R7128

3.1.5. TMC435350 (Tibotec-Medivir)

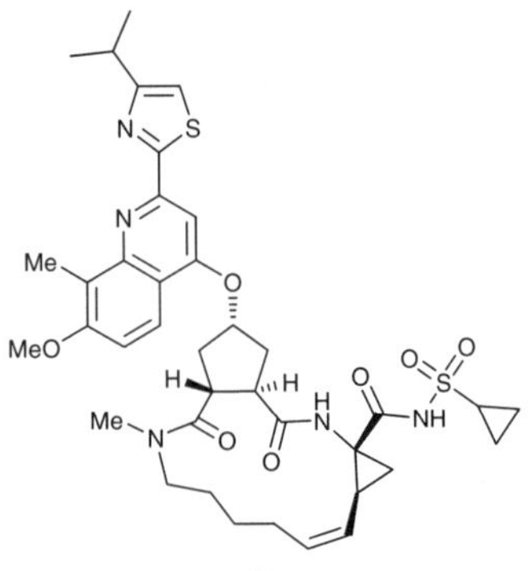

37

TMC435350

The PK properties of **34** were studied in rats and cynomolgus monkeys. Following oral dosing at 30 mg/kg, the concentration of the compound in the livers of both species is significantly above the *in vitro* EC_{50}. Furthermore, **34** exhibits a favorable liver-to-plasma exposure ratio of 127 with respect to the total observed exposure (AUC_{obs}), and 85 at C_{max}. These findings together with a high degree of selectivity in *in vitro* assays suggested that bid dosing in humans would give adequate exposure with minimal toxicity. Clinical evaluation of **34** in combination with standard of care, as well as with known polymerase inhibitors, is currently under way [183].

Medivir and Tibotec also launched a protease inhibitor program that utilized peptides as lead structures, ultimately resulting in clinical candidate **37** (TMC435350). A key finding was that the incorporation of an aryloxy-containing cyclopentane building block resulted in potent tetrapeptide inhibitors. Compound **38** was a potent inhibitor ($K_i^* = 22$ nM), despite lacking the proline moiety of earlier inhibitors [184]. Following the ciluprevir discovery strategy, efforts were made to convert this linear molecule into a cyclic structure. While macrocycle **39** was highly potent in the protease ($K_i^* = 0.41$ nM) and replicon assay ($EC_{50} = 9$ nM), it was poorly absorbed in the rat ($F = 2.5\%$) after an oral dose of 15 mg/kg. This poor bioavailability was attributed to rapid biliary excretion. Within 1 h, following an i.v. dose (1 mg/kg), 95% of the compound was excreted through the bile.

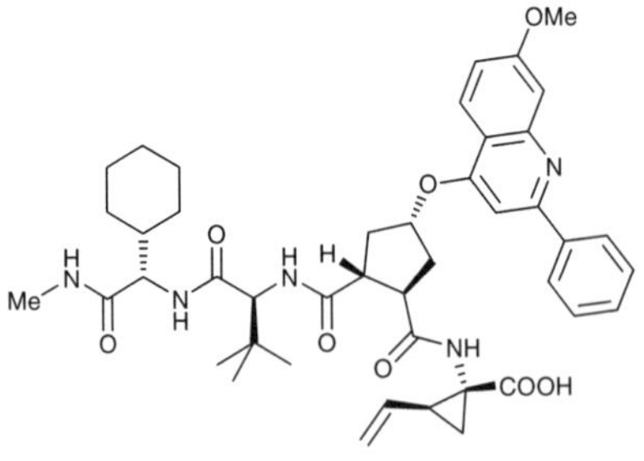

38

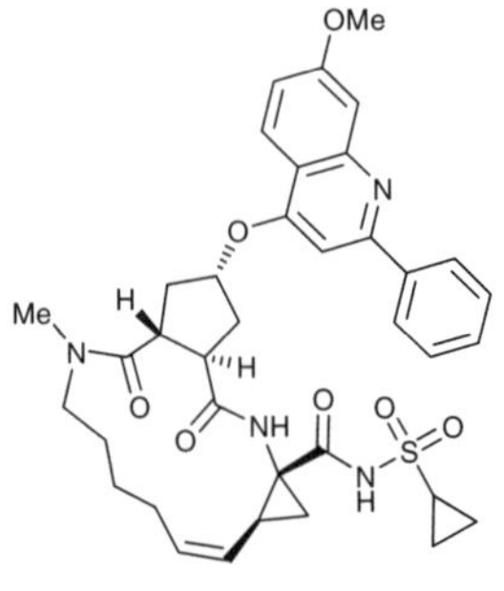

39

Further SAR studies of the aromatic heterocycle of **39** addressed the PK liabilities of

the compound. Systematic replacement of the phenyl substituent with numerous five- and six-membered heterocycles led to highly potent compounds in the replicon assay. Among these, TMC435350 (**37**) had the lowest intrinsic clearance in human liver microsomes. Three closely related compounds were evaluated for their pharmacokinetic properties in male Sprague-Dawley rats. In addition to its potency, **37** ($K_i^* = 0.36$ nM, $EC_{50} = 7.8$ nM) stood out for its low clearance (0.51 L/h/kg), volume of distribution (0.49 L/kg) and favorable liver/plasma ratio (63.5) after a 2 mg/kg i.v. dose. When dosed orally at 10 mg/kg, **37** demonstrated high exposure (AUC = 2.79 µMh), had a C_{max} of 0.73 µM and a $t_{1/2}$ of 2.8 h. The PK parameters in beagles after an oral 6.5 mg/kg dose were also determined, with bioavailability approaching 100%, a C_{max} of 4.72 µM, and a $t_{1/2}$ of 5.1 h. Compound **37** was subsequently advanced to clinical trials [185].

When dosed in healthy volunteers (Phase I trials) no adverse events were observed at single doses of **37** up to 600 mg and repeated doses of 400 mg for 5 days. Plasma levels of **37** were about threefold higher in patients compared to healthy volunteers after 5 days. A rapid reduction in the viral load was observed in all of the patients (genotypes 1a and 1b). Four weeks after dosing, viral RNA levels had returned to baseline levels in all patients [186].

Phase II trials were conducted in treatment-naïve patients infected with HCV genotype 1 for up to 28 days. The compound was well tolerated when dosed orally at 25 or 75 mg qd in combination with pegylated IFNβ-2a and ribavirin. Adverse events related to the drug were of mild to moderate severity. The 25 and 75 mg doses of **37** in combination with pegylated IFNβ-2a and ribavirin resulted in greater mean reduction of viral RNA levels than the standard of care alone. A dose-dependent reduction of RNA levels was observed which was enhanced by the addition of pegylated IFNβ-2a and ribavirin. When dosed at 75 mg qd for 4 weeks, nine out of nine patients had viral load below the lower limit of quantification, while eight out of nine patients achieved undetectable HCV RNA levels at day 28. Current studies are investigating higher doses of **37** as well as treatment options for nonresponders and patients who have experienced a relapse [187].

3.1.6. MK7009 (Merck)

40

MK7009

The Merck effort to design a structurally novel NS3/4A protease inhibitor was based on an *in silico* study of ciluprevir bound to the apo-form of the NS3/4A enzyme that included the helicase domain (Fig. 14). From the structural information obtained, it was hypothesized that the macrocyclic tether of ciluprevir could be broken and replaced by a linker installed between the quinoline and the carbamate moieties. An initial set of targeted compounds **41–44** with varying tether lengths, was evaluated in the binding and replicon assay.

A clear correlation between ring size and binding affinity was found, with the 5-carbon-linked macrocycle **43** being the most active analog in this series. When modeled into the active site of full length NS3/4A, superposition of large portion of **43** with BILD-2061 was obtained (Fig. 14). When evaluated in the cell-based replicon assay, compounds **41–44** showed only modest potency, probably because the carboxylic acid was detrimental to cell permeability. Replacement of the carboxylate by an acylsulfonamide substituent coupled with additional SAR work around the macrocycle led to analog **45**, which shows subnanomolar binding affinity for the enzyme ($K_i^* = 0.07$ nM). Furthermore, **45** retains its potency in the replicon assay in the presence of 10% fetal bovine serum (FBS) or 50% normal human serum (NHS $IC_{50} = 4.5$ and 14 nM, respectively). Importantly, **45** affords high concentrations in the rat liver for 24 h following a 5 mg/kg dose. This compound was active against neither the other proteases nor the hERG channel and was excreted unchanged, primarily in the bile, after i.v. dosing [188].

Figure 14. Model of ciluprevir (cyan) bound to full length NS3/4A (protease, green; helicase, purple) with key protein–inhibitor interactions shown overlaid with **43** [188]. Reproduced with permission by the American Chemical Society. (See color insert.)

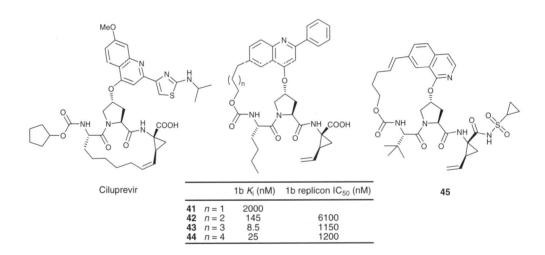

		1b K_i (nM)	1b replicon IC_{50} (nM)
41	$n = 1$	2000	
42	$n = 2$	145	6100
43	$n = 3$	8.5	1150
44	$n = 4$	25	1200

A series of bicyclic macrocycles, exemplified by **46**, hybrids of ciluprevir and macrocycles such as **44**, has also been reported. This series is noteworthy not only from a synthetic perspective but, **46**, also shows remarkable potency against the protease ($K_i^* = 0.029$ nM) and in the replicon assay in the presence of 10% FBS or 50% NHS ($IC_{50} = 2$ and 10 nM, respectively) [189].

46

Based on its potency in the replicon assay ($EC_{50} = 3.5$ nM) and favorable pharmaceutical properties **40** was studied in the chimpanzee model of hepatitis C. When chimpanzees chronically infected with HCV, they were dosed orally with 5 mg/kg bid for 7 days, a rapid $5 \log_{10}$ drop in viral load was observed. After the dosing was discontinued, the viral load rebounded to the initial level [190]. This led to the progression of **40** to human trials [191,192].

In Phase I clinical studies, **40** had acceptable PK and was generally safe and well tolerated, with only mild to moderate adverse events. The blood levels of **40** greatly exceeded the *in vitro* EC_{50}, allowing once- or twice-daily dosing [193]. A Phase II double-blind randomized placebo-controlled study of treatment-naïve or experienced patients demonstrated safety, tolerability and efficacy of **40** as a monotherapy. Viral RNA levels generally decreased rapidly, with the 700 mg bid dose group showing the greatest decline of $4.6 \log_{10}$ units after 8 days [194]. Additional Phase II clinical trials of **40** in combination with pegylated interferon and ribavirin are ongoing.

3.2. Nucleoside Inhibitors of HCV RNA-Dependent RNA Polymerase (RdRp)

Inhibitors of viral polymerases have provided successful therapeutics for the treatment of hepatitis B, herpes simplex, and HIV viruses. A variety of nucleoside competitive inhibitors of HCV NS5B, the RdRp encoded at the 3'-terminal portion of the HCV genome and required for viral replication, have also been thoroughly studied and advanced to clinical trials. These inhibitors function as chain terminators and are usually modified at the 2'-, 3'-, or 4'-position of the ribose moiety. In order for nucleosides to potently inhibit HCV replication in cells they must fulfill several requirements [195]. First, they must be able to enter the cell, usually as the 5'-hydroxy species, and then they must be a viable substrate for phosphorylation by a nucleoside kinase inside the cell, ultimately providing a nucleoside triphosphate, the active species. Conversion of the 5'-hydroxy compound to the corresponding monophosphate is the rate-determining step in the triphosphate formation process. After

the triphosphate has been produced inside the cell, it must be efficiently incorporated into the growing RNA chain. Once inserted into the nucleic acid chain, the inhibitor must act as a chain terminator to prevent further elongation of the strand. This occurs most often through either a steric or a conformational effect of a modified ribose segment of the inhibitor, thus blocking reaction at the 3'-hydroxyl group. Alternatively, inhibitors lacking a 3'-hydroxyl moiety cannot function as substrates for chain elongation at that position. Finally, nucleoside HCV inhibitors must possess oral bioavailability, must achieve therapeutic levels in the liver, and must have a pharmacokinetic half-life sufficient to enable efficacy with once or twice daily dosing.

3.2.1. Valopicitabine (NM283, Idenix)
An early nucleoside HCV polymerase inhibitory agent was 2'-C-methylcytidine, **47** (NM-107), identified in a bovine viral diarrhea virus (BVDV) surrogate assay for HCV inhibition with a K_i^* of 160 nM against BVDV polymerase [196]. Compound **47** is also an inhibitor of the yellow fever and West Nile RNA viruses, but does not inhibit DNA viruses [197]. The EC_{50} of **47** in an HCV replicon assay is 0.27 µM [198]. Interestingly, *in vitro* studies have suggested that ribavirin antagonizes the antiviral effect of **47** *in vitro* in an HCV replicon assay [198]. Due to poor oral bioavailability the *in vivo* utility of NM-107 was limited, leading to the evaluation of an amino ester prodrug, a strategy that had proven successful for other antivirals such as valacyclovir, the prodrug of acyclovir, and valganciclovir [199,200]. The 3'-O-valinyl ester **48**, valopicitabine (NM283), was evaluated in Phase II clinical trials for HCV [201,202]. This valine ester prodrug has 10-fold greater aqueous solubility (423 g/L) than **47**, very low protein binding, good stability at pH 4.5 ($t_{1/2} = 6$ days), enabling absorption prior to release of the parent 3'-hydroxy parent, and a half-life of ~4 h at pH 7.2 [196]. In human plasma and whole blood, **48** is cleaved by esterases to **47** with half-lives of 130 and 40 min, respectively. Compound **48** is also rapidly cleaved ($t_{1/2} < 1$ h) to release **47** in human liver and S9 fractions without the concomitant formation of the corresponding uridine. Rat pharmacokinetic

data for radiolabeled **48** were evaluated after a single 100 mg/kg oral dose and exposure of **47** (AUC = 30 μgh/mL) was threefold higher than exposure of the prodrug (AUC = 9 μgh/mL). The prodrug has a half-life of less than 1 h and is completely cleared from the plasma within 12 h postdose. In contrast, the half-life of **47** following a dose of **48** is 7 h. Bioavailability was determined to be 34%, relative to exposure following a single 60 mg/kg i.v. dose of **47**. A series of phosphoramidate prodrugs of **47** has also been explored [203].

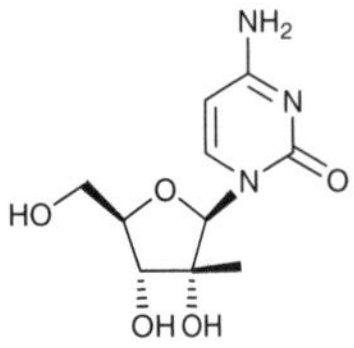

47 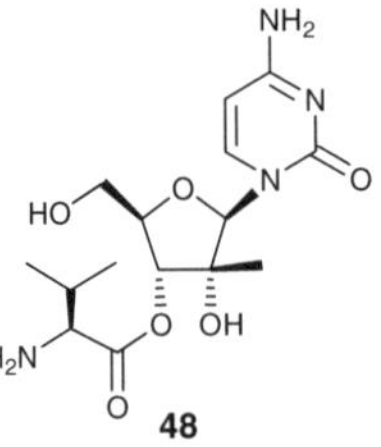   **48**

Clinical study data for valopicitabine has been thoroughly reviewed [163,204–206]. In a Phase I clinical study, after 15 days of oral dosing at 50 mg per day patient levels of HCV RNA were reduced by 0.2 $\log_{10}$. An 800 mg per day dose produced a 1.2 $\log_{10}$ drop after 15 days. A Phase IIb study at a dose of 200 mg of valopicitabine per day in combination with PEG-IFN (from day 8), afforded HCV viral RNA decreases of more than 2 $\log_{10}$ units in

87% of patients after 12 weeks, and a drop of more than 4 $\log_{10}$ units after 24 weeks. No resistant mutations were observed in clinical trials [207]. The development of **48** was discontinued due to significant gastrointestinal toxicity.

3.2.2. PSI-6130 (Pharmasset) Another early nucleoside inhibitor of HCV polymerase was 2′-deoxy-2′-fluorocytidine (FdC), **49**, the 2′-fluoro analog of cytidine. This compound is weakly active in a replicon assay with an EC_{90} of 6.5 μM [208] and is nonselective, with its triphosphate derivative acting as a substrate for RNA and DNA polymerases [209,210]. However, 2′-deoxy-2′-fluoro-2′-C-methylcytidine, **50** (PSI-6130), a hybrid of FdC and the 2′-C-methyl nucleoside class of HCV NS5B class of inhibitors, exemplified by 2′-C-methylcytidine **47** and related analogs [211–213], is a potent and selective inhibitor of HCV polymerase. Thus, **50** (EC_{90} = 5.4 μM), is slightly more active than FdC in an RT-PCR assay, but unlike FdC does not cause cytostasis at this concentration [214]. Compound **50** also has an EC_{90} of greater than 100 μM against BVDV, more than a 50-fold improvement over **47**, and a CC_{50} of >100 μM in an MTS assay. Furthermore, **50** shows only a 6.5-fold loss of activity against the HCV-1b S282T mutation, significantly less than that observed for other 2′-methylated nucleosides [215].

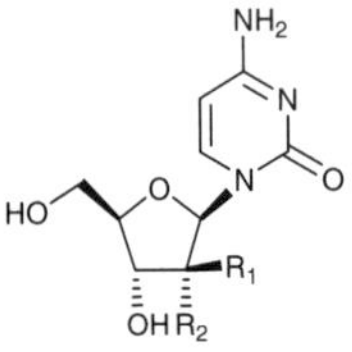

49 R_1 = H, R_2 = F
50 R_1 = CH_3, R_2 = F

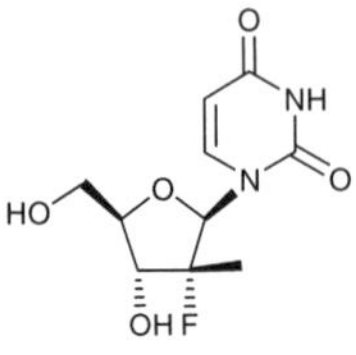

51

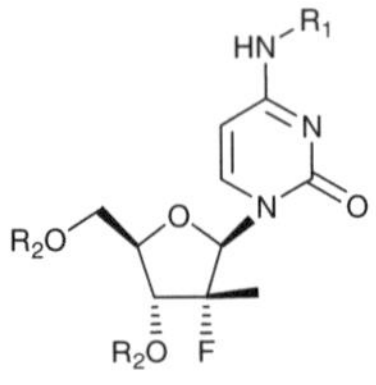

52 R_1 = $CO_2(CH_2)_4CH_3$, R_2 = H
36 R_1 = H, R_2 = $COCH(CH_3)_2$

The pharmacokinetics of **50** was evaluated in rhesus monkeys after 33.3 mg/kg i.v. and oral doses. Bioavailability was only 24% with slow absorption [216]. In an effort to improve these properties, two prodrugs were explored. N^4-Carbamate **52** (PSI-6419) does not show improved bioavailability as the carbamate is not readily cleaved to release **50** *in vivo*. However, diester **36** (R7128) entered clinical trials.

The mechanism of inhibition of HCV polymerase by PSI-6130 has been studied [217]. The rate-limiting conversion of PSI-6130 to its monophosphate is catalyzed by 2′-deoxycytidine kinase (dCK), followed by conversion into the diphosphate with UMP-CMP kinase, and finally phosphorylation to the triphosphate catalyzed by nucleoside diphosphate kinase. Incorporation of the PSI-6130 triphosphate into an elongating strand of viral RNA by the NS5B HCV polymerase ultimately results in chain termination, presumably through inhibition of phosphorylation of the 3′-hydroxy group due to steric hindrance from the 2′-C-methyl group. It has also been shown that in human hepatocytes PSI-6130 is metabolized via deamination of the monophosphate of PSI-6130 by deoxycytidylate deaminase (DCTD) to give the monophosphate of **51** (RO-2433), and subsequent transformation into RO-2433 triphosphate [218,219]. This metabolite has similar potency to the triphosphate of **47** against NS5B polymerase, but is considerably less active against the S282T mutant [218,219]. Uridine **51** is itself not active in a replicon assay due to poor conversion into its triphosphate under those conditions [214,219]. Replacement of the cytidine moiety of **50** with adenine or guanine also results in a loss of replicon activity [220].

In Phase Ib clinical trials, diester prodrug R7128 (**36**), at a dose of 1500 mg bid for 2 weeks, provided a 2.7 $\log_{10}$ order mean reduction in HCV RNA viral load in patients with genotypes 1a or 1b that did not respond to PEG-IFN/ribavirin standard of care, with no evidence of emergence of the S282T mutation after 14 days of dosing [221]. When administered at a 500 mg dose in combination with PEG-IFN and ribavirin for 28 days in 20 treatment-naïve patients, a 5.1 $\log_{10}$ order drop in HCV RNA was observed [204].

3.2.3. R1479/1626 (Roche)

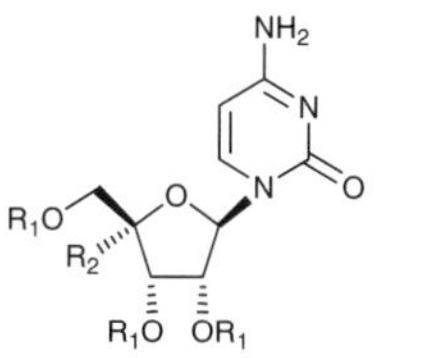

53 R_1 = H, R_2 = N_3
35: R_1 = COCH(CH$_3$)$_2$, R_2 = N_3
54 R_1 = H, R_2 = CN

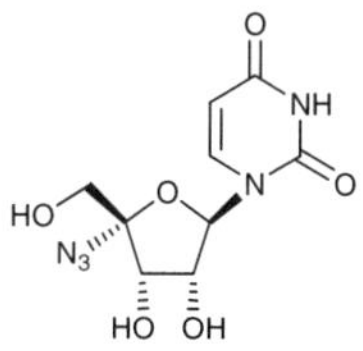

55

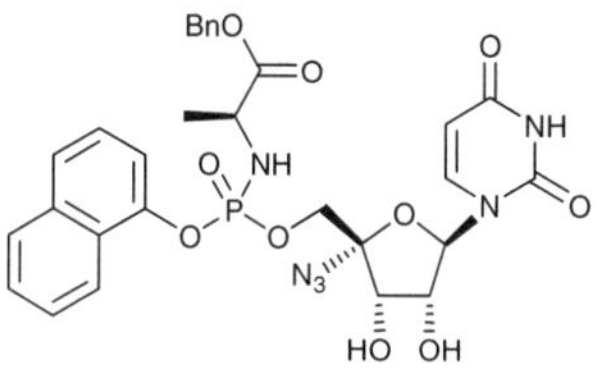

56

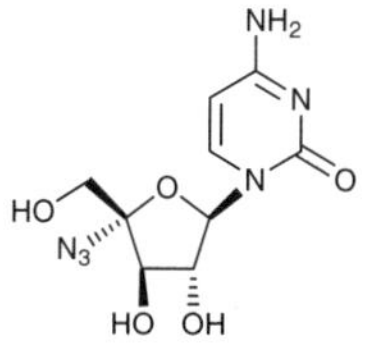

57

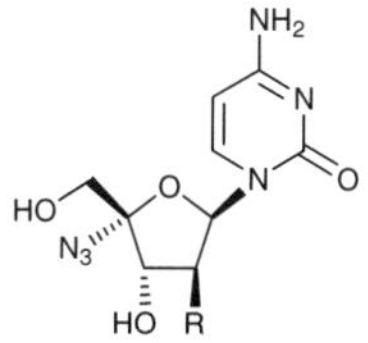

58 R = OH
59 R = F

A third class of cytidine-based inhibitors of HCV replication is exemplified by 4′-azidocytidine (R1479) (**53**), which was identified through targeted screening in combination with rational drug design [222]. Sixteen analogs were reported, exploring nine different 4′-α substituents in both cytidine and uridine series. Of these, only the 4′-azidocytidine **53** and the 4′-cyanocytidine **54** were active in a replicon assay. However, while **53** was not cytotoxic at concentrations of greater than 2 μM, cyano analog **54** was found to be cytotoxic and its activity was attributed to the inhibition of cell viability. Ethyl, ethoxy, and hydroxymethyl 4′-substituents gave less than 20% inhibition at 20 μM in the replicon assay. Unsaturated 4′-groups such as vinyl, allyl, and ethynyl were also only weakly active (~20 μM). Compound **53** has an IC$_{50}$ of 1.28 μM in the replicon assay, approximately twofold less active than **49**, but **53** does not cause cytostasis while **49** has a CT$_{50}$ of 0.8 μM. The triphosphate of **53** has been shown to be a potent inhibitor of HCV replicase activity and HCV polymerase mediated RNA synthesis activity [223].

Upon extended incubation of **53** with replicon cells at its IC$_{90}$, it can completely clear

HCV replicon RNA without selecting for resistance, and without effects on cell viability and proliferation. Unlike **50** (PSI-6130), **53** is as potent an inhibitor of replicon replication for HCV genotype 1b with the S282T mutation as for wild type. Conformational and steric factors have been invoked to account for the fact that the incorporation of a 4'-azido moiety is sufficient to provide a nucleoside that acts efficiently as a chain terminator [222]. Thus, in **53** this substituent adopts a pseudo-axial orientation, providing significant steric hindrance for the neighboring pseudo-equatorial 3'-hydroxyl group to be an effective nucleophile, as has been postulated for related 2'-deoxy nucleoside systems [224].

Although **53** displayed excellent *in vitro* activity as an inhibitor of HCV polymerase, it suffered from poor PK properties. The bioavailability ranged from 6–18%, likely due to a combination of low permeability (Caco-2 P_{app}: 0.2×10^{-6} cm/s), high solubility and a $\log p = 1.5$ [225]. Several approaches were taken to increase the lipophilicity of R1479, focusing on derivatization of one or more hydroxyl groups. Carbamate derivatives of **53** did not show improved exposure in monkeys due to poor conversion to the parent alcohols, and 5'-amino acid esters also failed to increase permeability or exposure. Lipophilic esters did afford the desired increase in exposure in monkeys, with the tri-isobutyrate ester **35** (R1626) achieving the correct balance of increased lipophilicity and acceptable solubility. The triester has solubility of 0.2 mg/mL at pH 7.4, greatly enhanced permeability (Caco-2 P_{app}: 15×10^{-6} cm/s), and a more drug-like $\log p$ of 2.5 [226].

A prodrug approach has also been applied to analogs of **53** that are potent polymerase inhibitors as their triphosphates, but are not active in the replicon assay as the 5'-alcohols. For example, compound **55**, the uridine analog of **53**, is not active in the replicon assay (13% inhibition at 20 µM), but the corresponding uridine triphosphate derivative is equipotent to **53** as an inhibitor of RNA polymerase ($IC_{50} = 0.3$ µM), demonstrating that inefficient intracellular phosphorylation of the uridine is responsible for its poor replicon activity. This problem has been addressed by the preparation of masked monophosphates that

have the ability to enter the cell and release the parent monophosphate, which is then readily converted into the active triphosphate. The monophosphates themselves are poorly cell permeable due to their negative charge at pH 7.4. Thus, while 4'-azidouridine **55** is inactive in the replicon assay, its naphthyloxy phosphoramidate **56** analog has an EC_{50} of 0.22 µM, an increase of greater than 450-fold over the activity of **55** [227]. The adenine analog of **56** is similarly active [228]. The suggested mechanism for release of the requisite monophosphate from **56** involves initial hydrolysis of the ester moiety, intramolecular attack of the resulting carboxylate on the phosphorus to give a cyclic mixed anhydride, hydrolysis of that anhydride and, finally, enzymatic cleavage of the phosphorus–nitrogen bond.

The excellent *in vitro* antiviral activity, acceptable physical properties and improved pharmacokinetics afforded by triester **35** (R1626), with exposure increased threefold relative to R1479, rapid *in vivo* conversion into **53** (R1479), and linear dose proportionality up to 12 g per day, supported its entrance into clinical trials. In a Phase Ib clinical study, after 14 days of monotherapy with twice-daily doses of 1500, 3000, and 4500 mg, viral load declines of 1.2, 2.6, and 3.7 $\log_{10}$ IU/mL, respectively, were observed without any indication of viral resistance [229–231]. A Phase II study, in combination with PEG-IFN, demonstrated potent reduction in HCV with or without ribavirin [232]. After 2 weeks of treatment with 1500 mg bid of R1626 and PEG-IFN a viral load reduction of 3.1 $\log_{10}$ IU/mL was observed, compared to 1.2 $\log_{10}$ IU/mL for R1626 alone at this dose. The addition of ribavirin to the 1500 mg bid of **35** and PEG-IFN regimen afforded an additional decrease of 3.0 $\log_{10}$ IU/mL of HCV RNA after 2 weeks, wherein 74% of patients who received this triple therapy had undetectable viral load after 4 weeks of treatment, as compared to only 5% of those on the combination of PEG-IFN and ribavirin alone.

Improvements in the antiviral activity and clinical efficacy of **53** and some of its analogs were sought to allow lower doses in the clinic and increase efficacy. The structural requirements for activity of analogs at the 2' and

3′positions in the 4′-azidocytidine series have also been explored [233]. The 3′-deoxy analog of **53**, and 4′-azido-2′-β-methylcytidine, and 4′-azido-2′-α-methylarabinocytidine are each inactive in an HCV replicon assay. The 4′-azidoxylocytidine compound **57**, the 3′-hydroxy epimer of **53**, is approximately 20-fold less active in the replicon assay than **53**. However, 4′-azidoarabinocytidine **58** (RO-9187), the 2′-hydroxy epimer of **53**, is more than fivefold more active than **53** in the replicon assay with an IC$_{50}$ of 0.17 μM [234]. The 2′-β-fluoro analog **59** (RO-0622) is even more active than **59**, and 50-fold more active than **53**, with a replicon IC$_{50}$ of 0.024 μM. Compounds **58** and **59** both inhibit NS5B genotypes 1a and 1b equally well, do not lose appreciable activity against S96T and S282T mutants, are not cytotoxic, and do not inhibit cell proliferation. The activity of **58** and **59** was unexpected since a hydrogen bond interaction between the 2′-α-hydroxy group of ribonucleosides and the RNA polymerases, Asp225 in the case of HCV polymerase [235], has been considered to be a required recognition element allowing discrimination against deoxyribonucleotides [234,236–238]. The extraordinary increase in replicon activity observed for **59** over **53** may be due in part to a 13-fold improvement in phosphorylation efficiency of this substrate by human dCK. In a two week rat toxicity study compound **58** was well tolerated with no toxicity findings at doses up to 2000 mg/kg/day [216].

3.2.4. MK0608 (Merck)

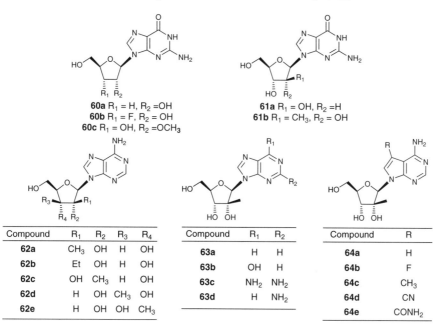

Compound	R$_1$	R$_2$	R$_3$	R$_4$
62a	CH$_3$	OH	H	OH
62b	Et	OH	H	OH
62c	OH	CH$_3$	H	OH
62d	H	OH	CH$_3$	OH
62e	H	OH	OH	CH$_3$

Compound	R$_1$	R$_2$
63a	H	H
63b	OH	H
63c	NH$_2$	NH$_2$
63d	H	NH$_2$

Compound	R
64a	H
64b	F
64c	CH$_3$
64d	CN
64e	CONH$_2$

The SAR of the 2′ and 3′-positions of adenine and guanine nucleoside inhibitors of HCV NS5B polymerase has been thoroughly investigated [212]. The guanosine triphosphates of **60a–60c** each are moderate inhibitors of NS5B catalyzed RNA synthesis, with IC$_{50}$ values of 0.6, 1.8, and 1.6 μM respectively. Since the nucleoside 3′-hydroxyl group is required for RNA chain elongation the ability of the 3′-deoxy analogs **60a** and **60b** to act as chain terminators is expected. The activity of the 2′-methoxy analog **60c** may result from the ability of increased steric bulk at this position to affect chain elongation efficiency. The corresponding adenine analogs of **60a–60c** each have polymerase IC$_{50}$ values greater than 20 μM. The triphosphate of 2′-β-hydroxyguanosine **61a** has an IC$_{50}$ of 20 μM in the polymerase assay, but the triphosphate of 2′-α-hydroxy-2′-β-methylguanosine **61b** is a potent polymerase inhibitor with an IC_{50} of $0.13\,\mu M$ and a replicon EC_{50} of $3.5\,\mu M$. In the adenosine series, the triphosphate of **62a** has an IC_{50} of $1.9\,\mu M$ in the polymerase assay, and **62a** has a replicon EC_{50} of $0.3\,\mu M$. The $2'$-β-ethyl analog **62b** is inactive, indicative of the strict steric requirements at the $2'$-position. Compounds **62c–62e** and their triphosphates are inactive in both the polymerase and the replicon assays. Conformational analysis of **62a** and **62c–62e** indicates that only in **62a** there is a conformational preference for the $2'$-hydroxy group in an axial orientation and the $3'$-hydroxyl in the equatorial orientation. With the modified ribose moiety that afforded the best polymerase and replicon activity (i.e., **61b** and **62a**) held constant, a survey of four analogs, **63a–63d**, with heterobase replacements for adenine and guanine, was undertaken. Of these, only **63c** provided any activity in the replicon assay with an EC_{50} of $7\,\mu M$, 2-fold less potent than the guanosine derivative **61b** and more than 20-fold less than **62a** in the replicon assay. $5'$-Phosphonate analogs of **62a** have been prepared, but have poor replicon activity indicative of the importance of the $5'$-hydroxyl moiety of **62a** for antiviral activity [239].

Analysis of the pharmacokinetic properties in rats of **61b** and **62a**, the compounds with the best replicon potency, revealed that $2'$-C-methylguanosine **61b** has excellent bioavailability ($F\% = 82$), but the more potent adenine analog **62a** had extremely high clearance on i.v. dosing ($>200\,mL/min/kg$) and extremely low exposure on oral dosing [212]. Adenosine **62a** was shown to be a substrate for both purine nucleoside phosphorylase (PNP), resulting in cleavage of the heterobase-ribose CN bond, and adenosine deaminase (ADA), that converts **62a** to the corresponding inosine analog **63b**.

The enzymatic lability and poor oral exposure of **62a** led to a search for more stable, orally active analogs through the synthesis of novel heterobases, including pyrrolo[3,4-d] pyrimidines **64a–64e** [213] in which N-7 of the adenine of **62a** has been replaced with a carbon, and pyrrolo[3,2-d]pyrimidines and furo[3,2-d]pyrimidines [240]. The replacement of the N-7 of adenine with a carbon has been shown to change the glycosyl torsion

angle and bond length [241]. The most active compounds in the replicon assay are the fluoro analog **64b** and primary amide **64e**, with EC_{50} values of 0.07 and $0.08\,\mu M$, respectively. The chloro and bromo analogs of **64b** are two- to threefold less active. Computer modeling suggests that for compounds **64b** and **64e** the fluoro and amide substituents may interact as hydrogen-bond acceptors with Lys141 in the NS5B active site. The unsubstituted pyrrolo[3,4-d]pyrimidine **64a** (MK0608) has a replicon EC_{50} of $0.25\,\mu M$, while the methyl and nitrile analogs, **64c** and **64d**, are considerably less active with EC_{50} values of approximately $3\,\mu M$. Compound **64a** also has fairly potent antiviral activity against the positive-strand RNA viruses BVDV ($EC_{50} = 0.3\,\mu M$) and rhinovirus type 2 ($EC_{50} = 0.5\,\mu M$), but relative to wild-type HCV NS5B loses 350-fold activity against the S282T mutant ($EC_{50} = 25\,\mu M$) [242]. Importantly, compounds **64a** and **64b** were evaluated as substrates of PNP and ADA and contrary to **62a** both were essentially unaffected by these enzymes. Consistent with the stability of **64b** to these enzymes, its plasma clearance in rats is $44\,mL/min/kg$ after a $1\,mg/kg$ i.v. dose, substantially lower than that for **62a**. Its bioavailability after a $2\,mg/kg$ oral dose is 51%. The 7-deaza-adenosine analog **64a** displays moderate clearance in rat ($25\,mL/min/kg$), dog, and rhesus monkey, and oral bioavailability of 51% in monkey and rat and 98% in the dog. Compound **64a** has been synthesized on a multikilogram scale [243]. Additional pyrrolo [3,4-d]pyrimidine nucleoside HCV polymerase inhibitors include analogs of 7-deazaneplanocin A, in which the ribose has been replaced with a carbocycle [244], and analogs of toyocamycin, modified at the 4-position of the pyrrolopyrimidine ring [245]. These analogs exhibit replicon activity in the low micromolar range.

A second strategy for improving the oral exposure of **62a** and related compounds has been through the use of prodrugs. The cyclic phosphate **65** is intended to reduce the conversion of the adenine to the corresponding inosine by ADA by protection of the $5'$-hydroxy group. Additionally, **65** is designed to release the $5'$-monophosphate derivative in the liver [246]. Thus, CYP3A4 mediated oxidation of the benzylic methine generates a hemiketal that can subsequently ring-open and eliminate an aryl vinyl ketone to liberate the 5'-monophosphate. Attaining acceptable bioavailability of analogs bearing the 5'-cyclic phosphate required tying up the 2'- and 3'-hydroxyl groups in a cyclic carbonate, thereby reducing the number of hydrogen-bond donors in the molecule. Compound **65** is 39% bioavailable.

Another prodrug approach utilizes *S*-acyl-2-thioethyl (SATE) masked 5'-phosphate derivatives to deliver the 5'-monophosphate to

the cell and bypass the initial rate-limiting intracellular phosphorylation of the 5'-hydroxy compound [247–250]. For example, compound **66** has a replicon EC_{50} of 0.08 μM, about 150-fold more active than the corresponding 5'-hydroxy compound [247]. Conversion of the SATE prodrug to the bare monophosphate occurs through enzymatic thioester hydrolysis followed by episulfide formation with release of the 5'-monophosphate. Despite the generation of episulfide, SATE prodrugs do not increase chromosomal aberration *in vitro* in CHO cells [248].

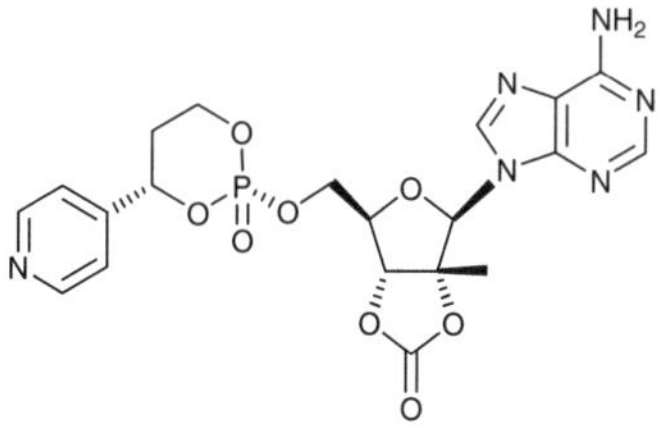

65

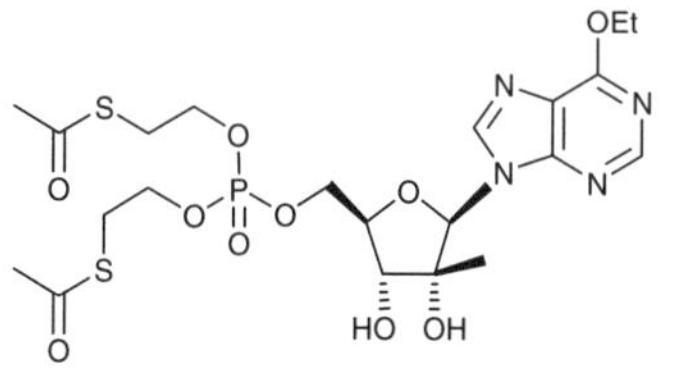

66

3.3. Nonnucleoside Inhibitors of NS5B

3.3.1. PF-00868554 (Pfizer)

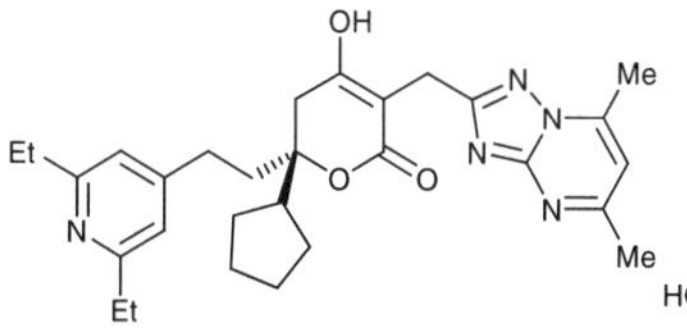

67

PF-00868554

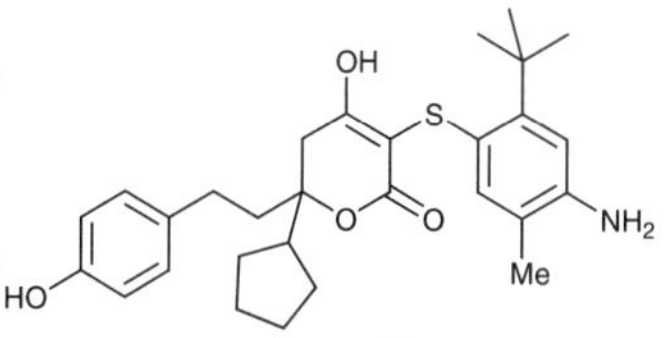

68

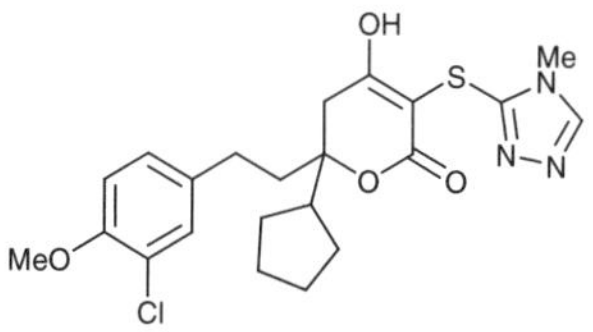

69

High-throughput screening of Pfizer's in-house library yielded racemic dihydropyrone **68**, a reversible nonnucleoside inhibitor of HCV RNA polymerase NS5B ($IC_{50} = 0.93$ μM, genotype 1b). The compound is an allosteric inhibitor, which binds noncompetitively with respect to GTP. It binds to the enzyme about 30 Å away from the active site, close to the junction of the palm and the finger regions [251]. Modification of substituents close to the phenol revealed the presence of a hydrophobic environment that tolerates a wide variety of substituents on the phenyl ring providing numerous compounds with improved binding affinity for the polymerase. The hydroxyl substituent on the pyrone core

is essential for activity. A brief survey of aryl and heteroaryl substituents replacing the aniline moiety yielded triazole analog **69** as a potent inhibitor of NS5B ($IC_{50} = 0.038$ μM). None of the reported compounds show appreciable activity in the replicon assay [251].

A substantial improvement in replicon activity was achieved when the triazole heterocycle was replaced with a dimethyltriazolopyrimidine system and the sulfur linker was replaced with a methylene. Racemic dihydropyrone **70** is potent in the enzyme ($IC_{50} = 0.020$ μM) and replicon assay ($EC_{50} = 0.33$ μM). This improvement in replicon activity correlates well with the respective Caco-2 permeability data. Further, SAR studies on the phenyl ring led to the discovery of optically pure **71** with a *gem*-dimethylcyano substituent $(IC_{50} = 3\,nM, EC_{50} = 15\,nM)$. When the pharmacokinetic properties of **71** were evaluated in rats, it showed low *in vivo* clearance (3.7 mL/min/kg) and volume of distribution

(0.3 L/kg). Compound **71** has a half-life of 0.88 h and bioavailability of 31% [252]. Of the two enantiomers, **71** showed a slightly better *in vivo* profile; therefore, this absolute stereochemistry was retained in subsequent analogs.

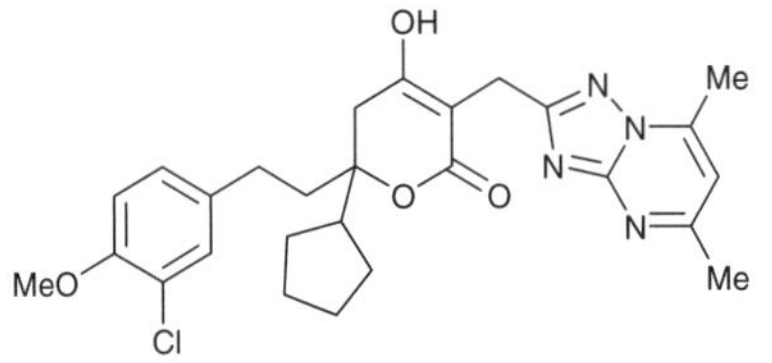

70

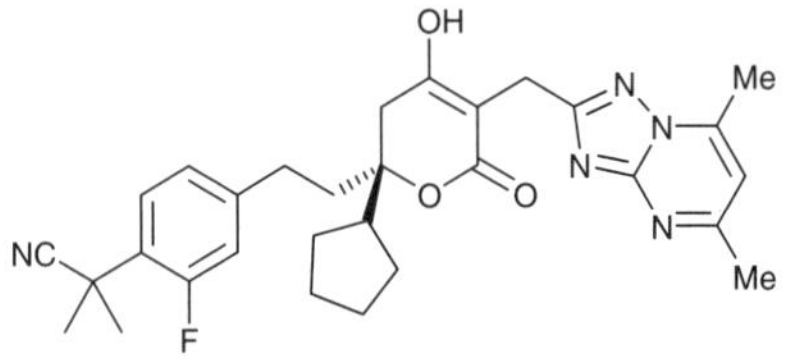

71

As **71** was found to crystallize in two distinct forms with significantly different solubility and *in vivo* properties, additional modification was required. In addition, **71** is a potent inhibitor of CYP2D6; an issue regarded as critical for patients with HCV receiving combination therapies. To avoid potential drug–drug interactions, improved analogs of **71** were expected to be devoid of any significant activity against the cytochrome P450 enzymes. It was demonstrated that the cyano group in compound **71** was responsible for its potency at CYP2D6 while structural modifications of the bicyclic heterocycle had little to no effect in this regard.

Detailed crystallographic analysis of **71** led to a series of compounds lacking the *gem*-dimethylcyano substituent but incorporating substituted phenyl and pyridine moieties. Among the reported compounds was PF-00868554 (**67**), which is potent in the enzyme and replicon assays $(IC_{50} = 7\,nM, EC_{50} = 41\,nM)$ and does not show cytotoxicity at concentrations up to 320 μM. More importantly, it does not inhibit any of the major cytochrome P450 isoforms and has an aqueous solubility of 2.55 mg/mL. Its hepatic clearance in monkey and rat microsomes (27 and <20 mL/min/kg) correlates with the *in vivo* clearance (21 mL/min/kg, both species) and volume of distribution (1.0 and 0.8 L/kg, respectively), whereas these values are low in the beagle dog (0.93 mL/min/kg and 0.25 L/kg). The oral bioavailability of **67** is 75% in the rat and 49% in dog. Based on these preclinical results, PF-00868554 was advanced for further clini-

cal studies [253]. When evaluated in healthy volunteers, **67** was well tolerated when dosed at 300 mg, three times per day for 14 days. If dosed at least 100 mg twice a day the measured blood levels of PF-00868554 were expected to reduce viral RNA levels in patients [254].

Subsequently, **67** was investigated in a double-blind placebo controlled study in treatment-naïve patients. The half-life of the drug was measured to be between 10 and 12 h and the measured blood concentration exceeded the *in vitro* EC_{50}, adjusted for protein binding. The mean C_{max} and AUC increased with higher doses; however, the increases were greater than the proportional increase in drug dose. Viral RNA levels decreased rapidly within the first 48 h after dosing was initiated. The maximum HCV RNA reduction ranged from 0.98 $\log_{10}$ units to 2.13 $\log_{10}$ units when dosed from 100 mg twice daily to 300 mg three times daily, respectively, for 8 days. Adverse events were only mild or moderate [255].

3.3.2. Benzothiadiazines (Abbott)

Using an enzyme-based high-throughput screen, a series of benzothiadiazines originally prepared as potential diuretics was identified as potent inhibitors of NS5B (Table 5) [256]. These inhibitors are noncompetitive and function by interfering with the binding of the requisite RNA primer to the enzyme [257]. The requirement for a moderately long *N*-alkyl chain is consistent with previous work [258] with the unsubstituted (**72a**) and *N*-methyl (**72b**) analogs being much less potent than the *n*-butyl

Table 5. Benzothiadiazine Screening Hits

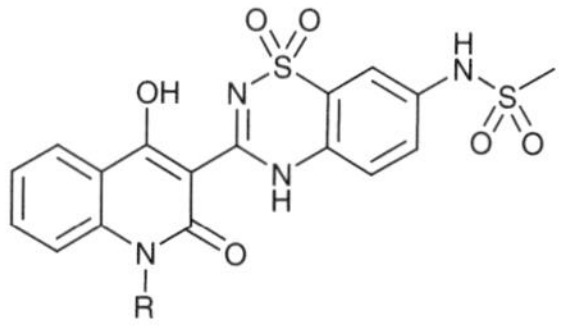

Compound	R	IC_{50} (μM)
72a	H	>50
72b	Me	>50
72c	n-Bu	0.10
72d	i-pentyl	0.08

and i-pentyl analogs. Both **72c** and **72d** are also potent replicon inhibitors, with EC_{50} values of about 0.50 μM.

Replacement of the quinolinone nitrogen of **72a–72d** with carbon was expected to improve solubility [259], and addition of a second identical alkyl group (to avoid racemates) led to a series of gem-dialkylbenzothiadiazines **73a–73h** (Table 6).

As was the case in **72a–72d**, larger alkyl substituents generally confer better potency. Methyl analog **73a** is about two- to threefold less potent than the longer chain analogs, **73e**

Table 6. Optimization of gem-Dialkylbenzo-thiadiazines

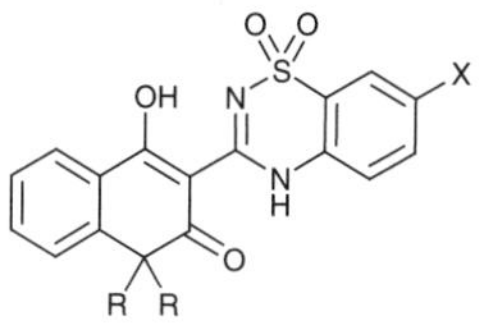

Compound	R	X	NS5B (1a) IC_{50} (μM)	NS5B (1b) IC_{50} (μM)
73a	Me	H	2.2	–
73b	Me	NHSO$_2$Me	0.93	6.26
73c	n-Pr	H	2.2	–
73d	n-Pr	NHSO$_2$Me	0.099	0.13
73e	n-Bu	H	0.99	2.27
73f	n-Bu	NHSO$_2$Me	0.01	0.073
73g	i-amyl	H	0.82	–
73h	i-amyl	NHSO$_2$Me	0.68	0.39

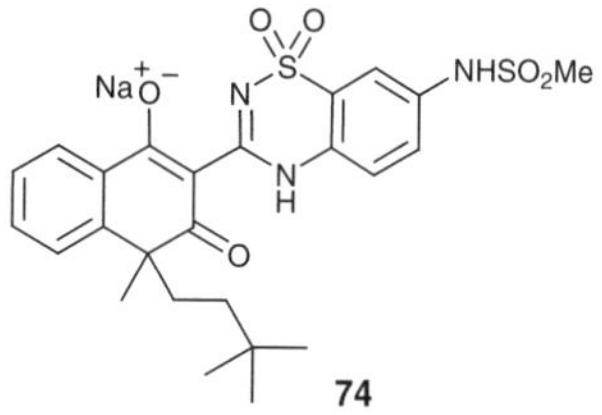

and **73g** [260]. This effect is more pronounced when a sulfonamide is added to the phenyl ring of the benzothiadiazine, which independently increases potency by about 10-fold. Analog **73f** is a potent inhibitor in the replicon assay with EC_{50} values of 0.28 and 0.048 μM against the 1a and 1b replicons, respectively. Compound **73f** displays excellent pharmacokinetic properties in rats. Oral administration of the compound at 5 mg/kg resulted in low clearance, a 4.3-hour half-life and 94% bioavailability. The compound also accumulated in the liver, with measurable levels out to 24 h postdose. Subsequent work [261] has investigated asymmetric analogs, where the gem-dialkyl groups are different. Of these, compound **74** is the most potent, inhibiting both the 1a and the 1b replicons in the 10 nM range.

74

3.3.3. Nesbuvir (HCV-796, Wyeth-ViroPharma)

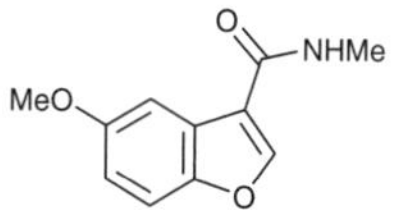

75

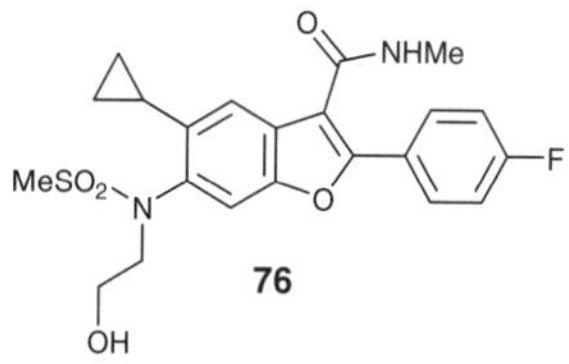

76

A high-throughput screening effort to discover novel nonnucleoside inhibitors of HCV polymerase identified benzofuran **75** with submicromolar activity against HCV NS5B [262]. Optimization of this lead, focusing on improving antiviral potency and physical properties, led to compound **76** (HCV-796, nesbuvir), a non-NTP competitive, allosteric, specific inhibitor of HCV NS5B with an enzyme IC_{50} of 0.03 μM, replicon EC_{50} values of 5 and 9 nM against HCV genotypes 1a and 1b, respectively, and CC_{50} values of greater than 50 μM in a variety of cell lines [263]. In a study comparing the in vitro replicon activity of a variety of nucleoside and nonnucleoside HCV polymerase inhibitors and HCV protease inhibitors, **76** was the most potent compound tested [109]. The X-ray crystal structure of **76** bound to HCV NS5B reveals that the inhibitor binds to an allosteric site in the palm domain of the protein, near the active site, with a hydrogen bond interaction between the amide NH of **76** and the side-chain hydroxyl group of Ser365 [264]. *In vitro* experiments to examine viral mutations after exposure to **76** showed that multiple amino acid substitutions, especially C316Y, arose in the binding pocket of the protein at positions that have direct interactions with the benzofuran carboxamide inhibitor [264,265].

In a Phase I clinical trial oral doses of 100–1000 mg of **76** given bid in combination with PEG-IFN produced mean viral reductions of up to 3.5 log at day 14, compared to 1.7 $\log_{10}$ for PEG-IFN alone, with no dose-limiting toxicity [204]. The C316Y mutation was observed in clinical isolates, and was associated with viral rebound seen in some patients in the Phase I study [264]. In a Phase II trial of **76** in combination with ribavirin and PEG-IFN, some patients presented with elevated liver enzymes after 8 weeks of dosing, leading to discontinuation of development [204,264,266].

4. CONCLUSION

After more than two decades of research, hepatitis C is gradually being conquered by a number of complementary strategies. This chapter has focused on the discovery efforts of the more advanced small-molecule inhibitors of the viral protease and polymerase; however, there are many newer candidates currently in preclinical studies. Additionally, a number of other approaches are being actively investigated. These include agents that are not specific antiviral agents, but act by other mechanisms, (modulation of immune response, inflammation, fibrosis, and other cellular functions) and may prove to be synergistic or additive when combined with STAT-C therapies.

The HCV area remains very active, with a steady stream of new literature. Additionally, more than 30 clinical candidates have been investigated in the last 2 years. Most of these have displayed efficacy and, although some have been discontinued, many have advanced to Phase II trials. It is reasonable to expect that the third decade of hepatitis C research will realize a diverse arsenal of drugs that will eradicate the virus and result in an improved cure rate for this devastating infection.

REFERENCES

1. Shepard CW, Finelli L, Alter MJ. Global epidemiology of hepatitis C virus infection. Lancet Infect Dis 2005;5(9): 558–567.

2. Tan SL, Pause A, Shi Y, Sonenberg N. Hepatitis C therapeutics: current status and emerging strategies. Nat Rev Drug Discov 2002; 1(11): 867–881.

3. Wasley A, Alter MJ. Epidemiology of hepatitis C: geographic differences and temporal trends. Semin Liver Dis 2000;20(1): 1–16.

4. Matsuura Y. Expression and characterization of hepatitis C virus proteins. Uirusu 1995; 45(2): 105–115.

5. Lo Re V 3rd, Kostman JR, Amorosa VK. Management complexities of HIV/hepatitis C virus coinfection in the twenty-first century. Clin Liver Dis 2008;12(3): 587–609, ix.

6. Thomas DL. The challenge of hepatitis C in the HIV-infected person. Annu Rev Med 2008; 59:473–485.

7. Detels R, Munoz A, McFarlane G, Kingsley LA, Margolick JB, Giorgi J, Schrager LK, Phair JP. Effectiveness of potent antiretroviral therapy on time to AIDS and death in men with known HIV infection duration. Multicenter AIDS Cohort Study Investigators. JAMA 1998;280(17): 1497–1503.

8. Pedersen C, Nielsen JO, Dickmeis E, Jordal R. Early progression to AIDS following primary HIV infection. AIDS 1989;3(1): 45–47.

9. Farci P, Alter HJ, Shimoda A, Govindarajan S, Cheung LC, Melpolder JC, Sacher RA, Shih JW, Purcell RH. Hepatitis C virus-associated fulminant hepatic failure. N Engl J Med 1996; 335(9): 631–634.

10. Baldo V, Baldovin T, Trivello R, Floreani A. Epidemiology of HCV infection. Curr Pharm Des 2008;14(17): 1646–1654.

11. McHutchison JG. Understanding hepatitis C. Am J Manag Care 2004;10(Suppl 2): S21–S29.

12. Di Bisceglie AM. Natural history of hepatitis C: its impact on clinical management. Hepatology 2000;31(4): 1014–1018.

13. Hirsch KR, Wright TL. "Silent killer" or benign disease? The dilemma of hepatitis C virus outcomes. Hepatology 2000;31(2): 536–537.

14. Thorp A. Hepatitis C: the silent killer. Paediatr Nurs 1999;11(3): 23–26.

15. Vento S, Cainelli F. Does hepatitis C virus cause severe liver disease only in people who drink alcohol?. Lancet Infect Dis 2002;2(5): 303–309.

16. Meanwell NA, Koszalka GW. 2007: a difficult year for HCV drug development. Curr Opin Investig Drugs 2008;9(2): 128–131.

17. Barre-Sinoussi F, Chermann JC, Rey F, Nugeyre MT, Chamaret S, Gruest J, Dauguet C, Axler-Blin C, Vezinet-Brun F, Rouzioux C, Rozenbaum W, Montagnier L. Isolation of a T-lymphotropic retrovirus from a patient at risk for acquired immune deficiency syndrome (AIDS). Science 1983;220(4599): 868–871.

18. Popovic M, Sarin PS, Robert-Gurroff M, Kalyanaraman VS, Mann D, Minowada J, Gallo RC. Isolation and transmission of human retrovirus (human t-cell leukemia virus). Science 1983;219(4586): 856–859.

19. Choo QL, Kuo G, Weiner AJ, Overby LR, Bradley DW, Houghton M. Isolation of a cDNA clone derived from a blood-borne non-A, non-B viral hepatitis genome. Science 1989;244(4902): 359–362.

20. Mitsuya H, Weinhold KJ, Furman PA, St Clair MH, Lehrman SN, Gallo RC, Bolognesi D, Barry DW, Broder S. 3′-Azido-3′-deoxythymidine (BW A509U): an antiviral agent that inhibits the infectivity and cytopathic effect of human T-lymphotropic virus type III/lymphadenopathy-associated virus in vitro. Proc Natl Acad Sci USA 1985;82(20): 7096–7100.

21. De Clercq E. Anti-HIV drugs. Verh K Acad Geneeskd Belg 2007;69(2): 81–104.

22. Roberts NA, Martin JA, Kinchington D, Broadhurst AV, Craig JC, Duncan IB, Galpin SA, Handa BK, Kay J, Krohn A, et al. Rational design of peptide-based HIV proteinase inhibitors. Science 1990;248(4953): 358–361.

23. Fischl MA, Richman DD, Grieco MH, Gottlieb MS, Volberding PA, Laskin OL, Leedom JM, Groopman JE, Mildvan D, Schooley RT, et al. The efficacy of azidothymidine (AZT) in the treatment of patients with AIDS and AIDS-related complex. A double-blind, placebo-controlled trial. N Engl J Med 1987;317(4): 185–191.

24. Collier AC, Coombs RW, Fischl MA, Skolnik PR, Northfelt D, Boutin P, Hooper CJ, Kaplan LD, Volberding PA, Davis LG, Henrard DR, Weller S, Corey L. Combination therapy with zidovudine and didanosine compared with zidovudine alone in HIV-1 infection. Ann Intern Med 1993;119(8): 786–793.

25. Sande MA, Carpenter CC, Cobbs CG, Holmes KK, Sanford JP. Antiretroviral therapy for adult HIV-infected patients. Recommendations from a state-of-the-art conference. National Institute of Allergy and Infectious Diseases State-of-the-Art Panel on Anti-Retroviral Therapy for Adult HIV-Infected Patients. JAMA 1993;270(21): 2583–2589.

26. Wainberg MA, Cahn P, Bethell RC, Sawyer J, Cox S. Apricitabine: a novel deoxycytidine analogue nucleoside reverse transcriptase inhibitor for the treatment of nucleoside-resistant HIV infection. Antivir Chem Chemother 2007; 18(2): 61–70.

27. Matthews T, Salgo M, Greenberg M, Chung J, DeMasi R, Bolognesi D. Enfuvirtide: the first therapy to inhibit the entry of HIV-1 into host CD4 lymphocytes. Nat Rev Drug Discov 2004; 3(3): 215–225.

28. Sepkowitz KA. AIDS: the first 20 years. N Engl J Med 2001;344(23): 1764–1772.

29. Clercq ED. The design of drugs for HIV and HCV. Nat Rev Drug Discov 2007;6(12): 1001–1018.

30. De Francesco R, Carfi A. Advances in the development of new therapeutic agents targeting the NS3-4A serine protease or the NS5B RNA-dependent RNA polymerase of the hepatitis C virus. Adv Drug Deliv Rev 2007;59(12): 1242–1262.

31. Zhan P, Liu X, De Clercq E. Recent advances in antiviral activity of benzo/heterothiadiazine dioxide derivatives. Curr Med Chem 2008; 15(15): 1529–1540.

32. Venkatraman S, Njoroge FG. Macrocyclic inhibitors of HCV NS3-4A protease: design and structure–activity relationship. Curr Top Med Chem 2007;7(13): 1290–1301.

33. Koch U, Narjes F. Recent progress in the development of inhibitors of the hepatitis C virus RNA-dependent RNA polymerase. Curr Top Med Chem 2007;7(13): 1302–1329.

34. Ronn R, Sandstrom A. New developments in the discovery of agents to treat hepatitis C. Curr Top Med Chem 2008;8(7): 533–562.

35. Sherman KE, Fleischer R, Laessig K, Murray J, Tauber W, Birnkrant D. Development of novel agents for the treatment of chronic

hepatitis C infection: summary of the FDA Antiviral Products Advisory Committee recommendations. Hepatology 2007;46(6): 2014–2020.

36. Zapf CW, Bloom JD, Levin JI. Recent progess on novel HCV inhibitors. Annu Rep Med Chem 2007;42:281–300.

37. Fried MW, Shiffman ML, Reddy KR, Smith C, Marinos G, Goncales FL Jr, Haussinger D, Diago M, Carosi G, Dhumeaux D, Craxi A, Lin A, Hoffman J, Yu J. Peginterferon alfa-2a plus ribavirin for chronic hepatitis C virus infection. N Engl J Med 2002;347(13): 975–982.

38. Manns MP, McHutchison JG, Gordon SC, Rustgi VK, Shiffman M, Reindollar R, Goodman ZD, Koury K, Ling M, Albrecht JK. Peginterferon alfa-2b plus ribavirin compared with interferon alfa-2b plus ribavirin for initial treatment of chronic hepatitis C: a randomised trial. Lancet 2001;358(9286): 958–965.

39. Leyssen P, Balzarini J, De Clercq E, Neyts J. The predominant mechanism by which ribavirin exerts its antiviral activity *in vitro* against flaviviruses and paramyxoviruses is mediated by inhibition of IMP dehydrogenase. J Virol 2005;79(3): 1943–1947.

40. Asahina Y, Izumi N, Enomoto N, Uchihara M, Kurosaki M, Onuki Y, Nishimura Y, Ueda K, Tsuchiya K, Nakanishi H, Kitamura T, Miyake S. Mutagenic effects of ribavirin and response to interferon/ribavirin combination therapy in chronic hepatitis C. J Hepatol 2005;43(4): 623–629.

41. Dixit NM, Perelson AS. The metabolism, pharmacokinetics and mechanisms of antiviral activity of ribavirin against hepatitis C virus. Cell Mol Life Sci 2006;63(7–8): 832–842.

42. Hayashi N, Takehara T. Antiviral therapy for chronic hepatitis C: past, present, and future. J Gastroenterol 2006;41(1): 17–27.

43. Davis GL, Lindsay KL. Treatment of chronic hepatitis C infection: one step at a time. Lancet Infect Dis 2005;5(8): 524–526.

44. McHutchison JG, Gordon SC, Schiff ER, Shiffman ML, Lee WM, Rustgi VK, Goodman ZD, Ling MH, Cort S, Albrecht JK. Interferon alfa-2b alone or in combination with ribavirin as initial treatment for chronic hepatitis C. Hepatitis Interventional Therapy Group. N Engl J Med 1998;339(21): 1485–1492.

45. Poynard T, Marcellin P, Lee SS, Niederau C, Minuk GS, Ideo G, Bain V, Heathcote J, Zeuzem S, Trepo C, Albrecht J. Randomised trial of interferon alpha2b plus ribavirin for 48 weeks or for 24 weeks versus interferon alpha2b plus placebo for 48 weeks for treatment of chronic infection with hepatitis C virus. International Hepatitis Interventional Therapy Group (IHIT). Lancet 1998;352(9138): 1426–1432.

46. McOmish F, Yap PL, Dow BC, Follett EA, Seed C, Keller AJ, Cobain TJ, Krusius T, Kolho E, Naukkarinen R, et al. Geographical distribution of hepatitis C virus genotypes in blood donors: an international collaborative survey. J Clin Microbiol 1994;32(4): 884–892.

47. Yoshioka K, Kakumu S, Wakita T, Ishikawa T, Itoh Y, Takayanagi M, Higashi Y, Shibata M, Morishima T. Detection of hepatitis C virus by polymerase chain reaction and response to interferon-alpha therapy: relationship to genotypes of hepatitis C virus. Hepatology 1992; 16(2): 293–299.

48. Nousbaum JB, Pol S, Nalpas B, Landais P, Berthelot P, Brechot C. Hepatitis C virus type 1b (II) infection in France and Italy. Collaborative Study Group. Ann Intern Med 1995; 122(3): 161–168.

49. Shakil AO, Conry-Cantilena C, Alter HJ, Hayashi P, Kleiner DE, Tedeschi V, Krawczynski K, Conjeevaram HS, Sallie R, Di Bisceglie AM. Volunteer blood donors with antibody to hepatitis C virus: clinical, biochemical, virologic, and histologic features. The Hepatitis C Study Group. Ann Intern Med 1995;123(5): 330–337.

50. De Franceschi L, Fattovich G, Turrini F, Ayi K, Brugnara C, Manzato F, Noventa F, Stanzial AM, Solero P, Corrocher R. Hemolytic anemia induced by ribavirin therapy in patients with chronic hepatitis C virus infection: role of membrane oxidative damage. Hepatology 2000;31(4): 997–1004.

51. Fried MW. Side effects of therapy of hepatitis C and their management. Hepatology 2002; 36(5 Suppl 1): S237–244.

52. Lindenbach BD, Thiel HJ, Rice CM. Flaviviridae: the viruses and their replication. In: Knipe DM, Howley PM, editors. Fields Virology. Philadelphia, PA: Lippincott-Raven; 2007. p. 1101–1152.

53. Moradpour D, Penin F, Rice CM. Replication of hepatitis C virus. Nat Rev Microbiol 2007;5(6): 453–463.

54. Simmonds P, Bukh J, Combet C, Deleage G, Enomoto N, Feinstone S, Halfon P, Inchauspe G, Kuiken C, Maertens G, Mizokami M, Murphy DG, Okamoto H, Pawlotsky JM, Penin F, Sablon E, Shin IT, Stuyver LJ, Thiel HJ, Viazov S, Weiner AJ, Widell A. Consensus proposals for a unified system of nomenclature

of hepatitis C virus genotypes. Hepatology 2005;42(4): 962–973.

55. Scarselli E, Ansuini H, Cerino R, Roccasecca RM, Acali S, Filocamo G, Traboni C, Nicosia A, Cortese R, Vitelli A. The human scavenger receptor class B type I is a novel candidate receptor for the hepatitis C virus. EMBO J 2002;21(19): 5017–5025.

56. Flint M, Maidens C, Loomis-Price LD, Shotton C, Dubuisson J, Monk P, Higginbottom A, Levy S, McKeating JA. Characterization of hepatitis C virus E2 glycoprotein interaction with a putative cellular receptor, CD81. J Virol 1999;73(8): 6235–6244.

57. Pileri P, Uematsu Y, Campagnoli S, Galli G, Falugi F, Petracca R, Weiner AJ, Houghton M, Rosa D, Grandi G, Abrignani S. Binding of hepatitis C virus to CD81. Science 1998; 282(5390): 938–941.

58. Zhang J, Randall G, Higginbottom A, Monk P, Rice CM, McKeating JA. CD81 is required for hepatitis C virus glycoprotein-mediated viral infection. J Virol 2004;78(3): 1448–1455.

59. Evans MJ, von Hahn T, Tscherne DM, Syder AJ, Panis M, Wolk B, Hatziioannou T, McKeating JA, Bieniasz PD, Rice CM. Claudin-1 is a hepatitis C virus co-receptor required for a late step in entry. Nature 2007;446(7137): 801–805.

60. Meertens L, Bertaux C, Cukierman L, Cormier E, Lavillette D, Cosset FL, Dragic T. The tight junction proteins claudin-1, -6, and -9 are entry cofactors for hepatitis C virus. J Virol 2008; 82(7): 3555–3560.

61. Dubuisson J, Helle F, Cocquerel L. Early steps of the hepatitis C virus life cycle. Cell Microbiol 2008;10(4): 821–827.

62. von Hahn T, Rice CM. Hepatitis C virus entry. J Biol Chem 2008;283(7): 3689–3693.

63. Gardner JP, Durso RJ, Arrigale RR, Donovan GP, Maddon PJ, Dragic T, Olson WC. L-SIGN (CD 209L) is a liver-specific capture receptor for hepatitis C virus. Proc Natl Acad Sci USA 2003;100(8): 4498–4503.

64. von Hahn T, McKeating JA. In vitro veritas? The challenges of studying hepatitis C virus infectivity in a test tube. J Hepatol 2007;46(3): 355–358.

65. von Hahn T, McKeating JA. In vitro veritas? The challenges of studying hepatitis C virus infectivity in a test tube. J Hepatol 2007;46(3): 355–358.

66. Blanchard E, Belouzard S, Goueslain L, Wakita T, Dubuisson J, Wychowski C, Rouille Y. Hepatitis C virus entry depends on clathrin-mediated endocytosis. J Virol 2006;80(14): 6964–6972.

67. Meertens L, Bertaux C, Dragic T. Hepatitis C virus entry requires a critical postinternalization step and delivery to early endosomes via clathrin-coated vesicles. J Virol 2006;80(23): 11571–11578.

68. Bartosch B, Vitelli A, Granier C, Goujon C, Dubuisson J, Pascale S, Scarselli E, Cortese R, Nicosia A, Cosset FL. Cell entry of hepatitis C virus requires a set of co-receptors that include the CD81 tetraspanin and the SR-B1 scavenger receptor. J Biol Chem 2003;278(43): 41624–41630.

69. Hsu M, Zhang J, Flint M, Logvinoff C, Cheng-Mayer C, Rice CM, McKeating JA. Hepatitis C virus glycoproteins mediate pH-dependent cell entry of pseudotyped retroviral particles. Proc Natl Acad Sci USA 2003;100(12): 7271–7276.

70. Tscherne DM, Jones CT, Evans MJ, Lindenbach BD, McKeating JA, Rice CM. Time- and temperature-dependent activation of hepatitis C virus for low-pH-triggered entry. J Virol 2006;80(4): 1734–1741.

71. Koutsoudakis G, Kaul A, Steinmann E, Kallis S, Lohmann V, Pietschmann T, Bartenschlager R. Characterization of the early steps of hepatitis C virus infection by using luciferase reporter viruses. J Virol 2006;80(11): 5308–5320.

72. Watanabe T, Umehara T, Kohara M. Therapeutic application of RNA interference for hepatitis C virus. Adv Drug Deliv Rev 2007; 59(12): 1263–1276.

73. Lorenz IC, Marcotrigiano J, Dentzer TG, Rice CM. Structure of the catalytic domain of the hepatitis C virus NS2-3 protease. Nature 2006;442(7104): 831–835.

74. Kolykhalov AA, Mihalik K, Feinstone SM, Rice CM. Hepatitis C virus-encoded enzymatic activities and conserved RNA elements in the 3' nontranslated region are essential for virus replication in vivo. J. Virol. 2000;74(4): 2046–2051.

75. Foy E, Li K, Wang C, Sumpter R Jr, Ikeda M, Lemon SM, Gale M Jr. Regulation of interferon regulatory factor-3 by the hepatitis C virus serine protease. Science 2003;300(5622): 1145–1148.

76. Li K, Foy E, Ferreon JC, Nakamura M, Ferreon AC, Ikeda M, Ray SC, Gale M Jr, Lemon SM. Immune evasion by hepatitis C virus NS3/4A protease-mediated cleavage of the Toll-like receptor 3 adaptor protein TRIF. Proc Natl Acad Sci USA 2005;102(8): 2992–2997.

77. Foy E, Li K, Sumpter R Jr, Loo YM, Johnson CL, Wang C, Fish PM, Yoneyama M, Fujita T, Lemon SM, Gale M Jr. Control of antiviral defenses through hepatitis C virus disruption of retinoic acid-inducible gene-I signaling. Proc Natl Acad Sci USA 2005;102(8): 2986–2991.

78. Lin K, Kwong AD, Lin C. Combination of a hepatitis C virus NS3-NS4A protease inhibitor and alpha interferon synergistically inhibits viral RNA replication and facilitates viral RNA clearance in replicon cells. Antimicrob Agents Chemother 2004;48(12): 4784–4792.

79. Pottage JC, Lawitz E, Mazur D, Wyles D, Vargas H, Ghalib R, Gugliotti E, Donohue M, Robison H. Short-term antiviral activity and safety of ACH-806 (GS-9132), an NS4A antagonist, in HCV genotype 1 infected individuals. J Hepatol 2007;46(Suppl 1): S294.

80. Gosert R, Egger D, Lohmann V, Bartenschlager R, Blum HE, Bienz K, Moradpour D. Identification of the hepatitis C virus RNA replication complex in Huh-7 cells harboring subgenomic replicons. J Virol 2003;77(9): 5487–5492.

81. Watashi K, Hijikata M, Hosaka M, Yamaji M, Shimotohno K. Cyclosporin A suppresses replication of hepatitis C virus genome in cultured hepatocytes. Hepatology 2003;38(5): 1282–1288.

82. Nakagawa M, Sakamoto N, Enomoto N, Tanabe Y, Kanazawa N, Koyama T, Kurosaki M, Maekawa S, Yamashiro T, Chen CH, Itsui Y, Kakinuma S, Watanabe M. Specific inhibition of hepatitis C virus replication by cyclosporin A. Biochem Biophys Res Commun 2004;313(1): 42–47.

83. Inoue K, Umehara T, Ruegg UT, Yasui F, Watanabe T, Yasuda H, Dumont JM, Scalfaro P, Yoshiba M, Kohara M. Evaluation of a cyclophilin inhibitor in hepatitis C virus-infected chimeric mice in vivo. Hepatology 2007;45(4): 921–928.

84. Paeshuyse J, Kaul A, De Clercq E, Rosenwirth B, Dumont JM, Scalfaro P, Bartenschlager R, Neyts J. The non-immunosuppressive cyclosporin DEBIO-025 is a potent inhibitor of hepatitis C virus replication in vitro. Hepatology 2006;43(4): 761–770.

85. Kwong AD, Rao BG, Jeang KT. Viral and cellular RNA helicases as antiviral targets. Nat Rev Drug Discov 2005;4(10): 845–853.

86. Einav S, Elazar M, Danieli T, Glenn JS. A nucleotide binding motif in hepatitis C virus (HCV) NS4B mediates HCV RNA replication. J Virol 2004;78(20): 11288–11295.

87. Elazar M, Liu P, Rice CM, Glenn JS. An N-terminal amphipathic helix in hepatitis C virus (HCV) NS4B mediates membrane association, correct localization of replication complex proteins, and HCV RNA replication. J Virol 2004;78(20): 11393–11400.

88. Einav S, Gerber D, Bryson PD, Sklan EH, Elazar M, Maerkl SJ, Glenn JS, Quake SR. Discovery of a hepatitis C target and its pharmacological inhibitors by microfluidic affinity analysis. Nat Biotechnol 2008;26(9): 1019–1027.

89. Blight KJ, Kolykhalov AA, Rice CM. Efficient initiation of HCV RNA replication in cell culture. Science 2000;290(5498): 1972–1974.

90. Neddermann P, Quintavalle M, Di Pietro C, Clementi A, Cerretani M, Altamura S, Bartholomew L, De Francesco R. Reduction of hepatitis C virus NS5A hyperphosphorylation by selective inhibition of cellular kinases activates viral RNA replication in cell culture. J Virol 2004;78(23): 13306–13314.

91. Murray CL, Jones CT, Rice CM. Architects of assembly: roles of Flaviviridae non-structural proteins in virion morphogenesis. Nat Rev Microbiol 2008;6(9): 699–708.

92. Cristofari G, Ivanyi-Nagy R, Gabus C, Boulant S, Lavergne JP, Penin F, Darlix JL. The hepatitis C virus Core protein is a potent nucleic acid chaperone that directs dimerization of the viral (+) strand RNA in vitro. Nucleic Acids Res 2004;32(8): 2623–2631.

93. Santolini E, Migliaccio G, La Monica N. Biosynthesis and biochemical properties of the hepatitis C virus core protein. J Virol 1994; 68(6): 3631–3641.

94. Kunkel M, Lorinczi M, Rijnbrand R, Lemon SM, Watowich SJ. Self-assembly of nucleocapsid-like particles from recombinant hepatitis C virus core protein. J Virol 2001;75(5): 2119–2129.

95. Matsumoto M, Hwang SB, Jeng KS, Zhu N, Lai MM. Homotypic interaction and multimerization of hepatitis C virus core protein. Virology 1996;218(1): 43–51.

96. Lo SY, Selby MJ, Ou JH. Interaction between hepatitis C virus core protein and E1 envelope protein. J Virol 1996;70(8): 5177–5182.

97. Nakai K, Okamoto T, Kimura-Someya T, Ishii K, Lim CK, Tani H, Matsuo E, Abe T, Mori Y, Suzuki T, Miyamura T, Nunberg JH, Moriishi K, Matsuura Y. Oligomerization of hepatitis C virus core protein is crucial for interaction with the cytoplasmic domain of E1 envelope protein. J Virol 2006;80(22): 11265–11273.

98. Murray CL, Jones CT, Tassello J, Rice CM. Alanine scanning of the hepatitis C virus core protein reveals numerous residues essential for production of infectious virus. J Virol 2007;81(19): 10220–10231.

99. Rouille Y, Helle F, Delgrange D, Roingeard P, Voisset C, Blanchard E, Belouzard S, McKeating J, Patel AH, Maertens G, Wakita T, Wychowski C, Dubuisson J. Subcellular localization of hepatitis C virus structural proteins in a cell culture system that efficiently replicates the virus. J Virol 2006;80(6): 2832–2841.

100. Miyanari Y, Atsuzawa K, Usuda N, Watashi K, Hishiki T, Zayas M, Bartenschlager R, Wakita T, Hijikata M, Shimotohno K. The lipid droplet is an important organelle for hepatitis C virus production. Nat Cell Biol 2007;9(9): 1089–1097.

101. Griffin SD, Beales LP, Clarke DS, Worsfold O, Evans SD, Jaeger J, Harris MP, Rowlands DJ. The p7 protein of hepatitis C virus forms an ion channel that is blocked by the antiviral drug. Amantadine. FEBS Lett 2003;535(1–3): 34–38.

102. Griffin SD, Harvey R, Clarke DS, Barclay WS, Harris M, Rowlands DJ. A conserved basic loop in hepatitis C virus p7 protein is required for amantadine-sensitive ion channel activity in mammalian cells but is dispensable for localization to mitochondria. J Gen Virol 2004; 85(Pt 2): 451–461.

103. Mangia A, Minerva N, Annese M, Leandro G, Villani MR, Santoro R, Carretta V, Bacca D, Giangaspero A, Bisceglia M, Ventrella F, Dell'Erba G, Andriulli A. A randomized trial of amantadine and interferon versus interferon alone as initial treatment for chronic hepatitis C. Hepatology 2001;33(4): 989–993.

104. von Wagner M, Hofmann WP, Teuber G, Berg T, Goeser T, Spengler U, Hinrichsen H, Weidenbach H, Gerken G, Manns M, Buggisch P, Herrmann E, Zeuzem S. Placebo-controlled trial of 400 mg amantadine combined with peginterferon alfa-2a and ribavirin for 48 weeks in chronic hepatitis C virus-1 infection. Hepatology 2008;48(5): 1404–1411.

105. Ferenci P, Formann E, Laferl H, Gschwantler M, Hackl F, Brunner H, Hubmann R, Datz C, Stauber R, Steindl-Munda P, Kessler HH, Klingler A, Gangl A. Randomized, double-blind, placebo-controlled study of peginterferon alfa-2a (40KD) plus ribavirin with or without amantadine in treatment-naïve patients with chronic hepatitis C genotype 1 infection. J Hepatol 2006;44(2): 275–282.

106. Jones CT, Murray CL, Eastman DK, Tassello J, Rice CM. Hepatitis C virus p7 and NS2 proteins are essential for production of infectious virus. J Virol 2007;81(16): 8374–8383.

107. Lohmann V, Korner F, Koch J, Herian U, Theilmann L, Bartenschlager R. Replication of subgenomic hepatitis C virus RNAs in a hepatoma cell line. Science 1999;285(5424): 110–113.

108. Yi M, Bodola F, Lemon SM. Subgenomic hepatitis C virus replicons inducing expression of a secreted enzymatic reporter protein. Virology 2002;304(2): 197–210.

109. Paeshuyse J, Vliegen I, Coelmont L, Leyssen P, Tabarrini O, Herdewijn P, Mittendorfer H, Easmon J, Cecchetti V, Bartenschlager R, Puerstinger G, Neyts J. Comparative in vitro anti-hepatitis C virus activities of a selected series of polymerase, protease, and helicase inhibitors. Antimicrob. Agents Chemother 2008;52(9): 3433–3437.

110. Zhou Y, Bartels DJ, Hanzelka BL, Muh U, Wei Y, Chu HM, Tigges AM, Brennan DL, Rao BG, Swenson L, Kwong AD, Lin C. Phenotypic characterization of resistant Val36 variants of hepatitis C virus NS3-4A serine protease. Antimicrob. Agents Chemother 2008;52(1): 110–120.

111. He Y, King MS, Kempf DJ, Lu L, Lim HB, Krishnan P, Kati W, Middleton T, Molla A. Relative replication capacity and selective advantage profiles of protease inhibitor-resistant hepatitis C virus (HCV) NS3 protease mutants in the HCV genotype 1b replicon system. Antimicrob. Agents Chemother 2008;52(3): 1101–1110.

112. Tong X, Chase R, Skelton A, Chen T, Wright-Minogue J, Malcolm BA. Identification and analysis of fitness of resistance mutations against the HCV protease inhibitor SCH 503034. Antiviral Res 2006;70(2): 28–38.

113. Flint M, Mullen S, Deatly AM, Chen W, Miller LZ, Ralston R, Broom C, Emini E, Howe AY. Selection and characterization of hepatitis C virus replicons dually resistant to the polymerase and protease inhibitors, HCV-796 and boceprevir (SCH 503034). Antimicrob Agents Chemother 2009;53:401–411.

114. Bartosch B, Dubuisson J, Cosset FL. Infectious hepatitis C virus pseudo-particles containing functional E1-E2 envelope protein complexes. J Exp Med 2003;197(5): 633–642.

115. Flint M, Logvinoff C, Rice CM, McKeating JA. Characterization of infectious retroviral pseu-

dotype particles bearing hepatitis C virus glycoproteins. J Virol 2004;78(13): 6875–6882.

116. Flint M, von Hahn T, Zhang J, Farquhar M, Jones CT, Balfe P, Rice CM, McKeating JA. Diverse CD81 proteins support hepatitis C virus infection. J Virol 2006;80(22): 11331–11342.

117. McKeating JA, Zhang LQ, Logvinoff C, Flint M, Zhang J, Yu J, Butera D, Ho DD, Dustin LB, Rice CM, Balfe P. Diverse hepatitis C virus glycoproteins mediate viral infection in a CD81-dependent manner. J Virol 2004;78 (16): 8496–8505.

118. Lindenbach BD, Evans MJ, Syder AJ, Wolk B, Tellinghuisen TL, Liu CC, Maruyama T, Hynes RO, Burton DR, McKeating JA, Rice CM. Complete replication of hepatitis C virus in cell culture. Science 2005;309(5734): 623–626.

119. Wakita T, Pietschmann T, Kato T, Date T, Miyamoto M, Zhao Z, Murthy K, Habermann A, Krausslich HG, Mizokami M, Bartenschlager R, Liang TJ. Production of infectious hepatitis C virus in tissue culture from a cloned viral genome. Nat Med 2005;11(7): 791–796.

120. Zhong J, Gastaminza P, Cheng G, Kapadia S, Kato T, Burton DR, Wieland SF, Uprichard SL, Wakita T, Chisari FV. Robust hepatitis C virus infection in vitro. Proc Natl Acad Sci USA 2005;102(26): 9294–9299.

121. Yi M, Villanueva RA, Thomas DL, Wakita T, Lemon SM. Production of infectious genotype 1a hepatitis C virus (Hutchinson strain) in cultured human hepatoma cells. Proc Natl Acad Sci USA 2006;103(7): 2310–2315.

122. Kolykhalov AA, Agapov EV, Blight KJ, Mihalik K, Feinstone SM, Rice CM. Transmission of hepatitis C by intrahepatic inoculation with transcribed RNA. Science 1997;277(5325): 570–574.

123. Mercer DF, Schiller DE, Elliott JF, Douglas DN, Hao C, Rinfret A, Addison WR, Fischer KP, Churchill TA, Lakey JR, Tyrrell DL, Kneteman NM. Hepatitis C virus replication in mice with chimeric human livers. Nat Med 2001;7(8): 927–933.

124. Kneteman NM, Weiner AJ, O'Connell J, Collett M, Gao T, Aukerman L, Kovelsky R, Ni ZJ, Zhu Q, Hashash A, Kline J, Hsi B, Schiller D, Douglas D, Tyrrell DL, Mercer DF. Anti-HCV therapies in chimeric scid-Alb/uPA mice parallel outcomes in human clinical application. Hepatology 2006;43(6): 1346–1353.

125. Migliaccio G, Tomassini JE, Carroll SS, Tomei L, Altamura S, Bhat B, Bartholomew L, Bosserman MR, Ceccacci A, Colwell LF, Cortese R, De Francesco R, Eldrup AB, Getty KL, Hou XS, LaFemina RL, Ludmerer SW, MacCoss M, McMasters DR, Stahlhut MW, Olsen DB, Hazuda DJ, Flores OA. Characterization of resistance to non-obligate chain-terminating ribonucleoside analogs that inhibit hepatitis C virus replication in vitro. J Biol Chem 2003;278(49): 49164–49170.

126. Ludmerer SW, Graham DJ, Boots E, Murray EM, Simcoe A, Markel EJ, Grobler JA, Flores OA, Olsen DB, Hazuda DJ, LaFemina RL. Replication fitness and NS5B drug sensitivity of diverse hepatitis C virus isolates characterized by using a transient replication assay. Antimicrob Agents Chemother 2005;49(5): 2059–2069.

127. Lin C, Gates CA, Rao BG, Brennan DL, Fulghum JR, Luong YP, Frantz JD, Lin K, Ma S, Wei YY, Perni RB, Kwong AD. In vitro studies of cross-resistance mutations against two hepatitis C virus serine protease inhibitors, VX-950 and BILN 2061. J Biol Chem 2005;280(44): 36784–36791.

128. Sarrazin C, Kieffer TL, Bartels D, Hanzelka B, Muh U, Welker M, Wincheringer D, Zhou Y, Chu HM, Lin C, Weegink C, Reesink H, Zeuzem S, Kwong AD. Dynamic hepatitis C virus genotypic and phenotypic changes in patients treated with the protease inhibitor telaprevir. Gastroenterology 2007;132(5): 1767–1777.

129. Lin C, Lin K, Luong YP, Rao BG, Wei YY, Brennan DL, Fulghum JR, Hsiao HM, Ma S, Maxwell JP, Cottrell KM, Perni RB, Gates CA, Kwong AD. In vitro resistance studies of hepatitis C virus serine protease inhibitors, VX-950 and BILN 2061: structural analysis indicates different resistance mechanisms. J Biol Chem 2004;279(17): 17508–17514.

130. Forestier N, Reesink HW, Weegink CJ, McNair L, Kieffer TL, Chu HM, Purdy S, Jansen PL, Zeuzem S. Antiviral activity of telaprevir (VX-950) and peginterferon alfa-2a in patients with hepatitis C. Hepatology 2007; 46(3): 640–648.

131. Yi M, Tong X, Skelton A, Chase R, Chen T, Prongay A, Bogen SL, Saksena AK, Njoroge FG, Veselenak RL, Pyles RB, Bourne N, Malcolm BA, Lemon SM. Mutations conferring resistance to SCH6, a novel hepatitis C virus NS3/4A protease inhibitor. Reduced RNA replication fitness and partial rescue by second-site mutations. J Biol Chem 2006;281(12): 8205–8215.

132. Tsantrizos YS. The design of a potent inhibitor of the hepatitis C virus NS3 protease: BILN 2061–from the NMR tube to the clinic. Biopolymers 2004;76(4): 309–323.

133. LaPlante SR, Llinas-Brunet M. Dynamics and structure-based design of drugs targeting the critical serine protease of the Hepatitis C virus - from a peptidic substrate to BILN 2061. Curr Med Chem anti-infective agents 2005;4:111–132.

134. Lamarre D, Anderson PC, Bailey M, Beaulieu P, Bolger G, Bonneau P, Bos M, Cameron DR, Cartier M, Cordingley MG, Faucher AM, Goudreau N, Kawai SH, Kukolj G, Lagace L, LaPlante SR, Narjes H, Poupart MA, Rancourt J, Sentjens RE, St George R, Simoneau B, Steinmann G, Thibeault D, Tsantrizos YS, Weldon SM, Yong CL, Llinas-Brunet M. An NS3 protease inhibitor with antiviral effects in humans infected with hepatitis C virus. Nature 2003;426(6963): 186–189.

135. Llinas-Brunet M, Bailey M, Fazal G, Goulet S, Halmos T, Laplante S, Maurice R, Poirier M, Poupart MA, Thibeault D, Wernic D, Lamarre D. Peptide-based inhibitors of the hepatitis C virus serine protease. Bioorg Med Chem Lett 1998;8(13): 1713–1718.

136. Llinas-Brunet M, Bailey M, Deziel R, Fazal G, Gorys V, Goulet S, Halmos T, Maurice R, Poirier M, Poupart MA, Rancourt J, Thibeault D, Wernic D, Lamarre D. Studies on the C-terminal of hexapeptide inhibitors of the hepatitis C virus serine protease. Bioorg Med Chem Lett 1998;8(19): 2719–2724.

137. Llinas-Brunet M, Bailey M, Fazal G, Ghiro E, Gorys V, Goulet S, Halmos T, Maurice R, Poirier M, Poupart MA, Rancourt J, Thibeault D, Wernic D, Lamarre D. Highly potent and selective peptide-based inhibitors of the hepatitis C virus serine protease: towards smaller inhibitors. Bioorg Med Chem Lett 2000;10(20): 2267–2270.

138. Bailey MD, Halmos T, Goudreau N, Lescop E, Llinas-Brunet M. Novel azapeptide inhibitors of hepatitis C virus serine protease. J Med Chem 2004;47(15): 3788–3799.

139. LaPlante SR, Cameron DR, Aubry N, Lefebvre S, Kukolj G, Maurice R, Thibeault D, Lamarre D, Llinas-Brunet M. Solution structure of substrate-based ligands when bound to hepatitis C virus NS3 protease domain. J Biol Chem 1999;274(26): 18618–18624.

140. LaPlante SR, Aubry N, Bonneau PR, Kukolj G, Lamarre D, Lefebvre S, Li H, Llinas-Brunet M, Plouffe C, Cameron DR. NMR line-broadening and transferred NOESY as a medicinal chemistry tool for studying inhibitors of the hepatitis C virus NS3 protease domain. Bioorg Med Chem Lett 2000;10(20): 2271–2274.

141. Tsantrizos YS, Bolger G, Bonneau P, Cameron DR, Goudreau N, Kukolj G, LaPlante SR, Llinas-Brunet M, Nar H, Lamarre D. Macrocyclic inhibitors of the NS3 protease as potential therapeutic agents of hepatitis C virus infection. Angew Chem Int Ed Engl 2003;42 (12): 1356–1360.

142. Rancourt J, Cameron DR, Gorys V, Lamarre D, Poirier M, Thibeault D, Llinas-Brunet M. Peptide-based inhibitors of the hepatitis C virus NS3 protease: structure–activity relationship at the C-terminal position. J Med Chem 2004;47(10): 2511–2522.

143. Poupart MA, Cameron DR, Chabot C, Ghiro E, Goudreau N, Goulet S, Poirier M, Tsantrizos YS. Solid-phase synthesis of peptidomimetic inhibitors for the hepatitis C virus NS3 protease. J Org Chem 2001;66(14): 4743–4751.

144. Goudreau N, Cameron DR, Bonneau P, Gorys V, Plouffe C, Poirier M, Lamarre D, Llinas-Brunet M. NMR structural characterization of peptide inhibitors bound to the Hepatitis C virus NS3 protease: design of a new P2 substituent. J Med Chem 2004;47(1): 123–132.

145. Llinas-Brunet M, Bailey MD, Ghiro E, Gorys V, Halmos T, Poirier M, Rancourt J, Goudreau N. A systematic approach to the optimization of substrate-based inhibitors of the hepatitis C virus NS3 protease: discovery of potent and specific tripeptide inhibitors. J Med Chem 2004;47(26): 6584–6594.

146. Llinas-Brunet M, Bailey MD, Bolger G, Brochu C, Faucher AM, Ferland JM, Garneau M, Ghiro E, Gorys V, Grand-Maitre C, Halmos T, Lapeyre-Paquette N, Liard F, Poirier M, Rheaume M, Tsantrizos YS, Lamarre D. Structure–activity study on a novel series of macrocyclic inhibitors of the hepatitis C virus NS3 protease leading to the discovery of BILN 2061. J Med Chem 2004;47(7): 1605–1608.

147. Goudreau N, Llinas-Brunet M. The therapeutic potential of NS3 protease inhibitors in HCV infection. Expert Opin Investig Drugs 2005;14 (9): 1129–1144.

148. Lin C, Kwong AD, Perni RB. Discovery and development of VX-950, a novel, covalent, and reversible inhibitor of hepatitis C virus NS3.4A serine protease. Infect Disord Drug Targets 2006;6(1): 3–16.

149. Summa V. VX-950 (Vertex/Mitsubishi). Curr Opin Investig Drugs 2005;6(8): 831–837.

150. Lin K, Perni RB, Kwong AD, Lin C. VX-950, a novel hepatitis C virus (HCV) NS3-4A protease inhibitor, exhibits potent antiviral activities in HCv replicon cells. Antimicrob Agents Chemother 2006;50(5): 1813–1822.

151. Leung D, Abbenante G, Fairlie DP. Protease inhibitors: current status and future prospects. J Med Chem 2000;43(3): 305–341.

152. Ede NJ, Eagle SN, Wickham G, Bray AM, Warne B, Shoemaker K, Rosenberg S. Solid phase synthesis of peptide aldehyde protease inhibitors. Probing the proteolytic sites of hepatitis C virus polyprotein. J Pept Sci 2000;6(1): 11–18.

153. Ingallinella P, Altamura S, Bianchi E, Taliani M, Ingenito R, Cortese R, De Francesco R, Steinkuhler C, Pessi A. Potent peptide inhibitors of human hepatitis C virus NS3 protease are obtained by optimizing the cleavage products. Biochemistry 1998;37(25): 8906–8914.

154. Attwood MR, Bennett JM, Campbell AD, Canning GG, Carr MG, Conway E, Dunsdon RM, Greening JR, Jones PS, Kay PB, Handa BK, Hurst DN, Jennings NS, Jordan S, Keech E, O'Brien MA, Overton HA, King-Underwood J, Raynham TM, Stenson KP, Wilkinson CS, Wilkinson TC, Wilson FX. The design and synthesis of potent inhibitors of hepatitis C virus NS3-4A proteinase. Antivir Chem Chemother 1999;10(5): 259–273.

155. Perni RB, Britt SD, Court JC, Courtney LF, Deininger DD, Farmer LJ, Gates CA, Harbeson SL, Kim JL, Landro JA, Levin RB, Luong YP, O'Malley ET, Pitlik J, Rao BG, Schairer WC, Thomson JA, Tung RD, Van Drie JH, Wei Y. Inhibitors of hepatitis C virus NS3.4A protease 1. Non-charged tetrapeptide variants. Bioorg Med Chem Lett 2003;13(22): 4059–4063.

156. Landro JA, Raybuck SA, Luong YP, O'Malley ET, Harbeson SL, Morgenstern KA, Rao G, Livingston DJ. Mechanistic role of an NS4A peptide cofactor with the truncated NS3 protease of hepatitis C virus: elucidation of the NS4A stimulatory effect via kinetic analysis and inhibitor mapping. Biochemistry 1997;36 (31): 9340–9348.

157. Ohmoto K, Yamamoto T, Okuma M, Horiuchi T, Imanishi H, Odagaki Y, Kawabata K, Sekioka T, Hirota Y, Matsuoka S, Nakai H, Toda M, Cheronis JC, Spruce LW, Gyorkos A, Wieczorek M. Development of orally active nonpeptidic inhibitors of human neutrophil elastase. J Med Chem 2001;44(8): 1268–1285.

158. Perni RB, Pitlik J, Britt SD, Court JJ, Courtney LF, Deininger DD, Farmer LJ, Gates CA, Harbeson SL, Levin RB, Lin C, Lin K, Moon YC, Luong YP, O'Malley ET, Rao BG, Thomson JA, Tung RD, Van Drie JH, Wei Y. Inhibitors of hepatitis C virus NS3.4A protease 2.

Warhead SAR and optimization. Bioorg Med Chem Lett 2004;14(6): 1441–1446.

159. Bennett JM, Campbell AD, Campbell AJ, Carr MG, Dunsdon RM, Greening JR, Hurst DN, Jennings NS, Jones PS, Jordan S, Kay PB, O'Brien MA, King-Underwood J, Raynham TM, Wilkinson CS, Wilkinson TC, Wilson FX. The identification of alpha-ketoamides as potent inhibitors of hepatitis C virus NS3-4A proteinase. Bioorg Med Chem Lett 2001;11(3): 355–357.

160. Perni RB, Farmer LJ, Cottrell KM, Court JJ, Courtney LF, Deininger DD, Gates CA, Harbeson SL, Kim JL, Lin C, Lin K, Luong YP, Maxwell JP, Murcko MA, Pitlik J, Rao BG, Schairer WC, Tung RD, Van Drie JH, Wilson K, Thomson JA. Inhibitors of hepatitis C virus NS3.4A protease. Part 3. P2 proline variants. Bioorg Med Chem Lett 2004;14(8): 1939–1942.

161. Yip Y, Victor F, Lamar J, Johnson R, Wang QM, Glass JI, Yumibe N, Wakulchik M, Munroe J, Chen SH. P4 and P1' optimization of bicycloproline P2 bearing tetrapeptidyl alpha-ketoamides as HCV protease inhibitors. Bioorg Med Chem Lett 2004;14(19): 5007–5011.

162. Yip Y, Victor F, Lamar J, Johnson R, Wang QM, Barket D, Glass J, Jin L, Liu L, Venable D, Wakulchik M, Xie C, Heinz B, Villarreal E, Colacino J, Yumibe N, Tebbe M, Munroe J, Chen SH. Discovery of a novel bicycloproline P2 bearing peptidyl alpha-ketoamide LY514962 as HCV protease inhibitor. Bioorg Med Chem Lett 2004;14(1): 251–256.

163. Sulkowski MS. Specific targeted antiviral therapy for hepatitis C. Curr Gastroenterol Rep 2007;9(1): 5–13.

164. Reesink HW, Zeuzem S, Weegink CJ, Forestier N, van Vliet A, van de Wetering de Rooij J, McNair L, Purdy S, Kauffman R, Alam J, Jansen PL. Rapid decline of viral RNA in hepatitis C patients treated with VX-950: a Phase Ib, placebo-controlled, randomized study. Gastroenterology 2006;131(4): 997–1002.

165. Lawitz E, Rodriguez-Torres M, Muir AJ, Kieffer TL, McNair L, Khunvichai A, McHutchison JG. Antiviral effects and safety of telaprevir, peginterferon alfa-2a, and ribavirin for 28 days in hepatitis C patients. J Hepatol 2008;49(2): 163–169.

166. Telaprevir phase 3 realize trial starts. AIDS Patient Care STDs 2008; 22(10):837.

167. Vertex Pharmaceuticals to start phase 3 "REALIZE" trial with telaprevir in treat-

ment-failure HCV patients. AIDS Patient Care STDs 2008; 22(9):766-767.

168. Lang L. Combination therapy with telaprevir and pegylated interferon suppresses both wild-type and resistant hepatitis C virus. Gastroenterology 2007;132(1): 5–6.

169. Sigal S, Jacobson I. Future therapies for hepatitis C: where do we go from here?. Nat Clin Pract Gastroenterol Hepatol 2007;4(2): 60–61.

170. Venkatraman S, Bogen SL, Arasappan A, Bennett F, Chen K, Jao E, Liu YT, Lovey R, Hendrata S, Huang Y, Pan W, Parekh T, Pinto P, Popov V, Pike R, Ruan S, Santhanam B, Vibulbhan B, Wu W, Yang W, Kong J, Liang X, Wong J, Liu R, Butkiewicz N, Chase R, Hart A, Agrawal S, Ingravallo P, Pichardo J, Kong R, Baroudy B, Malcolm B, Guo Z, Prongay A, Madison V, Broske L, Cui X, Cheng KC, Hsieh Y, Brisson JM, Prelusky D, Korfmacher W, White R, Bogdanowich-Knipp S, Pavlovsky A, Bradley P, Saksena AK, Ganguly A, Piwinski J, Girijavallabhan V, Njoroge FG. Discovery of (1R,5S)-N-[3-amino-1-(cyclobutylmethyl)-2,3-dioxopropyl]-3-[2(S)-[[[(1,1-dimethylethyl)amino]carbonyl]amino]-3,3-dimethyl-1-oxobutyl]-6,6-dimethyl-3-azabicyclo[3.1.0]hexan-2(S)-carboxamide (SCH 503034), a selective, potent, orally bioavailable hepatitis C virus NS3 protease inhibitor: a potential therapeutic agent for the treatment of hepatitis C infection. J Med Chem 2006;49(20): 6074–6086.

171. Arasappan A, Njoroge FG, Parekh TN, Yang X, Pichardo J, Butkiewicz N, Prongay A, Yao N, Girijavallabhan V. Novel 2-oxoimidazolidine-4-carboxylic acid derivatives as hepatitis C virus NS3-4A serine protease inhibitors: synthesis, activity, and X-ray crystal structure of an enzyme inhibitor complex. Bioorg Med Chem Lett 2004;14(23): 5751–5755.

172. Arasappan A, Njoroge FG, Chan TY, Bennett F, Bogen SL, Chen K, Gu H, Hong L, Jao E, Liu YT, Lovey RG, Parekh T, Pike RE, Pinto P, Santhanam B, Venkatraman S, Vaccaro H, Wang H, Yang X, Zhu Z, McKittrick B, Saksena AK, Girijavallabhan V, Pichardo J, Butkiewicz N, Ingram R, Malcolm B, Prongay A, Yao N, Marten B, Madison V, Kemp S, Levy O, Lim-Wilby M, Tamura S, Ganguly AK. Hepatitis C virus NS3-4A serine protease inhibitors: SAR of P'2 moiety with improved potency. Bioorg Med Chem Lett 2005;15(19): 4180–4184.

173. Bogen S, Saksena AK, Arasappan A, Gu H, Njoroge FG, Girijavallabhan V, Pichardo J, Butkiewicz N, Prongay A, Madison V. Hepatitis C virus NS3-4A serine protease inhibitors: use of a P2-P1 cyclopropyl alanine combination

for improved potency. Bioorg Med Chem Lett 2005;15(20): 4515–4519.

174. Bogen SL, Ruan S, Liu R, Agrawal S, Pichardo J, Prongay A, Baroudy B, Saksena AK, Girijavallabhan V, Njoroge FG. Depeptidization efforts on P3-P2' alpha-ketoamide inhibitors of HCV NS3-4A serine protease: effect on HCV replicon activity. Bioorg Med Chem Lett 2006;16(6): 1621–1627.

175. Bogen SL, Arasappan A, Bennett F, Chen K, Jao E, Liu YT, Lovey RG, Venkatraman S, Pan W, Parekh T, Pike RE, Ruan S, Liu R, Baroudy B, Agrawal S, Chase R, Ingravallo P, Pichardo J, Prongay A, Brisson JM, Hsieh TY, Cheng KC, Kemp SJ, Levy OE, Lim-Wilby M, Tamura SY, Saksena AK, Girijavallabhan V, Njoroge FG. Discovery of SCH446211 (SCH6): a new ketoamide inhibitor of the HCV NS3 serine protease and HCV subgenomic RNA replication. J Med Chem 2006;49(9): 2750–2757.

176. Njoroge FG, Chen KX, Shih NY, Piwinski JJ. Challenges in modern drug discovery: a case study of boceprevir, an HCV protease inhibitor for the treatment of hepatitis C virus infection. Acc Chem Res 2008;41(1): 50–59.

177. Malcolm BA, Liu R, Lahser F, Agrawal S, Belanger B, Butkiewicz N, Chase R, Gheyas F, Hart A, Hesk D, Ingravallo P, Jiang C, Kong R, Lu J, Pichardo J, Prongay A, Skelton A, Tong X, Venkatraman S, Xia E, Girijavallabhan V, Njoroge FG. SCH 503034, a mechanism-based inhibitor of hepatitis C virus NS3 protease, suppresses polyprotein maturation and enhances the antiviral activity of alpha interferon in replicon cells. Antimicrob Agents Chemother 2006;50(3): 1013–1020.

178. Kwo P, Lawitz E, McCone J, Schiff ER, Vierling JM, Pound D, Davis M, Galati JS, Gordon SC, Ravendhran N, Rossaro L, Anderson FH, Jacobson IM, Rubin R, Koury K, Chaudhri EI, Albrecht JK. HCV SPRINT-1: bocepravir plus peginterferon alfa-2b/ribavirin for treatment of genotype 1 chronic hepatitis C in previously untreated patients. Hepatology 2008; 48(Suppl 4): 1027A.

179. Seiwert SD, Andrews SW, Yang H-W, Tan H, Marafino B, Rieger R, Franklin RB, Pheneger J, Lee PA, Jiang Y, Kennedy AL, Wenglowsky SM, Madduru MR, Doherty GA, Condroski KR, Lemieux C, Pieti Opie L, Sullivan F, Neitzel N, Hingorani GP, Otten J, Brandhuber BJ, Vigers G, Josey JA, Blatt LM.Preclinical Characteristics of ITMN-191, an Orally Active Inhibitor of HCV NS3/4A Protease Nominated for Preclinical Development. Digestive Disease Week, May 20–25, 2006.

180. Seiwert SD, Hong J, Lim SR, Wang T, Ravi Rajagopalan PT, Kossen K, Tan H, Blatt LM. Sequence Variation of NS3/4A in HCV replicons exposed to ITMN-191 concentrations encompassing those likely to be achieved following clinical dosing. In: 42nd Meeting of the European Association for the Study of Liver Diseases, Apr 11–15, 2007, Barcelona. Abstract 647.

181. Blatt LM, Tan H, Seiwert SD. ITMN-191 concentrations achieved in the liver of animals promote HCV replicon clearance *in vitro* and this effect is enhanced by PEG-IFN-α-2a (Pegasys). In: 42nd Meeting of the European Association for the Study of Liver Diseases, Apr 11–15, 2007, Barcelona.

182. Tan H, Rajyaguru S, Wu T, McCown M, Ali S, Jiang W, Otto M, Furman P, Najera I, Klumpp K, Symons J, Cammack N, Blatt LM, Seiwert SD. Combination of the NS3/4A protease inhibitor ITMN-191 (R7227) with the active moiety of the NS5B inhibitors R1626 or R7128 enhances replicon clearance and reduces the emergence of drug resistant variants. In: 59th Annual Meeting of the American Association for the Study of Liver Diseases (AASLD), Oct 31–Nov 4, 2008, San Francisco, CA.

183. Seiwert SD, Andrews SW, Jiang Y, Serebryany V, Tan H, Kossen K, Rajagopalan PT, Misialek S, Stevens SK, Stoycheva A, Hong J, Lim SR, Qin X, Rieger R, Condroski KR, Zhang H, Do MG, Lemieux C, Hingorani GP, Hartley DP, Josey JA, Pan L, Beigelman L, Blatt LM. Preclinical characteristics of the hepatitis C virus NS3/4A protease inhibitor ITMN-191 (R7227). Antimicrob Agents Chemother 2008;52(12): 4432–4441.

184. Johansson PO, Back M, Kvarnstrom I, Jansson K, Vrang L, Hamelink E, Hallberg A, Rosenquist A, Samuelsson B. Potent inhibitors of the hepatitis C virus NS3 protease: use of a novel P2 cyclopentane-derived template. Bioorg Med Chem 2006;14(15): 5136–5151.

185. Raboisson P, de Kock H, Rosenquist A, Nilsson M, Salvador-Oden L, Lin TI, Roue N, Ivanov V, Wahling H, Wickstrom K, Hamelink E, Edlund M, Vrang L, Vendeville S, Van de Vreken W, McGowan D, Tahri A, Hu L, Boutton C, Lenz O, Delouvroy F, Pille G, Surleraux D, Wigerinck P, Samuelsson B, Simmen K. Structure–activity relationship study on a novel series of cyclopentane-containing macrocyclic inhibitors of the hepatitis C virus NS3/4A protease leading to the discovery of TMC435350. Bioorg Med Chem Lett 2008; 18(17): 4853–4858.

186. Reesink H, Verloes R, Abou Farha K, Van Vliet A, Weegink C, van Ot Klooster G, Aharchi F, Marien K, Van Remoortere P, De Kock H, Broeckaert F, Fanning G, Meyvisch P, Van Beirendonck E, Simmen K. Safety of the HCV protease inhibitor TMC435350 in healthy volunteers and safety and activity in chronic hepatitis C infected individuals: a Phase I study. In: 43rd Annual Meeting of the European Association for the Study of the Liver, Apr 23–27, 2008, Milan, Italy.

187. Manns M, Reesink H, Moreno C, Berg T, Benhamou Y, Horsmans Y, Dusheiko G, Flisiak R, Meyvisch P, Lenz O, Simmen K, Verloes R. Safety and antiviral activity of TMC435350 in treatment-naïve genotype 1 HCV-infected patients. In: 59th Annual Meeting of the American Association for the Study of Liver Diseases, Oct 31–Nov 4, 2008, San Francisco, CA.

188. Liverton NJ, Holloway MK, McCauley JA, Rudd MT, Butcher JW, Carroll SS, DiMuzio J, Fandozzi C, Gilbert KF, Mao SS, McIntyre CJ, Nguyen KT, Romano JJ, Stahlhut M, Wan BL, Olsen DB, Vacca JP. Molecular modeling based approach to potent P2-P4 macrocyclic inhibitors of hepatitis C NS3/4A protease. J Am Chem Soc 2008;130(14): 4607–4609.

189. McCauley JA, Rudd MT, Nguyen KT, McIntyre CJ, Romano JJ, Bush KJ, Varga SL, Ross CW 3rd, Carroll SS, DiMuzio J, Stahlhut MW, Olsen DB, Lyle TA, Vacca JP, Liverton NJ. Bismacrocyclic inhibitors of hepatitis C NS3/4a protease. Angew Chem Int Ed Engl 2008;47(47): 9104–9107.

190. Ludmerer S, Graham D, Handt L, Fandozzi C, Burlein C, Liverton N, McCauley J, Vacca J, Hazuda D, Carroll S, Olsen D. Evaluation of MK-7009, a novel macrocyclic inhibitor of NS3/4A protease, in the Chimpanzee model of chronic hepatitis C virus infection. Antivir Res 2008;78(2): A23–A23.

191. McCauley JA, Rudd MT, McIntyre CJ, Nguyen KT, Romano JJ, Butcher JW, Holloway MK, Wan B-L, Carroll SS, DiMuzio JM, Graham DJ, Ludmerer SW, Mao S-S, Stahlhut M, Fandozzi C, Trainor N, Olsen DB, Vacca JP, Liverton NJ. 2008. Discovery of MK-7009: a novel macrocyclic HCV NS3/4A protease inhibitor. In: 235th ACS National Meeting, Apr 6–10, 2008, New Orleans, LA.

192. Avolio S, Robertson K, Hernando JI, DiMuzio J, Summa V. Inhibitors of hepatitis C virus NS3/4A: alpha-ketoamide based macrocyclic inhibitors. Bioorg Med Chem Lett 2009; 19(8): 2295–2298.

193. Wright D, Miller J, Verlinden I, Cilissen C, Valentine J, Sun P, De Smet M, de Hoon J, Depré M, Cavens L, Chodakewitz J, Wagner J. Safety, tolerability, and pharmacokinetic data following single- and multiple-dose administration of MK-7009, a hepatitis C virus nonstructural 3/4a protease inhibitor, to healthy male subjects (1910). In: 59th Annual Meeting of the American Association for the Study of Liver Diseases (AASLD), Oct 31–Nov 4, 2008, San Francisco, CA.

194. Lawitz E, Sulkowski M, Jacobson I, Faruqui S, Kraft W, Maliakkal B, Al-Ibrahim M, Ghalib R, Gordon SG, Kwo P, Rockstroh J, Miller M, Hwang P, Gress J, Quirk E. 2008. Safety, tolerability and antiviral activity of MK-7009, a novel inhibitor of the hepatitis C virus NS3/4A protease, in patients with chronic HCV genotype 1 infection. In: 59th Annual Meeting of the American Association for the Study of Liver Diseases, Oct 31–Nov 4, 2008, San Francisco, CA.

195. Carroll SS, Olsen DB. Nucleoside analog inhibitors of hepatitis C virus replication. Infect Disord Drug Targets 2006;6(1): 17–29.

196. Pierra C, Amador A, Benzaria S, Cretton-Scott E, D'Amours M, Mao J, Mathieu S, Moussa A, Bridges EG, Standring DN, Sommadossi J-P, Storer R, Gosselin G. Synthesis and pharmacokinetics of valopicitabine (NM283), an efficient prodrug of the potent anti-HCV agent 2'-C-methylcytidine. J Med Chem 2006; 49(22): 6614–6620.

197. Pierra C, Benzaria S, Amador A, Moussa A, Mathieu S, Storer R, Gosselin G. NM 283, an efficient prodrug of the potent anti-HCV agent 2'-C-methylcytidine. Nucleosides Nucleotides Nucleic Acids 2005;24(5–7): 767–770.

198. Coelmont L, Paeshuyse J, Windisch MP, De Clercq E, Bartenschlager R, Neyts J. Ribavirin antagonizes the in vitro anti-hepatitis C virus activity of 2'-C-methylcytidine, the active component of valopicitabine. Antimicrob Agents Chemother 2006;50(10): 3444–3446.

199. Beauchamp LM, Orr GF, De Miranda P, Burnette T, Krenitsky TA. Amino acid ester prodrugs of acyclovir. Antivir Chem Chemother 1992;3(3): 157–164.

200. Pescovitz MD, Rabkin J, Merion RM, Paya CV, Pirsch J, Freeman RB, O'Grady J, Robinson C, To Z, Wren K, Banken L, Buhles W, Brown F. Valganciclovir results in improved oral absorption of ganciclovir in liver transplant recipients. Antimicrob Agents Chemother 2000; 44(10): 2811–2815.

201. Lawitz E, Nguyen T, Younes Z, Santoro J, Gitlin N, McEniry D, Chasen R, Goff J, Knox S, Kleber K, Belanger B, Brown NA, Dieterich D. Valopicitabine (NM283) plus peg-interferon in treatment-NAI⁻ve hepatitis c patients with HCV Genotype-1 infection: HCV RNA clearance during 24 weeks of treatment. Hepatology 2006;44(Suppl 1): S223.

202. Pockros P, O'Brien C, Godolfsky E, Rodriguez-Torres M, Afdahl N, Pappas SC, Lawitz E, Bzowej N, Rustgi VK, Sulkowski M, Sherman K, Jacobsen I, Chao G, Knox S, Pietropaolo K, Brown N. Gastroenterology 2006;130(Suppl. 2, Abstr. 4).

203. Donghi M, Attenni B, Gardelli C, Marco AD, Fiore F, Giuliano C, Laufer R, Leone JF, Pucci V, Rowley M, Narjes F. Synthesis and evaluation of novel phosphoramidate prodrugs of 2'-methyl cytidine as inhibitors of hepatitis C virus NS5B polymerase. Bioorg Med Chem Lett 2009;19(5): 1392–1395.

204. Stauber RE, Kessler HH. Drugs in development for hepatitis C. Drugs 2008;68(10): 1347–1359.

205. Sorbera LA, Castaner J, Leeson PA. Valopicitabine: anti-hepatitis C virus drug RNA-directed RNA polymerase (NS5B) inhibitor. Drugs Future 2006;31(4): 320–324.

206. Toniutto P, Fabris C, Bitetto D, Fornasiere E, Rapetti R, Pirisi M. Valopicitabine dihydrochloride: a specific polymerase inhibitor of hepatitis C virus. Curr Opin Invest Drugs 2007;8(2): 150–158.

207. Dutartre H, Bussetta C, Boretto J, Canard B. General catalytic deficiency of hepatitis C virus RNA polymerase with an S282T mutation and mutually exclusive resistance towards 2'-modified nucleotide analogues. Antimicrob Agents Chemother 2006;50(12): 4161–4169.

208. Stuyver LJ, McBrayer TR, Whitaker T, Tharnish PM, Ramesh M, Lostia S, Cartee L, Shi J, Hobbs A, Schinazi RF, Watanabe KA, Otto MJ. Inhibition of the subgenomic hepatitis C virus replicon in huh-7 cells by 2'-deoxy-2'-fluorocytidine. Antimicrob Agents Chemother 2004; 48(2): 651–654.

209. Richardson FC, Kuchta RD, Mazurkiewicz A, Richardson KA. Polymerization of 2'-fluoro- and 2'-O-methyl-dNTPs by human DNA polymerase alpha, polymerase gamma, and primase. Biochem Pharmacol 2000;59(9): 1045–1052.

210. Brox LW, LePage GA, Hendler SS, Shannahoff DH. Studies on the growth inhibition and

metabolism of 2′-deoxy-2′-fluorocytidine in cultured human lymphoblasts. Cancer Res 1974;34(8): 1838–1842.

211. Stuyver LJ, McBrayer TR, Tharnish PM, Hassan AE, Chu CK, Pankiewicz KW, Watanabe KA, Schinazi RF, Otto MJ. Dynamics of subgenomic hepatitis C virus replicon RNA levels in Huh-7 cells after exposure to nucleoside antimetabolites. J Virol 2003;77(19): 10689–10694.

212. Eldrup AB, Allerson CR, Bennett CF, Bera S, Bhat B, Bhat N, Bosserman MR, Brooks J, Burlein C, Carroll SS, Cook PD, Getty KL, MacCoss M, McMasters DR, Olsen DB, Prakash TP, Prhavc M, Song Q, Tomassini JE, Xia J. Structure–activity relationship of purine ribonucleosides for inhibition of hepatitis C virus RNA-dependent RNA polymerase. J Med Chem 2004;47(9): 2283–2295.

213. Eldrup AB, Prhavc M, Brooks J, Bhat B, Prakash TP, Song Q, Bera S, Bhat N, Dande P, Cook PD, Bennett CF, Carroll SS, Ball RG, Bosserman M, Burlein C, Colwell LF, Fay JF, Flores OA, Getty K, LaFemina RL, Leone J, MacCoss M, McMasters DR, Tomassini JE, Von Langen D, Wolanski B, Olsen DB. Structure-activity relationship of heterobase-modified 2′-C-methyl ribonucleosides as inhibitors of hepatitis C virus RNA replication. J Med Chem 2004;47(21): 5284–5297.

214. Clark JL, Hollecker L, Mason JC, Stuyver LJ, Tharnish PM, Lostia S, McBrayer TR, Schinazi RF, Watanabe KA, Otto MJ, Furman PA, Stec WJ, Patterson SE, Pankiewicz KW. Design, synthesis, and antiviral activity of 2′-deoxy-2′-fluoro-2′-C-methylcytidine, a potent inhibitor of hepatitis C virus replication. J Med Chem 2005;48(17): 5504–5508.

215. Stuyver LJ, McBrayer TR, Tharnish PM, Clark J, Hollecker L, Lostia S, Nachman T, Grier J, Bennett MA, Xie MY, Schinazi RF, Morrey JD, Julander JL, Furman PA, Otto MJ. Inhibition of hepatitis C replicon RNA synthesis by beta-D-2′-deoxy-2′-fluoro-2′-C-methylcytidine: a specific inhibitor of hepatitis C virus replication. Antivir Chem Chemother 2006; 17(2): 79–87.

216. Asif G, Hurwitz SJ, Shi J, Hernandez-Santiago BI, Schinazi RF. Pharmacokinetics of the antiviral agent beta-D-2′-deoxy-2′-fluoro-2′-C-methylcytidine in rhesus monkeys. Antimicrob Agents Chemother 2007;51(8): 2877–2882.

217. Murakami E, Bao H, Ramesh M, McBrayer TR, Whitaker T, Micolochick Steuer HM, Schinazi RF, Stuyver LJ, Obikhod A, Otto MJ, Furman PA. Mechanism of activation of beta-D-2′-deoxy-2′-fluoro-2′-C-methylcytidine and inhibition of hepatitis C virus NS5B RNA polymerase. Antimicrob. Agents Chemother 2007;51(2): 503–509.

218. Murakami E, Niu C, Bao H, Micolochick Steuer HM, Whitaker T, Nachman T, Sofia MA, Wang P, Otto MJ, Furman PA. The mechanism of action of beta-D-2′-deoxy-2′-fluoro-2′-C-methylcytidine involves a second metabolic pathway leading to beta-D-2′-deoxy-2′-fluoro-2′-C-methyluridine 5′-triphosphate, a potent inhibitor of the hepatitis C virus RNA-dependent RNA polymerase. Antimicrob Agents Chemother 2008;52(2): 458–464.

219. Ma H, Jiang WR, Robledo N, Leveque V, Ali S, Lara-Jaime T, Masjedizadeh M, Smith DB, Cammack N, Klumpp K, Symons J. Characterization of the metabolic activation of hepatitis C virus nucleoside inhibitor beta-D-2′-deoxy-2′-fluoro-2′-C-methylcytidine (PSI-6130) and identification of a novel active 5′-triphosphate species. J Biol Chem 2007;282(41): 29812–29820.

220. Clark JL, Mason JC, Hollecker L, Stuyver LJ, Tharnish PM, McBrayer TR, Otto MJ, Furman PA, Schinazi RF, Watanabe KA. Synthesis and antiviral activity of 2′-deoxy-2′-fluoro-2′-C-methyl purine nucleosides as inhibitors of hepatitis C virus RNA replication. Bioorg Med Chem Lett 2006;16(6): 1712–1715.

221. Ali S, Leveque V, Le Pogam S, Ma H, Philipp F, Inocencio N, Smith M, Alker A, Kang H, Najera I, Klumpp K, Symons J, Cammack N, Jiang W-R. Selected replicon variants with low-level *in vitro* resistance to the hepatitis C virus NS5B polymerase inhibitor PSI-6130 lack cross-resistance with R1479. Antimicrob Agents Chemother 2008;52(12): 4356–4369.

222. Smith DB, Martin JA, Klumpp K, Baker SJ, Blomgren PA, Devos R, Granycome C, Hang J, Hobbs CJ, Jiang W-R, Laxton C, Le Pogam S, Leveque V, Ma H, Maile G, Merrett JH, Pichota A, Sarma K, Smith M, Swallow S, Symons J, Vesey D, Najera I, Cammack N. Design, synthesis, and antiviral properties of 4′-substituted ribonucleosides as inhibitors of hepatitis C virus replication: the discovery of R1479. Bioorg Med Chem Lett 2007;17(9): 2570–2576.

223. Klumpp K, Leveque V, Le Pogam S, Ma H, Jiang W-R, Kang H, Granycome C, Singer M, Laxton C, Hang JQ, Sarma K, Smith DB, Heindl D, Hobbs CJ, Merrett JH, Symons J, Cammack N, Martin JA, Devos R, Najera I.

The novel nucleoside analog R1479 (4′-azido-cytidine) is a potent inhibitor of NS5B-dependent RNA synthesis and hepatitis C virus replication in cell culture. J Biol Chem 2006;281(7): 3793–3799.

224. Prisbe, E. J.; Maag, H.; Verheyden, J. P. H.; Rydzewski, R. M. In nucleosides and nucleotides an antitumor and antiviral agents; Chu, C. K.; Baker, D. C.; Plennum: Press New York, 1993; pp 101–113.

225. Li F, Maag H, Alfredson T. Prodrugs of nucleoside analogues for improved oral absorption and tissue targeting. J Pharm Sci 2008;97(3): 1109–1134.

226. Brandl M, Wu X, Holper M, Hong L, Jia Z, Birudaraj R, Reddy M, Alfredson T, Tran T, Larrabee S, Hadig X, Sarma K, Washington C, Hill G, Smith DB. Physicochemical properties of the nucleoside prodrug R1626 leading to high oral bioavailability. Drug Dev Ind Pharm 2008;34(7): 683–691.

227. Perrone P, Luoni GM, Kelleher MR, Daverio F, Angell A, Mulready S, Congiatu C, Rajyaguru S, Martin JA, Leveque V, Le Pogam S, Najera I, Klumpp K, Smith DB, McGuigan C. Application of the phosphoramidate ProTide approach to 4′-azidouridine confers sub-micromolar potency versus hepatitis C virus on an inactive nucleoside. J Med Chem 2007;50(8): 1840–1849.

228. Perrone P, Daverio F, Valente R, Rajyaguru S, Martin JA, Leveque V, Le Pogam S, Najera I, Klumpp K, Smith DB, McGuigan C. First example of phosphoramidate approach applied to a 4′-substituted purine nucleoside (4′-azidoadenosine): conversion of an inactive nucleoside to a submicromolar compound versus hepatitis C virus. J Med Chem 2007;50(22): 5463–5470.

229. Roberts S, Cooksley G, Dore G, Robson R, Shaw D, Berns H, Brandl M, Fettner S, Hill G, Ipe D, Klumpp K, Mannino M, O'Mara E, Tu Y, Washington C. Results of a phase 1B, multiple dose study of R1626, a novel nucleoside analog targeting HCV polymerase in chronic HCV genotype 1 patients. Hepatology 2006;44(Suppl 1): 692.

230. Roberts SK, Cooksley G, Dore GJ, Robson R, Shaw D, Berns H, Hill G, Klumpp K, Najera I, Washington C. Robust antiviral activity of R1626, a novel nucleoside analog: a randomized, placebo-controlled study in patients with chronic hepatitis C. Hepatology 2008; 48(2): 398–406.

231. McCown MF, Rajyaguru S, Le Pogam S, Ali S, Jiang WR, Kang H, Symons J, Cammack N, Najera I. The hepatitis C virus replicon presents a higher barrier to resistance to nucleoside analogs than to nonnucleoside polymerase or protease inhibitors. Antimicrob Agents Chemother 2008;52(5): 1604–1612.

232. Pockros PJ, Nelson D, Godofsky E, Rodriguez-Torres M, Everson GT, Fried MW, Ghalib R, Harrison S, Nyberg L, Shiffman ML, Najera I, Chan A, Hill G. R1626 plus peginterferon alfa-2a provides potent suppression of hepatitis C virus RNA and significant antiviral synergy in combination with ribarin. Hepatology 2008; 48(2): 385–397.

233. Smith DB, Kalayanov G, Sund S, Winqvist A, Pinho P, Maltseva T, Morisson V, Leveque V, Rajyaguru S, Le Pogam S, Najera I, Benkestock K, Zhou X-X, Maag H, Cammack N, Martin JA, Swallow S, Johansson NG, Klumpp K, Smith M. The design, synthesis, and antiviral activity of 4′-azidocytidine analogues against hepatitis C virus replication: the discovery of 4′-azidoarabinocytidine. J Med Chem 2009;52(1): 219–223.

234. Klumpp K, Kalayanov G, Ma H, Le Pogam S, Leveque V, Jiang WR, Inocencio N, De Witte A, Rajyaguru S, Tai E, Chanda S, Irwin MR, Sund C, Winqist A, Maltseva T, Eriksson S, Usova E, Smith M, Alker A, Najera I, Cammack N, Martin JA, Johansson NG, Smith DB. 2′-deoxy-4′-azido nucleoside analogs are highly potent inhibitors of hepatitis C virus replication despite the lack of 2′-alpha-hydroxyl groups. J Biol Chem 2008;283(4): 2167–2175.

235. Bressanelli S, Tomei L, Rey FA, De Francesco R. Structural analysis of the hepatitis C virus RNA polymerase in complex with ribonucleotides. J Virol 2002;76(7): 3482–3492.

236. Joyce CM. Choosing the right sugar: how polymerases select a nucleotide substrate. Proc Natl Acad Sci USA 1997;94(5): 1619–1622.

237. Brieba LG, Sousa R. Roles of histidine 784 and tyrosine 639 in ribose discrimination by T7 RNA polymerase. Biochemistry 2000;39(5): 919–923.

238. Sousa R, Padilla R. A mutant T7 RNA polymerase as a DNA polymerase. EMBO J. 1995;14(18): 4609–4621.

239. Koh YH, Shim JH, Wu JZ, Zhong W, Hong Z, Girardet JL. Design, synthesis, and antiviral activity of adenosine 5′-phosphonate analogues as chain terminators against hepatitis C virus. J Med Chem 2005;48(8): 2867–2875.

240. Butora G, Olsen DB, Carroll SS, McMasters DR, Schmitt C, Leone JF, Stahlhut M, Burlein C, Maccoss M. Synthesis and HCV inhibitory properties of 9-deaza- and 7,9-dideaza-7-oxa-

2'-C-methyladenosine. Bioorg Med Chem 2007;15(15): 5219–5229.

241. Abola J, Sundaralingam M. Refinement of the crystal structure of tubercidin. Acta Crystallogr B 1973;29(Pt. 4): 697–703.

242. Olsen DB, Eldrup AB, Bartholomew L, Bhat B, Bosserman MR, Ceccacci A, Colwell LF, Fay JF, Flores OA, Getty KL, Grobler JA, LaFemina RL, Markel EJ, Migliaccio G, Prhavc M, Stahlhut MW, Tomassini JE, MacCoss M, Hazuda DJ, Carroll SS. A 7-deaza-adenosine analog is a potent and selective inhibitor of hepatitis C virus replication with excellent pharmacokinetic properties. Antimicrob Agents Chemother 2004;48(10): 3944–3953.

243. Bio MM, Xu F, Waters M, Williams JM, Savary KA, Cowden CJ, Yang C, Buck E, Song ZJ, Tschaen DM, Volante RP, Reamer RA, Grabowski EJ. Practical synthesis of a potent hepatitis C virus RNA replication inhibitor. J Org Chem 2004;69(19): 6257–6266.

244. Kim HJ, Sharon A, Bal C, Wang J, Allu M, Huang Z, Murray MG, Bassit L, Schinazi RF, Korba B, Chu CK. Synthesis and anti-hepatitis B virus and anti-hepatitis C virus activities of 7-deazaneplanocin A analogues *in vitro*. J Med Chem 2009;52(1): 206–213.

245. Varaprasad CV, Ramasamy KS, Girardet JL, Gunic E, Lai V, Zhong W, An H, Hong Z. Synthesis of pyrrolo[2,3-d]pyrimidine nucleoside derivatives as potential anti-HCV agents. Bioorg Chem 2007;35(1): 25–34.

246. Hecker SJ, Reddy KR, van Poelje PD, Sun Z, Huang W, Varkhedkar V, Reddy MV, Fujitaki JM, Olsen DB, Koeplinger KA, Boyer SH, Linemeyer DL, MacCoss M, Erion MD. Liver-targeted prodrugs of 2'-C-methyladenosine for therapy of hepatitis C virus infection. J Med Chem 2007;50(16): 3891–3896.

247. Ding Y, Girardet JL, Hong Z, Lai VC, An H, Koh YH, Shaw SZ, Zhong W. Synthesis of 9-(2-beta-C-methyl-beta-d-ribofuranosyl)-6-substituted purine derivatives as inhibitors of HCV RNA replication. Bioorg Med Chem Lett 2005;15(3): 709–713.

248. Prakash TP, Prhavc M, Eldrup AB, Cook PD, Carroll SS, Olsen DB, Stahlhut MW, Tomassini JE, MacCoss M, Galloway SM, Hilliard C, Bhat B. Synthesis and evaluation of S-acyl-2-thioethyl esters of modified nucleoside 5'-monophosphates as inhibitors of hepatitis C virus RNA replication. J Med Chem 2005; 48(4): 1199–1210.

249. Gunic E, Chow S, Rong F, Ramasamy K, Raney A, Li DY, Huang J, Hamatake RK, Hong Z,

Girardet JL. 6-Hydrazinopurine 2'-methyl ribonucleosides and their 5'-monophosphate prodrugs as potent hepatitis C virus inhibitors. Bioorg Med Chem Lett 2007;17(9): 2456–2458.

250. Gunic E, Girardet JL, Ramasamy K, Stoisavljevic-Petkov V, Chow S, Yeh LT, Hamatake RK, Raney A, Hong Z. Cyclic monophosphate prodrugs of base-modified 2'-C-methyl ribonucleosides as potent inhibitors of hepatitis C virus RNA replication. Bioorg Med Chem Lett 2007;17(9): 2452–2455.

251. Li H, Tatlock J, Linton A, Gonzalez J, Borchardt A, Dragovich P, Jewell T, Prins T, Zhou R, Blazel J, Parge H, Love R, Hickey M, Doan C, Shi S, Duggal R, Lewis C, Fuhrman S. Identification and structure-based optimization of novel dihydropyrones as potent HCV RNA polymerase inhibitors. Bioorg Med Chem Lett 2006;16(18): 4834–4838.

252. Li H, Linton A, Tatlock J, Gonzalez J, Borchardt A, Abreo M, Jewell T, Patel L, Drowns M, Ludlum S, Goble M, Yang M, Blazel J, Rahavendran R, Skor H, Shi S, Lewis C, Fuhrman S. Allosteric inhibitors of hepatitis C polymerase: discovery of potent and orally bioavailable carbon-linked dihydropyrones. J Med Chem 2007;50(17): 3969–3972.

253. Li H, Tatlock J, Linton A, Gonzalez J, Jewell T, Patel L, Ludlum S, Drowns M, Rahavendran SV, Skor H, Hunter R, Shi ST, Herlihy KJ, Parge H, Hickey M, Yu X, Chau F, Nonomiya J, Lewis C. Discovery of (R)-6-cyclopentyl-6-(2-(2,6-diethylpyridin-4-yl)ethyl)-3-((5,7-dimethyl-[1,2,4]triazolo[1,5-a]pyrimidin-2-yl) methyl)-4-hydroxy-5,6-dihydropyran-2-one (PF-00868554) as a potent and orally available hepatitis C virus polymerase inhibitor. J Med Chem 2009;52(5): 1255–1258.

254. Hammond JL, Purohit VS, Fang J, DeBruin MF. 2008. Safety, tolerability and pharmacokinetics of the HCV polymerase inhibitor PF-00868554 following multiple dose administration in healthy volunteers. In: 59th Annual Meeting of the American Association for the Study of Liver Diseases, Oct 31–Nov 4, 2008, San Francisco, CA.

255. Hammond JL, Rosario MC, Wagner F, Mazur D, Kantaridis C, Purohit VS, Durham LK, Jagannatha S, DeBruin MF. 2008. Antiviral activity of the HCV polymerase inhibitor PF-00868554 administered as monotherapy in HCV genotype 1 infected subjects. In: 59th Annual Meeting of the American Association for the Study of Liver Diseases, Oct 31–Nov 4, 2008, San Francisco, CA.

256. Dhanak D, Duffy KJ, Johnston VK, Lin-Goerke J, Darcy M, Shaw AN, Gu B, Silverman C, Gates AT, Nonnemacher MR, Earnshaw DL, Casper DJ, Kaura A, Baker A, Greenwood C, Gutshall LL, Maley D, DelVecchio A, Macarron R, Hofmann GA, Alnoah Z, Cheng HY, Chan G, Khandekar S, Keenan RM, Sarisky RT. Identification and biological characterization of heterocyclic inhibitors of the hepatitis C virus RNA-dependent RNA polymerase. J Biol Chem 2002;277(41): 38322–38327.

257. Cocquerel L, Quinn ER, Flint M, Hadlock KG, Foung SK, Levy S. Recognition of native hepatitis C virus E1E2 heterodimers by a human monoclonal antibody. J Virol 2003;77(2): 1604–1609.

258. Pratt JK, Donner P, McDaniel KF, Maring CJ, Kati WM, Mo H, Middleton T, Liu Y, Ng T, Xie Q, Zhang R, Montgomery D, Molla A, Kempf DJ, Kohlbrenner W. Inhibitors of HCV NS5B polymerase: synthesis and structure–activity relationships of N-1-heteroalkyl-4-hydroxy-quinolon-3-yl-benzothiadiazines. Bioorg Med Chem Lett 2005;15(6): 1577–1582.

259. Rosen T, Chu DT, Lico IM, Fernandes PB, Marsh K, Shen L, Cepa VG, Pernet AG. Design, synthesis, and properties of (4S)-7-(4-amino-2-substituted-pyrrolidin-1-yl)quinolone-3-carboxylic acids. J Med Chem 1988; 31(8): 1598–1611.

260. Tedesco R, Shaw AN, Bambal R, Chai D, Concha NO, Darcy MG, Dhanak D, Fitch DM, Gates A, Gerhardt WG, Halegoua DL, Han C, Hofmann GA, Johnston VK, Kaura AC, Liu N, Keenan RM, Lin-Goerke J, Sarisky RT, Wiggall KJ, Zimmerman MN, Duffy KJ. 3-(1,1-dioxo-2H-(1,2,4)-benzothiadiazin-3-yl)-4-hydroxy-2(1H)-quinolinones, potent inhibitors of hepatitis C virus RNA-dependent RNA polymerase. J Med Chem 2006;49(3): 971–983.

261. Bosse TD, Larson DP, Wagner R, Hutchinson DK, Rockway TW, Kati WM, Liu Y, Masse S, Middleton T, Mo H, Montgomery D, Jiang W, Koev G, Kempf DJ, Molla A. Synthesis and SAR of novel 1,1-dialkyl-2(1H)-naphthalenones as potent HCV polymerase inhibitors. Bioorg Med Chem Lett 2008;18(2): 568–570.

262. Saha AK, Faitg TH, Kulkarni BA, Blackledge C, Masterson S, Deng Y, Rippin S, Rys D, Lessen T, Cebula C, Leister L, Swestock J, Nitz TJ, Feng H, Burns CJ, Young DC, Chunduru S. Benzofuran inhibitors of hepatitis-C RNA polymerase: synthesis of lead molecules including clinical candidate HCV-796. In: 233rd ACS National Meeting, Chicago, IL, March 25–29, 2007. Abstract MEDI-083.

263. Saha AK, Young C, Del Vecchio AM, Bailey TA, Reinhardt JA, Kulkarni BA, Faitg TH, Feng H, Rippin SR, Blackledge CW, Rys DJ, Lessen TA, Swestock J, Deng Y, Nitz TJ, Chunduru S, Chopra R, Collett M, Pevear D, Howe AYM, O'Connell J, Mansour T, Burns CJ. Discovery of HCV-796: a potent and orally bioavailable hepatitis-C polymerase inhibitor under clinical development. In: 233rd ACS National Meeting, Chicago, IL, March 25–29, 2007. Abstract MEDI-238.

264. Howe AY, Cheng H, Johann S, Mullen S, Chunduru SK, Young DC, Bard J, Chopra R, Krishnamurthy G, Mansour T, O'onnell J. Molecular mechanism of hepatitis C virus replicon variants with reduced susceptibility to a benzofuran inhibitor, HCV-796. Antimicrob Agents Chemother 2008;52(9): 3327–3338.

265. Flint M, Mullen S, Deatly AM, Chen W, Miller LZ, Ralston R, Broom C, Emini EA, Howe AYM. Selection and characterization of hepatitis C virus replicons dually resistant to the polymerase and protease inhibitors HCV-796 and boceprevir (SCH 503034). Antimicrob Agents Chemother 2009;53(2): 401–411.

266. Liu-Young G, Kozal Michael J, Hepatitis C protease and polymerase inhibitors in development. AIDS Patient Care STDs 2008;22(6): 449–457.

ANTI-DNA VIRUS AGENTS

Antonin Holý[1]
Erik De Clercq[2]
[1] Institute of Organic Chemistry &
Biochemistry, Academy of Sciences of
the Czech Republic, v.v.i., IOCB & Gilead
Sciences Joint Research Center,
166 10 Praha 6, Czech Republic
[2] Rega Institute for Medical
Research, K.U. Leuven,
Minderbroedersstraat 10,
B-3000 Leuven, Belgium

1. INTRODUCTION

Anti-DNA virus agents that are inhibitory to the replication of DNA viruses have been reviewed by Tim Middleton and Rockway in Burger's Medicinal Chemistry, 6th ed., volume 5 [1]. The chapter of Middleton and Rockway also provides a rather extensive description of the different DNA virus families: parvo-, polyoma-, papilloma-, adeno-, herpes-, pox-, and hepadnaviridae. Here we will address the various agents effective against these different viruses. For each of the (classes of) compound(s), we will, where applicable, specifically focus on (i) the antiviral compounds that are clinically available; (ii) the antiviral compounds that are under (pre)clinical development; (iii) the mechanism of action of the compounds; (iv) their structure–activity relationship (SAR); (v) resistance that may have arisen; (vi) recent clinical data obtained with the compounds while under development.

Previous reviews on antiviral agents have been dealing with "looking back in 2009 at the dawning of antiviral therapy now 50 years ago: an historical perspective" [2], highlighting the discovery of acyclovir [9-(2-hydroxyethoxymethyl)guanine] as a specific antiherpetic agent [3,4], "the design of drugs for HIV and HCV" [5], "HIV drug development: the next 25 years" [6], "interferons at age 50: past, current, and future impact on biomedicine" [7], "the way forward in HCV treatment-finding the right path" [8], "antiviral treatment of chronic hepatitis B virus infections: the past, the present, and the

future" [9], "antiviral agents active against influenza A viruses" [10], "the war against influenza: discovery and development of sialidase inhibitors" [11], "antivirals and antiviral strategies" [12], and "clinical potential of the acyclic nucleoside phosphonates (ANPs) cidofovir, adefovir, and tenofovir in treatment of DNA virus and retrovirus infections" [13].

2. THE COMPOUNDS

2.1. Introduction

Disregarding the character of their infectious nucleic acid, all viruses can replicate solely in the cells. The first step in the viral replication cycle is *virus adsorption*, wherein the virus particle adheres to appropriate structure(s) of the cell membrane. In the next step, it *penetrates* through the cellular membrane. During this process, the glycoproteins and lipid layer of the outer virion shells are left behind at the outside of the host cell membrane. At the end of this process, the infective viral DNA dissociates from the viral proteins (*uncoating*) some of which immediately begin to display their catalytic function making use of the DNA/RNA intermediates and peptide building blocks from the cell pool. The standard process of *transcription* and *translation* takes place followed by *maturation* processes and *splicing* of the polyproteins giving rise to a new supply of the fresh viral nucleic acids, proteins and other components required for building new virions. This process—*virus assembly*—is then followed by the *budding* of the virus particles from the host cell. The efficacy of this cycle is extremely high: For example, in one life-cycle of adenovirus 30,000 new virions are formed from a single parental virus particle that originally adsorbed to the host cell. All the above-mentioned individual steps can be targeted by specific agents, some of which evolved to approved antiviral drugs.

2.2. Antimetabolites

The background that could be envisaged in the rational design of the first efficient drugs used in antiviral treatment was based on the antimetabolites. By definition, these drugs are chemically modified analogs of natural metabolites. The drugs form a complex with an appropriate enzyme and either turn it in a partially or completely unfunctional form. Obviously, the *de novo* synthesis of viral DNA might be the most important step of the virus life cycle to identify a suitable target enzyme and/or drug candidate. In general, interference with this process could be induced by the modification of the monomers (nucleosides and/or nucleotides), the oligonucleotides or by analogs of inorganic diphosphate (a product that is formed during the dNTP polymerization process).

2.3. History

There are several generations of the small-molecule antivirals most of which belong to the category of nucleosides. Among them the first more broadly used antivirals are 5-iodo-2′-deoxyuridine (idoxuridine) (Herpid®, Stoxil®, **1**) [14,15] and 5-trifluoromethyl-2′-deoxyuridine (trifluridine) (Viroptic®, **2**) [16]. Both drugs are aimed at the use in ophthalmology (keratoconjunctivitis caused by HSV). Also to this early historical period belongs adenine arabinofuranoside (vidarabine, ara-A) (Vira-A®, **3**) [17], which was successfully applied to treatment of generalized herpes simplex infection and, most importantly, to neonatal HSV encephalitis [18]. Unfortunately, this drug is extremely insoluble in water and its applicability for infusion solution is thus very limited. Therefore, it is no longer used. Neither ara-A 5′-phosphate® nor its water-soluble sodium salt could be used in the therapy: it is rapidly dephosphorylated in the plasma to the insoluble ara-A that can have lethal consequences [19].

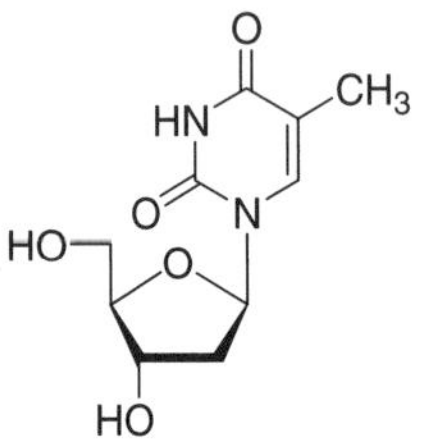

Thymidine
(2′-Deoxythymidine)

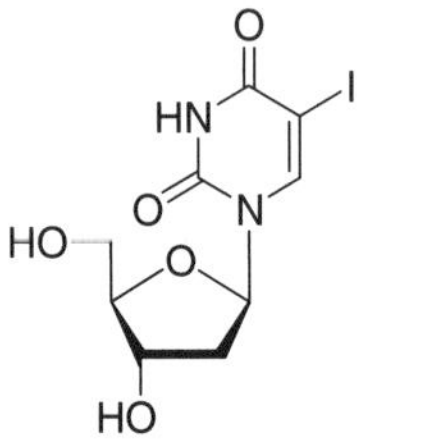

1 Idoxuridine
5-Iododeoxyridine

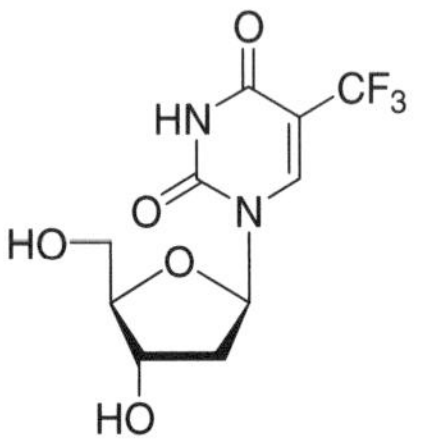

2 Trifluridine
Viroptic®

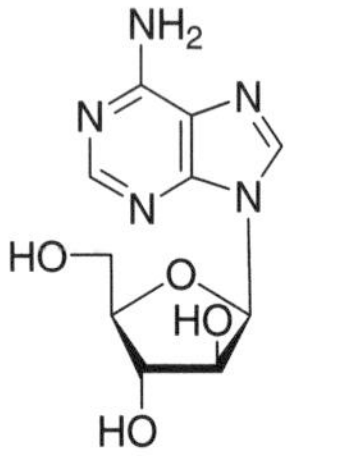

3 Ara-A
Vidarabine®

Generally, however, all these modified nucleosides must, *prior to* the anabolic reactions that result in the active antimetabolite (usually the 5′-triphosphate), be converted to their 5′-phosphomonoesters. The key-process is catalyzed by *nucleoside kinase*, a salvage pathway enzyme, whose presence or activity is thus decisive for the drug activity in a particular cell type.

2.4. SAR in the First Generation of Antimetabolites

The first generation of nucleoside antimetabolites was characterized by maximum possible similarity of the compound with its natural counterpart. It concerns both the general character of the groups in the molecule, as well as the overall geometry (conformation) of the molecule. It is considered to be rigid and enforces the adaptation of the enzyme active site during the formation of an ES (enzyme/substrate)-complex analog. In the first two compounds it was replacement of the 5-methyl group of the thymine part of thymidine by iodine or trifluoromethyl group. In ara-A the 2′-hydroxyl function was introduced in the *ara* configuration of the sugar part of the nucleoside (or of the sugar-5-phosphate moiety of the active metabolite), leaving the purine base intact, while fixing the conformation of the molecule by the intramolecular interactions. In the series of thymidine analogs or generally in the 5-halogeno-2′-deoxyuridines (**4**), there is often encountered a parallel enzyme-inhibitory activity; however, it is aimed at the thymidylate synthase activity, a cellular enzyme that is the only source of thymidine 5′-monophosphate *de novo* [20]. Therefore, these inhibitors were originally designed as potential anticancer drugs (e.g., 5-fluoro-2'-deoxyuridine). The 5-halogeno-2'-deoxyuridines are easily available from 2'-deoxyuridine by an addition–elimination reaction with elemental halogen or active halogeno compounds (*N*-halogenoamides, etc.) [21].

An interesting "double prodrug" is pyrimidin-2-one beta-D-ribofuranoside (zebularine, **5**) [22] that, in contrast to the base (**6**) or to

its 2-deoxyriboside (**7**), can cross the bacterial cell wall and release the base into the cytosol. The base is then converted to the 2'-deoxyribonucleotide (**8**, 4-deoxy derivative of dUMP or 4-desamino analog of dCMP), which is an efficient substrate/inhibitor of the bacterial thymidylate synthase. It would seem interesting to exploit this "double prodrug" approach for anti-DNA virus activity in eukaryotic cell systems.

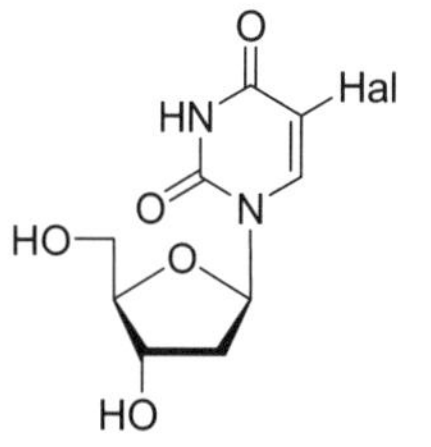

4, Hal = F, Cl, Br 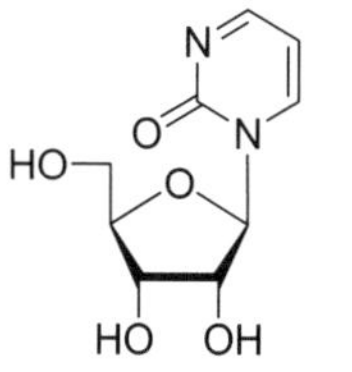   **5**, Zebularine 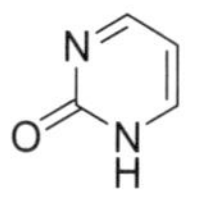   **6** 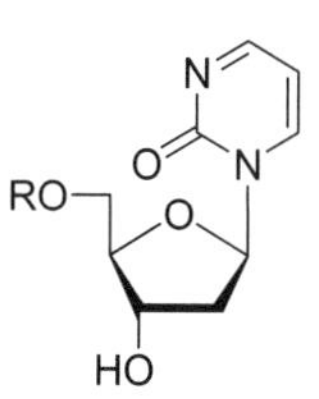   **7**, R = H, PymdRf
8, R = P(O)(OH)$_2$, PymdRf 5'P

Among 5-substituted 2'-deoxyuridines there are several important antiviral compounds; for example, 5-(*E*)-2-bromovinyl)-2'-deoxyuridine (brivudin, BVDU) (Zostex®, Brivirac®, Zerpex®, Helpin®, **9**) [23]. BVDU has been widely used for the treatment of herpesvirus infections, particularly varicel-

la-zoster virus (VZV). The D-*arabinofuranosyl* counterpart of BVDU (sorivudine) (BvaraU, Usevir®, Brovavir®, **10**) is also a potent anti-VZV agent but was not approved by the US FDA for clinical use [24] [*BVDU (brivudin) has never been submitted for consideration for approval by the US FDA*].

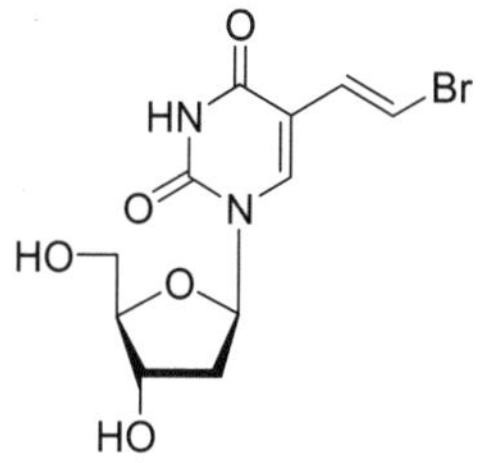

9, BVDU, Brivudin 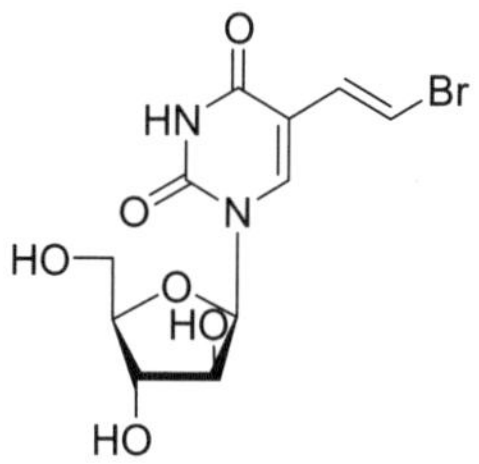   **10**, Sorivudine

However, there is an important drawback: the 5-(*E*)-2-bromovinyluracil base, which can be formed from both BVDU and sorivudine by a catabolic process in the cell cytoplasm, is a powerful inhibitor of dihydropyrimidine dehydrogenase, an enzyme whose level in the population is very variable. It is a key enzyme for the degradation of 5-fluorouracil, a cytostatic agent used regularly in the treatment of cancer patients. Thus, the use of the above anti-

virals (BVDU, BVaraU) in combination with cocktails containing FU or its prodrugs may have lethal consequences and is therefore prohibited [25].

Bicyclic pyrimidine nucleoside analogs (BCNA) are novel antiviral compounds with an absolute specificity for VZV and with very little toxicity [26,27]. Moreover, they are devoid of the undesirable inhibitory activity on dihydropyrimidine dehydrogenase, thus

avoiding a potential interaction with 5-fluor-
ouracil. This is important news, since the
majority of 5-fluorouracil treated cancer pa-

tients are at high risk of severe complications
caused by the latent VZV infection.

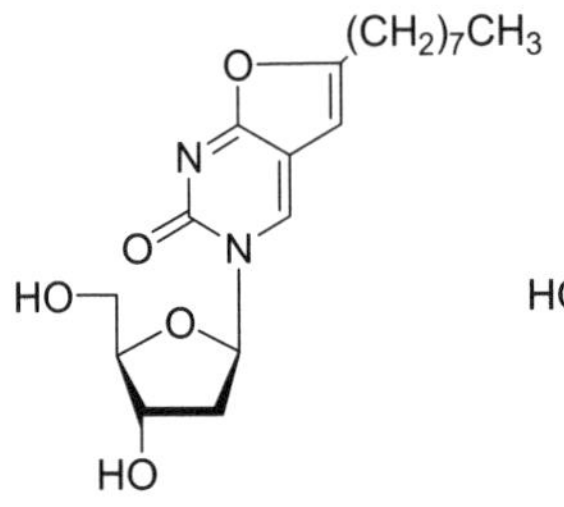

11, Cf 1368 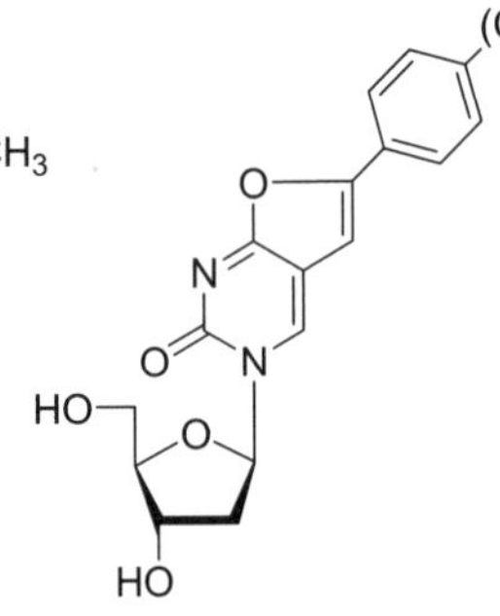   **12**, Cf 1743 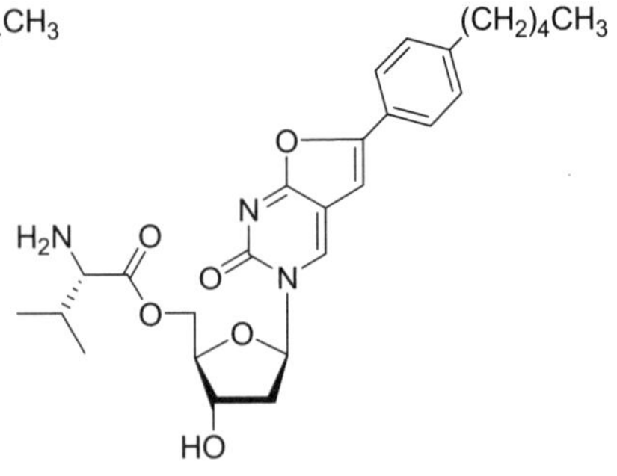   **13**, FV-100

FV-100 (**13**) [28] is a prodrug of the active
principle Cf 1743 (**12**) [27] that was selected by
an optimization of the original lead structure
Cf 1368 (**11**). The exquisite antiviral specificity might be explained by an alteration of the
active site structure of the appropriate VZV-
encoded (nucleoside) kinase. Although the existence of kinases exhibiting low structural
specificity toward the modified substrates is
not uncommon among the virus-encoded herpesvirus nucleoside kinases (see thymidine
kinase (TK) of herpes simplex virus) [29],
further excursions into this field could foster
the knowledge applicable to antiviral drug
design in general.

*Effect of the modification of nucleoside su-
gar moiety.* The multifunctional sugar moiety
in the nucleoside molecule offers manyfold
possibilities for structural changes. Numerous alternatives were examined and quite a
few interesting compounds were identified
among which the anomers, epimers, hydroxy,
or deoxy derivatives though their effect in all
cases shifted to the anticancer field. (One

should pay attention to the often confusing
nomenclature based upon the generally accepted term "thymidine" instead of the correct
"2'-deoxythymidine.")

At some time there was quite an expectation of the 5'-deoxy-5'-amino sugar analog of
idoxuridine devised by Cheng et al. [30] that,
however, was in vain, due to low potency and
unexpected clinical side reactions.

The presence or absence of hydroxyl groups
as well as their orientation (mutual or with
respect to the base) is essential for the biological activity of the analogs in general. Thus,
the absence of a 3'-hydroxyl group in the 2',3'-
dideoxynucleosides **14** [31] as well as in the
2,3'-unsaturated derivative **15** [32] or the azido derivative **16** (azidothymidine, zidovudine,
Retrovir®) [33] prevented the elongation of the
nucleic acid chain growth by the reverse tran-
scriptase-catalyzed reaction. All these compounds have proven to be clinically useful as
essential components of HAART therapy of
AIDS. However, as anti*retro*virals, they are
not subject of this chapter.

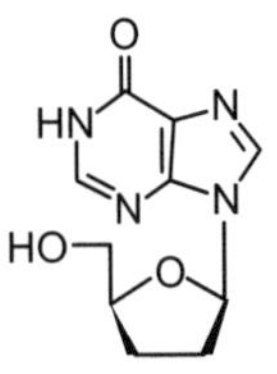

14, ddI, Didanosine 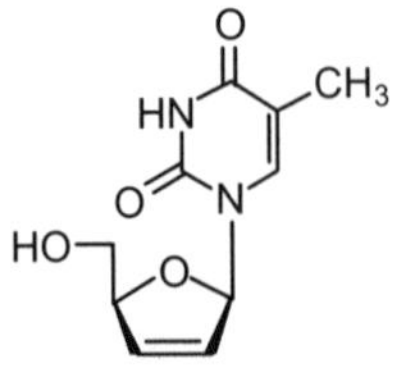   **15**, d4T, Stavudine 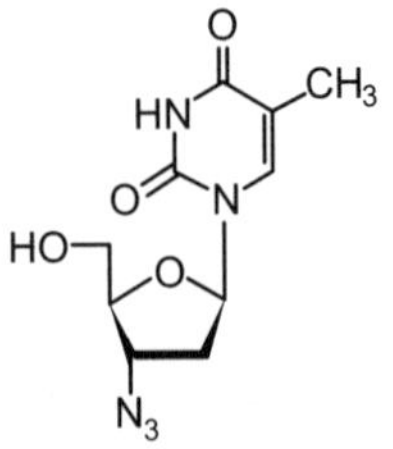   **16**, AZT, Zidovudine

The compounds discussed so far that were designed on the basis of the maximum similarity to their natural counterpart suffer from one logical consequence: they are also recognized by the enzymes catalyzing the catabolic reactions. There are three important groups of catabolic reactions that take place at the monomer level: (a) cleavage of the nucleotide phosphoric acid ester linkage ("dephosphorylation"), (b) oxidation or deamination at the nucleobase residue (followed by further degradation), and (c) cleavage of the nucleosidic linkage. All of these reactions limit the actual antiviral drug concentration at the target tissue. In order to circumvent this drawback, the patient must be burdened by an increased dosage of the xenobiotics or, by its more frequent dosage regimen. Moreover, the formation of decomposition products (some of them with undesirable properties, see above for brivudin or sorivudine) may cause a novel pharmacological situation.

These considerations led to the design of the *second generation of antimetabolites* that stresses the biological stability while maintaining the structural determinants of the first generation of antimetabolites.

The most important issue in this context is keeping the "nucleoside linkage" intact. The enzyme-catalyzed cleavage occurs by hydrolysis or by phosphorolysis; both reactions are reversible. The hemiacetal linkage is not particularly stable even under the conditions of general acido-basic hydrolysis. It was thus considered easier to convert it to a chemically an *a priori* stable analog replacing the sugar ring by its (substituted) carba analog, that is, the cycloalkyl ring system. Despite the fact that the majority of biologically active compounds among these analogs are directed to the antiparasitic field or to the posttranscriptional step of the virus multiplication cycle [34], there are at least two drug candidates that ought to be mentioned here: the cyclohexenylguanine (**17**) [35] and *N*-(methylenecyclopentyl)thymine (*N*-MCT, **18**) [36]. While the guanine derivative **17** is solely phosphorylated by the viral nucleoside kinase [35], the thymine derivative **18** is recognized by the host cell enzymes [37]. Related to this drug is entecavir, a carbocyclic 2′-deoxyguanosine analog (Baraclude®, **19**) [38,39] with an exomethylene function replacing the sugar ring oxygen atom.

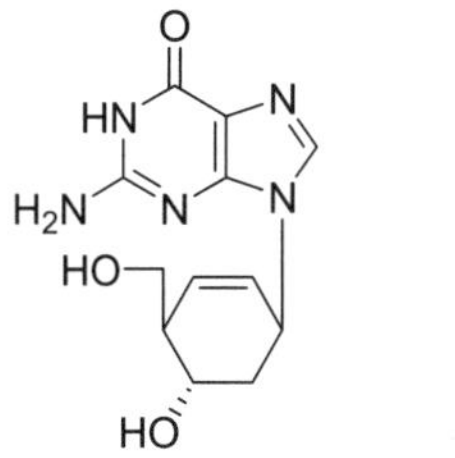

17, Cyclohexenylguanine 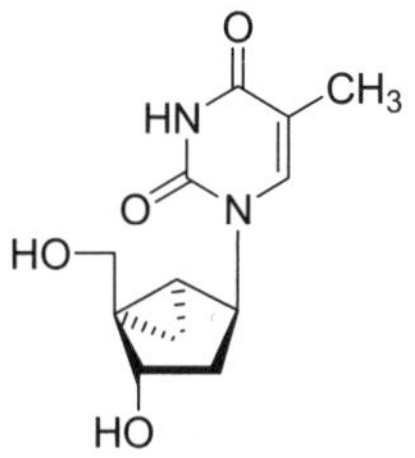   **18**, *N*-MCT 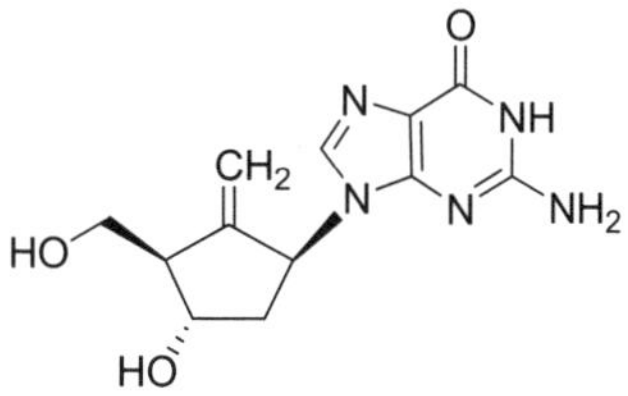   **19**, Entecavir

More than three decades ago we have been stimulated by the above idea of enzymatic resistance to design the L-nucleosides [40]. These compounds are true enantiomers of the natural compounds that are built from the sugars of the D-*ribo* configuration. All functional groups at the aldopentafuranose residue and the natural nucleobase are in essentially the same relation against each other. From a purely geometrical consideration it

follows that (a) compounds in question must be defined by three different points in space, if their response toward an enzyme is different, or, (b) in two or less points in space if they are both subject to the enzyme-catalyzed reaction. If one knows already something about the mechanism of the enzyme-catalyzed reaction, the thus obtained information can be quite useful. We have prepared and investigated the 2-deoxy-L-ribo- and L-ribonucleosides as well as their 5′-phosphates, and investigated their behavior *in vitro* and *in vivo* [41,42]. However, it was too early for investigating their antiviral activity against human hepatitis virus type B (*as at that time the required in vitro assay systems had not yet been developed*).

Human hepatitis virus type B has a special position with respect to the antiviral agents. It is due to the reverse transcription (RNA → DNA) step that is essential for the virus multiplication [43]. This fact illustrates the special position of HBV in the virus taxonomy. HBV infections can be successfully treated with drugs active against HIV [44]. There are, however, drugs that are aimed specifically at the individual viruses. For HBV, these are for example L-thymidine (telbivudine, Tyzeka™, **20**) [45] and clevudine (Levovir®, **21**) [46]. The D-enantiomer of a related compound, FIAU, had already entered the clinic for the same indication. Unfortunately, several fatalities caused its immediate withdrawal. It was shown that the crucial point was mitochondrial toxicity caused by the inhibition of DNA polymerase gamma by the triphosphate of FIAU [47,48] (*checking possible mitochondrial toxicity has now become a standard procedure for putative antiviral drugs*). The opposite enantiomer clevudine is evidently devoid of this drawback and is less toxic.

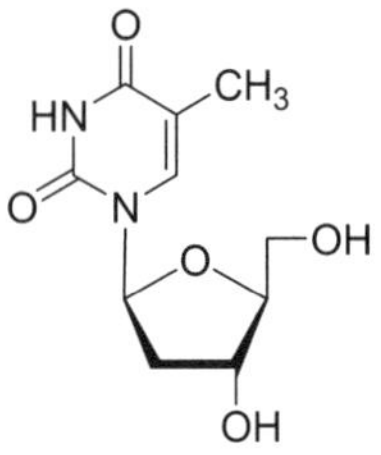

20, Telbivudine 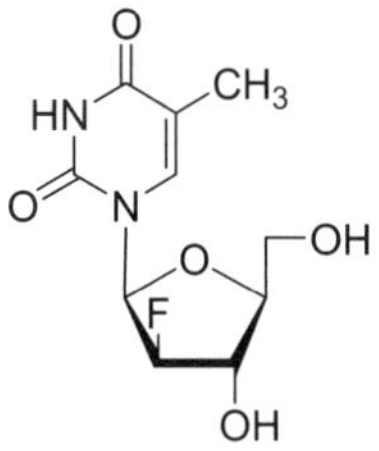   **21**, Clevudine

Mitochondrial thymidine kinase and deoxycytidine kinase catalyze phosphorylation of both enantiomers, albeit with greater preference for the "natural" D-series. This applies not only to the 2-deoxyribonucleosides, but also to the modified sugar moieties, for example, to the 2,3-didehydro-2,3-dideoxynucleosides (i.e., antiretroviral stavudine (Zerit®), one of the most widely used drugs in HAART therapy of AIDS). Both 5-fluorocytosine derivatives: the D-enantiomer (dexelvucitabine, beta-D-Fd4C, DPC-817,**22**) [49] and its L-enantiomer (elvucitabine, beta-L-Fd4C, ACH-126443, **23**) [50] are still in clinical trials for AIDS therapy.

Compound **24**, alovudine (FddThd, FLT, MIV-310), however, a very potent inhibitor of HIV, has not been further pursued for its potential activity against HBV [51].

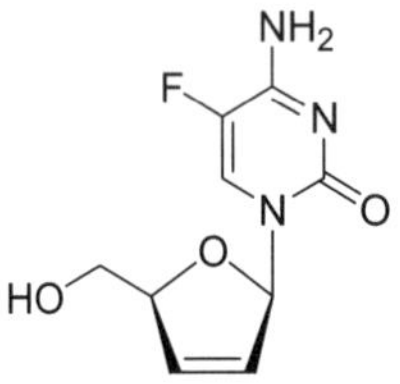

22, DPC-817 (β-D-Fd4C)   **23**, ACH-126443 (β-L-Fd4C)   **24**, MIV-310 (FddThd, FLT)
Dexelvucitabine   Elvucitabine   Alovudine
Reverset®

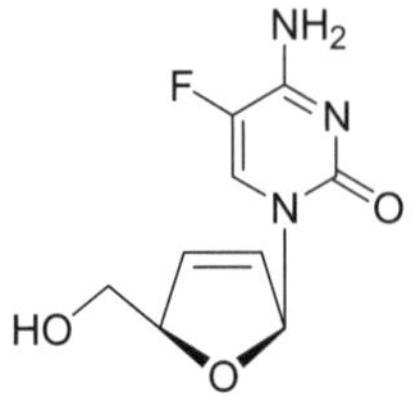

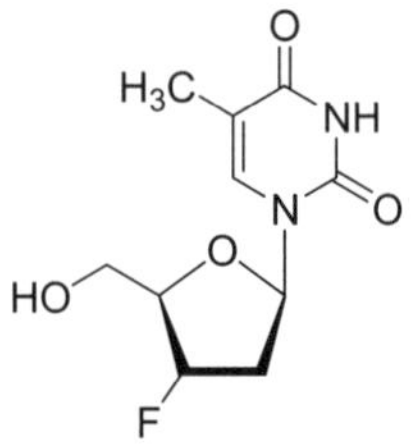

Vasu Nair et al. have developed the chemistry of so-called isodideoxynucleosides [52]. The characteristic feature of these interesting compounds is the transposition of the nucleobase from its "classical" position 1′ of the tetrahydrofurylmethanol to the neighboring 2′ position. According to the published

data [53,54], the major activity is expressed toward HIV. Interestingly, the activity is not limited to the standard stereochemistry, but active compounds are encountered in both series. However, the adenine derivative isoddA (**25**) of the 2*S*,4*S*-configuration (which corresponds to the D-ribo-series) was reported to have activity against HBV *in vitro* [55]; nonetheless, this finding was not corroborated by *in vivo* experiments, although the isoddA-5′-triphosphate has quite a long half-time under the *in vivo* conditions.

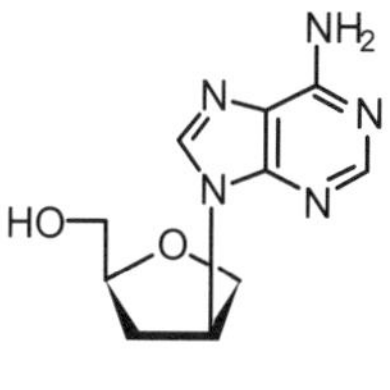

25, isoddA 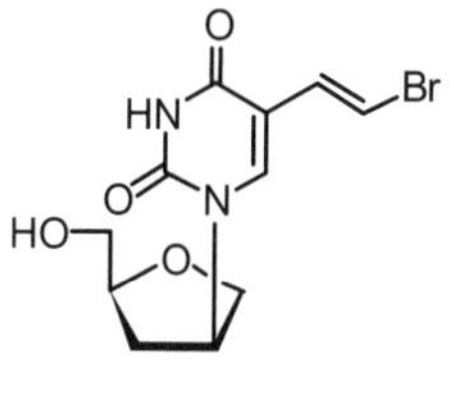   **26**, BVisoddU

The highly active 5-substituted uracil deoxynucleoside, BVDU, also proved to be an interesting congener among the isodideoxynucleosides. This compound, BVisoddU (**26**), exhibited pronounced biological activity by specific inhibition of HSV type-1 only [56]. There are no other herpesviruses, not even HSV-2, which have shown any sensitivity toward this agent. As the linkage of the base to

the tetrahydrofuran ring lost the hemiacetal nature, it must be stable against enzymatic cleavage, disregarding its mechanism of action. Thus, the "dangerous" bromovinyluracil cannot be generated from this analog that eliminates the risk of increased 5-fluorouracil toxicity.

1,3-Dioxolane and 1,3-oxathiolane derivatives. This family of compounds may be considered as composed of modified sugar nucleoside derivatives. They are isosteric analogs of nucleosides, similar enough in shape and main features to wobble the enzymes involved in *de novo* viral DNA synthesis. However, *prior to* their ultimate interaction with the HIV or HBV reverse transcriptase, they require at least three more erroneous consecutive anabolic reaction steps to be converted to the active 5′-triphosphate form. Such a situation requires a very efficient process at the end of the sequence, which is dead-end inhibition caused by the absence of any hydroxyl group in the last incorporated (analog) unit at the 5′-end of the growing DNA chain.

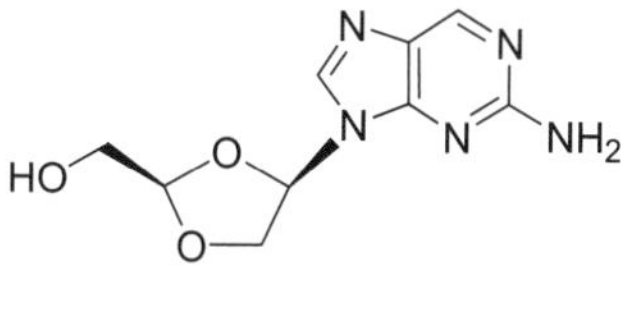

27, 2-Aminopurine dioxolane (APD)

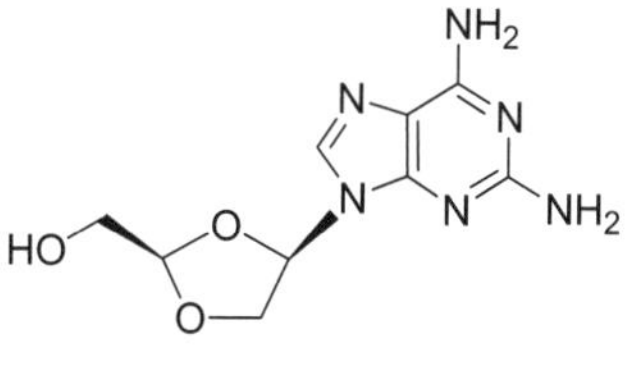

28, Diaminopurine dioxolane (DAPD)
Amdoxovir

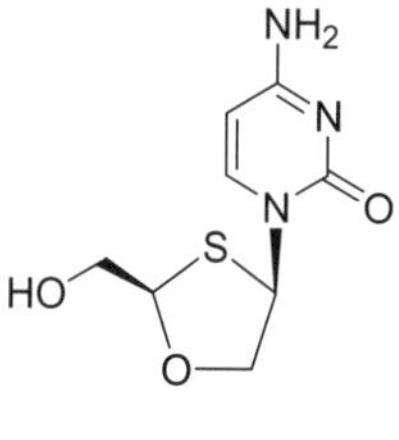

29, AVX-754 ((−)dOTC)
SPD-754
Apricitabine

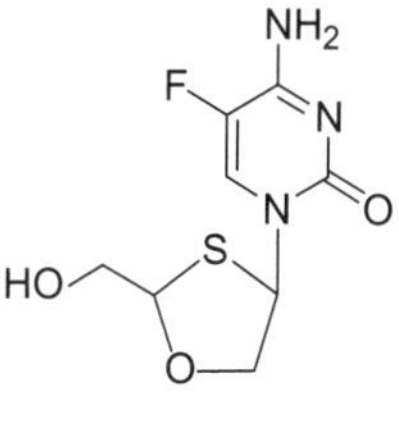

30, Racemic (±)-FTC (FdOTC)
Racivir®

Of this chemically very interesting group there can be listed at least few more frequently quoted compounds as drug candidates: 2-aminopurine dioxolane (APD, **27**) [57] and 2,6-

diaminopurine dioxolane (DAPD, *amdoxovir*, **28**) [58] and the cytosine derived oxathiolanes apricitabine [(−)-dOTC, AVX-754, SPD-754, **29**] [59] as well as the racemic 5-fluorocytosine analog FTC (FdOTC, Racivir®, **30**) [60]. Its L-(–)-enantiomer, emtricitabine ((–)FTC, Emtriva®, **31**) [61] was approved for the treatment of AIDS patients as a component of a *double combination* drug regimen with teno-

fovir disoproxil fumarate (Truvada®) [62] or a *triple combination* of these two drugs with a NNRTI (a nonnucleoside reverse transcriptase inhibitor) such as Sustiva®, as in Atripla® [63].

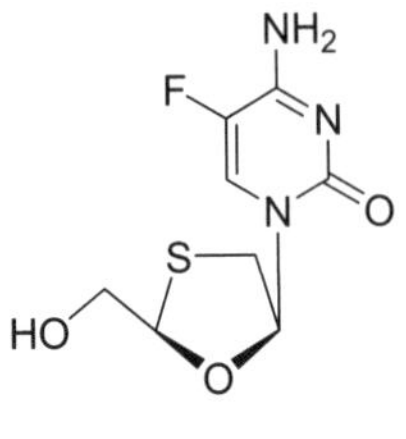

31, Emtricitabine 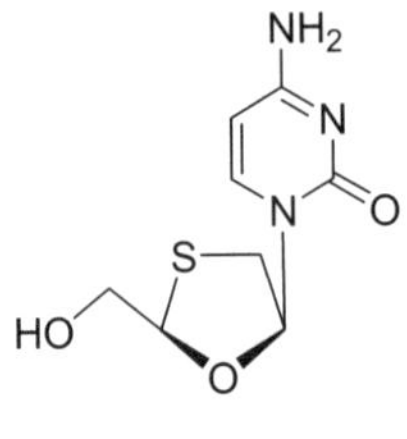   **32**, Lamivudine
                                              Epivir ®

However, the most important compound of the 1,3-oxathiolane derivatives from the viewpoint of hepatitis B therapy is most certainly the cytosine derivative of the L-series lamivudine (3TC, Epivir®, Zeffix®, **32**) [64]. It was originally targeted at AIDS, but nowadays it has also been routinely used for chronic hepatitis B therapy. Unfortunately, it is quite often impossible to eradicate the virus, which means that the drug should be applied to a patient for a long period of time, and this increases the risk of induction of the drug-resistant virus mutants under the drug pressure [65].

The third generation of nucleoside antimetabolites is characterized by a minimum necessary similarity to the metabolite structure. It means that the chemical structure of the analog must contain all the necessary parts and functional groups characteristic for the nucleoside molecule to be recognized by the enzyme and to render the enzyme-catalyzed reaction possible. From the whole spectrum of such configurations we selected those that can form the (thermodynamically or otherwise) optimum complexes with the enzyme(s). The easiest way to achieve it is to break the tetrahydrofuran ring of the sugar moiety and to replace it by an aliphatic hydroxyl groups bearing a chain linked to the heterocyclic moiety.

In the field of antivirals, there are mainly two groups of interest—the derivatives of adenine and guanine. However, since the former group acts generally at the stage of posttran-

scriptional modifications [66], there remains solely the field of guanine derivatives for discussion. A typical representative of this important class of antiherpetic agents is 9-(2-hydroxyethoxymethyl)guanine, acyclovir (ACV, Zovirax®, **33**) [3,4], a drug that opened the new era of antivirals. Its selectivity index was unheard of—owing to the highly nonspecific virus-encoded "thymidine kinase" of the herpes simplex viruses. That enzyme catalyzes an efficient phosphorylation of the primary hydroxyl group of the analog. This transformation is not followed by any of the "conservative" cellular nucleoside kinases of the salvage mechanisms of the cell (at least not to a comparable extent). This failure stands behind the fact that the drug activation proceeds solely in the virus-infected cells, while in the others its presence does not display any significant toxic effects.

This discovery did not only open up the new field of antimicrobial drug development, it also revived the interest in guanine chemistry that was not considered interesting enough and was greatly abandoned due to the unsuitable properties of the base. It is true that the alkylation reactions, disregarding the presence and/or the character of the base, always furnish mixtures of regioisomers that it is difficult to separate from each other and nearly always difficult to isolate. This problem was circumvented by the use of 2-amino-6-chloropurine that also gives a mixture of the regioisomers; however, it is in this case easily separable and the required 9-isomer is formed in an acceptable yield. The 6-chloro group can then be easily hydrolyzed to afford the guanine derivative by acid hydrolysis or by alkali in the presence of suitable catalysts [67].

Soon after the discovery of acyclovir there came ganciclovir (DHPG, GCV, Cytovene®, Cymevene®, Cymevan®, Virgan®, **34**) [17]. Its approval was delayed by a patent priority suit, as it had been evidently discovered simultaneously in three different laboratories all of which applied for patent protection. The drug was originally targeted at herpes simplex viruses; however, during the time its indications shifted to cytomegalovirus infections, which occur frequently in immunosuppressed (or AIDS) patients. Although ganciclovir itself has no center of asymmetry, on phosphorylation by deoxyribonucleoside kinase that takes place enantiospecifically at one of the mutually equivalent primary hydroxyl groups only, it turns into a chiral molecule—an acyclic analog of GMP [68]. The remaining two anabolic phosphorylation steps that result ultimately in the active antimetabolite, GCV triphosphate, are catalyzed consecutively by cellular guanylate kinase and NDP kinase [69].

The principle of carba-analogy, which was quite useful in the nucleoside drug design, was applied also to this field of guanine-containing acyclic nucleoside analogs. While the formal carba-analog of acyclovir 9-(4-hydroxybutyl) guanine (HBG, **35a**) has not attracted further attention, despite the fact that the reported activity of the (R)-3,5-dihydroxybutyl derivative **35b** against HSV-1 *in vitro* was higher than that of ganciclovir, solely penciclovir (PCV, Denavir®, Vectavir®, **36**) [70], became an approved antiviral drug clinically used in the therapy of VZV infections (i.e., herpes zoster).

Among the acyclic guanine nucleoside analogs it is noteworthy to mention the cyclopropylmethyl congener of GCV, *compound A-5021* (**37**). It also contains two primary hydroxyl groups; however, they are not quite identical [71].

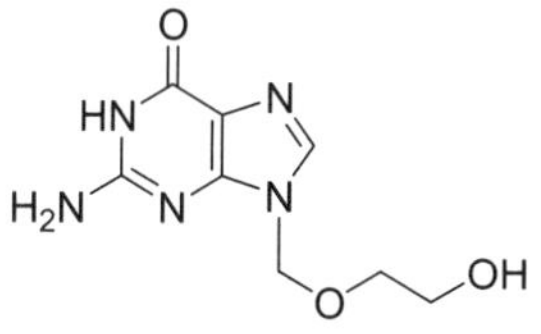

33, Acyclovir

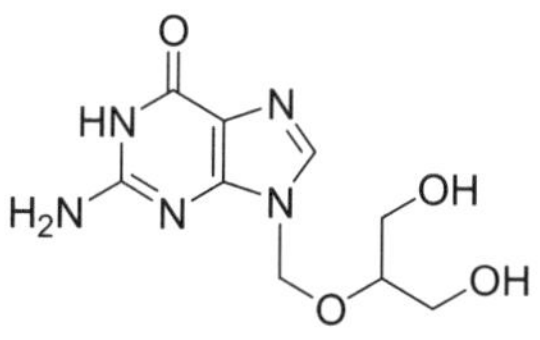

34, Ganciclovir

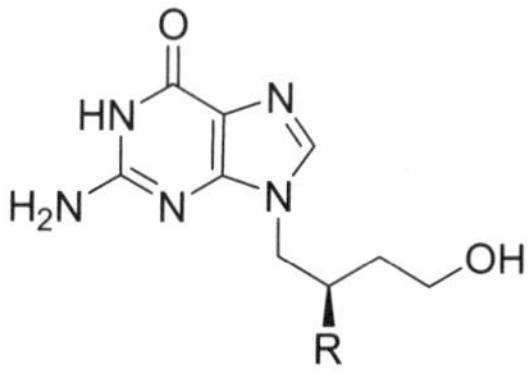

35a, HBG, R = H
35b, (R)-DHBG, R = OH

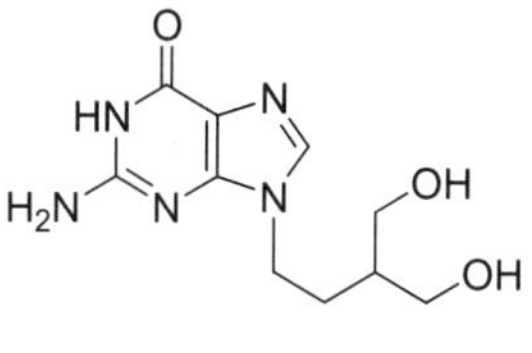

36, Penciclovir

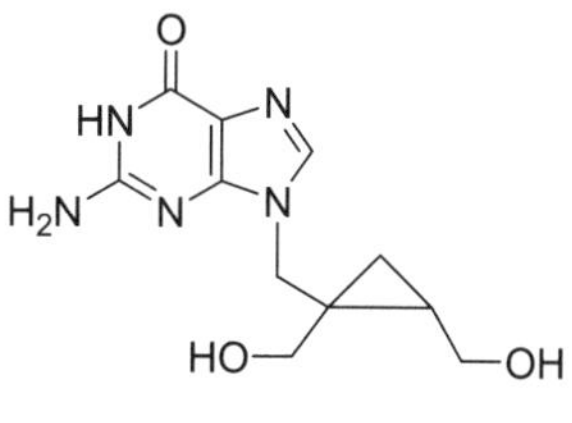

37, A-5021

There are several exhaustive reviews on this type of acyclic nucleoside analogs. Briefly, the hydroxyl group(s) must be present in the free form. They cannot be replaced either by hydrogen, fluorine, or by amino or sulfanyl groups or their respective substituted derivatives. The presence of an additional hydroxyl function at the side chain may improve the activity to some extent (e.g., 9-(R)-(2,4-dihydroxybutyl)guanine, DHBG, **35b**). The base is solely guanine or its 3- and 7-deaza derivatives. The substituent must be located solely at the N9-position, the other regioisomers, except for the N7-substituted congener S2242 [72], are inactive.

2.5. Nucleoside Prodrugs

In order to achieve a massive therapeutic effect, it is necessary to transport the antiviral nucleoside drug to the cytoplasm of the host cell in a sufficient amount. That problem is easily solved in the case of topical treatment (eye drops or creams for ophthalmic use, creams or ointments applicable to skin lesions, vaginal or rectal creams, etc.). However, when it comes to oral use, there are often difficulties, caused by the limited stability of the drug under the extreme pH conditions, poor absorption from the intestine to the blood circulation system as well as tedious pharmacological parameters ($t_{1/2}$, AUC). It can be often circumvented by a suitable

prodrug that liberates the active nucleoside analog inside the cell, if possible by the action of off cell (tissue)-specific enzymes. Also the physical parameters play an important role, for example, limited solubility in water that is notorious for guanine derivatives. It has been successfully overcome by the esterification of aciclovir with L-valine to obtain valaciclovir (Valtrex®, Zelitrex®, **38**) [73]. Similar esterification with L-valine gave valganciclovir (Valcyte®, **39**) [74]. Both L-valyl esters are easily hydrolyzed in the cytoplasm to afford the active drugs. Another alternative is to esterify the hydroxyl group(s) with a fatty acid, in order to enhance its fusion with an eukaryotic cell membrane. This is the case of ganciclovir elaidic acid ester (**40**) [69] that is in the cell cleaved to the active compound by the action of esterases.

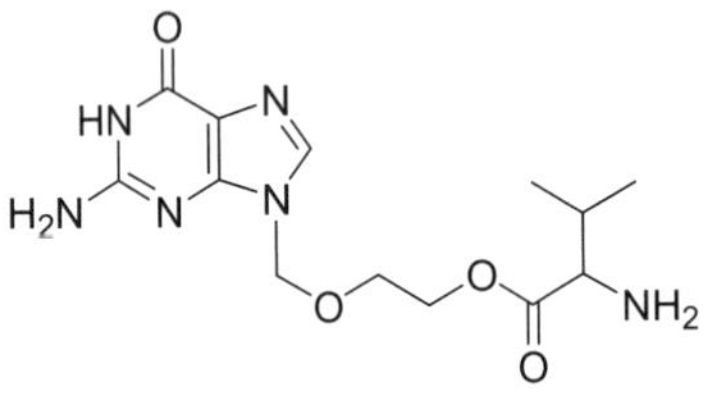

38, Valaciclovir

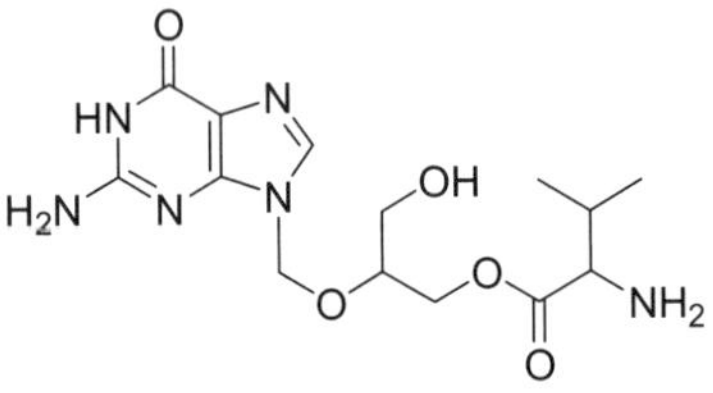

39, Valganciclovir

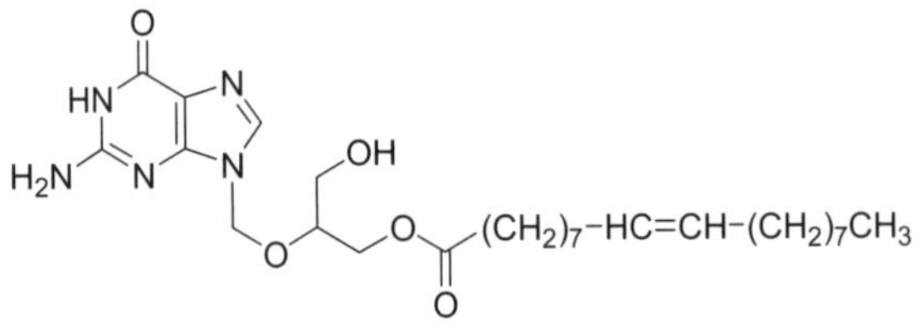

40, Ganciclovir elaidic acid ester

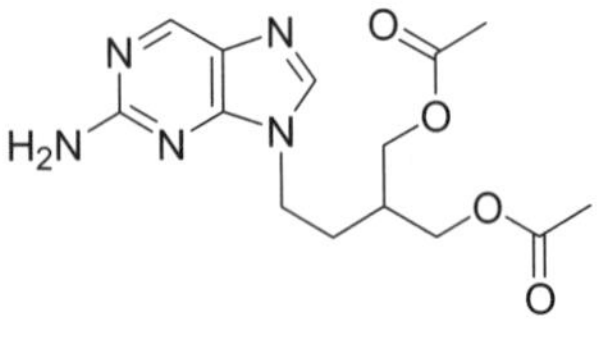

41, Famciclovir

A more complex prodrug design was applied in famciclovir (Famvir®, **41**) [17], a prodrug of penciclovir: in an attempt to increase the solubility of penciclovir, it was converted to its diacetyl analog and the guanine heterocyclic base was replaced by 2-aminopurine. In the target cells, it is converted to guanine by an oxidation at C-6 that can be catalyzed by xanthine oxidase via cytochrome P-450.

In this context it should be recalled that nucleosides themselves usually serve solely as the substrates for the consecutive phosphor-

ylations resulting in the 5'-triphosphates. Of key importance is the first phosphorylation that is catalyzed by a nucleoside kinase. The experiments to directly deliver the mononucleotides prepared by a routine chemical phosphorylation were unsuccessful (due to the strongly hydrophilic polar character of the phosphoric acid monoester residue and to the presence of a high level of diverse phosphomonoesterases in the plasma (cf. the intravenous administration of the water-soluble salt of ara-A 5'-monophosphate)). This also explains the lack of interest in the otherwise efficient and nonexpensive iontophoretic method for directly targeting the charged nucleotide molecules in the controlled treatment of herpetic lesions.

2.6. Nucleotide Prodrugs

Another application of the prodrug strategy is based on nucleotide prodrugs (protides) that can be transported through the eukaryotic cell membrane and should deliver the modified nucleotide in the appropriate cell compartment. Once there, they should undergo the anabolic pathways. They would resist the action of the active repulsion by the ATP-pump that removes the xenobiotics from the cells. Moreover, they retain the structure of the prodrugs in the blood plasma that, in turn, means that they can be eliminated by the urine without doing any harm to the kidneys. In principle, there are different ways on how to neutralize the negative charge at the phosphate group; this will be described later in connection with the acyclic nucleoside phosphonates (see below). In general, it is possible to design the phosphate-protecting groups that can be removed directly by beta-elimination (2-cyanoethyl group), or acid medium (phophoramidates), or by the action of enzymes (specifically nucleolytic enzymes, e.g., ribonucleases or phosphodiesterases), or, by the combination of both approaches (cascade prodrug decomposition).

2.7. Acyclic Nucleoside Phosphonates

Since the past 20 years we have been conducting research on these very promising topics that arose from the combination of the cumulative knowledge of principles of antiviral drug design. Their discovery [75] was preceded by several years of systematic study of enzyme responses toward modified nucleotides accompanied by a systematic search for antiviral and/or other biological activities. The conclusion that resulted from this investigation was straightforward: "in order to be recognized by the enzymes of nucleic acid metabolism, it is necessary to warrant (a) the isopolar and isosteric character of the phosphorus acid group in the phosphorus-modified nucleotide analog and (b) to keep the

oxygen atom in the vicinity of the phosphorus atom."

Compounds that would meet these conditions are simple isomers of phosphomonoesters (42), namely the etherified oxymethylphosphonates (43):

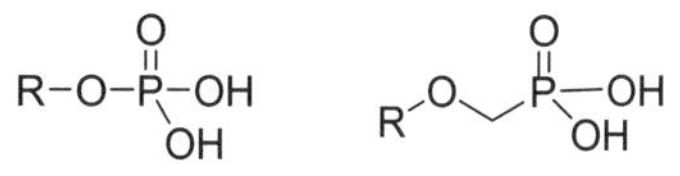

42   **43**

They contain a phosphonyl group that can dissociate twice and is thus isopolar with the phosphate, is practically stable both in alkali and acid, as well as against catabolic enzymes and, due to the presence of a sp^3-hybridized carbon atom at the ether function, it is well adjustable to suit steric (as well as electronic) requirements of anabolic (phosphorylating) enzymes. (*Note:* the term "hydrogen phosphonates" is in the oligonucleotide chemistry routinely used for the phosphorous acid monoesters (characterized by a P–H bond), whereas here it is used to describe compounds containing C–P bonds with the correct description of the residue as "phosphonyl," while the zwitterionic form is described by the prefix "phosphono-" and the neutral (e.g., dialkyl) diester will be called "dialkoxyphospho*n*yl." Moreover, in the case of cyclic ester the rational nomenclature designed for phosphorus heterocycles can also be applied.)

In accord with the expectations, the nucleoside 5'-phosphonates (44) clearly interact with some enzymes of nucleic acid metabolism as shown by the inhibition of 5'-nucleotidases and/or by their incorporation into the polyribonucleotides catalyzed by the DNA-dependent RNA polymerase of *E. coli* [76,77]. Nonetheless, there were no phosphorus-modified nucleotide analogs of the first generation of nucleoside antimetabolites that would demonstrate any inhibition of the growth of cells or their parasites (viruses). However, an exception to this rule are the isomers of d4T-5'-phosphate and d4A-5'-phosphate; compounds **45** and/or its 2'-fluoro derivative, compound **46**, which possess an explicit antiviral activity (albeit, against HIV). They are, in fact, derived from 1,2-dialdosugars [78,79].

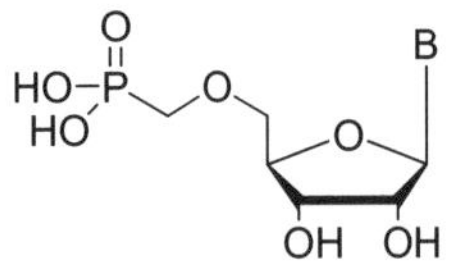

44 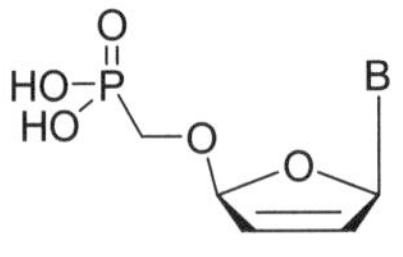   **45** 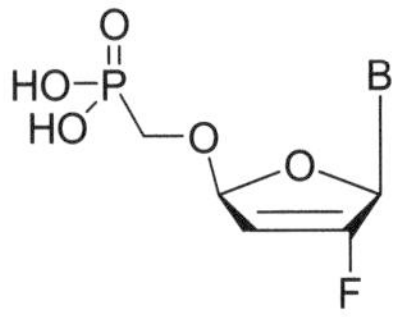   **46**

The situation is quite different, if the phosphonylmethyl group is linked by an ether bond to a hydroxyl group born by the alkyl chain of an acyclic nucleoside analog: the phosphonylmethyl group is linked by the C–O linkage to a hydroxyl group at the beta position of a short carbon atom (C2) chain that substitutes a purine base at the position N9, or a pyrimidine at the position N1. This basic structure comprises the so-called PME (*phosphonylmethoxyethyl*) derivatives. At the beta-position there can be a branching substituent: a methyl group (PMP derivatives for *phosphonylmethoxypropyl* residue), hydroxymethyl (HPMP) derivatives for 3-*hydroxy-2-phosphonylmethoxypropyl* residue), or 3-*fluoro-2-phosphonylmethoxy-propyl for fluoromethyl* (FPMP) derivatives. These are the only structures among the ANPs that proved to exhibit antiviral activity. Replacement of the methyl group by ethyl, cyclopropyl, phenyl, or cyclohexyl in PMP derivatives or of the hydroxyl group in the hydroxymethyl in the HPMP derivatives by an alkoxyl, azido or amino (dialkylamino or trialkylammonium) function is *not* allowed. This strangely narrow structural margin is strengthened by the critical distance of the phosphorus from the alpha-carbon of the chain that can only be *four linkages apart*: The homologous 2-[2-(2-phosphonyl*ethoxy*)ethyl] derivatives are antivirally inactive equally as the shortened phosphonylmethoxy*methyl* congeners, or the HPMP-isomers, the *2-hydroxy-3-phosphonylmethoxy*propyl derivatives [75,80,81].

The active ANP compounds contain a purine base bearing the amino groups at the pyrimidine ring, that is, 2-aminopurine, adenine, 2,6-diaminopurine, or guanine. Hypoxanthine or xanthine derivatives are totally inactive. Generally, all the active purine compounds in all series are the N9-isomers. The role of the amino groups is not evident. It is not solely based on basicity, as the corresponding

monoamino- or bis-(aminomethyl) derivatives of the heterocycle are inactive [67,80].

The bases should not be substituted at position C-8 of the imidazole ring of the purine moiety [82]. The isomeric 8-aza derivatives (with a nitrogen replacing CH) were in all series inactive; however, in the 9-regioisomers the activity was preserved in all three purine derivatives [83]. Likewise, a nitrogen for CH exchange was not acceptable at the C2-position of adenine; hence, the 2-aza analog of PMEA is inactive [84]. On the other hand, replacement of −N by −CH is permissible at the N3-position. While the N3-deazapurine derivatives are active in all series, the antiviral activity is lost in the corresponding N1-deazapurine analogs [85].

The hypothetical pharmacophore concept, in the pyrimidine series, should fit for most cytosine derivatives; however, solely the HPMP series gave the corresponding antivirally active compound. The uracil/thymine compounds were devoid of any activity whatsoever in all three series tested (PME, HPMP as well as the PMP series) [86,87].

Introduction of a branching substituent at the beta-position of the side chain brings about an asymmetric center in the molecule. In adenine and cytosine series solely the (*S*)-enantiomer ensures the antiviral activity. The situation is less unequivocal in the 2,6-diaminopurine or guanine-derived ANPs. It is most probably due to the different enantioselectivity of nucleotide kinases that applies to the first two compounds while the guanylate kinase that is responsible for the first phosphorylation step of the latter two compounds does not strictly distinguish between the two enantiomers [88].

Note: It should be kept in mind that, in accord with the Kahn–Ingold–Prelog rules, the order of preference for substituents at the asymmetric center in the PMP compounds differs from that in the HPMP and FPMP series, so that the absolute (*R*)-configuration of the PMP series formally corresponds to the (*S*)-configuration in the HPMP and FPMP series.

General methods for preparation of ANPs and their derivatives (prodrugs) [75,89] are as follows:

- Stepwise synthesis—alkylation of the heterocyclic base directly to the *N*-alkyl derivative with only one free hydroxyl group; reaction of thus obtained intermediate with dialkyl *p*-tolylsulfonyloxymethyl phosphonate or bromomethylphosphonic acid diester and a small excess NaH in DMF.

- Alkylation of the heterocyclic base in the presence of 1 equiv. NaH or 0.5 equiv. Cs_2CO_3 in DMF by a synthon with all the features of the side chain and ester-protected phosphonate function.

- The synthon will have a primary hydroxyl group that will be converted to an active ester (*p*-tolylsulfonyloxy, methylsulfonyloxy or trifluoromethylsulfonyl oxy group.

- Alternatively, the heterocyclic base will react with the hydroxyl group-bearing synthon under Mitsunobu conditions.

- Transformations of the reactive groups at the base.

- Transformations of the hydroxyl group of the phosphonate-protected HPMP derivatives.

(*Note:* It is recommended to use 2-propylester groups for protection of the phosphonate function, to avoid alkylation of the base by ester groups. The protected phosphonate obtained by these approaches will be deprotected by transsilylation reaction with bromotrimethylsilane followed by hydrolysis or by microwave-assisted reaction with an equimolar amount of HCl in water. *The residual traces of silicon containing contaminants, which may occur in the former case, can be removed by ion exchange chromatography.*)

Specifically the first ANP reported was the adenine derivative (*S*)-HPMPA (**47**); this compound has numerous biological activities: in addition to a general anti-DNA virus activity, (*S*)-HPMPA, though its diphosphate derivative, inhibits also the DNA polymerase of *Plasmodium* spp. (the causative agent(s) of malaria) [90] and suppresses the *Trypanosoma* spp. [91], which cause sleeping sickness, *Leishmania* spp. (causing *kala-azar* disease) [92], as well as the parasite *Schistosoma* [93] or *Cryptosporidia* spp. Despite its undisputable therapeutic potential (*S*)-HPMPA has never been developed as a drug.

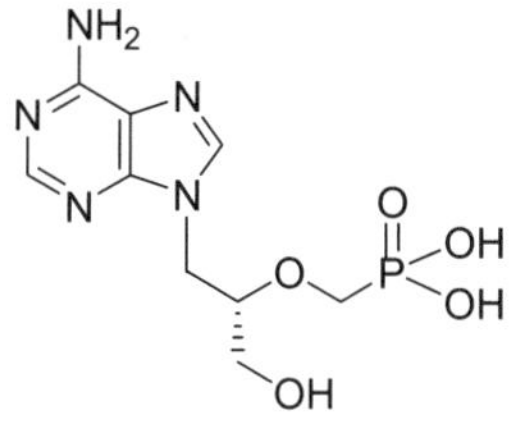

47, (*S*)-HPMPA 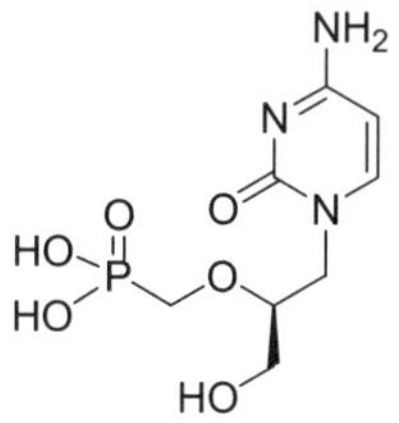   **48**, (*S*)-HPMPC   **49**, cHPMPC
                                  Cidofovir   Cyclic cidofovir

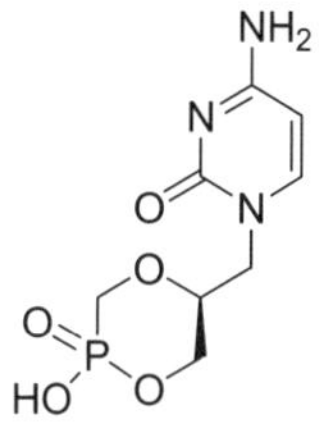

A possible explanation of this apparent anomaly might consist in the fact that its cytosine analog (*S*)-HPMPC (cidofovir, CDV, Vistide®, **48**), which has a nearly identical spectrum of antiviral activity, in the initial tests had lower toxicity compared to (*S*)-HPMPA. Formally, cidofovir was approved

for treatment of HCMV retinitis in AIDS patients [94]. Due to its low oral bioavailability it has to be administered by (intravenous) infusion; to prevent kidney damage it has to be given simultaneously with probenecid.

Under these circumstances, another positive quality of all the ANPs came into picture: due to the metabolic transformation of the ANP its efflux from the cell is much slower than that for the neutral compounds. In the case of cidofovir it is transformed to an ANP analog of CDP-choline, which serves as a depot form of the CDV-diphosphate (an analog of dCTP) [95]. This feature allows infrequent drug dosing (once per 2 or 3 weeks). This extraordinary fact might have been a decisive argument in the drug approval process, since the other drugs used for the treatment of (H)CMV disease (i.e., ganciclovir) have to be applied in much shorter intervals (several times a day). Cidofovir was applied in several critical cases of HCMV and other herpesvirus infections as the "drug of the last hope" [13].

The simplest prodrugs of the HPMP compounds are the cyclic monoesters that are formed easily by any of the phosphate activating agents (e.g., *N,N'*-dicyclohexylcarbodiimide, alkyl chloroformates, etc.). Contrary to the five-membered rings of the ribonucleoside 2',3'-cyclic phosphates, which are cleaved chemically, the six-membered rings (i.e., *the cyclic cidofovir* (cHPMPC, **49**) are cleaved by a decyclizing phosphodiesterase from the cells' cytosol [96].

Quite active against numerous DNA viruses is also the 5-azacytosine analog of HPMPC, 5-aza-(*S*)-HPMPC (**50**) [97], as well as its cyclic form 5-aza-(*S*)-cHPMPC, (**51**) [98]. In contrast to these compounds that are even more active against the herpesviruses (HCMV) or poxviruses, compared to their cytosine counterparts, their 6-azacytosine isomers **52** and **53** are essentially inactive.

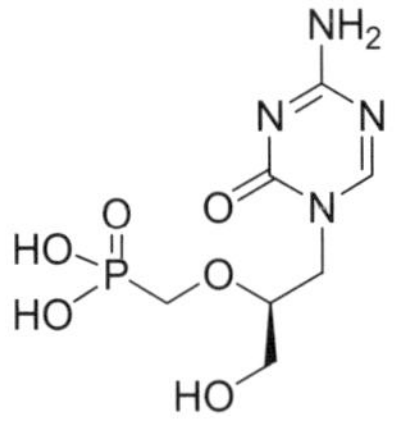

50, 5-*aza*-(*S*)-HPMPC 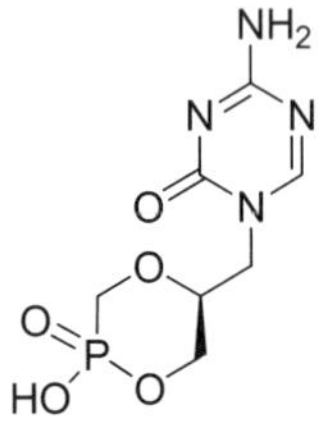   **51**, 5-*aza*-(*S*)-cHPMPC

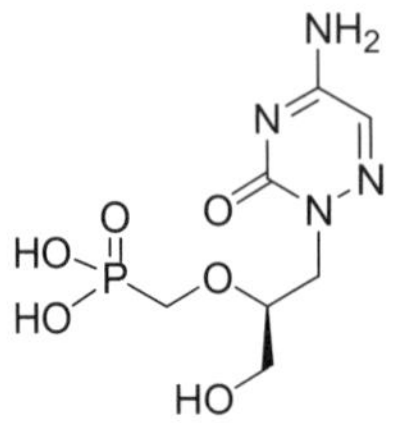

52, 6-*aza*-(*S*)-HPMPC 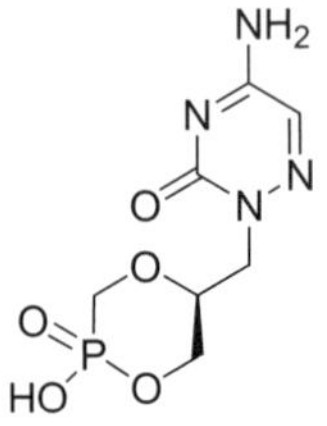   **53**, 6-*aza*-(*S*)-cHPMPC

There was a report in the literature about the N4-amidine derivative of HPMPC (**54**) that is easy to prepare by treatment of HPMPC with dimethylformamide dimethyl acetal and that would generate the parent drug by chemical hydrolysis [99]; also, there appeared a note about the activity of the 5-fluoro-HPMPC (**55**) [100].

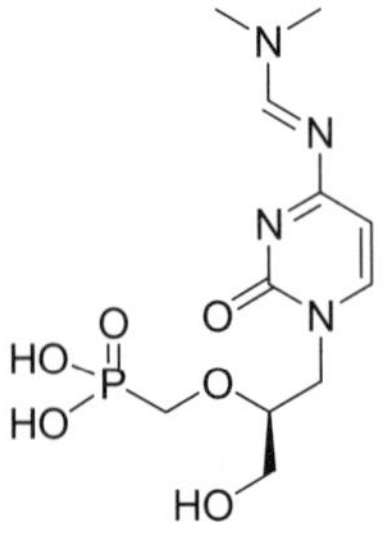

54 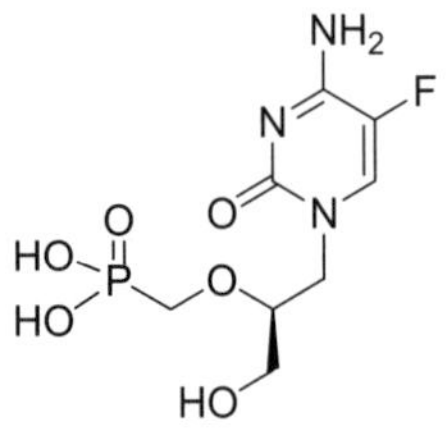   **55**

The following important types of ANP are composed of purines, their general order of activity being G (guanine) ≫ DAP (2,6-diaminopurine) > A (adenine) > MAP (2-aminopurine), the guanine compounds being in general the most toxic ones. In the range of low concentrations this toxicity is reversible, while at the higher concentrations the guanine derivatives turn the cells irreversibly into apoptosis [101]. This does not occur with the adenine, 2-aminopurine, and 2,6-diaminopurine derivatives, where under standard concentrations it is possible to endure mostly a reversible cell growth inhibition.

2.7.1. Adenine Derivatives 9-(2-Phosphono-methoxyethyl)adenine (PMEA, adefovir, **56**) [102] was discovered soon after (*S*)-HPMPA. It acts against both DNA viruses as well as retroviruses (HIV) and hepadnaviruses (HBV). It was developed for the therapy of chronic hepatitis B. As mentioned above, it was necessary to develop an oral formulation to achieve a suitable pharmacological profile. In this case, the pivaloyloxymethyl (POM)

ester group well known from the penicillin area was used for that purpose. It is comparatively easy to prepare the neutral [bis(POM)] ester by treatment of adefovir with the commercially available chloromethyl pivalate in the presence of alkali [103]. It was estimated at the beginning of the clinical phase that the dosage which would have been necessary to use in order to achieve a therapeutic effect in the treatment of HIV infections (AIDS) was already too high and caused unwanted alterations in biochemical markers. However, it was readily acceptable for the treatment of chronic hepatitis B, where the dosage of the drug could be much lower. Thus, the bis(pivaloyloxymethyl) ester of adefovir (bis(POM)PMEA, adefovir dipivoxil, Hepsera®, **57**) was approved by both FDA and EMEA for treatment of hepatitis B, specifically in patients with lamivudine-resistant HBV [104,105]. In contrast with lamivudine resistance, PMEA-induced resistant mutants of HBV rarely occur in clinical praxis (this is another common feature of ANPs that applies to both DNA viruses and retroviruses).

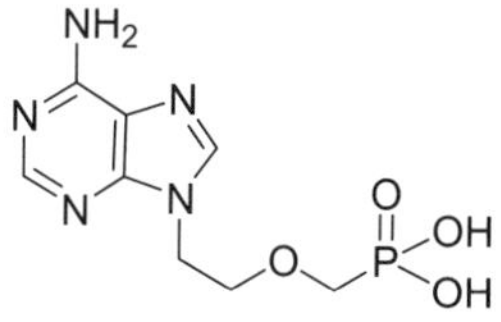

56, PMEA, Adefovir

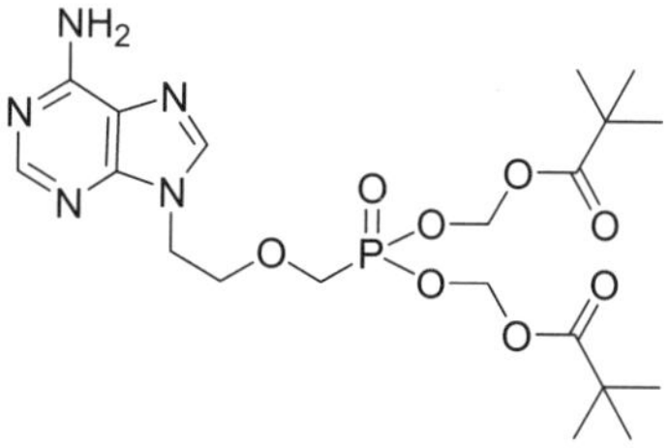

57, Adefovir dipivoxil

9-(*R*)-(2-Phosphonomethoxypropyl)adenine (Tenofovir, **58**). Contrary to PME- and HPMP derivatives the (*R*)-PMP compounds generally inhibit exclusively (DNA or RNA) viruses that utilize in their multiplication cycle the reverse transcription step [106]. The therapeutics' interest focuses mainly on AIDS and hepatitis B that are often present simultaneously as coinfection (due to similar ways of transmission). It has already been mentioned above that the drugs, which are active against HIV are often also able to

suppress HBV. This is exactly the situation with tenofovir (**58**) whose oral prodrug form tenofovir disoproxil fumarate (Viread®, **59**) is an important drug in AIDS therapy. Owing to its high efficacy and extraordinary low toxicity it has been granted approval to act as a drug against HBV as well as HIV infections [9,107].

Active drug liberation from the prodrugs **57** and **59** is very similar. In principle, it consists in the spontaneous decomposition of the ester linkages originally designed to stabilize

PMEA by acylation with pivalic acid (**57**) or (*R*)-PMPA by alkoxycarbonylation (**59**). In both cases, the stabilizing group is cleaved off by the action of an esterase. Formaldehyde, which is in both cases formed in a biequimolar amount, is rapidly oxidized by an oxidase/reductase. (Interestingly, the bad smell of pivalic acid in the original bottles had to be removed by active charcoal placed in the stopper.)

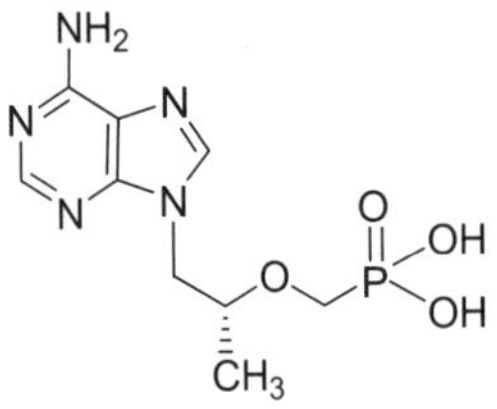

58, Tenofovir

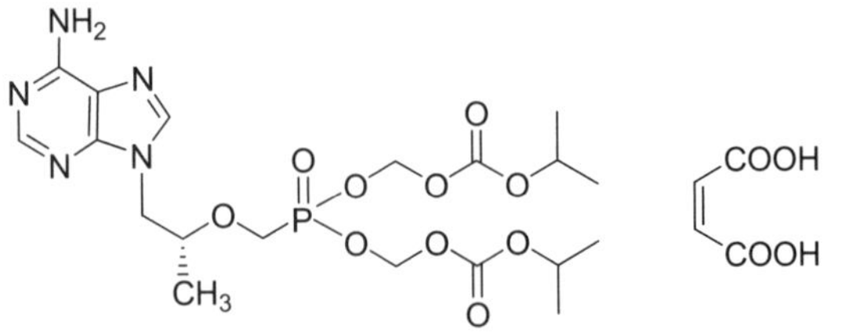

59, Tenofovir disoproxil fumarate

2.7.2. 2,6-Diaminopurine (DAP) Derivatives (60)   Both the PME, (*R*)-PMP- as well as the (*S*)-HPMP derivatives of DAP can be easily prepared by standard procedures. All the al-kylation reactions are regiospecific, forming exclusively the required N9-isomer. Although the activities are generally higher for the DAP derivatives than for the adenine deriva-tives [88,108], there is not any DAP compound being further pursued for antiviral drug development.

2.7.3. Guanine Derivatives   As already men-tioned, the guanine derivatives are usually not prepared by direct alkylation of guanine. On using the 2-amino-6-chloropurine instead, one can get usually homogeneous reaction solution with 0.5 equiv. of cesium carbonate or 1 equiv. of 1,8-diazabicyclo[5.4.0]undec-7-ene (DBU), or one equiv. of NaH. The required 9-isomer **61** is always formed as the main product (in the ratio 7 : 3). Its conversion to the guanine derivative **62** is performed by boiling in dilute aqueous hydrochloric acid or by treatment with DABCO followed by potas-sium carbonate in water [67].

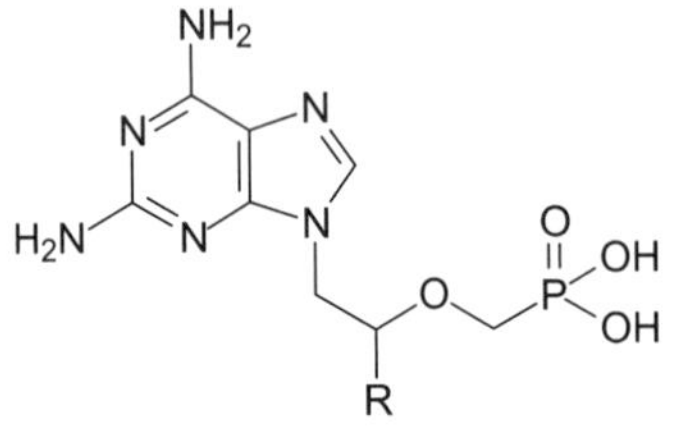

R = H, (*R*)-CH$_3$, (*S*)-CH$_2$OH

60, 2,6-Diaminopurine derivatives

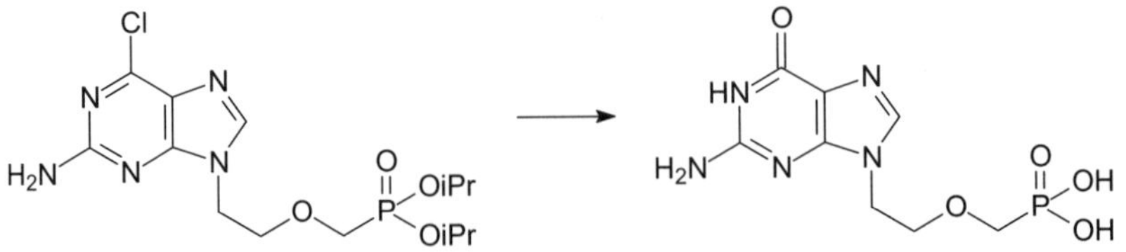

61

62, PMEG

2.7.4. 8-Azapurine Derivatives: Separation of Regioisomers [83] The mixture of isomeric diesters obtained by alkylation of 8-azapurine (8-azaadenine, 8-azaguanine, or 2,6-diamino-8-azapurine) in aqueous methanol (40%, 10 mmol) is applied on the column (100 ml) Dowex 50 × 8 in the H + form equilibrated in 40% aqueous methanol and eluted with the same solvent. The 9-isomer (**63**) elutes with consid-

erable retention. Aqueous ammonia (2.5%) in the same solvent mixture elutes the mixture of the 8-isomer with additional minor isomers (N7 and N3) of which the 8-isomer can be separated by silica gel column chromatography in chloroform with a gradient of ethanol in chloroform. The 8-isomer (**64**) is the main product; it has a characteristic blue fluorescence.

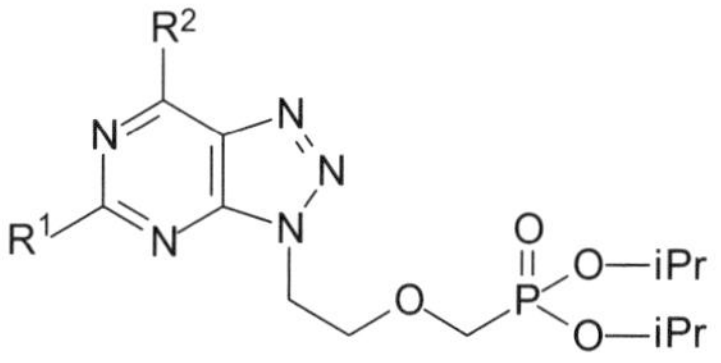

63

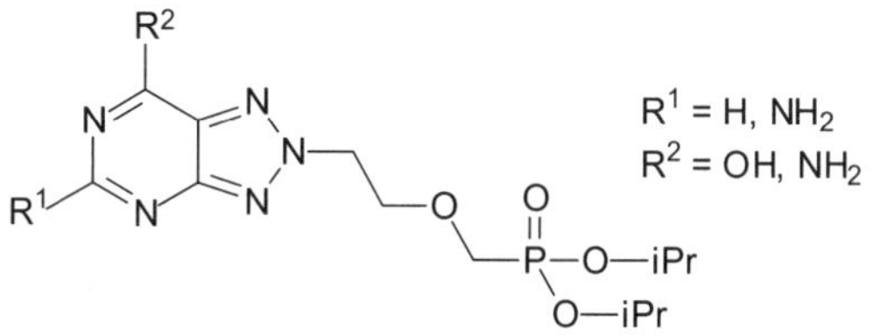

R^1 = H, NH_2
R^2 = OH, NH_2

64

2.7.5. Purine N6-Substituted Amino Derivatives [67] Another large and important group of ANP derivatives with an extraordinary high anti-DNA-viral activity, focused mainly on CMV and VZV, are the compounds derived from PME (and some PMP) derivatives containing 2-aminopurine bases bearing at the position N6, a mono- or disubstituted amino function. There is a special situation with the N6-cyclopropyl derivative (**65**) [109], which was shown to undergo deamination to give the guanine derivative PMEG (**62**) [110]. This rather unexpected behavior was encountered already with the antiviral drug *abacavir* [111]. The enzyme that catalyzes this conversion (*abacavir deaminase*) was found to be one of the salvage enzymes that is responsible for the utilization of the N6-methyladenine-containing oligonucleotides—the *N6-methylAMP/dAMP deaminase*. The study *in vitro* with the isolated enzyme and the selected compounds **65** unequivocally confirmed the relation between their antiviral activity and the enzymatic deamination. Thereby it is also explained why the analogous N6-substituted PMEA derivatives are inactive: the product of their transformation is the inactive hypoxanthine ANP derivative.

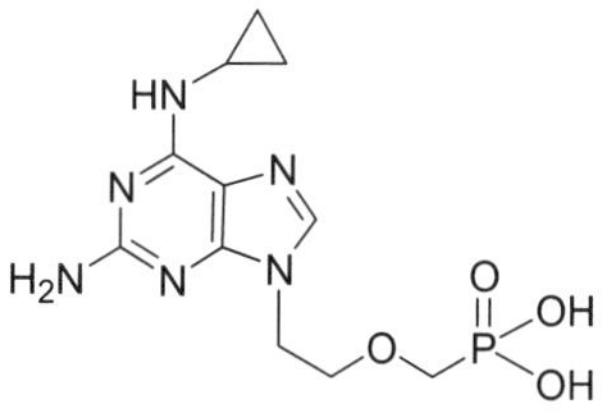

65

cPr PMEDAP

2.7.6. "Open-Ring" Purine Derivatives ("6-O-Substituted Pyrimidine" Derivatives) The 2,4-diamino- (**66**) and 2-amino-4-hydroxy-6-[2-(2-phosphonylmethoxy)ethoxy]-pyrimidines (**67**) often display an antiviral activity identical with (or very similar to) that of the corresponding purine (2,6-diaminopurine or guanine) [112]. This is obvious, if one consider these compounds to be analogs of guanine or 2,6-diaminopurine in which the imidazole ring has been opened and its N9-nitrogen atom replaced by oxygen with linked PME, (S)-HPMP-, (R)-PMP, or (S)-FPMP residues. Such compounds (abbreviated as DAPy series) are easily accessible from a commercially available 2,4-diamino-6-chloropyrimidine or 2-amino-4,6-dichloropyrimidine with the appropriate 2-hydroxyalkylphosphonate and NaH or by stepwise synthesis (reaction of the chloro derivatives with a glycol and the subsequent condensation of the 6-*O*-(2-hydroxyalkyl) intermediate with the active methylphosphonate synthon (see above). The 5-bro-

mo- and 5-methyl-PMEDAPy (**68a**, **68b**) are highly potent inhibitors of hepatitis B virus as well as of HIV and SIV *in vitro* [113].

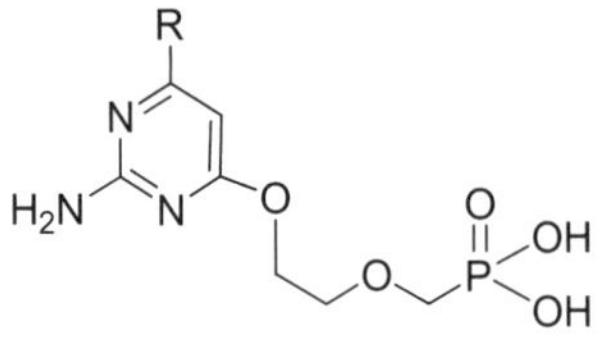

66, R = NH$_2$
67, R = OH

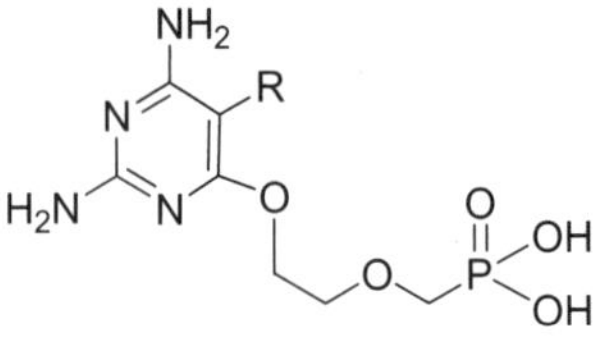

68a, R = Br
68b, R = CH$_3$

2.7.7. New Generation ANP Prodrugs The reasons for developing additional prodrugs of ANP are evident. The main concern is to improve the content of the drug in the target tissue compared to its content in the kidney.

Gosselin (Benzaria) et al. [114] introduced the SATE (*S*-acyl-2-thioethyl ester of the phosphonate) that, after removal of the *S*-acyl-2-thioethyl group, can be initiated by any nucleophilic attack, would generate the free phosphonate under spontaneous formation of the highly reactive thioxirane [114].

McGuigan et al. [115] systematically investigated the influence of the character of both the ester group as well as that of an amine in the phosphoramidate analogs derived from the phosphonate molecule. Phenol ester and L-alanine ester were suggested as the optimum combination for the phosphate masking groups [116]. This is indeed not very practical for application in the phosphonate field, where everything must start from the ANP with a free phosphonate group. Moreover, the esteramidates contain an asymmetric phosphorus atom that may cause difficulties in the evaluation of the drug. Although we have recently described an analytical method for separation of both the enantiomers and the P-stereoisomers by capillary electrophoresis [117], the technological procedure for obtaining a pure compound on a kilogram scale would be extremely difficult. Hence, it is more practical to use bis (amidates) where such problems cannot arise.

A notorious example is compound GS-9219, which is a bis(ethyl-L-alaninate) derivative (**69**). In this case, a special interest was due to the fact

that it accumulates in malignant lymphoid tissues such as non-Hodgkin's lymphomas (in Beagle dogs) where it liberates the free phosphonate, which is then converted to PMEG by the action of *N*6-methyl-2'-deoxyadenylate deaminase. PMEG that is formed at the site brings the transformed cells to apoptosis [118]. It remains to be seen, however, whether this prodrug will find any practical therapeutical use.

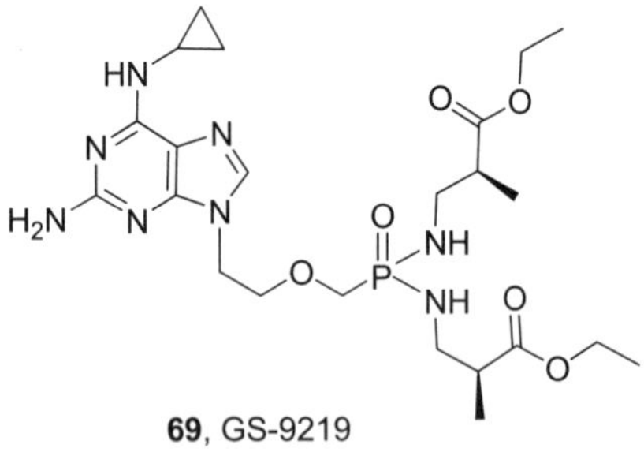

69, GS-9219

Hostetler et al. introduced an interesting alternative for substantial additional enhancement of the activity of the phosphonates by transforming them into monoesters with long aliphatic alcohols [119,120]. From these studies the following empirical rules can be obtained: (a) the optimum length of the ester is approximately C18–C21 atom units, (b) it is recommended to introduce an ether-bound oxygen atom to the beta or gamma position and (c) to achieve the expected enhancement effect, it is sufficient to introduce one such ester group only. There is a simple method on how to transform specifically a diester to monoester without further attacking the latter compound [121].

The data on nucleotide prodrugs, in particular those obtained with the ANPs would seemingly devaluate all the time vested into the investigation of the structure–antiviral activity relationship. However, it is only half of the truth: the prodrug concept might help to clarify some points of disagreement between the unexpected failures of some compounds.

2.7.8. Tissue-Targeted ANP Prodrugs

Among the recent trends of antiviral therapy there is an important issue of targeting the drug to the tissue where the virus has clearly established itself, or where it could cause the major damage. The obvious target is liver tissue. The

HepDirect technology [122,123] improves the therapeutic index by making use of the prodrugs that are activated by cytochrome P-450. The improvement is quite dramatic: there is a 15-fold increase of liver concentration of PMEA on application of remofovir mesylate (Hepavir B, MB06866Q) compared to adefovir dipivoxil [124]. The lead prodrug of this group is pradefovir mesylate (MB06866Q, **70**) that has proven its efficacy in volunteers [125]. The arylvinylketones that are formed from the cyclic prodrugs of the HepDirect type are rapidly absorbed at the site by the glutathione present in the hepatocytes.

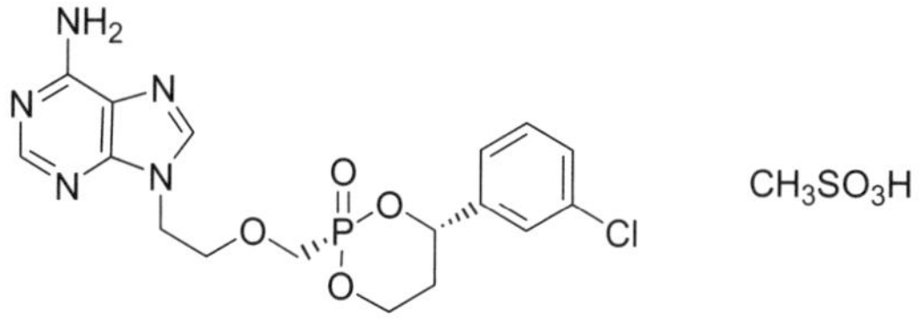

70, Pradefovir mesylate, MB06866Q

2.8. Nonnucleotide Inhibitors of Viral DNA-Polymerase

Most of these inhibitors are aimed at the HSV helicase–primase complex. The best known example is BAY 57-1923 (**71**) [126]: it is not only more active than the standard anti-HSV drugs based on acyclic guanosines; it is also effective in diverse animal models of disseminated herpes and human genital herpes [127]. However, spontaneous resistance of the HSV rapidly develops both against this compound as well as against two equally promising 2-aminothiazole derivatives BILS 22 BS (**72**) and BILS 179 BS (**73**) [128].

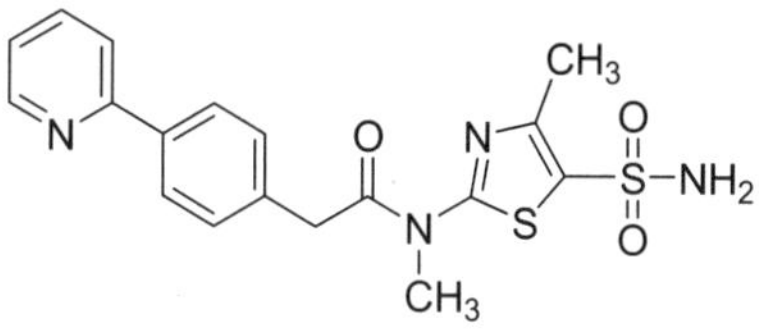

71, BAY-57-1293

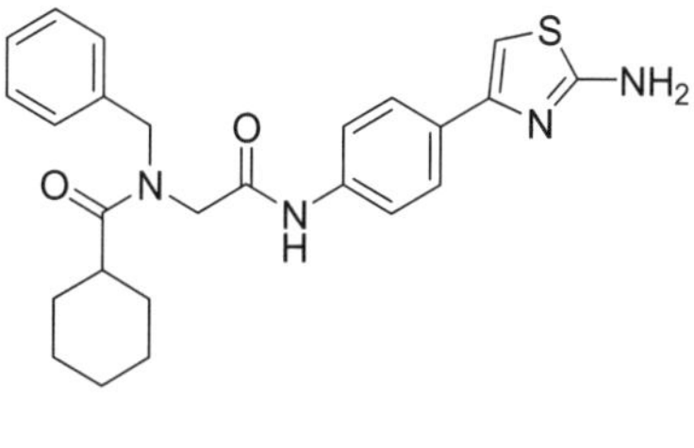

72, BILS 22 BS

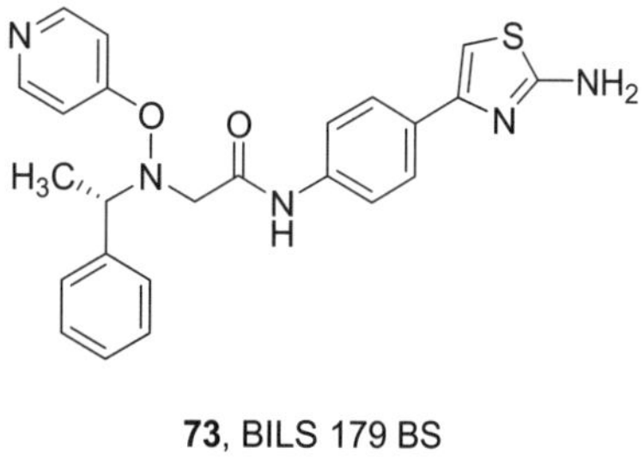

73, BILS 179 BS

Hopefully, suitable substituents in the bi-phenylsulfonacetic acid (74) might result in finding an inhibitor of general applicability against papillomavirus [129].

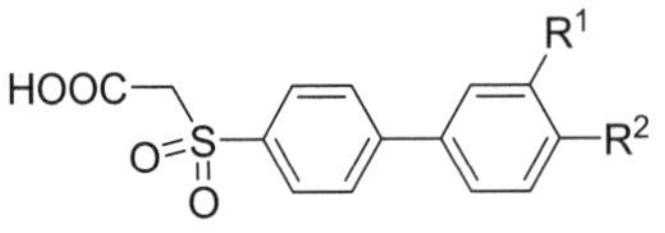

74, Biphenylsulfonacetic acid derivatives

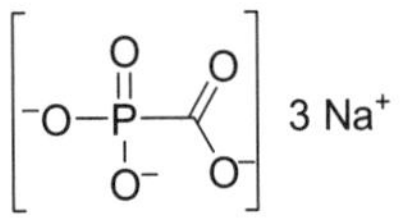

75, Foscarnet 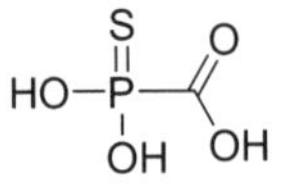   **76**, Thiovir 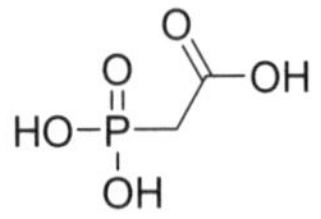   **77**, phosphonoacetic acid

2.9. Analogs of Inorganic Diphosphate

Any polymerization of nucleoside $5'$-tripho-sphate precursors of nucleic acids is bound to produce inorganic diphosphate ("pyrophos-phate"). It also happens during the synthesis of viral DNA. Obviously, pyrophosphate ana-logs might influence the polymerization pro-cess. Foscarnet (Foscavir®, **75**) [130] is a tri-sodium salt of phosphonoformic acid, PFA. Despite its side effects due to the disturbance in serum calcium and phosphate level (fatal cases of hypocalcemia), suppressing the differ-entiation of osteoblasts and a significant ne-phrotoxicity [131]. PFA has remained in clin-ical use, particularly in the therapy of HCMV infections. However, it should be kept in mind that PFA might interfere with all those nu-merous processes where a nucleoside $5'$-tri-phosphate is used as a source of activation energy. Thus, PFA affects the adenylyl cy-clases and guanylyl cyclases, and conse-quently it may exhibit far reaching distur-bances. Similarly as the nucleotide analogs, PFA has been also transformed into its lipid esters that were about $100\times$ more active than PFA [132]. Undoubtedly, this could be the correct way on how to lessen the risk of its clinical application.

Substantially improved parameters, in-cluding much better oral availability com-pared to PFA should have its phosphorothio-ate analog, Thiovir® (**76**) [133]. It exhibited in preclinical studies a potent antiviral activity against DNA viruses (HSV-1, HSV-2, CMV, VZV) and HIV. It could have synergistic action with *zidovudine*, not being accompanied by increased toxicity. On the contrary, it seems that the originally AZT-resistant HIV-mu-tants were re-sensitized by the drug action. Moreover, *thiovir* acts against multiple strains of influenza A and B, including the avian influenza H5N1 virus [134]. It remains to be seen whether it would also suffer from the unfortunate side reactions of its parent compound.

There is a certain mystery on the fate of the PFA homolog, the phosphonoacetic acid (PAA, **77**) [135]. This compound was inten-sively studied as an antiviral drug candidate in the 1970s of the past century and gave a positive response in the topical treatment of ocular herpes simplex both as eyedrops and as an ointment [136]. It was also active in the therapy of vaccinia virus-induced skin lesions in the rabbit model [137]. In contrast to other antivirals, it is not susceptible to metabolic transformations. Lipid prodrugs of phospho-noacetic acid have already been synthe-sized [138] and should deserve further attention.

Interference with kinases is a domain that should be further explored. The base-modified ribonucleoside maribavir (**78**) [139] sup-presses the activity of virus-associated protein kinase of both HCMV and HHV-6.

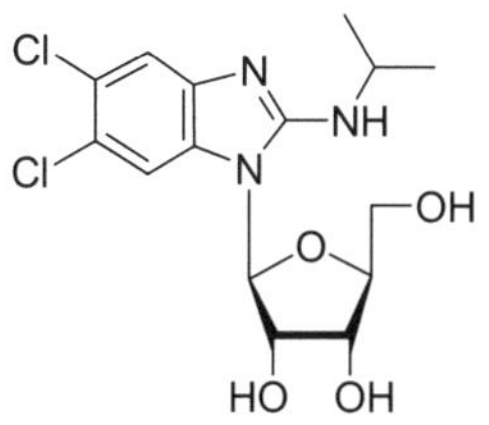

78, Maribavir (1263W94)

2.10. Posttranscriptional Methylation Inhibitors

Inhibition of methylation processes is usually discussed as a principle for rational drug de-

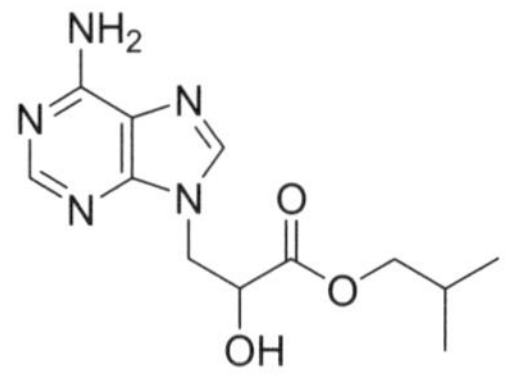

79, 3-(Adenin-9-yl)-2-hydroxypropanoic acid isobutyl ester

sign for RNA viruses. However, vaccinia virus is clearly inhibited by a SAH-hydrolase inhibitor, that is, 3-(adenin-9-yl)-2-hydroxypropanoic acid isobutyl ester (**79**) [140].

2.11. Virus Assembly Inhibitors

Virus assembly is the final intracellular process involved in virus multiplication. It can be specifically blocked by compound ST-246 (**80**) that has a pronounced effect on the replication of poxviruses [141].

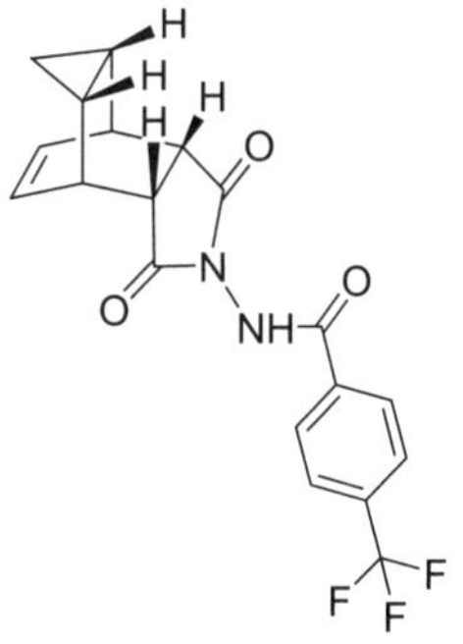

80, ST-246

3. THE VIRUSES

3.1. Polyomaviruses

The human polyomaviruses JC virus (JCV) and BK virus (BKV) can cause severe diseases, that is, progressive multifocal leukoencephalopathy (PML) and hemorrhagic cystitis, in immunosuppressed patients, that is, patients with AIDS. Currently, there is no approved specific antiviral treatment for JCV or BKV infections, although several anecdotal case reports have indicated that cidofovir [(S)-1-(3-hydroxy-2-phosphonylmethoxypropyl)cytosine, HPMPC] may be effective in the treatment of BKV- and JCV-associated infections in immunocompromised patients [13,142–145]. In addition to HPMPC (cidofovir) (**48**) and its cyclic analog cHPMPC (**49**), several newly synthesized acyclic nucleoside phosphonates, such as HPMP-5-azaC ((S)-1-(3-hydroxy-2-phosphonylmethoxypropyl)-5-azacytosine) (**50**), the cyclic derivative thereof

(cHPMP-5-azaC) (**51**) and the hexadecyloxyethyl ester of cHPMP-5-azacytosine (HDE-cHPMP-5-azaC) have recently been found to be selective inhibitors of different murine polyomavirus strains and the related simian virus 40 (SV40) [146]. Anti-BK virus activity has been reported for the alkoxyalkyl esters of (S)-9-(3-hydroxy-2-phosphonylmethoxypropyl)adenine (HPMPA) (**47**) [147].

3.2. Human Papillomavirus

Cidofovir (HPMPC) (**48**) has already been used for several years, albeit off-label, for the treatment of human papillomavirus (HPV)-associated diseases such as verruca vulgaris, plantar warts, hypopharyngeal, esophageal, laryngeal and respiratory papillomatosis, genital warts (condylomata acuminata), cervical intraepithelial neoplasia (CIN), vulvar intraepithelial neoplasia (VIN), penile intraepithelial neoplasia (PIN), and perianal intraepithelial neoplasia (PAIN) [13]. Especially in immunosuppressed patients, results obtained with cidofovir in the treatment of HPV-associated lesions have often been quite impressive [148].

In addition to HPMPC (cidofovir) (**48**), which has formally been approved only for the treatment of CMV retinitis in AIDS patients, 9-(2-phosphonylmethoxyethyl)-*N*6-cyclopropyl-2,6-diaminopurine (cPrPMEDAP) (**65**) offers considerable promise for the treatment of HPV-associated diseases [13]. This compound is converted intracellularly to 9-(2-phosphonylmethoxyethyl)guanine (PMEG) (**62**) by an *N*6-methyl-AMP aminohydrolase, which is also involved in the conversion of abacavir 5'-monophosphate to carbovir 5'-monophosphate [110]. Carbovir 5'-monophosphate and PMEG are then further phosphorylated intracellularly to carbovir 5'-triphosphate and PMEG diphosphate before interacting, in competition with dGTP, with viral DNA synthesis (in HIV-infected cells) or cellular DNA synthesis (in tumor cells), respectively.

A high capacity assay for detecting inhibitors of HPV DNA replication, targeted at the HPV E1 and E2 genes, has been described [149], and biphenylsulfonacetic acid derivatives have been found to inhibit HPV type 6 E1 helicase [129]. Possibly, biphenylsulfonacetic acid derivatives (**74**) could be optimized as antiviral agents against multiple HPV types as they target a single amino acid residue, Tyrosine 486, common to E1 helicase of several HPV types.

3.3. Herpes Simplex Virus (HSV)

Among the α-herpesviruses, HSV-1 and HSV-2 can cause both primary infections (HSV-1: gingivostomatitis, keratoconjunctivitis, encephalitis, and eczema herpeticum; HSV-2: genital herpes and neonatal herpes) and recurrent infections (HSV-1: herpes labialis, herpetic keratitis; HSV-2: genital herpes). For all manifestations of HSV-1 and HSV-2 infections, acyclovir (**33)** and its oral prodrug, valaciclovir (**38**), and the oral penciclovir prodrug famciclovir (**41**), have remained the indicated drugs. It should not be dismissed, however, that ganciclovir is more potent than acyclovir in its activity against both HSV-1

and HSV-2, both *in vitro* and *in vivo*, and this activity can be further enhanced if ganciclovir (**34**) is esterified with elaidic acid [69]. Other guanosine analogs that have been accredited with anti-HSV activity include cyclohexenylguanine (**17**) [35] and A-5021 (**37**) [150].

As the acyclic nucleoside analogs acyclovir (**33**) and penciclovir (**36**), and ganciclovir (**34**) for its anti-HSV activity, and the guanosine analogs at large require phosphorylation by the virus-encoded thymidine kinase to exert their antiviral activity, they do not inhibit TK-deficient HSV strains that can occasionally arise in the immunocompromised host. In this situation, HSV infections should be treated with foscarnet (**75**), a pyrophosphate analog, or the acyclic nucleoside phosphonate cidofovir, neither of which depend on the HSV TK for their antiviral action. The eventual target for the antiviral action of acyclovir, penciclovir, foscarnet, ganciclovir, and cidofovir is the HSV DNA polymerase.

An alternative and more recently recognized target is the viral helicase–primase complex associated with HSV-1 and HSV-2 DNA replication. The aminothiazolylphenyl derivatives BILS 179BS (**73**) (and BILS 22BS) (**72**) [128] and BAY 57-1293 (**71**) [126] were identified as potent HSV replication inhibitors based on their capacity to interfere with the viral helicase–primase complex. This complex comprises three viral proteins, the HSV UL5, UL8, and UL52 gene products, which together unwind the double-stranded viral DNA and generate primers for DNA synthesis by the viral DNA polymerase. In this heterotrimeric complex, UL5 is responsible for the helicase, whereas UL52 accounts for the primase activity. The first compound reported to interfere with the UL5-UL8-UL52 complex was the 2-aminothiazole derivative T157602 [151]. Later, BILS 179BS (and BILS 22BS) and BAY 57-1293 were discovered as therapeutically potential useful agents.

In particular, BAY 57-1293 has received much attention as a potentially therapeutic agent, as it was found to be superior to all compounds currently used (acyclovir, valaciclovir, and famciclovir) to treat HSV infections in several murine and rat models for disseminated herpes [127], a guinea pig model of human genital herpes [152], and a mouse model for HSV-1 infection [153]. Based on these findings, BAY 57-1293 can be considered as a highly promising antiviral compound for the treatment of HSV infections, including those HSV infections that are resistant to acyclovir (valaciclovir) or penciclovir (famciclovir) because of their thymidine kinase deficiency.

However, as first noted with BILS 22BS, drug-resistant viruses can be readily selected by serial passage or single-step plaque selection of HSV-1 in the presence of the aminothiazolylphenyl-based inhibitors [154], and the resulting amino acid changes reside in the N-terminus of the UL5 protein. Several spontaneous helicase/primase-drug-resistant variants have been detected, which were resistant to BAY 57-1293 and cross-resistant to BILS 22BS, and which did not revert to the sensitive phenotype in the absence of the inhibitor [155].

HSV-1 variants highly resistant to BAY 57-1293 have also been detected in clinical isolates of HSV-1, the most prominent resistant variant being based upon the mutation K356N in UL5 [156]. From plaque-purified strains, the K356Q and G352R mutations appeared as the most important helicase (UL5) mutations leading to resistance to BAY 57-1293; while leading to resistance to BAY 57-1293, they were associated with either increased (K356Q) or decreased (G352R) virus growth in cell culture [157].

3.4. Varicella-Zoster Virus

For the treatment of VZV infections, particularly herpes zoster (shingles, zona), four antiviral drugs have been licensed: acyclovir, its oral prodrug valaciclovir, the oral prodrug of penciclovir (famciclovir), and in many European countries brivudin (BVDU) (9) as well. As has been noted for most of the anti-HSV compounds, these anti-VZV compounds depend for their antiviral activity on a specific phosphorylation by the VZV-encoded thymidine kinase (TK), which converts acyclovir and penciclovir to their 5′-monophosphate and BVDU to its 5′-diphosphate, whereupon these compounds are further phosphorylated by cellular enzymes to their 5′-triphosphates. The latter then interfere with the viral DNA polymerization reaction [12].

Quite unexpectedly, a new class of highly specific VZV inhibitors, the so-called BCNAs (bicyclic furo[2,3-d]-pyrimidine nucleoside analogs) were discovered [26–28]. The prototype of the BCNAs [158] was found to inhibit VZV replication at subnanomolar concentrations, with a selectivity index (ratio of 50% cytotoxic concentration to 50% antivirally effective concentration) of more than 100,000 [159]. Cf 1743 (12) proved only active against VZV (and not HSV or any other virus) because of a highly specific recognition by the VZV-encoded thymidine kinase [29]. While recognition by the VZV-encoded TK is mandatory for the anti-VZV specificity of the BCNAs, their actual target of action (presumably the VZV DNA polymerase) still remains to be determined.

To improve oral bioavailability, as previously demonstrated for acyclovir and ganciclovir when esterified with valine, the 5′-valyl ester of Cf 1743, designated FV-100 (13), was constructed [28], and, based on its favorable antiviral and pharmacokinetic properties (i.e., uptake by the cells and oral bioavailability), FV-100 is now being pursued as a clinical candidate drug for the treatment of herpes zoster, and the first clinical studies point to its safety and favorable pharmacokinetics in healthy human subjects [160].

3.5. Human Cytomegalovirus (HCMV)

CMV infections are associated with severe morbidity and mortality in patients with immune system disabilities and, in particular, recipients of stem cell or solid organ recipients [161]. Since primary CMV infection in pregnancy can be transmitted at about 40% rate, causing severe fetal damage, there is an urgent need for safe and efficacious anti-CMV drugs in pregnant women and affected neonates. Three drugs have been approved for the systemic treatment of CMV infections: ganciclovir (and its oral prodrug valganciclovir, 39), foscarnet (75), and cidofovir (48). Furthermore, valaciclovir (38) has been approved for the prophylaxis of CMV infections in kidney transplant recipients [161].

Cyclic cidofovir (cHPMPC) (49) has been recently shown to prevent congenital CMV infection in a guinea pig model [162,163]; even when given as a single dose to the infected dams it raised pup survival from 28.2 to 83.7%. Oral prodrugs of HPMPA, that is, HDP-HPMPA and ODE-HPMPA are of great potential for the treatment of poxvirus infections (see below) as well as CMV infections [164]. Also, (Z)-methylenecyclopropane analogs of purine nucleosides, such as cyclopropavir, yield promise for the treatment of CMV infections [165,166].

Perhaps the most promising newly emerging anti-CMV agent is maribavir [1-(β-L-ribofuranosyl)-2-isopropylamino-5,6-dichloro-benzimidazole, 1263W94] (**78**). Maribavir has recently been shown to reduce the incidence of CMV infection (based on CMV pp65 antigenemia) in allogeneic stem cell transplant recipients (when given at a dosage of 200, 400, or 800 mg daily), and, unlike ganciclovir, it did not cause myelosuppression [167].

Maribavir is an inhibitor of UL97 kinase [139]. The UL97 kinase is an enzyme involved in the encapsidation and nuclear egress of CMV particles and the phosphorylation of virus replication-associated proteins, which means that maribavir has a mechanism of action distinct from the approved anti-CMV drugs (val)ganciclovir, foscarnet, and cidofovir that target the viral DNA polymerase. CMV UL97 kinase mutations have been shown to confer resistance to maribavir [168]. These are different from the UL97 mutations linked to ganciclovir resistance. Resistance mutations in the UL97 gene conferring resistance to maribavir may arise swiftly [169]. Their clinical relevance still needs to be determined.

3.6. Human Herpesvirus Type 6

For the treatment of human herpesvirus type 6 (HHV-6) infections no antiviral agents have been formally approved, although several compounds have been reported to inhibit HHV-6 replication, that is nucleoside analogs, such as S2242 [2-amino-7-[(1,3-dihydroxy-2-propoxy) methyl]purine], A-5021 [(1'S,2'R)-9-[[1',2'-bis (hydroxymethyl)cycloprop-1'-yl]methyl]guanine] (**37**), and cyclopropavir; nucleotide analogs (acyclic nucleoside phosphonates, such as cidofovir and its oral prodrugs hexadecyloxy-propyl-cidofovir (HDP-CDV) and octadecyloxy-ethyl-cidofovir (ODE-CDV), 2,4-diamino-6-

(R)-[3-hydroxy-2-(phosphonomethoxy)pro-poxy]-pyrimidine (HPMPO-DAPy), and (S)-9-[3-hydroxy-2-(phosphonomethoxy)propyl]-3-deazaadenine (3-deaza-HPMPA); and a number of nonnucleoside analogs, the most promising being CMV423, a protein tyrosine kinase inhibitor [170,171]. Also the anti-CMV agent maribavir (see above) has been recently reported to inhibit the replication of HHV-6 as well; it is targeted at the U69 protein kinase, which is homologous to the UL97 kinase in CMV [172].

HHV-6 as well as HHV-7 may be involved in the pathogenesis of chronic fatigue syndrome [173]. Valganciclovir (**39**), the drug of choice in the treatment of CMV infection (see above) may be potentially useful in the treatment of chronic fatigue syndrome in a subset of Epstein–Barr virus (EBV)-infected patients [174,175].

3.7. Epstein–Barr Virus

Epstein–Barr virus, which is responsible for infectious mononucleosis, Burkitt's lymphoma, and nasopharyngeal carcinoma and frequently involved in severe lymphoproliferative diseases in immunocompromised patients, has received little, if any, attention from an antiviral drug development viewpoint [12]. Some fluorinated methylenecyclopropane analogs of nucleosides, derivatives of cyclopropavir, have been accredited with rather potent *in vitro* activity against EBV [176,177]. These observations need to be followed up.

3.8. Poxviruses

Among the poxvirus infections (orthopox: variola, vaccinia, cowpox, monkeypox, ectromelia, camelpox; parapox: orf; molluscipox: molluscum contagiosum), smallpox, caused by variola virus, is the most feared bioterrorist threat: it is highly transmissible by the aerosol route from infected to susceptible (unvaccinated) persons; it is associated with high morbidity (90%), high mortality (30%); the initial diagnosis of a disease that has not been seen for 30 years is difficult, and, at present, other than the vaccinia-based vaccine, which should not be administered to immunocompromised individuals and that might be effective only if given before or in the first few days postinfection, there is no formally approved drug for the treatment of smallpox [12].

Off label, cidofovir has remained the drug of choice for the therapy and short-term prophylaxis of poxvirus infections (i.e., monkeypox) as well as for the treatment of complications of vaccinia that can arise in immunosuppressed patients inadvertently inoculated with the smallpox vaccine (vaccinia) [178]. In a murine model (athymic nude mice inoculated intracutaneously with vaccinia virus) that mimics progressive disseminated vaccinia in humans, systemic treatment with cidofovir caused the lesions to heal and regress [179]. Cidofovir has proved highly efficacious in the topical treatment of orf (contagious ecthyma) [178,180] and molluscum contagiosum [178,181], although in a recent review article on the various treatments for molluscum contagiosum, cidofovir was not mentioned [182].

Cidofovir (HPMPC) (48) and its predecessor HPMPA [(S)-9-[3-hydroxy-(2-phosphonomethoxypropyl)adenine] (47) are highly effective inhibitors of the vaccinia virus DNA polymerase: both compounds can be converted intracellularly to their diphosphates (HPMPCpp and HPMPApp, respectively), and it has been recently demonstrated that both compounds can be faithfully incorporated into the template strand, thereby inhibiting *trans*-lesion DNA synthesis [183]. In addition to HPMPC and HPMPA, various other acyclic nucleoside phosphonates such as HPMPO-DAPy and HPMP-5-azaC have been found to inhibit the replication of poxviruses, including camelpox virus [184] and orf [185]. Since the acyclic nucleoside phosphonates (HPMPA, HPMPC, etc.) are not readily bioavailable by the oral route, alkoxyalkyl (i.e., hexadecyloxypropyl (HDP) and octadecyloxyethyl (HDE)) esters of HPMPA or HPMPC [186], as well as oleyloxyethyl-HPMPA [187], 1-O-octadecyl-2-O-benzyl-sn-glycero-3-cidofovir [188] and alkoxyalkylphosphate conjugates of cidofovir and adefovir [189] have been prepared, and, as a rule, these alkoxyalkyl esters of HPMPC and/or HPMPC proved highly effective in the oral treatment of orthopoxvirus (i.e., cowpox, vaccinia, ectromelia) infections in mice [186,188].

Recently, a specific poxvirus inhibitor, ST-246 [4-trifluoromethyl-*N*-(3,3a,4,4a,5,5a,6,6a-octahydro-1,3-dioxo-4,6-ethenocycloprop(*f*)isoindol-2(1*H*)-yl)-benzamide] (80) [141] has been described to specifically target the F13L phospholipase involved in the p37-mediated extracellular virus particle production [190]. ST-246 has proven effective against vaccinia, cowpox, and camelpox viruses in human embryonic lung (HEL) and human keratinocyte (PHK) cell monolayers, as well as three-dimensional organotypic raft cultures [184]. The efficacy of ST-246 has been demonstrated in the oral treatment of monkeypox virus infection in squirrels [191] and the oral treatment of ectromelia virus infection in mice even if treatment was delayed up to 72 h after viral inoculation [192]. An anecdotal case report suggests that ST-246 may have prompted healing of eczema vaccinatum in a 2-year-old boy after he contacted vaccinia from his father [193]. ST-246 does not compromise protective immunity elicited by the smallpox vaccine [194], which implies it may be useful in preventing or treating the adverse events due to vaccination. Moreover, synergistic efficacy has been noted for the combination of ST-246 with hexadecyloxypropyl-cidofovir (CMX001) in mice infected with cowpox virus [195], which opens interesting perspectives for this drug combination in the treatment of orthopoxvirus infections. ST-246 has already been the subject of a phase I clinical study to assess its safety, tolerability, and pharmacokinetics in healthy human volunteers [196].

A conformationally locked (*North*) *N*-methanocarbathymidine (*N*-MCT) (18) has proven efficacious in the treatment of mice infected intranasally with vaccinia virus [197]. *N*-MCT also demonstrated potent activity against herpes simplex viruses (HSV-1 and HSV-2) and the Kaposi's sarcoma-associated herpesvirus (KSHV) [198]. The target of action of *N*-MCT is likely to be the viral DNA polymerase (after the compound has been converted to its 5′-triphosphate). The search for novel antipoxvirus agents has also led to the identification of an anticancer drug, mitoxantrone, as an inhibitor of vaccinia virus replication blocking the assembly of mature progeny virions [199].

3.9. Hepadnaviruses (Hepatitis B Virus (HBV))

Worldwide about 400 million people are chronically infected with the hepadnavirus hepatitis B virus (HBV) and complications of chronic HBV infection such as cirrhosis, hepatocellular carcinoma, and end-stage liver disease account for 1 million deaths each year. Approved therapies for chronic hepatitis B include standard and pegylated interferon-α, lamivudine (**32**), adefovir dipivoxil (**57**), entecavir (**19**), and telbivudine (**20**), but these therapies do not eradicate HBV so that (life) long-term treatment with nucleoside/nucleotide analogs is usually required [39]. This, in turn, engenders the risk for the emergence of virus-drug resistance toward these nucleoside or nucleotide analogs [200]. Resistance to lamivudine emerges in up to 66% of the patients after 4 years, but the signature mutation of lamivudine resistance, rT M204 I/V may disappear again with the concomitant or subsequent treatment with adefovir dipivoxil (**57**) [201].

Adefovir dipivoxil treatment may result in an improvement in the number and functionality of myeloid dendritic, but not plasmacytoid dendritic cells, thereby explaining why current antiviral therapy does not lead to a consistently sustained viral eradication [202]. Long-term clinical data from trials up to 5 years duration of adefovir dipivoxil treatment pointed to a sustained efficacy and safety in the majority of the patients [203], with the emergence of adefovir-associated mutations (rTA 181V and rT N236T) in 0, 3, 11, 18, and 29% of the patients after 48, 96, 144, 192, and 240 weeks of therapy, respectively [204]. Thus, adefovir has been quoted as the therapy with the best long-term resistance profile following 5-year duration [205], the best 2-year resistance profile hitherto being attributed to entecavir monotherapy [205].

However, 10% of the patients previously treated with lamivudine-developed resistance to entecavir after 2 years of therapy [206]. More specifically, only 1% of the patients experienced rebounds of entecavir-resistant strains in year 1 with an additional 9% experiencing entecavir resistance rebounds in year 2 [207]. Entecavir treatment of patients with lamivudine-resistant HBV mutants led to >30% resistance after 3 years and >50% after 5 years, while the cumulative probability of developing genotypic resistance to entecavir in nucleoside-naïve chronic hepatitis B patients was only 1.2% after 5 years of entecavir treatment [208,209].

Surprisingly [210], entecavir led to the emergence of HIV-1 variants with the lamivudine-resistant mutation M184V in patients with HIV-1 and HBV coinfection [211]. This argues against the use of entecavir in persons with HIV-1 and HBV coinfection who are not receiving fully suppressive anti-HIV drug regimens.

The position of telbivudine (**20**) as a new option for the treatment of chronic hepatitis B [212] still has to be validated. Meanwhile, peginterferon α-2b has gained wider acceptance in the treatment of chronic hepatitis B patients with advanced fibrosis or cirrhosis [213]. Sequential pegylated interferon α-2a with tenofovir has been advocated for HBV infection in patients coinfected with HIV [214].

Why do we not have combination chemotherapy for chronic hepatitis B [215]? There is now an emerging body of data suggesting that combination therapy can decrease antiviral resistance in HBV infection, and, rather than adding or replacing an antiviral agent after resistance develops, it is likely to be more effective in treatment-naïve patients [215]. Further pointing to the potential of combination therapy is that in patients with chronic hepatitis B peginterferon α-2b plus adefovir dipivoxil led to a marked decrease in serum HBV DNA, accompanied by a strong decline of intrahepatic covalently closed circular DNA (cccDNA), the hallmark of persistent HBV infection [216].

Which are the newly emerging anti-HBV drugs that in the future may be used for the therapy of HBV infections? In clinical development is clevudine [1-(2-deoxy-2-fluoro-β-L-arabinofuranosyl)thymine, L-FMAU] (**21**), which was previously found in woodchucks infected with woodchuck hepatitis virus (WHV) to lead to a prompt and profound suppression of WHV that was sustained for more than 12 weeks after cessation of dosing [217]. Clevudine showed potent and durable antiviral activity in HBeAg-positive chronic hepatitis B, which lasted for 6 months after a 12-week treatment period [218]. No evidence of virus-drug resistance was noted during the treatment period if extended to 24 weeks [219]. The sustained viral suppression achieved by clevudine appeared to be associated with, and may be attributed to, a significant reduction of covalently closed circular DNA (cccDNA) in hepatocytes [220,221].

In preclinical development are $(-)$-β-D-2-aminopurine dioxolane (APD) (**27**) (which, like the closely related $(-)$-β-D-2,6-diaminopurine dioxolane (DAPD) (**28**), is converted to 9-(β-D-1,3-dioxolan-4-yl)guanine (DXG)) [222], the hexadecyloxypropyl esters of 5-phosphono-pent-2-en-1-yl nucleosides [223] and 2,4-diamino-6-[2-(phosphonomethoxy)ethoxy]pyrimidine (PMEO-DAPy) [224]. Also a prodrug of adefovir, pradefovir mesylate (MB06866Q) (**70**), has been reported to specifically target adefovir to the liver for the treatment of hepatitis B, with pradefovir exhibiting a 12-fold improvement in the liver/kidney ratio over adefovir dipivoxil (**57**) [225].

Yet, the most imminent new drug for the treatment of chronic HBV infection is tenofovir disoproxil fumarate (TDF) (**62**), which, in the mean time has become well established for the treatment of HIV infection, particularly in combination with emtricitabine and efavirenz, and which, at the dosage used (300 mg per day), has proven to be more effective in suppressing HBV replication than adefovir dipivoxil (at 10 mg per day). Tenofovir disoproxil fumarate has in the mean time been formally approved in the EU, New Zealand, Turkey, and the United States, and is expected to be formally approved very soon, in Canada and Australia, for the treatment of chronic hepatitis B.

ACKNOWLEDGMENTS

We thank Mrs Christiane Callebaut for her never failing editorial dedication, Dr Dana Hockova for drawing the formulae, and Dr Petra Brehova for help with the references.

REFERENCES

1. Middleton T, Rockway T. Antiviral agents, DNA. In: Abraham DJ, editor. Burger's Medicinal Chemistry and Drug Discovery. 6th ed., Vol. 5. John Wiley & Sons, Inc.; 2003. Chapter 9.

2. De Clercq E. Looking back in 2009 at the dawning of antiviral therapy now 50 years ago: an historical perspective. Adv Virus Res 2009;73:1–53.

3. Elion GB, Furman PA, Fyfe JA, de Miranda P, Beauchamp L, Schaeffer HJ. Selectivity of action of an antiherpetic agent, 9-(2-hydroxyethoxymethyl) guanine. Proc Natl Acad Sci USA 1977;74:5716–5720.

4. Schaeffer HJ, Beauchamp L, de Miranda P, Elion GB, Bauer DJ, Collins P. 9-(2-hydroxyethoxymethyl) guanine activity against viruses of the herpes group. Nature 1978;272:583–585.

5. De Clercq E. The design of drugs for HIV and HCV. Nat Rev Drug Discov 2007;6:1001–1018.

6. Flexner C. HIV drug development: the next 25 years. Nat Rev Drug Discov 2007;6:959–966.

7. Borden EC, Sen GC, Uze G, Silverman RH, Ransohoff RM, Foster GR, Stark GR. Interferons at age 50: past, current and future impact on biomedicine. Nat Rev Drug Discov 2007;6:975–990.

8. Manns MP, Foster GR, Rockstroh JK, Zeuzem S, Zoulim F, Houghton M. The way forward in HCV treatment—finding the right path. Nat Rev Drug Discov 2007;6:991–1000.

9. Férir G, Kaptein S, Neyts J, De Clercq E. Antiviral treatment of chronic hepatitis B virus infections: the past, the present and the future. Rev Med Virol 2008;18:19–34.

10. De Clercq E. Antiviral agents active against influenza A viruses. Nat Rev Drug Discov 2006;5:1015–1025.

11. von Itzstein M. The war against influenza: discovery and development of sialidase inhibitors. Nat Rev Drug Discov 2007;6:967–974.

12. De Clercq E. Antivirals and antiviral strategies. Nat Rev Microbiol 2004;2:704–720.

13. De Clercq E. Clinical potential of the acyclic nucleoside phosphonates cidofovir, adefovir, and tenofovir in treatment of DNA virus and retrovirus infections. Clin Microbiol Rev 2003;16:569–596.

14. Kulikowski T. Structure–activity relationship and conformational features of antiherpetic

pyrimidine and purine nucleoside analogues. A review Pharm World Sci 1994;16:127–138.

15. Prusoff WH. Synthesis and biological activities of iododeoxyuridine, an analog of thymine. Biochim Biophys Acta 1959;32:295–296.

16. Carmine AA, Brogden RN, Heel RC, Speight TM, Avery GS. Trifluridine—a review of its antiviral activity and therapeutic use in the topical treatment of viral eye infections. Drugs 1982;23:329–353.

17. Superti F, Ammendolia MG, Marchetti M. New advances in Anti-HSV chemotherapy. Curr Med Chem 2008;15:900–911.

18. Whitley RJ, Nahmias AJ, Soong SJ, Galasso GG, Fleming CL, Alford CA, Connor J, Bryson Y, Linnemann C. Vidarabine therapy of neonatal herpes simplex virus infection. Pediatrics 1980;66:495–501.

19. Pavan-Langston D. Ocular viral infections: herpes simplex virus, Epstein–Barr virus, adenovirus, and poxviruses. In: Galasso GJ, Whitley RJ, Merigan TC, editors. Antiviral Agents and Human Viral Diseases. 4th ed. Raven: Lippincott; 1997. p 202.

20. Carreras CW, Santi DV. The catalytic mechanism and structure of thymidylate synthase. Annu Rev Biochem 1995;64:721–762.

21. Bradshaw TK, Hutchinson DW. 5-Substituted pyrimidine nucleosides and nucleotides. Chem. Soc. Rev. 1977;6:43–62.

22. Votruba I, Holý A, Pischel H. Inhibition of DNA synthesis in *Escherichia coli* by 1-(β-D-ribofuranosyl)-2-pyrimidinone. Collect Czech Chem Commun 1972;37:2213–2220.

23. De Clercq E. (*E*)-5-(2-Bromovinyl)-2'-deoxyuridine (BVDU). Med Res Rev 2004;25:1–20.

24. Whitley RJ. Sorivudine: a potent inhibitor of varicella zoster virus replication. Antiviral chemotherapy 4. Adv Exp Med Biol 1996;394:41–44.

25. Okuda H, Nishiyama T, Ogura Y, Nagayama S, Ikeda K, Yamaguchi S, Nakamura Y, Kawaguchi K, Watanabe T. Lethal drug interactions of sorivudine, a new antiviral drug, with oral 5-fluorouracil prodrugs. Drug Metabol Disp 1997;25:270–273.

26. Mc Guigan C, Yarnold CJ, Jones G, Velazquez S, Barucki H, Brancale A, Andrei G, Snoeck R, De Clercq E, Balzarini J. Potent and selective inhibition of varicella-zoster virus (VZV) by nucleoside analogues with an unusual bicyclic base. J Med Chem 1999;42:4473–4732.

27. McGuigan C, Barucki H, Carangio A, Blewett S, Andrei G, Snoeck R, De Clercq E, Balzarini

J, Erichsen JT. Highly potent and selective inhibition of varicella-zoster virus by bicyclic furopyrimidine nucleosides bearing an aryl side chain. J Med Chem 2000;43:4993–4997.

28. McGuigan C, Pathirana RN, Migliore M, Adak R, Luoni G, Jones AT, Diez-Torrubia A, Camarasa MJ, Velázquez S, Henson G, Verbeken E, Sienaert R, Naesens L, Snoeck R, Andrei G, Balzarini J. Preclinical development of bicyclic nucleoside analogues as potent and selective inhibitors of varicella zoster virus. J Antimicrob Chemother 2007;60:1316–1330.

29. Sienaert R, Naesens L, Brancale A, De Clercq E, McGuigan C, Balzarini J. Specific recognition of the bicyclic pyrimidine nucleoside analogs, a new class of highly potent and selective inhibitors of varicella-zoster virus (VZV), by the VZV-encoded thymidine kinase. Mol Pharmacol 2002;61:249–254.

30. Cheng YC, Goz B, Neenan JP, Ward DC, Prusoff WH. Selective-inhibition of herpes-simplex virus by 5'-amino-2',5'-dideoxy-5-iodouridine. J Virol 1975;15:1284–1285.

31. Faulds D, Brogden RN. Didanosine—a review of its antiviral activity, pharmacokinetic properties and therapeutic potential in human-immunodeficiency-virus infection. Drugs 1992;44:94–116.

32. Lea AP, Faulds D. Stavudine—a review of its pharmacodynamic and pharmacokinetic properties and clinical potential in HIV infection. Drugs 1996;51:846–864.

33. Langtry HD, Campolirichards DM. Zidovudine—a review of its pharmacodynamic and pharmacokinetic properties, and therapeutic efficacy. Drugs 1989;37:408–450.

34. Borchardt RT, Keller BT, Patelthombre U. Neplanocin-A—a potent inhibitor of *S*-adenosylhomocysteine hydrolase and of vaccinia virus multiplication in mouse L929 cells. J Biol Chem 1984;259:4353–4358.

35. Wang J, Froeyen M, Hendrix C, Andrei G, Snoeck R De Clercq E. Herdewijn P. The cyclohexene ring system as a furanose mimic: synthesis and antiviral activity of both enantiomers of cyclohexenylguanine. J Med Chem 2000;43:736–745.

36. Prichard MN, Keith KA, Quenelle DC, Kern ER. Activity and mechanism of action of *N*-methenocarbathymidine against herpesvirus and orthopoxvirus infections. Antimicrob Agents Chemother 2006;50:1336–1341.

37. Zalah L, Huleihel M, Manor E, Konson A, Ford H, Marquez VE, Johns DG, Agbaria R. Metabolic pathways of *N*-methanocarbathymidine,

a novel antiviral agent, in native and herpes simplex virus type 1 infected Vero cells. Antiviral Res 2002;55:63–75.

38. Palumbo E. Entecavir for chronic hepatitis B: a review. Ther Drug Monitor 2008;30:1–4.

39. Osborn MK, Lok ASF. Antiviral options for the treatment of chronic hepatitis B. J Antimicrob Chemother 2006;57:1030–1034.

40. Jurovcik M, Holý A. Metabolism of pyrimidine L-nucleosides. Nucleic Acids Res 1976;3:2143–2154.

41. Jurovcik M, Holý A, Sorm F. The utilization of L-adenosine by mammalian tissues. FEBS Lett 1971;18:274–276.

42. Votruba I, Holý A, Sorm F. L-Ribonucleosides do not penetrate bacterial cell walls. FEBS Lett 1971;19:136–138.

43. Nassal M. Hepatitis B viruses: reverse transcription a different way. Virus Res 2008;134: 235–249.

44. Schildgen O, van Bommel F, Rockstroh JK. Current and future therapies for chronic HBV-infections. Rev Med Microbiol 2007;18:79–88.

45. Lui YYN, Chan HLY. A review of telbivudine for the management of chronic hepatitis B virus infection. Exp Opin Drug Metab Toxicol 2008;4:1351–1361.

46. Sharon A, Chu CK, Clevudine. (L-FMAU): a unique antiviral agent for the treatment of chronic hepatitis B virus infection. Collection Symp Series, Academy of Sciences of the Czech Republic, Prague, Czech Republic 2008;10:239–243.

47. Cui LX, Yoon SY, Schinazi RF, Sommadossi JP. Cellular and molecule events leading to mitochondrial toxicity of 1-(2-deoxy-2-fluoro-1-beta-D-arabinofuranosyl)-5-iodouracil in human liver-cells. J Clin Invest 1995;95:555–563.

48. Mckenzie R, Fried MW, Sallie R, Conjeevaram H, Dibisceglie AM, Park Y, Savarese B, Kleiner D, Tsokos M, Luciano C, Pruett T, Stotka JL, Straus SE, Hoofnagle JH. Hepatitic-failure and lactic-acidosis due to fialuridine (FIAU), an investigational nucleoside analog for chronic hepatitis-B. N Engl J Med 1995;333:1099–1105.

49. McIntyre JA, Castaner J. Dexelvucitabine—anti-HIV agent—reverse transcriptase inhibitor. Drugs Future 2005;30:1205–1211.

50. Dunkle LM, Gathe JC, Pedevillano DE, Robison HG, Rice WG, Pottage JC. Elvucitabine: potent antiviral activity demonstrated in multidrug-resistant HIV infection. Antiviral Ther 2003;8:U21.

51. Ghosn J, Quinson AM, Sabo ND, Cotte L, Piketty C, Dorleacq N, Bravo ML, Mayers D, Harmenberg J, Mardh G, Valdez H, Katlama C. Antiviral activity of low-dose alovudine in antiretroviral-experienced patients: results from a 4-week randomized, double-blind, placebo-controlled dose-ranging trial. HIV Med 2007;8:142–147.

52. Nair V, Nuesca ZM. Isodideoxynucleosides—a conceptually new class of nucleoside antiviral agents. J Am Chem Soc 1992;114:7951–7953.

53. Bolon PJ, Jahnke TS, Nair V. Homologues of anti-HIV active isodideoxynucleosides. Tetrahedron 1995;51:10443.

54. Bolon PJ, Sells TB, Nuesca ZM, Purdy DF, Nair V. Novel isomeric dideoxynucleosides as potential antiviral agents. Tetrahedron 1994;50:7747.

55. Nair V, St Clair MH, Reardon JE, Krasny HC, Hazen RJ, Paff MT, Boone LR, Tisdale M, Najera I, Dornsife RE. Antiviral, metabolic, and pharmacokinetic properties of the isomeric dideoxynucleoside 4(S)-(6-amino-9H-purin-9-yl)tetrahydro-2(S)-furanmethanol. Antimicrob Agents Chemother 1995;39: 1993–1999.

56. Guenther S, Balzarini J, De Clercq E, Nair V. A thymidine phosphorylase-stable analogue of BVDU with significant antiviral activity. J Med Chem 2002;45:5426–5429.

57. Kim HO, Schinazi RF, Nampalli S, Shanmuganathan K, Cannon DL, Alves AJ, Jeong LS, Beach JW, Chu CK. 1,3-Dioxolanylpurine nucleosides (2R,4R) and (2R,4S) with selective anti-HIV-1 activity in human-lymphocytes. J Med Chem 1993;36:30–307.

58. Thompson MA, Kessler HA, Eron JJ, Jacobson JM, Adda N, Sheng G, Zhong J, Harris J, Moxham C, Rousseau FS. Short-term safety and pharmacodynamics of amdoxovir in HIV-infected patients. AIDS 2005;19:1607–1615.

59. Revill P, Serrandell N, Apricitabine. Anti-HIV agent, nucleoside reverse transcriptase inhibitor. Drugs Future 2006;31:1035–1041.

60. Otto MJ. New nucleoside reverse transcriptase inhibitors for the treatment of HIV infections. Curr Opin Pharmacol 2004;4:431–436.

61. Frampton JE, Perry CM. Emtricitabine—a review of its use in the management of HIV infection. Drugs 2005;65:1427–1448.

62. De Clercq E. From adefovir to Atripla™ via tenofovir, Viread™ and Truvada™. Future Virol 2006;1:709–715.

63. Feng JY, Ly JK, Myrick F, Goodman D, White KL, Svarovskaia ES, Borroto-Esoda K, Miller MD. The triple combination of tenofovir,

emtricitabine and efavirenz shows synergistic anti-HIV-1 activity *in vitro*: a mechanism of action study. Retrovirol 2009;6:44.

64. Jarvis B, Faulds D. Lamivudine—a review of its therapeutic potential in chronic hepatitis B. Drugs 1999;58:101–141.

65. Degertekin B, Lok ASF. Update on viral hepatitis: 2008. Curr Opin Gastroenterol 2009;25: 180–185.

66. De Clercq E. Biochemical aspects of the selective antiherpes activity of nucleoside analogues. Biochem Pharmacol 1984;33:2159–2169.

67. Holý A, Votruba I, Tloustová E, Masojídková M. Synthesis and cytostatic activity of *N*-[2-(phosphonomethoxy)alkyl] derivatives of N6-substituted adenines 2,6-diaminopurines and related compounds. Collect Czech Chem Commun 2001;66:1545–1592.

68. Zimmermann A, Michel D, Pavić I, Hampl W, Lüske A, Neyts J, De Clercq E, Mertens T. Phosphorylation of acyclovir, ganciclovir, penciclovir and S2242 by the cytomegalovirus UL97 prote: a quantitative analysis using recombinant vaccinia viruses Antiviral Res 1997;36:35–42

69. Andrei G, Snoeck R, Neyts J, Sandvold ML, Myhren F, De Clercq E. Antiviral activity of ganciclovir elaidic acid ester against herpesviruses. Antiviral Res 2000;45:157–167.

70. Boyd MR, Bacon TH, Sutton D, Cole M. Anti-herpesvirus activity of 9-(4-hydroxy-3-hydroxymethylbut-1-yl)guanine (BRL 39123) in cell culture. Antimicrob Agents Chemother 1987;31:1238–1242.

71. Sekiyma T, Hatsuya S, Tanaka Y, Uchiyama M, Ono N, Iwayama S, Oikawa M, Suzuki K, Okunishi M, Tsuji T. Synthesis and antiviral activity of novel acyclic nucleosides: discovery of a cyclopropyl nucleoside with potent inhibitory activity against herpesviruses. J Med Chem 1998;41: 1284–1298.

72. Neyts J, Andrei G, Snoeck R, Jahne G, Winkler I, Helsberg M, Balzarini J, De Clercq E. The *N*-7-substituted acyclic nucleoside analog 2-amino-7-[(1,3-dihydroxy-2-propoxy)methyl]purine is a potent and selective inhibitor of herpesvirus replication. Antimicrob Agents Chemother 1994;38:2710–2716.

73. Guo A, Hu P, Balimane PV, Leibach FH, Sinko P. Interactions of a nonpeptidic drug, valaciclovir, with the human intestinal peptide transporter (hPEPT1) expressed in a mammalian cell line. J Pharmacol Exp Ther 1999;289:448–454.

74. Sugawara M, Huang W, Fei YL, Leibach FH, Ganapathy V, Ganapathy ME. Transport of valganciclovir, a ganciclovir prodrug, via peptide trasporters PEPT1 and PEPT2. J Pharm Sci 2000;89:781–789.

75. Holý A. Phosphonomethoxyalkyl analogs of nucleotides. Curr Pharm Design 2003;9: 2567–2592.

76. Holý A, Rosenberg I. Preparation of 5′-*O*-phosphonomethyl analogs of nucleoside-5′-phosphates, 5′-diphosphates and 5′-triphosphates. Collect Czech Chem Commun 1982;47: 3447–3463.

77. Cvekl A, Horská K, Šebesta K, Rosenberg I, Holý A. Phosphonate analogues of dinucleotides as substrates for DNA-dependent RNA polymerase from *Escherichia coli* in primed abortive initiation reaction. Int J Biol Macromol 1989;11:33–38.

78. Cihlar T, Ray AS, Boojamra CG, Zhang L, Hui H, Laflamme G, Vela JE, Grant D, Chen J, Myrick F, White KL, Gao Y, Lin KY, Douglas JL, Parkin NT, Carey A, Pakdaman R, Mackman RL. Design and profiling of GS-9148, a novel nucleotide analog active against nucleoside-resistant variants of human immunodeficiency virus type 1, and its orally bioavailable phosphonoamidate prodrug, GS-9131. Antimicrob Agents Chemother 2008;52:655–665.

79. Ray AS, Vela JE, Boojamra CG, Zhang L, Hui H, Callebaut C, Stray K, Lin KY, Gao Y, Mackman RL, Cihlar T. Intracellular metabolism of the nucleotide prodrug GS-9131, a potent anti-human immunodeficiency virus agent. Antimicrob Agents Chemother 2008;52:648–654.

80. Holý A. Antiviral acyclic nucleoside phosphonates structure activity studies. Antiviral Res 2006;71:248–253.

81. De Clercq E, Holý A. Acyclic nucleoside phosphonates: a key class of antiviral drugs. Nat Rev Drug Discov 2005;4:928–940.

82. Janeba Z, Holý A, Masojídková M. Synthesis of acyclic nucleoside and nucleotide analogs derived from 6-amino-7*H*-purin-8(9H)-one. Collect Czech Chem Commun 2000;65: 1126–1144.

83. Holý A, Dvořáková H, Jindřich J, Masojídková M, Buděšínský M, Balzarini J, Andrei G, De Clercq E. Acyclic nucleotide analogs derived from 8-azapurines: synthesis and antiviral activity. J Med Chem 1996;39: 4073–4088.

84. Hocková D, Masojídková M, Buděšínský M, Holý A. Acyclic nucleoside and nucleotide analogs derived from 2-azaadenine. Collect Czech Chem Commun 1995;60:224–236.

85. Dvořáková H, Holý A, Alexander P. Synthesis and biological effects of 9-(3-hydroxy-2-phosphonomethoxypropyl)derivatives of deazapurines. Collect Czech Chem Commun 1993;58: 1403–1418.

86. De Clercq E, Holý A, Rosenberg I, Sakuma T, Balzarini J, Maudgal PC. A novel selective broad-spectrum anti-DNA virus agent. Nature 1986;323:464–467.

87. De Clercq E, Sakuma T, Baba M, Pauwels R, Balzarini J, Rosenberg I, Holý A. Antiviral activity of phosphonylmethoxyalkyl derivatives of purine and pyrimidines. Antivral Res 1987;8:261–272.

88. Balzarini J, Holý A, Jindřich J, Naesens L, Snoeck R, Schols D, De Clercq E. Differential antiherpesvirus and antiretrovirus effects of the (S) and (R) enantiomers of acyclic nucleoside phosphonates: potent and selective *in vitro* and *in vivo* antiretrovirus anctivities of (R)-9-(2-phosphonomethoxypropyl)-2,6-diaminopurine. Antimicrob Agents Chemother 1993;37:332–338.

89. Holý A. Synthesis of acyclic nucleoside phosphonates. In: Current Protocols in Nucleic Acid Chemistry 2005; Chapter 14: Unit 14.2, John Wiley and Sons, Inc., Hoboken, New Jersey.

90. Smeijsters LJJW, Fransen FFJ, Naesens L, de Vries E, Holý A, Balzarini J, De Clercq E, Overdulve JP. Inhibition of the *in vitro* growth of *Plasmodium falciparum* by acyclic nucleoside phosphonates. Int J Antimicrob Agents 1999;12:53–61.

91. Kaminsky R, Nickel B, Holý A. Arrest of *Trypanosoma brucei* rhodesiense and *T. brucei brucei* in the S-phase of the cell cycle by (S)-9-(3-hydroxy-2-phosphonylmethoxypropyl) adenine (S)-HPMPA. Mol Biochem Parasitol 1998;93:91–100.

92. Kaminsky R, Schmid C, Grether Y, Holý A, De Clercq E, Naesens L, Brun R. (S)-9-(3-Hydroxy-2-phosphonylmethoxypropyl)adenine (S)-HPMPA): a purine analogue with trypanocidal activity *in vitro* and *in vivo*. Trop Med Int Health 1996;1:255–263.

93. Botros S, William S, Hammam L, Zidek Z, Holý A. Activity of 9-(S)-[3-hydroxy-2-(phosphonomethoxy)propyl]adenine against *Schistosomiasis mansoni* in mice. Antimicrob Agents Chemother 2003;47:3853–3858.

94. Plosker GL, Noble S. Cidofovir: a review of its use in cytomegalovirus retinitis in patients with AIDS. Drugs 1999;58:325–345.

95. Ho HT, Woods KL, Bronson JJ, De Boeck H, Martin JC, Hitchcock MJ. Intracellular metabolism of the antiherpes agent (S)-1-[3-hydroxy-2-(phosphonylmethoxy)propyl]cytosine. Mol Pharmacol 1992;41:197–202.

96. Mendel DB, Cihlar T, Moon K, Chen MS. Conversion of 1-[(S)-2-hydroxy-2-oxo-1,4,2-dioxaphosphorinan-5-yl)methyl]cytosine to cidofovir by an intracellular cyclic CMP phosphodiesterase. Antimicrob Agents Chemother 1997;41:641–646.

97. Krecmerová M, Holý A, Piskala A, Masojídková M, Andrei G, Naesens L, Neyts J, Balzarini J, De Clercq E, Snoeck R. Antiviral activity of triazine analogues of 1-(S)-[3-hydroxy-2-(phosphonomethoxy)propyl]cytosine (cidofovir) and related compounds. J Med Chem 2007;50:1069–1077.

98. Krecmerová M, Holý A, Pohl R, Masojídková M, Andrei G, Naesens L, Neyts J, Balzarini J, De Clercq E, Snoeck R. Ester prodrugs of cyclic 1-(S)-[3-hydroxy-2-(phosphonomethoxy)propyl]-5-azacytosine: synthesis and ativiral activity. J Med Chem 2007;50:5765–5772.

99. Zemlicka J, Holý A. Preparation of N-dimethylaminomethylene derivatives—a new method of a selective substitution of nucleoside amino groups. Collect Czech Chem Commun 1967;32:3159.

100. Krecmerová M, Masojídková M, Holý A. Preparation of C-5 substituted cidofovir derivatives. Collect Czech Chem Commun 2006;71: 579–594.

101. Otova B, Francova K, Franek F, Koutnik P, Votruba I, Holý A, Sladka M, Schramlova J. 9-[2-(Phosphonomethoxy)ethyl]-2,6-diaminopurine (PMEDAP)—a potential drug against haematological malignancies—induces apoptosis. Anticancer Res 1999;19:3173–3182.

102. Balzarini J, Naesens L, Herdewijn P, Rosenberg I, Holý A, Pauwels R, Baba M, Johns DG, De Clercq E. Marked *in vivo* antiretrovirus activity of 9-(2-Phosphonylmethoxyethyl)adenine, a selective anti-human immunodeficiency virus agent. Proc Natl Acad Sci USA 1989;86:332–336.

103. Naesens L, Balzarini J, Bischofberger N, De Clercq E. Antiretroviral activity and pharmacokinetics in mice of oral bis(POM)-PMEA, the bis(pivaloyloxymethyl)prodrug of 9-(2-phosphonylmethoxyethyl)adenine. Antimicrob Agents Chemother 1996;40:22–28.

104. Pardo M, Bartolome J, Carreno V. Current therapy of chronic hepatitis B. Arch Med Res 2007;38:661–667.

105. Dai CY, Chuang WL, Hsieh MY, Lee LP, Huang JF, Hou NJ, Lin ZY, Chen SC, Hsieh MY, Wang LY, Tsai JF, Chang WY, Yu ML.

Adefovir dipivoxil treatment of lamivudine-resistant chronic hepatitis B. Antiviral Res 2007;75:146–151.

106. Grim SA, Romanelli F. Tenofovir disoproxil fumarate. Ann Pharmacother 2003;37: 849–859.

107. Matthews G. The management of HIV and hepatitis B coinfection. Curr Op Infect Dis 2007;20:16–21.

108. Naesens L, Neyts J, Balzarini J, Holý A, Rosenberg I, De Clercq E. Efficacy of oral 9-(2-phosphonylmethoxyethyl)-2,6-diaminopurine (PMEDAP) in the treatment of retrovirus and cytomegalovirus infections in mice. J Med Virol 1993;39:167–172.

109. Andrei G, Snoeck R, Piette J, Delvenne P, De Clercq E. Antiproliferative effects of acyclic nucleoside phosphonates on human papillomavirus (HPV)-harboring cell lines compared with HPV-negative cell lines. Oncol Res 1998;10:523–531.

110. Schinkmanova M, Votruba I, Holý A. N6-Methyl-AMP aminohydrolase activates N6-substituted purine acyclic nucleoside phosphonates. Biochem Pharmacol 2006;71:1370–1376.

111. Schinkmanova M, Votruba I, Shibata R, Han B, Liu X, Cihlář T, Holý A. Human N6-methyl-AMP/damp aminohydrolase (abacavir 5′-monophosphate deaminase) is capable of metabolizing N6-substituted purine acyclic nucleoside phosphonates. Collect Czech Chem Commun 2008;73:275–291.

112. Holý A, Votruba I, Masojidkova M, Andrei G, Snoeck R, Naesens L, De Clercq E, Balzarini J. 6-[2-(Phosphonomethoxy)alkoxy]pyrimidines with antiviral activity. J Med Chem 2002;45:1918–1929.

113. Hockova D, Holý A, Masojidkova M, Andrei G, Snoeck R, De Clercq E, Balzarini J. 5-Substituted-2,4-diamino-6-[2-(phosphonomethoxy)ethoxy]-pyrimidines—acyclic nucleoside phosphonate analogues with antiviral activity. J Med Chem 2003;46:5064–5073.

114. Benzaria S, Pelicano H, Johnson R, Maury G, Imbach JL, Aubertin AM, Obert G, Gosselin G. Synthesis, in vitro antiviral evaluation, and stability studies of bis(S-acyl-2-thioethyl) ester derivatives of 9-[2-(phosphonomethoxy) ethyl]adenine (PMEA) as potential PMEA prodrugs with improved oral bioavailability. J Med Chem 1996;39:4958–4965.

115. Ballatore C, McGuigan C, De Clercq E, Balzarini J. Synthesis and evaluation of novel amidate prodrugs of PMEA and PMPA. Bioorg Med Chem Lett 2001;11:1053–1056.

116. Birkus G, Kutty N, He GX, Mulato A, Lee W, McDermott M, Cihlar T. Activation of 9-[(R)-2-[[(S)-[[(S)-1-(isopropoxycarbonyl)ethyl]amino]-phenoxyphosphinyl]-methoxy]propyl]adenine (GS-7340) and other tenofovir phosphonoamidate prodrugs by human proteases. Mol Pharmacol 2008;74:92–100.

117. Dolakova P, Dracinsky M, Masojidkova M, Solinova V, Kasicka V, Holý A. Acyclic nucleoside bisphosphonates: synthesis and properties of chiral 2-amino-4,6-bis[(phosphonomethoxy)alkoxy]pyrimidines. Eur J Med Chem 2009;44:2408–2424.

118. Reiser H, Wang JY, Chong L, Watkins WJ, Ray AS, Shibata R, Birkus G, Cihlar T, Wu S, Li B, Liu X, Henne IN, Wolfgang GH, Desai M, Rhodes GR, Fridland A, Lee WA, Plunkett W, Vail D, Thamm DH, Jeraj R, Tumas DB. GS-9219—a novel acyclic nucleotide analogue with potent antineoplastic activity in dogs with spontaneous non-Hodgkin's lymphoma. Clin Cancer Res 2008;14:2824–2832.

119. Hostetler KY, Beadle JR. Orally active lipid esters of antiviral nucleoside phosphonates. In: Hocek M, editor. Chemistry of Nucleic Acid Components, Collection Symposium Series. Vol. 7,Academy of Sciences of the Czech Republic, Prague, Czech Republic 2005. p 95–103.

120. Hostetler KY. Alkoxyalkyl prodrugs of acyclic nucleoside phosphonates enhance oral antiviral activity and reduce toxicity: current state of art. Antiviral Res 2009;82:A84–A89.

121. Holý A. Simple method for cleavage of phosphonic acid diesters to monoesters. Synthesis 1998;4:381–385.

122. Erion MD, van Poelje PD, Mackenna DA, Colby TJ, Montag AC, Fujitaki JM, Linemeyer DL, Bullough DA. Liver-targeted drug delivery using HepDirect prodrugs. J Pharmacol Exp Ther 2005;312:554–560.

123. Erion MD, Bullough DA, Lin CC, Hong Z. HepDirect prodrugs for targeting nucleotide-based antiviral drugs to the liver. Curr Opin Investig Drugs 2006;7:109–117.

124. Lin CC, Yeh LT, Vitarella D, Hong Z, Erion MD. Remofovir mesylate: a prodrug of PMEA with improved liver-targeting and safety in rats and monkey. Antivir Chem Chemother 2004;15:307–317.

125. Tillmann HL. Pradefovir, a liver-targeted prodrug of adefovir against HBV infection. Curr Opin Invest Drugs 2007;8:682–690.

126. Kleymann G, Fischer R, Betz UA, Hendrix M, Bender W, Schneider U, Handke G, Eckenberg

P, Hewlett G, Pevzner V, Baumeister J, Weber O, Henninger K, Keldenich J, Jensen A, Kolb J, Bach U, Popp A, Mäben J, Frappa I, Haebich D, Lockhoff O, Rübsamen-Waigmann H. New helicase–primase inhibitors as drug candidates for the treatment of herpes simplex disease. Nat Med 2002;8:392–398.

127. Betz UAK, Fischer R, Kleymann G, Hendrix M, Rübsamen-Waigmann H. Potent *in vivo* antiviral activity of the herpes simplex virus primase–helicase inhibitor BAY 57-1293. Antimicrob Agents Chemother 2002;46:1766–1772.

128. Crute JJ, Grygon CA, Hargrave KD, Simoneau B, Faucher AM, Bolger G, Kibler P, Liuzzi M, Cordingley MG. Herpes simplex virus helicase–primase inhibitors are active in animal models of human disease. Nat Med 2002;8:386–391.

129. White PW, Faucher A-M, Massariol M-J, Welchner E, Rancourt J, Cartier M, Archambault J. Biphenylsulfonacetic acid inhibitors of the human papillomavirus type 6 E1 helicase inhibit ATP hydrolysis by an allosteric mechanism involving tyrosine 486. Antimicrob Agents Chemother 2005;49:4834–4842.

130. Chrisp P, Clissold SP. Foscarnet—a review of its antiviral activity, pharmacokinetic properties and therapeutic use in immunocompromised patients with cytomegalovirus retinitis. Drugs 1991;41:104–129.

131. Jacobson MA. Review of the toxicities of foscarnet. J AIDS Hum Retrovirol 1992;5: S11–S17.

132. Hammond JL, Koontz DL, Bazmi HZ, Beadle JR, Hostetler SE, Kini GD, Aldern KA, Richman DD, Hostetler KY, Mellors JW. Alkylglycerol prodrugs of phosphonoformate are potent *in vitro* inhibitors of nucleoside-resistant human immunodeficiency virus type 1 and select for resistance mutations that suppress zidovudine resistance. Antimicrob Agents Chemother 2001;45:1621–1628.

133. Lynn A. ADVENTRX to present positive thiovir antiviral activity results. http://www.actions-traitements.org/spip.php?breve2444; April 2006.

134. Waringer S, Ramos S, Robbins J. Combinations of thiovir and neuraminidase inhibitors exert synergistic antiviral activity on human, equine and avian influenza *in vitro*. Antiviral Res 2007;74:A82.

135. Overby LR, Duff RG, Mao JCH. Antiviral potential of phosphonoacetic acid. Ann NY Acad Sci 1977;284:310–320.

136. Overby LR, Robishaw EE, Schleich JB, Rueter A, Shipkowi NL, Mao JCh. Inhibition of herpes-simplex virus replication by phosphonoacetic acid. Antimicrob Agents Chemother 1974;6:360–365.

137. Friedman-Kien AE, Fondak AA, Klein RJ. Phosphonoacetic acid treatment of shope fibroma and vaccinia virus skin infections in rabbits. J Invest Dermatol 1976;66:99–102.

138. Hostetler KY, Kini GD, Beadle JR, Aldern KA, Gardner MF, Border R, Kumar R, Barshak L, Sridhar CN, Wheeler CJ, Richman DD. Lipid prodrugs of phosphonoacids: greatly enhanced antiviral activity of 1-*O*-octadecyl-*sn*-glycero-3-phosphonoformate in HIV-1, HSV-1 and HCMV-infected cells, *in vitro*. Antiviral Res 1996;31:59–67.

139. Biron KK, Harvey RJ, Chamberlain SC, Good SS, Smith AA 3rd, Davis MG, Talarico CL, Miller WH, Ferris R, Dornsife RE, Stanat SC, Drach JC, Townsend LB, Koszalka GW. Potent and selective inhibition of human cytomegalovirus replication by 1263W94, a benzimidazole L-riboside with a unique mode of action. Antimicrob Agents Chemother 2002;46: 2365–2372.

140. De Clercq E, Holý A. Alkyl esters of 3-adenin-9-yl-2-hydroxypropanoic acid: a new class of broad-spectrum antiviral agents. J Med Chem 1985;28:282–287.

141. Bailey TR, Rippin SR, Opsitnick E, Burns CJ, Pevear DC, Collett MS, Rhodes G, Tohan S, Huggins JW, Baker RO, Kern ER, Keith KA, Dai D, Yang G, Hruby D, Jordan R. *N*-(3,3a,4,4a,5,5a,6,6a-Octahydro-1,3-dioxo-4,6-ethenocycloprop[*f*]isoindol-2-(1*H*)-yl)carboxamides: identification of novel orthopoxvirus egress inhibitors. J Med Chem 2007;50: 1442–1444.

142. Kuypers DR, Vandooren AK, Lerut E, Evenepoel P, Claes K, Snoeck R, Naesens L, Vanrenterghem Y. Adjuvant low-dose cidofovir therapy for BK polyomavirus interstitial nephritis in renal transplant recipients. Am J Transplant 2005;5:1997–2004.

143. Shitrit D, Lev N, Bar-Gil-Shitrit A, Kramer MR. Progressive multifocal leukoencephalopathy in transplant recipients. Transpl Int 2004;17:658–665.

144. Viallard JF, Lazaro E, Lafon ME, Pellegrin JL. Successful cidofovir therapy of progressive multifocal leukoencephalopathy preceding angioimmunoblastic T-cell lymphoma. Leuk Lymph 2005;46:1659–1662.

145. Josephson MA, Williams JW, Chandraker A, Randhawa PS. Polyomavirus-associated nephropathy: update on antiviral strategies. Transpl Infect Dis 2006;8:95–101.

146. Lebeau I, Andrei G, Krečmerová M, De Clercq E, Holý A, Snoeck R. Inhibitory activities of three classes of acyclic nucleoside phosphonates against murine polyomavirus and primate simian virus 40 strains. Antimicrob Agents Chemother 2007;51:2268–2273.

147. Randhawa P, Zemlicka J, Sauerbrei A, Meier C, Hostetler KY, Beadle JR, Farasati NA, Huang Y, Bradley M. Anti-BK virus activity of nucleoside analogs. Antimicrob Agents Chemother 2008;52:1519–1521.

148. Bonatti H, Aigner F, De Clercq E, Boesmueller C, Widschwendner A, Larcher C, Margreiter R, Schneeberger S. Local administration of cidofovir for human papilloma virus associated skin lesions in transplant recipients. Transpl Int 2007;20:238–246.

149. Plumpton M, Sharp NA, Liddicoat LH, Remm M, Tucker DO, Hughes FJ, Russell SM, Romanos MA. A high capacity assay for inhibitors of human papillomavirus DNA replication. Biotechnology 1995;13:1210–1214.

150. De Clercq E, Andrei G, Snoeck R, De Bolle L, Naesens L, Degrève B, Balzarini J, Zhang Y, Schols D, Leyssen P, Ying C, Neyts J. Acyclic/carbocyclic guanosine analogues as anti-herpesvirus agents. In: Proceedings of the XIV International Round Table on Nucleosides, Nucleotides and Their Biological Applications; 2000 September 10-14; San Francisco, CA, USA. Nucleos Nucleot Nucleic Acids 2001;20:271–285.

151. Spector FC, Liang L, Giordano H, Sivaraja M, Peterson MG. Inhibition of herpes simplex virus replication by a 2-amino thiazole via interactions with the helicase component of the UL5-UL8-UL52 complex. J Virol 1998;72:6979–6987.

152. Baumeister J, Fischer R, Eckenberg P, Henninger K, Ruebsamen-Waigmann H, Kleymann G. Superior efficacy of helicase–primase inhibitor BAY 57-1293 for herpes infection and latency in the guinea pig model of human genital herpes disease. Antiviral Chem Chemother 2007;18:35–48.

153. Biswas S, Jennens L, Field HJ. The helicase primase inhibitor, BAY 57-1293 shows potent therapeutic antiviral activity superior to famciclovir in BALB/c mice infected with herpes simplex virus type 1. Antiviral Res 2007;75:30–35.

154. Liuzzi M, Kibler P, Bousquet C, Harji F, Bolger G, Garneau M, Lapeyre N, McCollum RS, Faucher AM, Simoneau B, Cordingley MG. Isolation and characterization of herpes simplex virus type 1 resistant to aminothiazolyl-phenyl-based inhibitors of the viral helicase–primase. Antiviral Res 2004;64:161–170.

155. Biswas S, Swift M, Field HJ. High frequency of spontaneous helicase–primase inhibitor (BAY 57-1293) drug-resistant variants in certain laboratory isolates of HSV-1. Antiviral Chem Chemother 2007;18:13–23.

156. Biswas S, Smith C, Field HJ. Detection of HSV-1 variants highly resistant to the helicase–primase inhibitor BAY 57-1293 at high frequency in 2 of 10 recent clinical isolates of HSV-1. J Antimicrob Chemother 2007;60:274–279.

157. Biswas S, Jennens L, Field HJ. Single amino acid substitutions in the HSV-1 helicase protein that confer resistance to the helicase–primase inhibitor BAY 57-1293 are associated with increased or decreased virus growth characteristics in tissue culture. Arch Virol 2007;152:1489–1500.

158. De Clercq E. Highly potent and selective inhibition of varicella-zoster virus replication by bicyclic furo[2,3-d]pyrimidine nucleoside analogues. Med Res Rev 2003;23:253–274.

159. Andrei G, Sienaert R, McGuigan C, De Clercq E, Balzarini J, Snoeck R. Susceptibilities of several clinical varicella-zoster virus (VZV) isolates and drug-resistant VZV strains to bicyclic furano pyrimidine nucleosides. Antimicrob Agents Chemother 2005;49:1081–1086.

160. Canas SM, Wargin B, Boehlecke B, Henson G, Patti JM, Morris AM. A single accelerating dose study to evaluate safety and pharmacokinetics (PK) of FV-100 in healthy subjects. In: Abstracts of the Twenty-First International Conference on Antiviral Research; 2008 April 13–17; Montreal, Quebec, Canada. Antiviral Res 2008;A32: no. 40.

161. Biron KK. Antiviral drugs for cytomegalovirus diseases. Antiviral Res 2006;71:154–163.

162. Schleiss MR, Anderson JL, McGregor AM. Cyclic cidofovir (cHPMPC) prevents congenital cytomegalovirus infection in a guinea pig model. Virology J 2006;3:9.

163. Bravo FJ, Cardin RD, Bernstein DI. Effect of maternal treatment with cyclic HPMPC in the guinea pig model of congenital cytomegalovirus infection. J Infect Dis 2006;193:591–597.

164. Quenelle DC, Collins DJ, Pettway LR, Hartline CB, Beadle JR, Wan WB, Hostetler KY,

Kern ER. Effect of oral treatment with (S)-HPMPA, HDP-(S)-HPMPA or ODE-(S)-HPMPA on replication of murine cytomegalovirus (MCMV) or human cytomegalovirus (HCMV) in animal models. Antiviral Res 2008;79:133–135.

165. Zhou S, Breitenbach JM, Borysko KZ, Drach JC, Kern ER, Gullen E, Cheng YC, Zemlicka J. Synthesis and antiviral activity of (Z)- and (E)-2,2-[bis(hydroxymethyl)cyclopropylidene] methylpurines and -pyrimidines: second-generation methylenecyclopropane analogues of nucleosides. J Med Chem 2004;47:566–575.

166. Kern ER, Bidanset DJ, Hartline CB, Yan Z, Zemlicka J, Quenelle DC. Oral activity of a methylenecyclopropane analog, cyclopropavir, in animal models for cytomegalovirus infections. Antimicrob Agents Chemother 2004;48:4745–4753.

167. Winston DJ, Young J-A, Pullarkat V, Papanicolaou GA, Vij R, Vance E, Alangaden GJ, Chernaly RF, Petersen F, Chao N, Klein J, Sprague K, Villano SA, Boeckh M. Maribavir prophylaxis for prevention of cytomegalovirus infection in allogeneic stem cell transplant recipients: a multicenter, randomized, double-blind, placebo-controlled, dose-ranging study. Blood 2008;111:5403–5410.

168. Chou S, Van Wechel LC, Marousek GI. Cytomegalovirus UL97 kinase mutations that confer maribavir resistance. J Infect Dis 2007;196:91–94.

169. Chou S, Marousek GI. Accelerated evolution of maribavir resistance in a cytomegalovirus exonuclease domain II mutant. J Virol 2008;82:246–253.

170. De Clercq E, Naesens L. In search of effective anti-HHV-6 agents. J Clin Virol 2006;37:Suppl 1: S82–S86.

171. Naesens L, Bonnafous P, Agut H, De Clercq E. Antiviral activity of diverse classes of broad-acting agents and natural compounds in HHV-6-infected lymphoblasts. J Clin Virol 2006;37 Suppl 1:S69–S75.

172. Prichard M, Daily S, Perry A, Kern E. Maribavir inhibits the replication of human herpesvirus 6 and the activity of the U69 protein kinase. In: Abstracts of the Twenty-First International Conference on Antiviral Research; 2008 April 13-17; Montreal, Quebec, Canada. Antiviral Res 2008;A29: no. 34.

173. Chapenko S, Krumina A, Kozireva S, Nora Z, Sultanova A, Viksna L, Murovska M. Activation of human herpesviruses 6 and 7 in patients with chronic fatigue syndrome. J Clin Virol 2006;37 Suppl 1:S47–S51.

174. Kogelnik AM, Loomis K, Hoegh-Petersen M, Rosso F, Hischier C, Montoya JG. Use of valganciclovir in patients with elevated antibody titers against Human Herpesvirus-6 (HHV-6) and Epstein–Barr Virus (EBV) who were experiencing central nervous system dysfunction including long-standing fatigue. J Clin Virol 2006;37 Suppl 1:S33–S38.

175. Lerner AM, Beqaj SH, Deeter RG, Fitzgerald JT. Valacyclovir treatment in Epstein-Barr virus subset chronic fatigue syndrome: thirty-six months follow-up. In vivo 2007;21:707–714.

176. Zhou S, Kern ER, Gullen E, Cheng Y-C, Drach JC, Tamiya S, Mitsuya H, Zemlicka J. 9-{[3-Fluoro-2-(hydroxymethyl)cyclopropylidene] methyl}-adenines and -guanines. Synthesis and antiviral activity of all stereoisomers1. J Med Chem 2006;49:6120–6128.

177. Li C, Prichard MN, Korba BE, Drach JC, Zemlicka J. Fluorinated methylenecyclopropane analogues of nucleosides. Synthesis and antiviral activity of (Z)- and (E)-9-{[(2-fluoromethyl-2-hydroxymethyl)-cyclopropylidene] methyl}adenine and -guanine. Bioorg Med Chem 2008;16:2148–2155.

178. De Clercq E. The acyclic nucleoside phosphonates from inception to clinical use: historical perspective. Antiviral Res 2007;75:1–13.

179. Neyts J, Leyssen P, Verbeken E, De Clercq E. Efficacy of cidofovir in a murine model of disseminated progressive vaccinia. Antimicrob Agents Chemother 2004;48:2267–2273.

180. Geerinck K, Lukoto G, Snoeck R, De Vos R, De Clercq E, Vanrenterghem Y, Degreef H, Maes B. A case of human orf in an immunocompromised patient treated successfully with cidofovir cream. J Med Virol 2001;64:543–549.

181. Fery-Blanco C, Pelletier F, Humbert P, Aubin F. Disseminated molluscum contagiosum during topical treatment of atopic dermatitis with tacrolimus: efficacy of cidofovir. Ann Dermatol Venereol 2007;134:457–459.

182. Jones S, Kress D. Treatment of molluscum contagiosum and herpes simplex virus cutaneous infections. Cutis 2007;79 Suppl 4:11–17.

183. Magee WC, Aldern KA, Hostetler KY, Evans DH. Cidofovir and (S)-9-[3-hydroxy-(2-phosphonomethoxy)propyl]adenine are highly effective inhibitors of vaccinia virus DNA polymerase when incorporated into the template strand. Antimicrob Agents Chemother 2008;52:586–597.

184. Duraffour S, Snoeck R, de Vos R, van Den Oord JJ, Crance JM, Garin D, Hruby DE, Jordan R, De Clercq E, Andrei G. Activity of the anti-orthopoxvirus compound ST-246 against vaccinia, cowpox and camelpox viruses in cell monolayers and organotypic raft cultures. Antiviral Ther 2007;12:1205–1216.

185. Dal Pozzo F, Andrei G, Lebeau I, Beadle JR, Hostetler KY, De Clercq E, Snoeck R. *In vitro* evaluation of the anti-orf virus activity of alkoxyalkyl esters of CDV, cCDV and (*S*)-HPMPA. Antiviral Res 2007;75:52–57.

186. Quenelle DC, Collins DJ, Herror BP, Keith KA, Trahan J, Beadle JR, Hostetler KY, Kern ER. Effect of oral treatment with hexadecyloxypropyl-[(*S*)-9-(3-hydroxy-2-phosphonylmethoxy-propyl)-adenine] [(*S*)-HPMPA] or octadecyloxyethyl-(*S*)-HPMPA on cowpox or vaccinia virus infections in mice. Antimicrob Agents Chemother 2007;51:3940–3947.

187. Beadle JR, Wan WB, Ciesla SL, Keith KA, Hartline C, Kern ER, Hostetler KY. Synthesis and antiviral evaluation of alkoxyalkyl derivatives of 9-(*S*)-(3-hydroxy-2-phosphono-methoxypropyl)adenine against cytomegalovirus and orthopoxviruses. J Med Chem 2006;49:2010–2015.

188. Hostetler KY, Beadle JR, Trahan J, Aldern KA, Owens G, Schriewer J, Melman L, Buller RM. Oral 1-*O*-octadecyl-2-*O*-benzyl-*sn*-glycero-3-cidofovir targets the lung and is effective against a lethal respiratory challenge with ectromelia virus in mice. Antiviral Res 2007;73:212–218.

189. Ruiz JC, Beadle JR, Aldern KA, Keith KA, Hartline CB, Kern ER, Hostetler KY. Synthesis and antiviral evaluation of alkoxyalkylphosphate conjugates of cidofovir and adefovir. Antiviral Res 2007;75:87–90.

190. Yang G, Pevear DC, Davies MH, Collett MS, Bailey T, Rippen S, Barone L, Burns C, Rhodes G, Tohan S, Huggins JW, Baker RO, Buller RL, Touchette E, Waller K, Schriewer J, Neyts J, DeClercq E, Jones K, Hruby D, Jordan R. An orally bioavailable antipoxvirus compound (ST-246) inhibits extracellular virus formation and protects mice from lethal orthopoxvirus challenge. J Virol 2005;79:13139–13149.

191. Sbrana E, Jordan R, Hruby D, Mateo RI, Xiao SY, Siirin M, Newman PC, DA Rosa AP, Tesh RB. Efficacy of the antipoxvirus compound ST-246 for treatment of severe orthopoxvirus infection. Am J Trop Med Hyg 2007;76:768–773.

192. Quenelle DC, Buller RML, Parker S, Keith KA, Hruby DE, Jordan R, Kern ER. Efficacy of delayed treatment with ST-246 given orally against systemic orthopoxvirus infections in mice. Antimicrob Agents Chemother 2007;51: 689–695.

193. Kaiser J. Smallpox vaccine. A tame virus runs amok. Science 2007;316:1418–1419.

194. Grosenbach DW, Jordan R, King DS, Berhanu A, Warren TK, Kirkwood-Watts DL, Tyavanagimatt S, Tan Y, Wilson RL, Jones KF, Hruby DE. Immune responses to the smallpox vaccine given in combination with ST-246, a small-molecule inhibitor of poxvirus dissemination. Vaccine 2008;26:933–946.

195. Quenelle DC, Prichard MN, Keith KA, Hruby DE, Jordan R, Painter GR, Robertson A, Kern ER. Synergistic efficacy of the combination of ST-246 with CMX001 against orthopoxviruses. Antimicrob Agents Chemother 2007;51:4118–4124.

196. Jordan R, Tien D, Bolken TC, Jones KF, Tyavanagimatt SR, Strasser J, Frimm A, Corrado ML, Strome PG, Hruby DE. Single-dose safety and pharmacokinetics of ST-246, a novel orthopoxvirus egress inhibitor. Antimicrob Agents Chemother 2008;52:1721–1727.

197. Smee DF, Hurst BL, Wong MH, Glazer RI, Rahman A, Sidwell RW. Efficacy of *N*-methanocarbathymidine in treating mice infected intranasally with the IHD and WR strains of vaccinia virus. Antiviral Res 2007;76:124–129.

198. Marquez VE, Hughes SH, Sei S, Agbaria R. The history of *N*-methanocarbathymidine: the investigation of a conformational concept leads to the discovery of a potent and selective nucleoside antiviral agent. Antiviral Res 2006;71:268–275.

199. Deng L, Dai P, Ciro A, Smee DF, Djaballah H, Shuman S. Identification of novel antipoxviral agents: mitoxantrone inhibits vaccinia virus replication by blocking virion assembly. J Virol 2007;81:13392–13402.

200. Zoulim F. Antiviral therapy of chronic hepatitis B. Antiviral Res 2006;71:206–215.

201. Suzuki F, Kumada H, Nakamura H. Changes in viral loads of lamivudine-resistant mutants and evolution of HBV sequences during adefovir dipivoxil therapy. J Med Virol 2006;78:1025–1034.

202. Van der Molen RG, Sprengers D, Biesta PJ, Kusters JG, Janssen HLA. Favorable effect of adefovir on the number and functionality of myeloid dendritic cells of patients with chronic HBV. Hepatology 2006;44:907–914.

203. Delaney WEIV. Progress in the treatment of chronic hepatitis B: long-term experience with

adefovir dipivoxil. J Antimicrob Chemother 2007;59:827–832.

204. Qi X, Xiong S, Yang H, Miller M, Delaney WE. *In vitro* susceptibility of adefovir-associated hepatitis B virus polymerase mutations to other antiviral agents. Antiviral Ther 2007;12:355–362.

205. Hadziyannis SJ. New developments in the treatment of chronic hepatitis B. Expert Opin Biol Ther 2006;6:913–921.

206. Zoulim F. Entecavir: a new treatment option for chronic hepatitis B. J Clin Virol 2006;36:8–12.

207. Tenney DJ, Rose RE, Baldick CJ, Levine SM, Pokornowski KA, Walsh AW, Fang J, Yu CF, Zhang S, Mazzucco CE, Eggers B, Hsu M, Plym MJ, Poundstone P, Yang J, Colonno RJ. Two-year assessment of entecavir resistance in La-mivudine-refractory hepatitis B virus patients reveals different clinical outcomes depending on the resistance substitutions present. Antimicrob Agents Chemother 2007;51:902–911.

208. Dimou E, Papadimitropoulos V, Hadziyannis S. The role of entecavir in the treatment of chronic hepatitis B. Ther Clin Risk Manag 2007;3:1077–1086.

209. O'Brien WA, Entecavir has low resistance rates after 5-year treatment of chronic hepa-titis B. http://www.docguide.com/news/content.nsf/news/, 30 May 2008.

210. Hirsch MS. Entecavir surprise. N Engl J Med 2007;356:2641–2643.

211. McMahon MA, Jilek BL, Brennan TP, Shen L, Zhou Y, Wind-Rotolo M, Xing S, Bhat S, Hale B, Hegarty R, Chong CR, Liu JO, Siliciano RF, Thio CL. The HBV drug entecavir—effects on HIV-1 replication and resistance. N Engl J Med 2007;356:2614–2621.

212. Ruiz-Sancho A, Sheldon J, Soriano V. Telbivu-dine: a new option for the treatment of chronic hepatitis B. Expert Opin Biol Ther 2007;7:751–761.

213. Buster EHCJ, Hansen BE, Butti M, Delwaide J, Niederau C, Michielsen PP, Flisiak R, Zon-dervan PE, Schalm SW, Janssen HL. Pegin-terferon alpha-2b is safe and effective in HBeAg-positive chronic hepatitis B patients with advanced fibrosis. Hepatology 2007;46:388–394.

214. Johnson RM, Ristig MB, Overton ET, Lisker-Melman M, Cummings OW, Aberg JA. Safety and tolerability of sequential pegylated IFN-alpha2a and tenofovir for hepatitis B infection in HIV(+) individuals. HIV Clin Trials 2007;8:173–181.

215. Sasadeusz JJ, Locarnini SL, Macdonald G. Why do we not yet have combination che-motherapy for chronic hepatitis B? Med J Aust 2007;186:204–206.

216. Wursthorn K, Lutgehetmann M, Dandri M. Volz T, Buggisch P, Zollner B, Longerich T, Schirmacher P, Metzler F, Zankel M, Fischer C, Currie G, Brosgart C. Petersen J. Peginter-feron alpha-2b plus adefovir induce strong cccDNA decline and HBsAg reduction in pa-tients with chronic hepatitis B. Hepatology 2006;44:675–684.

217. Peek SF, Cote PJ, Jacob JR, Toshkov IA, Horn-buckle WE, Baldwin BH, Wells FV, Chu CK, Gerin JL, Tennant BC, Korba BE. Antiviral activity of clevudine [L-FMAU, (1-(2-fluoro-5-methyl-beta, L-arabinofuranosyl) uracil)] against woodchuck hepatitis virus replication and gene expression in chronically infected woodchucks (*Marmota monax*). Hepatology 2001;33:254–266.

218. Lee H-S, Chung Y-H, Lee K, Byun KS, Paik SW, Han J-Y, Yoo K, Yoo H-W, Lee JH, Yoo BC. A 12-week clevudine therapy showed potent and durable antiviral activity in HBeAg-posi-tive chronic hepatitis B. Hepatology 2006;43:982–988.

219. Yoo BC, Kim JH, Chung YH, Lee KS, Paik SW, Ryu SH, Han BH, Han JY, Byun KS, Cho M, Lee HJ, Kim TH, Cho SH, Park JW, Um SH, Hwang SG, Kim YS, Lee YJ, Chon CY, Kim BL, Lee YS, Yang JM, Kim HC, Hwang JS, Choi SK, Kweon YO, Neony SH, Lee MS, Choi JY, Lim DG, Kim YS, Lee HY, Yoo K, Yoo HW, Lee HS. Twenty-four-week clevudine therapy showed potent and sustained antiviral activity in HBeAg-positive chronic hepatitis B. Hepa-tology 2007;45:1172–1178.

220. Zhu Y, Yamamoto T, Cullen J, Saputelli J, Aldrich CE, Miller DS, Litwin S, Furman PA, Jilbert AR, Mason WS. Kinetics of hepadna-virus loss from the liver during inhibition of viral DNA synthesis. J Virol 2001;75:311–322.

221. Summers J, Mason WS. Residual integrated viral DNA after hepadnavirus clearance by nucleoside analog therapy. Proc Natl Acad Sci USA 2004;101:638–640.

222. Menne S, Asif G, Narayanasamy J, Butler SD, George AL, Hurwitz SJ, Schinazi RF, Chu / surname> CK, Cote PJ, Gerin JL, Tennant BC. Antiviral effect of orally administered (−)-beta-D-2-aminopurine dioxolane in wood-chucks with chronic woodchuck hepatitis virus infection. Antimicrob Agents Chemother 2007;51:3177–3184.

223. Choo H, Beadle JR, Kern ER, Prichard MN, Keith KA, Hartline CB, Trahan J, Aldern KA, Korba BE, Hostetler KY. Antiviral activities of novel 5-phosphono-pent-2-en-1-yl nucleosides and their alkoxyalkyl phosphonoesters. Antimicrob Agents Chemother 2007;51:611–615.

224. Brunelle MN, Lucifora J, Neyts J, Villet S, Holý A, Trepo C, Zoulim F. *In vitro* activity of 2,4-diamino-6-[2-(phosphonomethoxy) ethoxy]-pyrimidine against multidrug-resistant hepatitis B virus mutants. Antimicrob Agents Chemother 2007;51:2240–2243.

225. Reddy KR, Matelich MC, Ugarkar BG, Gómez-Galeno JE, DaRe J, Ollis K, Sun Z, Craigo W, Colby TJ, Fujitaki JM, Boyer SH, van Poelje PD, Erion MD. Pradefovir: a prodrug that targets adefovir to the liver for the treatment of hepatitis B. J Med Chem 2008;51:666–676.

β-LACTAM ANTIBIOTICS

Sebastian A. Testero
Jed F. Fisher
Shahriar Mobashery
Department of Chemistry and Biochemistry,
The University of Notre Dame,
Notre Dame, IN

1. INTRODUCTION

The β-lactam class of antibacterials has been a cornerstone of human health for nearly seven decades. Their preeminence in the treatment of bacterial infection is the result of their unparalleled clinical efficacy and clinical safety. Nonetheless, the history of the β-lactams is not static. Rather, the relatively brief period in human history during which the β-lactams have exerted their profound benefit, is a period characterized by continuous innovation—most visibly seen in the evolution of structures within the β-lactam subclasses—driven by the hardly lesser ability of bacteria to innovate resistance mechanisms to each successive β-lactam generation. While at this time there is no evidence that human innovation of the β-lactam structure will falter, there is abundant evidence that the recent appearance of highly resistant bacteria (not only primarily in the hospital but also increasingly in the community) profoundly challenges the way medicinal chemists contemplate innovation of β-lactam structure, the way the pharmaceutical industry develops β-lactam (and other antibacterial) structures, and the way the medical community uses antibacterials. The continuing preeminence of this extraordinary class is hardly assured.

Nonetheless, this review imbues optimism. Following a concise summary of the history of the β-lactams, we emphasis the breadth of recent innovation within this class. This innovation is found not only within the chemistry of the β-lactams but also within the entire biological framework that empowers the medicinal chemist, from microbiology through genetics, and to structural and mechanistic biochemistry. While the continuing efficacy of the β-lactams is indeed challenged by resistance (as is true for all other antibac-

terial structure), the knowledge base necessary to drive the continued innovation of the β-lactam class continues to expand.

1.1. Early History

The history of the β-lactams begins with Alexander Fleming's observation in 1928 that the *Penicillium* mold produced an antibacterial agent [1]. Although Fleming was well aware of the momentous importance of his observation [2], it was the collective enterprise of Florey, Chain and Heatley [3,4] under the dire circumstance of world war that ultimately vindicated Fleming's surmise. Recent books summarize this parlous history [5–7]. The debate as to the correct structure to Fleming's antibacterial agent—a penicillin—was contentious [8,9], settled with finality by the revelation in 1945 by Hodgkin's crystal structure of the presence of a 2-azetidinone, or β-lactam, ring [10]. The underlying basis for this debate was the presumption that the β-lactam, as a four-membered cyclic amide, would possess sufficient ring strain as to result in diminished amide resonance and hence profound instability toward nucleophiles. Indeed, the difficulty in the first efforts addressing the synthetic challenge of closing a β-amino acid to a β-lactam seemingly supported this assumption. It is partly from this difficulty that Sheehan, who was the first to solve this synthetic problem using carbodiimide activation for intramolecular closure of a β-aminoacid, proposed the β-lactam as the "enchanted ring" [11]. Rigorous study has dispelled, however, the presumption of an extraordinary reactivity for the β-lactam either for hydrolysis or for acyl transfer to other nucleophiles [12–14].

1.2. The β-Lactam Structural Classes

An antibiotic is a natural product with cytotoxic biological activity. The first β-lactam antibiotic discovered—having cytotoxic activity toward bacteria—was a penicillin, and this β-lactam was followed in 1945 by the discovery of a second β-lactam class, the cephalosporins [15]. The cephalosporins are formed by biosynthetic transformation from penicillin N (**1**) [16], first by enzyme-catalyzed oxidative ring expansion [17–19] followed by

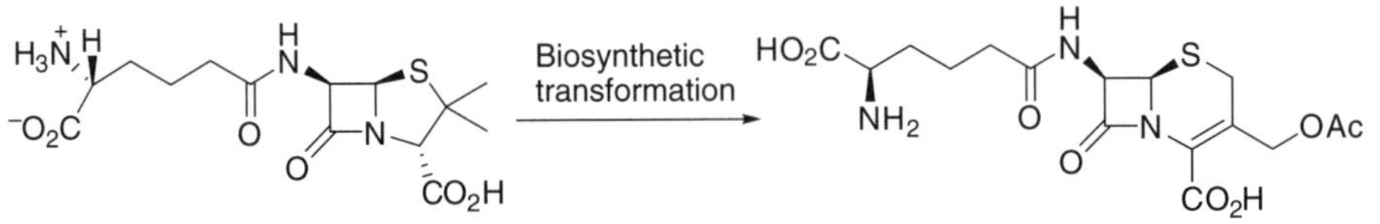

(1) Penicillin N   **(2)** Cephalosporin C

Figure 1. Biosynthetic transformation of penicillin N into cephalosporin C.

enzyme-catalyzed *O*-acetylation [20]. The product of this transformation from penicillin N is cephalosporin C (**2**) (Fig. 1). The structures of these two β-lactams are used to introduce key terms of nomenclature.

The core rings of the penicillins are the β-lactam and the thiazolidine fused as the 4-thia-1-azabicyclo[3.2.0]heptane or *penam*. The systematic name for the β-lactam, azetidin-2-one, is not used in the literature. The CAS name for penicillin N is (2*S*,5*R*,6*R*)-3,3-dimethyl-7-oxo-6-[(phenylacetyl)amino]-4-thia-1-azabicyclo[3.2.0]heptane-2-carboxylic acid. In customary usage, 7-oxo, 6*R*-amino, and 2*S*-carboxylate substitutents are implicit to the penam. The ring fusion is *cis* with respect to this amine and the sulfur atom, and the 6*R*-amine is customarily described as having 6β-stereochemistry. Cephalosporin C (CAS name (6*R*,7*R*)-3-[(acetyloxy)methyl]-7-{[(5*R*)-5-amino-5-carboxy-1-oxopentyl]amino}-8-oxo-5-thia-1-azabicyclo[4.2.0]oct-2-ene-2-carboxylic acid) preserves the *cis*-ring fusion. The ring fusion is also *cis* with respect to the 7β-amine. The 7β-amino-4-thia-1-azabicyclo[3.2.0]heptane-2-carboxylic acid ring is a *cephem*. As an important word of caution, in the historical literature (and still often continuing to this day) a nonsystematic numbering of the thiazolidine (for the penams) and 3,6-dihydro-2*H*-thiopyran (for the cephem) rings is used, where the numbering is the order as if these rings were detached (starting with the sulfur atom at the 1-position). Regardless of the starting positioning for numbering, the amine is located at C-6 of the penam and C-7 of the cephem. Continuing efforts in natural product isolation and synthesis have identified entirely new classes over the past 55 years. The most important of these classes (not presented in chronological order) are

- *Penems*: These differ from the penams by a double bond, instead of a single bond, between C-2 and C-3 of the thiazolidine. Penems are not natural products, being made by total synthesis.

- *Carbapenams and Carbapenems*: These β-lactams are cognate structures of penams and penems, respectively, where the sulfur atom is replaced by a carbon atom. Many natural and synthetic members of this class are known, including important and clinically used antibacterials. Systematic numbering of the carbapenem ring, corresponding to 7-oxo-1-azabicyclo[3.2.0]hept-2-ene-2-carboxylic acid, likewise begins at the β-lactam nitrogen.

- *Oxapenems*: Cognate structures of the penems having an oxygen atom replacing the sulfur atom. Although prepared for antibacterial evaluation, no member of this class is used clinically.

- *Oxacephems and Cabacephems*: These compounds are cognate structures of the cephems, where the sulfur atom is replaced by an oxygen or carbon atom. As noted above, the cephems or cephalosporins ring system retains continuing importance for drug discovery, moving through several generations of structure. At this time, β-lactam treatment of the most difficult infections is dominated by members of carbapenem and cephem classes.

- *Monobactams*: The monocyclic β-lactam obtained by reductive desulfurization of penicillin is biologically inactive. Two subclasses of monocyclic β-lactams possessing antibacterial activity were isolated subsequently as natural products. One subclass (the nocardicins) is weakly antibacterial, while in the second subclass the β-lactam is activated by *N*-sulfation. The monocyclic *N*-sulfo-β-lactam is the core

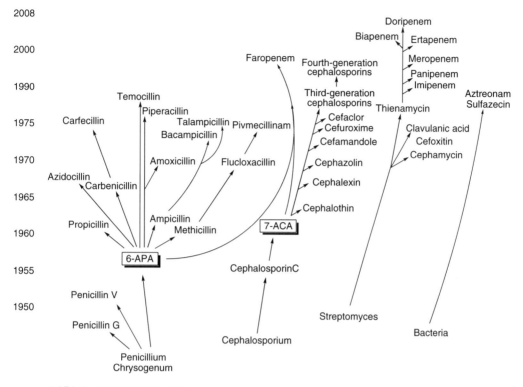

Figure 2. Evolution of the β-Lactam class.

ring of the monobactam class. One monobactam is used clinically. This class has,
however, received renewed attention due
to its potential for the treatment of β-lactam-resistant Gram-negative pathogens.

A chronological summary of these classes,
including the names of important class members, is given as Fig. 2. Generic structural
representations of the different classes, using
traditional (that is, nonsystematic) numbering, are given in Fig. 3.

2. MECHANISM OF ACTION

2.1. The Bacterial Cell Wall as an Essential Structural Component of the Bacterium

Despite the observation of that the β-lactam
ring has appreciable chemical stability, the

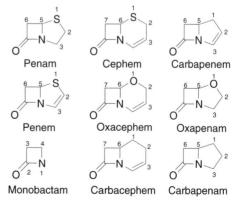

Figure 3. β-Lactam skeletons.

reactivity of the β-lactam is indeed central to the mechanism of its antibacterial activity. The basis for the efficacy of the β-lactams is that they target an enzymatic activity that is essential to bacterial viability. The basis for the safety of the β-lactams is the uniqueness of this enzymatic activity to bacteria. Clearly, an understanding of the relationship between β-lactam recognition by this enzyme, and of β-lactam reactivity toward this enzyme, is central to the mechanistic understanding of the β-lactam antibacterial activity. While a full discussion of these matters is beyond the scope of this review, the following summary provides a basic perspective for this mechanistic understanding. Bacteria are unicellular microorganisms. Like eukaryotic cells, bacteria are surrounded by a lipid membrane. In contrast to eukaryotic cells, but reflecting the necessity to the bacterium of osmotic and mechanical stability, the membranes of bacteria are integrated with a thin, polymeric shell also surrounding their cell. This polymeric shell is described by several interrelated terms. If the bacterium is boiled vigorously in a detergent, all soluble matter is removed leaving behind for each bacterium this polymeric shell, as a single molecule. The term describing the intact shell is the sacculus. If the isolated sacculus is further degraded into its molecular constitutents, both saccharides and amino acids are recovered. Accordingly, the composition of the sacculus is described as that of a peptidoglycan. If the sacculus is partially degraded, structures showing covalent attachment between the sacharides and the amino acids are isolated, termed murein (also a synonym for peptidoglycan) strands or muropeptides. Human bacterial pathogens are divided between those that are Gram-positive and those that are Gram-negative. While this distinction refers specifically to the relative abilities of the two classes toward experimental staining [21], it also directly differentiates two different means for the cellular organization of the peptidoglycan and membrane substructures. In Gram-positive bacteria, the sacculus is relatively thick (10–30 nm in *Staphylococcus aureus*) and comprises the outside of the bacterium, under which is found a thin space (called the periplasm) and the cell membrane [22–24].

Gram-negative bacteria, in contrast, have a membrane exterior directly juxtaposed to their sacculus, which is typically 3.5–7 nm in thickness [25]. Underneath the sacculus of the Gram-negative bacterium is also found a periplasmic space [26], itself overlaying a second membrane. In addition to the cryomicroscopy studies of bacteria noted above, the application cryotomography analysis of bacterial ultrastructure [27] is providing extraordinary insight into the subcellular organization of bacteria [28–30]. These two methods, as well as fluorescent bacterial imaging methods [31], represent unprecedented opportunities for imaging bacterial infection, [32] and for the phenotypic characterization of bacterial structure [33–36] including in response to exposure to antibiotics [37].

2.2. The Penicillin Binding Proteins

The molecular targets of the β-lactam antibiotics are the enzymes involved in the biosynthesis, structural maintenance, and reannealing (following cell wall septation in cell division) of the sacculus. For obvious historical reasons, these enzyme targets were termed penicillin binding proteins (PBPs), a nomenclature that persists to this day [38]. The presence of the term "binding" in this name implies more than mere recognition, but *covalent* binding: following recognition by the PBP of the β-lactam, an active site serine of the PBP adds to the β-lactam carbonyl to open the ring, in a functionally irreversible reaction of serine acylation. The β-lactam-acylated PBP is catalytically inactive. Why does this happen? The answer begins with a closer examination of the structure of the peptidoglycan, and the catalytic events accomplished by the PBP in its synthesis. We have already noted that the peptidoglycan contains covalently interconnected saccharides and amino acids. The core saccharide structure, common to both Gram-positive and -negative bacteria, is an *N*-acetylglucosamine (NAG) β-1,4-linked to *N*-acetylmuramic acid (NAM). The NAM structure differs from the NAG structure by the presence of an ether-linked *O*-(R-1-carboxyethyl)- (that is, D-lactate) substituent on the 3-hydroxyl of the 2-deoxyglucosamine core of NAM. In both Gram-positive and -negative bacteria, the NAG-NAM glycan pair is polymerized as a $(NAG-NAM)_n$ glycan strand, primarily as oligoglycans ($n \leq 10$) but with substantial populations of (NAG-NAM) polymers ($10 < n < 100$). The second structural dimension of the peptidoglycan is an oligopeptide stem attached, in an amide linkage, to the carboxylate of the ether-linked lactate of the NAM. The *core* structure of this stem in many Gram-positive bacteria is NAM-L-Ala-γ-D-Glu-L-Lys-D-Ala-D-Ala. The *full* structure of the stem in the Gram-positive pathogen *S. aureus* is NAM-L-Ala-γ-D-Glu-L-Lys[ε-Gly-Gly-Gly-Gly-Gly]-D-Ala-D-Ala (wherein the pentaglycine extension at the ε-amino group of the lysine is termed the "bridge" substructure). Among the Gram-positive bacteria, the core structure is relatively constant but the bridge structure is highly variable (in terms of both length and amino acid composition). In Gram-negative bacteria, the diaminodiacid *meso*-diaminopimelate replaces the L-Lys residue of the core, and the bridge structure is typically absent.

It is now evident that the complexity of this structure indicates exceptional biosynthetic enterprise (Section 5.1.4). The central question is the assembly of the pivotal biosynthetic building block—termed Lipid II—to form the polymeric structure of the sacculus. The structure of the Lipid II of *S. aureus* is NAG-NAM[-L-Ala-γ-D-Glu-L-Lys-D-Ala-D-Ala]-OP(O$_2$)OP(O$_3$)-Undecaprenyl, corresponding to an intact NAG-NAM[-L-Ala-γ-D-Glu-L-Lys-D-Ala-D-Ala] disaccharide in nucleotidyl α-glycosidic linkage to an undecaprenyldiphosphate lipid (Fig. 4). Lipid II is biosynthesized in the cytoplasm of the cell, and localized (by virtue of the undecaprenyl tail) in the inner face of the cytosolic membrane [39,40]. Carrier-mediated translocated across the membrane [41,42], to the outer leaflet of the cytosolic membrane, presents Lipid II as a substrate for peptidoglycan synthesis. The enzyme catalyst for this process is the biosynthetic PBP. These PBPs are usually bifunctional (two different active sites, single polypeptide) enzymes, also described as the high molecular mass class A and class B PBPs [43]. They comprise four structural domains [44–46]. The first domain is an amphipathic polypeptide sequence that colocalizes these enzymes in the outer leaflet of the cytosolic membrane with their Lipid II. The second domain is a glycosyltransferase catalytic domain, wherein Lipid II is transferred to a nascent glycan strand with liberation of the undecaprenyldiphosphate as a leaving group [47]. The third domain of the PBP is again structural, a primary purpose of which is believed [48] to be the spatial separation of the second domain (the catalytic glycosyltransferase domain) from the fourth and final domain (also a catalytic domain, having *transpeptidase* activity). This fourth domain is the molecular target of the β-lactam antibiotics.

All bacteria also contain one or more low molecular weight PBPs [49,50]. These enzymes comprise three domains: the amphiphilic terminus (again for the purpose of lipid insertion), connected to the second domain believed to be primarily structural, so as to elevate the third and catalytic domain into the periplasmic space, presumably into contact with the cell wall. The precise catalytic roles of the individual enzymes are not well understood. Although these enzymes collectively have been shown to be intimately involved in the control of bacterial cell shape [51,52] and daughter cell septation [53], they are not critical for cell survival. An example is *Escherichia coli* PBP 5, an enzyme having both *in vitro* and *in vivo* DD-carboxypeptidase activity (hydrolytic cleavage of the terminal D-Ala of the -D-Ala-D-Ala terminus of the peptide stem, thereby preventing transpeptidation). Loss of its activity by gene deletion results in viable *E. coli* of aberrant morphology, while its overexpression is lethal [54,55]. Depending on the chemical structure of the β-lactam, both the high M_r biosynthetic transpeptidase and the low M_r carboxypeptidase structural PBPs may be inactivated by serine acylation. From the perspective of drug design, a β-lactam that has differential activity toward these two classes is highly desirable [56]. Inactivation of the high M_r transpeptidases is bacteriocidal, and the successful antibacterial β-lactam will accomplish this task. Coinactivation of the low M_r carboxypeptidases is a key event used by the Gram-negative bacterium to sense the presence of β-lactams leading to derepression resistance mechanisms to the β-lactam, notably the gene encoding for β-lactamase expression [57,58]. β-Lactamases are highly

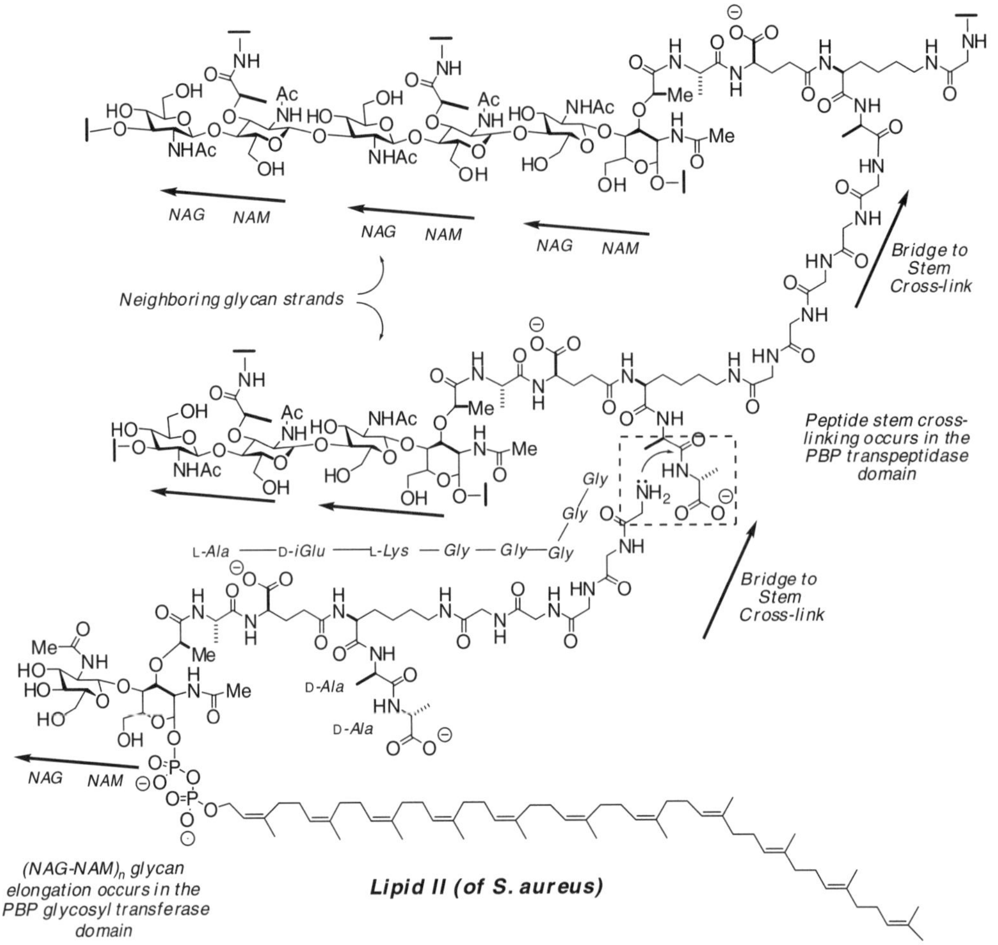

Figure 4. The cross-linking event in the peptidoglycan biosynthesis by Gram-positive bacterium *S. aeureus*.

efficient hydrolytic enzymes, which selectively recognize the β-lactam (to the exclusion of the cell wall -D-Ala-D-Ala terminus) and deactivate it by ring opening to the β-amino acid. β-Lactamase expression is a key mechanism for β-lactam resistance by Gram-negative bacteria (Section 3).

2.3. The Tipper–Strominger Hypothesis for D-Ala-D-Ala Mimicry

The function of the PBP transpeptidase domain is the cross-linking of adjacent glycan strands. This cross-linking is accomplished by an acyl transfer reaction, using one peptide stem structure as an acyl-donor, and a second as the acyl acceptor. The acyl donor in the

transpeptidation is the D-Ala-D-Ala terminus of the core stem. Nucleophilic addition of an active site serine to the amide carbonyl linking these two amino acids transfers the acyl moiety of the penultimate D-Ala to the serine, and releases the ultimate D-Ala as the leaving group. Acyl transfer of this D-Ala to serine completes the first half-reaction of transpeptidation. In the second half-reaction, the amine terminus of an adjacent glycan strand acts as the acyl acceptor, freeing the serine for another catalytic event. In *S. aureus* the amine terminus used is that of the fifth glycine of the bridge. As a result, a covalent linkage by amide bond formation occurs between the D-Ala of one strand and the Gly terminus of a second. The chemistry involved in this cross-

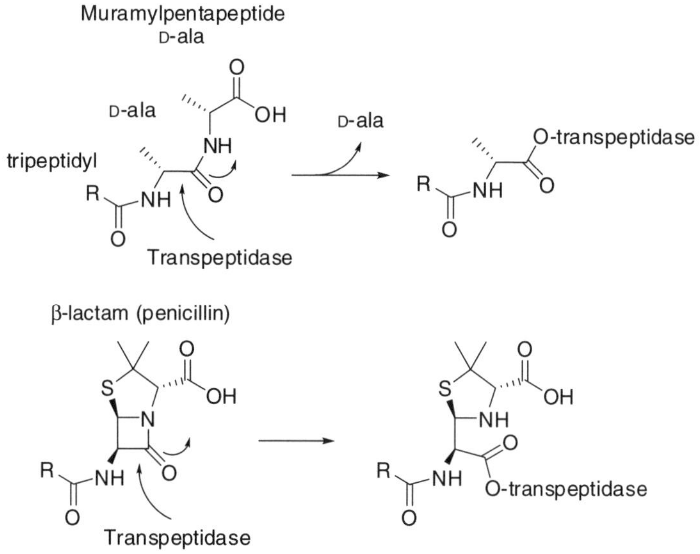

Figure 5. Mechanism of action of β-lactams.

linking event is depicted in Fig. 4. The mechanism used by the β-lactam is functional mimicry of the D-Ala-D-Ala terminus (Fig. 5). The same catalytic serine adds to the β-lactam carbonyl, and successfully completes acyl transfer (the first half-reaction). As the leaving group in the β-lactam structure in the course of enzyme acylation is actually tethered by the virtue of it being a part of the antibiotic structure, there exists a steric impediment for a second half-reaction, which would be needed for regeneration of the enzyme. In the laboratory hydrolytic acyl transfer to water is observed (thus a net reaction of hydrolysis of the β-lactam), but this occurs on a time scale that is much slower—in the order of days— than bacterial viability. Concisely, the mode of action of the β-lactams is mechanism-based irreversible acylation of the active

site domain of the biosynthetic PBPs, accomplished by their structural mimicry of the D-Ala-D-Ala terminus of the core stem *and* the intrinsic acylation reactivity of their β-lactam structure. This mechanistic proposal was first articulated by Strominger, from his pioneering studies on the reaction of β-lactams with PBPs [59], and is known as the Tipper-Strominger hypothesis [60–62]. All subsequent study supports this hypothesis. Nonetheless, there remain numerous unanswered questions. The fundamental question—how do the β-lactams mimic the D-Ala-D-Ala structure, and why are the β-lactam-derived PBP acyl-enzymes so stable?—very much remains as open to experimental study.

A comparison of the D-Ala-D-Ala and penicillin (and cephalosporin) structures is given in Fig. 6. This perspective, simultaneously

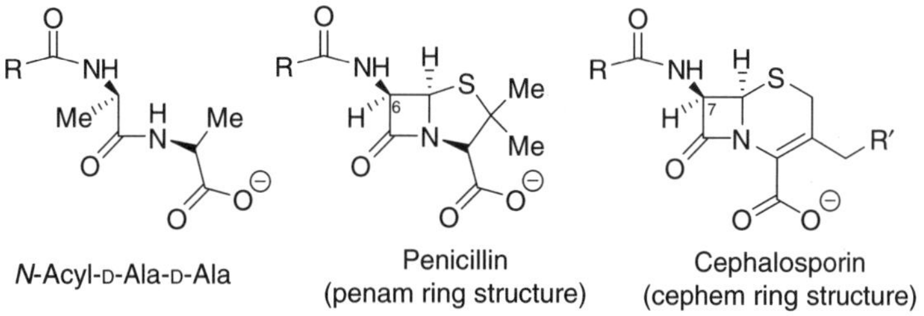

Figure 6. Comparison of the structures of D-Ala-D-Ala, penicillin and cephalosporin.

and independently articulated by Lee [63] and Sweet [64], emphasizes key points of similarity and difference. The features on the left sides of the penicillin and cephalosporin structures are identical. This identity coincides with the presence of an *N*-acyl group (top left), the positioning of the two amides, and the placement of the carboxylate terminus. There are two notable points of difference. The space occupied by the methyl group of the penultimate D-Ala corresponds to unsubstituted space (that of the C—H hydrogen at C-6 of the penicillin and at C-7 of the cephalosporin) of the β-lactams. Pratt [65] has argued forcefully that this point of difference is a key aspect of the evolutionary divergence of the PBPs into enzymes—the serine class β-lactamases—that are capable of efficient hydrolytic deacylation and are now widely distributed, as resistance enzymes, especially in Gram-negative pathogens. The evolutionary origin and role of the β-lactamases in β-lactam resistance are discussed in Section 3.3. A necessary aspect of evolutionary divergence is that the β-lactamase not be capable of hydrolytic degradation of the D-Ala-D-Ala terminus of Lipid II. This methyl is a probable steric barrier, used for this substrate differentiation. As we shall also see later, replacement of the 7-hydrogen with an appropriate substitutent, such as the 7α-methoxyl found in the cephamycin class, gives a structure that is β-lactamase-stable but still antibiotic. Again comparing D-Ala-D-Ala to the two β-lactams, the key point of difference is the dissimilarity of the top right quadrants. Whereas this quadrant is empty in the D-Ala-D-Ala structure, it is occupied in the β-lactams, and the nature of this occupancy for the β-lactams (the thiabicyclo structures) serves to covalently retain the equivalent of the distal D-Ala, which is otherwise lost (as a leaving group) upon completion of the acylation half-reaction. The retention of this segment by the β-lactams following acylation may be conjectured to result in a serine-acyl enzyme improperly positioned for further reaction (whether transpeptidation of hydrolysis) and/or sterically impeded for transpeptidation. Depending on the β-lactam structure (and whether the enzyme is a PBP or β-lactamase) one or both conjectures are likely true [66].

2.4. Structural Organization of the Cell Wall

Cell wall biosynthesis is multistep, commencing in the cytoplasm from fructose-6-phosphate and proceeding through 2-deoxy-2-aminoglucose (glucosamine) as an intermediate, to Lipid II as the last biosynthetic intermediate of the cytoplasm [39,40,67]. Translocation of Lipid II across the membrane into the periplasm follows. Although these events are common to both Gram-positive and -negative bacteria, the precise structure of the peptide stem of the NAM saccharide is variable [68,69]. In most Gram positives, a lysine is found in the third position of the peptide stem (-L-Ala-γ-D-Glu-L-Lys-D-Ala-D-Ala) whereas in most Gram negatives this position is occupied by *meso*-diaminopimelate (-L-Ala-γ-D-Glu-*m*DAP-D-Ala-D-Ala). Following translocation of Lipid II into the periplasm—now recognized to be present in both Gram-negative and -positive bacteria [23]—the peptide stem may be further modified, depending again on the bacterium [70]. Figure 7 shows in schematic summary (lower left) the cell wall structure for *S. aureus* (which adds a pentaglycine bridge to the ε-amine of the lysine) as the representative Gram-positive bacterium, and (lower right) for *E. coli* (which does not further modify the peptide stem of Lipid II) as the representative Gram-negative bacterium [71]. Table 1 summarizes representative bridge structures for several Gram-positive bacteria. Either prior to the peptide stem modification(s) or following these modifications, Lipid II is elongated into a glycan strand catalyzed by the transglycosylase domain of the biosynthetic (high M_r) PBP enzymes. The final step of cell wall assembly is transpeptidation of adjacent glycan strands, using the amine terminus of either the lysine or *m*DAP as the acyl-acceptor of one glycan, and with release of the D-Ala terminus of the stem of the second glycan. [72] As is previously discussed, this cross-linking is catalyzed by the transpeptidase doman of the biosynthetic PBPs, and it is this cross-linking that is inhibited by the β-lactams.

The peptidoglycan of the cell wall forms the exterior surface (outer wall) of the Gram-positive bacterium. High-resolution microscopy of dividing *S. aureus* indicates the thickness of

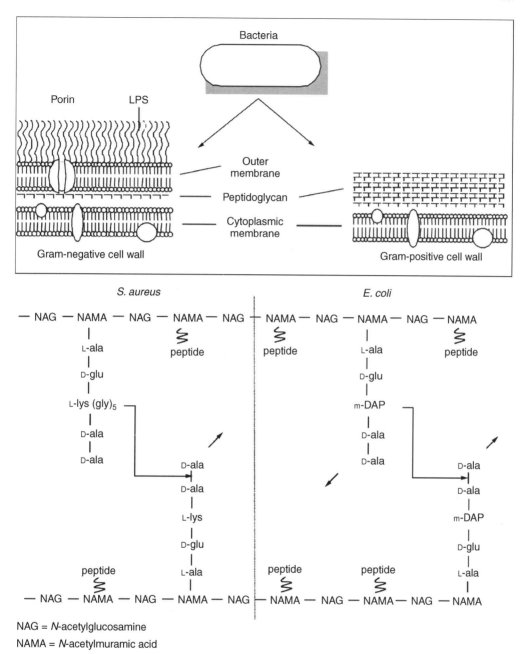

NAG = *N*-acetylglucosamine

NAMA = *N*-acetylmuramic acid

Figure 7. Bacterial cell wall of Gram-positive and Gram-negative strains.

its mature cell wall to be approximately 20 nm. At the septal zone of cell division, a thinner nascent cell wall is observed (10 nm) with a thicker cell wall (40 nm) at the "bridging" cell wall interconnecting the two daughter cells. Removal of this bridging cell wall—so as to allow separation of the two daughter cells—is catalyzed by enzymes ("autolysins") that hydrolytically degrade the peptidoglycan. These enzymes include D,

Table 1. Bridge in the Peptidoglycans of Bacteria[a]

Organism	Amino Acid 3, Chain 1[b]	Bridge[b]	Amino Acid 4, Chain 2[b]
S. aureus	L-Lys	(Gly)$_5$	D-Ala
S. epidermidis	L-Lys	(Gly)$_{4-5}$-L-Ala	D-Ala
Streptococcus agalacticae	L-Lys	L-Ala (or L-Ser)-L-Ala	D-Ala
Streptococcus group G	L-Lys	L-Ala (or L-Ser)-L-Ala	D-Ala
Streptococcus salivarius	L-Lys	Gly-L-Thr	D-Ala
Streptococcus bovis	L-Lys	L-Ser-Ala-L-Thr	D-Ala
E. faecium	L-Lys	D-Asn	D-Ala
E. faecalis	L-Lys	(L-Ala)$_{2-3}$	D-Ala
Streptococcus sp.	L-Lys	Gly-L-Ala	D-Ala
Gram-negative bacilli	*m*-Dap[c]	Direct; no bridge	D-Ala

[a] See Refs [70,77].
[b] Positions of amino acids 3 and 4 and of the bridge are indicated in Fig. 7.
[c] *m*-DAP, *m*-diaminopimelic acid.

D-endopeptidases, which cleave the cross-link synthesized by D-alanyl-D-alanine transpeptidases; *N*-acetylmuramyl-L-alanine amidase, which cleaves peptides from muramyl residue; and (3) lytic glycosylases [73], β-*N*-acetylglucosaminidases, and β-*N*-acetylmuraminidases, all of which hydrolyze the glycan strand of the peptidoglycan (Fig. 8). The peptidoglycan of the Gram-negative bacterium is located in the periplasmic space between the inner and the outer membranes. While its precise location is uncertain, the presence of L,D-transpeptidase enzymes that covalently attach membrane-bound proteins of the inner leaflet of the outer membrane to the peptidoglycan [74–76], suggest that this leaflet and the peptidoglycan may directly juxtapose. The cell wall of Gram-negative bacteria appears as a uniformly even surface within the periplasm that is thinner (*E. coli*, approximate thickness

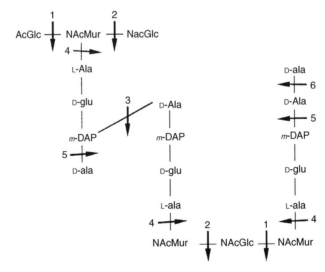

Figure 8. Action of autolysins. 1, β-*N*-acetylglucosaminidase; 2, lytic transglycosylase and β-*N*-acetylmuraminidase (lysozyme); 3, D,D-endopeptidase; 4, *N*-acetylmuramyl- L-alanine amidase; 5, L,D-carboxypeptidase; 6, D,D-carboxypeptidase. Although lytic transglycosylase and β-*N*-acetylmuraminidase (lysozyme) cleave the same target bond, the former enzyme additionally catalyzes transfer of the glycosyl bond to the 6′-hydroxyl group of the same muramic acid, yielding 1,6-anhydromuramic acid. NacGlc, *N*-acetylglucosamine; NacMur, *N*-acetylmuramic acid; *m*-DAP, *m*-diaminopimelic acid.

of 7 nm; *Pseudomonas aeruginosa*, 3.5 nm) than the Gram-positive cell wall [25].

The inactivation of the catalytic activities of PBPs by the β-lactams is bactericidal (in contrast to some other antibiotics, which are bacteriostatic in action). The molecular mechanism leading to this bacteriocidal outcome is uncertain. An attractive hypothesis is loss of regulation of cell wall homeostasis, possibly resulting in uncontrolled activation of one or more of the autolysins [78,79]. Many bacteria have multiple autolysins. As one example, *E. coli* has at least 11 different enzymes catalyzing 5 modes of cleavage [80]. The transglycosylases, transpeptidases, and autolysins are often (but not always) membrane bound, allowing their activities to be localized. Their main role is to provide sites for insertion of new peptidoglycans [81], but they may also assist in daughter cell cleavage [82–84] and for the insertion into (and adherence to) the peptidoglycan of the pili [85], secretion apparati, and flagella [86,87]. In this respect, the outcome of uncontrolled autolytic activity would be analogous to use of autolysins by phages in their entry and exit [88–90]. Evaluation of the effect of subinhibitory β-lactam exposure in *S. aureus* establishes that PBP inhibition is directly linked to autolysin activity [91]. However, the relationship seen in this study was strong repression of the autolytic system. A new and alternative mechanism for the bacteriocidal effect of the β-lactams, and which encompasses several antibacterial families, is induction of an envelope stress response that ultimately manifests lethal levels of intracellular reactive oxygen species [92–95].

In many Gram-negative bacteria, but not all, peptidoglycan fragments are actively released during cell growth and are then efficiently reabsorbed, internalized, and recycled.

3. MECHANISM OF RESISTANCE TO β-LACTAMS

The therapeutic use of an antibiotic selects for eventual resistance to it [96]. It is not necessary for the microorganism to identify a single resistance mechanism, nor is it necessary for the resistance mechanism to result in complete evasion of the antibiotic. Rather, the appearance of resistance in a microorganism typically coincides with acquisition of a single decisive resistance mechanism, abetted by the further selection of secondary resistance mechanisms. The molecular basis of the resistance mechanisms used by bacteria against the β-lactams are known [97,98], although in many cases important details as to how the resistance mechanism is fully implemented by the bacterium are not known. The combination of these mechanisms raises the concentration of the β-lactam needed for bacteriocidal efficacy to a level greater than what can be reached by chemotherapy. For the Gram-positive microorganisms, the decisive stroke is the use of acquired PBP enzymes with intrinsically poor recognition of the β-lactam, or to remodel peptidoglycan biosynthesis so as to obviate the role of the D-Ala-D-Ala terminus in transpeptidation. For the Gram-negative microorganisms, the decisive stroke is acquisition of a β-lactamase enzyme, having increasing greater ability to destroy advanced generation β-lactams. For both (but especially the Gram negatives), the secondary resistance mechanisms are selection of porins (proteins that control egress of solutes into the bacterium) with reduced ability to transport inward the β-lactams, and the use of active transporters to facilitate egress of the β-lactam.

As will be seen in the ensuing sections, the current themes for new β-lactam discovery coincide with these resistance patterns. For the newly resistant Gram negatives, it is the discovery of new β-lactams with intrinsic resistance to β-lactamase inactivation yet retaining high affinity for inactivation of their HMM PBP targets. For the newly resistant Gram positives, it is the discovery of new β-lactams possessing structural features that restore affinity to the otherwise resistant (to previous generation β-lactams) PBPs.

3.1. Acquisition and Spread of Resistance to β-Lactams

Bacteria acquire resistance by mutation of existing genes, or acquisition of new genes. Bacteria acquire new genes by bacteriophage transduction, or by transformation (uptake of DNA from the external environment). These transfers tend to occur mainly between members of the same species. Such narrow host range resistance transfer can be important clinically. For example, transformation is probably spreading PBP-type resistance genes between clinical isolates of *Streptococcus pneumoniae*, a common cause of bacterial pneumonia. A major clinical problem is the transfer of resistance genes across genus and species lines. Such broad host range transfer is most likely to be mediated by conjugation (transfer of DNA through a pore formed in the fused membranes of two bacteria). There are two types of conjugative elements, plasmids and chromosomal elements known as conjugative transposons.

3.1.1. Plasmids Plasmids are the best-studied conjugative mechanism. Plasmids that transfer themselves by conjugation must carry a number of genes encoding proteins needed for the conjugation process itself (*tra* genes). Thus, self-transmissible plasmids are usually at least 25 kb (kilobases). Some plasmids that cannot transfer themselves can still be transferred by conjugation because they are mobilized by self-transmissible plasmids. Such plasmids are called mobilizable plasmids, and can be much smaller than self-transmissible plasmids because they need only one or two genes (*mob* genes) that allow to them to take advantage of the transfer machinery provided by the other plasmids. Self-transmissible (or mobilizable) plasmids can acquire and transmit multiple antibiotic resistance genes. There are two ways plasmids can acquire multiple resistance genes. One way is to acquire sequential transposon insertions. However, most multiresistance plasmids apparently did not arise in this way. A more recent integrating element, called the integron, is probably responsible for evolution of many of the plasmids that carry multiple resistance genes (Fig. 9). Integrons, like transposons, are linear DNA segments that insert into DNA. Unlike transposons, however, integrons integrate at a single site and do not encode a transposase. The first integron inserted into a plasmid is inserted at an 8 bp consensus site on the plasmid. Integration is mediated by an integrase encoded on plasmid that receives the integron. The plasmid must also provide a promoter because

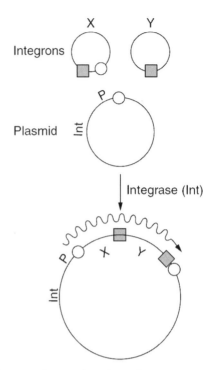

Figure 9. Integration of two integrons, carrying promoterless resistance genes X and Y, into a plasmid. The plasmid supplies the promoter (P) and integrase (Int). ◯, 8 bp consensus site; ■ 59- to 60 bp shared sequence.

most integrons contain promoterless antibiotic resistance genes.

3.1.2. Conjugative Transposons A second type of conjugative element is the conjugative transposon. Conjugative transposons are usually located in the bacterial chromosome and can transfer themselves from the chromosome of the donor to the chromosome of the recipient. They can also integrate into plasmids. Their mechanism of transfer is different from that of other known gene transfer elements. They excise themselves from the donor genome to form a covalently closed circle that does not replicate. This circular intermediate transfers with a mechanism similar to that of plasmids. In the recipient, the circular intermediate integrates in the chromosome by a mechanism that does not duplicate the target site. Conjugative transposons are probably responsible for at least as much resistance gene transfer as plasmids, especially among Gram-positive bacteria, and they have a very broad host range. Conjugative transposons can transfer not only among species within the Gram-positive group or within the Gram-negative group but also between Gram-positive and -negative bacteria. Conjugative transposons were overlooked for a long time because they are located in the chromosome and thus cannot be detected as easily as plasmids. Moreover, one of the few groups of bacteria in which conjugative transposons have not been found is the group of species closely related to *E. coli*. Like self-transmissible plasmids, conjugative transposons can mediate the transfer of the other DNA. They can mobilize coresident plasmids, and some can also mediate the transfer of unlinked segments of chromosomal DNA.

3.2. Modification of Native PBPs

The PBP content of bacteria shows surprising diversity. All bacteria have at least four PBPs, distributed among classes A, B, and C. All of these PBPs are membrane bound, through a hydrophobic peptide *N*-terminus. Classes A and B PBPs are high molecular mass (HMM) PBPs, while the class C PBPs are low molecular mass (LMM). Class A PBPs are bifunctional (transglycosylase and transpeptidase) catalysts. Class B PBPs are monofunctional catalysts of transpeptidation. The position of the transglycosylase domain in class B PBPs (in comparison to class A PBPs) is occupied by a domain whose function is believed to be protein–protein recognition. Class C PBPs are involved in peptidoglycan trimming and maturation, cell separation, and peptidoglycan recycling. The HMM PBPs are essential, whereas the LMM PBPs while important to the control of shape and possibly long-term viability are not.

The spherical-shaped Gram-negative *Neisseria gonorrhoeae* has four PBPs: one class A HMM PBP, PBP-1; one class B PBP, PBP-2; and two class C LMM PBPs, PBP-3, and PBP-4. The HMM PBPs are both essential, as is the possession of one of the LMM PBPs [99]. The rod-shaped Gram-negative *E. coli* has 12 PBPs; the sporulating rod-shaped Gram-positive *Bacillus subtilis* has 16 PBPs. The genetic, structural, and functional characteristics of

these enzymes are summarized in four exquisite reviews [38,43,49,100]. Considerable progress has been made (especially in *E. coli*) to understand the functional cooperativity among the PBPs [53,101], especially relating to the control of bacterial cell shape [102,103] and in bacterial cell division. In this latter role, the HMM PBPs participate in a "hyperstructure" involving numerous proteins and enzymes, the full composition of which is only now in its early stage of revelation [104–107].

3.2.1. Resistant PBPs Obtained by Mosaic Gene Formation
Modification of the normal PBPs is the sole cause of resistance to β-lactams in pneumococci [108–110] and other α-hemolytic streptococci [111] and, together with impermeability [112], is a major component of non-β-lactamase-mediated "intrinsic" resistance in *Neisseria* sp. [113–116] and *Haemophilus influenzae* [117–120]. Target modification of the PBP contributes to β-lactam resistance in *Acinetobacter* [121] but it is the ability of this microorganism to use the entire spectrum of resistance mechanisms (β-lactamases, efflux, and impermeability) that have conferred to these Gram-negatives high-level resistance [122,123]. Although modifications of normal PBPs are very rare, in some instances they have been thought to cause resistance in staphylococci, enterococci, enterobacteria, and pseudomonas [124,125]. Critically, the organisms in which PBP modification has proved important (i.e., α-hemolitic streptococci, hemophili, and *Neisseria* sp.) are transformable with naked DNA [126]. They can acquire fragments of PBP genes from other organisms with inherent or acquired β-lactam resistance and insert this into their own PBP genes. The resulting "mosaic" gene encodes β-lactam-resistant PBPs. The transformation can occur when sequence divergence between the incoming DNA and the native material is less than 25–305 bp, permitting interspecies recombination [126]. Restriction and mismatch repair systems do not limit exchange as much as might be anticipated and may even serve to correct errors during replication. Mosaic gene formation is understood for *Neisseria meningitidis*, where penicillin insensitive strains have alteration only in

PBP-2. In particular, the PBP-2 gene has regions of normal meningococcal sequence interspersed with inserts with 14% to 23% divergences [127,128]. These inserts closely resemble the corresponding section of the PBP-2 genes of *Neisseria flavescens* and *Neisseria cinerea*, which are throat commensals that are inherently unsusceptible to penicillin.

Penicillin-resistant gonococci have mosaic PBP-2 genes with inserts identical to those in resistant meningococci [128,129]. In addition, however, gonococci with high-level penicillin resistance commonly have modifications of PBP-1 and reduced permeability [130–132]. Mosaic gene formation has also been extensively studied in pneumococci [126]. High-level benzylpenicillin resistance (MIC values of more than 1 μg/mL, compared to MIC values of ≤0.06 μg/mL for "normal" isolates) requires modification, through mosaic gene formation, of each PBP-1a, -2x, -2a, and -2b, although low level resistance (MIC values of 0.12–1 μg/mL) arise when only three of these are altered [126]. Mosaic PBP-1a, -2x, and -2b genes of different resistant isolates have diverse inserts, whereas corresponding PBP gene sequences from susceptible isolates are highly conserved [133–137]. It is concluded that resistance has evolved on many separate occasions. The source of the foreign DNA is uncertain. Recombination events between penicillin-resistant *S. pneumoniae* and *Streptococcus mitis* are implicated [110,138–140]. Mosaic gene formation has not yet been proved in *H. influenzae* isolates with non-β-lactamase-mediated ampicillin resistance but seems likely, inasmuch as the resistance is associated with reduced PBP affinity [117,141,142] and is readily transformable in the laboratory [143]. The PBPs affected are 68- and 63 kDa proteins, numbered 3a and 3b or 4 and 5, respectively. Alternative routes of peptidoglycan synthesis allow a different form of target-mediated resistance, compared with that described above, and are important in staphylococci and *Enterococcus faecium* [144,145].

3.2.2. PBPs of *N. gonorrhoeae*   Chromosomal resistance in *N. gonorrhoeae* [146,147] involves five genes (*penA*, *penB*, *mtrR*, *ponA*, and *penC*). A mutation of the *penC* gene disrupts secretin assembly, reducing β-lactam ingress [148]. The role of the *mtrR* gene is efflux pump expression, further coordinated to porin (*penB*) selection [112,149]. A single class A PBP (PBP-1) is encoded by the *ponA* gene and a single class B PBP (PBP-2) by the *penA* gene. High-level β-lactam resistance correlates to mutations in PBP-1 [150] or PBP-2 [129], or acquisition of a mosaic PBP-2 [113,115,151,152]. The crystal structure of a mutant PBP-2 from β-lactam-resistant *N. gonorrhoeae* emphasizes the incremental and remarkable subtlety involved in the acquisition of resistance [116]. The location of the catalytic residues in the active site is virtually identical, and the rate constant for acylation of this PBP by β-lactams is reduced—likely as a result of thermal disordering—by only fivefold.

3.2.3. Methicillin-Resistant Staphylococci: Mechanism and Genetics   During the past decade, highly β-lactam-resistant *S. aureus*, the methicillin-resistant *S. aureus* (MRSA), has emerged from the hospital into the community as a serious Gram-positive pathogen [153–163]. Staphylococci that are β-lactam susceptible have two essential PBPs, 2 and 3 [100,164,165]. These two PBPs are β-lactam sensitive, including sensitivity to the penicillin, methicillin. MRSA retain the β-lactam-sensitive PBP-1 to PBP-3 but express an additional transglycosylase/transpeptidase, PBP-2a (also referred to as PBP-2′) encoded by the *mecA* gene [166–169]. PBP-2a continues to function when PBP-1, -2, and -3 have been inactivated [153,170] and yields a stable peptidoglycan, albeit with many fewer cross-links than that of the normal wall [171–173].

The *mecA* gene in MRSA is now believed to have arisen by horizontal gene transfer [174] of an endogenous PBP gene of the animal-resident *Staphylococcous sciuri* [175–178]. *S. sciuri* is not pathogenic to humans. The selection in *S. sciuri* of a PBP that is intrinsically resistant to β-lactam acylation may have occurred in response to veterinary use of β-lactams as antibiotics. The mechanistic pathway for the successful mobilization of the gene from *S. sciuri* to *S. aureus* is uncertain [158,179,180]. The *mecA* gene does not necessarily impose a fitness cost to *S. aureus* [181–184]. The *mec* determinant is not readily self-transmissible but has spread within *S. aureus* and several coagulase-negative species [185–187], indicating an ability for horizontal transfer. Several chromosomal genes have been implicated in the control of *mecA* [100], including those in the *fem* cluster, particularly *femA* [188–190], and the analogous *fib* locus in *S. pneumoniae* [191], as well as a second determinant, *chr* [192]. Curiously, loss of β-lactamase from MRSA causes *mecA* to be homogeneously expressed; the relation is unclear but implies a linkage in the control of the two-resistance determinant [193,194]. Expression of *mecA* and of resistance is induced by β-lactams and is also influenced by the environmental conditions, being promoted by high osmolality, low temperature, and neutral to alkaline pH [195,196]. These influences may also account for the observation of MRSA heteroresistance [161]. An additional aspect of MRSA heteroresistance of particular importance to MRSA chemotherapy is concurrent vancomycin heteroresistance [197–199].

A basis for the understanding of the molecular origin of the intrinsic β-lactam resistance exhibited by PBP-2a was provided by the crystallographic structure of this enzyme [200]. Comparison of the apo-enzyme with β-lactam-acylated enzyme shows a 1.8 Å movement of the nucleophilic oxygen (Oγ) of the catalytic serine (Ser403) coinciding with a tilt in the proximal helical domains of the active site [100]. This movement may coincide with the observation that the rate of PBP-2a acylation by β-lactams is substantially diminished [201]. In addition, an additional protein loop covers the PBP-2a active site, clearly impeding access of both substrate and inhibitor to the active site. Substantial evidence supports allosteric manipulation of the PBP-2a active site by peptidoglycan mimics of the cell wall [202]. The improved ability of newer generation β-lactams to acylate (and thus inactivate PBP-2a), in response to this allosteric manipulation by the cell wall, correlates to their improved antibacterial efficacy against MRSA [203,204]. In addition, a low pH-induced alteration of the PBP-2a structure, resulting also in improved efficacy for β-lactam acylation [205], likewise correlates to greater antibacterial efficacy against MRSA at lower pH values [206].

3.2.4. PBP-5 of E. faecium

Bypass resistance is also important in *E. faecium*, although rare in *Enterococcus faecalis*. *E. faecium* has six PBPs, with PBP-3 serving as the main D-alanyl-D-alanine transpeptidase. This protein is inhibited by penicillins and carbapenems, but not by cephalosporins and monobactams. At low temperature (32°C), or following mutation, *E. faecium* can switch to using PBP-5, a transpeptidase that has minimal affinity for any β-lactam. Acting alone, PBP-5 can manufacture a stable peptidoglycan [207,208]. Unlike PBP-2a of MRSA, PBP-5 is universal in *E. faecium*, and its permanent expression requires only a regulatory mutation, not acquisition of foreign DNA [209]. PBP-5 is a class B PBP, as is also the *S. aureus* PBP-2a (that is, do not catalyze transglycosylation). Many isolates of *E. faecium* have undergone this mutation and are consequently (and obviously) resistant to all β-lactams [210,211]. Both the structure of this PBP following penicillin inactivation [212] and the kinetics of its inactivation with several β-lactams are known [213]. This latter kinetic study correlated the rate of PBP acylation by the β-lactam with its antibacterial efficacy, suggesting in turn a correlation of critical side-chain interactions also with efficacy. Expression of the *fem* genes of *S. aureus* in *E. faecalis* and *E. faecium* resulted in mosaic peptidoglycan synthesis, and likewise expression of *S. aureus* PBP-2a in *E. faecalis* and *E. faecium* conferred β-lactam resistance [144].

3.2.5. PBP-2x of S. pneumoniae

PBP-2x is an essential PBP (and one of two class B enzymes) found in *S. pneumoniae*, and is the primary basis for *S. pneumoniae* β-lactam resistance [136]. While the native enzyme shows very high reactivity toward inactivation by β-lactams, a small number of mutations (including mutations quite distant from the active site) significantly reduce this reactivity and confer β-lactam resistance [214–217]. Mosaic PBP-2x enzymes that confer resistance are also known, and the study of these mosaic enzymes suggest a possible fitness cost, ameliorated by preservation of the cooperativity between PBP-2x and a second PBP, PBP-1a. The acyl-enzyme structure of this PBP, obtained by inactivation with a diversity of β-lactam structure, has been solved on a number of occasions [118,218–220]. Due to the availability of these different structures, intensive effort has been made to correlate these structures with the location of the resistance mutations [221–224]. As is also the case with the other well-studied resistant PBPs, the basis for the change from high to low β-lactam reactivity is subtle. Nonetheless, these studies have identified the active site contacts made by those β-lactams that retain PBP-2x affinity, and this identification have value for further structure-based design of new generation β-lactams [118,220,224]. The value of this approach, however, presumes that the structure of the acyl-enzyme is more useful than the structure of the transition state for acylation by the β-lactam, a presumption that is by no means proven [100,225].

3.3. β-Lactamase Enzymes: Biological Evolution of PBP and β-Lactamases

The serine β-lactamases (classes A, C, and D) are ancient enzymes with divergent origins from among the bacterial PBPs [226–230]. Correlation of the amino acid sequence of these β-lactamases with the PBPs describes this evolutionary history, with the low molecular weight enzymes most related to these β-lactamases. The diverse classes of β-lactamases are more closely akin to the different PBP classes from which they arose, than they are to each other. This is a further clear indication that β-lactamases originated from different groups of PBPs rather than from an immediate shared common ancestor. Class A β-lactamases cluster together with the class C low molecular mass PBPs, and the class C β-lactamases with the class B LMM PBPs. Here, the simpler domain structure of the low molecular weight PBPs provided the template for β-lactamase evolution. On the other hand, the sequence of the class D β-lactamases clusters with that of the high molecular mass PBPs. As the role of the HMM PBPs is different, the structural relationships among these three serine β-lactamase classes are at once similar

(sharing common catalytic motifs) yet different. The evolutionary origins of the class B metallo-β-lactamases are uncertain [231]. Nonetheless, these β-lactamases are also ancient, and constitute two distinct phylogenic groups each with an independent evolutionary origin [231–234]. Metzoan serine protease analogs of the PBP/β-lactamase family are known [235], such as the LACTB protease found in muscle [236] and believed to function within the metabolic syndrome network [237]. The purpose for retention of a PBP/β-lactamase homolog in eukaryotes is suggested as peptidoglycan degradation, such as during phagocytotic feeding [235].

The kinetic schemes for the PBPs and for the serine β-lactamases are similar. Both enzymes catalyze β-lactam ring opening by a serine nucleophile (the Enz-OH of Fig. 10), yielding an acyl-enzyme intermediate. The deacylation step (k_3) for the PBPs is exceptionally slow, while for the β-lactamases this deacylation can be very fast. A common mechanistic feature of serine β-lactamase inhibitors (Section 5.6) is intramolecular reaction of this acyl-enzyme into longer-lived acyl-enzyme species.

3.4. Classification and Relevance of β-Lactamases in Clinics

From a clinical perspective, the most important β-lactamases are those that threaten the use of the most beneficial β-lactam-containing antimicrobial agents. The importance of the β-lactamases as targets correlates directly with the spectacular ability of these enzymes to respond via evolutionary mutation, to the appearance of new generation β-lactams [238–244]. It is not merely the customary β-lactams—such the oral penicillins and cephalosporins, and β-lactams in combination with β-lactamase inhibitors (such as amoxicillin-clavulanic acid) that are used frequently for community infections such as otitis media—that are threatened, but the very newest β-lactams are also threatened.

3.4.1. β-Lactamase Classifications Many attempts have been made to classify the β-lactamases. The earliest basis for their distinction was whether a penicillin (such as

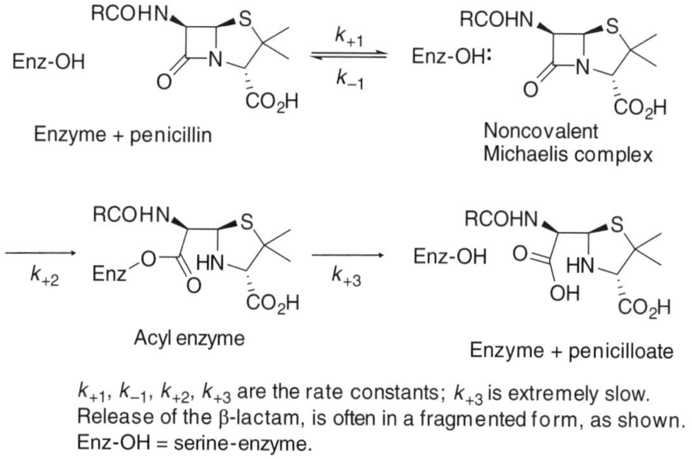
Enz-OH
RCOHN
S
N
O
CO2H
Enzyme + penicillin
k+1
k−1
Enz-OH:
Noncovalent
Michaelis complex
k+2
Enz
HN
Acyl enzyme
k+3
OH
Enzyme + penicilloate
k+1, k−1, k+2, k+3 are the rate constants; k+3 is extremely slow.
Release of the β-lactam, is often in a fragmented form, as shown.
Enz-OH = serine-enzyme.

Figure 10. Mechanism of action of serine β-lactamases.

benzylpenicillin) was hydrolyzed in preference to a cephalosporin (such as cephaloridine), thus distinguishing a penicillinase from a cephalosporinase. Table 2 summarizes the substrate spectrum of common β-lactamases. Other phenotypic properties used to categorize the β-lactamases include whether enzyme inhibition is achieved by cloxacillin, clavulanate, aztreonam, *p*-chloro-mercuribenzoate, or EDTA; and whether the enzyme is chromosomally encoded or plasmid encoded. Phenotypic categorizations are useful and convenient, in that they can sort all β-lactamases, can relate antibiogram data from clinical laboratories, and because they allow "weighting" of minor structural changes that critically alter the hydrolytic spectrum. The first phenotypic classification achieving wide acceptance was proposed by Richmond and Sykes in 1973 [245]. A convention emerged, concurrent with the appearance of these classification efforts, to identify plasmid-mediated β-lactamases (such as those falling into the Richmond–Sykes classes III and V) with a three letter–number code [246,247]. By 1984, plasmid-mediated β-lactamases could be clustered into three groups according to relative activity against benzylpenicillin, oxacillin, or carbenicillin. Broad-spectrum β-lactamases corresponded to Richmond–Sykes class III, but the oxacillinases and carbenicillinases—although very different from each other—both fell into class V. Other problems emerged with the Richmond–Sykes scheme [248]. Class I included two different classes of cephalosporinases, a clavulanate-insensitive, molecular weight 40 kDa, chromosomally encoded enzyme found in the enterobacteria; and the 30 kDa cefuroxime-hydrolyzing β-lactamase from *Proteus vulgaris*. Finally, many enzymes placed in class II proved to be transposon-mediated, and accordingly were transferred to classes III and V. These deficiencies prompted Bush to propose a major reorganization [249] on the basis of functional grouping within the Ambler molecular classification. In the Ambler classification [250], the serine β-lactamases are separated into three subclasses (A, C, and D) on the basis of amino acid sequence of the enzyme. The serine class A β-lactamases are distinguished (relative to a cognate PBP, and to the other two serine classes) by a loop structure, termed the Ω-loop [251], that places a catalytic glutamate into contact with an active site lysine for cooperative general base catalysis of serine acylation and deacylation [252,253]. The serine class C enzymes use lysine general base catalysis, in cooperation with either substrate or(/and) an active site tyrosine [254,255], for serine activation. The class D enzymes use a carboxylated-lysine for serine activation [256]. As an alternative and complement to the Ambler classes A–D,

Table 2. Correspondence Between Molecular and Phenotypic Classification of β-Lactamases

Structural Class (Ambler)	Functional Group (Bush)	Richmond–Sykes class	Activity[a]							Inhibition[b]		
			Penicillin	Carbenicillin	Oxacillin	Cephaloridine	Cefotaxime	Aztreonam	Imipenem	Clavulanate	Aztreonam	EDTA
Serine β-lactamases												
A	2a	NL[c]	+++	+	–	±	–	–	–	++	–	–
	2b	II and III	+++	+	+	++	–	–	–	++	–	–
	2be	IV	+++	++	++	++	++	++	–	++	–	–
	2br	NL	+++	+	+	+	–	–	–	+	–	–
	2c	II and V	++	+++	+	++	+	–	–	++	–	–
	2e	Ic	++	++	–	++	++	++	–	+	–	–
	2f	NL	++	+	?	+	+	++	++	+	–	–
C	1	I, except Ic	++	±	+	+++	+	–	–	–	++	–
D	2d	V	++	++	+++	+	–	–	–	V	++	–
Undetermined[d]	4[d]	NL	++	++	++	V	V	–	++	–	–	–
Zinc β-lactamases												
B	3	NL	++	++	++	++	++	–	++	–	–	++

[a] Activity: ++, preferred substrate (highest V_{max}); +, good substrate; ±, barely hydrolyzed; +, hydrolyzed; –, stable; V, varies within group; ?, uncertain.
[b] Inhibition: ++, strong inhibitor of all members of class; +, moderate inhibition; V, inhibition varies within the class; –, negligible inhibition.
[c] NL, not listed.
[d] None of Bush's group 4 enzymes has yet been sequenced. They are assumed to be serine types because they lack carbapenemase activity and are not inhibited by EDTA.

Bush classified β-lactamases according to their relative ability to hydrolyze penicillin, oxacillin, carbenicillin, cephaloridine, expanded-spectrum cephalosporins, and imipenem; and on their susceptibility to inhibition by clavulanate, aztreonam, and EDTA. Four "functional groupings" were recognized. The Group 2 enzymes (clavulanate-sensitive, aztreonam-resistant penicillinases) were divided into six subgroups. The enzymes in Group 4 are partly characterized. At this time, the dramatic increase in the number and variety of β-lactamases has resulted in the concurrent use in the literature of the letter–number, Ambler class A–D, and Bush descriptors. Table 3 [257] cross-correlates these descriptors using the more important letter–number β-lactamases for exemplification. The Richmond–Sykes classification is no longer in use. Correct classification of the metallo-β-lactamases with Class B remains a matter of debate [258,259]. The complete β-lactamase compilation maintained by the Lahey Clinic (http://www.lahey.org/studies/webt.html) is authoritative [260].

The Ambler sequence-based classification reflects fundamental relationships, unlike phenotypic classification, and cannot be distorted by mutations that alter substrate specificity and inhibitor susceptibility. Each of the four Ambler classes (A–D) shows distinct sequence motifs [261]. The distinction between chromosomally encoded and plasmid-mediated β-lactamases has lost relevance, as the trend for β-lactamase mobilization from the chromosome to the plasmid continues. Nevertheless, the distinction between chromosomal β-lactamases and those coded by plasmids (or other inserts) remains fundamental to the clinical microbiologist: chromosomal β-lactamases are ubiquitous in species, whereas plasmid-mediated types are less universal and cross interspecies lines. Table 3 summarizes Table 2 and cross-correlates many of the common three letter–number identified β-lactamases with their Ambler/Bush classifications.

The clinical introduction of the first serine β-lactamase inhibitors (clavulanate, sulbactam) was promptly followed by the appearance of inhibitor-resistant β-lactamases, especially the class A inhibitor-resistant TEM

(IRT) enzymes [262]. Evaluation of the mechanistic basis for this resistance revealed that straightforward mutation (within the active site, but in many cases also distant to the active site) were sufficient to incrementally diminish the inactivation kinetics, and thus meaningfully attenuate the potency of the inhibitor [239,263–268]. Rapid mutational response to clinically introduced β-lactams has become certain expectation: the uncertainty is only whether the resulting attenuation of the clinical potency will be meaningful. Indeed, there is excellent evidence that the durability of the class A TEM enzymes directly reflects their high tolerance to mutational events [269,270]. Efforts toward the prediction of the natural evolution of the class A TEM [240] and class C AmpC [271] β-lactamases have shown promise [228].

Following the clinical introduction of the oxyiminocephalosporins in the mid-1980s, mutant β-lactamases appeared encompassing these same cephalosporins as substrates. These β-lactamases, initially TEM and SHV mutants assigned to class A and Functional class 2be, were described as "extended-spectrum β-lactamases" or ESBLs [241,242,272–274]. With time—and with the appearance of many new additional β-lactamases having extended substrate spectra—the meaning of the term "ESBL" has been lost [275]. Several important events account for this loss of meaning. The first of these events is appearance new serine ESBLs, including the CTX-M (class A, Functional class 2be) [276], plasmid-mediated AmpC (class C, Functional class 1) [277,278], and OXA (class D, Functional class 2d) enzymes. The second of these events is the introduction into clinical use of the carbapenems, resulting in the emergence of "carbapenemases" [279–282]. Clinically important carbapenemases are found among the class A serine [282], class D serine [283], and class B metallo [231,281] β-lactamase families. The clinical threat of these carbapenemases cannot be overestimated [284]. The third of these events is the reemergence of interest in β-lactams, such as the monobactams and the 6α-methoxypenams, which combine a potent Gram-negative spectrum with intrinsic β-lactamase stability. Indeed,

Table 3. Molecular and Functional Classification of the β-Lactamases[a]

Molecular Class	Functional Class	Class Descriptor	Preferred Substrates	Inhibited by Clavulanate	Inhibited by EDTA	Examples
A	2a	Gram-positive penicillinase	Penicillins	Yes	No	PC1
A	2b	Broad spectrum	Penicillins and narrow-spectrum cephalosporins	Yes	No	TEM-1, TEM-2; SHV-1, OHIO-1
A	2be	Extended spectrum	Penicillins, all cephalosporins, monobactams	Yes	No	TEM-3, -10, -26; SHV-2, -5; CTX-M-1
A	2br	Inhibitor resistant	Penicillins and narrow-spectrum cephalosporins	No	No	TEM-30 to -36, SHV-10
A	2c	Carbenicillin capable	Penicillins including carbenicillin	Yes	No	PSE-1, -3, -4; AER-1; CARB-3, -4
D	2d	Oxacillin capable	Penicillins including oxacillin and cloxacillin	Variable	No	OXA-1 to -30
A	2e	Clavulanate-sensitive cephalosporinase	Cephalosporins	Yes	No	CepA, FPM-1, L2
A	2f	Serine carbapenemase	Penicillins, cephalosporins carbapenems	Yes	No	IMI-1, NMC-1; Sme-1
B	3a	Metallo (MBL)	Penicillins, cephalosporins carbapenems	No	Yes	B. cereus II, CcrA, IMP-1, L1, VIM-1 VIM-2, SPM-1
B	3b	Metallo (MBL)	Carbapenems	No	Yes	CphA, ASA-1 ASA-1, ImiS
B	3c	Metallo (MBL)	Cephalosporins, carbapenems	No	Yes	L. gormanii BLA
C	1	AmpC	Cephalosporins	No	No	Enterobacter, Citrobacter, Serratia, and Pseudomonas inducible; CMY, ACT-1, FOX plasmid
ND	4	Clavulanate-insensitive penicillinase	Penicillins	No	No	SAR-2

[a] See Ref. [257].

278

Table 4. Classification of the Extended-Spectrum β-Lactamases[a]

ESBL Class	Class Descriptor	Functional Class	Common Examples	Operational Criteria
$ESBL_A$	ESBL-Class A	Class 2be	CTX-M, TEM, SHV,	• Nonsusceptible to extended-spectrum cephalosporins
			VEB, PER	• Clavulanate synergy
$ESBL_{M-C}$	Plasmid-mediated ESBL-AmpC	Class 1	CMY, FOX, MIR, MOX, DHA, LAT, BIL, ACT, ACC	• Nonsusceptible to extended-spectrum cephalosporins; and
$ESBL_{M-D}$	ESBL-OXA	Class 2d	OXA-10 group OXA-13 group OXA-2 group OXA-18 OXA-45	•Phenotypic ($ESBL_{M-C}$) or genotypic ($ESBL_{M-D}$) detection
$ESBL_{CARBA-A}$	Carbapenemase-A	Class 2f	KPC, GES, NMC, SME, IMI	•Nonsusceptible to extended-spectrum
$ESBL_{CARBA-B}$	Carbapenemase-B (Carbapenemase-MBL)	Classes 3a–3c	IMP, VIM, SPM-1,	cephalosporins and at least one carbapenem and phenotypic and/or
			GIM-1, SIM-1, AIM-1	genotypic $ESBL_{CARBA}$ detection
$ESBL_{CARBA-C}$	Carbapenemase-OXA	Classes 2d	OXA-23 group	
			OXA-24 group OXA-48 OXA-58	

[a] See Ref. [285].

the assessment of all new β-lactams is measured by their efficacy against their PBP targets and their ESBL stability (whether alone, or in combination with a β-lactamase inhibitor). As a result of these three events, a new and comprehensive definition of the term "ESBL" is proposed [285]. Six ESBL subclasses (Table 4) encompass the oxyiminocephalosporin and carbapenem substrates. The first three classes are serine ESBLs with oxyiminocephalosporin activity: class A ($ESBL_A$), miscellaneous class C ($ESBL_{M-C}$), and miscellaneous class D ($ESBL_{M-D}$) enzymes. The remaining three classes are the carbapenemases, drawn from class A ($ESBL_{CARBA-A}$), from the metallo-β-lactamase class B ($ESBL_{CARBA-B}$), and from class D ($ESBL_{CARBA-D}$). This proposed classification is intended to provide scientific clarity, preserve clinical relevance, and retain a simplicity that will encourage its adoption. With the proliferation of ESBL variants there is universal agreement that the

unmodified descriptor "ESBL" is inadequate [275].

3.5. β-Lactam Resistance Attributed to Decreased Outer Membrane Permeability and Active Efflux

Antibiotic exposure selects all possible resistance mechanisms. In Gram-positive bacteria cell wall-acting antibacterials have in principle unhindered access to their PBP targets. In reality, one resistance response to β-lactams (and especially to glycopeptides) is the thickening of the Gram-positive cell wall [286]. In Gram-negative bacteria, the outer membrane acts as a barrier [287,288]. The balance between β-lactam influx and clearance (whether as a result of β-lactamase hydrolysis or active efflux) contributes to the susceptibility (or resistance) of the cell, given that permeability barriers alone rarely produce significant levels of resistance. In *E. coli* and other Gram-negative bacteria, β-lactams diffuse across the outer membrane primarily through water channels consisting of a specific class of proteins, termed porins. Mutations that reduce expression of porins, or reduce β-lactam accessibility to the existing porins, result in decreased susceptibility to the β-lactams.

3.5.1. Porin Loss in Enterobacteria Permeability mutants of enterobacteria, lacking one or more porins, are easily isolated in the laboratory [289,290]. The MICs of β-lactams (including penicillins, cefoxitin, and narrow- and extended-spectrum cephalosporins) for *E. coli* increase in a stepwise manner as first the OmpC porin and then OmpF porin are lost [291,292]. Loss of OmpF has a greater effect because it forms larger pores than OmpC. Despite this ease of selection, porin-deficient enterobacteria are rarely found in clinical settings, probably because they are nutritionally disadvantaged [293]. Nonetheless, Gram-negative mutants showing substantive β-lactam resistance as a result of porin loss are by no means unusual. Examples include *Klebsiella pneumoniae* with cefoxitin or carbapenems [294–300], a β-lactamase-depressed *Enterobacter cloacae* with carbapenems [290,301,302], *Salmonella enterica* (serovar Wien) with imipenems [303], and β-lactam-resistant *Neisseria* [112,149]. In some cases, the combination of impermeability with weak β-lactamase production confers clinical resistance, whereas the β-lactamase alone fails to do so [295,304]. Porin-deficient mutants of *Serratia marcescens*, lacking a 40 kDa protein, were selected more often than analogous mutants of other enterobacteria [293].

3.5.2. β-Lactam Resistance in *P. aeruginosa* *P. aeruginosa* is one of the "ESKAPE" bacterial pathogens (Section 4.3) currently representing either unmet or just barely met, medical needs for effective antibacterial therapy [305,306]. Rates of infection due to resistant (β-lactams, quinolones, and also increasingly aminoglycosides) *P. aeruginosa* are increasing globally, especially in patients that are ventilator dependent, immunocompromized, or have cystic fibrosis [307,308]. The basis for this concern is that *P. aeruginosa* is not simply intrinsically resistant to antibac-

terials, but when challenged it uses the entire array of resistance mechanisms (limited ingress, facilitated egress, resistance enzymes, target alteration) to attain high levels of multidrug resistance. Moreover, the fitness cost of this array may be minimal [309]. As the synergistic interplay of the full breadth of these individual resistance mechanisms still remains to be understood, study of *P. aeruginosa* resistance remains an important undertaking.

It is evident already that there is not a unique answer. The precise interplay is specific to the β-lactam structure, and indeed *P. aeruginosa* β-lactam resistance can result from prolonged non-β-lactam chemotherapy [310]. For this reason, current studies of *P. aeruginosa* resistance focus on the characteristics of clinical isolates [311]. For example, carbapenem resistance has been correlated to diminished expression of the oprD porin, sustained or increased (either ampC or metallo) β-lactamase expression, and activation of several different efflux systems [312–315]. Other clinical isolates show reduced transcription of PBP-2 and PBP-3 as further contributing to β-lactam resistance [316]. Imipenem (a carbapenem) resistance can result from loss of the ompD porin, while cephaloridine (a cephalosporin) retains activity [317]. Moreover, sensitivity to carbapenem may diminish irrespective of whether the OprD is lost, as evidenced by an increase of the MIC values of imipenem from 1–2 to 8–32 µg/mL and those of meropenem from 0.25–0.5 to 2–4 µg/mL [318]. The greater effect on imipenem than on meropenem reflects the slight liability of imipenem to the class C β-lactamase of *P. aeruginosa*. This enzyme gives greater protection when permeability is reduced by porin loss [319]. Meropenem has greater β-lactamase stability and is less affected by the porin loss [320].

The important role of efflux systems in *P. aeruginosa* resistance has made this pathogen a system of choice for the understanding of the role of these efflux systems in resistance. The molecular mechanism for induction of mexAB, the most important of these efflux systems, is redox driven, presumably by peroxide-dependent oxidation of a cysteine pair on the MexR regulator resulting in its dissociation from the DNA [321]. *P. aeruginosa* is regarded as an appropriate target for development of efflux inhibitors for synergy with antibacterials [322].

4. CLINICAL APPLICATION (HOSPITAL AND COMMUNITY)

4.1. Pharmacokinetic Properties

4.1.1. Penicillins Renal excretion is the major route of elimination of most penicillins. With few exceptions, renal clearance exceeds the glomerular filtration rate. In all cases studied, there is evidence of active renal tubular secretion, in that the coadministration of probenecid invariably decreases renal clearance, increases serum concentrations, and/or prolongs serum-life. Likewise, renal dysfunction profoundly affects the elimination rate, serum levels, and drug accumulation. Although homodialysis or peritoneal dialysis can be effective in some patients with end-stage renal failure, the rate of drug removal is not simply related to serum protein binding. Even though antimicrobial activity in bile is usually high compared to that in serum, biliary excretion contributes only insignificantly to the elimination of most penicillins. Notable exceptions are metampicillin, nafcillin, and the ureidopenicillins. β-Lactam ring cleavage appears to be a common metabolic pathway among penicillins. Penicilloic acid formation, although variable, may represent as much as 50% of total clearance of a given agent. Part of this clearance may occur in the gastrointestinal lumen or during initial transit through the gut wall and liver after oral administration. Although there is evidence of *N*-deacylation for some penicillins, only traces of 6-aminopenicillanic acid or penicilloic acid are found in human urine.

4.1.2. Cephalosporins The cephalosporin and cephamycin (7α-methoxycephalosporin) classes typically require parenteral administration. Notable orally absorbed cephalosporins include cephaloglycine, cephalexin, cephradine, cefadroxil, cefaclor, and cefratrizine [323]. Urinary excretion is the primary route of elimination for all cephalosporins, although biliary excretion and metabolism contribute to the elimination of several. For

most, urinary excretion involves both glomerular filtration and renal tubular secretion. As might be expected, kidney dysfunction or the coadministration of probenecid causes dramatic changes in drug elimination [324]. Cephalosporin antibiotics are remarkably stable *in vivo*, with few exceptions. The metabolism of cephalosporins has generally not been studied with discriminating assay technique. Those that have been studied show insignificant metabolism. Ceftobiprole medocaril (Section 5.2.8.8), a new fourth generation cephalosporin prodrug with broad-spectrum Gram-negative and -positive (including MRSA) activities [325], is an example. Upon infusion it is immediately converted to the parent in the serum, distributes well (volume of distribution of 18.4 L), undergoes minimal hepatic metabolism (hydrolytic β-lactam ring opening of approximately 5% of dose) thus failing to induce cytochrome P450 expression, with rapid renal excretion (terminal elimination half-life of 3 h) [326–328]. These pharmacokinetics were correlated to a dosing schedule [329]. As with all β-lactams, the ceftobiprole dose must be correlated to renal function [330].

The pharmacological properties of the parenteral penicillins and cephalosporins are summarized in Table 5 [331–333]. In general, β-lactam antibiotics penetrate most areas of the body except the eye, prostate (except aztreonam), and uninflamed meninges. Although entry into the cerebrospinal fluid (CSF) is satisfactory with most of the penicillins and carbapenems, only certain cephalosporins reach therapeutic levels in the CSF. Protein binding varies from 2% to 98%. The serum half-life of penicillins is short, ranging from 0.5 to 1.5 h. The half-life of cephalosporins, and especially the third-generation cephalosporins, tends to be longer. The half-life of ceftriaxone, the longest of all these agents, is 8 h [334]. Most penicillins, cephalosporins, and aztreonam are removed intact by renal excretion, and those require dose modification in patients with renal impairment. However, the isoxazolyl penicillins (nafcillin and oxacillin), the ureidopenicillins (such as piperacillin), and a few cephalosporins (ceftriaxone, cefoperazone, and cefotetan) have partial to predominant biliary excretion [335]. Dose modification is needed less often for the urei-

Table 5. Pharmacokinetic Properties of the β-Lactams

Antimicrobial	Protein Binding	$t_{1/2}$ (h)	Cerebrospinal Fluid Penetration	Route of Excretion
Penicillin G	55	0.5	Yes	Renal
Nafcillin	87	0.5	Yes	Biliary and Renal
Oxacillin	93	0.5	Yes	Biliary and Renal
Ampicillin	17	1	Yes	Renal
Carbenicillin	50	1.1	Yes	Renal
Ticarcillin	50	1.2	Yes	Renal
Piperacillin	50	1.3	Yes	Renal and biliary
Mezlocillin	50	1.1	Yes	Renal and biliary
Azlocillin	20	0.8	Yes	Renal and biliary
Aztreonam	56	1.8	Yes	Renal
Imipenem/cilastatin	20/40	1	Yes	Renal
Meropenem	2	~1	Yes	Renal
Cephalothin	71	0.6		Renal
Cefazolin	80	1.8		Renal
Cephradine	10	0.7		Renal
Cefamandole	75	0.8		Renal
Cefonicid	98	4.5		Renal
Cefuroxime	35	1.3	Yes	Renal
Cefoxitin	70	0.8		Renal
Cefotetan	90	3.5		Renal
Cefotaxime	35	1	Yes	Renal
Ceftizoxime	30	1.7	Yes	Renal
Ceftriaxone	90	8	Yes	Renal and biliary
Cefoperazone	90	2		Renal and biliary
Ceftazidime	17	1.8	Yes	Renal
Cefepime	20	2.1	Yes[a]	Renal

[a] Animal studies only.

dopenicillins and these cephalosporins, and is not needed at all for the isoxazolyl penicillins.

4.1.3. Carbapenems Imipenem is hydrolyzed in the renal tubules by the dehydropeptidase (DHP-1) enzyme, producing nephrotoxic metabolites, and requires coadministration of cilastatin, an inhibitor of DHP-1 [336]. This prolongs its half-life and preserves renal function. Newer generation carbapenems incorporate a 1β-methyl substituent, conferring stability toward the dehydropeptidase, and therefore do not require coadministration of a DHP-1 inhibitor [337]. An intravenous dose of ertapenem, for example, undergoes primarily renal clearance. Approximately 90% of the ertapenem dose is excreted in the urine (approximately one-half unchanged, one-half β-lactam opened) with biliary clearance of the remainder [338]. Carbapenems also require dose reductions in patients with renal impairment. The serum half-life of meropenem (4.5 h) allows single daily dosing, an option not possible with imipenem due to its shorter serum half-life (1.5 h).

4.2. Side Effects and Drug Interactions

A remarkably favorable chemotherapeutic index has been one of the most important qualities of the animal and human pharmacology of the first penicillins. Aside from problems of local irritation and of neurotoxicity with extremely large doses, these antibiotics have minimal direct toxicity. For nearly 20 years, allergic or immune-mediated reactions represented the only common complications of the use of penicillins. However, while the development of newer penicillins and cephalosporins (as well as other β-lactam classes) has largely preserved this exceptional safety profiles, other toxicity problems have emerged, particularly in the carbapenem subclass.

Pain and sterile inflammatory reactions at the site of intramuscular injection are among the most common local effects of therapy with the penicillins and cephalosporins. With benzylpenicillin these reactions appear to be related to the concentration of the antibiotic, and this also may be the case for the other penicillins [339]. Phlebitis develops in many patients receiving intravenous penicillins or cephalosporins [340]. The relative risk of phlebitis among the different cephalosporins is small [341–343], but is still seen with the newer β-lactams [344]. Phlebitis is more frequently seen with intravenous as compared to intramuscular or oral dosing [345].

Gastrointestinal side effects are among the most common adverse reactions to oral treatment with the β-lactam antibiotics. Some degree of gastric irritation is reported in 2–7% of patients [346]. The discomfort occasionally results in discontinuation of the drug, although serious consequences are rare. Diarrhea is also a relatively common problem, which may be of mild or life-threatening severity. Three types (nonspecific diarrhea, pseudomembranous colitis, presumed ischemic colitis) are distinguishable. Given the efficacy of oral cephalosporins for the treatment of community-acquired respiratory and other infections [323], and the correlation of oral β-lactam administration not only with diarrhea but also with resistance selection [347–349] and pathogen—such as *Clostridium difficile*, often causative of the diarrhea [350]—displacement of desirable microbiota [351,352], innovative β-lactamase cotherapy for β-lactam administration is receiving pharmacological assessment. Oral administration of a β-lactamase concurrent parenteral administration of the β-lactam [353–355], or slow-release colonic β-lactamase release for oral β-lactams [356,357], have delivered encouraging results. These approaches are fully consistent with the necessity for improved antibacterial stewardship in the clinic (Section 4).

Some of the most important reactions to β-lactam antibiotics result from the involvement of humoral or cellular immunity [358]. Almost all patients receiving benzylpenicillin develop antibodies to it [339]. The frequency of allergic reactions to penicillins has been reported as 0.7–10%, and the frequency for cephalosporins as 0.8–7.5% [359,360]. The larger number in this range coincides with patient reporting, while the lower number is believed to more closely coincide with true incidence [361]. Humoral hypersensivity produces some of the most serious adverse effects, including urticaria, angioedema, bronchospasm, and anaphylaxis. The frequency of anaphylactic reactions to penicillin has been estimated to be 0.045–0.15% [339,362]. A history of previous exposure to penicillin is common but not invariable. Skin testing may be helpful in distinguishing those patients at risk for anaphylaxis, especially if testing is conducted with both major and minor antigenic determinants of the penicillin [363]. Skin rashes during the administration of a penicillin or cephalosporin are relatively common, occurring in approximately 2% of cases [346,364,365]. Aztreonam, however, is safe for administration to penicillin-allergic patients [366–368].

Current clinical experience indicates that allergic reactions to cephalosporins are comparable in frequency to those for penicillins [369]. Given the importance of the β-lactams to antibacterial therapy, and the structural diversification of classes within the β-lactams, a decision as to appropriate antibacterial therapy for the allergic patient continues as an important clinical issue [370]. Sensitivity toward a penicillin does not implicate sensitivity toward a cephalosporin [371], and an understanding of these cross-reactivities is required for the correct (measured in terms of cost and efficacy) chemotherapeutic decision [361,370,372]. Since the available allergic tests are available only for penicillins, one central question is whether a penicillin-test positive patient is at risk for cephalosporin therapy. Alternative testing methods, given the commercial absence of the benzylpennicilloyl-polylysine (major determinant) reagent, are reviewed [373]. The present consensus is that there should indeed be the presumption of risk for patients with a history of penicillin allergy, regardless of whether the skin test is negative or positive. Where cephalosporin therapy is unavoidable, it should be initiated very cautiously, with independent skin and provocation evaluations and with graded challenges [374,375]. A recent retrospective study on clinical experience with meropenem (a carbapenem) gave no evidence for allergic cross-reactivity to the carbapenem in patients reporting penicillin allergies [376].

It is now recognized that the β-lactams, as a class, exhibit dose-dependent neurotoxicity [377–380]. This neurotoxicity is seen particularly among the carbapenems at very high dosing, or high dosing concurrent with renal insufficiency [381]. Imipenem produces seizures in 0.4–1.5% of patients, predominantly those affected by renal insufficiency with underlying central nervous system (CNS) disease. The newer carbapenems (having DHP-1 stability) have a lower risk of CNS toxicity compared to imipenem [382–384].

A more recent and apparently unrelated discovery is the ability of the β-lactams, notably the cephalosporin ceftriaxone (Section 5.2.4), to induce increased expression of the EAAT2 glutamate transporter at the synapse [385]. This outcome was first shown to be ameliorative and neuroprotective in a pharmacological model of ALS [385], and subsequently in other models of excitotoxic inflammatory CNS damage including HIC dementia [386], multiple sclerosis and autoimmune encephalomyelitis [387], Huntington's disease [388], stroke [389], and hyperbaric hypoxia [390]. In addition, ceftriaxone attenuated morphine-evoked hyperthermia in rats [391], which attenuates the development of physical dependence and abstinence-induced withdrawal from cocaine and amphetamine [392], and abolishes tolerance to kappa opiod receptor agonists [393]. The molecular mechanism of this epigenetic effect involves promotion of the nuclear translocation of p65 and activation of NF-κB [394]. Biochemical and pharmacological evaluation of the ability of ceftriaxone to ameliorate neurodengerative disease through modulation of extracellular glutamate [394] is intense, and the literature cited is only representative.

A second cephalosporin, ceftiofur, impairs bacterial lipopolysaccharide induced proinflammatory cytokine secretion (including TNF-α, interleukin IL-6, and interleukin IL-10) through inhibition of the activation of NF-κB and MAP kinase, including inhibition of p65-NF-κB translocation [395,396]. It remains to be determined if these effects of ceftiofur and ceftriaxone represent different molecular mechanisms, or reflect different outcomes reflecting the difference in structures, within a similar molecular mechanism.

4.3. Indications for Use

The β-lactams are the drugs of choice for the treatment of a variety of infections caused by specific bacteria. While there are many bacterial infections where they retain efficacy (summarized in Table 6), over the past decade a new array of bacterial pathogens—found both in the hospital and in the community—has appeared. Each member of this array represents a challenge to empirical treatment, not just by the β-lactams but other antibacterials as well. This array is summarized by the acronym "ESKAPE." It includes "E" for vancomycin-resistant *E. faecium* (VRE), "S" for methicillin-resistant *S. aureus*, "K" for extended-spectrum β-lactamase and carbapenemase-expressing *Klebsiella* and *E. coli*, "A" for *Acinetobacter baumannii*, "P" for *Pseudomonas*, and "E" for ESBL-expressing *Enterobacter* [305,397]. Given the exceptional resistance of these pathogens, in the face of a diminished clinical pipeline of new antibacterials, the necessity for improved antibacterial "stewardship" has been recognized [398–401]. This stewardship (as defined by Gerding) involves optimization of antibacterial selection, dose, and duration for the combined objectives of safety, efficacy, and minimal impact on resistance development. The driving forces behind resistance development to the β-lactams were summarized in the previous section. The subsequent sections of this review focus largely on the correlation of structure to the therapeutic need defined by these pathogens. As will be noted, it is not only the discovery of new structure but also the reevaluation of old structure to meet this need. The presumption that the optimal therapeutic antibacterial must always be broad-spectrum is now balanced against the understanding that a pathogen-selective (especially in term of Gram positive versus Gram negative) antibacterial may have intrinsic clinical advantage. Aspects of this treatment dilemma (including consideration of both β-lactam and

Table 6. Recommendations for the Use of β-Lactams

β-Lactam	Recommendation	Organism or Condition	Notes
Penicillin G	Primary indication	*Streptococcus pyogenes, S. pneumoniae,* and enterococcal infections	
	Drug of choice	Treponemal infection, prevention of rheumatic fever.	
	Can be used	Puerperal infection: anaerobic strepto-cocci, *Streptomyces agalactiae,* clos-tridial infection, and infection attri-buted to mouth flora: Gram-positive cocci, Gram-negative cocci, and *Actiomyces*	
Penicillinase-resis-tant penicillins	Can be used	Susceptible *S. aureus* infection	
Aminopenicillins	Recommended	Prevention of endocarditis	
	Can be used	Infection of respiratory tract in areas with low prevalence of β-lactamase and *H. influenzae.* Urinary tract infection	
Extended spectrum	Primary indication	*Pseudomonas* sp.	
	Can be used	Infection of urinary tract, respiratory tract, and bone with Gramnegative bacilli and mixed aerobic/anaerobic infections	
Combination drugs	Can be used	Mixed bacterial infection: community and hospital-acquired pneumonia, especially if aspiration, intra-ab-dominal and gynecological infections, osteomyelitis, and skin-structure infection	
Timentin (ticarcil-lin and clavula-nic acid)			
Unasyn (ampicillin and sulbactam)	Can be used	Mixed bacterial infection: intra-abdom-inal: obstetric, gynecologic, soft tis-sue, bone infection	
Zosyn (piperacillin and tazobactam)	Can be used	Mixed bacterial infection: lower re-spiratory tract, intra-abdominal, skin, and soft tissue infection	
Monobactams aztreonam	Can be used	Urinary tract, lower respiratory tract, skin structure, and intra-abdominal infections, patients with penicillin allergy	
Carbapenems	Can be used	Resistant Gram-negative bacilli infec-tion with ESBL.	
Imipenem	Drug of choice	Nosocomial infection, when multiresis-tant Gram-negative bacilli or mixed infections are suspected	
Meropenem	Can be used	Nosocomial infection when multiresis-tant Gram-negative bacilli or mixed infections are suspected.	
First-generation cephalosporins	Drug of choice	Prophylaxis of surgical procedures	
	Can be used	Infection attributed to *S. aureus* or nonenterococcal streptococci (e.g, skin and soft tissue infections, pharyngitis)	

Table 6. (*Continued*)

β-Lactam	Recommendation	Organism or Condition	Notes
Second-generation cefuroxime	Can be used	Respiratory tract infections: pneumonia epiglottis, complicated sinusitis, soft-tissue infections, bacteremia	Good *H. influenzae* coverage
Cefoxitin	Drug of choice	Pelvic inflammatory disease (+ doxycicline)	
	Recommended	Prophylaxis of colorectal surgery	
	Can be used	Mixed aerobic/anaerobic infections: intra-abdominal infections, skin and soft-tissue infections, including diabetic foot infections and decubitus ulcers	
Cefotetan		Mixed aerobic/anaerobic infections: intra-abdominal infections, skin and soft-tissue infections, including diabetic foot infections and decubitus ulcers	Slightly less anaerobic coverage but better Gram-negative coverage than cefoxitin
Third-generation ceftriaxone	Drug of choice	*Neisseria gonorroea* chancroid, Lyme disease if neurological involvement, carditis, arthritis, or refractory late constitutional symptoms	Once-daily dosing, good CSF penetration
	Recommended	Meningitis attributed to *H. influenzae, Neisseria* meningitis, and penicillin-resistant *S. pneumoniae*	
	Can be used	Nosocomial infection caused by a sensitive Gram-negative baccilli: pneumoniae, wound, and complicated urinary tract infections	
		Home treatment of chronic infections	
Ceftazidime	Should be used	Infections that are likely attributable to *P. aeruginosa*	
	Can be used		
	Drug of choice	Empiric treatment of febrile neutropenia	
		Meningitis attributed to *P. aeruginosa*	
Cefoperazone	Can be used	Empiric treatment of febrile neutropenia	Moderate antipseudomonal activity
Cefepime	Can be used	Infections of lower respiratory tract, urinary tract, skin and soft tissue, and in female reproductive tract	
	Can be used	Nosocomial infection caused by a sensitive Gram-negative baccilli: pneumoniae, wound, and complicated urinary tract infections	

non-β-lactam antibacterial therapy) are reviewed recently for Gram-negative pathogens including *P. aeruginosa, A. baumannii,* and *K. pneumoniae* [402], for Gram-positive MRSA [403–405], for acute bacterial rhinisinustis [406], and for *S. pneumoniae* community-acquired pneumonia [407,408].

The β-lactam drugs remain stalwart agents for the empirical treatment of febrile neutropenic patients [409–412]. However, the choice of empirical therapy is less straightforward compared to the choices of the past. No best regime exists. Important factors influencing the choice of empirical therapy for febrile neutropenia include the type of cancer chemotherapy being used, expected severity and duration of neurotropenia, the presence of an indwelling long-term catheter, previous use of prophylactic antibiotics or gut decontamination, the patients' symptoms, and the bacterial resistance pattern of the hospital. Supportive evidence also exists for the empiric use of β-lactam drugs in combination with an aminoglycoside. Piperacillin, mezlocillin, azlocillin, and ticarcillin all have shown similar efficacy, with response rates of 55–88% [413,414]. A convenient regimen of once-daily dosing of ceftriaxone and amikacin, and ceftriaxone and amikacin, proved as effective as multiple daily-dosing regimens [415,416]. Toxicity for aminoglycoside use led to trials with combinations of two β-lactam agents. Good results were achieved with multiple regimens, including carbenicillin plus cephalotin, cefoperazone plus aztreonam, cefoperazone plus mezlocillin, ceftazidime plus piperacillin, and ceftazidime plus ticarcillin/clavulanate [409,413,414]. However, double β-lactam therapy remains controversial because of the possibilities of increased selection of resistant organisms, drug antagonism, prolongation of neutropenia, and potentiation of bleeding disorders. Recent studies include reports of the successful implementaton of ceftazidime [417,418], piperacillin/tazobactam [419,420], imipenem/cilastatin, meropenem [421], and both ceftriaxone [422] and cefepime as monotherapy [423].

β-Lactam antibiotics have played a key role in improving the care of both immunocompromized and nonimmunocompromized patients. These agents are bactericidal, well tolerated, widely distributed throughout the body, and clinically effective.

5. CHEMISTRY OF THE β-LACTAMS

The discovery of the penicillin class of the β-lactam antibiotics is a milestone in medicinal chemistry. The β-lactam class has endured, not only as the preeminent antibiotic class for the treatment of bacterial infection but also as that

continues to reveal truly remarkable breadth of structure and biological activity. Indeed, the simple term "β-lactam," with its emphasis on the small and deceptively simple four-membered ring, poorly emphasizes this breadth. Rather, the history of the β-lactams can be compared to a sky full of stars. The terse pages that follow describe the most important β-lactam classes, and embrace both β-lactams that are antibacterials, and those that as β-lactamase inhibitors antagonize a primary bacterial resistance mechanism.

5.1. Penicillin

Alexander Fleming made the remarkable observation in 1928 that the partial lysis of staphylococci colonies occurred on plates contaminated with *Penicillium notatum*. The antibiotic era was initiated in 1940 with the proof by Florey and his colleagues [424] that penicillin, the chemical basis for Fleming's discovery, was a chemotherapeutic agent of unprecedented potency [425]. The life-saving capacity of penicillin was first demonstrated in animals, and in humans the following year, when the small quantities of penicillin available necessitated the recovery of the antibiotic from the urine of the patient for reuse [426]. Once penicillin was shown to be effective in humans, the search for improved production was initiated. War-torn Britain was thought unsuitable for such research, so key scientists moved to the United States to continue the effort alongside their American colleagues. Here, replacement of the surface cultures of the low-yielding *P. notatum* with the first use of an aerated deep fermentation of a high yielding strain of *Penicillium chrysogenus*, and the use of corn-steep liquor as growth promoter, led to greatly improved penicillin production. This provided sufficient material for the treatment of infections associated with serious battle casualties during the end of World War II, and so confirmed the important role of penicillin in the saving of life.

Soon after the demonstration of the extraordinary efficacy in treating infections, penicillin was the subject of in-depth studies by groups on both sides of the Atlantic to solve the structure of penicillin. The correct structure of benzylpenicillin (Pen-G) was eventually identified as the fused β-lactam-thiazolidine bicyclic structure (3), as opposed to an oxazolone alternative, by an X-ray crystallographic analysis in 1945 [427].

Isolation of reasonably pure samples of penicillin revealed differences in chemical behavior and biological properties between the materials studied by different groups. This arose as a consequence of the different acyl side chains (RCO) attached to the C-6 amino group. The source of the acyl side chains is the carboxylic acids present in the culture media producing that penicillin; thus, the phenylacetic acid in corn-steep liquor resulted in the phenylacetamido group (RCO=PhCH$_2$CO) of penicillin G (3). From among the many penicillins that have been isolated from *Penicillium* sp. fermentations, either unaided or resulting from the incorporation of added precursor acids (RCO$_2$H), several of the better known examples are shown (Table 7) with their British and U.S. designations.

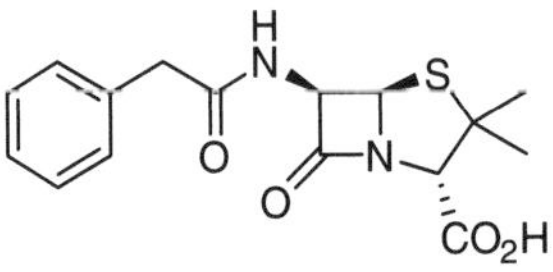

The next major advance was the isolation and characterization of the penicillin nucleus, 6-amino-penicillanic acid (6-APA) (4) [435], in 1957 by the Beecham group at Brockham Park [436]. This major breakthrough provided a source of chiral material for the preparation of semisynthetic penicillins. Concurrently with identification of 6-APA (2) from biochemical investigations, Sheehan and Henerey-Logan concluded their total synthesis of penicillin (1) [437,438] (see Section 5.1.1) and 6-APA [439,440].

However, this synthesis gave a low overall yield and lacked stereospecificity, so it could not compete with the biochemical route as a practical source of material for chemical modifications. Today, 6-APA (4), obtained from penicillin G by enzymatic cleavage of the phenylacetyl side chain, is readily available in bulk quantities for use in the semisynthesis of new penicillins.

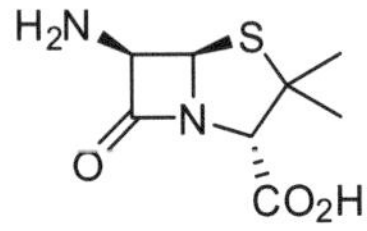

(3) Penicillin G (1929–1940)

(4) 6-Amino-penicillanic acid (6-APA)

Table 7. Biosynthetic Penicillins

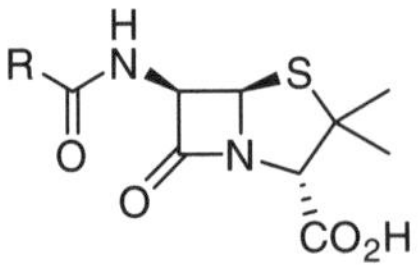

	Name	British Name	United States Name	R	Reference
a	2-Pentenyl penicillin	I	F	CH$_3$CH$_2$CH=CHCH$_2$–	[428]
b	Pentyl penicillin	Dihydro I	Dihydro F	CH$_3$(CH$_2$)$_4$–	[429]
c	Heptyl penicillin	IV	K	CH$_3$(CH$_2$)$_6$–	[428]
d	Benzyl penicillin	II	G	PhCH$_2$–	[430]
e	*p*-Hydroxybenzyl penicillin	III	X	4-HO–PhCH$_2$–	[430]
f	(D)-4-Amino-4-carboxybutyl penicillin		N	(D)–HO$_2$C–CH (NH$_2$)(CH$_2$)$_3$–	[431]
g	(L)-4-Amino-4-carboxybutyl penicillin		*iso*-N	(L)–O$_2$C–CH (NH$_2$)(CH$_2$)$_3$–	[432]
h	Phenoxymethyl penicillin		V	PhOCH$_2$–	[429]
i	Butylthiomethyl penicillin	BT		C$_4$H$_9$SCH$_2$–	[433]
j	Allylthiomethyl penicillin	AT	O	CH$_2$=CHCH$_2$SCH$_2$–	[433]
k	*p*-Aminobenzyl penicillin		T	4-H$_2$N–PhCH$_2$–	[434]
l	*p*-Nitrobenzyl penicillin			4-O$_2$N–PhCH$_2$–	[434]

5.1.1. Synthesis of Penicillin

Three major synthetic approaches to penicillin were developed from the considerable synthetic effort first initiated in the 1940s. The first approach was the Sheehan carbodiimide-mediated closure of the penicilloic methyl ester (5) to the β-lactam.

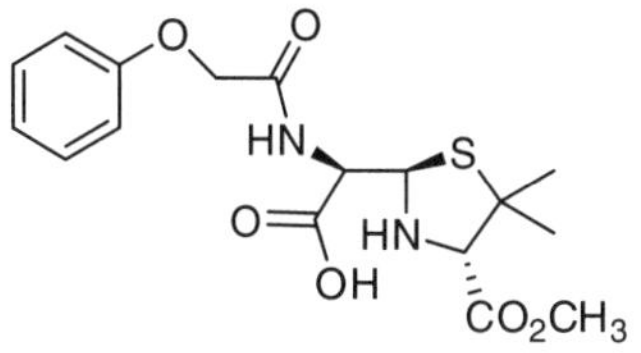

(5)

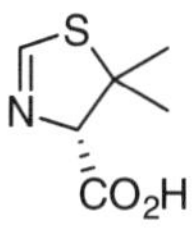

(6) 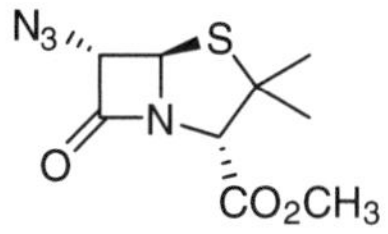   (7) 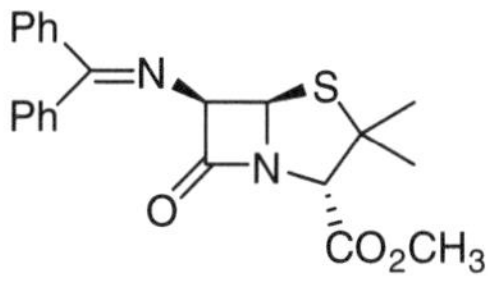   (8) 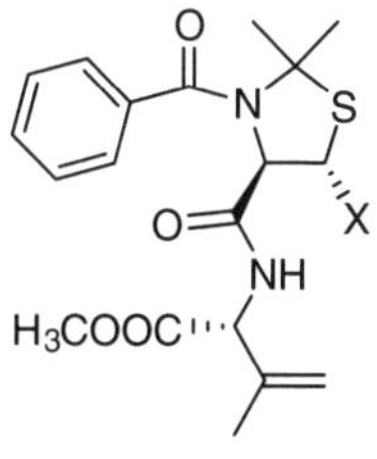   (9) X = H
                     (10) X = Cl

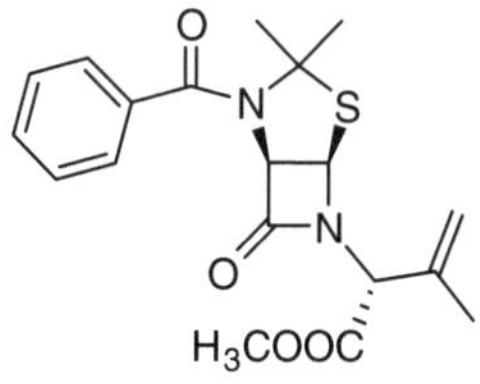

(11) 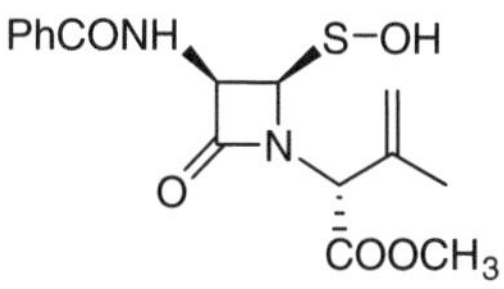   (12) 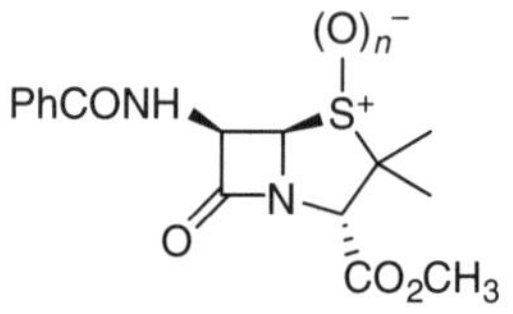   (13) n = 1
                (14) n = 0

It was not until 1976 that the only stereoselective synthesis of penicillin was described by Baldwin [443]. Thus, the peptide precursor (9), derived from cysteine and D-isodehydrovalinemethyl ester, was cyclized through the chloride (10) to the β-lactam (11). Conversion of (11) by a multistep process then generated the sulfenic acid (12), which cyclized to the sulfoxide (13). Reductive deoxygenation of the sulfoxide gave the penicillin ester (14).

5.1.2. Derivatives of 6-APA: Biological Activity and Structure–Activity Relationship (SAR)

The availability of 6-APA led to the preparation of many thousands of semisynthetic penicillins by N-acylation of the 6-amine [444]. This increase in the scope of side-chain variation

A second approach to the β-lactam was devised by Bose using dihydrothiazoline (6) cycloaddition with the ketene derived from azidoacetyl chloride. The reaction product is, however, the thermodynamically favored unnatural *trans*-penicillin (7) [441]. Subsequently, equilibration of the C-6 stereochemistry by kinetic quenching of the anion generated from imine (8) provided some quantities of the natural *cis*-β-lactam stereochemistry [442].

allowed significant improvements in the biological properties of the derived analogs, including greater stability to penicillinase (β-lactamase) and an expanded spectrum of antibacterial activity. Some early examples of semisynthetic penicillins studied in humans were the acid-stable penicillin V (15), phenethicillin (16) and propicillin (17). Despite the latter two being a mixture of diastereoisomers, increased oral absorption (thus giving higher and more prolonged blood levels) was seen compared to penicillin V [445].

The fast widespread use of penicillin G, and probable misuse or abuse of this antibiotic, had already resulted in an increase in the occurrence of penicillinase-producing strains of *S. aureus*. Penicillinase is an enzyme that hydrolytically opens the β-lactam, destroying its antibiotic activity. The broader term "β-lactamase" has now replaced the term penicillinase, reflecting the increasing and broader role that these enzymes contribute to clinical β-lactam resistance. By 1960 penicillinase-dependent resistance was a worldwide clinical problem [446]. Often these strains of *S. aureus* were virulent and resistant to most other antibiotics, thus making them difficult to eradicate. Much early research was therefore directed at identifying new penicillins resistant to inactivation by these penicillinases. Methicillin (18) was introduced into clinical usage in 1960 [447], followed by nafcillin (19) [448]

and the isoxazole penicillins oxacillin (20a) [449], cloxacillin (20b) [450], dicloxacillin (20c) [451], and flucloxacillin (20d) [452]. In each of these, the steric bulk of the side-chain group adjacent to the amide carbonyl group protected the β-lactam ring from the unwanted hydrolysis by the bacterial penicillinase.

The aminopenicillins such as ampicillin (21) [453], epicillin (22) [454], amoxycillin (23) [455,456], and cyclacillin (24) [457] introduced into the clinic between 1961 and 1972, are characterized by their broad spectrum of antibacterial activity against both Gram-positive and -negative bacteria and good oral absorption.

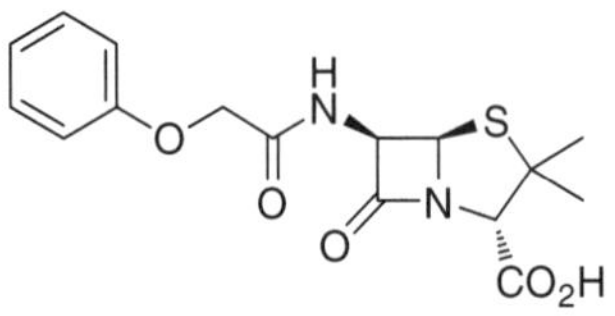

(15) Penicillin V

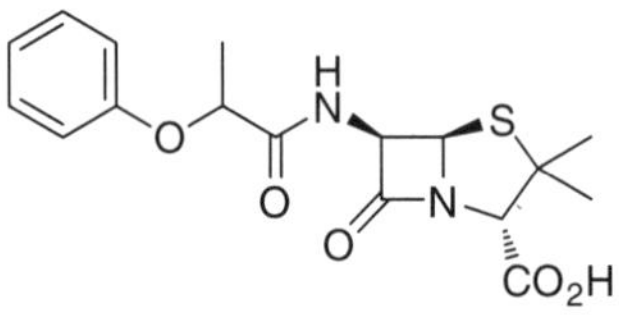

(16) Phenethicillin

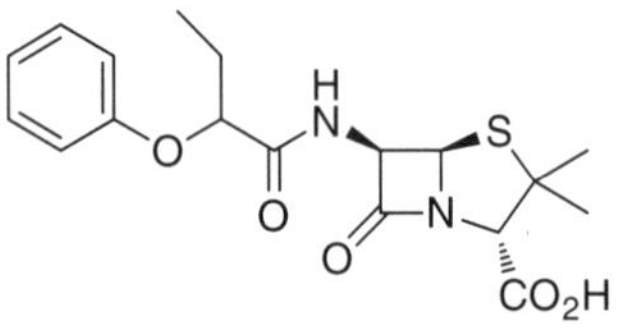

(17) Propicillin

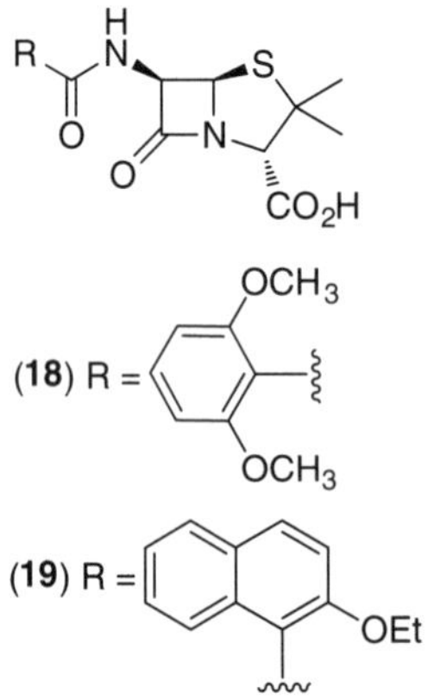

(18) R =

(19) R =

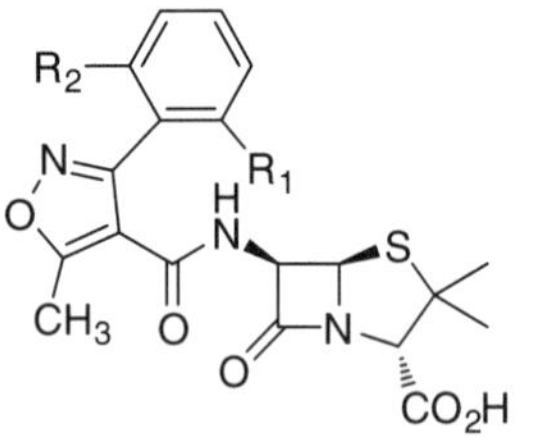

(20a) R₁ = R₂ = H
(20b) R₁ = H, R₂ = Cl
(20c) R₁ = R₂ = Cl
(20d) R₁ = F, R₂ = Cl

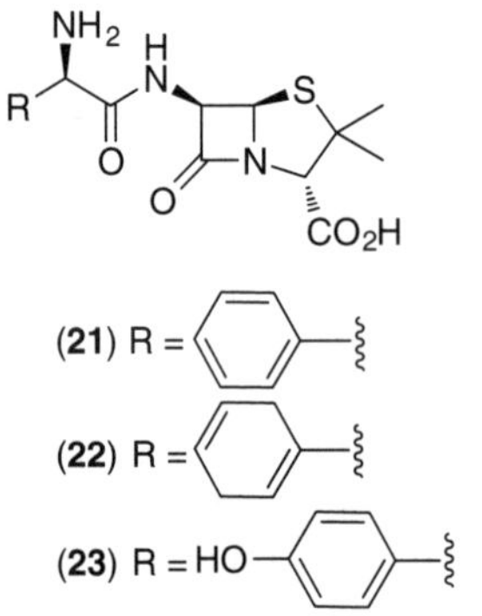

(21) R =

(22) R =

(23) R = HO

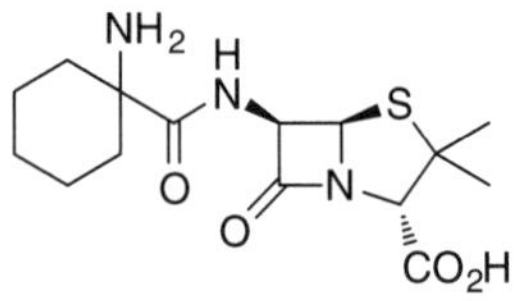

(24)

Subsequently the prodrug esters talampicillin (**25**) [458], bacampicillin (**26**) [459], pivampicillin (**27**) [460], and lenampicillin (**28**) [461], which all release ampicillin (**21**) once absorbed, were developed as agents that improve the oral absorption of ampicillin. With these ester prodrugs, the oral absorption of ampicillin approaches the excellent level achieved by amoxycillin (**23**).

One of the next challenges to be addressed was to extend the spectrum of antibacterial acitivity to cover the opportunistic pathogen *P. aeruginosa*. Carbenicillin (**29**) [462], ticarcillin (**30**) [463], and sulbenicillin (**31**) [464] are deri-

vatives with an acidic group in the acylamino side chain. They have found clinical use as parenteral agents with adequate antipseudomonas potency combined with good safety tolerance.

A second generation of penicillins active against *Pseudomonas* sp. was obtained by acylation of the side-chain amino group of ampicillin (**21**) or amoxycillin (**23**). A selection from the many *N*-acylated aminopenicillin analogs (**32–37**) that have been considered for development as antipseudomonas agents is shown in Table 8. Among the many penicillins, piperacillin (**36**) and ticarcillin (**30**) are particularly effective against *Pseudomonas*.

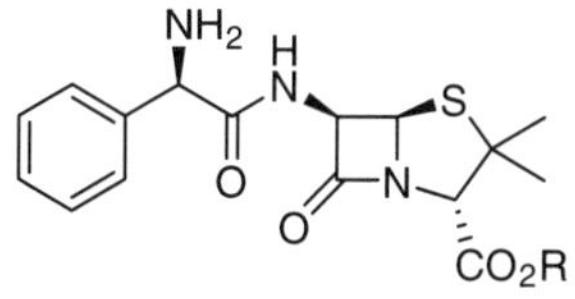

(**26**) R = CH(CH$_3$)OCO$_2$Et
(**27**) R = CH$_2$OCOC(CH$_3$)$_3$
(**28**) R = 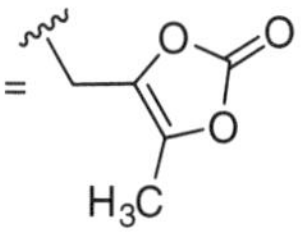
(**25**) R =

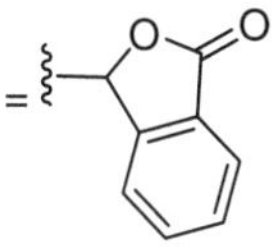

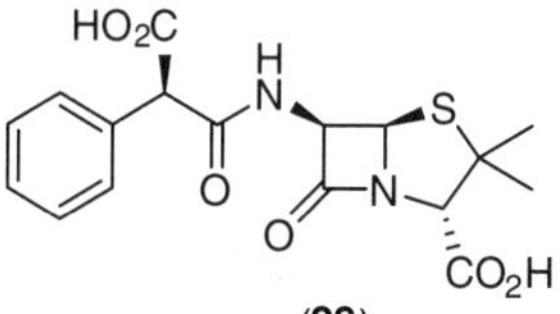

(**29**)

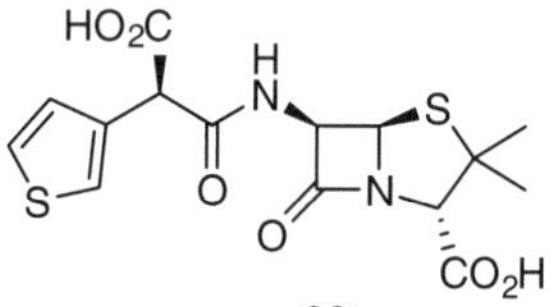

(**30**)

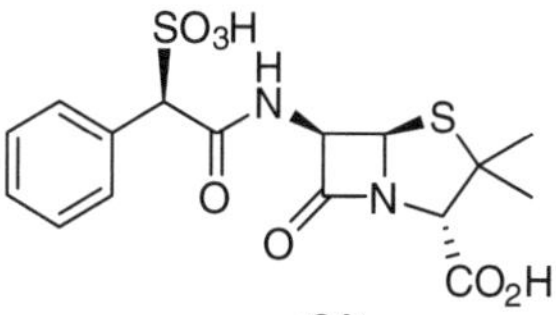

(**31**)

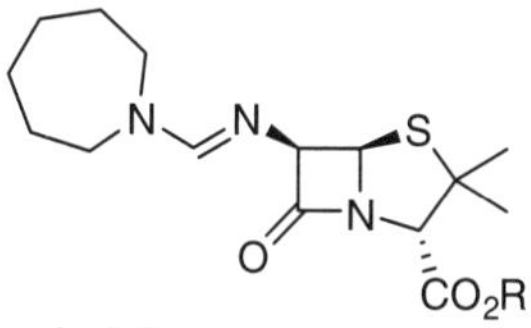

(**38**) R = H
(**39**) R = CH$_2$OCOC(CH$_3$)$_3$
(**40**) R = CH(CH$_3$)OCO$_2$Et

In the 1970s, the amidino penicillin, mecillinam (**38**), which is unusual in that it has a non-acyl side-chain and antibacterial activity limited to Gram-negative organisms, was reported [465]. Also, the oral pivaloyloxymethyl [466] and carbonate pro-

drug esters were described [467]. BRL-44154 (**41**) exemplifies a 6-acylaminopenicillin with improved β-lactamase stability and high activity *in vitro* against Gram-positive organisms including methicillin-resistant staphylococci (MRSA) [468]. BRL-

Table 8. *N*-Acylated Aminopenicillins with Activity Against *P. aeruginosa*

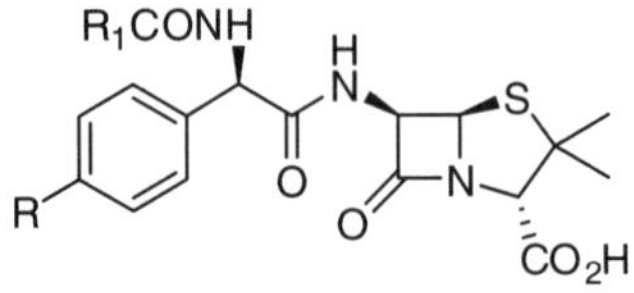

Compound	Name	R	R$_1$	CAS Reg. No.
32	Apalcillin	H	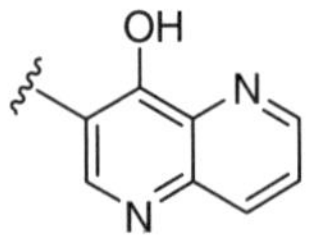	63469-19-2
33	Timoxicillin	OH	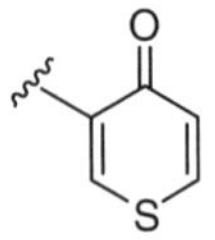	56453-01-1
34	Azlocillin	H	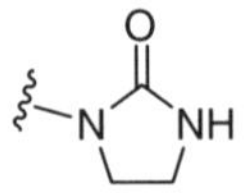	37091-66-0
35	Mezlocillin	H	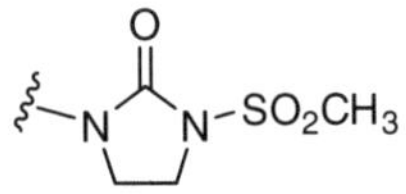	51481-65-3
36	Piperacillin	H	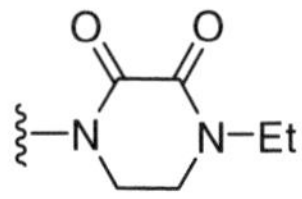	61477-96-1
37	Aspoxicillin	OH	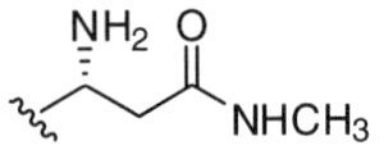	63358-49-6

44154, however, has poor oral availability [469].

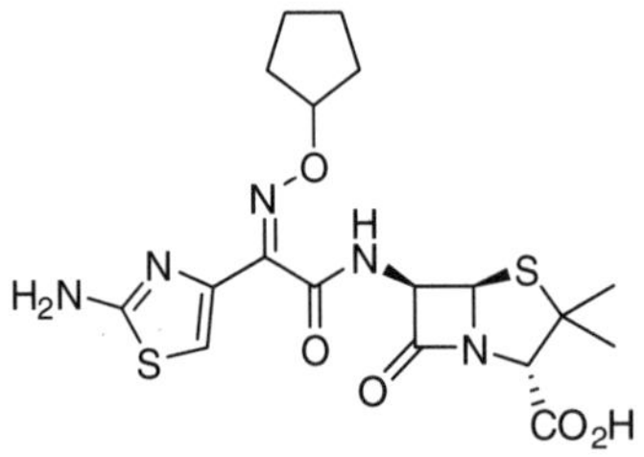

(41) BRL-44154

Table 9 compares the *in vitro* antibacterial activities of representative penicillins, and includes the 6α-substituted derivatives described below (see Section 5.1.2.1). More comprehensive summaries of the breadth of penicillin structure and activity are found in the reviews by Rolinson [470,471] and by Wright [472].

C-6-Substituted Penicillins Early interest in C-6-substituted penicillins arose from the idea that the presence of a C-6-α-methyl group in a penicillin molecule would provide a closer mimic of the D-alanyl-D-alanine component of the cell wall [473,474]. Although this was not shown to be the case [475,476], the discovery of the naturally occurring 7α-methoxy cephalosporin derivatives (the cephamycins, Section 5.2.5), turned attention to the synthesis of penicillins having this and other substituents in the C-6 position. In many cases the methodology for the introduction of the methoxy substituent parallels that developed for the cephalosporin [477]. A method for direct methoxylation of a 6-acylaminopenicillin relies on the addition of methoxide to an acylimine

Table 9. *In Vitro* Antibacterial Activity of Penicillins[a,b]

Organism	Pen G	Meth	Clox	Amox	Ticar	Pip	Mecill	BRL-44154	6α-Substituted	
									Temo	Form
E. coli	50–100	>100	>100	2–100	0.8–100	0.06–64	<0.4–50	1–64	2–16	<0.03–0.5
K. pneumoniae	0.5–100	>100	>100	16–100	25–100	1–64	<0.4–100	8–64	1–100	<0.03–2
Enterobacter sp.	50–100	>100	>100	12.5–100	0.8–100	1–64	<0.4–100	16–64	1–32	<0.03v0.12
Citrobacter sp.	>100	>100	>100	5–100	<1.6–100	1–64	0.5–100	8–32	2–16	<0.03–16
S. marcescens	>100	>100	>100	>100	4–100	2–64	0.8–100	16–64	8–100	<0.03–8
P. mirabilis	16–32	>100	>100	0.8–100	<1.6–100	0.06–64	3.2–100	2–64	0.5–16	0.06–0.25
Proteus sp (In. +)	0.4–100	6.3–100	50–100	0.4–100	<1.6–100	0.06–64	1.6–100	2–64	1–4	<0.03–2
P. aeruginosa	>100	>100	>100	>64	3.2–100	1–64	12.5–100	16–64	>100	0.12–16
H. influenzae	0.08–100	—	2–100	0.05–64	0.25–100	<0.03–2	16–100	0.06–2	0.5–4	0.06–0.5
B. fragilis	0.08–25	>100	>100	0.12–32	<1.6–100	3–100	>100	8–64	16–128	32
S. aureus	<0.005–100	0.4–2.5	0.12–2	0.05–>100	0.4–25	0.8–100	1.6–100	0.25–1	>100	>100
S. pyogenes	0.005–50	0.1–0.8	<0.03–0.06	<0.03–0.12	0.2–0.8	<0.015–0.12	0.8–6.3	0.03–0.06	>100	4
S. pneumoniae	0.006–2	0.1–0.2	0.12	<0.03–4	1.25–2	0.015–0.06	0.8–12.5	<0.03–8	>100	4
N. gonorrhoeae	0.003–100	0.05–2	0.12–64	0.01–16	0.02–16	0.015–1	0.03–8	—	0.03–8	<0.008–0.06

[a]Minimum inhibitory concentrations (range in milligram per liter). See Refs [470,471,499], and GSK in house data.
[b]Pen G, benzylpenicillin; Meth, methicillin; Clox, cloxacillin; Amox, amoxicillin; Ticar, ticacillin; Pip, piperacillin; Mecill, mecillinam; Temo, temocillin; Form, Formidacillin.

293

(**42**) [478,479], whereas an indirect procedure involves the addition of methanol to the putative acylamine formed from the 6α-methylthiopenicillin (**43**) in the presence of a mercuric salt [480]. The 6α-methylthio substituent, as well as alkyl and substituted alkyl, is available from the anion of imine (**44**) with a suitable reagent [476,480,481]. The 6α-stereochemistry of the new substituents is ensured, given that the incoming group always approaches from the less-hindered α-face of the β-lactam ring [481]. Other methods for introduction of methoxy and a variety of alkyl or substituted alkyl variations make use of diazo-intermediates [482] or isonitrile chemistry [483]. Alternative reactive intermediates for the insertion of a C-6-α-substituent have been generated by way of keteneimines [484], sulfenimines [485], and quinolone methide intermediates [486].

After the methoxy series a wide variety of the other C-6-α-substituents were investigated on the penicillin ring system. A 6α-formamidino group with an appropriate side chain provided a series of highly active antibiotics [487]. At the time of this discovery naturally occurring β-lactams possessing this substituent were not known. Introduction of the 6α-formamido substituent followed similar approaches as were used for 6α-methoxy introduction. Initially, displacement of the methylthio group from (**43**) by ammonia in the presence of a mercury salt was used, followed by formylation of the 6α-amino group. Subsequently, a more direct addition used *N,N-bis*-trimethylsilylformamide (BSF) [487,488]. In both the methoxy and formamido series it is also possible to generate the C-6 amino nucleus (**45**), which can be acylated with the appropriate side-chain acid as needed [488]. Other methods for the introduction of the formamido group make use of the *N*-trifluoromethylsulfonylamino penicillin (**46**) [489] or the 6α-methylsulfinyl penicillin (**47**) [490] to generate the acylimine, which is then trapped with BSF.

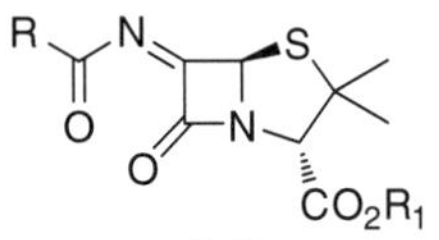

(**42**) 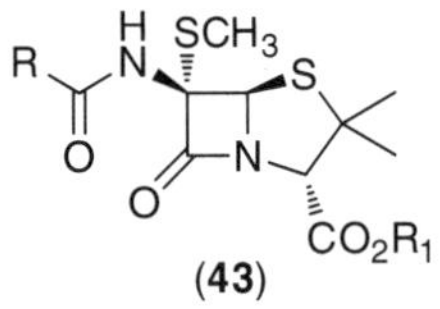 (**43**) 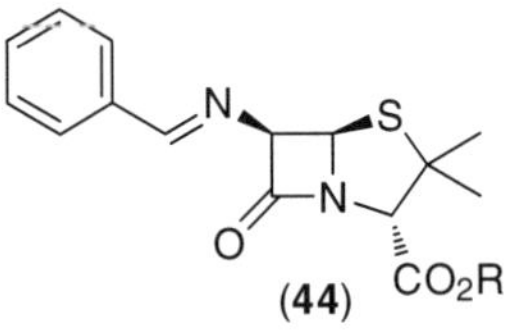 (**44**)

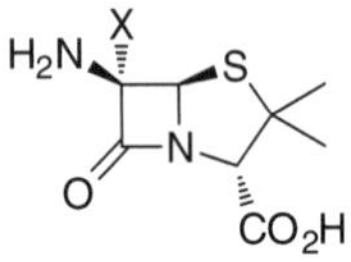

(**45**) X=OCH₃, NHCHO 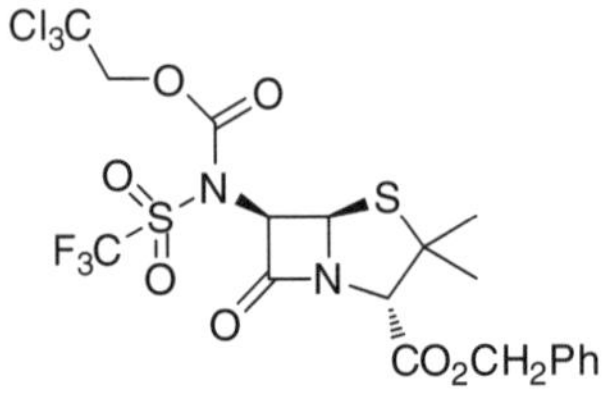   (**46**) 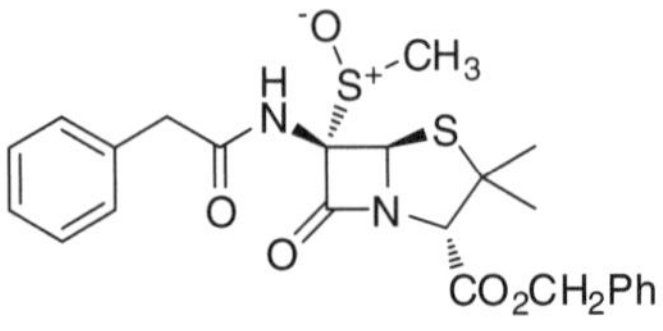   (**47**)

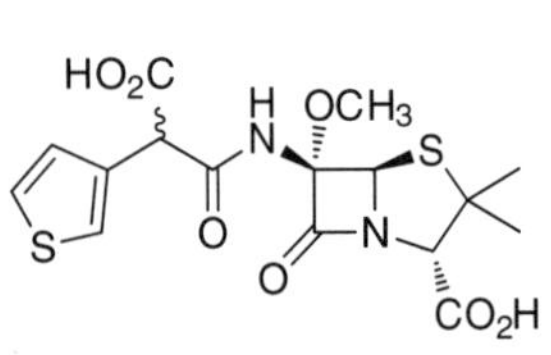

(**48**) 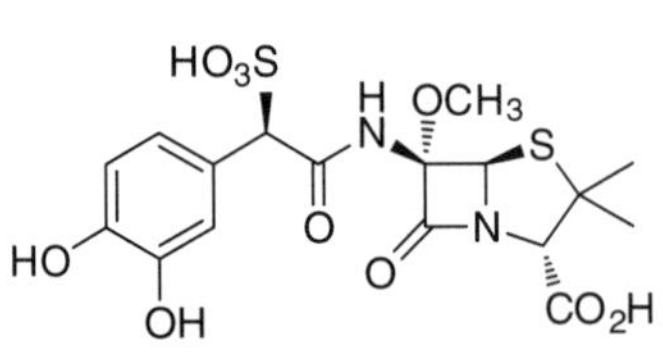   (**49**) 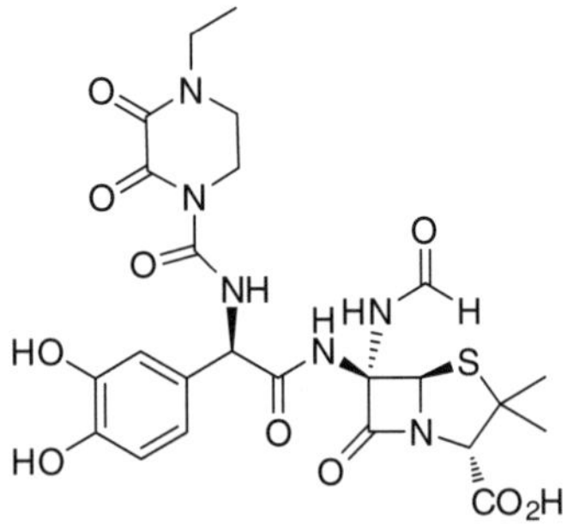   (**50**) BRL-36650

Although the 6,6-disubstituted penicillins have stability toward hydrolysis by β-lactamases, their antibacterial potency is compromised in comparison to 6α-unsubstituted (hydrogen) analogs. Only one derivative, temocillin (**48**) [491,492], was advanced to the clinic. In spite of its prolonged blood levels in humans ($t_{1/2} = 4.5-5$ h), it has found limited utility due to its limited Gram-negative activity (it is not active against Gram positives, anerobes, and *P. aeruginosa*). Given current concerns for the growing presence of highly resistant Gram negatives as a result of β-lactamase expression, and the stability of temocillin to many of these β-lactamases [493,494], there is renewed interest in its clinical use [495,496]. When the thienyl carboxylic acid of temocillin was replaced by a catecholic sulfonic acid to give (**49**), the spectrum of antibacterial activity was expanded to include *P. aeruginosa*, but still not Gram-positive bacteria [497]. After an extensive research program [498] the combination of the *N*-acylated dihydroxyphenylglycyl 6α-formamidino group produced formidacillin (BRL-36650, **50**) [499,500]. This derivative was highly potent against Gram-negative organisms, including *Pseudomonas* sp., and possessed some activity against streptococci but not against the staphylococci.

5.1.3. Other Modified Penicillins

Chemical modifications of most of the other positions (S1, C-2, C-3, and C-6) of the penicillin are summarized elsewhere [444]. More recent reports have described novel 2-carboxypenam analogs T5575 (**51**) and T5578 (**52**), in which both the C-2 and C-3 substituents have been changed compared to natural penicillins [501,502]. These compounds displayed potent antibacterial activity against Gram-negative organisms, including *P. aeruginosa*, with improved stability to β-lactamases.

5.1.4. Biosynthesis of Isopenicillin N and Deacetoxycephalosporin C

The biosynthetic transformation of the δ-(L-α-aminoadipyl)-L-cysteinyl-D-valine ("LLD") tripeptide [503–508] to isopenicillin N [509] by a single nonheme, iron-dependent synthase (IPNS) [510–516], is one of several outstanding examples of peptide-derived structure

with potent biological activity [517]. Computational study of the mechanism of this synthase suggests the likely radical intermediates and direction for ring cyclization (β-lactam ring formation preceding thiazoline ring formation) involved in the ring cyclizations [518]. In a no less remarkable succeeding reaction, thiazoline ring expansion transforms isopenicillin N—by a nonheme, iron and α-oxoglutarate-dependent synthase [18,519]—into deaceoxycephalosporin. The biosynthesis of the β-lactam rings of clavulanate [512,520–522] (Section 5.6.1), the nocardicins (Section 5.4.1.1) and the carbapenems (Section 5.5.1.2) involve mechanistically similar synthases. Excellent progress has been made toward the understanding of the evolutionary relationships within the penicillin biosynthetic gene cluster [523].

5.2. Cephalosporins and Synthetic Analogs: Oxacephems, Carbacephems

The cephalosporins were the second class of β-lactams discovered, as natural products, and they likewise follow the penicillins in recognition as a β-lactam class. Moreover, the circumstances of the discovery of the cephalosporins have similarities to the discovery of the penicillins. On the presumption that environments with microbial diversity might yield interesting secondary metabolites, Brotzu in 1945 collected microorganisms from a sewage outfall in Sardinia. A metabolite produced by *Cephalosporium acremonium*, from this collection, had antibacterial activity. Abraham at Oxford University subsequently isolated and characterized the principle active component as cephalosporin C (**2**) [524–527]. Confirmation of its structure as a substituted cephem (the cephem core is the (6*R*,7*R*)-7-amino-8-oxo-5-thia-1-azabicyclo[4.2.0]oct-2-ene-2-carboxylicacid substructure) was obtained by X-ray crystallography [528]. Upon catalytic hydrogenation of (**2**), a single mole of H_2 was consumed with transformation of (**2**) to deacetoxycephalosporin C (**53**), but with loss of 90% of the antibacterial potency [529].

Cephalosporin C attracted attention mainly because of its relative stability to penicillinases. Cephalosporins (**54**) are characterized by a bicyclic ring system, in which the β-lactam is fused to a six-membered ring bearing a sulfur atom at position 1 (traditional, but nonsystematic numbering); oxacephalosporins (**55**), an oxygen atom; and carbacephalosporins (**56**), a carbon atom [530]. The isolation of the first cephalosporin was followed by the discovery of other natural metabolites from fungi and actinomycetes, including those with a 7α-methoxy substituent (**57**) [531,532] and a 7α-formamido group (**58**) [533].

5.2.1. Total Synthesis of Cephalosporin C Intermediates such as (**59**) [534] have been used to provide the cephalosporin lactone ring system (**60**) and deacetylcephalothin [535]. Later, [2 + 2] cycloaddition reaction between the thiazine (**61**) and the ketene derived from azidoacetyl chloride was key to the total racemic synthesis of cephalothin [536–538].

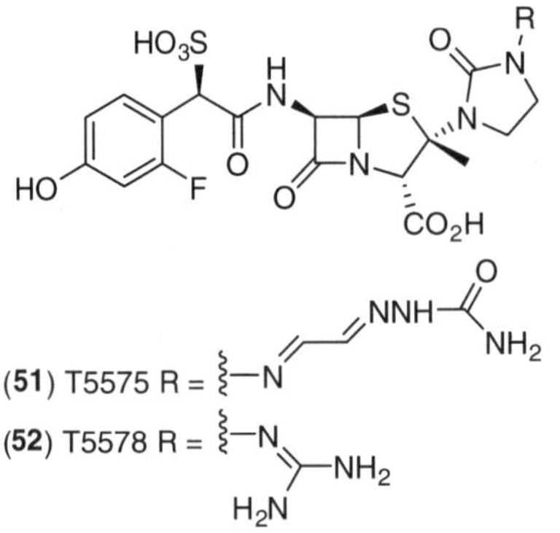

(**51**) T5575 R =

(**52**) T5578 R =

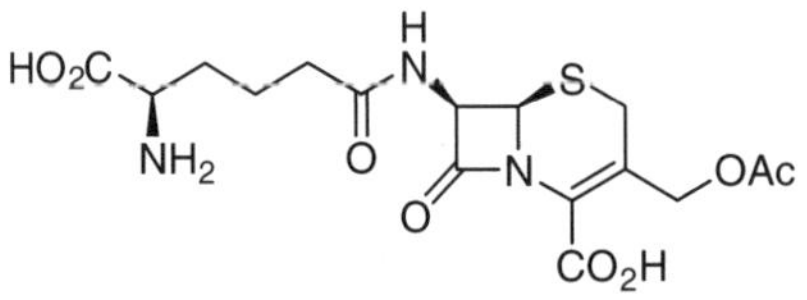

(**2**) Cephalosporin C (1948)

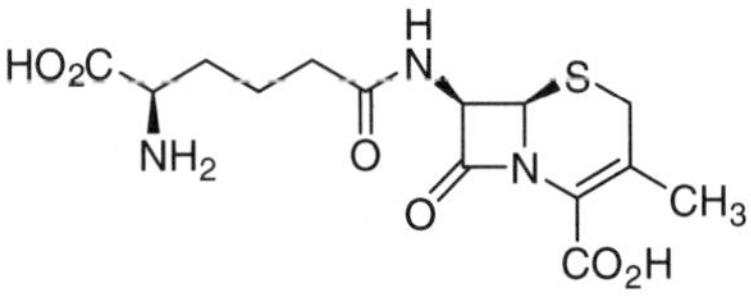

(**53**) Deacetoxycephalosporin C

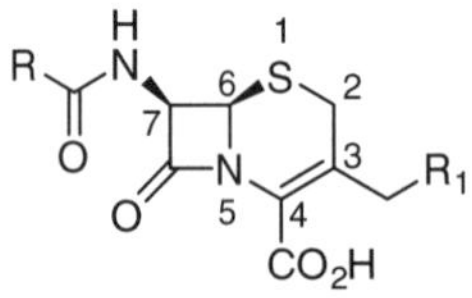

(**54**) Cephalosporins

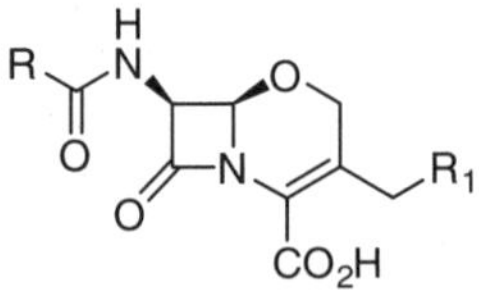

(**55**) Oxacephalosporins

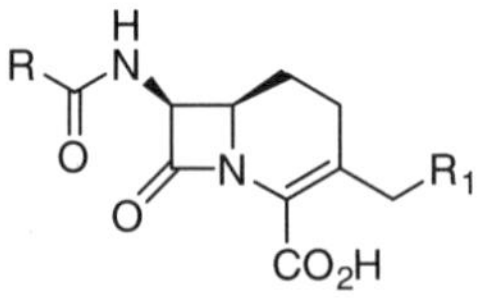

(**56**) Carbacephalosporins

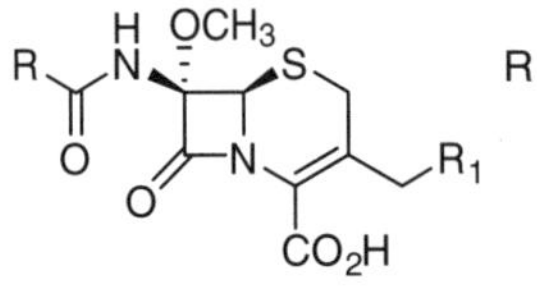

(**57**) Cephamycins

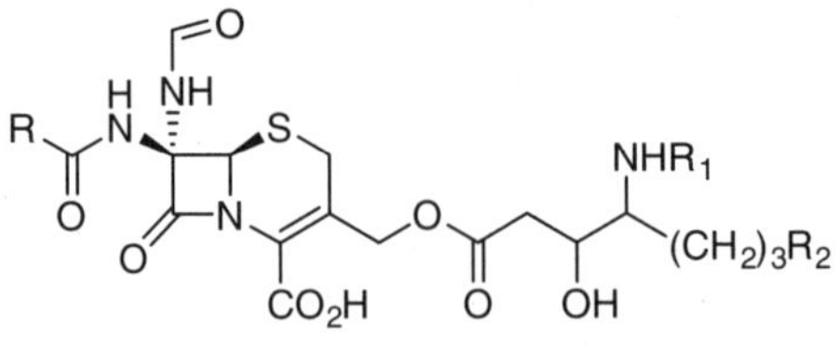

(**58**) Cephabacins

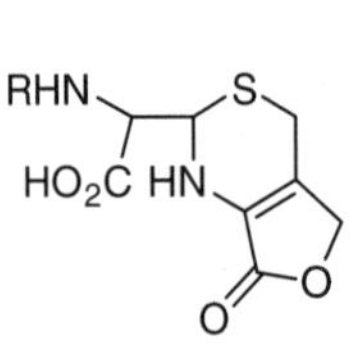

(**59**)

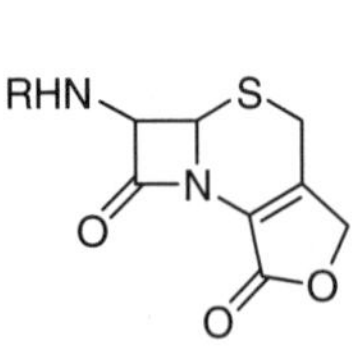

(**60**)

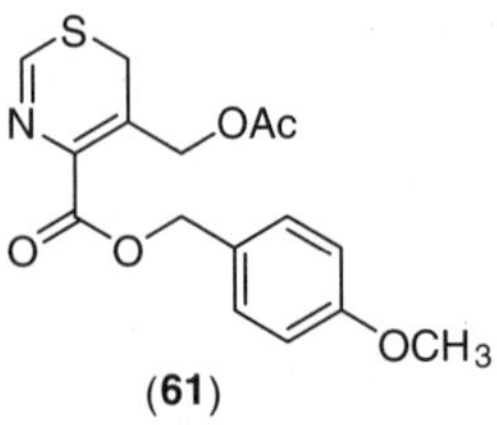

(**61**)

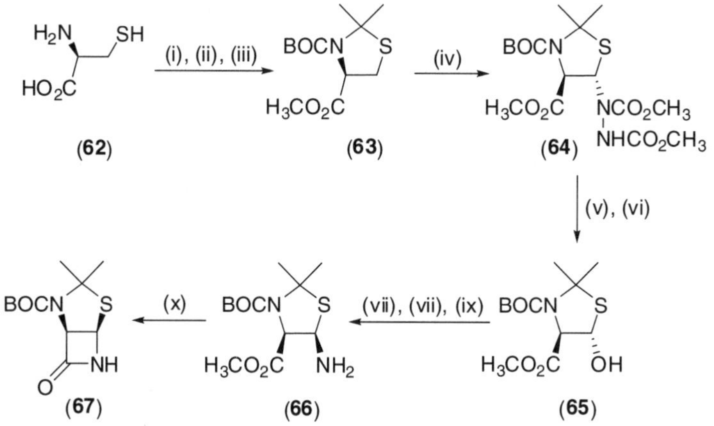

Reagents: (i) acetone; (ii) BOCCl, pyridine; (iii) CH₂N₂;
(iv) MeO₂CN = NCO₂Me; (v) Pb(OAc)₄; (vi) NaOAc, MeOH;
(vii) MeSO₂Cl, DIPEA; (viii) NaN₃; (ix) Al/Hg; (x) triisobutylaluminium.

Figure 11. Woodward's synthesis of cephalosporin C.

The only complete synthesis of cephalos-porin C was described by Woodward in his Nobel lecture of 1965 [539] and published in 1966 [540] (Figs 11 and 12). Protection of the nitrogen, sulfur, and carboxylic acid of L-cy-steine (62) provided the cyclic intermediate (63). Introduction of the hydrazino group gave

(64) that, by oxidation with lead tetracetate and treatment with sodium acetate, was converted into the *trans*-hydroxy ester (65). Formation of the mesylate, inversion of the stereochemistry by displacement with azide, and reduction provided the *cis*-amino ester (66) that gave the key β-lactam intermediate

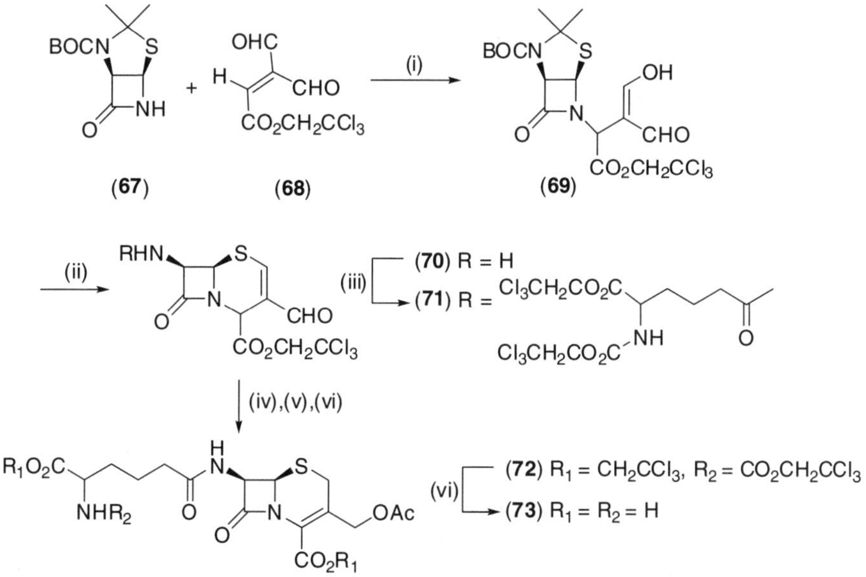

Reagents: (i) 80°C; (ii) CF₃CO₂H; (iii) acylation; (iv) diborane; (v) Ac₂O, pyridine;
(vi) pyridine; (vii) Zn, CH₃CO₂H.

Figure 12. Woodward's synthesis of cephalosporin C.

(67). The absolute stereochemistry was confirmed by X-ray crystallography.

This β-lactam derivative was reacted with dialdehyde (68) in a Michael addition manner to yield (69). Treatment with trifluoroacetic acid removed both nitrogen- and sulfur-protecting groups and resulted in cyclization to the cephalosporin precursor (70), in which the amino group was then acylated with the suitably protected D-α-aminoadipic acid side chain, forming (71). Reduction, acetylation, and equilibration provided the cephalosporin C ester (72), from which the protecting groups were removed with zinc and acetic acid to give the free acid (73), which was identical to a sample of authentic material.

5.2.2. Penicillin Sulfoxide-Cephalosporin Conversion
Early work on the chemistry of penicillin sulfoxide by Morin [541] demonstrated the thermal rearrangement of (74) in the presence of acid to the deacetoxycephalosporin ring system (76). Speculation that this transformation occurred through the sulfenic acid intermediate (75) was later confirmed by its isolation in a crystalline form [542]. The rearrangement of (74) to (76) afforded an attractive route to cephalosporins lacking the C-3 acetoxymethyl group of the natural derivative, starting from a relatively cheap chiral starting material, while retaining the stereochemical integrity of the β-lactam ring. The chemistry of the penicillin sulfoxides and their use for the

interconversion of β-lactam antibiotics have been extensively reviewed by Cooper et al. [542–544]. Here we report only the process leading to the commercially available cephalexin (79) and cefaclor (80) [545] (Fig. 13).

In the case of cephalexin (79) the trichloroethyl ester of penicillin V sulfoxide (74) was successfully rearranged to the deacetoxycephalosporin, followed by cleavage of the C-7 side chain and acylation with a suitably protected D-α-phenylglycine. Removal of the amine- and acid-protecting groups gave a synthesis that could be adapted for the production of cephalexin (79) on a multikilogram scale [546]. The synthesis of cefaclor (80) stems from work that showed that penicillin sulfinyl chlorides (77), generated from (74) afforded 3-exomethylene cepham sulfoxides (78) on treatment with tin (IV) chloride or other Lewis acids [547]. Reduction of the sulfoxide and ozonolysis of the double bond gave the C-3 hydroxycephem, which was converted to the corresponding chloride. Side-chain exchange and deprotection provided a viable synthesis of cefaclor (80) [548]. 4-Arylsulfonylthioazetidin-4-ones (81) have been efficiently converted (yields of 70–90%) to 3-chloromethyl cephalosporins (83) through an electrolytic ene-type chlorination to (82) and subsequent base-catalyzed ring closure (Fig. 14) [549]. This procedure has provided the basis for the successful development of a commercially viable process for the synthesis of the key cephalosporin

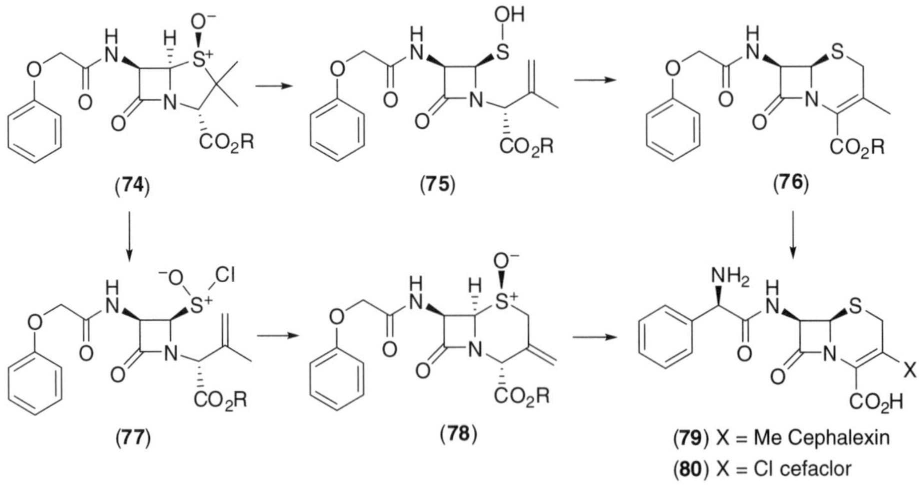

Figure 13. Rearrangement of penicillin sulfoxide to cephalosporins.

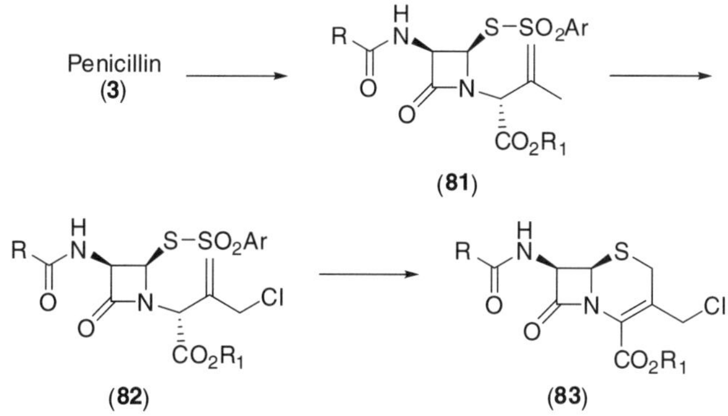

Figure 14. Conversion of penicillin into cephalosporin.

intermediate 7-amino-3-chloromethyl-3-ce-phem-4-carboxylic acid, *p*-methoxybenzyl es-ter (7-ACLE) (**84**), as well as other derivatives, by the Otsuka Chemical Company of Japan. Variations of the process also afford 3-hydro-xymethyl cephalosporins [550].

5.2.3. Derivatives of 7-Aminocephalosporanic Acid

The structures of naturally occurring members of this series have an α-aminoadipic side chain at C-7 [524,527,531,551–554]. Some variations have been isolated that have the side chain derived from glutaric acid [555,556] or 5-hydroxy-5-carboxyvaleric acid [557,558].

The naturally occurring cephalosporins have low levels of antibacterial activity. Clea-vage of the amide bond of the aminoadipoyl side chain of cephalosporin C (**2**) is high yield-ing [559], affording 7-amino-cephalosporanic acid (7-ACA, **85**), ideally suited for the synth-esis of a wide range of semisynthetic cepha-losporins by acylation of its C-7 amine.

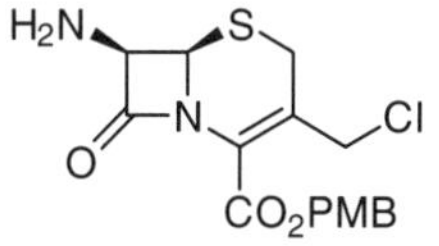

(**84**) 7-ACLE

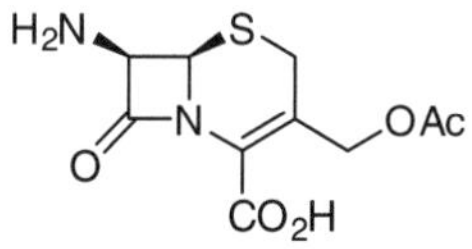

(**85**) 7-Amino-cephalosporanic acid (7-ACA)

Cephalosporins have two positions avail-able for structural manipulation, C-3 and C-7. A wide variety of amine acylation meth-ods are used (including acyl chlorides, mixed anhydrides, active esters, and carbodiimide-mediated carboxylic acid acylation) for the production of 7-acylamino derivatives [560]. To improve the efficiency of the acylation, the solubility of 7-ACA in organic solvents is increased by esterification of the carboxylic acid at C-4 (**85**), typically the *tert*-butyl dimethylsilyl, benzhydryl, *p*-nitrobenzyl, or *p*-methoxybenzyl esters. However, ester de-rivatives of 7-ACA (**85**) are very sensitive to basic conditions, wherein Δ^3 double bond isomerization into the unwanted (and biolo-gically inactive) Δ^2 isomer is competitive with acylation [561].

Reactions at C-3 have mainly involved dis-placement of 3′-acetate, to give substitution with heteroatoms (especially sulfur and nitro-gen) [562], whereas elimination followed by catalytic hydrogenation [563] or acid-cata-lyzed reduction by use of trialkylsilanes leads to 3-methyl cephalosporins [560]. An alterna-tive to the displacement of the 3′-acetoxy for the synthesis of 3′-heteroatom cephalosporins is through functionalization of a 3-methyl derivative of a cephalosporin sulfoxide, by allylic bromination to the 3′-bromomethyl compound suitable for subsequent displace-ment reactions [561]. Hydrolytic deacylation by base or esterase gives 3′-hydroxymethyl cephalosporins [564], which can be converted into carbamoyl compounds such as cefuroxime (**86**) [565].

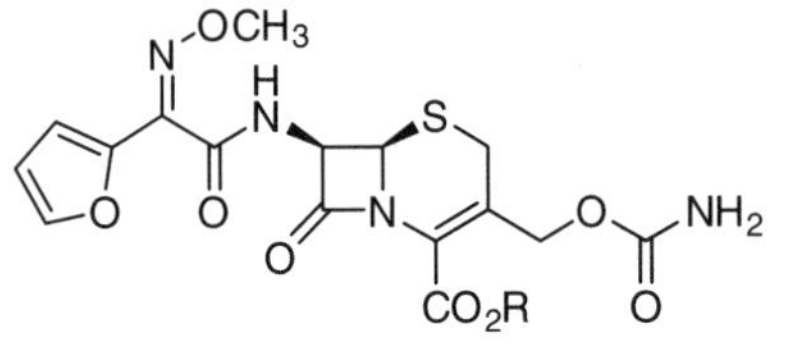

(**86a**) Cefuroxime R = H

(**86b**) Cefuroxime axetil R = CH(CH$_3$)OAc

Other important intermediates are 3-exomethylene derivatives that, by ozonolysis of the exocyclic double bond, provide an entry to cephalosporins having a heteroatom attached directly at C-3 as in the commercially important cefaclor (**80**) [548]. The exomethylene compounds are also easily converted to 3'-bromomethyl derivatives with bromine and base [566]. A summary of many of the common reactions and derivatives of 7-ACA (**85**) is given in Fig. 15.

5.2.4. Classification, Biological Activity, and Structure–Activity Relationship of Cephalosporins

Some 50 different cephalosporins are in clinical use or at an advanced stage of development [470,560,567,568]. Many attempts have been made to classify these based on stability to β-lactamases, potency, antibacterial spectrum, and pharmacological properties. The most common approach is division of the cephalosporins into generations, defined primarily on the basis of their antibacterial spectrum—with both parenteral and oral agents being covered [569,570]—and also on the basis of their chemical sophistication. The first cephalosporins were designated as first generation. The cephalosporins that closely followed, having a more extended spectrum, were classified as second generation. Each newer generation of cephalosporins has significantly greater Gram-negative antimicrobial properties than the preceding generation, in most

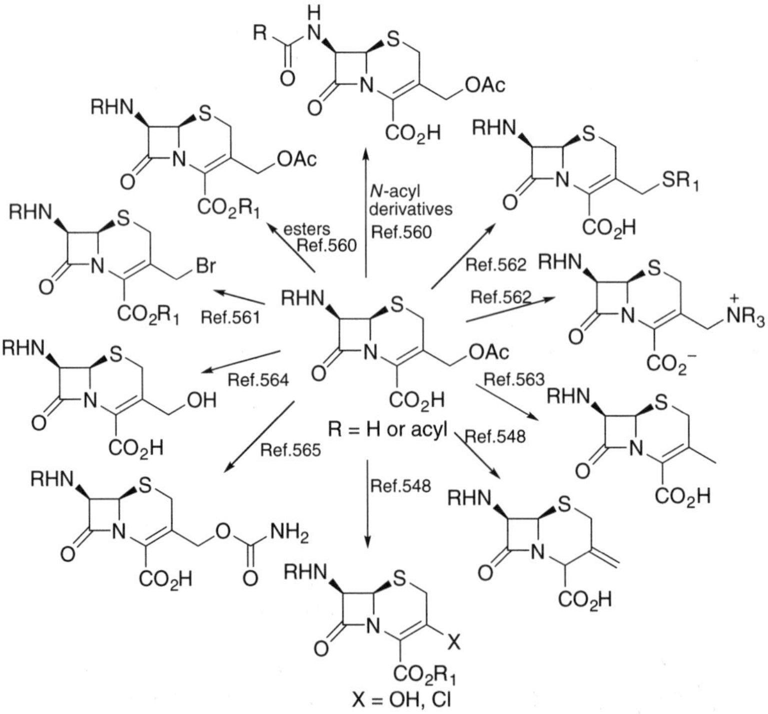

Figure 15. Summary of some common reactions and derivatives of 7-ACA.

cases with decreased activity against Gram-positive organisms. However, the fourth-generation cephalosporins exhibit remarkable broad-spectrum activity.

First-generation derivatives possess activity against Gram-positive bacteria, but a relatively narrow spectrum against Gram-negative strains attributed in part to their susceptibility to β-lactamases. Although oral first-generation agents are tolerated and have been broadly used, there have been calls to restrict their use since now better alternatives are available. These drugs possess activity against staphylococci and streptococci, although the activity against Gram-negative bacteria is relatively modest. Cephalexin (Keflex™) (79) [571], Cephalothin (Keflin™) (87) [572], Cefazolin (Ancef®) (88), Cefadroxil (Duricef®, Ultracef) (89), Cephapirin (Cefa-

dyl™) (90), and Cefradine (Velosef™) (91) are some of the drugs that belong to this category.

Second-generation compounds have a broader spectrum of activity, including activity against *H. influenzae* and the Enterobacteriaceae resulting from an increased stability to β-lactamases. Examples of compounds in this group are Cefamandole nafate (Mandol®) (92) [573], Cefuroxime (Ceftin™, Zinacef®) (86a) [574], Cefprozil (Cefzil™) and the oral agent Cefaclor (Cefaclor) (80) [575]. The highly β-lactamase stable cephamycins such as Cefoxitin (Mefoxin®) (92) and Cefotetan (Cefotan®) (93) are also included in this group and show excellent activity against *Bacteroides fragilis* [573]. The carbacephem Loracarbef (Lorabid®) is also included in this category.

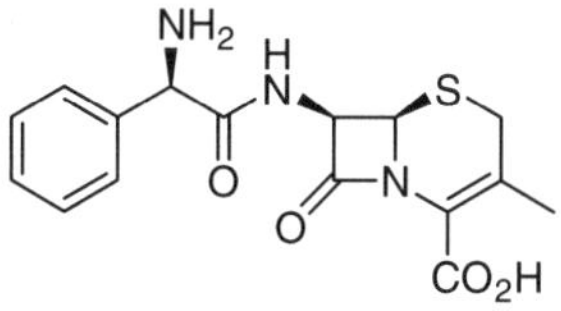

(79) Cephalexin (first generation)

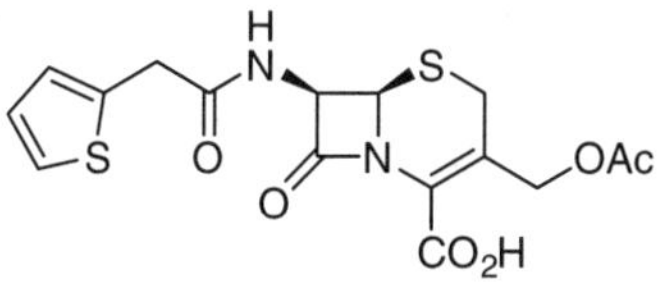

(87) Cephalothin (first generation)

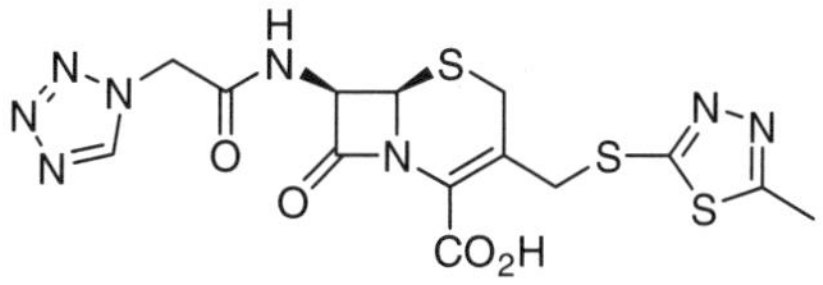

(88) Cefazolin (first generation)

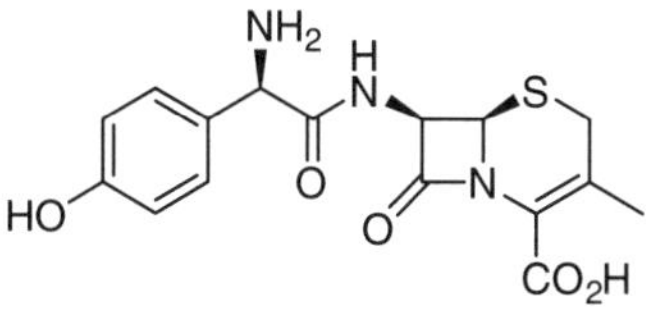

(89) Cefadroxil (first generation)

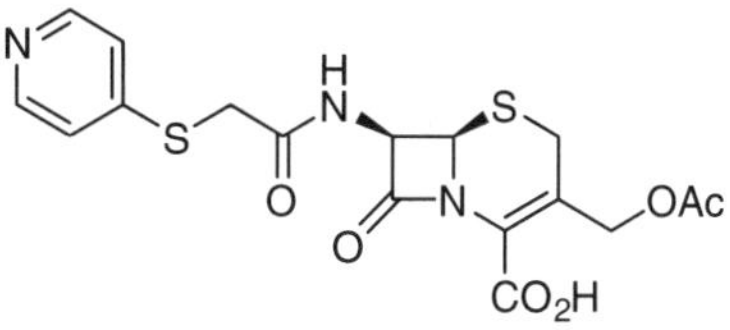

(90) Cephapirin (first generation)

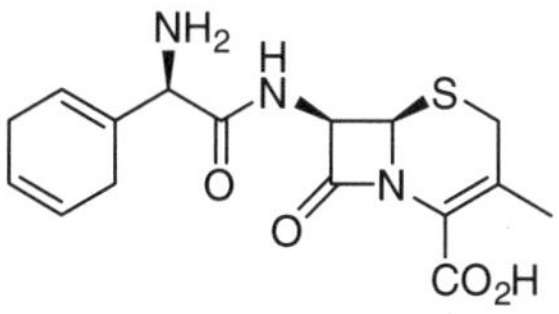

(91) Cefradine (first generation)

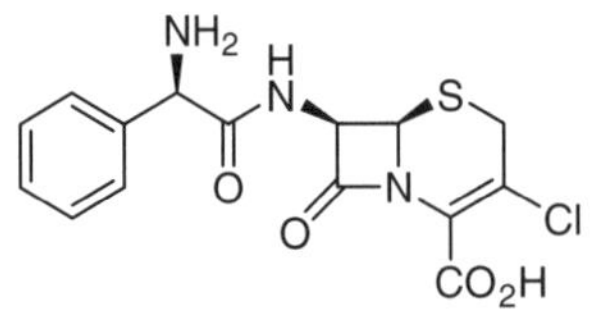

(80) Cefaclor (second generation)

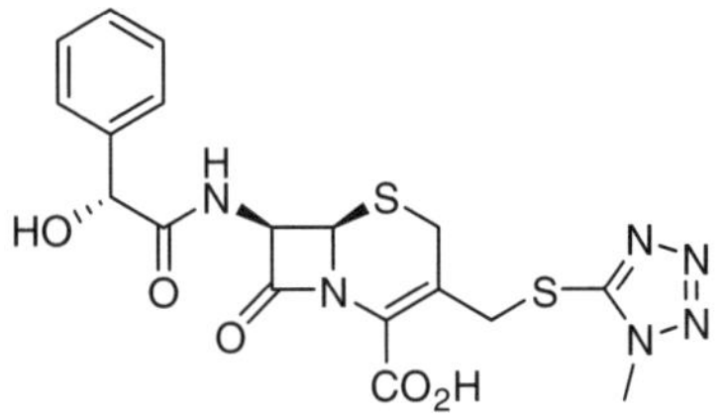

(89) Cefamandole (second generation)

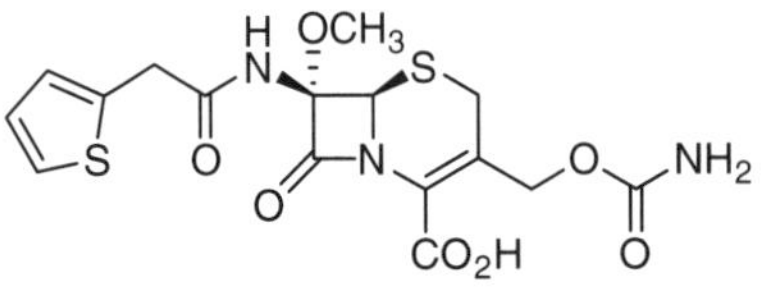

(92) Cefoxitin (second generation)

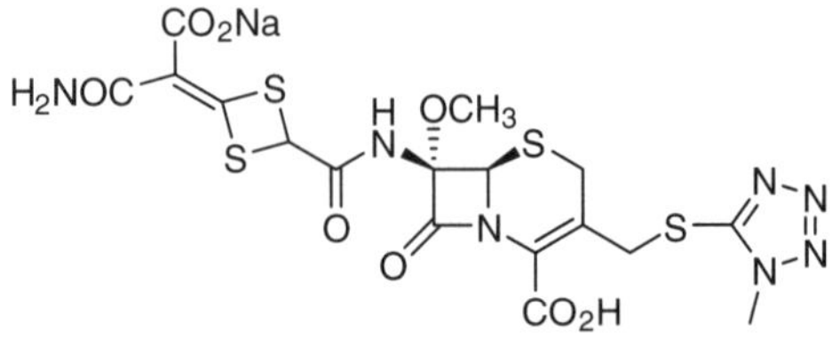

(93) Cefotetan (second generation)

The third-generation cephalosporin compounds[576,577], which originated with Cefotaxime (Claforan®) (94) [578–581], have a yet broader spectrum of activity than the earlier generation cephalosporins, especially against the Enterobacteriaceae. They show several important advantages over the first- and second-generation compounds, including increased resistance to many plasmid-mediated and chromosomal β-lactamases. Third-generation agents have acquired a good reputation for efficacy and tolerability. The third-generation cephalosporins show potent anti-Gram-negative but modest anti-Gram-positive activity, being inferior to the first-generation agents in this respect, and like the majority of cephalosporins described so far, show no activity against MRSA [569].

The typical spectrum includes *E. coli*, *Klebsiella*, *Enterobacter*, *Acinetobacter*, *Serratia*, *Providencia*, *Proteus*, *Morganella* and *Neisseria*. Some drugs are also active on *B. fragilis* and *Pseudomonas* sp. Examples of third-generation cephalosporins include, Cefpodoxime proxetil (Vantin®)(95), Ceftazidime (Fortaz®)(96), Cefdinir (Omnicef®)(97), Ceftibuten (Cedax®) (98), Ceftriaxone (Rocephin®) (99) [582], and the oral agent Cefixime (Suprax®) (100) [583].

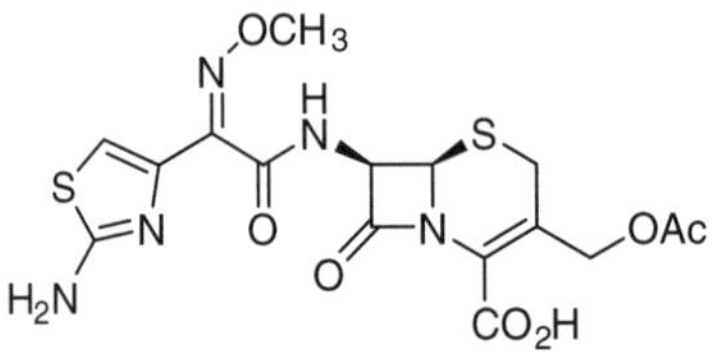

(94) Cefotaxime (third generation)

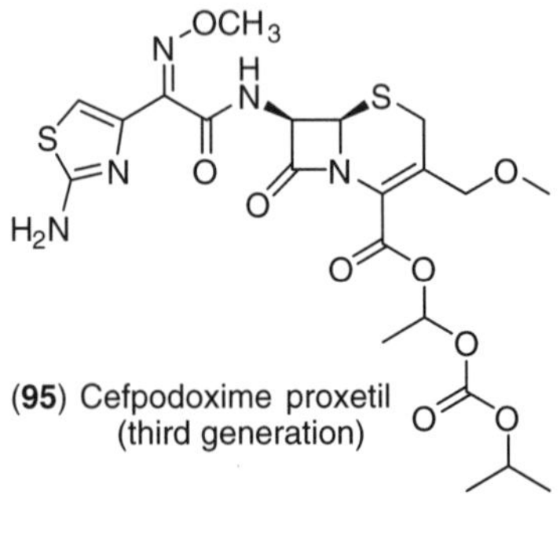

(95) Cefpodoxime proxetil
(third generation)

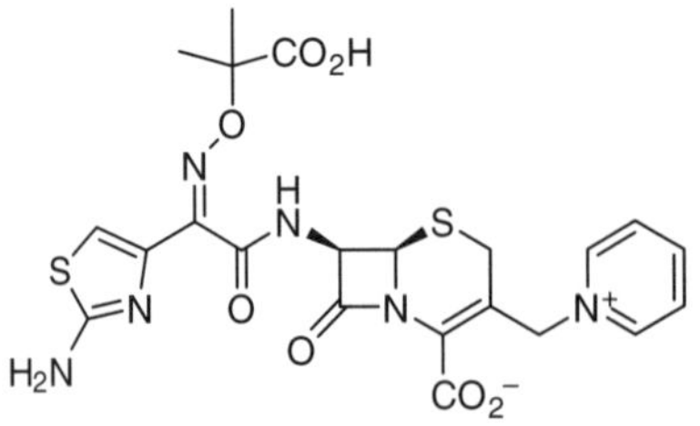

(96) Ceftazidime (third generation)

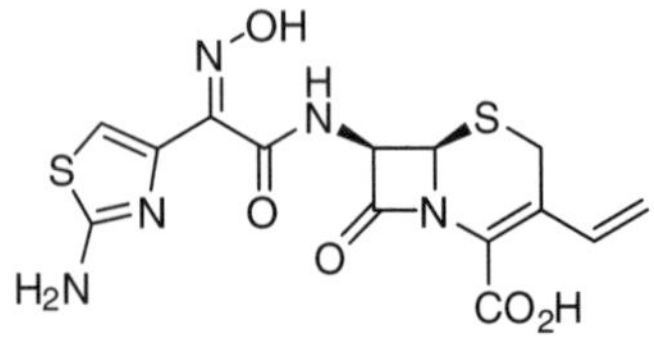

(97) Cefdinir (third generation)

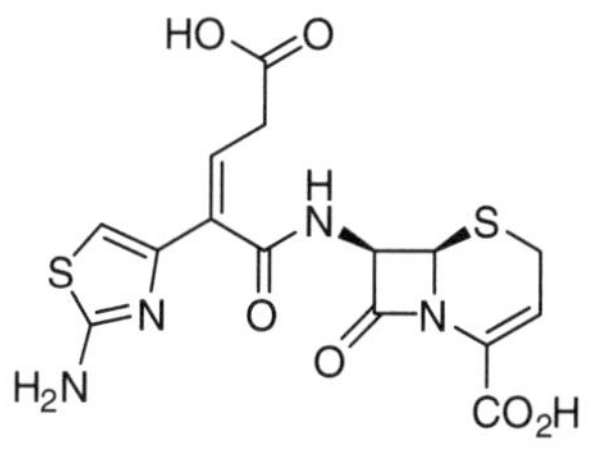

(98) Ceftibuten (third generation)

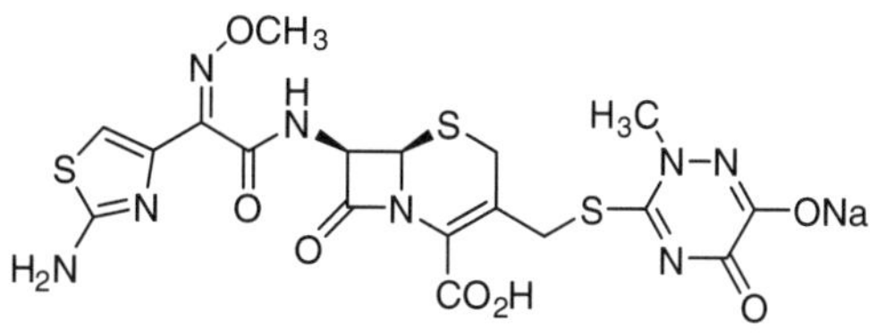

(99) Ceftriaxome (third generation)

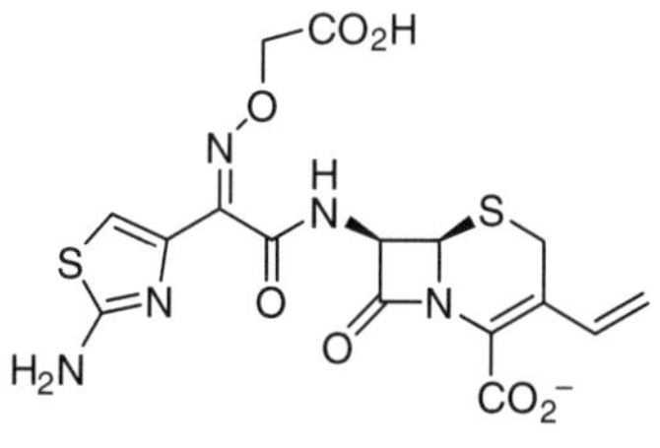

(100) Cefixime (third generation)

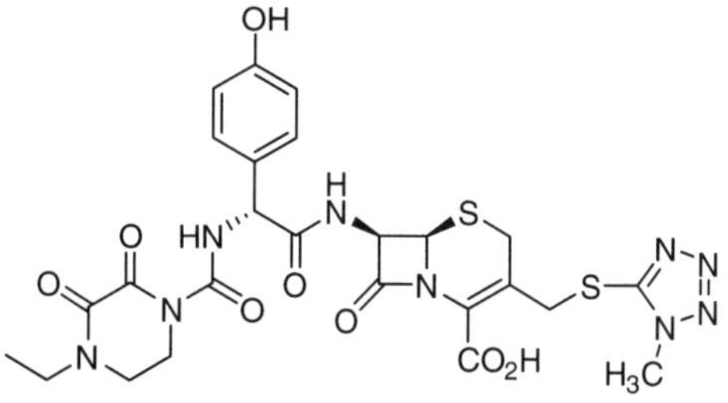

(101) Cefoperazone (third generation)

Compounds such as Cefoperazone (Cefobid®) (101) [584] and Ceftazidime (102) [585] show improved activity against *P. aeruginosa*, which is also a predominant feature of Cefsulodin (103) [578,586].

The fourth-generation cephalosporins possess extended Gram-negative coverage compared with third-generation cephalosporins, due to increased stability toward hydrolysis by β-lactamases and, perhaps, lower induction of β-lactamase-mediated resistance. They possess similar activity against Gram-positive organisms as first-generation cephalosporins and simultaneously have activity against Gram-negative organisms with multiple drug resistance patterns such as *Enterobacter, Klebsiella*, and *P. aeruginosa*. Cefepime (Maxipime®) (104) [587–589] and Cefpirome (105) [590] belong to this group.

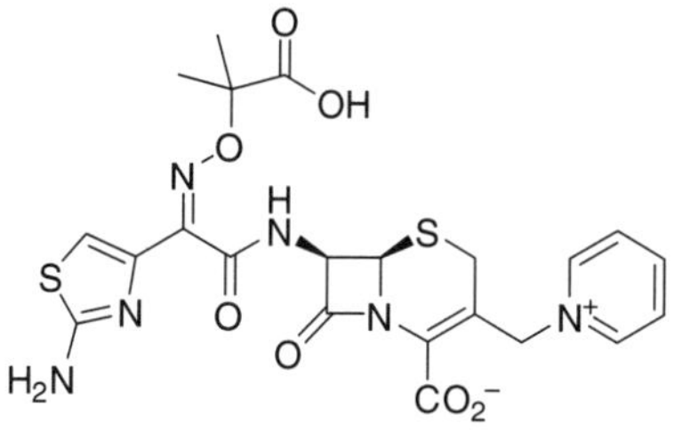

(102) Cefazidime (third generation)

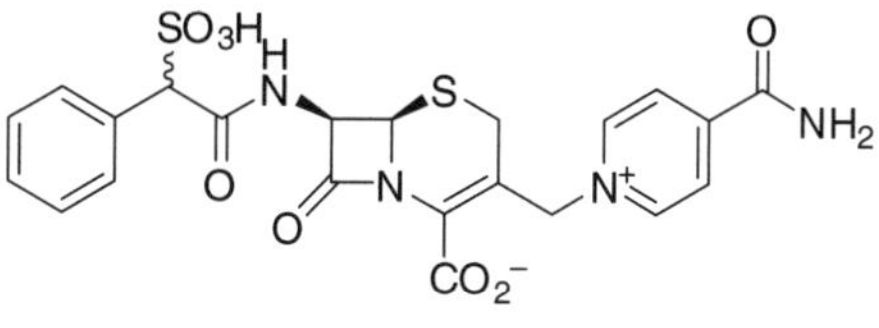

(103) Cefsulodin (third generation)

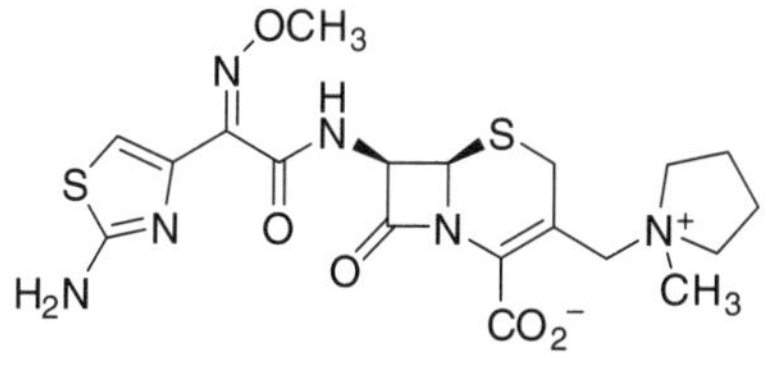

(104) Cefepime (fourth generation)

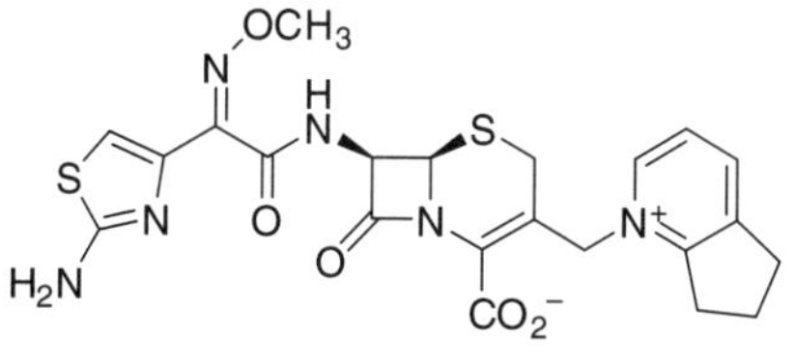

(105) Cefpirome (fourth generation)

Table 10. Antibacterial Activity (mg/L) of Some Representative Cephalosporins[a,b]

Organism	First			Second			Third				Fourth	
	CET	CEZ	CEX (os)	CMD	CXM	CFL (os)	CTX	CTR	CAZ	CFM (os)	CPR	CPM
E. coli	4–64	2–128	4–128	1–32	1–8	1–128	0.03–1	0.12–1	0.12–1	0.4–32	0.03–0.25	0.02–1
K. pneumoniae	4–128	2–128	4–128	0.5–128	2–4	1–128	0.03–0.12	0.06–0.12	0.06–0.25	0.05–0.4	0.06–NA	0.01–2
Enterobacter sp.	>128	>128	>128	32–128	16–128	>128	0.12–64	0.25–NA	0.25–64	64–100	0.12–4	0.01–32
Citrobacter sp.	64	>128	>128	8	8	>128	0.25	0.5	0.5	64–100	0.12	0.01–0.5
S. marcescens	>128	>128	>128	>64	64–128	>128	0.12–64	0.25–NA	0.12–2	2–100	0.12–4	0.03–3.2
P. mirabilis	2–4	4–8	8	1–2	1–2	1	0.03	0.03–NA	0.06	0.05	0.03–NA	0.02–0.25
Proteus sp. (In +)	>128	>128	>128	8	8	>128	0.12	0.12	0.12	NA	0.25	NA
P. aeruginosa	>128	>128	>128	>128	>128	>128	32–128	32–64	2–16	NA	4–16	0.5–16
H. influenzae	4	8	8	1–81–8	0.5	1–2	0.03–0.06	0.03–0.06	0.12	0.12	0.03	0.02–0.06
B. fragilis	64	64	64	64	32	>128	32	64	64	NA	32	8–125
S. aureus	0.25–0.5	0.25–1	2–4	0.5–1	1	1–4	2	4	4–8	8–100	0.5	1–4
S. pyogenes	0.12	0.12	0.5	0.06	0.03	0.25	0.03	0.03	0.12	0.2	0.03	<0.01–0.06
S. pneumoniae	0.12	0.12	2	0.25	0.12	1	0.12	0.25	0.25	0.4	0.12	0.01–0.25
N. gonorrhoeae	0.5	0.5–2	2	0.5	0.06	0.12–0.5	<0.01–0.03	<0.01–0.01	0.06–0.12	NA	<0.01	<0.01–0.06

[a] See Refs [470,583,587].

[b] CET, cephalotin; CEZ, cefazolin; CEX, cephalexin; CMD, cefamandole; CXM, cefuroxime; CFL, cefaclor; CTX, cefotaxime; CTR, ceftriaxone; CAZ, ceftazidime; CFM, cefixime; CPR, cefpirome; CPM, cefepime.

Table 10 compares the *in vitro* antibacterial activities of representative cephalosporins of these groups. Ultimately, the biological activity of the cephalosporins depends on their affinity and interaction with their PBP enzyme targets. However, other factors such as penetration to the target site, β-lactamase stability, pharmacokinetic parameters, and metabolic stability influence their absolute antibacterial effectiveness. Most SAR studies focus on *in vitro* antibacterial activities measured against individual bacterial strains using MIC values as the basis of comparison. Major factors influencing these properties result from changes in the 7-acylamino substituent or C-3 variations, although virtually all positions of the cephalosporin nucleus have been modified (Fig. 16) [569].

A large number of acyl groups have been introduced at C-7 and significantly change both potency and spectrum of activity [560]. Introduction of the aminothiazole group improves the activity against Gram-negative strains [591], and in combination with the *syn*-oximino grouping confers resistance to β-lactamases [592]. The nature of the C-3 substituent predominantly influences the pharmacokinetic and pharmacological properties, and secondarily the antibacterial activity. Thus, 3-methyl compounds with a C-7 phenylglycinyl side chain are orally absorbed, whereas C-3 vinyl derivatives, even with the oximino-containing C-7 side chains, also show promise as oral agents [560]. Some interesting synthetic methodologies have been developed for these vinyl compounds by use of allenyl

azetidinone intermediates and a variety of organometallic reagents [593,594].

Several highly active derivatives have resulted from replacement of the sulfur atom with oxygen or carbon, or by transposition of the heteroatom from position 1 to position 2 ("isocephem" derivatives). Substitution at C-7 strongly affects β-lactamase stability.

The synthesis of potent antipseudomonal β-lactam derivatives can be achieved by introducing siderophore-like moieties that allow use of the *ton* B transport system, overcoming resistance caused by a reduced permeation barrier. In general, siderophores are high affinity iron binding compounds that the bacteria release in their surroundings [595,596]. These bacterial products, which are capable of chelating ferric iron, are actively transported into the bacteria.

Catechol groups have been used to enhance the activity, particularly against *P. aeruginosa*. Many examples are described [568]. The effect of the catechol group seems to be similar irrespective of whether it is incorporated into the C-7 acylamino side chain as in M-14659 (**106**) [597], or the C-3-position as illustrated by (**108**) [598]. BRL-57342 (**107**) [599] is noteworthy in that it not only exhibits antipseudomonal activity but also retains some anti-Gram-positive activity, an unusual feature for cephalosporins bearing a catechol group. Evidence has been presented to show that these compounds penetrate into the cell through use of the bacterial *ton* B-dependent iron-transport system [600,601].

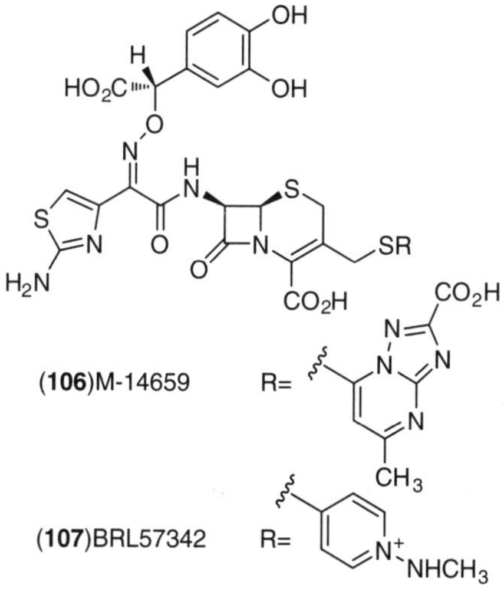

(**106**)M-14659   R=

(**107**)BRL57342   R=

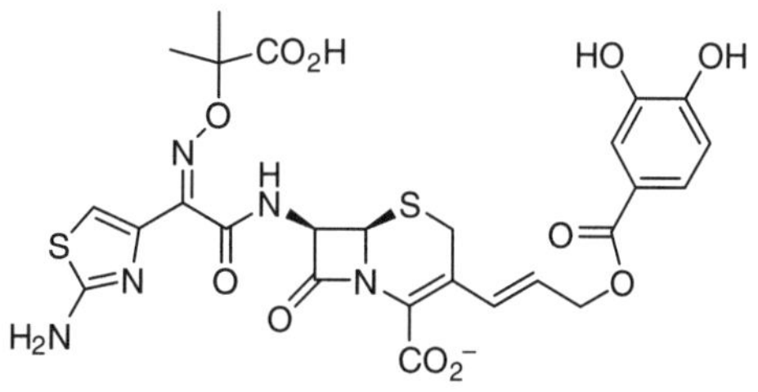

(**108**)

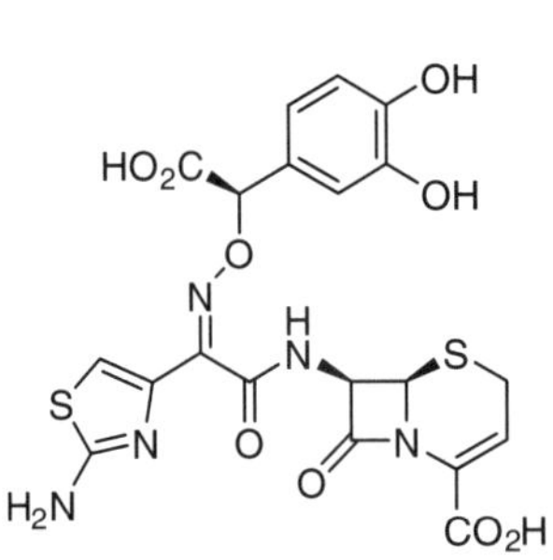

(109) GR-69153

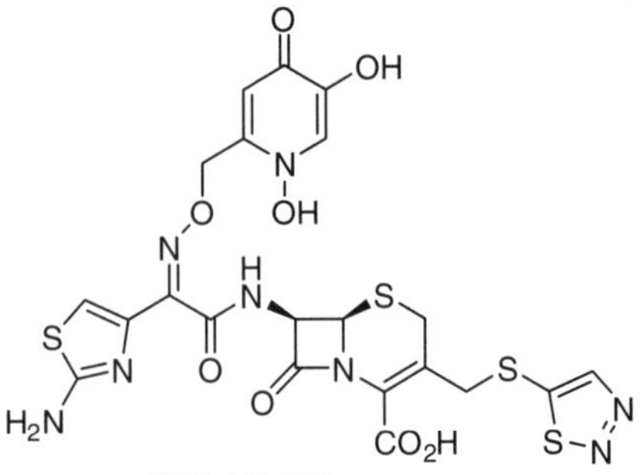

(110) KP-736

Other examples of cephalosporin derivatives bearing a catechol moiety are GR-69153 (**109**) [602] and KP-736 (**110**) [603]. However, bacteria commonly develop resistance to siderophore-like drugs.

5.2.5. 7α-Substituted Cephalosporins In 1971 two naturally occurring cephalosporins possessing a 7α-methoxy substituent were isolated from a *Streptomyces* strain. Its structure was shown to be 7α-methoxycephalosporin C (**111**) and the 3-carbamate (**112**) [531]. Subsequently, several further examples of this type of natural product were discovered and characterized [560,604]. All possess the D-α-aminoadipic acid side chain, but with different 3-substituents. Interest in this class of compounds arose primarily from their intrinsically higher resistance to hydrolysis by β-lactamases. Collectively,

they are called cephamycins. Their chemistry and biology have been comprehensively reviewed [477,532].

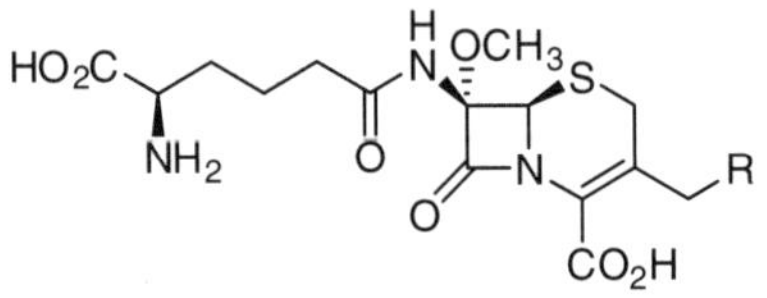

(111) R = OCOCH$_3$
(112) R = OCONH$_2$

Subsequently, a range of 7α-methoxycephalosporins (**113**) of bacterial origin and possessing oligopeptide side chains at C-3, known as the cephabacins M, were reported [605]. A new structural class,

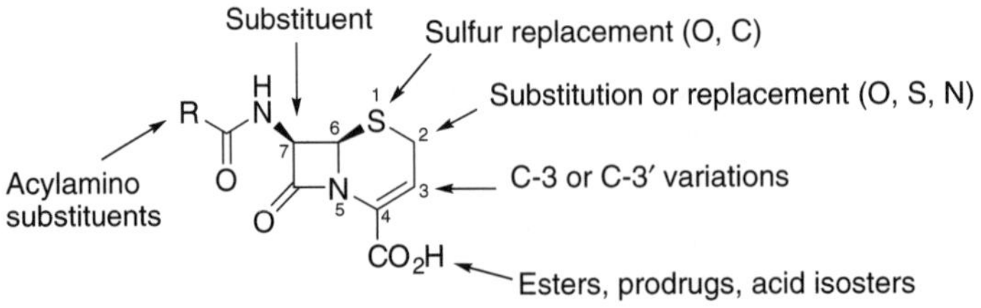

Figure 16. Structural variations of the cephalosporin ring system.

incorporating a 7α-formylamino substituent (114), was also isolated [533,606,607]. These were named the cephabacins F, or alternatively as the chitinovorins A–D [533,607,608].

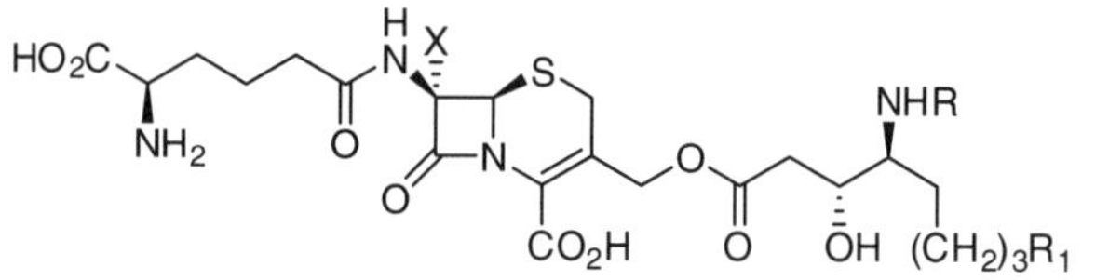

(113) Cephabacins-M   X = OCH₃
(114) Cephabacins-F   X = NHCHO

7α-Methoxy Cephalosporins As with the cephalosporins, the first area of SAR to be investigated was the replacement of the α-aminoadipic acid side chain with other acylamino variations. Methods involving acyl exchange [609] and removal of the side chain using imines and imidoyl chlorides [610–612] or through an oxamic acid derivative [613] have been described, together with the effect on antibacterial activity [477]. Numerous approaches have been directed toward the chemical introduction of the 7α-methoxy, and other substituents into the cephalosporin ring system [477]. Many have also found application in the penicillin field (Section 5.1). Of the range of groups introduced, however, it is the methoxy and the formamido groups that provide the best combination of stability to β-lactamases and antimicrobial potency [614,615].

Although initial approaches to methoxylation used C-7-diazo cephalosporins [482], as in the penicillins, the most widely used methods rely on addition of methoxide to acylimine intermediates such as (115) [616], sulfenimines (116) [485], or ketenimines [617]. Addition to the quinone methide derivative (117) is a method that has found application in the synthesis of Cefmetazole (118) [618,619], a semisynthetic cephamycin.

Again, in a manner similar to that of the penicillins, an alternative approach to acylimine formation uses carbanion formation α to the β-lactam carbonyl followed by reaction with an electrophile, to give a substrate suitable for the introduction of the methoxy group. Thus, generation of the anion from imine (119) and reaction with methyl methanethiosulfate gave the 7α-thiomethyl cephalosporin (120), which was then converted to the acylamino derivative (121). Solvolysis in methanol in the presence of mercury salts then led to the 7α-methoxy cephalosporin [480].

Factors related to the methylthiolation of cephalosporins have been extensively studied, particularly by workers at Squibb [620]. Approaches to the total synthesis of the 7α-methoxycephalosporins were described by the Merck group [536–538] and Kishi [621,622]. The first member of this group to be used clinically was cefoxitin (92), which is very stable to the class A β-lactamases. Its carbamoyl group provides stability to esterases [573]. Cefoxitin (92) has a fairly broad spectrum of activity, including anaerobic bacteria such as *B. fragilis*, a common pathogen following abdominal surgery [623]. Examples of newer cephamycins having a 3-*N*-methyltetrazolylthiomethyl substituent are cefmetazole (118) [619,624] and cefotetan (93) [625], reported as showing improved Gram-positive activity or pharmacokinetic properties over those of cefoxitin.

7α-Formamido Derivatives Before the discovery of the natural products, the Beecham group had already shown the utility of the formamido substituent with the synthesis of several highly active, β-lactamase stable 6α-substituted penicillins and 7α-substituted cephalosporins [487,488]. One of the initial approaches to the conversion of the unsubstituted cephalosporin ring system into the formamido nucleus was by way of (123), readily available from work on the methoxy series. Acylation provides (124), from which the methylthio group can be displaced with ammonia in the presence of a mercury salt followed by formylation and acid deprotection, to give the appropriate 7α-formamido cephalosporin acid (125).

Alternatively, the formamido group can be introduced directly by treatment of (126) with *N,N*-bis(trimethylsilyl)formamide in the presence of mercuric acetate [488,626]. Other methods for incorporating the forma-

mido substituent have been reported [489,490], as well as high yielding "one-pot" large scale preparation of the formamido nucleus by use of silyl protection and quinone methide methodology [627].

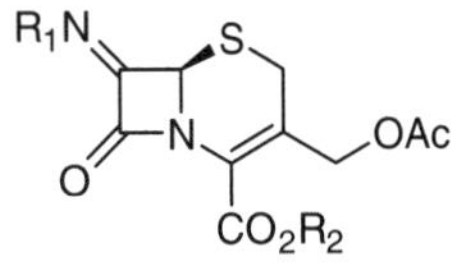

(115) R$_1$ = RCO
(116) R$_1$ = RS

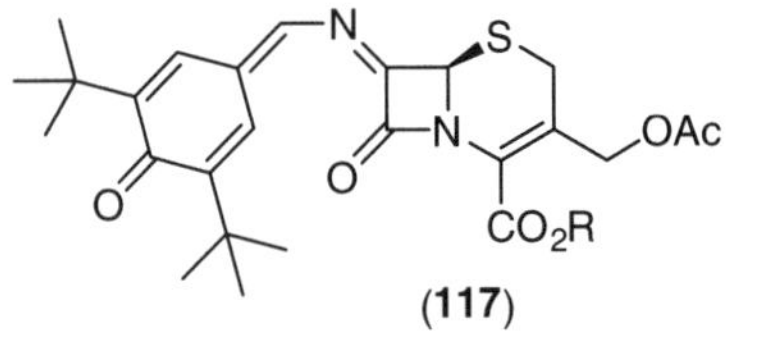

(117)

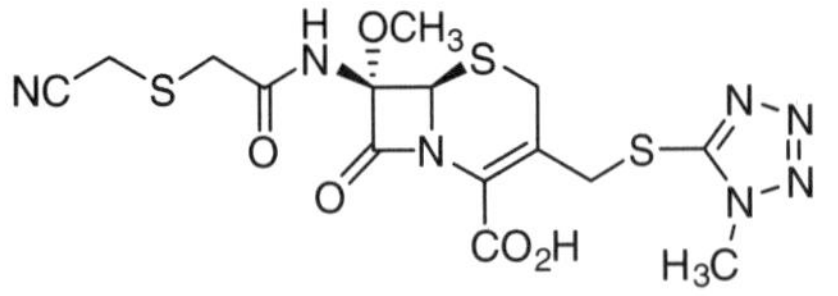

(118) Cefmetazole

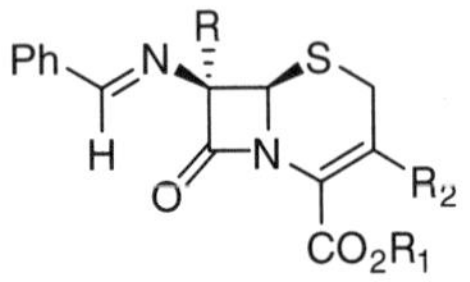

(119) R = H
(120) R = SCH$_3$

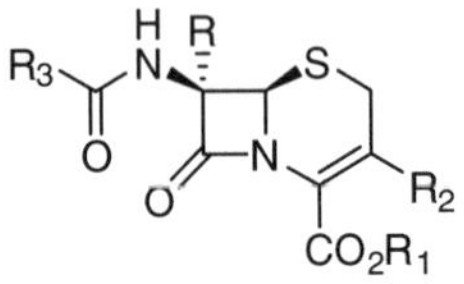

(121) R = SCH$_3$
(122) R = OCH$_3$

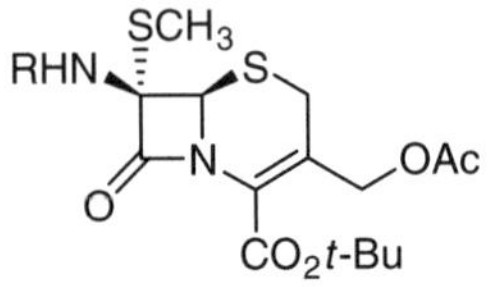

(123) R = H
(124) R = R$_1$CO

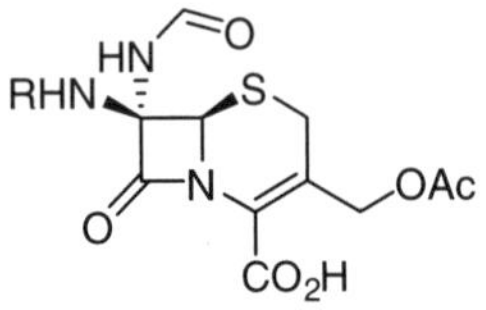

(125) R = R$_1$CO
(126) R = H

In a series of structure–activity studies varying both the 7-acylamino side chain and 3-substituent, it was demonstrated that the formamido cephalosporins in many cases showed advantages over the cephamycins in conferring high β-lactamase stability without compromising antimicrobial activity [628,629]. In particular the catecholic derivative (127, BRL-41897) was identified as a broad-spectrum agent active against both Gram-negative and -positive bacteria with high potency against *P. aeruginosa*. Its efficacy correlated to its uptake occurred via the ferri-pyochelin siderophore transporter [630]. BRL-41897 reached the stage of single dose volunteer studies, before adverse toxicological effects caused its withdrawal from development [631].

5.2.6. Oxacephalosporins (1-Oxa-1-Dethiacephems) The synthesis of 1-oxadethiaceph-3-

em-4-carboxylic acids (1-oxacephems) was initially carried out by the Merck group in 1974 with the synthesis of racemic 1-oxacephalothin (128) [632]. The 1-oxacephalothin showed biological activity comparable to cephalothin (87). Subsequent examples also demonstrated the potential value of these nonnatural 1-oxa analogs over the natural cephalosporins [633–635]. Extensive SAR studies by the Shionogi group led to the identification and development of moxalactam (latamoxef, 129) as a broad-spectrum clinical agent equal to or better than many third-generation cephalosporins [636,637]. However, moxalactam possesses poor activity against *S. aureus*, while the manifestation of side effects, including problems associated with blood clotting due to decreased vitamin K synthesis, have considerably restricted its clinical use [638,639]. Further studies identified flomoxef (130) with improved Gram-positive activity as an agent to overcome these problems [640,641].

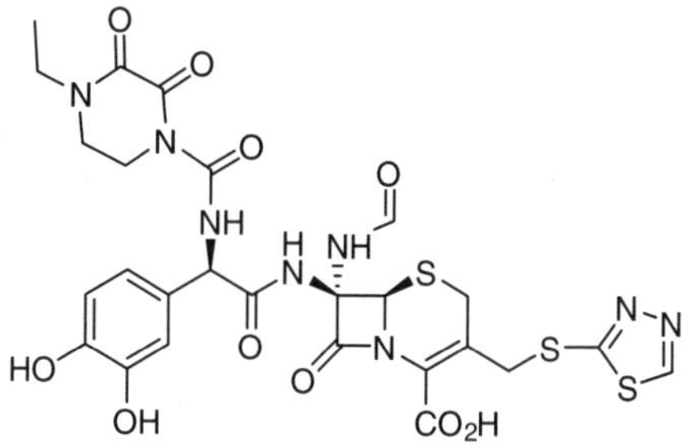

(**127**) BRL-41897

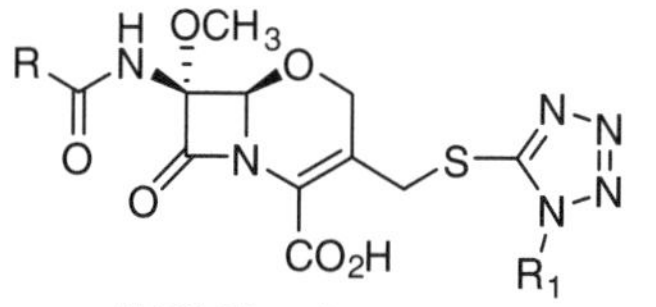

(**129**) Moxalactam

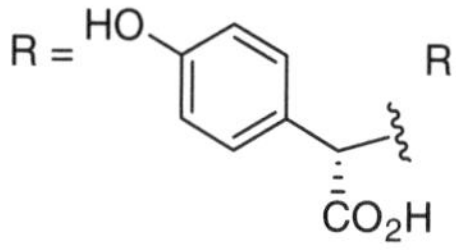

R = [structure] R₁ = CH₃

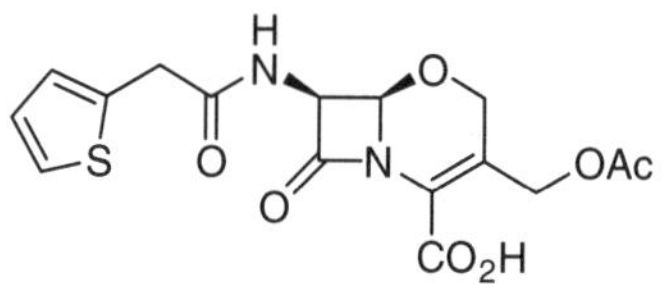

(**130**) Flomoxef R = F₂CHSCH₂
R₁ = CH₂CH₂OH

(**128**)

The identification of moxalactam (**129**) and flomoxef (**130**) as clinical candidates led to an intensive effort by Shionogi to establish a stereocontrolled, commercially viable process synthesis of 1-oxacephems. The culmination of this effort is illustrated (Fig. 17) by the conversion of the readily available penicillin nucleus (6-APA) to the 1-oxacephem nucleus (**138**) used for the production of both moxalactam (**129**) and flomoxef (**130**) [642,643]. Protection, oxidation, and epimerization of the benzoyl derivative of 6-APA (**131**) readily gave the epipenicillin β-sulfoxide (**132**), which was converted to the key epi-oxazolinone azetidinone intermediate (**133**). Transformation to the allylalcohol (**134**) was followed by Lewis acid catalyzed cyclization to the oxacepham ring system (**135**), and then photochemical halogenation to the chloromethyl 1-oxo-cephem ester (**136**). Introduction of the methoxy group and appropriate tetrazole substituent

gave (**137**). Deacylation yielded ester (**138**) in high overall yield, as a suitable substrate for conversion to moxalactam (**129**) or flomoxef (**130**) on a commercially viable scale. A range of 2-methyl analogs (e.g., **139**) have been reported but no clinical candidates were selected [644].

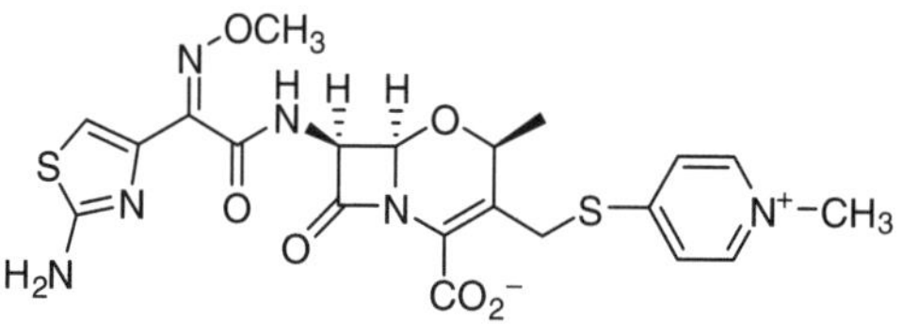

(**139**)

Subsequent to the discovery of the 7α-formamido-substituted cephalosporins the synthesis of a series of analogous 1-oxacephem

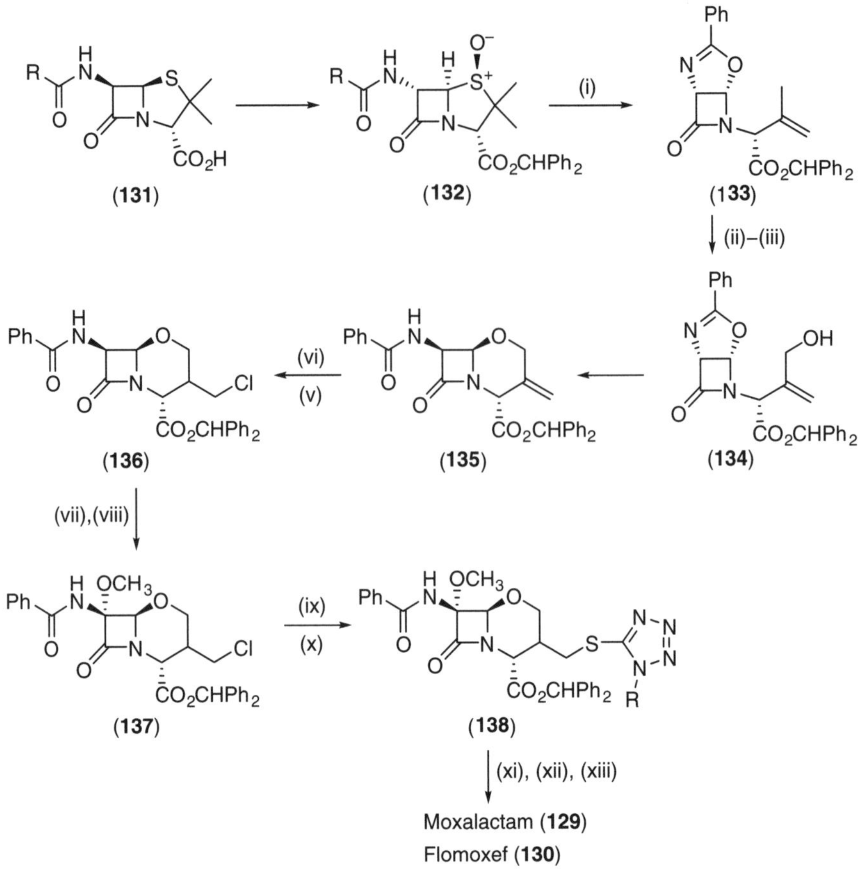

Reagents: (i) Δ/Ph₃P; (ii)Cl₂/base, (iii) I₂/CuO/DMSO/H₂O; (iv) BF₃-Et₂O; (v) Cl₂/hν;
(vi) DBN; (vii) t-BuOCl/LiOMe; (viii)H⁺; (ix) Na₂S₂O₃; (x) NaS-tetrazole; (xi) PCl₅/pyridine;
(xii) MeOH; (xiii) acylation.

Figure 17. Conversion of penicillin to 1-oxacephems.

antibiotics was described [631]. A general method for their synthesis was reported by Kamachi et al. from either the iminopenam or iminocephem [645]. Many of these show a level of antibacterial activity and β-lactamase stability comparable to that of moxalactam, or cephalosporins such as ceftazidime (**96**) [629,646].

5.2.7. Carbacephalosporins   (Carbacephems)
Another series of nonnatural cephalosporins of interest are the 1-carbacephems, particularly with the discovery of the oral compound loracarbef (**140**), which has a spectrum of activity similar to that of cefaclor, but with greater chemical stability, a longer half-life, and better oral absorption [647,648]. The additional chemical stability conferred by the carbacephem nucleus has been further demonstrated by the synthesis of directly linked quaternary derivatives such as (**141**), which have not been reported in the cephalosporin series [649]. This same stability may, however, correlate to increased likelihood of nephrotoxicity [650]. The Lilly group has also described detailed SAR lead-

ing to the identification of agents, exemplified by (142), with activity against methicillin-resistant staphylococci [651]. While there are occasional reports in the literature concerning exploratory chemistry within this class [652–654], there is no evidence of further interest in clinical candidates from this cephem subclass.

5.2.8. New Cephalosporins
In contrast to the penicillin class, which can be argued to have a fully matured structure–activity relationship, new cephalosporin structures continue to emerge [655,656]. Nonetheless, all of these new cephalosporin structures are nuanced variations within the same substructure class: an O-substituted heterocyclic (often an aminoazolyl) oxyiminoacetamido at C-7, and hydrophilic-substituted heteroarene substitution at C-3. The oxyiminoacetamido substitutent combines antibacterial potency with resistance to β-lactamase hydrolysis, while the basis for optimization of the hydrophilic-substituted heteroarene is particular affinity for the PBP2a enzyme of methicillin-resistant $S. aureus$.

CB-181963
CB-181963 (formerly CAB-175) (143), possessing an azomethine substituent at position 3 of the cephem nucleus, has excellent $in vitro$ activity against a broad range of Gram-positive pathogens including methicillin-susceptible and methicillin-resistant $S. aureus$. The spectrum of activity extends to glycopeptide-intermediate and vancomycin-resistant $S. aureus$, as well as a variety of Gram-negative pathogens [657]. The anti-MRSA activity correlates with elevated binding to PBP2a. Spontaneous mutants resistant to CB-181963 did not arise either in MSSA or in MRSA hosts under conditions where mutants resistant to other antistaphylococcal antibiotics could be recovered. Human pharmacokinetic or pharmacodynamic data for CB-181963 are not available. CB-181963 had a short postantibiotic effect compared with other β-lactam antibiotics; therefore, possibly requiring more frequent or prolonged infusion administration [658]. Development of CB-181963 was

terminated by Cubist in 2004, although the compound continues to be pursued by the Antibiotic Research Institute of Sandoz as ABRI-1175 [659]. Other Sandoz cephalosporins (ABRI 2901 and ABRI 1974) show antibacterial activities against MRSA, including the clinically important vancomycin-resistant strain [203].

CXA-101
CXA-101 (formely FR264205) (144) (Astellas Pharma, Inc.) is a novel parental 3-(2,4-disubstituted 3-aminopyrazolyl) methyl cephalosporin currently in preclinical development [660]. CXA-101 has potent $in vitro$ activity against clinical isolates of $P. aeruginosa$ and $in vivo$ efficacy in various animal models [661]. The MIC_{90} value was an impressive 1 µg/mL against 193 isolates of $P. aeruginosa$, 8- to 16-fold more potent than ceftazidime, ciprofloxacin, or imipenem. In murine models of pulmonary, urinary tract, and burn wound infection caused by $P. aeruginosa$, CXA-101 was highly effective. Also, resistance characterization showed very low propensity for induce resistance [662]. In another study, CXA-101 demonstrated high stability of toward the class C AmpC β-lactamase [662].

LB-11058
LB-11058 (145) is a parenteral cephalosporin with a C-3 pyrimidinyl-substituted vinyl sulfide and a C-7 2-amino-5-chloro-1,3-thiazolyl group [663]. LB-11058 encompasses high PBP2 and PBP2a affinity. It is active $in vitro$, and in some $in vivo$, models against MRSA and several other gram-positive pathogens [663]. The good anti-MRSA activity of LB-11058 correlated with its ability to inhibit PBP2a (IC_{50} 0.8 µg/mL). A remarkable feature of LB-11058 is its $in vitro$ activity against oxacillin-resistant staphylococci. LB 11058 was very active against penicillin-resistant $S. pneumoniae$. Against Gram-negative pathogens, LB-11058 showed activity against $H. influenzae$ (MIC_{90}, 0.25–0.5 µg/mL) and $Moraxella catarrhalis$ ($MIC_{90} = 0.25$ µg/mL), with MICs not influenced by β-lactamase production. It has, however, a less broad coverage of the Gram-negative pathogens [664]. Its development status is uncertain [659].

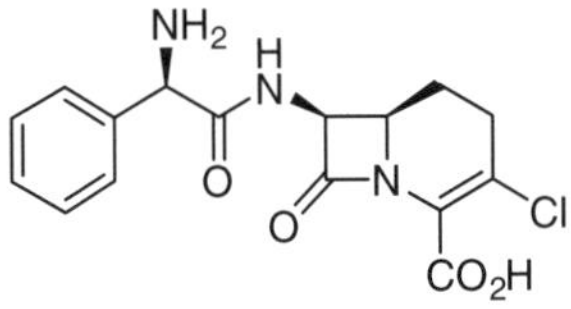

(**140**) Loracarbef

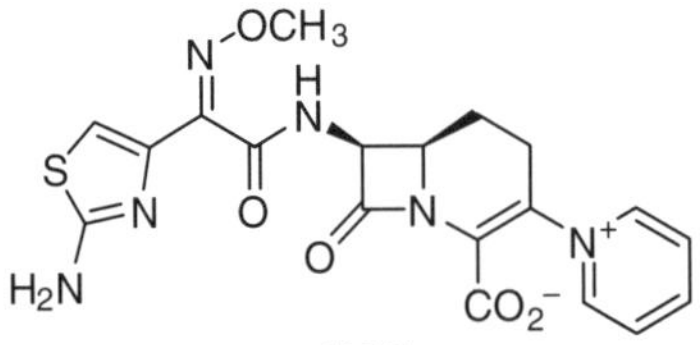

(**141**)

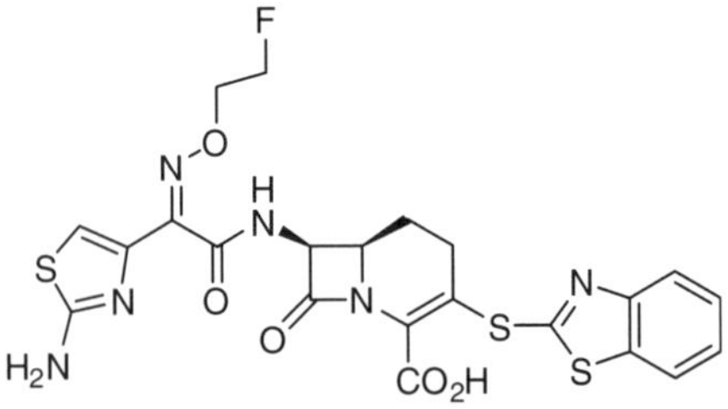

(**142**)

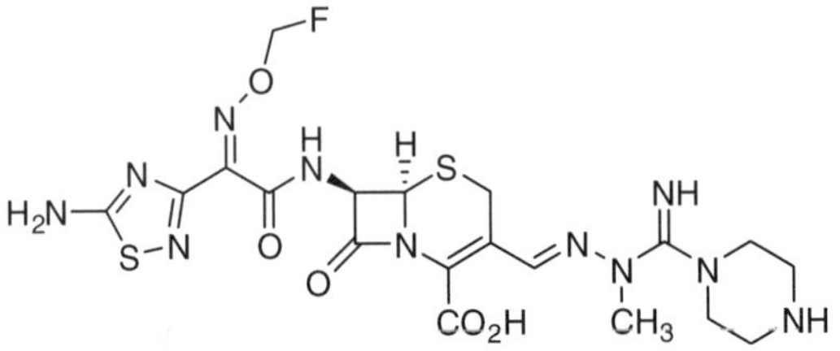

(**143**) CB-181963

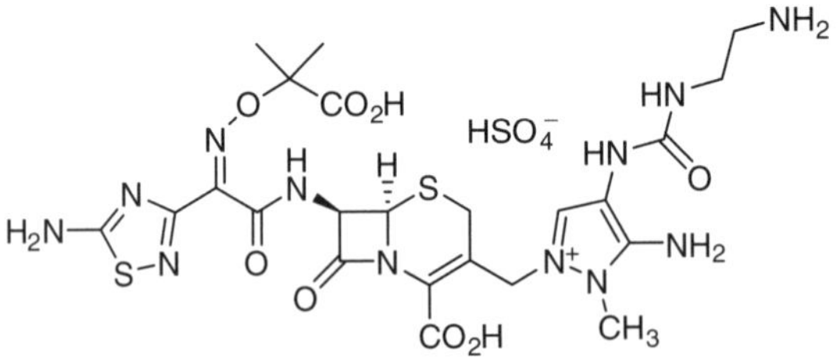

(**144**) CXA-101

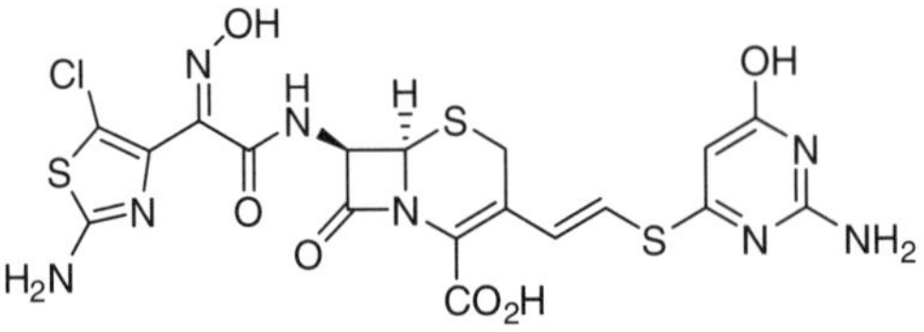

(**145**) LB11058

RWJ-442831   RWJ-442831 (**146**) is the aspartyl prodrug of the cephalosporin RWJ-54428 (formerly MC-02,479) (**147**)[665,666]. This prodrug has greatly improved solubility over the zwitterionic RWJ-54428 parent. The pro-drug is rapidly converted to RWJ-54428 by liver and serum enzymes. This cephalosporin has several unique structural features, notably a 4-pyridinethiol directly linked to the cephalosporin core (that is, without a methylene spacer between them) and a 2-aminoethylthio-methyl substituent. The pyridine ring, in particular, is crucial for both activity and solubility [667].

RWJ-54428 shows high antibacterial activity in vitro against most Gram-positive bacteria including multiresistant staphylococci, streptococci, and E. faecalis but not ampicillin-resistant E. faecium. The MIC$_{90}$ of RWJ-54428 was ≤2 µg/mL for all bacteria tested, with this single exception of the ampicillin-resistant E. faecium [668,669]. The activity against four strains of vancomycin-intermediate S. aureus was similar to that for other MRSA isolates (range 0.5–2 µg/mL) [670]. RWJ-54428 was more active than penicillin G and cefotaxime against penicillin-resistant strains of S. pneumoniae (MIC$_{90}$ = 0.25 µg/mL). RWJ-54428 did not select resistant mutants of MRSA or enterococci by the methods used [659]. The difficulty for RWJ-54428 to select for resistance by standard methods has been attributed to the potent inhibition of multiple PBPs and stability to β-lactamases [671]. RWJ-54428 was only marginally active against most Gram-negative bacteria but activity was observed against H. influenzae and M. catarrhalis (MIC$_{90}$ = 0.25 and 0.5 µg/mL, respectively). RWJ-54428 also had low MIC values against most β-lactamase-negative isolates, with the exception of C. difficile [672].

RWJ-442831 was effective against both methicillin-susceptible S. aureus and MRSA in a mouse model of sepsis, demonstrating activity comparable to that of vancomycin. Its MRSA activity correlates to PBP2a affinity [671]. RWJ-442831 also showed activity similar to that of vancomycin in a single-dose neutropenic mouse thigh model of infection with MRSA and exhibited a prolonged in vivo postantibiotic effect [673]. Efficacy superior to that shown by either penicillin G or cefotaxime was obtained in a mouse model of pneumonia due to a penicillin-susceptible strain of S. pneumoniae. RWJ-442831 had bactericidal effects similar to those shown by vancomycin and ampicillin in a mouse model of pyelonephritis caused by E. faecalis but the necessary daily doses were two- to threefold lower [673]. Its pharmacokinetic and pharmacodynamic parameters in these mouse models were very acceptable [674].

S-3578 S-3578 (**148**) is a highly water soluble (>100 mg/mL, at pH 2–7) and broad-spectrum parenteral cephalosporin, with potent activity against both methicillin-resistant S. aureus and P. aeruginosa [675,676]. The MIC$_{90}$ values of S-3578 against MRSA clinical isolates were 4 µg/mL, and 2 µg/mL for MRSE. These values were, respectively, fourfold higher than, and equal to, those of vancomycin against the same strain collection. S-3578 was also highly active against PRSP, with a MIC$_{90}$ of 1 µg/mL, which was comparable to that of ceftriaxone. In time-kill studies with MRSA and methicillin-susceptible S. aureus, S-3578 caused more than a 4 log$_{10}$ decrease of viable cells on the average at twice the MIC after 24 h of exposure, indicating that it had potent bactericidal activity [677]. It was reported that S-3578 did not select resistant mutants of MRSA or enterococci. S-3578 also had antibacterial activity against a variety of Gram-negative bacteria including P. aeruginosa, although it was not superior to cefepime.

A mouse lung infection model with PRSP and a neutropenic mouse systemic infection model with MRSA were used to determine the PK-PD parameters that best correlated with the efficacy of S-3578 [678]. The plasma concentration remained above the MIC was again the PK-PD parameter that best correlated with efficacy. There was a twofold increase in the dose of S-3578 required in the systemic infection model compared with that in the pneumonia model, although the area under curves (AUCs) were the same, which is probably due to the different MIC values of S-3578 for the two pathogens [678]. S-3578 maintains a spectrum resembling a third-generation cephalosporin against clinically important Gram-negative species, making it potentially suitable for broad-spectrum use.

The efficacy of S-3578 in a mouse model of septicemia caused by MRSA was almost the same as that of vancomycin [679]. In contrast, cefepime and imipenem-cilastatin were less active against this pathogen. S-3578 was the most effective of these compounds in a mouse model of septicemia caused by PRSP. S-3578 (10 mg/kg) had significant activity against MRSA and P. aeruginosa in polymicrobial pulmonary infections. The therapeutic efficacy of S-3578 was more potent than that of the combination of vancomycin and ceftazidime.

S-3578 was in Phase I development by Shionogi in 2003, but appears to be no longer pursued by this company [655].

TD-1792 The structure of TD-1792 (149) combines a proprietary cephem structure with vancomycin, giving a hybrid heterodimer antibacterial structure [680,681]. The cephem-vancomycin heterodimer TD-1792 is designed to exploit the affinity of vancomycin for the D-Ala-D-Ala termini of bacterial peptidoglycan precursors, to enhance cephem inactivation of the proximal PBP enzymes. Thus, TD-1792 is directed against two key bacterial cell wall targets and indeed, it inhibits both the PBP transpeptidation and the transglycosylation reactions [682]. TD-1792 showed extremely potent activity against Gram-positive isolates from skin and blood specimen sources [683]. The MIC$_{90}$ values against MRSA and MSSA

were 64-fold lower than those of vancomycin [684]. Time-kill assays against three MRSA strains showed that TD-1792 was bactericidal at 2× the MIC (MIC = 0.015–0.03 µg/mL). Against VISA, TD-1792 was bactericidal at low multiples of the MIC, whereas vancomycin was bacteriostatic. This compound presents prolonged postantibiotic effect against MSSA and MRSA [685]. The potent activity of TD-1792 could not be reproduced by its individual components administered either alone, or in combination. Covalent linkage of the component moieties is required for the potent activity of TD-1792, in accordance with a multivalent mode of action [686]. In Phase II evaluation by Theravance TD-1792 was as effective as vancomycin, and as well or better tolerated, in the treatment of Gram-positive cSSSIs. Attempts to select and recover *S. aureus* isolates resistant to TD-1792 were not successful.

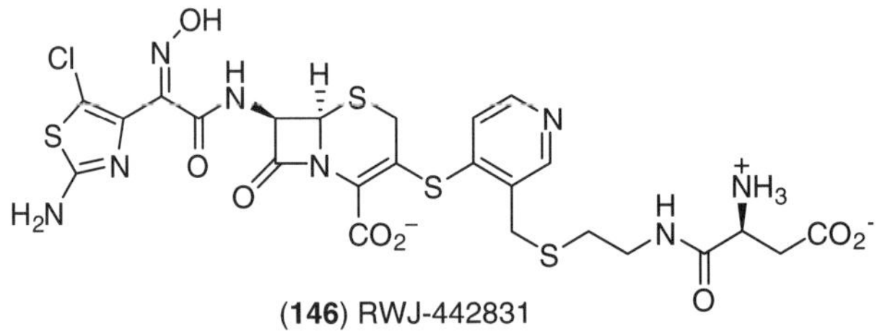

(**146**) RWJ-442831

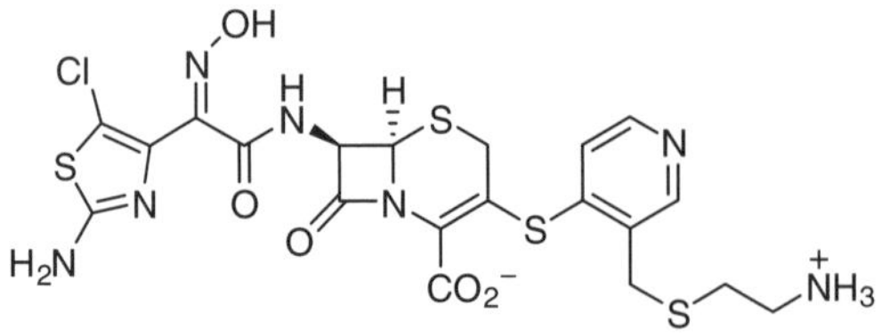

(**147**) RWJ-54428

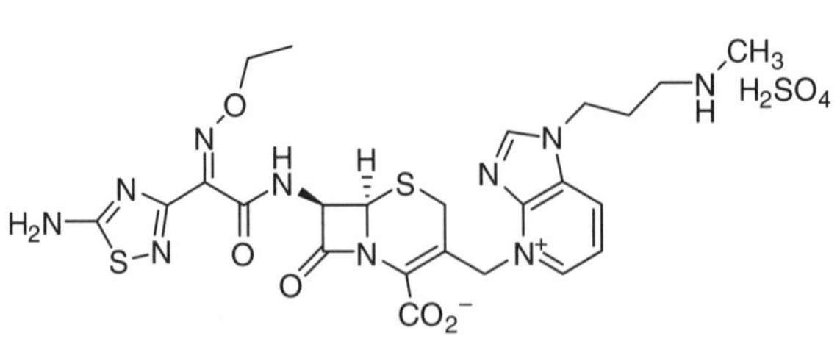

(**148**) S-3578

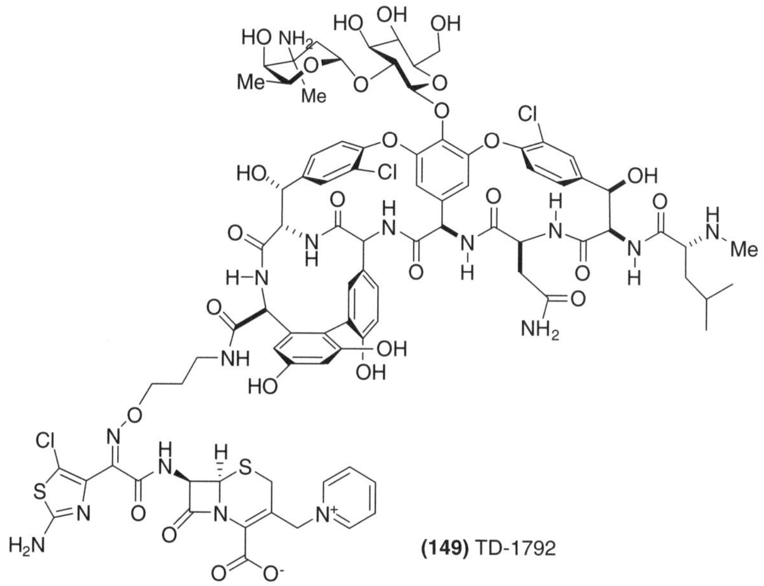

(149) TD-1792

Ceftaroline Fosamil   Ceftaroline fosamil (formerly known as both PPI-0903 and TAK-599) **(150)**, a water-soluble N-phosphono cephalosporin prodrug, was discovered by Takeda Chemical Industries Ltd. [687–689] and is being developed by Forest Laboratories [690]. The parent, ceftaroline, is released upon *in vivo* hydrolysis. Ceftaroline has a high affinity for the MRSA PBP2a enzyme ($IC_{50} = 0.9\,\mu g/$ mL) [204], and as a result it exerts potent *in vitro* activity against oxacillin (methicillin)-resistant *S. aureus* (as well many other Gram-positive organisms), while retaining activity against Gram-negative bacilli [691,692]. *Staphylococcus* sp., including MRSA and oxacillin-resistant coagulase-negative staphylococci, appear to be particularly susceptible to ceftaroline ($MIC_{90} = 0.25–2\,\mu g/mL$) [693]. Ceftaroline also has good activity against vancomycin-nonsusceptible MRSA, a pathogen of increasing concern, and it was highly active against *S. pneumoniae* ($MIC_{50} = 0.12\,\mu g/mL$, $MIC_{90} = 0.25\,\mu g/mL$), including cephalosporin-resistant isolates [694,695] as well as β-lactamase-positive and -negative isolates of *H. influenzae* ($MIC_{50}/MIC_{90} \leq 0.016\,\mu g/mL$) and *M. catarrhalis*, pathogens frequently associated with respiratory tract infections [696]. Ceftaroline MIC_{90} values were $4\,\mu g/mL$ against *E. faecalis*.

The spectrum of activity of ceftaroline against the Gram-negative bacteria is similar to those of the broad-spectrum cephalosporins. Among the Enterobacteriaceae, the vast majority of *C. freundii* ($MIC_{90} = 2\,\mu g/$ mL), nonextended-spectrum β-lactamase (ESBL)-producing *E. coli* ($MIC_{90} = 0.12\,\mu g/$ mL), *K. pneumoniae* ($MIC_{90} = 0.5\,\mu g/mL$), *Morganella morganii* ($MIC_{90} = 0.12\,\mu g/mL$), *Proteus mirabilis* ($MIC_{90} = 0.12\,\mu g/mL$), and *S. marcescens* ($MIC_{90} = 2\,\mu g/mL$) strains are inhibited at $\leq 2\,\mu g/mL$ [692]. However, like other broad-spectrum cephalosporins, the ceftaroline MICs for some *E. cloacae*, *P. vulgaris*, and *Providencia* sp. strains and ESBL-producing strains (regardless of species) were elevated. Ceftaroline has poor activity against anaerobes and nonfermenters, particularly *P. aeruginosa* and *E. faecium*. In a comprehensive evaluation, ceftaroline had activity comparable to, or better than, ceftriaxone [697]. Ceftaroline is labile to the action of the ESBL and AmpC β-lactamases, and some vulnerability to enterobacterial penicillinases. Much of this lability was overcome by combination with clavulanate [692]. Resistance selection occurred with Enterobacteriaceae, but was not seen with *S. aureus, H. influenzae,* or the pneumococci.

Ceftaroline fosamil demonstrated superior bacteriocidal activity to linezolid and vancomycin in a MRSA endocarditis model in the rabbit [698]. It is eliminated in humans mainly by renal excretion, with $t_{1/2}$ values of 2.0–2.9 h [690]. Cefatroline exhibits excellent tolerability and safety profile. On the basis of successful completion of a Phase II cSSSI study [699], Ceftaroline fosamil was advanced to Phase 3 cSSSI and CAP clinical trials [690,700].

Ceftobiprole Ceftobiprole (formerly known as both BAL9141 and Ro-63-9141) (**151**) is the active component of the parenteral prodrug ceftobiprole medocaril (formerly known both as BAL5788 and Ro-65-5788) (**152**) [701–704]. It is a fourth-generation cephalosporin having a pyrrolidinone-3-ylide-nemethyl cephem with a basic C-3 side chain. A synthetic route to ceftobiprole medocaril is described [705]. The water-soluble prodrug ceftobiprole medocaril is rapidly cleaved in plasma to give ceftobiprole [326]. The *in vitro* activity of ceftobiprole encompasses a wide range of Gram-positive and -negative pathogenic bacteria [706–714]. In addition to the organisms normally susceptible to cephalosporins (including *P. aeruginosa*), ceftobiprole exhibits strong antibacterial activity against MRSA and methicillin-resistant *Staphylococcus epidermidis*, penicillin-resistant *S. pneumoniae* (PRSP) and even *E. faecalis*, which is an unusual activity for a cephalosporin [659]. Importantly, ceftobiprole was uniformly efficacious across the entire spectrum of MRSA strains [715].

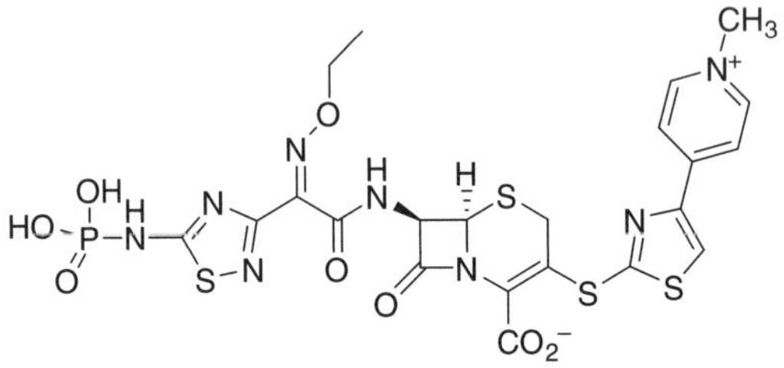

(**150**) Ceftaroline fosamil

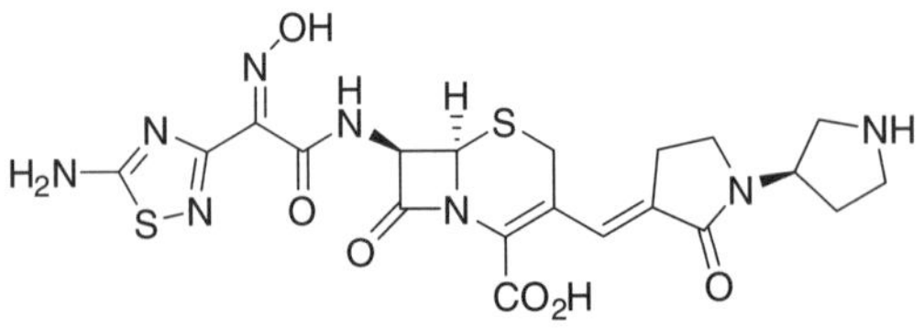

(**151**) Ceftobiprole

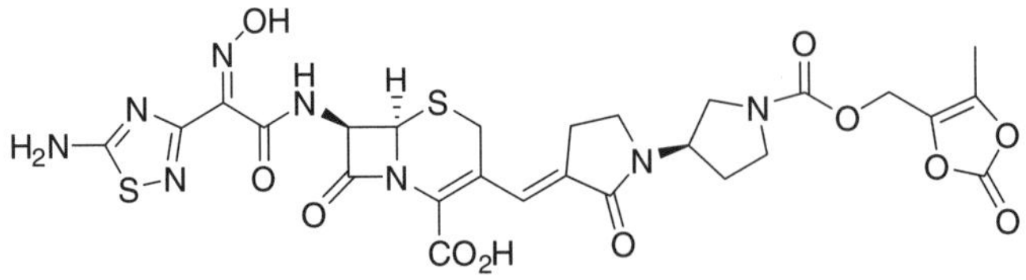

(**152**) Ceftobiprole medocaril

Ceftobiprole shows strong binding to the PBP 2a of MRSA (IC$_{50}$ = 0.3–0.5 µg/mL) [715–717]. Its overall PBP affinity is also strong for representative PBPs of Gram-negative and -positive bacteria [718]. Ceftobiprole is relatively stable toward class C β-lacta-mases, and shows a low propensity to induce these enzymes or to select for stably dere-pressed mutants in strains producing the enzymes. One study showed that ceftobiprole is resistant to hydrolysis by the common staphylococcal PC1 β-lactamase, the class A

TEM-1 β-lactamase, and the class C AmpC β-lactamase but was labile to hydrolysis by class B, class D, and class A extended-spectrum β-lactamases [719].

Ceftobiprole medocaril is being developed jointly by Johnson & Johnson and Basilea. It has shown efficacy in several pharmacological models of infection including against *E. faecalis* [720], *S. aureus* [721], and *S. pneumoniae* [722]. The pharmacokinetics and pharmacodynamics of ceftobiprole in humans were reported [328,723]. Ceftobiprole medocaril was well tolerated in clinical trials. The most common adverse event was a caramel-like taste disturbance during infusion. It is currently under regulatory review for the treatment of cSSSI, and has completed Phase 3 community-acquired pneumonia (CAP) and NP clinical trials [700]. Initial summaries of its clinical experience are available [325,724–726]. If approved, ceftobiprole will likely be an attractive choice for formulary consideration. It is a β-lactam that is effective in the treatment of MRSA, for which there are no other β-lactam options currently available. However, ceftobiprole will likely be considered a second-line antibiotic for the treatment of cSSSIs, as it has not demonstrated greater efficacy than vancomycin monotherapy, or vancomycin plus ceftazidime.

5.3. Penems

Penems—unlike the penams (penicillins), carbapenems, and cephalosporins—are not precedented in nature. The fully synthetic template of the penems was conceived first by Woodward [727,728] as a hybrid incorporating key structural attributes of the penams (the azathiobicyclo[3.2.0] core) and cephems (the alkene of the larger ring) [729–731]. While the penem hybrids obtained by the straightforward union of the penam and cephalosporin pharmacophores—the penems having 6β-*N*-acylamino substitution— are unexceptional (see below), penems that use 6α-side chains seen in the carbapenems and 2-substitutents precedented also by recent-generation carbapenems and cephalosporins, have exceptional antibacterial activities. These activities include strong Gram-positive and -negative activities (with the precise spectrum, however, very closely defined by the particular structures of these side chains), excellent resistance toward hydrolysis by the class A, C, and D serine β-lactamases (but typically not toward the class B metallo-β-lactamases), and excellent renal dehydropeptidase stability. These properties have led to one marketed oral penem (faropenem, Farom®), a series of expired clinical candidates (including BRL-42715, ritipenem, AMA-3176, Sch29482, Sch34343, Men-10700, and CGP-31608), and one continuing clinical candidate (sulopenem). Nonetheless, at this time, neither the open nor the patent literature suggests significant current medicinal effort within the penem class. This section reviews the history of the conception, summarizes key synthetic reactions and early generation penem properties, and closes with particular summaries pertaining to faropenem and sulopenem.

5.3.1. Synthesis of the Penems

Woodward's Phosphorane Route   The synthesis of 6-phenoxyacetamido penem (**159**, an analog of Penicillin G) was the first penem synthesized (Fig. 18) [732]. The strategy used a semisynthetic approach based on the penicillin-derived Kamiya disulfide (**153**), and employing an intramolecular Wittig reaction as the key step (**154–158**) forming the fused thiazoline. Despite limited chemical stability, penem (**159**) possessed antibacterial activity. This observation vindicated Woodward's conception, and led to a proliferation of studies on the penem β-lactam system.

Extension of the Phosphorane Route   Although alternative routes have been developed (Section 5.3.1.3), the most versatile routes to penems use the Woodward phosphorane strategy (or closely related methods) for 2,3-double bond formation. Total syntheses embodying this strategy have prepared a range of 2- and 6-substituted racemic penems. Nucleophilic displacement of the acetyl of 4-acetoxyazetidinone (**160**) [733] provided azetidinones (**161–163**) that were then elaborated to penems (**164**) [734] and (**165**) [735]. Similar reactions of 3-substituted (or disubstituted) acetoxyazetidinones gave 2-substituted 6-alkyl and 6,6-dialkylpenems. Acetoxyazetidinone (**160**) also provided the starting point for

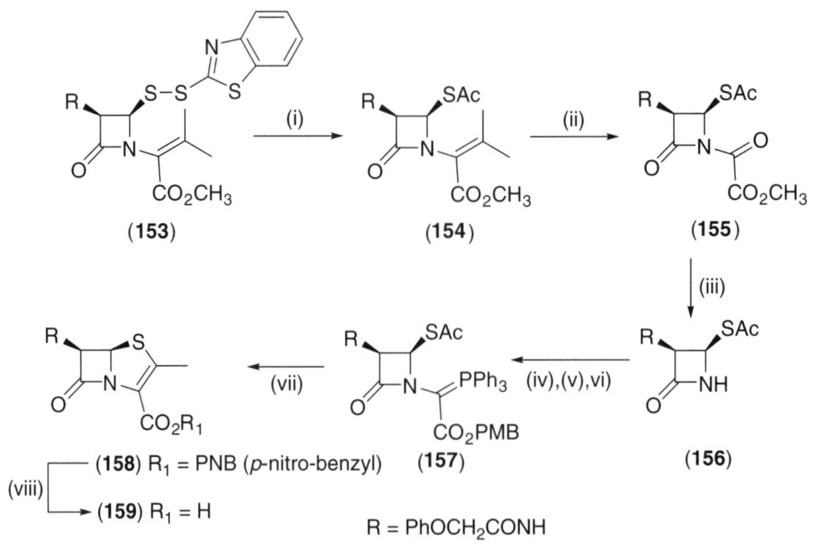

(i)
(ii)
(iii)
(iv),(v),vi)
(vii)
(viii)
(153)
(154)
(155)
(156)
(157)
(158) R1 = PNB (p-nitro-benzyl)
(159) R1 = H
R = PhOCH2CONH

Reagents: (i) Ph_3P, Ac_2O, AcOH, pyridine; (ii) O_3; (iii) MeOH; (iv) *p*-nitro-benzyl glyoxylate ethyl hemiacetal; (v) $SOCl_2$, base; (vi) Ph_3P, base; (vii) Δ, toluene; (viii) H_2, Pd/C.

Figure 18. Woodward's synthesis of penems.

the racemic synthesis of a penem (**167**) having the 1-hydroxyethyl substituent of the naturally occurring carbapenems [736]. The demonstration (in common with the carbapenems) that maximal antibacterial activity resided in the racemate with *trans*-6-(1*R*-hydroxyethyl) substitution, together with the earlier indication that optimal activity correlated to 5*R*-stereochemistry [737], set the stereochemical objectives for chiral penem syntheses.

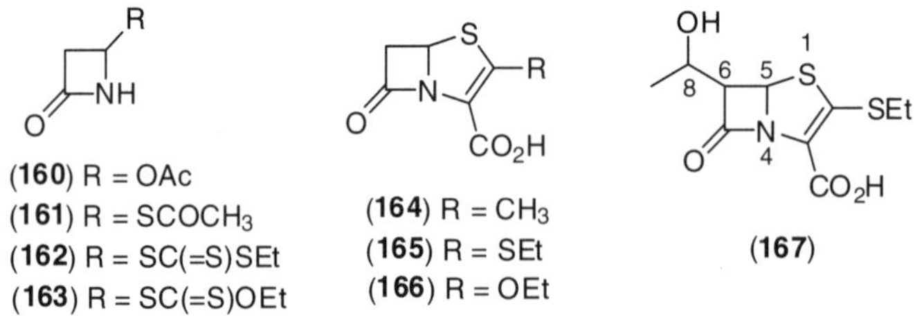

(160) R = OAc
(161) R = SCOCH3
(162) R = SC(=S)SEt
(163) R = SC(=S)OEt
(164) R = CH3
(165) R = SEt
(166) R = OEt
(167)

The favorable stereochemical outcome of the condensation of the readily available 6,6-dibromopenicillanate (**168**) with acetaldehyde [738] made these adducts attractive starting materials (Fig. 19). Reductive debromination from the major product (**169**) and also having the desired 8*R* stereochemistry, provided the 5*R*,6*S*,8*R*-penam (**170**). Several methods may be used to open the thiazolidine ring so as to give intermediates suitable for elaboration to penems. For example, chlorinolysis of (**170**) gives chloroazetidinone (**171**) [739], whereas $Hg(OAc)_2$ oxidative cleavage gives (after oxidative removal of the *N*-substituent) the acetoxy azetidinone (**172**) [740]. Reaction of either (**171**) [739] or (**172**) [741] with sodium trithiocarbonate proceeded with retention of configuration to give azetidinones (**173**). These were converted to the desired *trans*-8*R*-penems (**174**). In these studies, the high temperatures required to cyclize the intermediate phosphoranes were also responsible for a novel 5-epimerization of the penem (possibly involving the intermediacy of a betaine) leading to the unwanted *cis*-penems (**175**) [741].

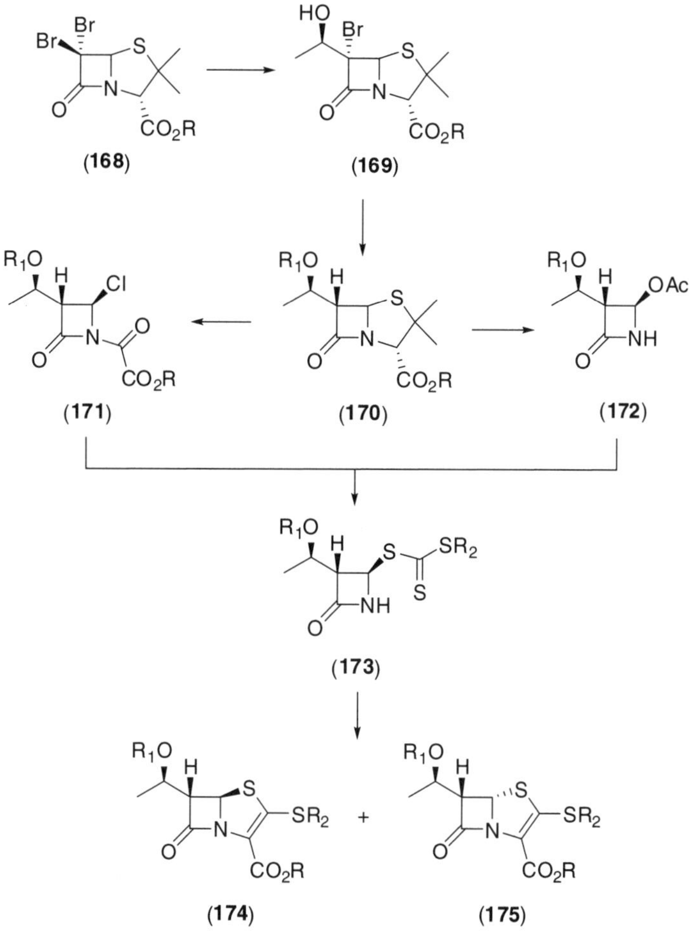

Figure 19. Synthesis of chiral penems.

Other methods that retain the stereochemistry of the carbon bearing the sulfur atom upon cleavage of the thiazolidine ring of penicillanates, to produce suitable intermediates for penem synthesis, include Ag(I)-assisted cleavage to mercaptides [742], whereas the sulfenic acids generated by the thermolysis of penicillanate sulfoxides have been trapped by terminal alkynes [743] and thiols [744]. Among the more efficient synthesis are those using the commercial, *tert*-butyldimethylsilyl-protected acetoxyazetidinone (**172**), which is prepared by total synthesis.

Alternative Methods for the Synthesis of Penems
Figure 20 summarizes the more widely applicable strategies for synthesis of penems (**182**). Although demonstrated, syntheses involving

S-C-2 and N-C-3 ring closures have been little used. The diazoketone/carbene insertion route widely used for the synthesis of carbapenems (see Section 5.5) has not been demonstrated for penems [745]. The lack of reactivity appears related to the interaction of the sulfur with the diazo-derived carbenoid.

The reactivity of the oxalimide carbonyl provides two useful alternatives to the original phosphorane route for 2,3-alkene formation. Treatment of thioesters (**179a**) [746] and trithiocarbonates (**180a**) [747,748] with trialkylphosphites at high temperatures gave the corresponding *C*- and *S*-substituted penems (**182**). A detailed study demonstrated [749] that for the thioesters, carbene generation and interception gave the

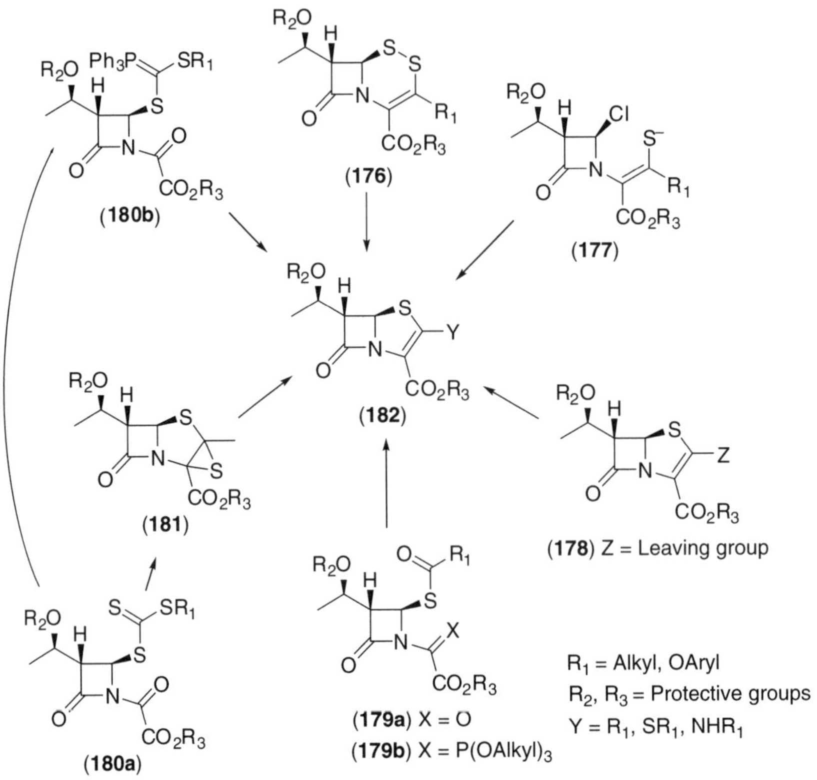

Figure 20. Alternative methods for the synthesis of penems.

intermediate trialkoxyphosphoranes (**179b**), which underwent Wittig-type cyclization. In contrast, it has been proposed that cyclization of the trithiocarbonates proceeds through insertion of the carbene into the more reactive thiocarbonyl group, to form a tricyclic episulfide (**181**), which is readily desulfurized to penem (**182**) [747,750]. The lower temperatures and shorter reaction times required for cyclization of trithiocarbonates, by this procedure avoid the C-5 epimerization experienced with the conventional phosphorane route. The high reactivity of the oxalimide carbonyl has also been exploited in the cyclization of "inverse phosphoranes" of the type (**180b**) [751]. Bond formation between the sulfur and the C-5 was used for the synthesis of the first examples of 2-aryloxy penems (**182**, Y = OAryl) [752].

Stereospecific cyclization of intermediate (**177**), exploiting chloride as the leaving group (Z), inverted configuration to give the 5R-pe-

nem (**182**) as product. Ring contraction of 2-thiacephems (**176**) has been studied extensively [753]. The unpredictable stereoselectivity of desulfurizations with P(III) reagents was overcome by oxidation to the 1,1-dioxides. These sulfones undergo stereospecific thermal desulfonylation to the 5R-penems. Despite this, it was concluded that the route offered no practical advantage over routes that used 2,3-alkene-forming strategies. Penems possessing leaving groups at the two positions have proved to be useful intermediates. Regioselective oxidation of the sulfide provided 2-ethylsulfinylpenems (**178**, Z = S(O)Et), which underwent displacement reactions with thiolates to give thio-substituted penems [754]. In a conceptually similar approach, amines were shown to displace phenolate leaving groups from penems of the type (**178**, Z = OAr) as a general route to the 2-substituted aminopenems (**182**, Y = NHR$_1$) [755]. The triflate nucleofuge of penems (**178**, Z = OSO$_2$CF$_3$) is displaced by thiolates to give *S*- and by cuprates to give *C*-substituted penems [756].

5.3.2. Biological Properties Unlike the antibacterially inactive penicillanic and cephalosporanic acids, 6-unsubstituted penems exhibited good activity against Gram-positive bacteria and have modest potency against Gram-negative strains [734]. Penems, incorporating a 6β-acylamino side chain (such as **159**) have limited stability and weak antibacterial activity [732]. In contrast to 6α-methoxylation, 6α-methylation of (**159**) improved stability but failed to improve the antibacterial activity [757]. 6,6-Dialkylpenems are extremely stable but devoid of antibacterial activity [758].

Early Penem Candidates Incorporation of the 1*R*-hydroxyethyl side chain, such as is found in the naturally occurring carbapenem thienamycin, proved crucial for creation of penems having both a broad-spectrum of activity and a stability toward β-lactamases. As with the carbapenems, activity was markedly affected by the relative stereochemistry at the three stereogenic centers. Evaluation of the stereoisomers within the penem mixture (**167**) revealed the *trans*-8*R* isomer to be over 20-fold more potent than the *trans*-8*S* isomer. The two *cis*-isomers had intermediate potency. Removal, or *O*-alkylation of the 8-hydroxyl, lost β-lactamase stability and reduced potency against non-β-lactamase-producing bacteria. Increased bulk resulting from an additional methyl group or substitution of the 8-methyl group was not tolerated: the 6-hydroxyisopropyl-, 6-(1-hydroxy-1-propyl)-, and 6-(1-hydroxy-2-phenylethyl)-penems were without antibacterial activity [759]. With the exception of the 6-benzylidene penems, which are potent β-lactamase inhibitors (Section 5.6), all penems that have progressed have 5*R*,6*S*,8*R*-stereochemistry. The less critical choice of the 2-substituent is amply demonstrated by the wide range of 2-substituted 6-(1-hydroxyethyl)penems having potent antibacterial activity. Typically, these penems show excellent activity against Gram-positive bacteria (including β-lactamase-producing strains) whereas activity against Gram-negative organisms is more modest and generally

inferior to the carbapenem analog. Except for penems having a basic amine as part of in the 2-substituent, penems are devoid of useful activity against *Pseudomonas* sp. [760]. Changes in the 2-substituent often alter susceptibility toward the β-lactamases and toward human renal dehydropeptidase-1, as well as pharmacokinetics and oral absorption. These properties are optimized in the selection of the clinical candidate.

Table 13 lists several penems that entered development. Some, such as Sch-29482 (**183**) and faropenem (**191**, SUN 5555), are orally absorbed as a carboxylate salt. Others, such as ritipenem (**185**, FCE-22101) and sulopenem (**192**), use ester prodrugs to attain good blood levels. Ritipenem acoxil (FCE-22891) is the oral acetoxymethyl ester of ritipenem (**185**, FCE 22101). Ritipenem is an injectable penem for the treatment of urinary tract and lower respiratory tract infections. Sch-29482 (**183**) was in Phase II studies for treatment of gonorrhea, pneumonia, and UTI. In humans, it was rapidly absorbed when administered orally, with a plasma half-life of 1.5–2 h. It was highly active (MIC < 8 µg/mL) against Gram-positive and -negative bacteria, including some strains resistant to third-generation cephalosporins. It was inactive against pseudomona. Its development was discontinued by Schering–Plough, however, due to an odor problem. Only two of the penems listed in Table 11, faropenem medoxomil and sulopenem, are currently under development in the United States.

Faropenem Faropenem (as the sodium salt) (**191**) has been available in Japan since 1997 (Farom). Faropenem medoxomil (**197**) is an orally administered [761] penem, licensed to Replydine by Daiichi Suntory Pharma. Following absorption, faropenem medoxomil is rapidly hydrolyzed to the active drug faropenem. The structural differences between faropenem relative to both the carbapenems and the cephems give a unique profile in terms of spectrum of activity, pharmacology, clinical utility, and safety [56,731,762]. The 2-tetrahydrofuranyl substituent improves chemical stability and reduces CNS effects as compared to imipenem.

There are several ways to prepare faropenem (**191**) and faropenem medoxomil (**197**) [763]. Here, we show only one of these

Table 11. Penems Selected for Detailed Investigation

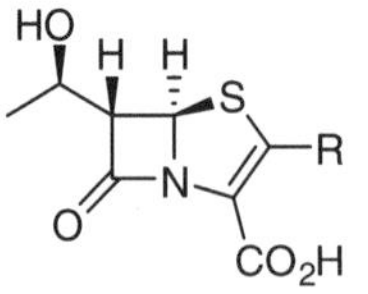

Compound	Name/Code	R	CAS Reg. No.
183	SCH 29482	SCH_2CH_3	77646-83-4
184	SCH 34343	$S(CH_2)_2OCONH_2$	95415-91-1
185	Ritipenem (FCE 22101)	CH_2OCONH_2	84845-57-8
186	FCE 29464	CH_2OCH_3	
187	MEN-10700	$CH_2N(CH_3)CH_2CONH_2$	195874-55-6
188	CGP-31608	CH_2NH_2	107740-67-0
189	HRE 664	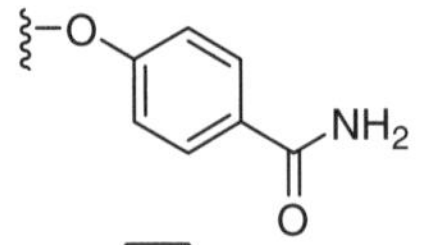	114549-95-0
190	AMA-3176	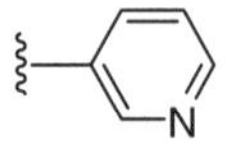	113141-75-6
191	Faropenem (SUN 5555)	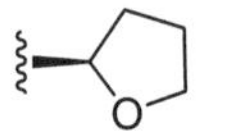	106560-14-9
192	Sulopenem (CP 70429)	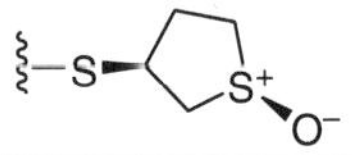	120788-07-0

synthetic routes [764] (Fig. 21). Condensation of the commercial 4-acetoxy azetidinone (**172**) and tetrahydrofuran-2R-thiocarboxylic S-acid by means of NaOH in THF/water gives the azetidinone thioester (**193**), which is coupled with allyl oxalyl chloride in presence of triethylamine to afford (**194**). The penem structure (**195**) was obtained by an intramolecular Wittig cyclization reaction using triethyl phosphite. Treatment of the silylated penem (**195**) with tetrabutylammonium fluoride in AcOH gives faropenem allyl ester (**196**), which is hydrolyzed with tetrakistriphenylphosphine Pd(0) in the presence of sodium 2-ethylhexanoate to provide faropenem sodium (**191**). Finally, faropenem medoxomil (**197**) can be obtained by esterification with 4-(iodomethyl)-5-methyl-1,3-dioxol-2-one.

Faropenem demonstrates broad-spectrum *in vitro* antimicrobial activity against many Gram-positive and -negative aerobes and anaerobes, and is resistant to hydrolysis by classes A, C, and D β-lactamases including extended-spectrum β-lactamases and AmpC

β-lactamases [765,766]. It is several-fold poorer a substrate against several *B. fragilis* metallo-β-lactamases [767]. Faropenem medoxomil has excellent *in vitro* activity against *S. pneumoniae, H. influenzae* and other key pathogens implicated in acute bacterial rhinosinusitis [768] and otits [769]. However, faropenem is not active against methicillin-resistant *S. aureus*, vancomycin-resistant *E. faecium, P. aeruginosa,* or *Stenotrophomonas maltophilia* [730,763]. Faropenem has a low propensity for resistance development, β-lactamase induction, and selection of carbapenem-resistant *P. aeruginosa*.

Prospective, multicenter, randomized, double-blind, comparative (not versus placebo) clinical trials of acute bacterial sinusitis (ABS), acute exacerbations of chronic bronchitis (AECB), CAP, and uncomplicated skin and skin structure infections (uSSSIs) have demonstrated that faropenem medoxomil to have equivalent efficacy and safety compared with cefuroxime, clarithromycin, azithromycin, amoxicillin, cefpodoxime, and amoxicillin-

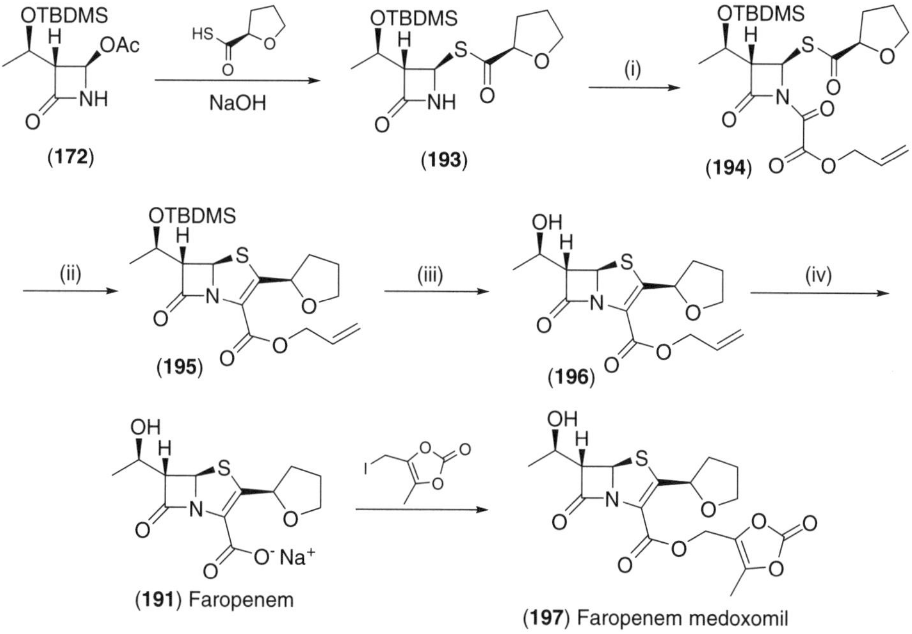

(i) ClCOCO$_2$Allyl, Et3N; (ii) (EtO)$_3$P, reflux in xylene; (iii) Bu$_4$NF, AcOH, THF; (iv) (Ph$_3$P)$_4$Pd, sodium 2-ethylhexanoate.

Figure 21. Synthesis of faropenem medoxomil.

clavulanate [56]. This evidence supported faropenem medoxomil as a promising new oral β-lactam with proven efficacy and safety for treatment of a variety of community-acquired infections [730]. Faropenem is relatively highly bound to human serum albumin (95–99%), resulting in diminished antibacterial efficacy (two to three dilutions) [770–772]. Faropenem medoxomil also was being developed for the treatment of tonsillitis, pharyngitis, and otitis media in children. It was the lone β-lactam under development for the oral treatment of respiratory pathogens. Following a nonapprovable letter from the FDA in late 2006 [56], its further development was discontinued (including a randomized, double-blind, placebo-controlled trial for chronic bronchitis). In April 2008, Replidyne announced that they had planned two trials for CAP and one trial for ABS, using the FDA-recommended NDA protocols, but initiation of these trials are currently on hold [700].

Sulopenem The thiopenem sulopenem (Pfizer CP-70429) (**192**) has good activity against both Gram-positive and negative bacteria, with the exception of *P. aeruginosa* [730,773]. The MIC$_{90}$ values were 1 μg/mL or less for most clinical pathogens of the 1101 tested. Sulopenem had MICs 10–100-fold lower than those of cefoxitin, cefotaxime, ceftazidime, and ceftriaxone against Gram positives and anaerobes. However, sulopenem had higher MICs than those of imipenem against staphylococci, group A streptococci, and *E. faecalis*, although it had twofold lower MICs than those of imipenem against members of the Enterobacteriaceae. Interestingly, sulopenem was more bactericidal than imipenem, ceftazidime, and cefotiam against *S. aureus, E. coli, E. cloacae,* and *C. freundii,* and for some strains, efficacy was seen at concentrations much lower than those required to achieve a similar level of kill with broad-spectrum cephalosporins [774]. This may be a consequence of the high affinity of sulopenem for PBP2, 1a, 1b, and 3 as detected by using cell-free preparations of *E. coli* W-7 [774]. Sulopenem was only slightly susceptible to hydrolysis by type 1 cephalosporinases and TEM-1, SHV-1, and PSE-2 plasmid-encoded β-lactamases. In another study, sulopenem was found to have lower MICs than those of imipenem, ceftazidime, and cefotiam against a range of β-lactamase–producing Gram-positive and -negative strains (with the exception of *P. aeruginosa* and *S. maltophilia*). Sulopenem was not active against penicillin-resistant staphylococci [775].

Despite being developed in the 1980s, the clinical trials of sulopenem never completed. However, Pfizer has resumed evaluation of sulopenem, and an oral ester prodrug, PF-03709270. The oral prodrug, PF-03709270, could potentially be the only oral option available for ESBL-producing and quinolone-resistant Gram-negative pathogens [774]. In a more recent study of the comparative activity of sulopenem against a collection of recently isolate Gram-positive and -negative aerobic organisms, sulopenem MIC_{90} range between 0.03 and $1\,\mu g/mL$ against all clinically significant bacterial species tested. This high *in vitro* potency was also confirmed by *in vitro* time-kill studies [776].

5.4. Monobactams and Nocardicins

The isolation of the nocardicins in 1976 [777,778] and the monobactams in 1981 [779,780] revealed for the first time the potential for antimicrobial activity in simple monocyclic β-lactams, as opposed to the fused-ring systems of the penams and cephems. This discovery provided great impetus for new ideas concerning β-lactam recognition and activation, together with the development of methods for their synthesis [781].

5.4.1. Nocardicins

The nocardicins were detected in a fermentation broth of a strain of *Nocardia uniformis* by screening against a mutant strain of *E. coli* made supersensitive to β-lactams. The first nocardicin characterized was nocardicin A, which shows a modest level of antibacterial activity *in vitro* against Gram-negative bacteria [777]. Structural determination was made by degradation and by NMR analysis [782,783]. The related nocardicins B-G were also characterized [778],

whereas a more recent chloro-substituted derivative was isolated from a *Streptomyces* sp. [784,785]. The structures of the natural nocardicins are shown in Table 12.

Derivatives of 3-Amino Nocardicinic Acid and the Synthesis of Nocardicins

As with the penicillins and cephalosporins, the initial improvements in the potency of the nocardicins focused on alteration of the acylamino side chain of the 3-amino norcardinic acid (3-ANA) nucleus (**206**). Initially, 3-ANA was prepared by deacylation of nocardicin C using either microbial amidases or chemical hydrolysis [786]. A more practical approach made use of the reaction of the oxime group of nocardicin A with a large excess of Boc_2O, to give (**207**), which upon treatment with CF_3CO_2H afforded 3-ANA in excellent yield [787].

Although semisynthetic approaches to the nocardicins from penicillin-derived β-lactams have been reported [786,788,789], by far the greatest effort has been directed toward total synthesis, affording breadth of structure. An early approach used the cycloaddition of thioimidate (**208**) with the ketene generated from phthalimidoacetyl chloride. This reaction gave the *cis*-substituted β-lactam (**209**), which was readily converted to 3-ANA, and thence to derivatives [790]. Another synthesis of nocardicin A reported by the Lilly group used the L-cysteine-derived thiazolidine (**210**). Intramolecular displacement of the chloride demonstrated one of the first examples of β-lactam formation by N1-C-4 ring closure [791]. The most widely used cyclizations of this type is the hydroxamate method developed by Miller, which provides the opportunity to use readily available amino acids in a high yielding process to afford chiral β-lactams of virtually any description with neither racemization nor elimination [792]. Thus, use of the Mitsunobu reaction or base-catalyzed cyclization of β-halo hydroxamates (**211**) provides good yields of (**212**), from which the β-lactam (**213**) is obtained by $TiCl_3$ reduction of the free *N*-hydroxy-β-lactam [793]. Miller synthesized (**214**) by this method, starting from L-Ser-*O*-*t*Bu. Following introduction of the phenylglycine residue by alkylation, or diazo insertion using (**215**), β-lactam (**216**)— a fully protected version of 3-ANA—was obtained in an overall yield of 45% [794].

Table 12. Structures of Natural Nocardicins

Compound	Nocardicin	X	R	Reference(s)
198	A	H	HO₂C—…—O—…—N–OH (NH₂)	[782,783,785]
199	B	H	HO₂C—…—O—…—OH/N (NH₂)	[782,785]
200	C	H	HO₂C—…—O—…—NH₂ (NH₂)	[782,785]
201	D	H	HO₂C—…—O—…—C=O (NH₂)	[782,785]
202	E	H	HO—…—N–OH	[782,785]
203	F	H	HO—…—OH/N	[782,785]
204	G	H	HO—…—NH₂	[782,785]
205	Chlorocardicin	Cl	HO₂C—…—O—…—N–OH (NH₂)	[784]

A synthesis featuring a biomimetic ring closure was demonstrated by Salituro and Townsend [795]. The Townsend group has also made notable progress toward an understanding of the biosynthesis of the nocardicins [796–799]. In their biomimetic synthesis, intermediate (**217**) was cyclized by a modi-

fied cyclodehydration procedure using P(OMe)₃ rather than PPh₃, thus avoiding epimerization at C-5. After deprotection and acylation, nocardicins A–G were obtained in good yields. For example, nocardicin A was produced in an overall yield of 22% from L-serine and D-(p-hydroxyphenyl)glycine. Other approaches to the nocardicin core use α-methylidene-β-lactams [795] as well as other novel β-lactam-forming reactions [800]. General aspects of the synthesis of monocyclic β-lactams and 3-amino-2-azetidinones are reviewed [781,801,802].

Biological Activity and SAR Nocardicin A shows *in vitro* activity (3.1–50 μg/mL) against several Gram-negative organisms including *P. aeruginosa*, *Proteus* sp., *S. marcescens*, and strains of *Neisseria*. No significant activity is seen against staphylococci or *E. coli*. Nocardicins C–E show weak activity, whereas nocardicins F and G are inactive, illustrating the importance of the *syn*-oxime function and the homoserine residue for activity [803,804]. Functional group modifications of the side chain (oxime, ketone, and amine) of nocardicins A, C, and D almost always lead to reduced activity. While acetamido derivatives of 3-ANA show weak activity, replacement of the *p*-hydroxyphenyl residue by other aromatic or heteroaromatic groups generally does not reduce potency. After extensive SAR (involving the preparation of several hundred derivatives) nocardicin A was concluded to be the

only useful antibiotic in the series. To maintain an effective level of activity, only limited modification of the nocardicin A structure is tolerated [803]. The most interesting property of nocardicin A relates to its *in vivo* mechanism, where it acts synergistically with serum bactericidal factors against *P. aeruginosa* and with polymorphonuclear leukocytes (PMNs) against *P. aeruginosa*, *E. coli*, and *P. vulgaris*. Unlike most antibiotics the bactericidal activity of nocardicin A increased markedly in the presence of fresh serum and PMNs, an effect that was reflected in more potent *in vivo* activity than was anticipated from the *in vitro* MIC values [803,805].

Formadicins The most recently described members of the nocardicin class are the formadicins A–D, isolated from a species of *Flexibacter* [806]. Formadicins A (**218**) and C (**219**) have a formamido substituent at C-3 of the β-lactam [807]. The formadicins show a fairly narrow spectrum of activity that is similar to that for nocardicin A, of which those with the formamido substituent were significantly more stable to hydrolysis by β-lactamases. No synthetic analogs have been reported.

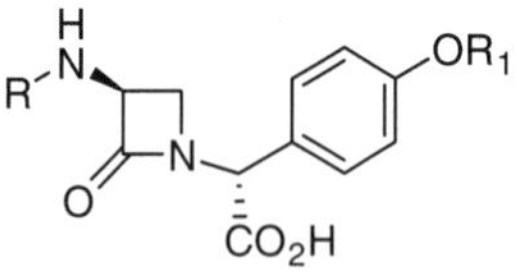

(**206**) R = R$_1$ = H (3-ANA)
(**207**) R = R$_1$ = CO$_2$*t*-Bu

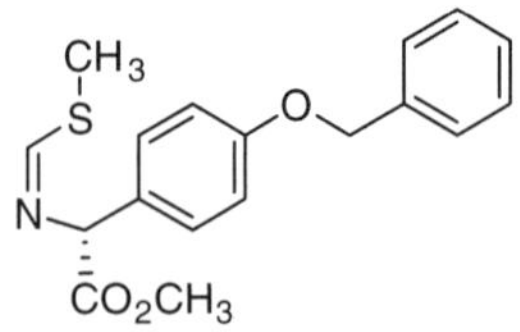

(**208**)

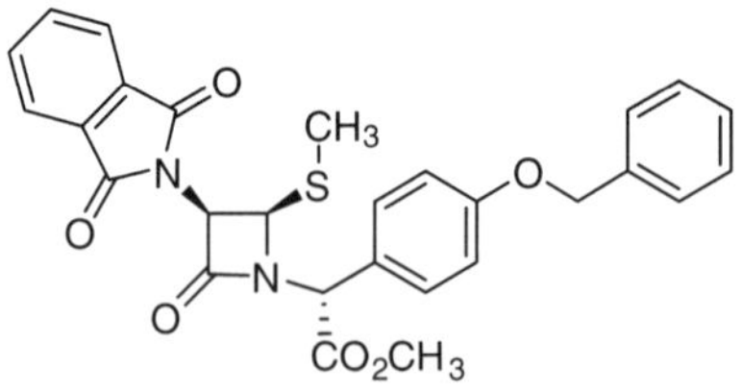

(**209**)

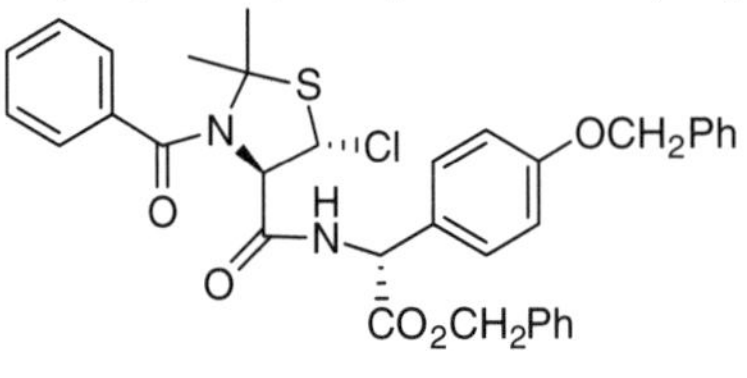

(**210**)

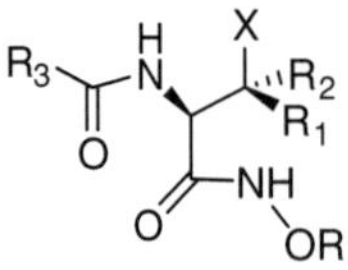

(**211**)

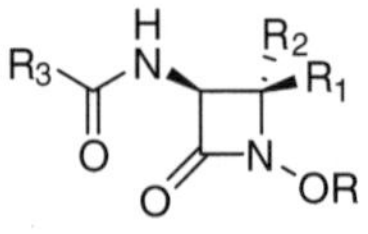

(**212**)

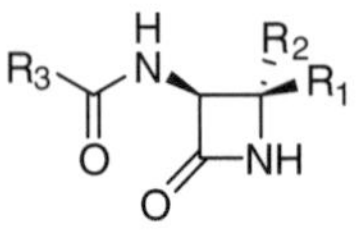

(**213**)

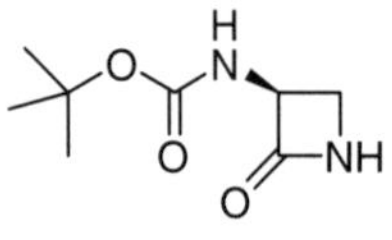

(**214**)

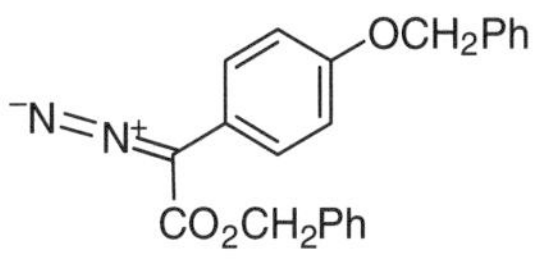

(215) 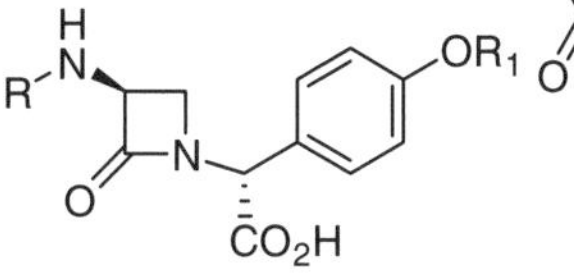   **(216)** 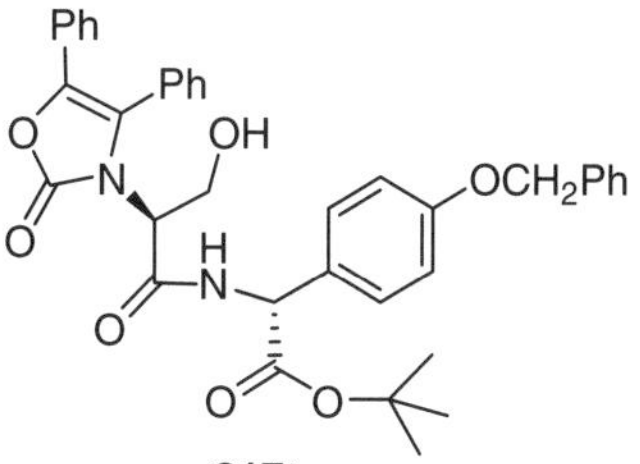   **(217)**

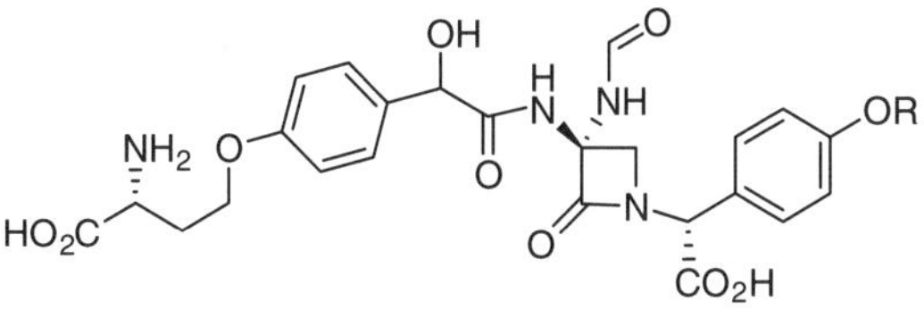

(218) R = D-Glucuronic acid; Formadicin A
(219) R = H; Formadicin C

5.4.2. Monobactams In 1980 groups at Takeda and Squibb reported the isolation of a new class of monocyclic β-lactams from bacteria [779,780]. Until this discovery, the only producers of β-lactam antibiotics were the fungi and actinomycetes. These monocyclic β-lactams, collectively known as the monobactams, are characterized by N^1-sulfonyl substitution of the β-lactam ring [808,809]. The simplest member is the acetamido derivative SQ-26180 (**220**) [810]. Other members of the series are sulfazecin (**221**) [811], isosulfazecin (**222**) [812], and several related members based on structure (**223**) [813] together with others having oligopeptide side chains [814–816]. One member (**224**) has been reported to have a 4-methyl group [817].

Structure Determination and Synthesis The structure of SQ 26180 (**220**) was readily determined from spectroscopic data. Confirmation was made by degradation of the thiazine ring of an appropriately substituted methoxylated cephalosporin to a simple acetamido β-lactam. *N*-Sulfonation then gave material identical with the natural product, thus establishing that the stereochemistry at the C-3-position of SQ 26180 (**220**) was the same as found in the cephalosporins and cephamycins [810]. The structure and stereochemistry of sulfazecin (**221**) was unambiguously established by X-ray crystallography [818], whereas for the other natural monobactams

stereochemistry was assigned by combination of spectroscopy and hydrolytic separation of the peptide side chains. Isolation of the monobactams has led to the synthesis of many acylamino derivatives of 3-amino-monobactamic acid (3-AMA) (**225**) or the 3β-amino-3α-methoxy- monobactamic acid (**226**). Because deacylation of the natural products was not satisfactory, β-lactams (**225**) and (**226**) were initially prepared by degradation of 6-APA (**2**) followed by sulfonation of the derived β-lactam. In the case of (**226**) only racemic material was obtainable [808,819]. Total synthesis has been extensively used, and is now almost always the method of choice. The first method used for formation of the β-lactam was direct base-catalyzed cyclization of the acyl sulfamate (**227**) [820]. Subsequently, additional methods were developed using β-hydroxy amino acid starting materials. Intermediate (**228a**) ($R_1 = H$, obtained from serine) and intermediate (**228b**) ($R_1 = Me$, obtained from threonine) provide ready access to (**229**) ($R_1 = H$ or Me), ideally suited for acylation of its 3-amine [821].

Biological Activity of Natural Products and Synthetic Derivatives Like penicillins, cephalosporins, and other β-lactam antibiotics, the monobactams interfere with the synthesis of bacterial cell walls by binding to PBPs [822]. Aztreonam (**232**), which is clinically efficacious [823], binds specifically to

PBP-3 [824–826]. Remarkably, inhibition by aztreonam of the *E. coli* PBP-3 alters the cytoskeletal localization of a second PBP, PBP-2 [827]. The differential PBP affinity of aztreonam (and of other β-lactams) has provided evidence for the allosteric regulation of PBP activity [828]. All of the natural monobactams exhibit poor activity. However, extensive optimization of the 3-amido side chain (by acylation of 3-AMA) has provided several highly potent compounds. In addition, structural modification at C-4 and N-1 of the β-lactam ring profoundly affect antibacterial activity and β-lactamase stability [829]. The importance of the stereochemistry at C-3 was demonstrated by comparison of the enantiomers of (**230**). Only the *S*-isomer (MIC < 0.05 µg/mL against *Providencia rettgeri*; *R*-isomer 100 µg/mL), corresponding to the configuration of the natural penicillins and cephalosporins, was active [821]. Compared to benzyl penicillin, the analogous monobactam (**231**) shows a similar pattern of activity but with reduced potency. With a carbenicillin side

chain, activity was reduced. Ureido side-chain derivatives had activity that was similar to that of the ureido penicillin. A similar pattern appeared with the corresponding analogs of the cephalosporins [829]. One early observation revealed that 4-alkyl substituents considerably influenced both antimicrobial potency and β-lactamase stability. Extensive SAR studies resulted in the identification of the totally synthetic derivative aztreonam (**232**) as a product with a potent and useful spectrum of clinical activity against Gram-negative bacteria, but with virtually no activity against Gram-positive pathogens [821,830–832]. A second synthetic monobactam to reach the clinic is carumonam (**233**), which shows some improvement in activity over that of aztreonam against the Enterobacteriaceae family of bacteria [833,834]. The process synthesis reported for carumonam also gives a critical assessment of the synthetic routes available for monobactam synthesis [835]. Table 13 shows representative activities of several of monobactams [836].

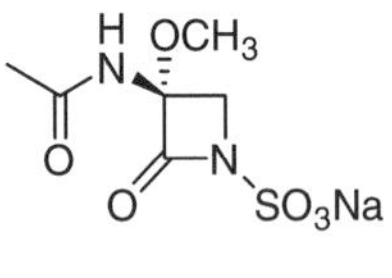

(**220**) SQ 26180

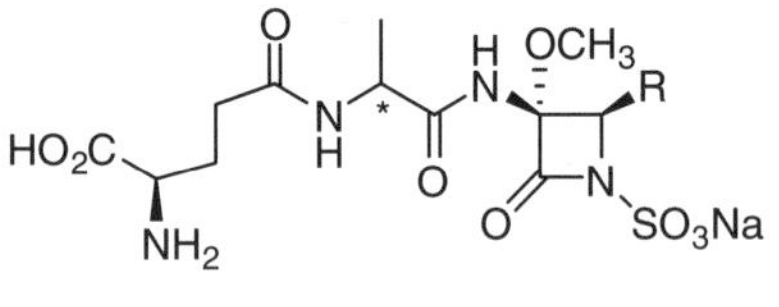

(**221**) R = H; Sulfazecin; *= D
(**222**) R = H; isosulfazecin; * = L
(**223**) R = CH₃; * = D

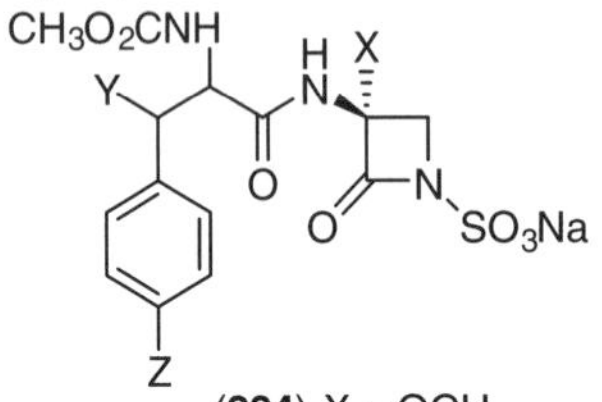

(**224**) X = OCH₃
Y = OSO₃M
Z = H, OH, OSO₃M

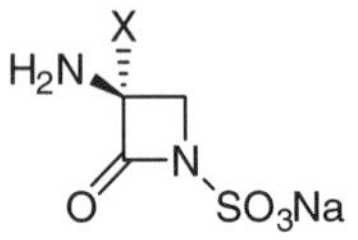

(**225**) X = H
(**226**) X = OCH₃

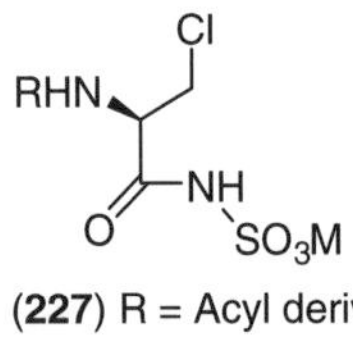

(**227**) R = Acyl derivative

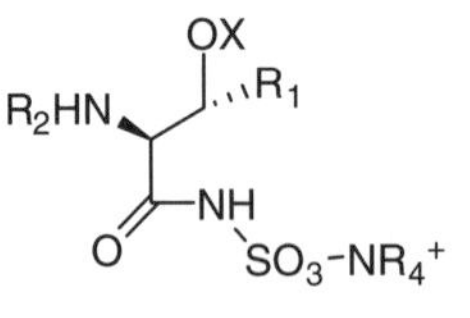

(**228a**) R₁ = H
(**228b**) R₁ = Me

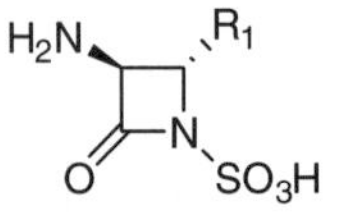

(**229**)

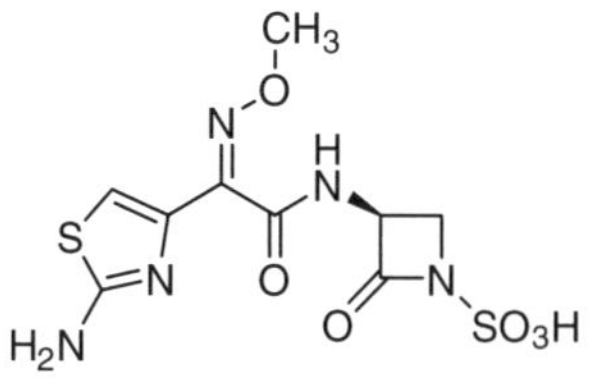

(230) 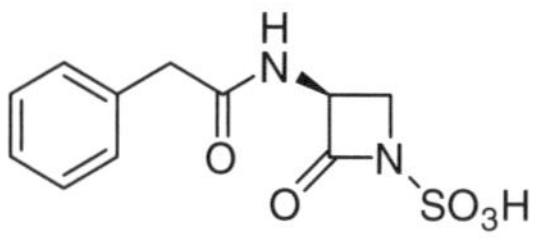   **(231)** 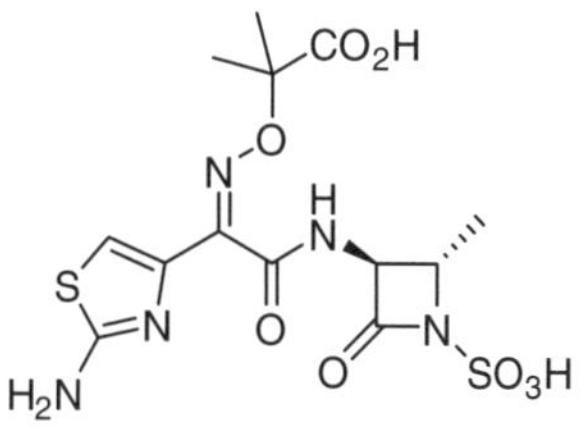   **(232)** Aztreonam

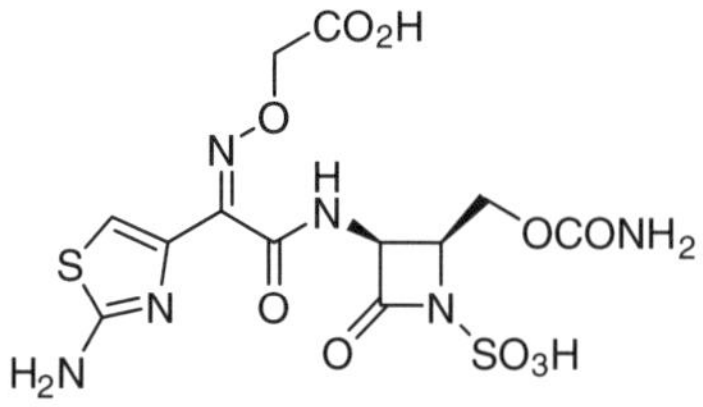

(233) Carumonam

There is renewed interest in Gram-negative therapy, stimulated in large part by the recent emergence of highly drug resistant *A. baumannii* [123,837–839], and highly drug resistant *P. aeruginosa* as causative in the complications of cystic fibrosis [308] and COPD [840]. For this reason, the potential advantages of aerosol delivery of antibiotics to the lung are currently receiving attention [841]. Initial data with an aerosol formulation of aztreonam, currently undergoing clinical evaluation by Gilead, are encouraging [842,843]. In addition, aztreonam has low cross-reactivity in humans with β-lactam allergy [368].

5.4.3. New Monobactams The renewed interest in Gram-negative therapy has likewise renewed interest in monobactam SAR development. A new monobactam, BAL30072 (**234**), and a new monobactam and β-lactamase inhibitor formulation, BAL30376, are both undergoing clinical development by Basilea.
BAL30072 BAL30072 (**234**), (3*S*)-3-4,4-dimethyl-2-oxoazetidinyl hydroxysulfonate, is a new siderophore monobactam with activity against a broad range of Gram-negative bacteria. The dihydropyridinone substituent confers potent inhibitory activity against *Acinetobacter*, *Burkholderia* and *Pseudomonas* sp. as well as many species of Enterobacteriaceae. Against carbapenem-resistant isolates, BAL30072 showed MICs ≤ 8 mg/L [844]. BAL30072 not only had high affinity

for PBP 3 but also had $IC_{50} \leq MIC$ for the equivalents of PBP 1a and PBP 1b in most strains examined. PBP 2 was also inhibited in some strains [845]. Also, *in vitro*, BAL30072 was significantly more potent than meropenem and imipenem against multidrug resistant *A. baumannii* (including imipenem resistant strains containing *bla*OXA-23 [846].
BAL30376 BAL30376 is a threefold combination antibacterial composed of a siderophore monobactam (BAL19764) (**235**), a class C β-lactamase inhibitor (BAL29880) (**236**), and clavulanic acid (**237**) to inhibit ESBLs. The principle behind this combination is to overcome resistance by dual protection of the monobactam (which is inherently stable to metallo-β-lactamases) with inhibitors of the AmpC and ESBLs enzymes. MIC_{90} of BAL30376 against *P. aeruginosa* was 8 μg/mL, eightfold more active than aztreonam, ceftazimide or cefepime; two- to eightfold more active than meropenem; and 8–32-fold more active than piperacillin/tazobactam [847]. In a second study against multiresistant Enterobacteriaceae, BAL30376 overcame most AmpC- or ESBLs-mediated resistance, though less consistently than a carbapenem. However, unlike the circumstance with the carbapenem, BAL30376 remained active against most metallo-β-lactamase producers. A few ESBL and AmpC isolates required high MICs, suggesting an unusual codeterminant of susceptibility, possible related to permeability [848].

Table 13. *In Vitro* Antibacterial Activity of Monobactams and Analogs[a,b]

Organism	Pen G	CAZ	(230)	AZTR (232)	CAR (233)	TIG (238)	(239)	(240)	OXIM (241)
E. coli	>100	0.4	50–100	0.1–0.2	0.1–0.2	0.4–0.8	0.4–0.8	0.4–0.8	0.25–0.5
K. aerogenes	12.5–100	0.1–1.6	50	0.2–100		0.4–0.8	0.4–0.8	0.4–100	
E. cloacae	25–100	0.2–100	>100	0.01–50	0.25–16	0.8–50	0.8–100	0.8–50	1–64
P. rettgeri	3.1	<0.05	25	0.05	0.06–0.12	<0.05	0.2	<0.05–0.4	0.12
P. aeruginosa	>100	1.6	>100	3.1	1–4	1.6–100	0.3–100	0.8–12.5	>64
S. aureus	0.05–3.1	12.5	3.1–6.3	>100	>128				>64

[a]Minimum inhibitory concentrations (range in milligram per liter). See Refs [821,829,833,836].

[b]Pen G, benzyl penicillin; CAZ, ceftazidime; AZTR, aztreonam; CAR, carumonam; TIG, tigemonam; OXIM, oximonam.

Alternative N1-Activating Groups Knox has suggested that the *N*-sulfamate of the monobactams both activates the β-lactam ring for interaction with the active site serine of the PBP, and provides the anionic charge required for binding [821,849]. This hypothesis has stimulated the synthesis of other monocyclic derivatives with similar but new *N*-activating substituents. Several, exemplified by structures (**238–241**), exhibit various levels of antibacterial activity (Table 13) and β-lactamase stability [821]. Tigemonam (**238**) is a potent anti-Gram-negative agent with good stability to β-lactamases [850,851]. It is orally absorbed, which is unusual among the monobactams, and while encouraging results were obtained in early clinical studies [821] it was not further developed.

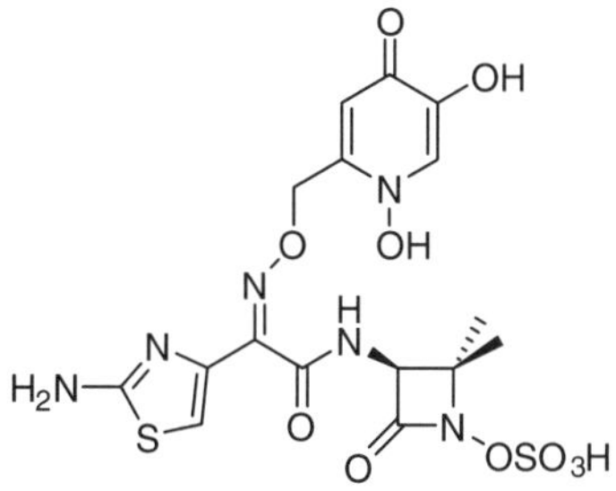

(**234**) BAL30072

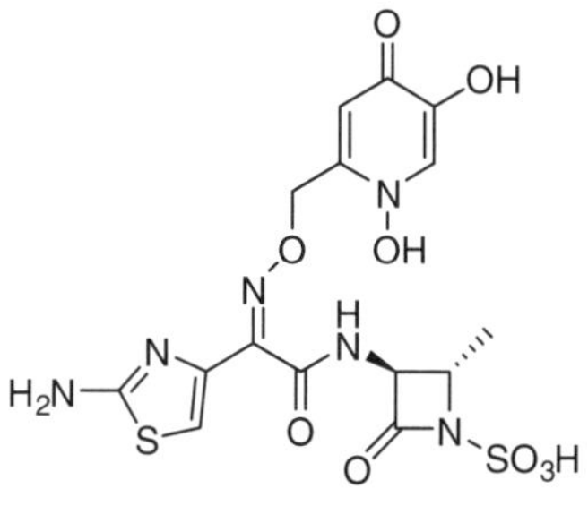

(**235**) BAL19764

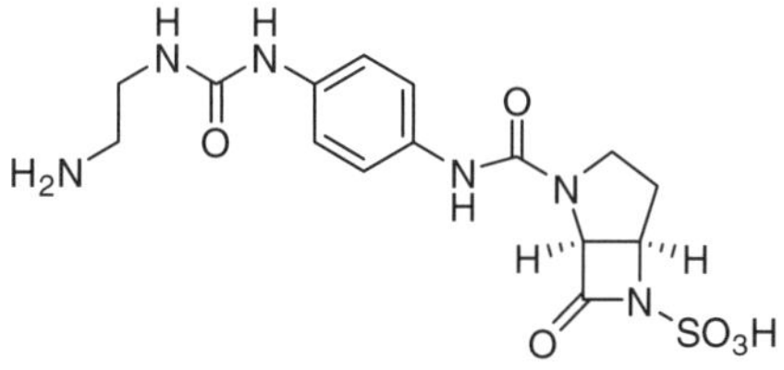

(**236**) BAL29880

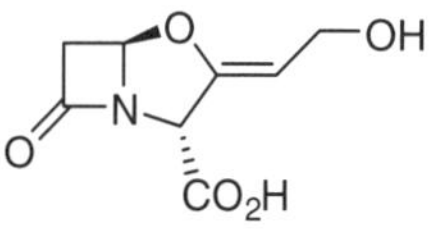

(**237**) Clavulanic acid

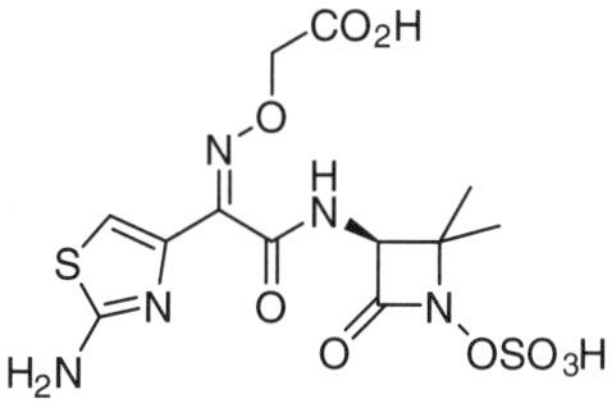

(**238**) Tigemonam

A second example of heteroatom activation is exemplified by oximonam (**241**), a member of oxamazin class [852–854]. The *t*-butyl glycolate ester prodrug (gloximonam) of (**241**) is also absorbed by the oral route, giving good therapeutic levels of the parent drug [821]. Efforts to improve potency against *P. aeruginosa* led to the discovery of SQ-83360 (**242**), having a 3-hydroxy-4-pyridone substituent as a catechol bioisotere, leading to uptake by the

bacterial *ton* B-dependent iron transport pathway in a manner similar to that of the catecholic β-lactams [855]. A related series has a tetrazole replacement of the sulfonate, exemplified by RU-44790 (**243**) that has *in vitro* activity that compares favorably to aztreonam [856]. In contrast, N^1-sulfonyl monobactams having the (*R*)-1-hydroxyethyl of the carbapenems (Section 5.4) at the C-3-position show weak activity [857]. 3-Alkylidene derivatives such as (244), with a neutral *N*-acyl activating group, are antibacterial showing particularly good *in vitro* anaerobe activity [858].

N-Thiol Monocyclic β-**Lactams**   *N*-Alkylthio β-lactams (245) are a recently discovered family of antibacterial compounds that selectively inhibit the growth of *Bacillus anthracis* [859] and *Staphylococcus* bacteria, including MRSA [860,861]. A wide range of other Gram-positive and -negative microbes is otherwise unaffected. The mode of action of these *N*-thiolated lactams is distinct from other β-lactam antibiotics [862]. Following

facile entry into the bacterium, these β-lactams engage in thiol-disulfide exchange. The alkyl-CoA disulfides formed from this exchange inhibit the FabH enzyme of type II fatty acid biosynthesis [861]. Evaluation of these compounds in eukaryotic cells (where the same mechanism may be presumed to operate) has shown antifungal [863] and anticancer activity [864]. The most active derivatives obtained after extensive SAR study are (246) and (247). The substituents at C-3 and C-4 of the lactam ring make secondary contributions to the biological properties [865].

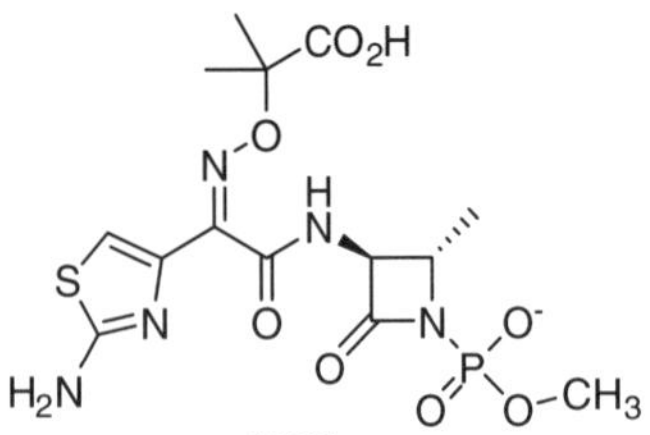

(239)

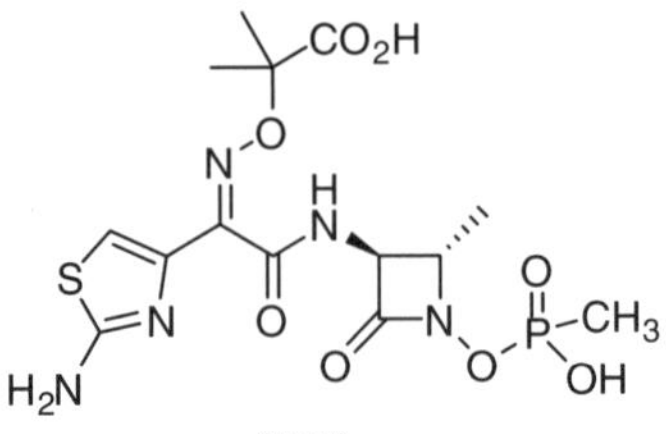

(240)

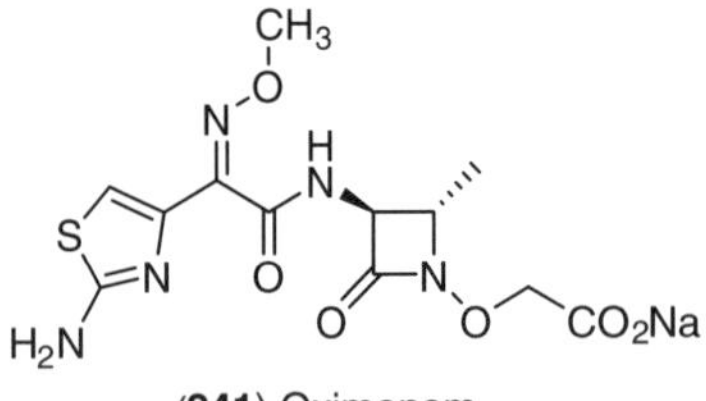

(241) Oximonam

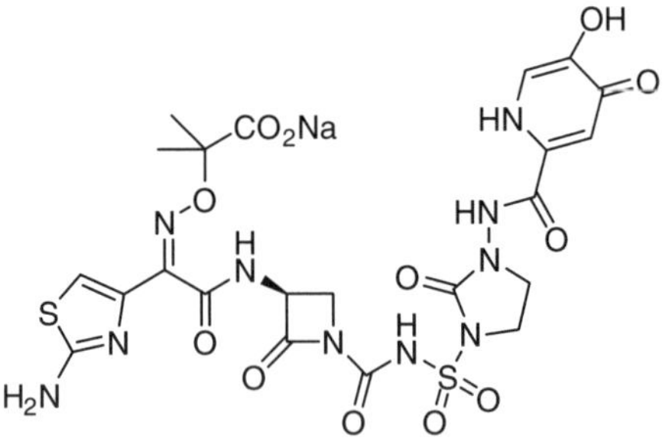

(242) SQ 83360

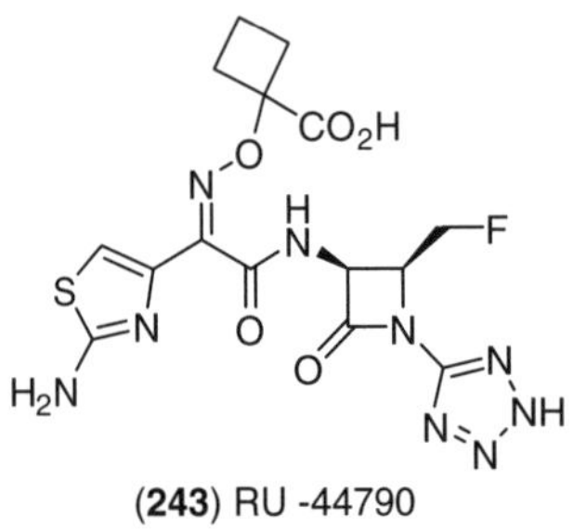

(243) RU -44790

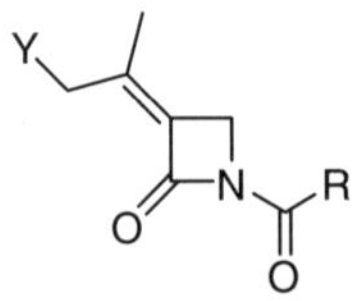

(244)

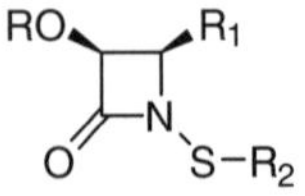

(245)

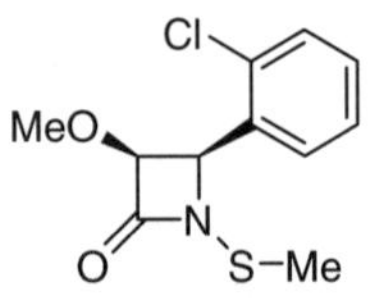

(246)

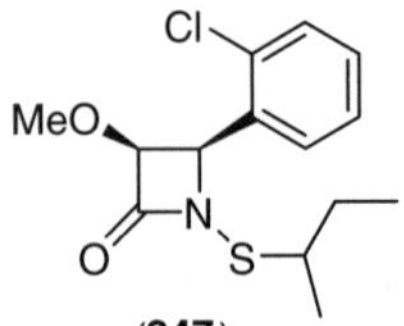

(247)

The Monocyclic β-Lactam as a Nonantibacterial Pharmacophore A monocyclic β-lactam is often regarded as an undesirable pharmacophore, reflecting the presumption of excessive intrinsic reactivity with biological nucleophiles. In the absence of an activating group, however, this presumption is unfounded [866]. Among the recent biological targets targeted by the monocyclic β-lactam [867–870] are leukocyte elastase [871,872], thrombin, cytomegalovirus protease, cathepsin, phospholipase A$_2$, and the PSA antigen protein [873]. The β-lactam ring is central to the pharmacophore of the cholesterol absorption inhibitor ezetimibe [874,875]. Its precise role in the molecular mechanism of ezetimibe is uncertain, given the very recent discovery of the Niemann-Pick C-1-like protein as the ezetimibe target [876–879].

5.5. Carbapenems

The carbapenems and the fourth-generation cephalopsporins are the two most important classes currently being explored for the discovery of new β-lactam antibacterials. The carbapenems were discovered in the 1970s as natural products, as a result of screening of microbial metabolites. Following several key SAR developments, nearly one dozen carbapenems have been approved or are in late-stage development, as totally synthetic (that is, not produced by Nature nor by semisynthesis) antibacterials [337,880–885]. Four carbapenems (imipenem (**248**), meropenem (**249**), ertapenem (**250**), and doripenem (**251**)) currently are approved, and a detailed review on the comparative properties of the four is available [886]. The trinems are also wholly synthetic carbapenem analogs, designed with the expectation of improved biological properties, but as yet without clinical impact.

5.5.1. Discovery of Carbapenems
In the course of screening for inhibitors of cell wall biosynthesis, a Merck group in the mid-1970s isolated thienamycin (**252**) from *Streptomyces cattleya*, followed by other members of this family [887]. At the same time at Beecham, a screen to identify new β-lactamase inhibitor isolated the olivanic acids from *Streptomyces olivaceus* [888,889]. Both families contained a (5*R*)-7-oxo-1-azabicyclo[3.2.0]hept-2-ene-2-

carboxylic acid ring system, now generally called a 1-carbapen-2-em-3-carboxylic acid or carbapenem (**253**). Other carbapenem natural products have been isolated from *Serratia* sp. and *Erwinia* sp. [890]. All possess substituents at C-2 and C-6, and over 50 variations are known [890–892]. The substituent structure and stereochemistry are critical to the definition of the biological activity. These highly active β-lactams—so similar to, yet so markedly different from (compare especially the functional group structure *and* stereochemistry at C-6) the penams and cephems—are central to on-going β-lactam drug discovery.

Natural Products: Occurrence, Structural Variations, and Chemistry While a variety of *Streptomyces* sp. produce carbapenems, only *S. cattleya* and *S. penemfaciens* have been reported to produce thienamycin [892]. These natural carbapenems are found typically in low yield (1–20 µg/L) and as a mixture of stereoisomers [893–897]. Considerable effort has been expended on strain improvement and optimization of the fermentation conditions [898]. Thienamycin (**252**) is distinguished by a (8*R*)-configuration at the stereogenic carbon of the alcohol on the C-6 side chain, and (2*S*) stereochemistry for this side chain at the β-lactam, corresponding to *trans* stereochemistry with respect to the C-5 and C-6 hydrogens of the β-lactam ring [899]. The early history of the discovery, structural elucidation, and chemistry of thienamycin and related carbapenem antibiotics was documented by the Merck discovery group [900]. The first metabolites isolated from *S. olivaceus* were a series of sulfated derivatives such as MM13902 (**254a**: R = SO$_3$H), the sulfoxide MM4550 (**255a**), and the side-chain-saturated derivative MM17880 (**256**) [889,893,901]. Later, nonsulfated members (for example **254b**, **255b**, **256**, **257**, and **258**) were also obtained from *S. olivaceus* [902,903], corresponding to a series of thienamycins and epi-thienamycins analogs isolated from *S. parvogriseus* [900]. The stereochemistry at the stereogenic carbon of the side chain is (8*S*), with a *cis*-substituted β-lactam in the olivanic acid sulfated series, whereas both *cis*- and *trans*-β-lactams are found for the C8-alcohols [904,905]. Following the isolation of thienamycin and the olivanic acids (**254–258**) additional carbapenems isolated from a variety of sources were reported, and having differing C-2 and C-6 substitutions. Representative examples are PS-5 and PS-6 (**259**, **260**) [906], carpetimycin A (**261**) [907], asparenomycin A (**262**) [908], and pluracidomycin A (**263**) [897].

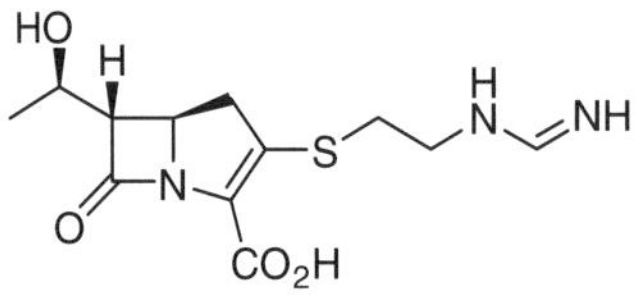

(**248**) Imipenem (1982)

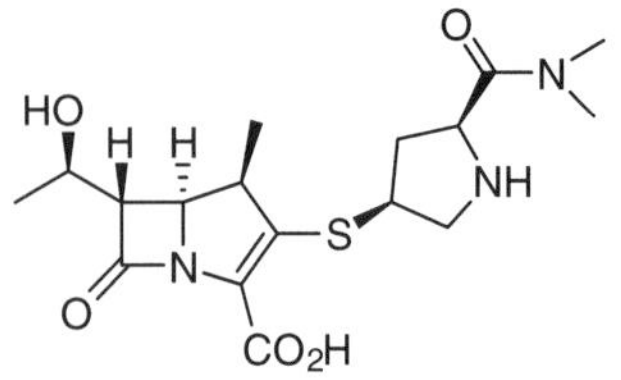

(**249**) Meropenem (1987)

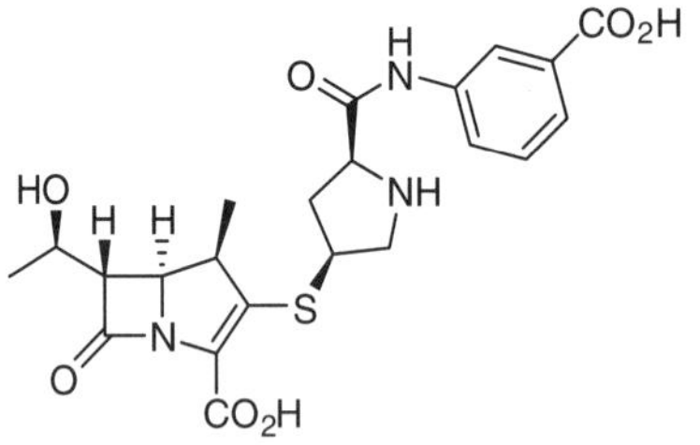

(**250**) Ertapenem (2001)

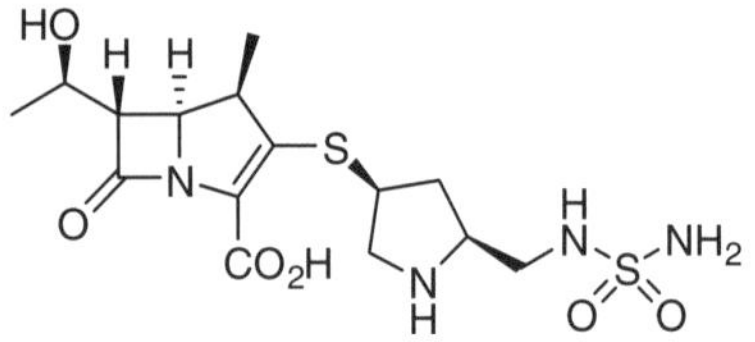

(**251**) Doripenem (2005)

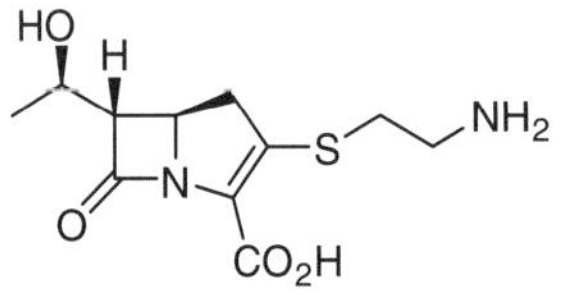

(**252**) Thienamycin (1977)

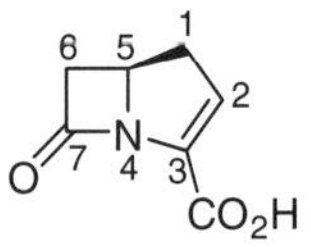

(**253**)

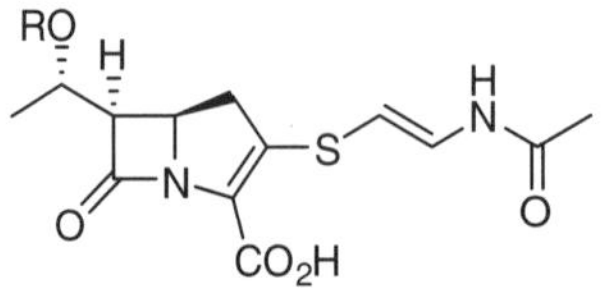

(**254a**) MM13902 R = SO₃H
(**254b**) MM22380 R = H

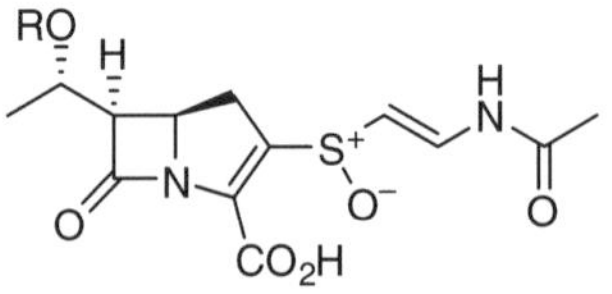

(**255a**) MM4550 R = SO₃H
(**255b**) MM22382 R = H

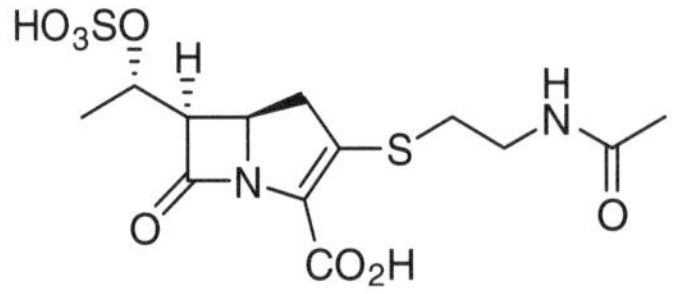

(**256**) MM17880

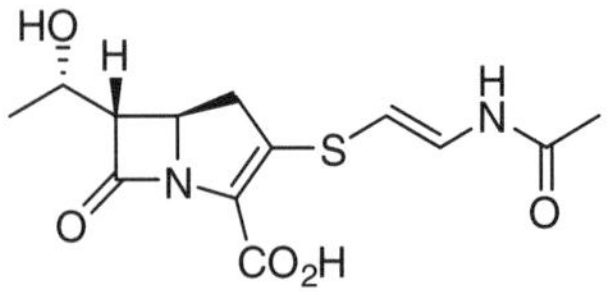

(**257**) MM22383

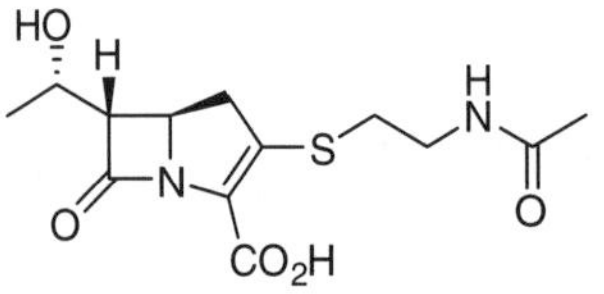

(**258**) MM22381

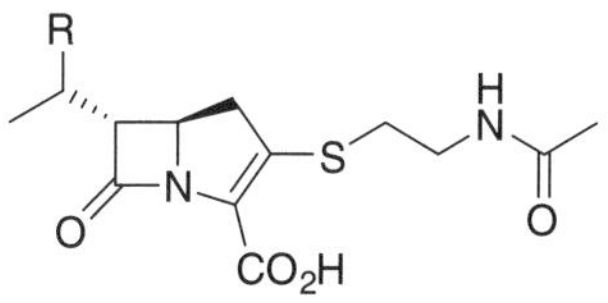

(259)PS-5 R = H
(260) PS-6 R = CH₃

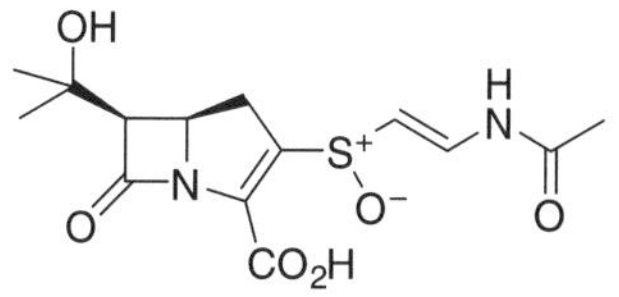

(261) Carpetimycin A

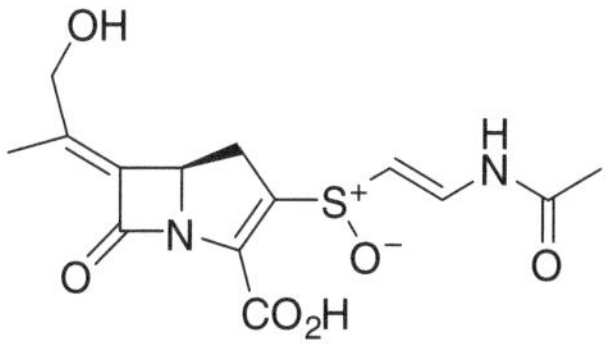

(262) Asparenomycin A

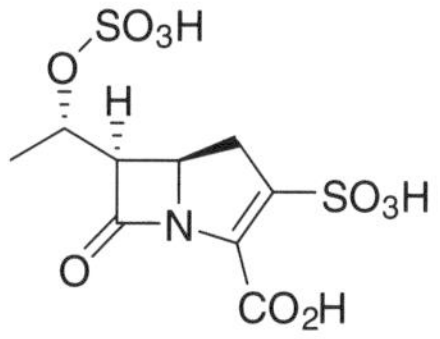

(263) Pluracidomycin A

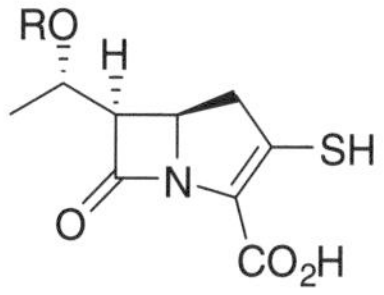

(264)

The carbapenems often show chemical instability and can be extremely sensitive to reaction conditions. Nevertheless, extensive functional group modifications have been carried out on the natural products. Many derivatives of the amino, hydroxy, and carboxy groups of thienamycin have been obtained for SAR studies; other reactions cover oxidation or removal of the cysteaminyl side chain and isomerization of the double bond [900,909]. The largest class of derivatives is comprised of those obtained by modification of the amino group, particularly amidines, which greatly improve chemical stability without compromising potency. This series that gave the N-formimidoyl substituted thienamycin derivative, imipenem (248) [910], as the first member of the carbapenem family approved for parenteral antibacterial therapy [911].

In the olivanic acids the side-chain vinylether can be isomerized to the (Z)-isomer [912]. It reacts readily with HOBr to give an unstable bromohydrin, which on decomposition gives the thiol (264), ideally suited for further synthesis [913]. Inversion of the C-8 stereochemistry of the 8-hydroxyolivanic acids affords entry into the (8R)-thienamycin type series. A second useful method for substitution at the sulfur of the C-2 side chain is displacement of the S-oxide with other thiols [914] used in the synthesis of PS-5 (259). Detailed reviews [881,892,900,909,915–922] further summarize these aspects of carbapenem chemistry and SAR.

Biosynthesis of the Carbapenems As noted previously, imipenem (248) a carbapenem in clinical use, although conceptually inspired by the natural product thienamycin (252), is obtained by total synthesis. Although key aspects of thienamycin biosynthesis were discovered in the decade following its discovery—especially that there were fundamental points of difference when compared to penicillin biosynthesis via the Arnstein tripeptide [923]—the low and variable biosynthetic yield of thienamycin was a barrier to new discovery. Two recent discoveries have reinvigorated interest in carbapenem biosynthesis. The first was the isolation of the thienamycin gene cluster in 2003 [923] and the coincident discovery by Nunez et al. [923] that carbapenem biosynthesis (as well as those of other antibiotics [924,925]) is regulated by bacterial quorom sensing [926–928]. Biosynthesis of the core carbapenem ring (Fig. 22)

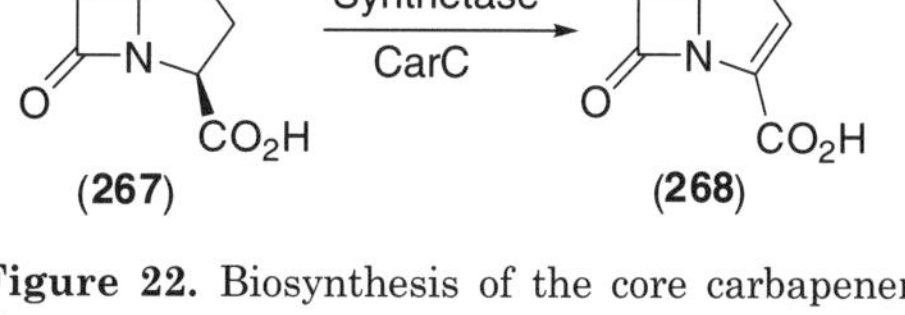

(265)   (266)

(267)   (268)

Figure 22. Biosynthesis of the core carbapenem ring.

commences from the reaction of iminoproline (glutamate semialdehyde) **(265)** with malonyl-CoA to give (2*S*,5*S*)-carboxymethylproline **(266)** [929,930], followed by ATP-dependent cyclization to **(267)** catalyzed by the *carA*-encoded carbapenam synthetase [931]. The contra-thermodynamic O_2- and 2-oxogluta-rate-dependent epimerization and concurrent dehydrogenation to the carbapenem **(268)** is catalyzed by the *carC*-encoded carbapenem synthase [932,933]. Stereochemical study indicates these two transformations, of this remarkable single-enzyme catalyzed biosynthetic transformation, are in substantial part mechanistically coupled [934]. Possible mechanisms incorporating these two events into a coherent mechanism are discussed [935,936]. Likewise, no less fascinating later stage biosynthetic events in thienamycin biosynthesis [937,938] have recently been shown to involve acetyl-CoA degradation, as opposed to a direct cysteamine route for incorporation of the side chain [939].

Chemical Synthesis of Natural Carbapenems
The structural novelty, the potent antibacterial activity, and the low fermentation yields of the carbapenems compelled intensive synthetic efforts toward wholly synthetic analogs having improved chemical and metabolic stability [899,940–942]. The most common strategy is early stage synthesis of an appropriately substituted β-lactam of defined stereochemistry, followed by cyclization to the strained bicyclic system. Variations within this approach have yielded virtually all of the natural products. The unsubstituted system **(253)** was synthesized by several groups, before the discovery of the natural carbapenems, in both racemic and chiral forms starting from azetidinones **(269)** or **(270)**, obtained from reaction of chlorosulfonyl isocyanate and the appropriate alkene [943–946]. Progression to

the phosphorane **(271** or **272)**, followed by oxidation to the aldehyde **(273)**, allowed ready intramolecular Wittig cyclization. Ester deprotection gave the unstable sodium salt of **(253)**. Formation of the 2,3-alkene by this procedure has been used extensively in both natural product and analog synthesis [947]. Thienamycin **(217)** has been the focal point for innumerable synthetic studies [900], and the methods that originated from the Merck group remain widely used. The first Merck synthesis of racemic thienamycin also used **(269)** as an intermediate, with introduction of the hydroxyethyl side chain by aldol reaction giving the *trans* β-lactam, further elaborated by a lengthy process to the dibromide **(274)**. Cyclization and decarboxylation, followed by elimination and deprotection, completed the synthesis [948]. The chiral synthesis (Fig. 23) used the L-aspartate-derived β-lactam **(275)** in a 3,4-bond formation sequence [949]. Stereo-controlled introduction of the side chain, and elaboration to dithiane **(276)**, was followed by introduction of the hydroxyethyl side chain **(277)** and elaboration to the diazo intermediate **(278)**. Intramolecular $Rh_2(OAc)_4$-catalyzed cyclization proceeded extremely efficiently to give the bicyclic ketoester **(279)**, a key intermediate in the synthesis of a wide range of carbapenem analogs. Introduction of the cysteaminyl side chain at C-2 uses the vinyl-phosphate **(280)**. Final deprotection gave thienamycin **(252)**. Introduction of the amidine to provide imipenem **(248)** is straightforward [950]. By similar routes, 2-thio-substituted derivatives were obtained including cyclic amidines **(281)** and *S*-aryl and *S*-heteroaryl derivatives **(282, 283)** [951,952]. A similar approach using the stable vinyltriflate **(284)** allowed the synthesis of aryl and vinyl carbapenems (such as **285–287)** by organometallic-catalyzed coupling [953].

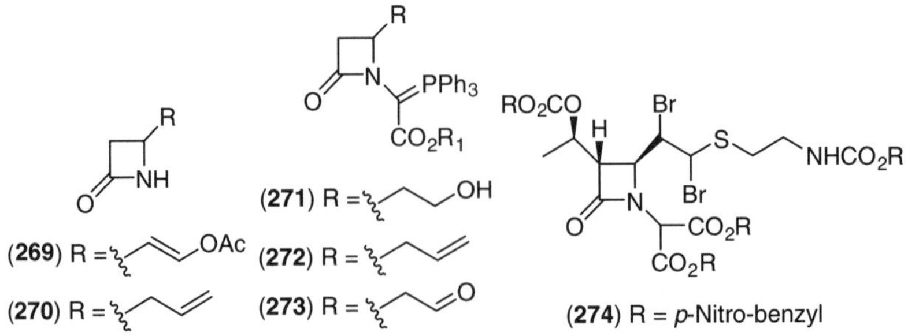

(269) R = ⌇⌇OAc   (271) R = ⌇⌇OH   (272) R = ⌇⌇
(270) R = ⌇⌇   (273) R = ⌇⌇O

(274) R = *p*-Nitro-benzyl

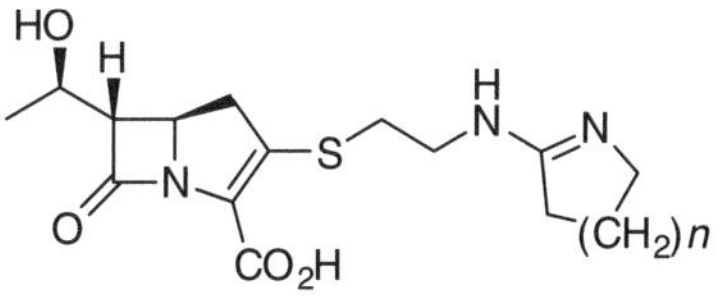

(281)

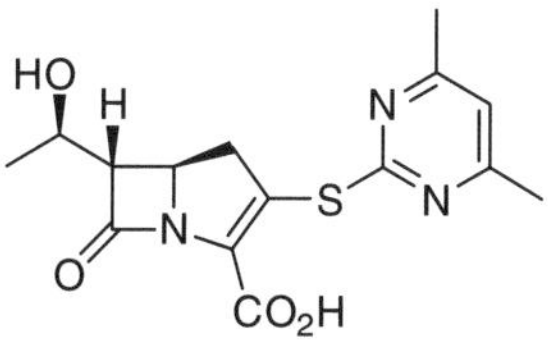

(282)

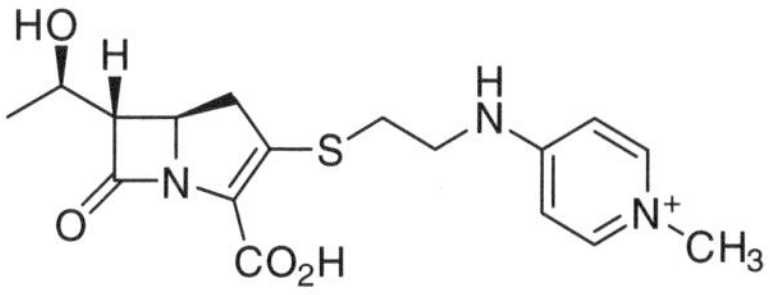

(283)

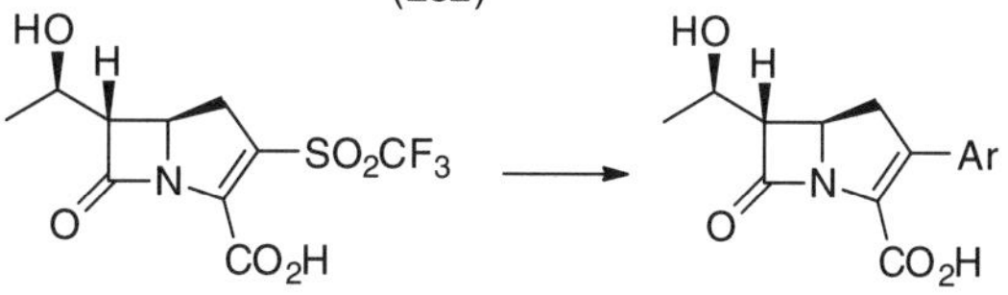

(284)

(285) Ar =

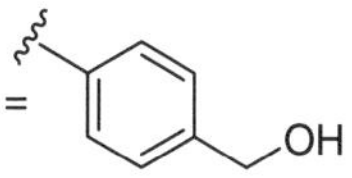

(286) Ar =

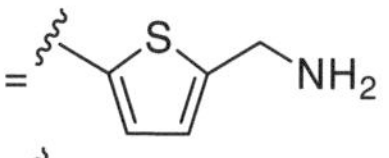

(287) Ar =

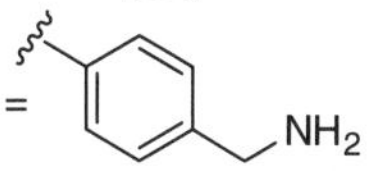

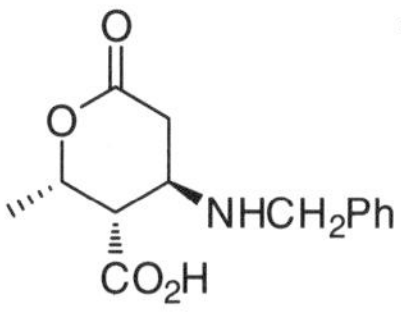

(288)

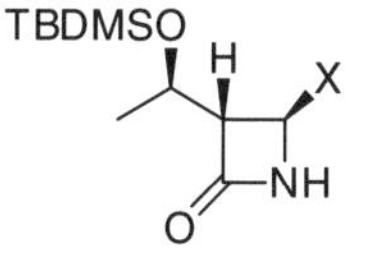

(289) X=Cl
(172) X=OAc

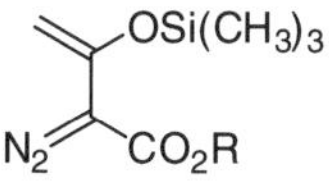

(290)

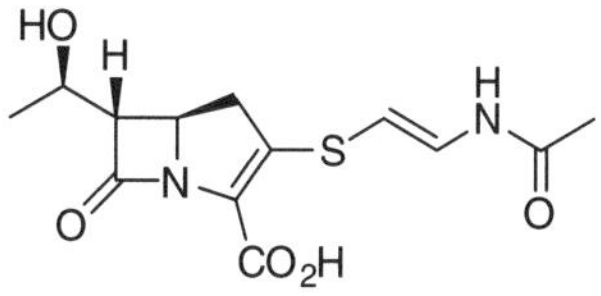

(291)

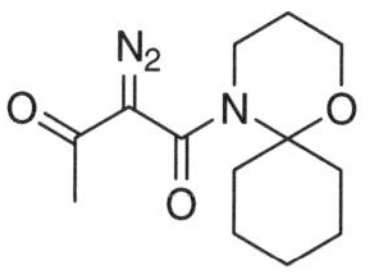

(292)

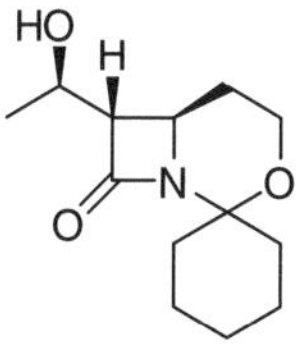

(293)

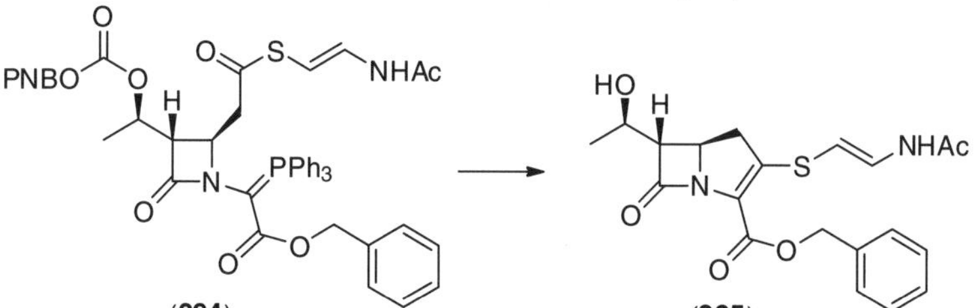

(294)

(295)

A second approach uses (±)-lactone (288), obtained from acetonedicarboxylic acid [942]. This route gave a practical synthesis of (±)-thienamycin, although requiring inversion of the side-chain stereochemistry from (S) to (R). A subsequent enantioselective route used chiral lactone (288) [954]. Displacement of the 4-acetoxy or 4-chloro group from azetidinones

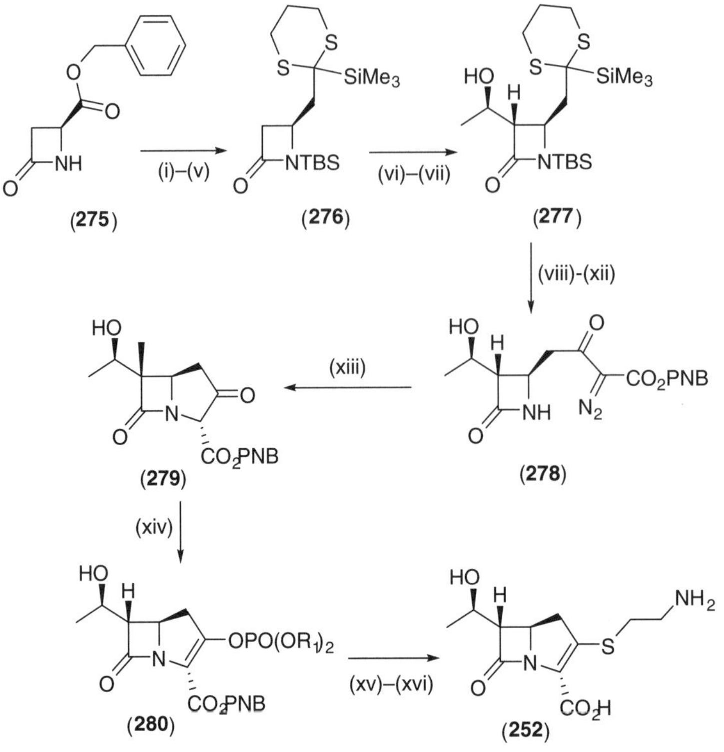

Reagents: (i) NaBH$_4$, MeOH; (ii) MeSO$_2$Cl, TEA, DCM 0°C, (iii) NaI acetone, Δ; (iv) TBSCl, TEA, DMF

(v) 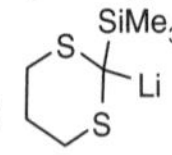 [structure: S, S, SiMe$_3$, Li] , THF, −78°C; (vi) LDA, N-acetyl imidazole, THF, −78°C; (vii) K selectride, KI, ether;

(viii) HgCl$_2$, HgO, MeOH, H$_2$O, Δ; (ix) H$_2$O$_2$, MeOH, H$_2$O; (x) CDI, THF, then Mg[structure: COO$^-$, COOPNB] ;

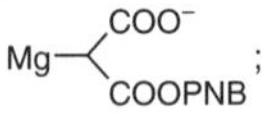

(xi) HCl, MeOH; (xii) p-carboxy benzene sulfonyl azide, TEA, CH$_3$CN; (xiii) Rh(OAc)$_4$, toluene, 80°C;

(xiv) ClPO(OPh)$_2$, DIPEA, CH$_3$CN, 0°C; (xv) HSCH$_2$CH$_2$NHCO$_2$PNB, DIPEA, CH$_3$CN, −5°C; (xvi) H$_2$, Pd/C, 3.5 atm.

Figure 23. A stereocontrolled synthesis of thienamycin.

such as (289) and (172), by silyl enol ether (290), further improved the synthesis of thienamycin (252) and its analogs [955,956]. The value of this route is shown by the use of 4-acetoxyazetidinone (172) as a pivotal intermediate in penem, carbapenem, and trinem synthesis. Two very successful syntheses use 3-hydroxybutyric, or lactic acid, derived starting materials for subsequent synthesis of the β-lactam ring by cycloaddition [957,958]. Other syntheses use β-lactams derived

from penicillin [955,959,960], carbohydrates [961,962], amino acids [963,964], isoxazolidines [965], and organo-iron or -cobalt complexes [966,967]. Alternative methods for bicyclic ring formation use the Dieckmann cyclization [968] or intramolecular Michael reactions [969]. The discovery that thioesters participate in the Wittig cyclization to give C-2 derivatives was the basis for the total synthesis of the olivanic acid MM22383 (257) and N-acetyldehydrothienamycin (291) [903]. In this case, formation of the β-lactam ring used $Rh_2(OAc)_4$-catalyzed cyclization of diazo intermediate (**292**), giving the *trans*-β-lactam (**293**) as a mixture of hydroxy epimers after ketone reduction. Cyclization of thioester (**294**) provided (**295**) as an epimeric mixture. Separated of the epimers and deprotection completed the racemic synthesis [970,971].

Another route to the olivanic acids used the ready reaction of (**296**) [972] with acetamidoethanethiol, forming carbapenam (**297**). Reintroduction of the alkene gave the ester of (+) MM22381 (**298**) [973]. This method has also been used for the synthesis of PS-5 (**259**), although most other approaches used the chiral (3*R*,4*R*) 4-acetoxy-3-ethylazetidinone (**299**) and diazoketone (**300**). For the carpetimycins

(such as **261**) the major problem is obtaining the thermodynamically less-favored *cis*-arrangement of hydrogens around the β-lactam ring in precursors such as (**301**). One attractive method involves the directed aldol condensation between (**302**) and acetone, using metal chelation of the β-lactam enolate with the neighboring methoxyethoxymethoxy (MEM) group in the presence of the bulky silyl residue, to give predominant β-face addition and thus the *cis*-product (**303**) [974]. The asparenomycin natural products (such as **262**) have an alkylidene substituent at C-6. Syntheses in this series have used a similar route by way of a bicyclic ketoester derived from an appropriately substituted monocyclic precursor. These elegant routes are reviewed [920,947].

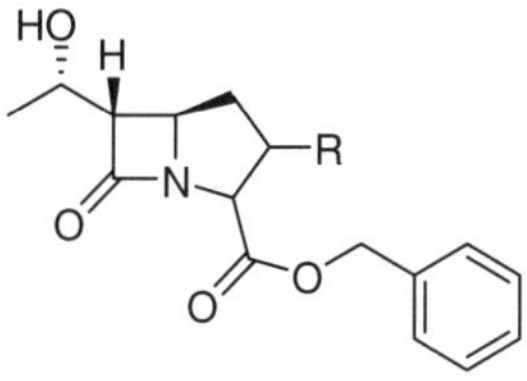

(**296**) R = H
(**297**) R = S—NHAc

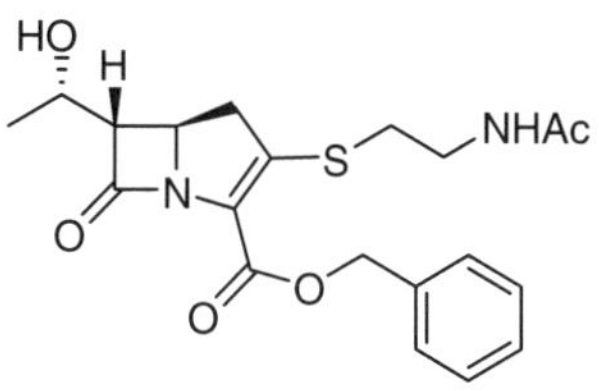

(**298**)

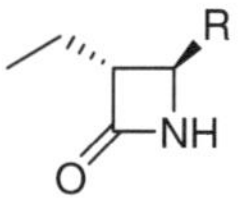

(**299**) R = OAc
(**300**) R = —CO₂R₁ N₂

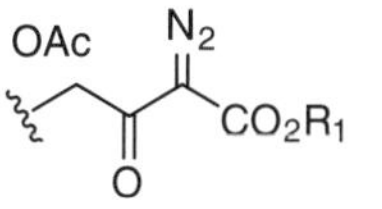

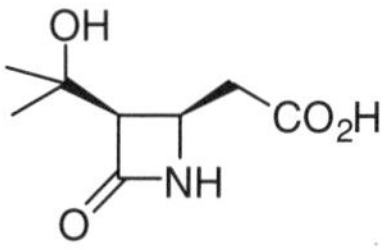

(**301**)

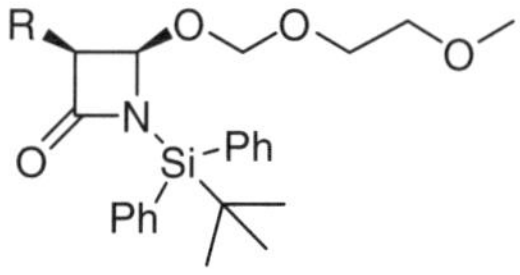

(**302**) R = H
(**303**) R =

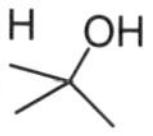

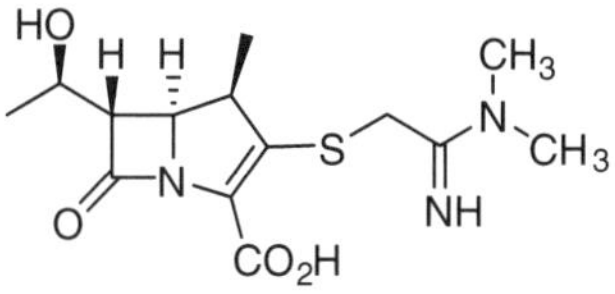

(**304**)

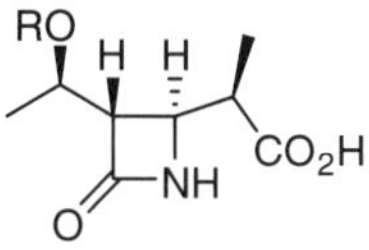

(**305**)

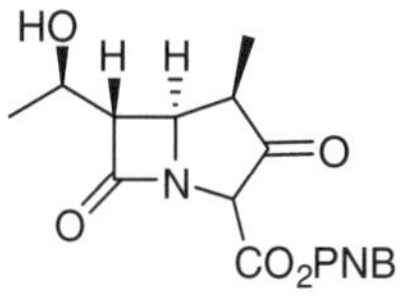

(**306**)

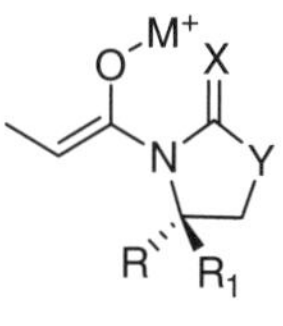

(**307**) X, Y = O, S
      R, R₁ = alkyl

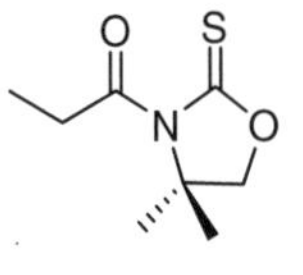

(308) 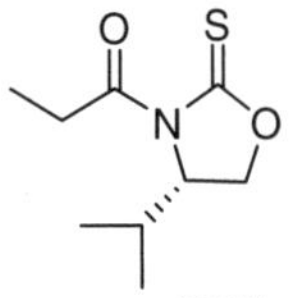   (309) 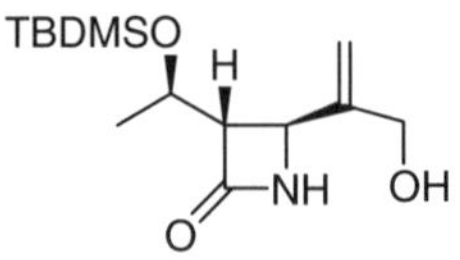   (310) 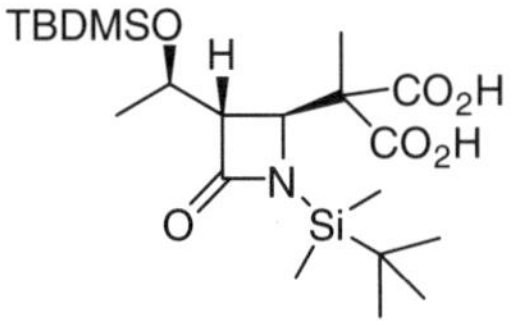   (311)

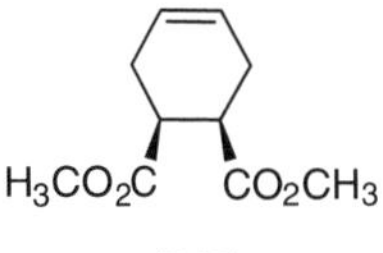

(312)

Synthesis of 1β-Methylcarbapenems   An unexpected clinical discovery with the first-generation carbapenems was enzymatic hydrolysis of the carbapenems catalyzed by a human renal dipeptidase (DHP-1, Section 5.5.3) enzyme. The result of this enzyme-catalyzed hydrolysis was loss of the antibacterial activity of the carbapenems. Although the slow rate of this reaction *in vivo* was believed acceptable, concerns about potential nephrotoxicity required coformulation of imipenem with a specific inhibitor of this enzyme (Section 5.5.3). As imipenem is fully synthetic, the possibility that a revised synthesis might incorporate a substituent that would abolish DHP-1 recognition without compromise of the antibacterial activity, was aggressively pursued. In 1984, the Merck group reported the 1β-methyl-substituted carbapenem (304) fulfilling both of these criteria [975]. Its synthesis was achieved by alkylation of the methyl ester of (274, R = TBS), followed by elaboration of the acid (305) to ketoester (306), albeit with poor stereocontrol. The advantages of the 1β-methyl series led to the stereoselective synthesis of (300) and other intermediates leading to (301). Most often, a tin or boron enolate of general structure (307) displaces the acetoxy group of the chiral 4-acetoxyazetidinone (172). The pro-

ducts are readily converted to the acid. Yields are generally good, with a ratio of β:(isomers ranging from 24:1 with (308) [976] to greater than 90:1 with (309) [977]. Other variations have been reported [881]. Direct incorporation of the diazo side chain is also possible. Alternative variations for 1β-methyl carbapenem ring synthesis use (*R*)- or (*S*)-methyl 2-methylhydroxypropionate [978,979], alcohol (310) [980], malonic acid derivative (311) [981], and an enzymatic approach starting from (312) [982]. Numerous SAR efforts have further examined 1β-methyl carbapenem structure in the search for broad-spectrum antibacterials for the treatment of severe infections. Compounds (313–324) are representative examples [983–987]. Alternative possibilities for the 1β-methyl examined include ethyl (325), hydroxy (326), methoxy (327), or 1,1′-*spiro*-cyclopropane (328). All are less active [988,989]. A Sankyo group evaluated the 1α-methyl and 1,1-dimethyl panipenem derivatives (329) and (330) [990–992]. Further modifications studied by Roche eventually gave Ro 19-8928 (331) having good activity against *P. aeruginosa*. Fluorination at position 1 was reported by Merck to give very unstable compounds such as (332) [993].

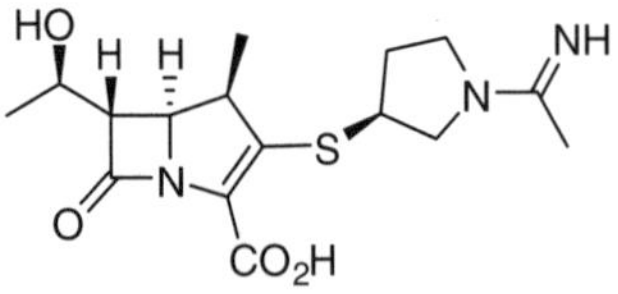

(313) 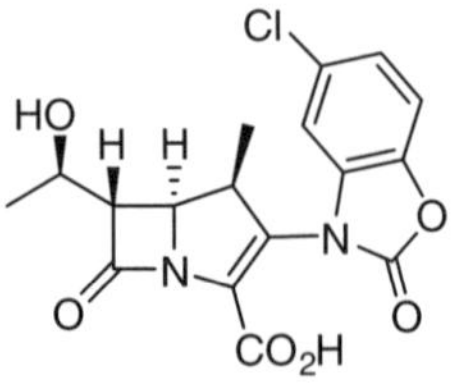   (314) 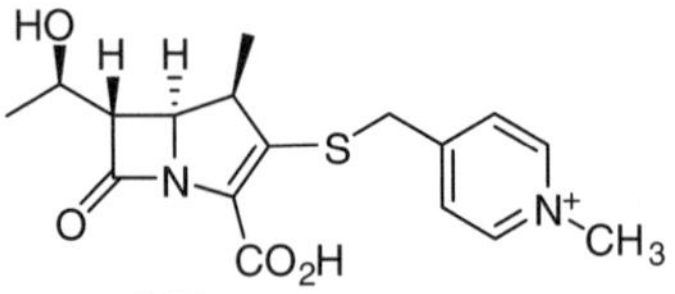   (315)

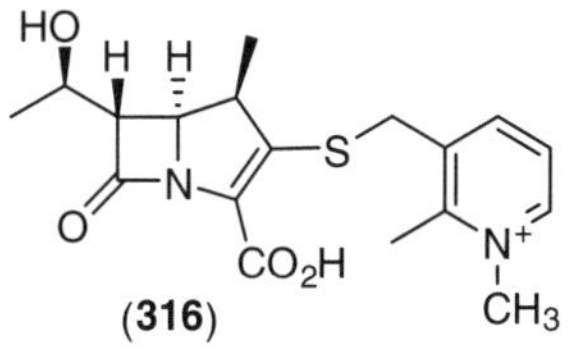

(316)

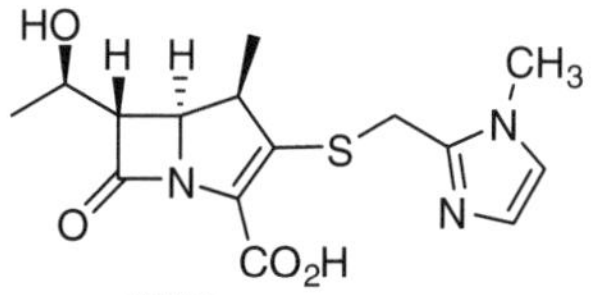

(317)

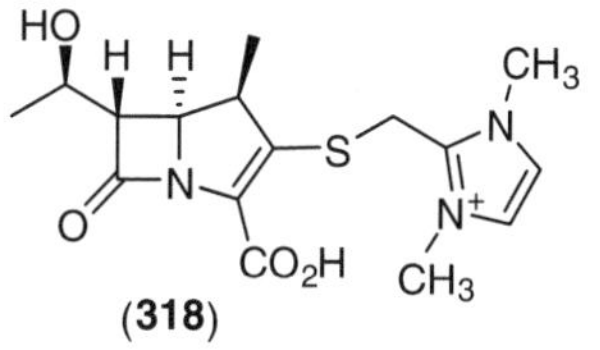

(318)

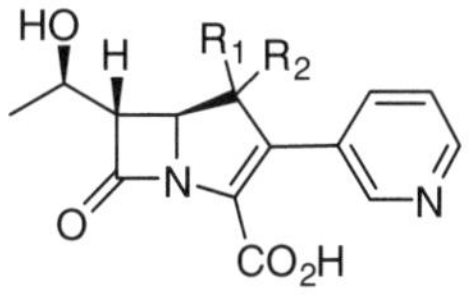

(319) R₁, R₂ = H or CH₃

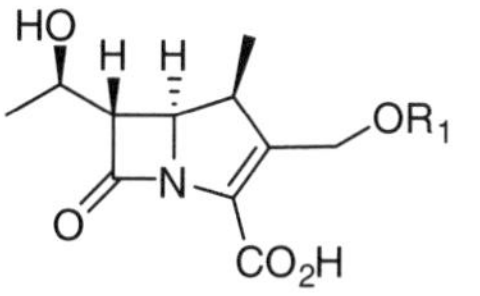

(320) R₁ = H, Ac, CONH₂, CON(CH₃)₂, CONHAr, CONH(CH₂)₂Py⁺

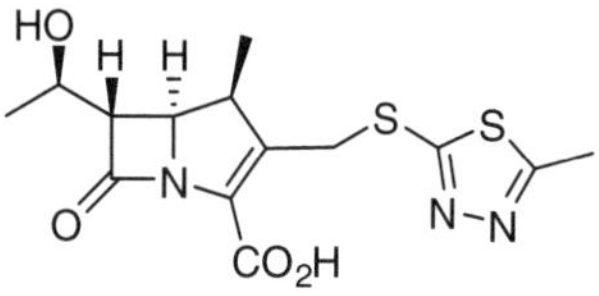

(321)

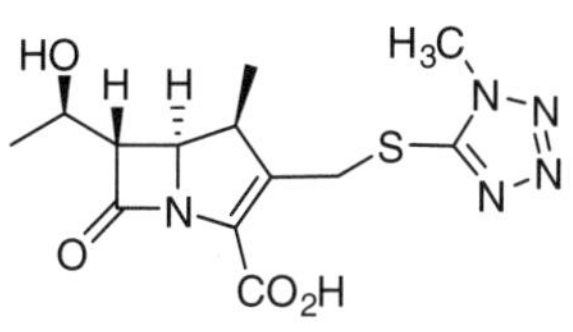

(322)

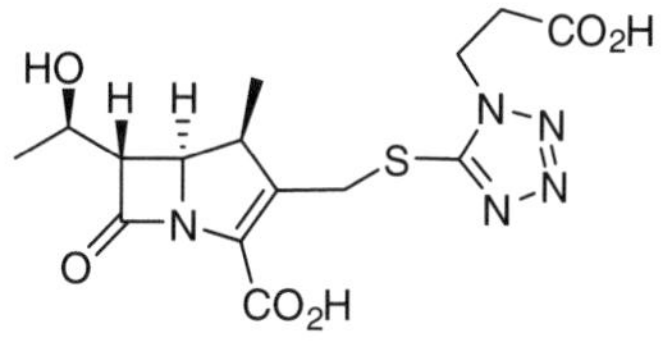

(323)

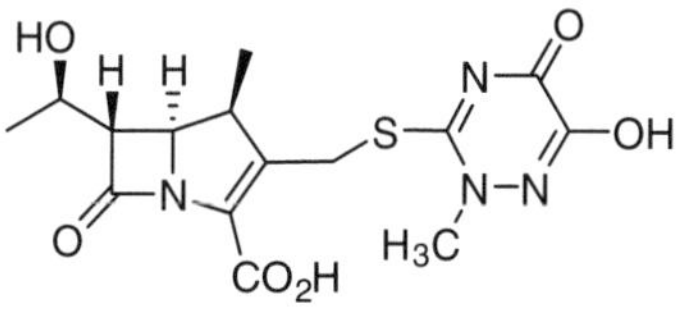

(324)

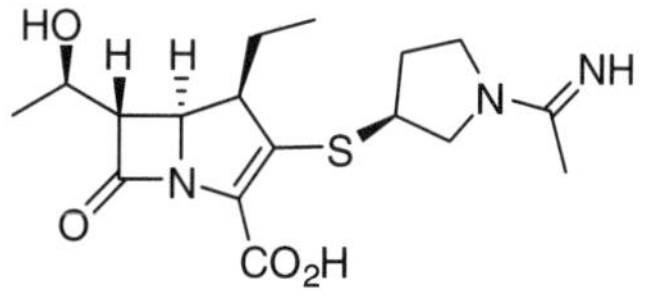

(325)

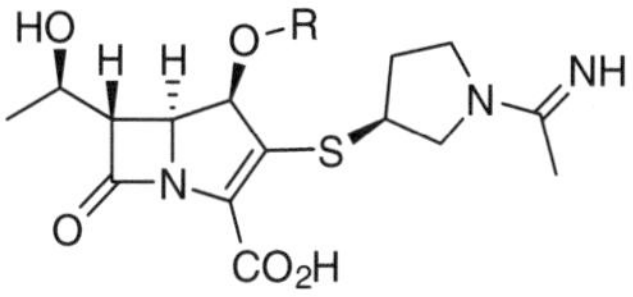

(326) R = H
(327) R = CH₃

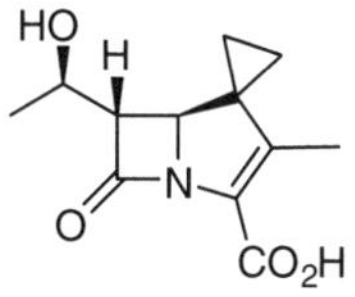

(328)

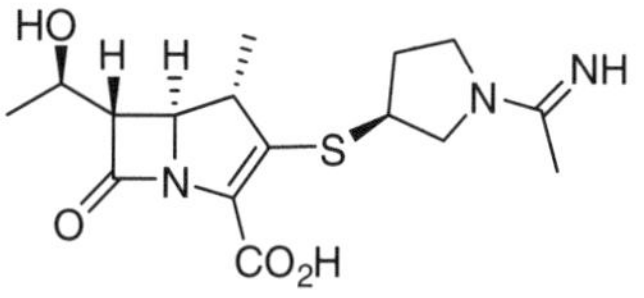

(329)

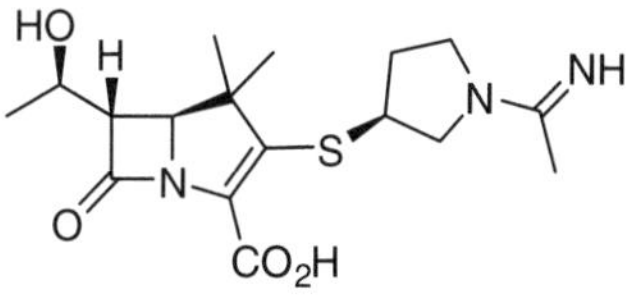

(330)

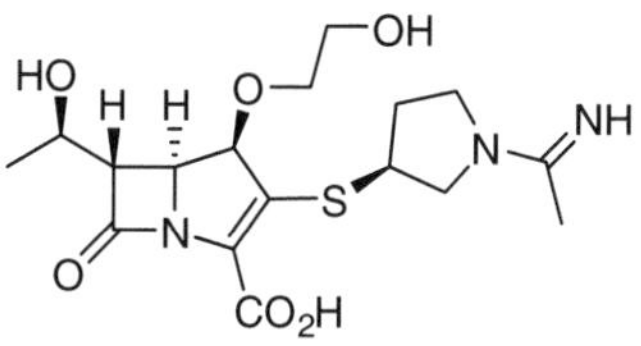

(331) Ro 19-8928

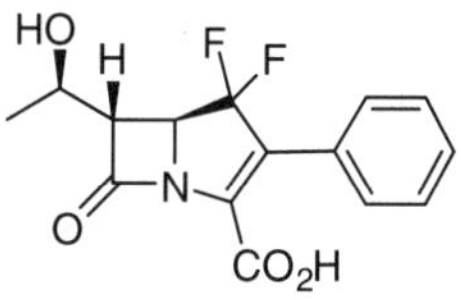

(332)

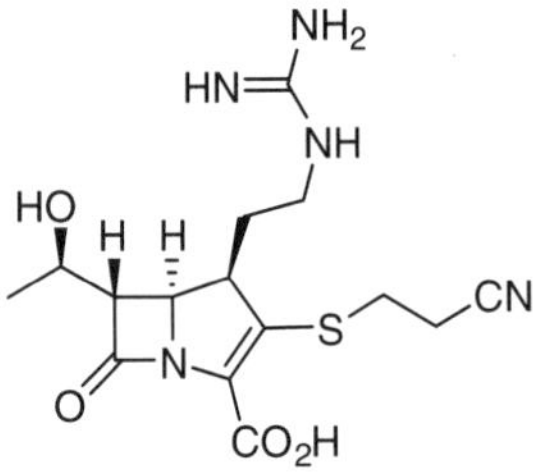

(**333**) BMS-181139

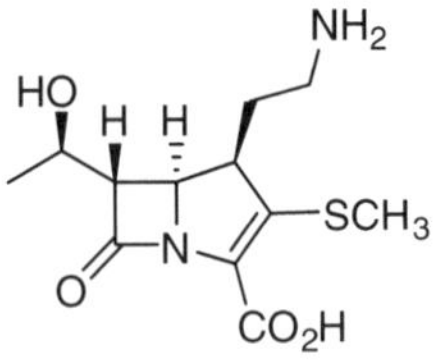

(**334**) BMY-43975

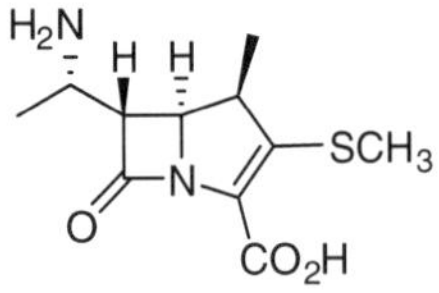

(**335**) BMY-40383

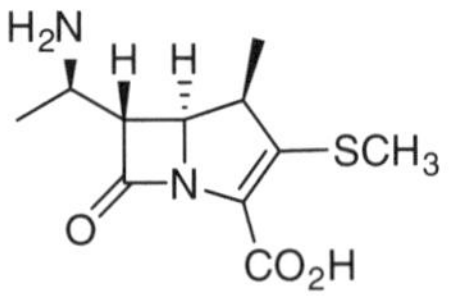

(**336**) BMY-40591
Carbapenems bearing a basic
group at C-6 position

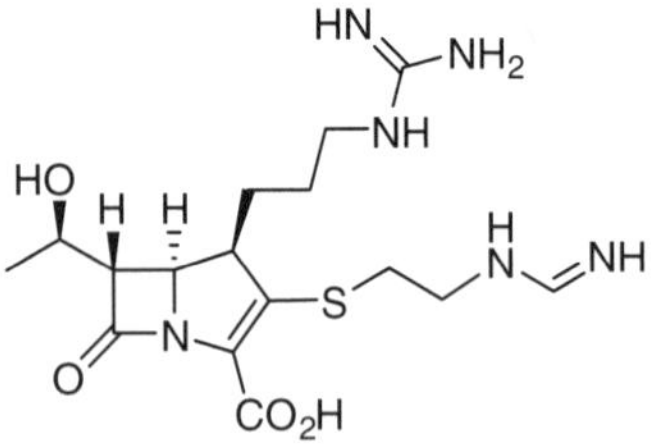

(**337**) BMY-45742

A series of 1β-aminoalkyl-substituted car-bapenems [994] was extensively explored at Bristol-Myers-Squibb. Compounds (**333**) and (**334**) exemplify the series [995]. Compari-son [994,996] of carbapenems with amino substitution either at C-6- or at C-1-position (**335–340**), to derivatives with the hydro-xyethyl side chain (**341, 342**), led to three conclusions: (1) The presence of a cationic group was confirmed as essential to retain antipseudomonal activity. (2) Antipseudomo-nal activity was observed, regardless of the position of the cationic group at C-1, C-2, or C-6. (3) The presence of a second basic group at C-1 or C-6-position of a carbapenem already with a cationic center at C-2 allows the carbapenem to exert its antipseudomo-nal activity without the need for egress

through via porin protein D2, thereby over-coming an important resistance mechanism of *P. aeruginosa*. Besides the introduction of a basic functional group, Bristol-Myers Squibb also evaluated other modifications of the hydroxyethyl side chain [997]. This eva-luation confirmed that the incorporation of an electron-withdrawing group at C-6 was not practical due to the low chemical stabi-lity of these carbapenems (such as **343–345**). The hydroxyethyl side chain is the best compromise between chemical stability and microbiological activity [996,998–1000]. Another interesting modification at C-6 was reported by Nagao et al. [1001], wherein formation of a C-6 carbanion led to the synthesis of the 6-methylthiocarbapenems (**346**) and (**347**).

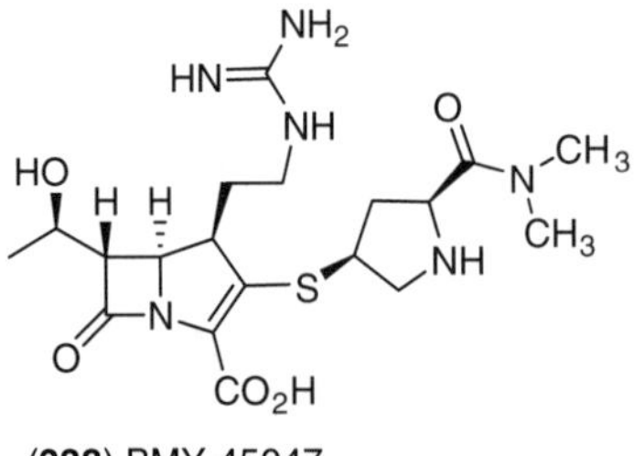

(**338**) BMY-45047
Carbapenems bearing a basic group
at C-1 and C-2 positions

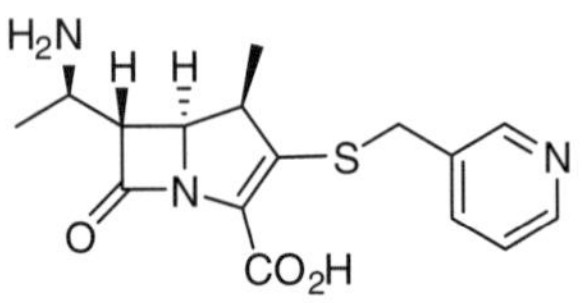

(**339**) BMY-40732

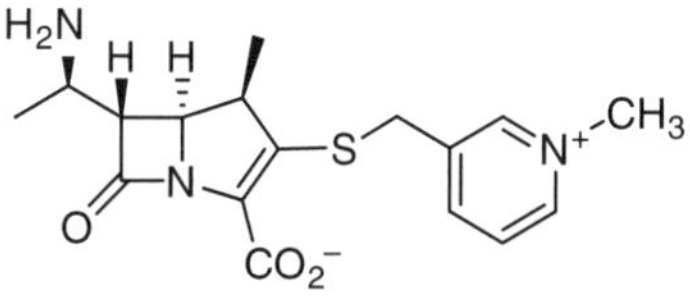

(340) BMY-40886

Carbapenems bearing a cationic or
basic group at C-2 and C-6 positions

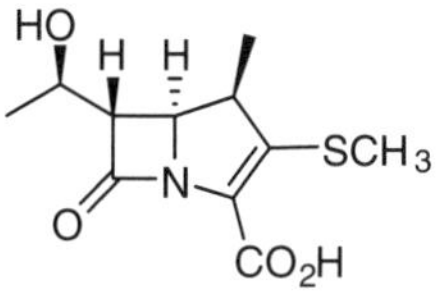

(341) BMY-27946

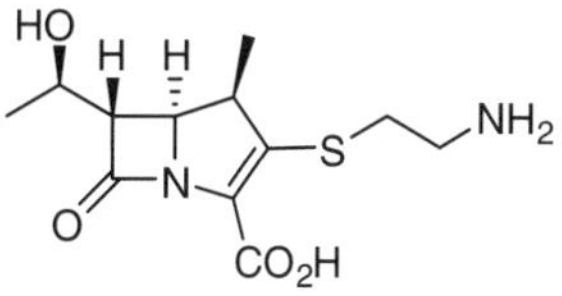

(342) BMS-182880

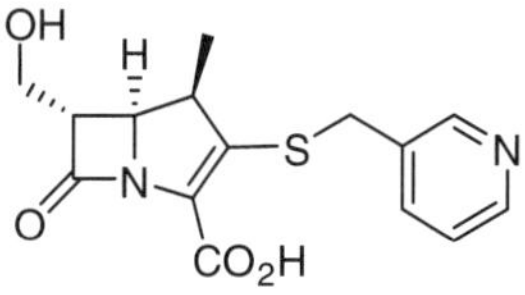

(343)

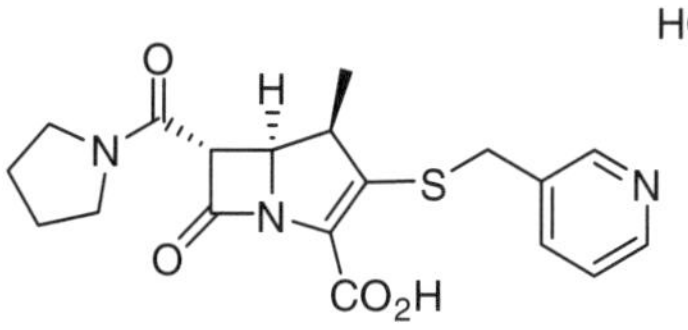

(344)

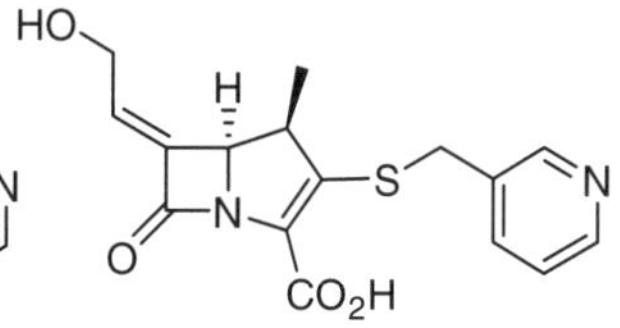

(345)

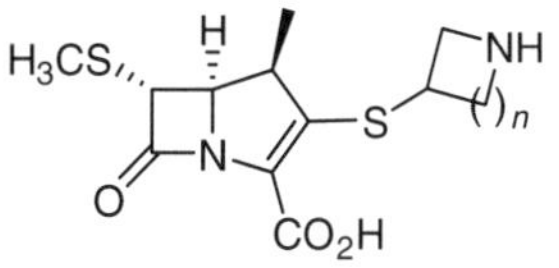

(346) n = 1
(347) n = 2

Sumitomo presented meropenem (249) as a drug candidate, featuring improved efficacy and safety over previous carbapenems, in 1987. The very potent antibacterial activity and wide spectrum of action (against both Gram-positive and -negative organisms including *Pseudomonas* sp.) of meropenem stimulated the synthesis of a variety of analogs combining 1β-methyl substitution with a 2,4-disubstituted pyrrolidine moiety on the C-2 side chain [1002–1005].

N-Methylation of the pyrrolidine and modification of the carboxamide group enhanced DHP-I stability [922] and, in particular, the introduction of hydrophilic groups (348, 349) on the amido moiety increased the antipseudomonal activity. Addition of a second cationic (basic) center was explored to improve the biological profile. Following this approach, Nishi et al. reported the piperazine derivative (350), also having antipseudomonal activity.

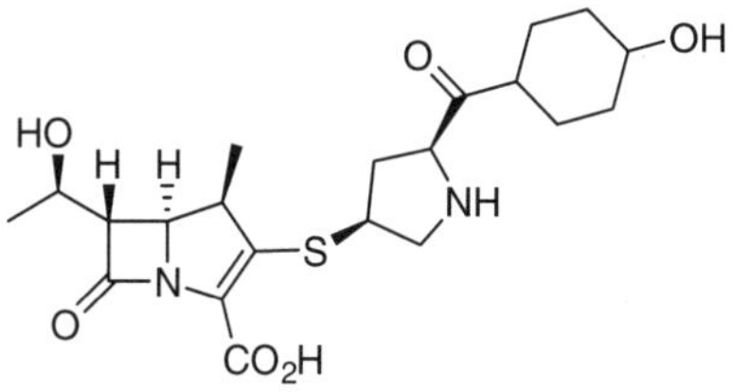

(348)

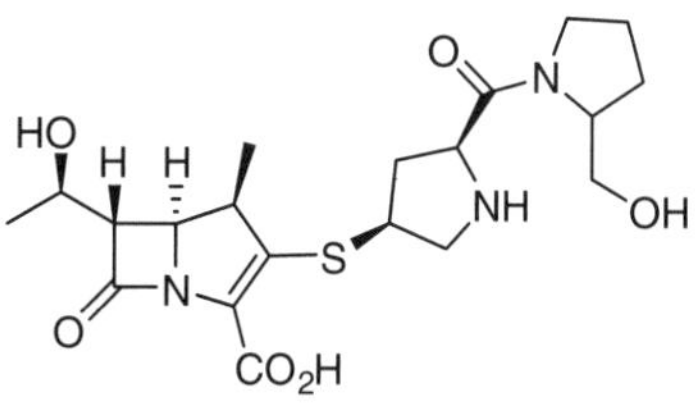

(349)

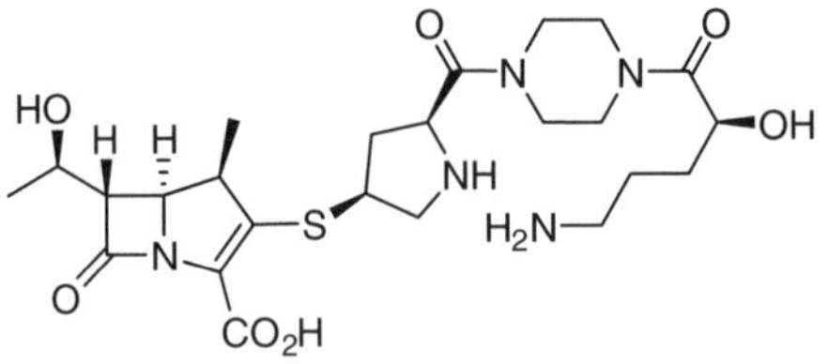

(**350**) DX-8739

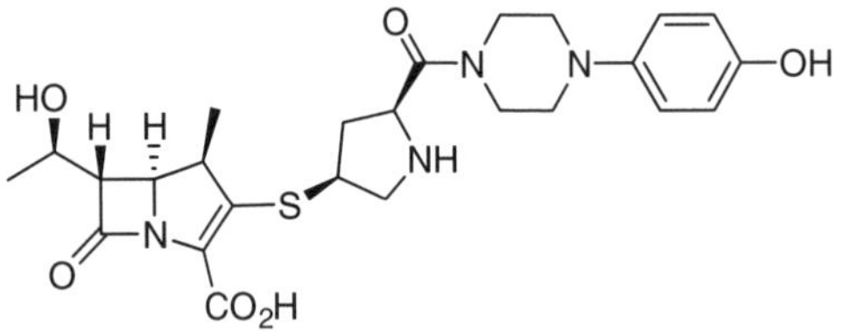

(**351**)

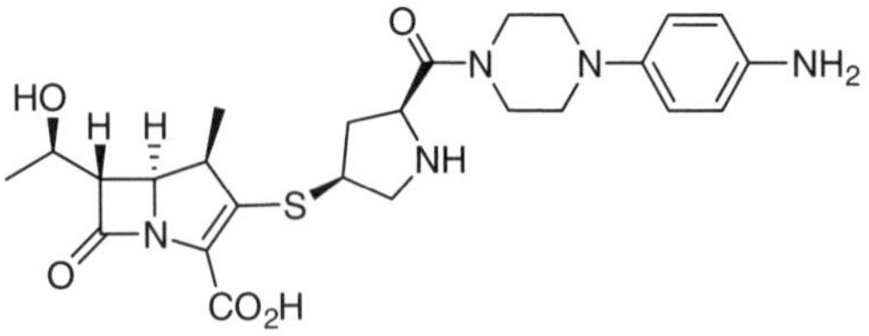

(**352**)

Other piperazine derivatives (**351**, **352**) are distinguished by their good activity against *P. aeruginosa*. Introduction of a quaternary ammonium moiety in the C-2 proline side chain (**353**) was particularly effective for improving serum half-life by reduction of renal clearance. Alternatively, a sulfonium moiety was used to provide an extra cationic center (**354**) by Oh [1006]. Zeneca and Merck groups achieved a remarkable improvement in terms of human serum half-life through the synthesis of MK-826 (**355**). The compound is significantly (approximately 95%) protein bound in serum, contributing to a mean terminal $t_{1/2}$ of 4.5 h after intravenous administration, allowing single daily dosing [1007,1008]. However, the overall negative charge of MK-826 limits its antibacterial spectrum. It lacks activity against the Gram-negative *P. aueruginosa* and the Gram-positive penicillin-resistant *S. pneumoniae* [1009]. Another class of merope-

nem derivatives incorporates a catechol moiety (**356**), in a manner similar to a cephalosporin class (see Section 5.2). This modification improved the *in vivo* antipseudomonal activity [1010].

Although most compounds exhibited an antibacterial profile similar to that of meropenem, Banyu, first with J-111,347 (**357**) and then with J-111,225 (**358**), J-114,870 (**359**), and J-114,871 (**360**), demonstrated that it is possible to further expand the antibacterial spectrum of meropenem mimics, including antimethicillin-resistant *S. aureus* (anti-MRSA) activity [1011]. Further evaluation of the prototype compound J-111,347 (319) has been suspended because of its epileptogenicity. This activity was eliminated by *N*-methylation (**358**) or carbamoylmethyl substitutions (**359**, **360**) in the other three compounds. *In vitro* and *in vivo* data are reported by Nagano et al. [1011].

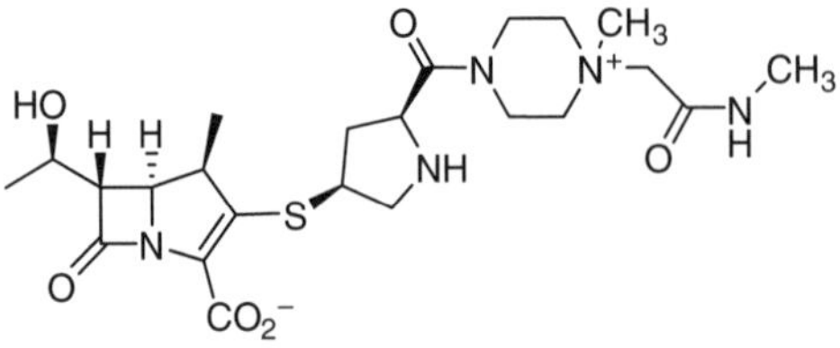

(**353**)

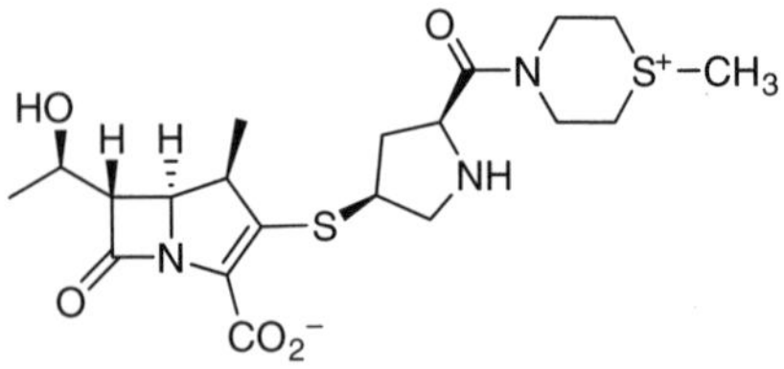

(**354**)

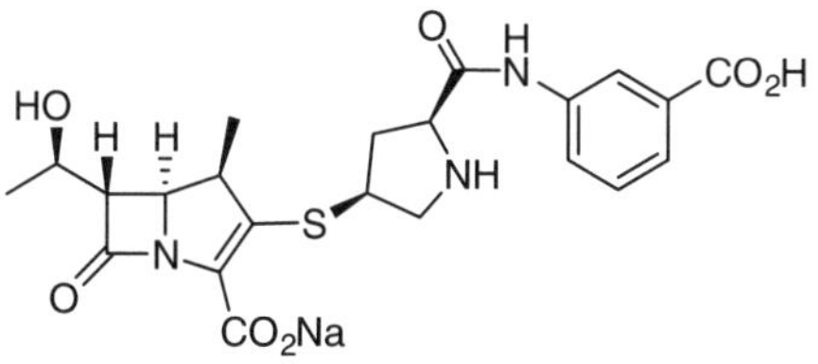

(355) MK-826

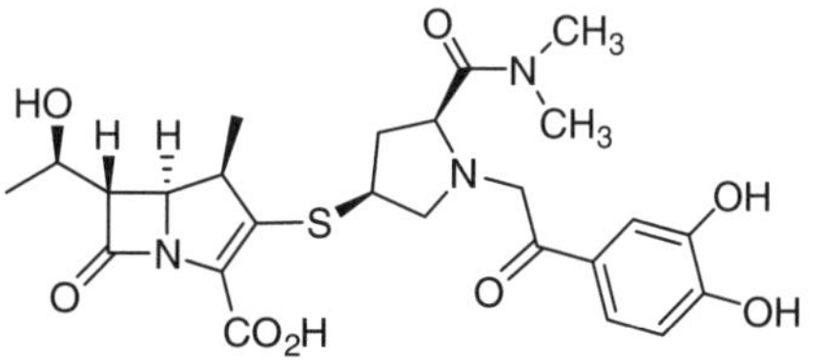

(356)

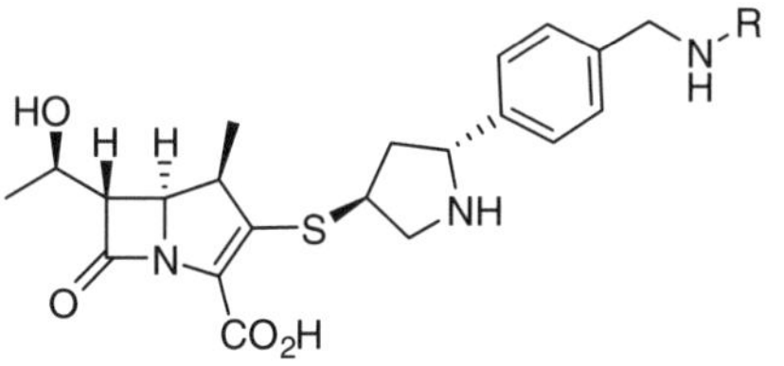

(357) J-111,347 R = H
(358) J-111,225 R = CH$_3$

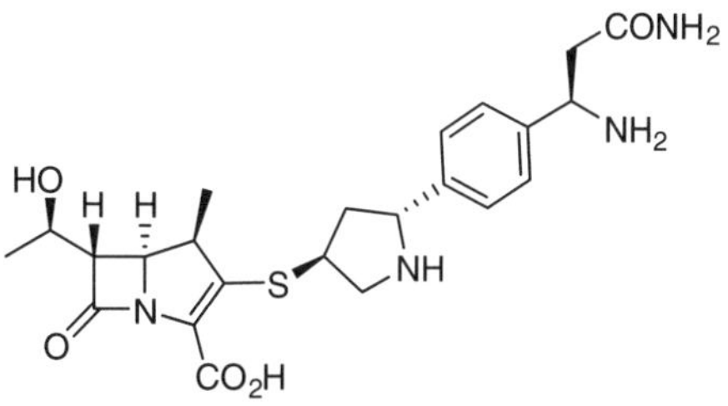

(359) J-114,870

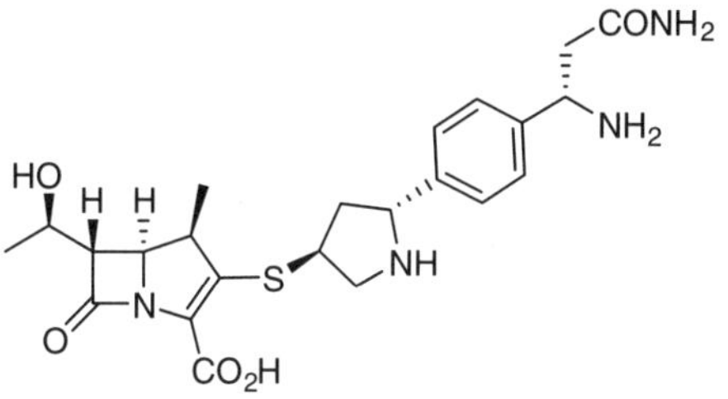

(360) J-114,871

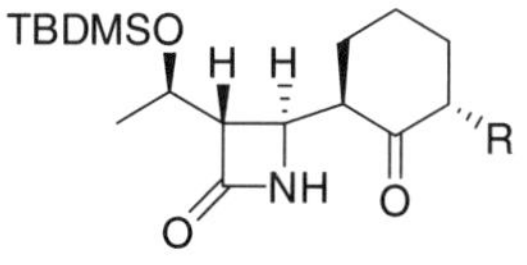

(361)

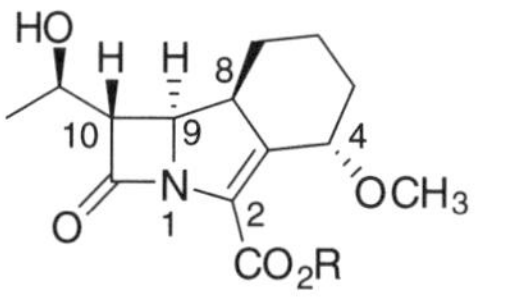

(362) Sanfetrinem R = Na
(363) Sanfetrinem cilexetil

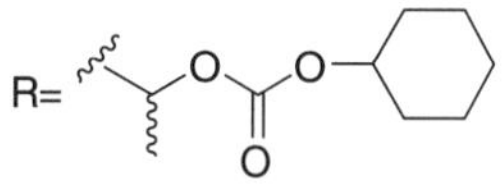

R=

5.5.2. Trinems and Polycyclic Carbapenems

Further efforts for improvements within the carbapenem class gave tricyclic and oligocyclic analogs. From azetidinone (361), a Glaxo group used the phosphorane route to prepare a series of so-called *tribactams* (later renamed *trinems*), exemplified by the 4-methoxy-substituted GV104326 (sanfetrinem, 362) [1012] showing very potent microbiological activity. Its prodrug ester (363) demonstrated a safety profile and pharmaceutical stability to warrant further progression into the clinic [1013–1016]. The trinem antibacterial spectrum was broad, including aerobic and anaerobic Gram-positive and -negative bacteria. The trinems also showed good stability toward many relevant β-lactamases and to the human dehydropeptidase (DHP-I) [1017]. SAR studies showed the best biological profile to coincide to a (4S,8S) absolute configuration and heteroatom attachment to C-4.

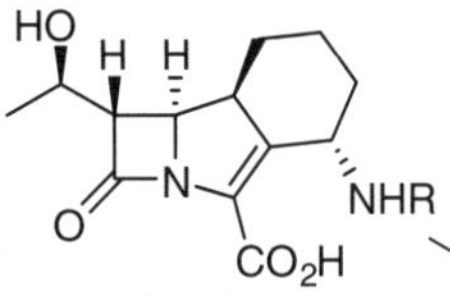

(377)

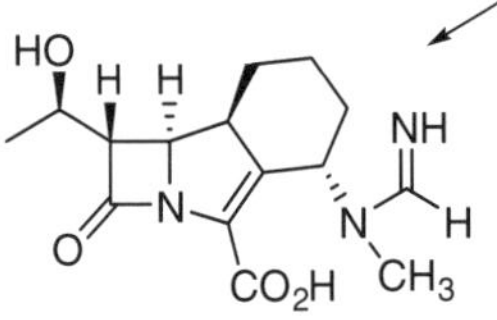

(380) GV129606x

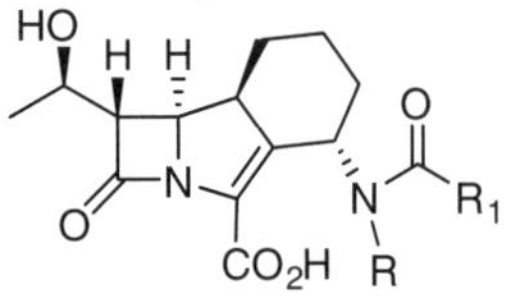

(379)

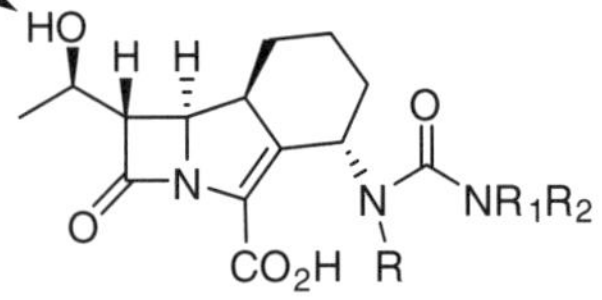

(378) R = H, CH₃

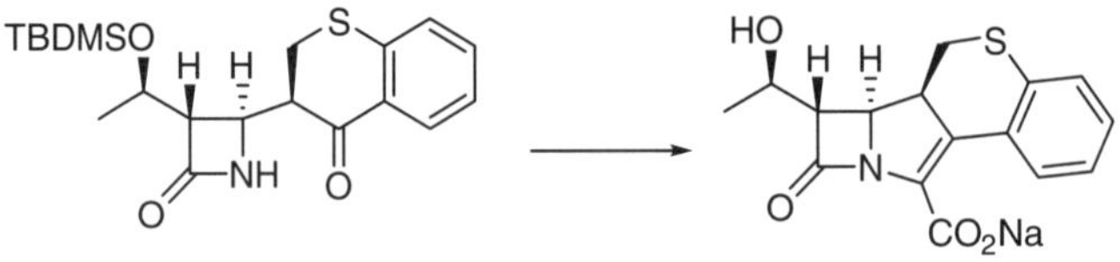

(381)

(382)

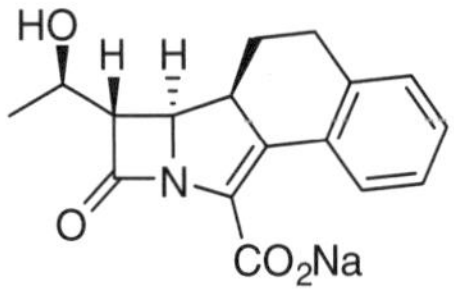

(383)

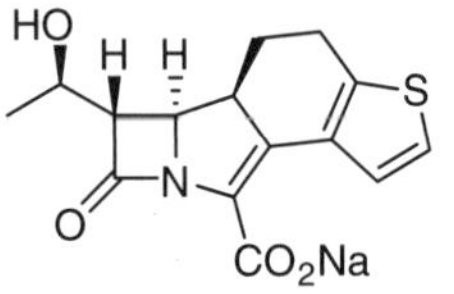

(384)

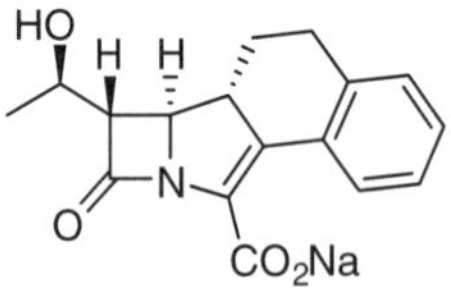

(385)

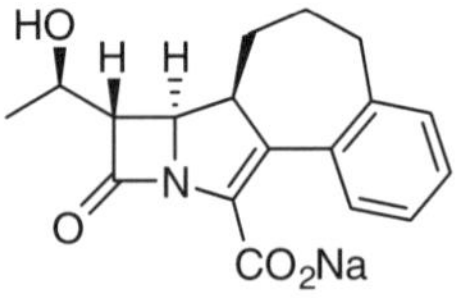

(386)

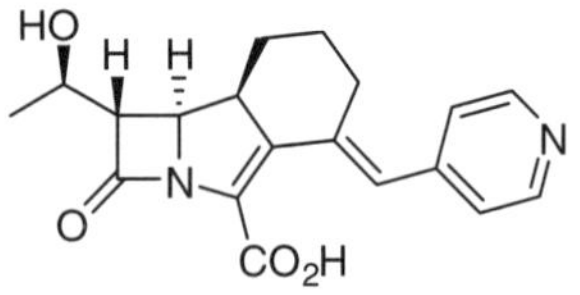

(387) GV143253X

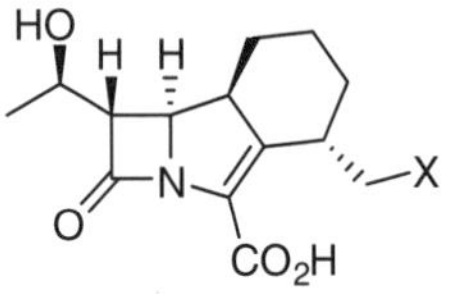

(388) X = NH₂

(389) X = HN

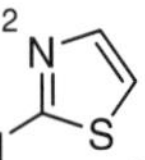

(390) X = S

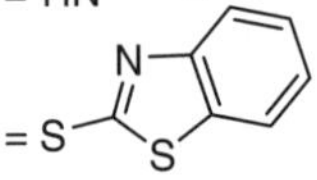

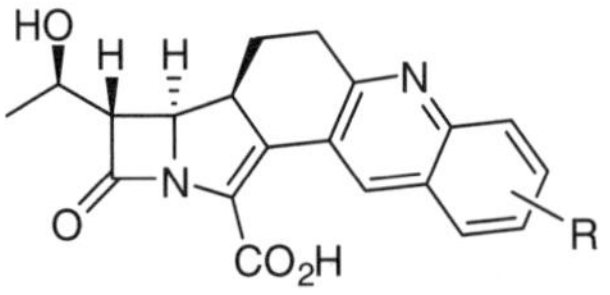

(391)

The difficult challenge of the trinem synthesis is stereochemical control of the five stereogenic centers. Advanced intermediates such as epoxide (366) and epoxyphosphate (372) allowed the introduction at C-4 of sulfur-, oxygen-, and nitrogen-containing functional groups (Figs 24 and 25). Reaction of 4-acetoxyyazetidinone (172) with 2-cyclohexenylborane

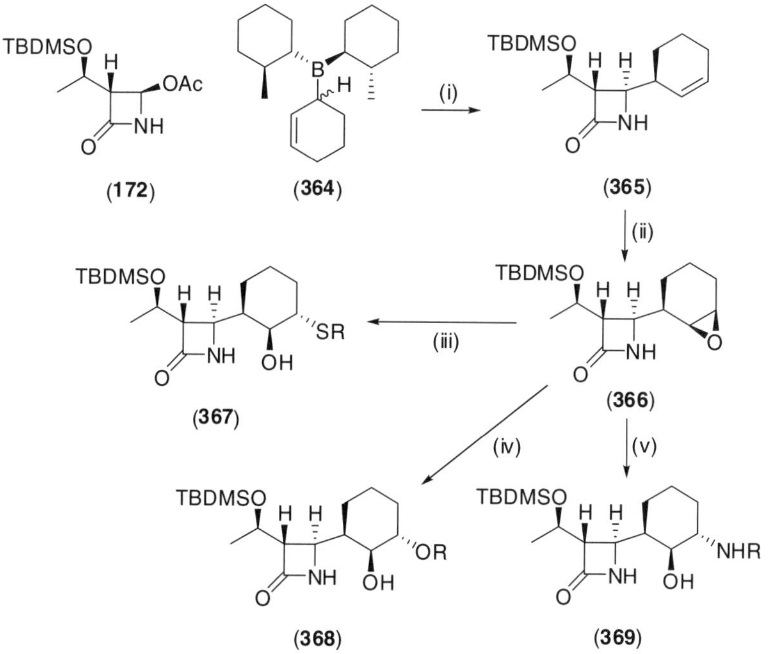

Reagents: (i) ZnEt$_2$, THF, 25°C; (ii) Magnesium monoperoxyphthalate, CH$_2$Cl$_2$; (iii) RSH, H$^+$; (iv) ROH, H$^+$; (v) RNH$_2$, H$^+$.

Figure 24. Highly diastereoselective synthesis of intermediates to trinems.

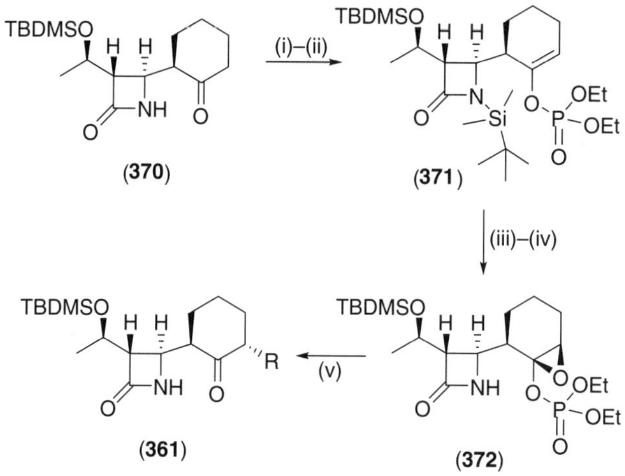

Reagents: (i) TBDMSCl, TEA, DMF; (ii) LHMDSA, ClP(O)(OEt), −70°C; (iii) KF, MeOH; (iv) MCPBA, CH$_2$Cl$_2$; (v) nucleophile.

Figure 25. Synthesis and use of epoxyphosphate (372).

(364) gave cyclohexenyl derivative (365) in high yield and selectivity [1018]. This intermediate was converted into epoxide (366) for nucleophilic substitution to afford sulfide (367), alkoxide (368), and amine (369) derivatives, further elaborated to derivatives of general formula (361). A second diastereoselective synthesis used reaction of N-protected (at the β-lactam) ketoazetidinone (370) with diethylchlorophosphate to give (371). Epoxidation gave the advanced intermediate (372), then transformed to azetidinone (361) [1019]. A synthetic improvement was direct condensation [1020–1022] in which the enantiomerically enriched silyl enol ether of 2-methoxycyclohexanone (373) [1023,1024] reacted with 4-acetoxyazetidinone (172) to yield the 6′-methoxy ketoazetidinone (374), with high stereoselectively. Intramolecular cyclization of an oxalimido derivative (375) produced the protected trinem (376). Depro-

tection gave sanfetrinem (362). Hanessian et al. [1025] reported a practical synthesis of sanfetrinem using the highly diastereoselective protonation (with diethyl malonate) of the zinc enolate of 6′-methoxy ketoazetidinone as the key step to diastereomerically pure (374). Figure 26 shows a multikilogram scale synthesis of sanfetrinem (362).

Furthermore, 4-N-substituted trinems (such as 377) allowed the preparation of urea (378) and amide (379) [1026], and most importantly the 4-N-methylformamidino GV129606X (380) [1012,1027]. GV129606X, although having broad antibacterial spectrum (including *Pseudomonas* sp.) as a parenteral trinem, was abandoned after toxicity problems were identified in preclinical studies. Through similar chemistry, both Hoechst and Bayer described tetracyclic analogs [1028,1029]. Thus, (381) was elaborated to the tetracyclic carbapenem (382) [1029].

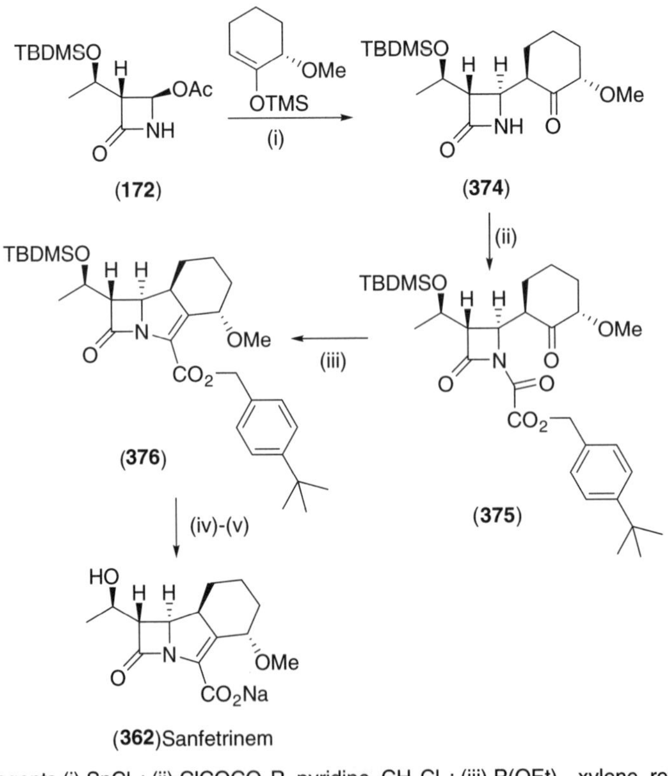

Reagents (i) SnCl₄; (ii) ClCOCO₂R, pyridine, CH₂Cl₂; (iii) P(OEt)₃, xylene, reflux; (iv) TBAF, AcOH, THF; (v) H₂, Pd/C.

Figure 26. Highly diastereoselective and practical synthesis of sanfetrinem.

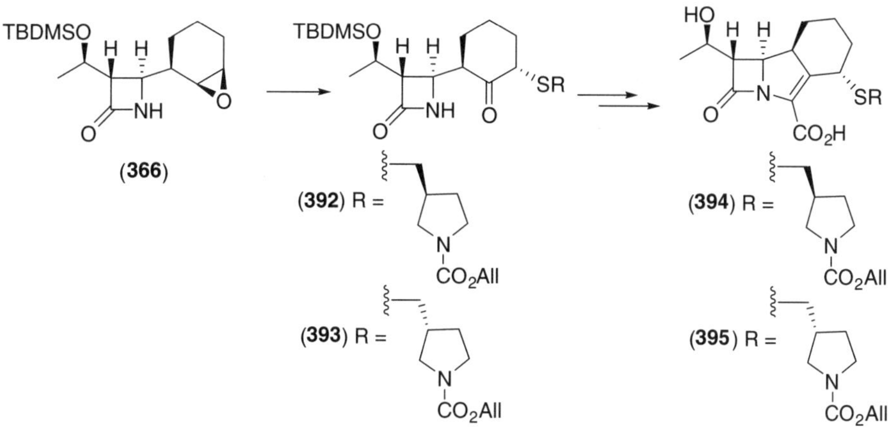

Figure 27. Preparation of derivatives starting from epoxide (366).

Ring size, stereochemistry, and heteroatom position were modified (**383–386**) but failed to attain improved antibacterial activity. Introduction of a 4-exo-arylidene or heteroarylidene provided a series that showed high potency against resistant Gram-positive strains such as penicillin-resistant *Pneumococci* and MRSA. In particular, GV143253X (**387**) showed a broad spectrum, including vancomycin-resistant enterococci and *H. influenzae*, good *in vivo* efficacy against MRSA

in septicemia and in thigh infections in the mouse. Sankyo synthesized a series of 4-substituted trinems (**388–390**) bearing a heteroaryl substituent, having an antibacterial spectrum similar to that of 4-exo methylenyl trinems [1030]. An interesting pyrrolidinyl series of anti-MRSA trinems (Fig. 27) was prepared by Sankyo [1031] from epoxide (**366**), or from the hydroxymethyl intermediate (**396**) (Fig. 28). Epoxide (**366**) was converted in two steps into ketoazetidinones

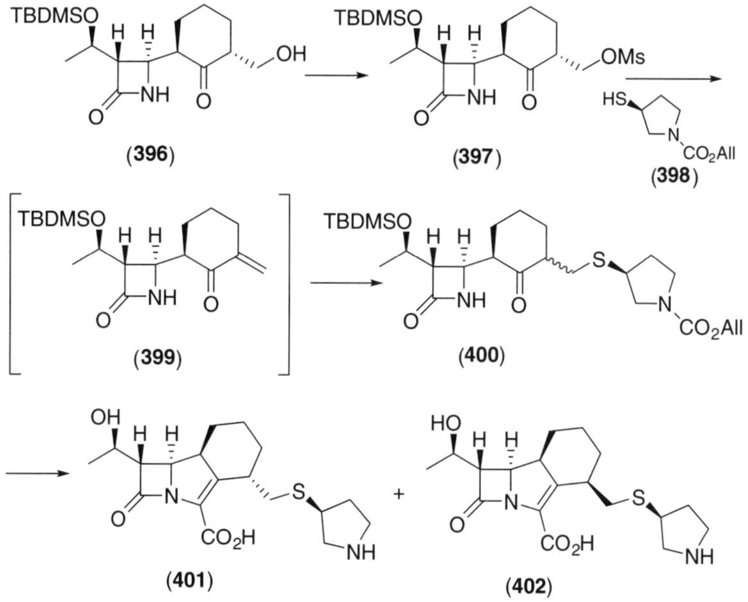

Figure 28. Preparation of derivatives from hydroxymethyl intermediate (396).

(392) and (393). Standard procedures gave trinems (394) and (395). Reaction of mesylate (397) with thiol (398) gives both 6′-isomers (400), possibly through elimination of mesylate to (399) and subsequent thio-Michael addition. Trinems (401) and (402), sulfur regioisomers of (394) and (395), were obtained by subsequent reaction. Interestingly, pyrrolidinyl group orientation was found to correlate with good antibacterial activity against Gram-positive strains including MRSA. Best results—comparable to vancomycin—were obtained with (402). GlaxoWellcome also reported the synthesis of pentacyclic β-lactams (391), conceived as conformationally constrained analogs of the 4-exo-arylidene trinems [1032]. This class has *in vitro* antibacterial activity, and affinity to the PBP2a of MRSA, similar to those of 4-arylidene trinems but with an inferior pharmacokinetic profile [1033].

5.5.3. Biological Properties of Carbapenems and Trinems

As a class the carbapenems are broad-spectrum antibacterial agents showing good stability to β-lactamases deactivation. Thienamycin (252) is the most potent of the natural products, having activity against a wide range of Gram-positive and Gram-negative bacteria including *P. aeruginosa*. An important aspect to this latter property is its very low molecular mass, enabling very efficient bacterial permeability. SAR studies indicate its exceptional biological activity correlates to the structural combination of the unusual C-6-*trans*-substituted β-lactam with the basic C-2 cysteaminyl side chain. *N*-acylation of the primary amine of this side chain greatly reduces activity [909]. Olivanic acid MM13902 (254a; R = SO$_3$H) is also a broad-spectrum agent but lacks significant activity against *Pseudomonas* sp. [1034]. Many carbapenems —and particularly [889] the olivanic acid sulfoxide MM4550 (255a; R = SO$_3$H)— are good β-lactamases inhibitors (Section 5.6). The *in vitro* activities of representative carbapenems are shown in Table 14.

Unlike the penicillins and cephalosporins, adherence to *cis*-stereochemistry at the β-lactam ring is not necessary for activity. In the olivanic acids the des-sulfate derivatives are less active than the corresponding sulfates,

and the *cis*-isomers are better than the *trans*-isomers [1034]. Thienamycin (252) is the most stable to β-lactamases. This stability is attributed to the (8*R*)-hydroxyethyl side chain, given that synthetic congeners lacking the C-6 substituent are much more susceptible to β-lactamase hydrolysis [1035,1036]. In the nonsulfated hydroxyethyl series, SAR indicates the order of potency as *trans*-β-lactam with 8(*R*) stereochemistry > *cis* 8(*S*) > *trans* 8 (*S*) [909]. Binding studies in *E. coli* indicate thienamycin as having greatest affinity for PBP-2, whereas most of the newer cephalosporins bind to PBP-3 [1037]. Thienamycin (252) was not suitable for further development because of its chemical instability both in concentrated solution and in the solid state. However, imipenem (248), the *N*-formimidoyl derivative of thienamycin, gave a stable crystalline product also with much improved solution stability [910]. Imipenem exhibits an outstanding spectrum of activity against aerobic and anaerobic Gram-positive and Gram-negative bacteria. It has a potent bactericidal effect against *P. aeruginosa*, *Serratia*, *B. fragilis*, enterococci, and many other species [1038]. Imipenem inhibited the majority of 800 clinical isolates at concentrations below 1 µg/mL, and was not hydrolyzed by plasmid or chromosomal β-lactamases, although both *Pseudomonas maltophilia* and *P. cepacia* were resistant [1039]. The plasma half-life of imipenem (1 h) in humans was considered satisfactory, although with quite variable urinary recoveries (6–40%) [1040]. This variability was the result of extensive metabolism by a renal tubular brush border dipeptidase (DHP-1) enzyme. All *natural* carbapenems are susceptible to this enzymatic hydrolysis [1041]. To overcome this obstacle, imipenem was developed by Merck in combination with an inhibitor (cilastatin, 403) of DHP-1, to give an acceptable urinary recovery of the antibiotic [1042]. The formation of any potential nephrotoxic degradation products was reduced. After successful clinical trials, this combination was developed successfully as the broad-spectrum parenteral agent Primaxin [881]. Although large numbers of imipenem analogs have been synthesized, particularly with modified *S*-linked C-2 side chains, the only other compound developed in

Table 14. *In Vitro* Antibacterial Activity of Carbapenems [MIC (μg/mL)][a]

Organism	Thienamycin (252)	Imipenem (248)	MM13902 (254a)	PS-5 (259)	Asparenomycin A (262)	Pluracidomycin A (263)	Meropenem (249)	Biapenem (407)	Sanfetrinem (362)
E. coli	0.2–0.4	0.25	0.2–1.6	1.56	0.39–3.13	6.3	0.03	0.25	0.5
K. pneumoniae	0.4	0.25	0.4–3.1	3.13	0.78	6.3	0.06	0.25	2
Enterobacter sp.	1.6	0.5–1				12.5	0.12	0.25	2
S. marcescens	1.6	0.5–2				12.5	0.12	2	16
P. mirabilis	3.1	2	0.2	6.25	3.13	12.5	0.12	2	2
P. aeruginosa	3.1	2–4	25–50	50–100	25	>100	8	4	>32
H. influenzae	—	0.25–0.5	0.1	—	—	—	0.12	1	0.25
B. *fragilis*	0.4	0.25	0.4	—	—	—	1	0.5	—
S. aureus	0.04	0.03–0.06	1.6	0.025–0.39	1.56	25–50	0.12	0.06	0.12
S. pyogenes	0.01	0.01	0.2	0.08	1.56	25–50	0.12	0.008	0.015
S. pneumoniae	1.6	0.03	6.2	0.02	—	—	0.06	0.03	0.007
Enterobacter sp.	1.6	0.5–1				12.5	0.12	0.25	2

[a] See Refs [470,881,897,1012,1034].

351

this series is panipenem (**404**). Although a broad-spectrum agent, panipenem (**404**) still requires co-administration with betamipron for concurrent DHP-I inhibition [1043]. One thienamycin series of some interest has an aryl group directly attached at C-2. Some have good activity and stability [1044,1045] with promising anti-MRSA activity.

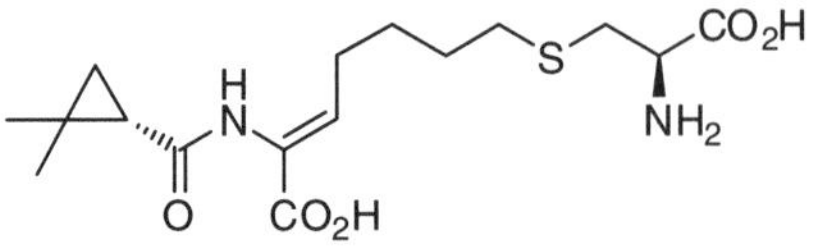

(**403**) Cilastatin

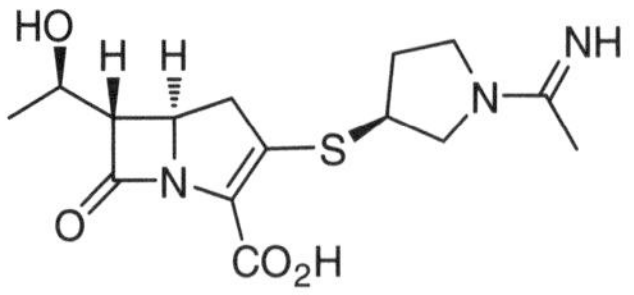

(**404**)Panipenem

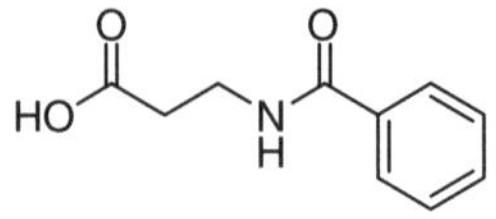

Betamipron

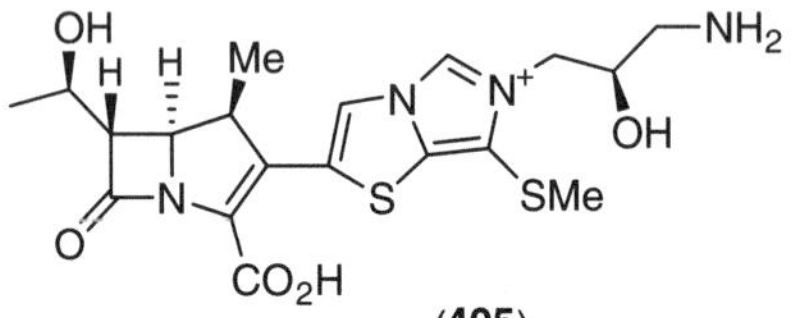

(**405**)

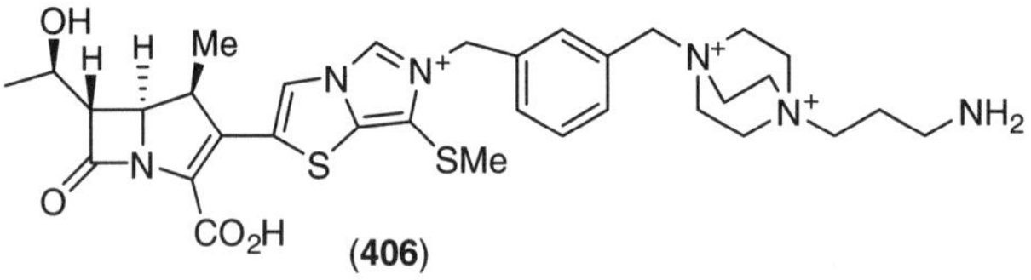

(**406**)

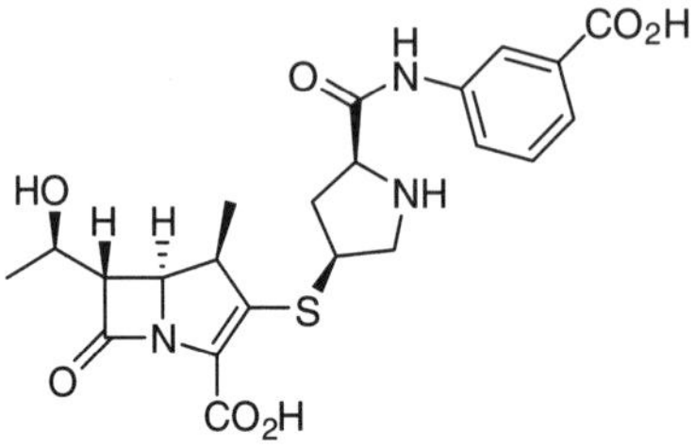

(**250**) Ertapenem

The 1β-methyl series has seen the development of meropenem (**249**), a broad-spectrum agent comparable to imipenem (Table 14), and which is sufficiently stable to DHP-I as to not require an inhibitor. Sanfetrinem (**362**) is not active against *Pseudomonas* sp. but it has a broad spectrum of antimicrobial activity (Table 14) and is stable to DHP-I. Of particular interest is the cilexetil prodrug ester (**363**), which is orally absorbed in humans [881]. Oral absorption was also demonstrated with the pivaloyloxymethyl ester of the tetracyclic β-lactam derivative (**382**) [1029]. The antibacterial activity of trinems is highly influenced by the substituent at C-4 [1046], and could be targeted toward broad-spectrum agents including *Pseudomonas* sp. [1047], as shown by GV129606X (**380**) or highly resistant Gram-positive bacteria such as MRSA and penicillin-resistant streptococci such as GV143253X (**387**).

A particularly interesting development with respect to the carbapenems was made from the study of the molecular bases for *in vitro* high-level β-lactam resistance in the Gram-positive bacterium *E. faecium* [145]. A key event resulting in this high level of resistance is the appropriation of a peptidoglycan LD-transpeptidase for catalysis of glycan strand cross-linking [1048]. This donor stem structure used in this reaction is not the customary -L-Ala^1-D-iGln^2-L-Lys[D-iAsx]^3-D-Ala^4-D-Ala^5 terminus of this bacterium, but a -L-Ala^1-D-iGln^2-L-Lys[D-iAsx]^3-D-Ala^4 terminus. The LD-transpeptidase accepts this stem, in the first step of transpeptidation cross-linking, forming a lysyl acyl-enzyme with loss of the -D-Ala^4 residue. In the second half-reaction that completes the cross-linking, the amine terminus of the D-iAsx residue located on the ε-amino of L-Lys^3 intercepts the acyl-enzyme to form a L-Lys[D-iAsx]^3-L-Lys$^{3'}$ cross-link. As the catalytic residue of the LD-transpeptidase is cysteine *and* as this reaction involves LD-transpeptidation (in contrast to the serine of PBP-dependent DD-transpeptidation), the observation that thienamycin was an irreversible inactivator of the LD-transpeptidase was unexpected [1049]. This observation suggests the possibility of synergistic β-lactam therapy, should these resistant mutants appear in the clinic. Moreover, the peptidoglycan of stationary phase *Mycobacterium tuberculoisis* shows LD-transpeptidation cross-links, and the LD-transpeptidase catalyst here is also carbapenem susceptible [1050].

5.5.4. Exploratory Carbapenem SAR

Exploratory carbapenem synthesis is no longer strongly represented in the medicinal chemistry literature. This conclusion may be seen to reflect the abundance of these structures in the clinic and also in clinical development, the absence of oral activity within the class, and the lack of a basis for structure-based drug design. The lack of oral activity is being addressed by prodrug strategies [1051] as also

exemplified by tebipenem (Section 5.5.5.8). Classical empirical structure interchange remains the driving force behind the few disclosures appearing within the medicinal chemistry literature, such as recent structures within the CP5068 series. CP5484 (**405**) [1052] was substantially more active than imipenem against both MRSA (MIC 0.8 μg/mL versus 25 μg/mL) and imipenem-resistant MRSA (MIC 1.6 μg/mL versus 100 μg/mL). A more recent, and even more highly charged, structure from the same group (**406**) suggests (its excellent MRSA activity notwithstanding), with regard to its molecular complexity and high relative molecular mass, the end-stage limitations of empirical SAR study.

The profound limitation of the Tipper–Strominger hypothesis as applied to β-lactam SAR was discussed (Section 2.3). This limitation is believed to reflect a relative lack of subsite recognition by the PBPs for their endogenous substrates [66]. This is not the case, however, for β-lactam recognition by PBPs: it was known from the earliest studies on these enzymes that the relative affinity of β-lactams among the several PBPs of the bacterium was highly dependent on the β-lactam structure. Notwithstanding the existence of several PBP structures of outstanding resolution, these enzymes do not easily lend themselves to structure-based design due to the certainty—not likelihood—that their catalysis coincides with substantial conformational fluctuation [165]. This is now changing. With the realization that the *in vitro* ability of new β-lactams to inhibit target PBPs (especially PBP 2a of MRSA) strongly correlates to their antibacterial activity [203,204], the value of crystallographic examination of target PBPs following β-lactam inactivation is now appreciated. The first study toward this objective was reported in 2008 by Yamada et al. [220], comparing (at the moderate resolutions of 2.5–3.0 Å) the structures of biapenem-inhibited and tebipenem-inhibited *S. pneumoniae* PBPs 2X and 2A. The importance of the C-2 hydroxyethyl side chain in the positioning of the acyl-enzymes was observed, and the probable value from this understanding of the side-chain interaction toward the design of future carbapenems with modified C-2 side chains was specifically addressed. SAR development of the C-2 side chain has progressed little beyond the first carbapenem structural studies. It remains to be seen, however, whether the most important interactions governing β-lactam inactivation of PBPs are kinetic (involving the positioning of the β-lactam as it enters the active site) or thermodynamic (the structure of the resulting acyl-enzyme).

5.5.5. Evolution of the Carbapenem SAR
Carbapenems possess a broad spectrum of bacterial activity against both Gram-positive and -negative aerobes and anaerobes. They are also stable to almost all β-lactamases, although as noted in Section 3.3 the appearance of β-lactamases with the ability to hydrolyze carbapenems is a matter of grievous future clinical concern [281]. As discussed above, the first carbapenem discovered was thienamycin in the mid-1970s. Imipenem, the fully synthetic and chemically more stable analog of thienamycin, was the first parenteral carbapenem. Five parenteral carbapenems have followed: panipenem in 1993, meropenem [1053] in 1996, ertapenem in 2001, biapenem in 2002, and doripenem in 2005. The introduction of the 1β-methyl substituent to prevent DHP-1 degradation, as exemplified by meropenam (and continuing through all subsequent carbapenam structures), was the first major SAR advance. Four new carbapenems are in clinical trials.

New Carbapenems   The four new carbapenems are tomopenem (Phase II), PZ-601 (Phase II), ME-1036 (Phase I), and tebipenem pivoxil (Phase III). Progress with these four is given, following (for purposes of comparison) the properties and characteristics of ertapenem, biapenem, and doripenem.

Ertapenem   [CAS Reg. No. 153832-46-3] (formerly Merck MK-0826) (**251**) is a once-a-day parenteral carbapenem approved in the United States in November 2001 and in Europe in April 2002 [1054–1062]. Ertapenem is structurally similar to meropenem, including the presence of a 1β-methyl substituent providing relative stability to dehydropeptidase-1 degradation [338]. However, its N-acylated meta-aminobenzoic acid terminus on its C-2 substituent increases its both molecular weight and lipophilicity, thus imparting an

overall negative charge to the C-2 substituent at physiological pH. This charge accounts for extensive protein binding [1063], resulting in a longer serum half-life for ertapenem relative to other carbapenems [1064]. Moreover, also for these reasons ertapenem is likely to permeate Gram-negative cell walls more slowly than meropenem, and this difference probably contributes to its unique antimicrobial spectrum. A detailed study of the hydrolytic stability in buffer (as a function of pH and temperature) was reported [1065]. Ertapenem is susceptible to deactivation by some carbapenemases [1066], while it is inhibitory to others [1067].

Like imipenem (**248**) and meropenem (**249**), ertapenem (**251**) demonstrates *in vitro* activity against Gram-positive and Gram-negative aerobes and anaerobes and is resistant to nearly all β-lactamases, including extended-spectrum β-lactamases and AmpCs. However, unlike the other carbapenems, ertapenem exhibits minimal activity against nosocomial pathogens including *P. aeruginosa*, MRSA, *Actineobacter* sp., the enterococci as well as other nonfermentative Gram-negative bacteria [1068]. Because of its pharmacologic properties and spectrum of activity are different enough from those of imipenem and meropenem, it is generally considered to belong to its own separate class within the carbapenem group [1057]. Imipenem and meropenem represent carbapenems suitable for nosocomial infections, whereas ertapenem is suitable for community-acquired infections. Ertapenem challenges the traditional view of carbapenems as agents to be used as a last resort [1059]. Ertapenem has showed equivalent efficacy and safety when compared with piperacillin/tazobactam or ceftriaxone.

Ertapenem is both clinically efficacious in randomized, comparative studies in the treatment of community-acquired infections including complicated intra-abdominal infections, complicated SSSI, and CAP. Ertapenem is used to treat mild to moderately ill patients with community-acquired infections, and for patients requiring outpatient intravenous antibacterial therapy [883,1062].

Biapenem   [CAS Reg. No. 120410-24-4] (formerly LJC-10627) (**407**) is a synthetic carbapenem in clinical use in Japan (marketed in

2002 as Omegacin®) for parenteral administration [337,1069,1070]. As a newer generation carbapenem, biapenem has a 1β-methyl substituent that confers excellent stability toward hydrolysis by human renal DHP-I. Biapenem has broad-spectrum antibacterial activity encompassing many Gram-negative and Gram-positive aerobic and anaerobic bacteria, including β-lactamase-producers. On the basis of many *in vitro* investigations, biapenem is considered to be more active than imipenem against Enterobacteriaceae having extended-spectrum β-lactamases [882]. However, biapenem has variable activity against *S. marcescens* (MIC$_{90}$ range 0.5–8 mg/mL) and was inactive against *P. rettgeri* (MIC$_{90}$ > 8 mg/mL). MIC$_{90}$ values against strains of *P. aeruginosa* (from January 1994 to December 1996) showed a tendency toward less resistance to biapenem than to the other carbapenems. Although the *in vitro* activity of biapenem against *P. aeru-*

ginosa was similar to imipenem, biapenem was more active than imipenem in several studies [1069]. In common with imipenem, meropenem, and panipenem, biapenem was essentially inactive against methicillin-resistant *S. aureus* (MIC$_{90}$ values ranged from 32 to 128 mg/mL) and *E. faecium* (MIC$_{90}$ typically >128 mg/mL). Biapenem is active against MSSA (MIC$_{90}$ range 0.06–0.5 mg/mL), *S. epidermidis* (MIC$_{90}$ values were 0.12–1 mg/mL) and methicillin-susceptible coagulase-negative streptococci (MIC$_{90}$ range 0.5–2 mg/mL). In general, biapenem was at least as active as imipenem against Gram-positive bacteria, although imipenem showed a trend toward slightly better activity than biapenem against some Gram-positive pathogens in some studies [1069]. Biapenem is generally well tolerated by adults with complicated intra-abdominal infections, lower respiratory tract infections, and complicated urinary tract infections.

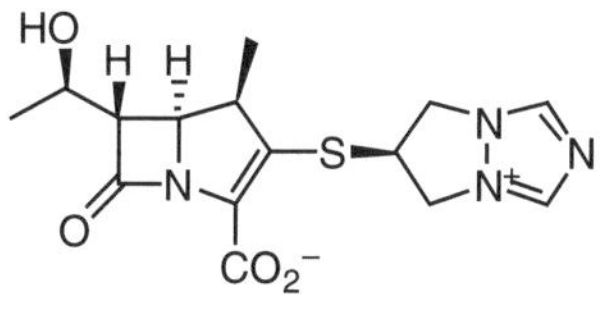

(**407**) Biapenem

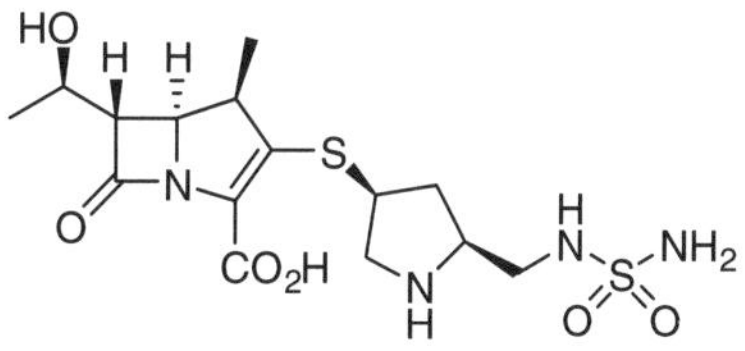

(**251**) Doripenem

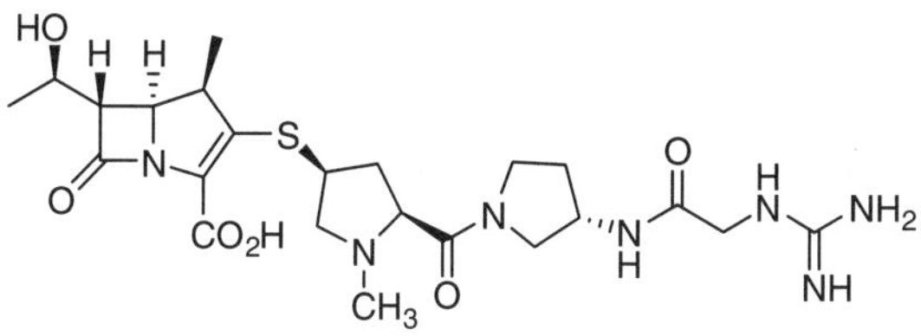

(**408**) Tomopenem

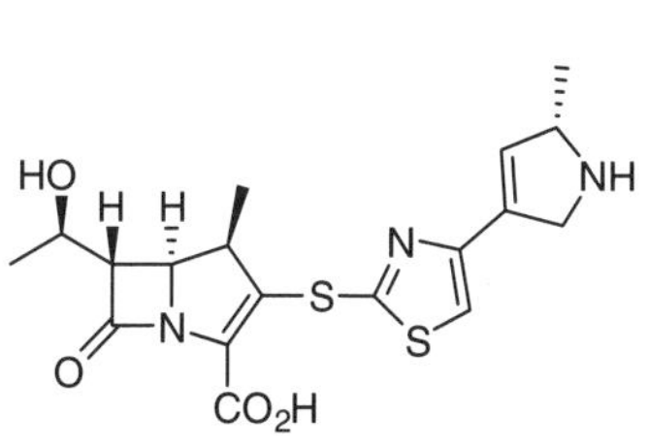

(**409**) PZ-601

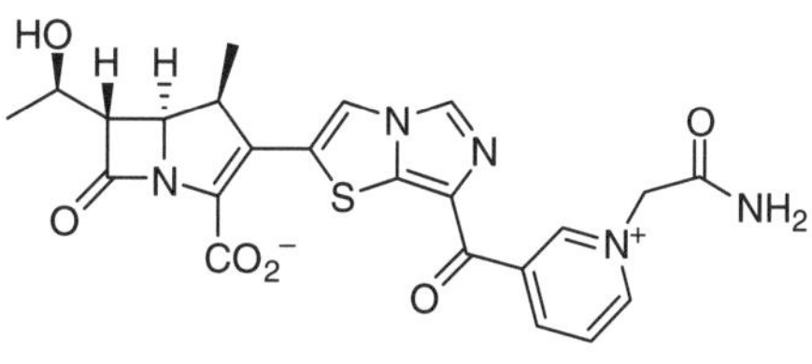

(**410**) ME-1036

Biapenem is used often as the substrate for the computational [1071,1072] and experimental [1073,1074] study of β-lactamase-catalyzed hydrolysis of carbapenems. Of the 1β-methyl carbapenems examined, only biapenem was not a substrate of the Mex transporters of *P. aeruginosa* [1075].

With respect to the undesirable convulsant activity induced by some β-lactams, biapenem appeared weaker than imipenem, panipenem, and cefazolin in *in vitro* and in *in vivo* investigations. Biapenem did not induce severe convulsions or show neurotoxic potential in rats and showed a substantially lower potential than imipenem for evoking convulsions in mice. This favorable result was attributed to the presence of the 1β-methyl and the bicyclic triazole at C-2, lowering the affinity of biapenem for the GABA receptor compared to imipenem [1076].

Doripenem (Finibax, Doribax) [CAS Reg. No. 148016-81-3] (**251**) is a synthetic carbapenem for parenteral administration [1077–1079] launched in 2005 in Japan by Shionogi & Co. as a broad-spectrum antibiotic [1080–1082]. Its rights outside of Japan were ultimately acquired by Ortho-McNeil Pharmaceutical (New Brunswick, NJ, USA: a subsidiary of Johnson & Johnson). FDA approval was granted in October 2007 for the use of doripenem in the treatment of complicated intra-abdominal and complicated urinary tract infections, including pyelonephritis. The use of doripenem for treatment of nosocomial pneumonia (HAP) is under FDA review, while in Europe its use against HAP and complicated urinary tract infections are under review [775]. In these clinical trials, doripenem was generally well tolerated with headache, nausea, diarrhea, and phlebitis as occasional drug-related adverse events. Doripenem lacked CNS convulsive activity in rodent pharmacological assay [383].

The presence of a 1β-methyl substituent (as is also found in ertapenem and meropenem) renders doripenem stable to dehydropeptidase-I cleavage, and eliminates the need for coadministration of a DHP-I inhibitor. Similar to other carbapenems, doripenem has a basic side chain—a [[(sulfamoylaminoethyl)pyrrolidinyl]thio] group—at position 2. The lower basicity of this substituent, compared to those of meropenem or imipenem, probably explains its enhanced Gram-negative antibacterial activity [883,1083]. The activity profile of doripenem combines the best features of imipenem and meropenem [884,1084–1090]. This profile includes better activity against Gram-positive organisms than meropenem, and better activity against Gram-negative organisms than imipenem. In addition, its MIC values against *P. aeruginosa* are lower than other antipseudomonal agents, including the available carbapenems, while still maintaining potency against ESBL-containing pathogens. Doripenem is effective against the major causative pathogens of complicated intra-abdominal infections, including *E. coli, K. pneumoniae, P. aeruginosa, Streptococcus intermedius, Bacteroides caccae, Bacteroides thetaiotaomicron, B. fragilis*, and *Bacteroides uniformis*. Its exceptional activity against *E. coli* and *P. aeruginosa* may correlate to its good selectivity for bacteriocidal PBPs [1091]. Doripenem has the lowest *in vitro* rate for emergence of resistant *P. aeruginosa* of all presently available carbapenems, likely because multiple mechanisms are needed for resistance [1092]. This rate is further reduced by the presence of an aminoglycoside [1093].

Doripenem has demonstrated extended stability at room temperature in normal saline (8 h) compared to other carbapenems (4 h for imipenem/cilastatin and for meropenem; 6 h for ertapenem). This extended stability allows for prolonged infusion times [1094]. Its ADME profile in man [1095] and preliminary clinical data [1096,1097] have been reported.

Tomopenem [CAS Reg. No. 222400-20-6] (formerly CS-023, R-1558, R-115685, and RO-4908463) (**408**) is a parenteral 1β-methyl-carbapenem characterized by a unique guanidinium terminus for its C-2 substituent. It was discovered by Sankyo [1098], and acquired subsequently by Roche. It is more stable against human renal dehydropeptidase-I (DHP-I) than meropenem or imipenem [1099] and hence does not require coadministration with an inhibitor of this enzyme. Likewise, tomopenem has greater β-lactamase stability (including Gram-negative ESBLs) compared to these two carbapenems [1099–1101]. The *in vitro* Gram-positive activity of tomopenem is comparable to imipenem, and the Gram-negative activity (and anaerobe) activities of tomopenem are comparable to meropenem [1102]. The relatively modest antibacterial activity of tomopenem against MRSA (MIC$_{90}$ 8 µg/mL) correlated with good affinity toward PBP2a [1103]. Tomopenem is, however, four- to eightfold more active than meropenem against meropenem-resistant *P. aeruginosa* [1104]. This increased *P. aeruginosa* activity, coupled with its relatively slow *in vivo* clearance, give tomopenem efficacy in a pharmacological model of *P. aeruginosa* respiratory infection [1105]. The basis for its slow clearance is reduced renal transport [1106–1111]. These results suggested potential for tomopenem against nosocomial bacterial infections by both Gram-positive and -negative pathogens, including MRSA and *P. aeruginosa*. Tomopenem entered in phase 2 clinical trials, but was returned to Daiichi Sankyo in 2007, and now is reported as discontinued [700].

PZ-601 [CAS Reg. No. 426253-04-5] (Sumitomo, formerly SMP-601 and SM-216601) (**409**) is a parenteral 1β-methylcarbapenem with antimicrobial activity against a wide range of Gram-positive and Gram-negative bacteria, especially multiresistant MRSA and VISA *S. aureus*. The basis for the selection of this particular structure from among a series of 2-(4-tetrahydropyridinylthiazol-2-ylthio) and 4-dihydropyrrolylthiazole 2-substituted 1β-methylcarbapenems [1112,1113] was made on the basis of the antibacterial potency and CNS safety. In particular, the introduction of an *S*-methyl substituent to the 2,5-dihydropyrrol-3-yl terminus of the 2-thiazolylthio ring at C-2 markedly attenuated the undesirable convulsant activity of this class, with only small loss of Gram-negative activity [1114]. Its activity against Gram-negative bacteria is slightly less (MIC two- to fourfold higher) compared to imipenem. However, the excellent activity of PZ-601 against MRSA, *S. epidermidis* and *E. faecium* distinguish it from other carbapenems. In agar dilution susceptibility testing, PZ-601 attained an MIC$_{90}$ of 2 µg/mL for 90% of the MRSA strains tested, comparable to vancomycin and linezolid. PZ-601 was very potent against *E. faecium*, including vancomycin-resistant strains (MIC$_{90}$ = 8 µg/mL). PZ-601 exhibited potent activity against penicillin-resistant *S. pneumoniae*, ampicillin-resistant *H. influenzae*, *M. catarrhalis*, *E. coli*, *K. pneumoniae*, and *P. mirabilis* with MIC$_{90s}$ values of less than 0.5 µg/mL. Intermediate activity was seen against *C. freundii*, *E. cloacae*, *S. marcescens* (8 µg/mL), and *P. aeruginosa* (32 µg/mL). The therapeutic efficacy of PZ-601 against *S. aureus*, *E. faecium*, *E. coli*, and *P. aeruginosa* infections in mice reflected its *in vitro* activity and plasma levels [1115]. The basis for the lowered activity against *P. aeruginosa* was a diminished ability of this carbapenem to ingress via the outer membrane porins and the operation of the MexAB-OprM efflux system, and not as a result of reduced PBP affinity [1116]. Indeed, the notably high affinities of PZ-601 for PBP2a of MRSA and PBP5 of ampicillin-resistant *E. faecium* suggest the importance of the lipophilic C-2 thiazole for binding to these often low-affinity PBPs [1115]. PZ-601 has *in vivo* efficacy against both MRSA and vancomycin-intermediate *S. aureus* (VISA) [1117]. A safety and multiple dose pharmacokinetic study of PZ-60l in healthy male volunteers assessed adverse events, EKGs, and plasma and urinary levels of PZ-601 and its ring-opened metabolite. No serious adverse events were found [1101]. It is currently in Phase 2 clinical trials for the treatment of complicated skin and skin structure infections (cSSSI) [700].

ME-1036 [CAS Reg. No. 432038-96-5] (Forest & Meiji Aeika, formerly CP5609) (**410**) is a parenteral carbapenem with 7-[(3-pyridinium)carbonyl]-substitution to the imidazo [5,1-*b*]thiazole-2-yl group at the C-2-position of the carbapenem [1118]. ME1036 has high affinity for the staphylococcal PBP2a enzyme of MRSA, and this is reflected in potent *in vitro* activity against MRSA. ME1036 was very active against a well-characterized collection of community-acquired MRSA (CA-MRSA) isolates obtained from patients throughout the United States [693]. Moreover, similarly potent *in vitro* activities were observed against penicillin-resistant *S. pneumoniae*, *H. influenzae*, and *E. faecalis*. When tested against the Enterobacteriaceae, ME1036 was more active than ceftriaxone and other broad-spectrum cephalosporins (including ceftaroline), due to its higher level of resistance to hydrolysis by the ESBLs and AmpC β-lactamases of these bacteria [1119]. Like most other carbapenems, ME1036 was inactive against *E. faecium*. ME1036 had no activity against *P. aeruginosa*. SAR analysis of the ME1036 structure showed compounds with potent activities against Gram-positive bacteria (and MRSA in particular) and also penicillin-resistant *S. pneumoniae* (PRSP) [1052,1120,1121]. Members of this series also exhibited potent activity against β-lactamase-negative ampicillin-resistant *H. influenzae* (BLNAR). ME1036 has superior efficacy to vancomycin in models of MRSA infection [1122,1123]. ME1036 is in Phase I evaluation for possible use as a broad-spectrum carbapenem for respiratory infection.

Tebipenem pivoxil   [CAS Reg. No. 161715-24-8], (**411**) formerly L-084 and ME 1211, is an oral carbapenem developed by Wyeth-Lederle (Japan). The prodrug structure is that of a typical acyloxy ester of the C-3 carboxylate of tebipenem (L-036, LJC-11036), the active parent [1124]. The parent has 1-(1,3-thiazolin-2-yl)azetidin-3-ylthio substitution at the C-2-position of a 1β-methylcarbapenem core [1125], and exhibits excellent renal dehydropeptidase stability. Its synthesis uses the condensation of a thiol with an enolphosphate as a key step [1126].

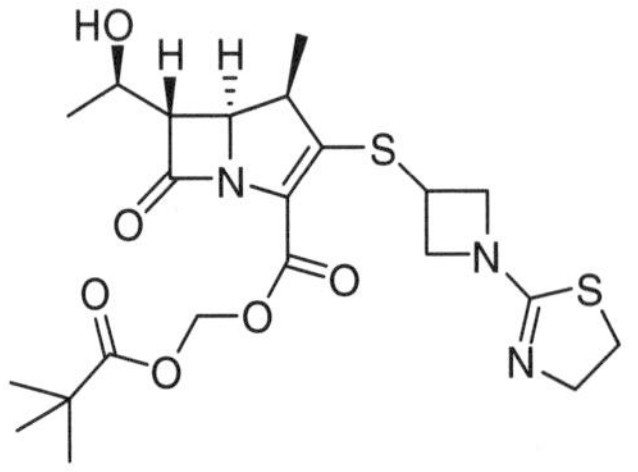

(**411**) Tebipenem pivoxil

Tebipenem pivoxil has high bioavailability in humans. Phase III clinical studies are now being conducted by Meiji Seika Kaisha (Tokyo, Japan) in Japan [775]. A comparison of the *in vitro* activity of tebipenem against multidrug-

resistant *S. pneumoniae* to other β-lactams showed MIC_{90} values for penicillin-susceptible, penicillin-intermediate and penicillin-resistant strains of 0.002, 0.004-0.016, and 0.063 μg/mL, respectively. Tebipenem was bactericidal against the resistant strains [1127]. The crystal structure of the *S. pneumoniae* PBP 2X acyl-enzyme obtained upon reaction with tebipenem emphasizes the importance of the C-2 substituent for PBP recognition [220]. This aspect is discussed in the introductory comments on the evolution of carbapenem SAR. The activity of tebipenem was greater than imipenem, faropenem, and cefdinir against the main causative organisms of respiratory and urinary-tract infections including *S. pneumoniae*, *S. pyogenes*, *H. influenzae*, *K. pneumoniae*, *M. catarrhalis*, and *E. coli* [1127,1128]. Tebipenem pivoxil was active in an animal model of *S. pneumoniae* otitis infection [1129]. The anticipated therapeutic utility of tebipenem is its broad spectrum of activity for outpatient management of infections [883].

5.6. β-Lactamase Inhibitors

The existence among bacteria of a catalytic (that is, enzymatic) mechanism for the deactivation of the β-lactam was recognized even prior to clinical use of the β-lactams as antibacterials [1130]. The mechanism of the deactivation reaction is hydrolysis, exemplified in Fig. 29 with penicillin G, and the name given to the enzyme in this early literature was "penicillinase." As the use of the β-lactams became more widespread, the number of β-lactam-hydrolyzing increased, encompassing new enzymes capable of preferentially hydrolyzing cephalosporins, termed "cephalosporinases." With yet new classes of β-lactams—and the now virtually continuous emergence of not just simply more capable mutant forms of old enzymes, but new enzymes, both "penicillinase" and "cephalosporinase" have been replaced with the more generic (and also more accurate) appellation "β-lactamase" (BLA). Among the first discovered β-lactamases were the "569/H penicillinase" from the Gram-positive *B. cereus* and the "RTEM penicillinase" from the

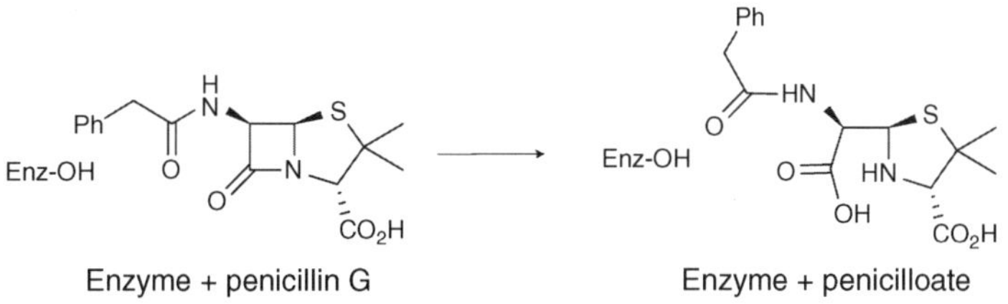

Figure 29. Hydrolysis of penicillin G by "penicillinase".

Gram-negative *E. coli*. Today, the variation among the β-lactamase enzymes arguably rivals in breadth the variation within β-lactam structure. More than 650 β-lactamase variants are now known (see www.lahey.org/studies and http://www.pasteur.fr/ip/easysite/go/03b-00002u-03q/beta-lactamase-enzyme-variants). Consequently, β-lactamase nomenclature has increased to a level of complexity justifying publication of a glossary of modifier origins, synonyms, and abbreviations [247]. The β-lactamases divide between two fundamentally different mechanistic classes. The first of these classes uses nucleophilic serine participation in an acylation, deacylation mechanistic sequence. This mechanism is not mere similarity to the mechanism used by the PBPs in peptidoglycan biosynthesis (transpeptidation) and structural maturation (peptide stem hydrolytic degradation). Rather, the "serine" β-lactamases are ancient evolutionary descendants of the PBPs [98,1131] [226–228,230,235] retaining remarkable points of similarity between the catalytic machinery of the PBP and the β-lactamase active sites. The second class of β-lactamases is the zinc-dependent hydrolases. While the precise mechanism used by these enzymes has yet to yield to intensive mechanistic study [1132–1134], an acyl-enzyme is not a catalytic intermediate [1135]. This distinction (an acyl-enzyme intermediate in serine β-lactamases, but not metallo β-lactamase turnover) is critical with respect to the use of β-lactams in resistant microorganisms due to β-lactamase production.

The serine β-lactamases divide into three subclasses (Molecular class A, C, and D). The large class A (containing the *E. coli* RTEM enzyme, more often referred to now as "TEM") may be further subdivided into Functional Group (substrate) classes (2a–2c, 2e, 2f). In this alternate classification system the class D enzymes comprise Functional Group 2d (Table 3), and the class C (also called AmpC) enzymes comprise Functional Group 1 [257]. The class B metallo-β-lactamases (MBLs) divide into three subclasses, still with some debate as to optimal arrangement of the MBL subclasses [258,259]. The clinical use of the β-lactams has driven the evolutionary development and dissemination of genes of progressively more capable β-lactamases in both the serine- and metallo- β-lactamase subclasses. This progression continues, and directly impacts both the clinical use [400,1136,1137] and drug development [305,1138] of the β-lactam antibacterials. At this time β-lactamase expression is the dominant mechanism—abetted by manipulation of the porin proteins used by bacteria to control small molecule ingress [288], and active transporter catalysis of small molecule egress [1139,1140]—used by Gram-negative pathogens to secure β-lactam resistance [97,98]. Two strategies are used to thwart this resistance. The first strategy is to yet further optimize structure within β-lactam classes that intrinsically evade β-lactamase recognition and hydrolysis. This principle is seen in the design of newer generation cephalosporins, monobactams, and carbapenems. A corollary to this structure–activity design challenge is the simultaneous optimization of structure to also evade the sensing system used by bacteria to detect the presence of β-lactams and thus induction of β-lactamase expression. Cefoxitin (the first-generation cephamycin) and thienamycin (the first carbapenem) have the notable ability to activate, via the very poorly understood β-lactam sensing system, β-lactmase expression [1141]. The structural features of the new β-lactams incorporated with this objective are emphasized in the discussions of the previous sections. The second strategy is the coadministration with the β-lactam antibacterial of a β-lactamase inhibitor. Both strategies are proven effective. While the β-lactams remain the dominant antibacterial in clinical use, both strategies are threatened by the ability of the newest β-lactamases to hydrolyze even the newest generation β-lactams. The mechanisms of β-lactamase inhibition by inactivators, and the role of the β-lactamases in driving β-lactam drug development, are reviewed regularly [241,242,280,1142–1146].

Current commercial inhibitors include clavulanic acid, sulbactam and tazobactam, shown below which are administered in the antibiotic/inhibitor combinations: Augmentin[TM] (amoxicillin/clavulanic acid), Timentin[TM] (ticarcillin/clavulanic acid), Unasyn[TM] (ampicillin/sulbactam), and Zosyn[TM] (piperacillin/tazobactam) (Fig. 30). As discussed below, these combinations are effective against susceptible organisms expressing Ambler class A enzymes, which are the most commonly encountered. These inhibitor/antibiotic combinations are much less effective against class C and class D β-lactamase-producing bacteria (including extended-spectrum β-lactamases), and ineffective against class B metallo-β-lactamase-producing bacteria. Progress toward inhibitors with a broader β-

lactamase-inhibitory spectrum completes this section.

5.6.1. Discovery of Clavulanic Acid The identification of β-lactamase inhibitors for coadministration with a β-lactam, thereby protecting it from hydrolysis by β-lactamase-producing organisms [1147], is the focus of this section. The search for inhibitors has involved both the natural product screening and the creative ingenuity of the medicinal chemist. Clavulanic acid (**412**) is the first, and arguably remains the clinically most important, of the β-lactamase inactivators [1148]. It was isolated, as a β-lactam natural product of unprecedented structure, from a strain of *Streptomyces clavuligerus* using an assay to detect β-lactamase inhibitors by their ability to protect penicillin G from hydrolysis by a β-lactamase-producing strain of *Klebsiella aerogenes* [1149]. In contrast to the sulfur-containing 4-thio-1-azabicyclo[3.2.0] heptane penicillins, clavulanate is a 4-oxa-7-oxo-1-azabicyclo[3.2.0]heptane. A C-2 carboxylate is found in the expected position, and with the expected stereochemistry, but a 6-substituent on the β-lactam ring is lacking and the 3,3-dimethyls of the penicillin are replaced by a (2-hydroxyethylidene) moiety. The juxtaposition of this ethylidene with the oxygen is critical to the mechanism for β-lactamase inactivation. The biosynthesis of clavulanate continues as an active research area [521,1150–1154]. Clavulanic acid is a potent inhibitor of a wide range of clinically important class A β-lactamases, with more modest activity against class D and none against the class B and C enzymes [1155]. Comparative inhibition data for clavulanic acid (against three other inhibitors, discussed below) are shown in

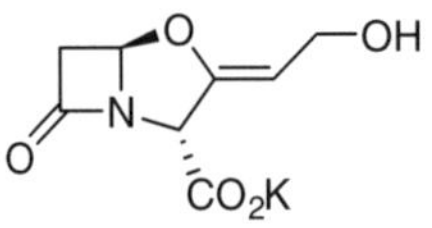

(412) Potassium Clavulanate

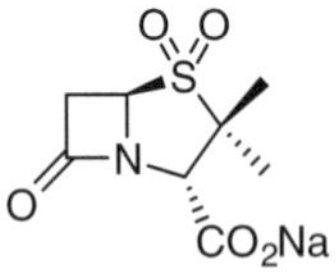

(413) Sulbactam Sodium Salt

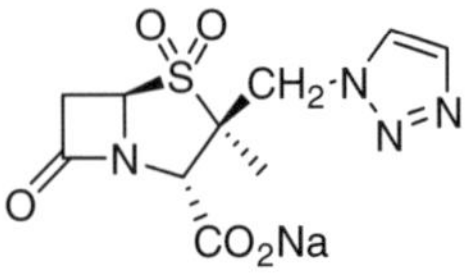

(414) Tazobactam Sodium Salt

Figure 30. Current commercial inhibitors.

Table 15. β-Lactamase Inhibitory Activity [IC$_{50}$ (μg/mL)]^a

Organism	Enzyme Class	Clavulanic Acid (412)	Sulbactam (413)	Tazobactam (414)	BRL-42715 (423)
S. aureus	A	0.063	1.4	0.27	0.016
E. coli (TEM-1)	A	0.055	1.7	0.028	0.002
E. coli (SHV-1)	A	0.035	13.0	0.14	0.001
E. cloacae (P99)	C	>50	5.0	0.93	0.002
E. coli (OXA-1)	D	0.71	2.2	1.1	0.001

^{a} IC$_{50}$ determined after 5 min preincubation of enzyme and inhibitor.

Table 15 [1156]. Clavulanic acid (412) is itself a poor antibacterial, but significantly synergizes the activity of β-lactams against a range of Gram-positive and Gram-negative β-lactamase-producing bacteria [1157]. Comparative synergy data from a study in which low inhibitor concentrations were used are shown in Table 16 [1158]. These data emphasize the differences in spectrum and potency of the four inhibitors featured in this review. Clavulanic acid markedly reduces the MIC of amoxycillin (23) against bacteria with the class A. However, at this inhibitor level, the modest potency of clavulanate against bacteria with class D β-lactamases is not translated into whole-cell activity.

Clavulanate, marketed as Augmentin (potassium clavulanate combined with amoxycillin) and Timentin (potassium clavulanate combined with ticarcillin), has found widespread use (particularly Augmentin for community-acquired respiratory infection), with outstanding efficacy and safety [1159–1162]. Extensive reviews of

the clinical data for clavulanate, published 15 years ago (after more than a decade of Augmentin clinical use) concluded that there was no significant increase in resistance to Augmentin [1163–1165]. Although this conclusion was sustained by subsequent study one decade later, a background continuous increase in β-lactamase resistance prompted clinical entry of a higher dose Augmentin formulation [1159].

5.6.2. Mechanism-Based Inactivation by Clavulanic Acid
Clavulanic acid is a rare example of a drug having ""mechanism-based" (also less correctly called "suicide") enzyme inactivation as its mechanism of action. Due to its clinical importance, and also reflecting its position as a paradigm for other important mechanism-based inactivators of these same serine β-lactamases (see below), the details of the clavulanate inactivation events—this plurality is important—have been thoroughly studied. The pivotal intermediate initiating inactivation is the acyl-enzyme, derived from

Table 16. Amoxycillin MIC (μg/mL) in the Presence of microgram per milliliter of Inhibitor

Organism	Enzyme Class	No Inhibitor	Clavulanic Acid (412)	Sulbactam (413)	Tazobactam (414)	BRL-42715 (423)
P. mirabilis	A	>512	16	64	16	2
E. coli (TEM-1)	A	>512	8	128	8	2
K. pneumoniae	A	256	4	64	16	2
E. cloacae	C	512	>512	256	256	1
E. coli (OXA-1)	D	>512	>512	>512	>512	2

enzyme-catalyzed β-lactam opening by its active site serine. As a result of the *N*-deacylation of β-lactam ring opening, the 5-ethylideneoxazolidine substructure is rendered chemically unstable. While still as the acylenzyme, spontaneous ring opening of this 1,3-oxazolidine occurs, taking advantage of the enolate leaving group. The outcome of these two ring-opening events is an acyclic, conformationally mobile acyl-enzyme. Neither this intermediate (414) nor the ensuing structures resulting from further tautomerization, hydrolysis, and nucleophilic trapping (415–417) is capable of hydrolytic deacylation. The enzyme is inactivated. The salient events of this mechanism are shown in Fig. 31.

Mechanistic study of class A β-lactamases with diminished sensitivity to clavulanate (termed inhibitor-resistant β-lactamases have emphasized the importance of two particular events in the clavulanate inacti-

vation pathways. The first is entry of a second active site nucleophile (as shown for 415) to stabilize the β-lactamase in the inactivated state. In clavulanate-sensitive TEM β-lactamases, this nucleophile is a second active site serine. Mutational loss of this second serine (or perturbation of its reactivity by neighboring residues) attenuates clavulanate inhibition [239,263,264,1166]. Second, flow of a substantial portion of acyl-enzyme into the *trans*-enamine intermediate (373) is preferable, as compared to lower yields of this enamine, or accumulation of the *cis*-enamine [1167–1169]. Simple mutations that incrementally decrease the binding affinity of clavulanate also confer inhibitor-resistance [238]. Despite extensive structural modifications, especially to the oxygen of the allylic alcohol, no semisynthetic clavulanate derivative has been identified as an improved structure.

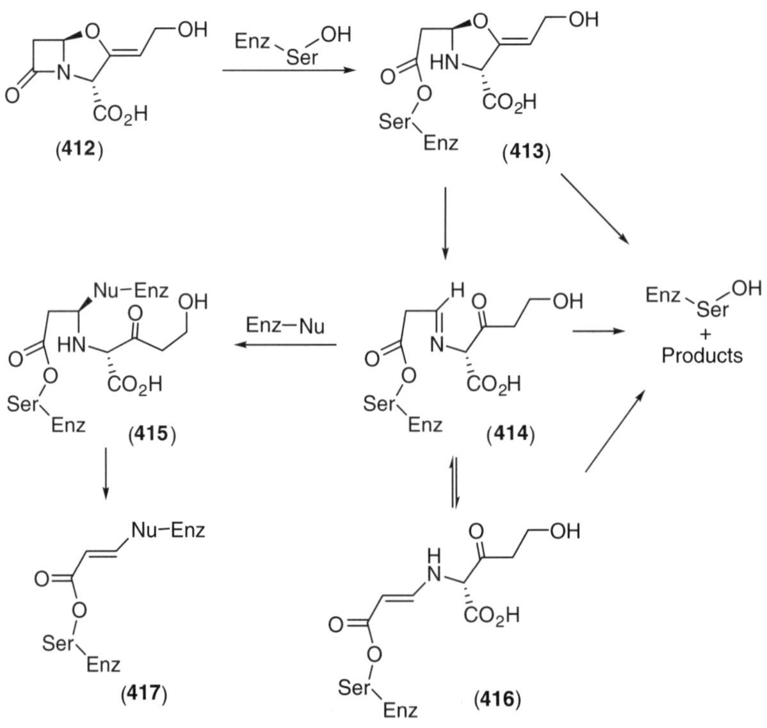

Figure 31. Mechanism of action of clavulanic acid.

The continued entry, and subsequent distribution, of increasingly more efficacious β-lactamases to the Gram negative pathogens is driving evaluation of further "unorthodox" experimental evaluation of clavulanate-β-lactam synergy pairings, especially with fourth-generation (ampC-resistant) cephalosporins [1170]. Such a pairing is based on possible therapeutic advantage, rather than advantageous melding of intellectual property. Clavulanate is being examined more broadly. *Mycobacterium tuberculosis* is highly β-lactam resistant due to constitutive expression of a chromosomal and highly capable ESBL β-lactamase [1171]. However, this β-lactamase retains a moderate level of clavulanate sensitivity and structure-based design from structure of the clavulanate-inactivated enzyme may lead to efficacious β-lactam-β-lactamase combination therapy for tuberculosis [1171–1173]. Augmentin was efficacious in an experimental model of murine pneumonia caused by a nonhyperproducing, cefoxitin-resistant *E. coli* clinical isolate [1174].

5.6.3. Penam Sulfones

The penam sulfones are semisynthetic derivatives of 6-aminopenicillanic acid. These structures were conceptualized at Pfizer [1175,1176] at virtually the same time as clavulanate was discovered. Although the penam sulfones share structural (absence of a C-6 substitutent) and mechanistic similarities to clavulanate (as briefly discussed below), apart from these similarities there exist key biological differences between the clavulanate and the penam sulfone classes.

Sulbactam Brominative diazotization of 6-aminopenicillanic acid 6-APA (**4**), followed by thioether oxidation to the sulfone, give 6,6-dibromopenicillanic acid sulfone (**418**). Reductive debromination by catalytic hydrogenation provided sulbactam (**413**) [1177]. Sulbactam is an irreversible inhibitor of several β-lactamases by a mechanism that strongly parallels that of clavulanic acid. Following acylation of the β-lactamase, intramolecular opening of the thiazolidine dioxide generates an imine intermediate upon loss of the sulfinic acid. Tautomerization of this imine gives an enamine-containing acyl-enzyme, again analogous to what is seen with clavulanate. Sulbactam is a modest inhibitor of the class A enzymes (Table 15) compared to clavulanic acid [1168,1178,1179] but is an improved inhibitor against class C β-lactamases, although at levels not considered to be of clinical value. The levels of synergy achieved against whole bacteria with sulbactam (Table 16) reflect its poorer potency against the class A enzymes. Synergistic combination with ampicillin (**21**) led to a 1:1 formulation, marketed as Unasyn for parenteral use [1180,1181]. Poor absorption of sulbactam (**416**) precludes use of this combination by the oral route. For this reason, the synthesis of the mutual prodrug sultamicillin (**419**) was undertaken [1182,1183]. After absorption from the gut this double ester undergoes rapid cleavage by nonspecific esterases, to give good serum levels of both ampicillin (**21**) and sulbactam (**413**). Sulbactam has also been coformulated with a third-generation cephalosporin for parenteral use. Reviews of the properties of these sulbactam-β-lactam synergistic combinations note the continuing efficacy of these combinations (similar to clavulanate) in both nosocomial and community respiratory and skin infection [1184,1185]. One point of difference between sulbactam and clavulanate is the intrinsic activity of sulbactam against *A. baumannii* [1186], a Gram-negative bacterium that has emerged suddenly as a highly drug-resistant human pathogen [837,1187]. Dissipation of this intrinsic activity has occurred, however, in more recent *A. baumannii* isolates that are highly β-lactam resistant due to carbapenemase expression [1188]. Sulbactam combinations have not demonstrated strong selective pressures for extended-spectrum β-lactamase-producing Enterobacteriaceae and vancomycin-resistant enterococci [1184,1189]. A second difference is the poorer ability of sulbactam to activate the ampC sensor pathway detecting the presence of β-lactams [1184]. This is a desirable advantage, as activation of this pathway induces β-lactamase expression. Despite the structural similarity, the intrinsic ability of the penam sulfone class to penetrate to the Gram-negative periplasm is inferior to clavulanate [1190].

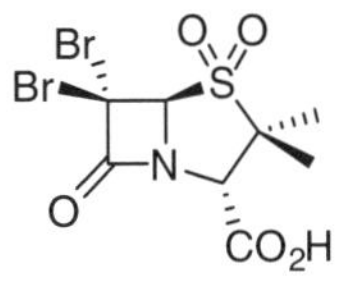

(418) 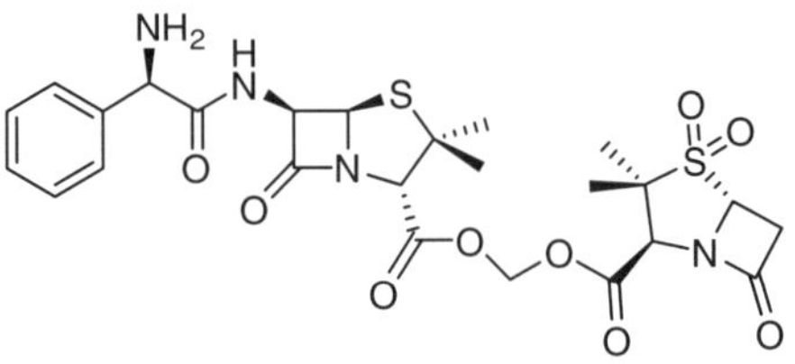   (419) Sultamicillin 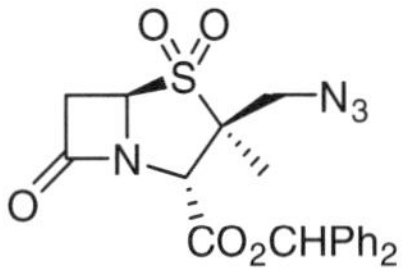   (420)

Tazobactam The spare structure of sulbactam opened the possibility that advantageous substitution might further improve the efficacy of the penam sulfone class as β-lactamase inhibitors [1191,1192]. Substitution to the 2-methyl group, exploiting the azide reactivity of 2-β-azidomethylpenam (**420**) toward alkyne dipolar cycloaddition, gave the 2β-(triazolyl)methylpenam series with potent β-lactamase inhibitory activity. This class is represented in the clinic by tazobactam (**414**) having an unsubstituted triazole, in combination with piperacillin (**36**) as a parenteral formulation [1193,1194]. Tazobactam, synthesized by reaction of (**420**) with vinyl acetate, was selected on the basis of its potency and ease of preparation. Its mechanism is analogous to sulbactam, as supported by chemical solvolysis studies [1195]. Tazobactam is, however, more potent than sulbactam (Table 15) with good activity against the clinically important TEM-1 class A enzymes. Mechanistic enzymology to ascertain the basis for this improvement continues [1166,1196], as well as to understand the basis for β-lactamase resistance to tazobactam, as is seen with the OXA class D enzymes [1197]. While tazobactam shows a modest level of activity against the class C enzymes [1198], which are not inhibited by clavulanic acid, this activity is not clinically meaningful [1194]. In combination with amoxicillin, levels of synergism similar to those of clavulanic acid are observed for bacteria producing class A β-lactamases

(Table 16). The piperacillin-tazobactam combination has excellent safety and tolerability, and with its continued efficacy (including as an improved formulation) it remains a reliable choice for the empirical treatment of moderate-to-severe nosocomial infection [1194].

5.6.4. 6-Heteroarylmethylene Penems
Notwithstanding the features of low resistance induction, safety, and efficacy, the poorer activity of both the clavulanate and the penam sulfone combinations against bacteria that are β-lactam-resistant due to the presence of either a class C or a class D β-lactamase is a significant shortcoming. Efforts toward β-lactamase inhibitors encompassing the class C and class D serine β-lactamase classes have focused primarily on 6-methylidene penems having (**421**) as a generic structure [1199]. The promise of this class was established from initial studies with SB-206999z (**422**) [1200] and especially BRL-42715 (**423**) [1158]. Continued synthetic activities established the 6-methylidene as the key functional group conferring mechanism-based β-lactamase inhibition to this class, but the stereochemistry and heteroaryl substituent of the methylidene substituent as key to the biological activity. Considerable effort since these first structures toward both empirical, and structure-based, identification of the optimal bicyclic and tricyclic heteroarene [257]. Robust synthetic routes to this class are disclosed [1199,1201,1202].

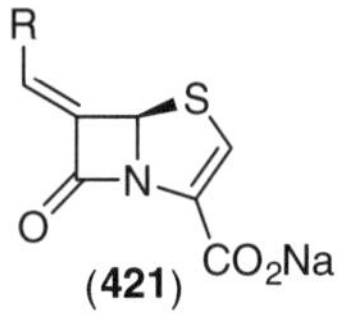

(421) 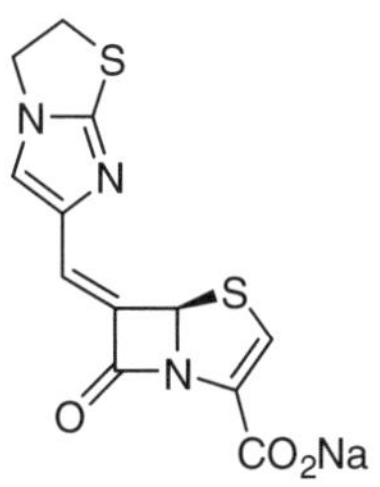   (422) SB-206999Z 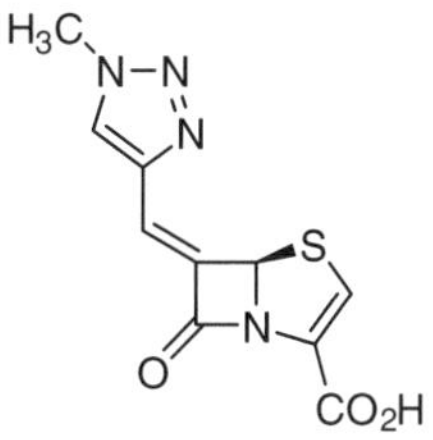   (423) BRL-42715

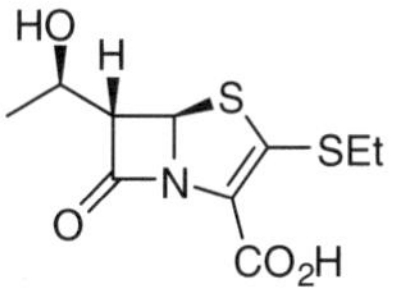

(424) 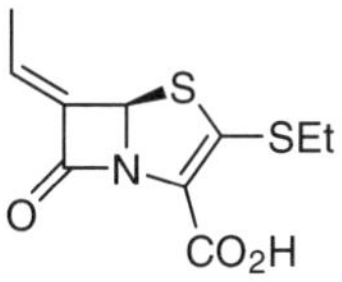   (425)

Sch-29482 (424) was reported to inhibit class C and class D β-lactamases [1203]. Relatively little data are available for 6-(1-hydroxyethyl)-substituted penems, despite the proven versatility of this substituent in other classes. Dehydration of (424) gave the *E*- and *Z*-isomers of the 6-ethylidenepenem (425). Both isomers are potent broad-spectrum β-lactamase inhibitors, although with much weaker antibacterial activity than that of the parent penem [1199]. Extensive structure–activity studies involving modification at both the C-2 and the C-8 positions are described [1204].

From these studies the *Z*-triazolylmethylenepenem (423, BRL-42715) was selected for further evaluation. BRL-42715 potently inhibits a broad range of β-lactamases, including the plasmid-mediated class A TEM, SHV and staphylococcal; plasmid-mediated class D OXA, as well as the chromosomally mediated *Bacteroides*, *Enterobacter*, *Citrobacter*, *Serratia*, *Morganella*, *Escherichia*, *Klebsiella*, and *Proteus* sp. enzymes [1156,1205]. Nearly all of these bacteria are brought into a susceptible range of $\leq 8\,\mu g/mL$ upon synergistic pairing of BRL-42715 with amoxicillin [1206]. BRL-42715, included as a comparator in Tables 15 and 16, reveal BRL-42715 (423) as a more potent inhibitor than clavulanic acid (412), sulbactam (413), and tazobactam (414) against classes A, C, and D enzymes. This potency is translated into impressive syner-

gism in whole-cell assays. Its Gram-negative penetration is comparable to the penam sulfones, but is less than clavulanate [1190]. BRL-42715 is a substrate, and not an inactivator, of the metallo-β-lactamases [1207]. It is not a dehydropeptidase substrate [1208].

Detailed kinetics confirming the efficiency of inactivation have been described for a number of β-lactamases [1207,1209,1210]. The mechanism by which the acyl-enzyme competitively transforms to a new and more stable acyl-enzyme [1200] has been studied extensively, confirming a novel acyl-enzyme rearrangement to the dihydrothiazepine (387) [1211–1214]. Despite its impressive inhibitor profile, development of BRL-42715 was terminated.

The first BRL-42715 successors were imidazolyl-substituted 6-methylidenepenems (Figs 32 and 33) having excellent *in vitro* activity against both class A and class C enzymes [1215,1216]. 2-Benzylimidazol-5-yl derivative (426) is a potent inhibitor of both the class A TEM-1 ($IC_{50} = 0.4\,nM$) and the class C AmpC ($IC_{50} = 2\,nM$). The imidazole moiety of these structures was succeeded by a series of [5] and [5,6] bicyclic-fused azole (particularly pyrazole, imidazole) congeners, closely related to SB-206999z (422). Compounds (435) and (436) have nearly identical *in vitro* activities (approximately $1\,nM\ IC_{50}$ values against both the TEM-1 and the AmpC enzymes). Synergistic activity of these two

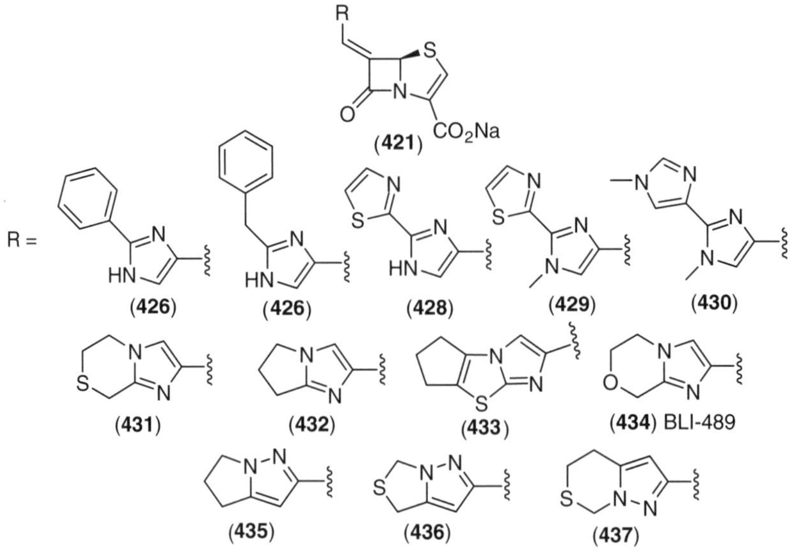

Figure 32. Bicyclic-fused azole.

with piperacillin was excellent [1216]. The *E*-diastereomer of (**435**) was much less active. An initial disclosure indicates this class also to have activity against the OXA-1 class D β-lactamase, also via the acyl-enzyme rearrangement mechanism [1217]. While compounds (**436**) and (**437**) showed identical k_{inact} rate constants (of $0.1\,s^{-1}$) with this enzyme, the affinity of (**437**) for the enzyme ($K_i = 12$ nM) was fourfold smaller than that of (**436**). Nonetheless, the two structures were equipotent (each was evaluated at 4 mg/L) at reducing the MIC values (from 1024 mg/L to 2 mg/L) of an OXA-1-expressing *E. coli* [1217]. In this same assay, tazobactam, a much poorer class D inhibitor [1197], was much less active

(MIC reduction to 512 mg/L at 4 mg/L tazobactam).

Among the [5,6]-fused bicyclic structures, BLI-489 (**434**) was a potent and broad-spectrum inhibitor (IC$_{50}$ TEM-1 = 0.4 nM; IC$_{50}$ AmpC = 2 nM) and showed the anticipated piperacillin synergy against β-lactamase-producing bacteria [1218]. As a continuation of this series the Wyeth group described the synthesis and biological activities of several 5,5,6-fused tricyclic heterocycles substituting at the 6-methylidene of the penem (**438**), (**439**), and (**440**). These structures likewise synergize piperacillin activity against class A and class C β-lactamase producers [1219]. Optimal activity within the tricyclic class was

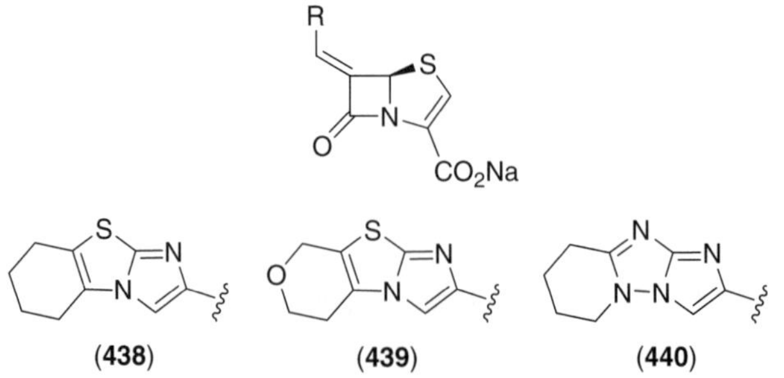

Figure 33. 5,5,6-Fused tricyclic heterocycles substituting at the 6-methylidene of the penem.

suggested, on the basis of computational modeling, to derive in part from hydrophobic subsite interactions attained after rearrangement to the 4,7-dihydro-1,4-thiazepine [1220].

5.6.5. Carbapenems

Many of the carbapenems described in Section 5.5 are potent β-lactamase inhibitors with a spectrum that includes the class C enzymes not inhibited by clavulanic acid [1221]. The mechanistic basis for this inhibition also involves formation of a stabilized acyl-enzyme, following carbapenem acylation of the β-lactamase serine, but via stabilization of a different sort than that seen for the clavulanate/penam sulfone- and methylidenepenem-derived stable acyl-enzymes. The molecular basis driving the formation of stable carbapenem-derived acyl-enzymes likely originates in their unprecedented 6α-hydroxyethyl side chain. Transfer of this motif to penams (where in contrast to the above inhibitors, β-lactam ring opening gives a stable thiazolidine substructure) gives an acyl-enzyme behavior suggestive of a mispositioning of the hydrolytic water in the β-lactamase active site (of all three serine classes) induced by this unusual side chain [1222–1225]. A possible consequence of the longer-lived acyl-enzyme is opportunity for tautomeric rearrangement, first suggested by Knowles [1226] to correspond to Δ^1-pyrroline (441) formation. More recent structural study with the class A SHV enzyme indicates two different positions for the acyl-enzyme in the inactivated enzyme, as well as direct contact of the side-chain alcohol with the hydrolytic water molecule [1227–1229]. A complementary approach to the challenge of understanding how carbapenems interact with β-lactamases is comparison of the active site of a carbapenemase to cognate β-lactamases incapable of carbapenem hydrolysis. An initial comparison of the OXA-24 carbapenemase to noncabapenem hydrolyzing OXA β-lactamases is given by Santillana et al. [1230]. At this time limitations on the level of carbapenem that is used, imposed by their potent antibacterial activities, have precluded the demonstration of significant synergy. Accordingly, no carbapenem has progressed as a β-lactamase inactivator for the purpose of β-lactam synergy.

A series of tricyclic carbapenems ("trinems") were potent inhibitors of the class A and C enzymes, exemplified by LK-157 (442) showing an IC_{50} against the TEM-1 enzyme of 0.6 nM and an IC_{50} against the class C AmpC enzyme of 62 nM [1231]. The trinem structure is an essential aspect of the structure–activity relationship.

5.6.6. Structurally Modified Penams, Penam Sulfones, and Cephem Sulfones

6β-Bromopenicillanic acid (443), often called brobactam, was described as a β-lactamase inhibitor as early as 1978 [1232]. Extensive studies of its mechanism of action [1233] gave powerful evidence for an active-site serine-bound dihydrothiazine (446) in the inactivated enzyme [1234–1236], as a result of a mechanistically similar transformation as is seen from the methylidenepenem-derived acyl-enzymes. Dihydrothiazine (446) has a similar enamine moiety as is seen in the transiently inhibited species (416) from clavulanate and the penam sulfones. Despite the demonstration of good synergistic properties and a favorable pharmacokinetic profile in humans [1237], brobactam did not found clinical application. The inactivation behavior of 6β-iodopenicillanic acid (444) is similar to brobactam [1238–1240], whereas the chloro analog (445) is less potent [1241]. Stimulated by the discoveries of sulbactam (413), tazobactam (414), and brobactam (443), further modification of the penam nucleus has provided a large number of β-lactamase inhibitors. Tables 17 and 18 exemplify these inhibitors.

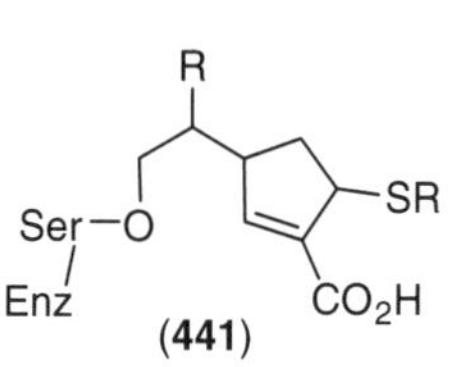

(441) 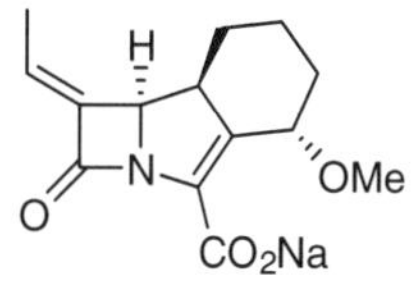   (442) LK-157

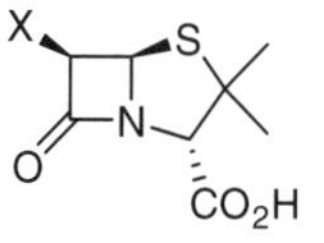

(443) X = Br
(444) X = I
(445) X = Cl   (446)

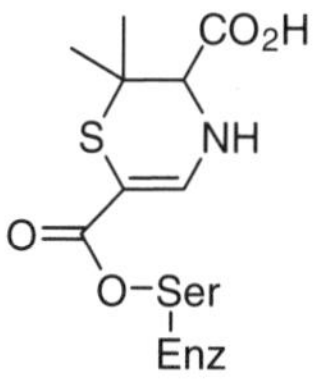

Table 17. Penam Inhibitors of β-Lactamases

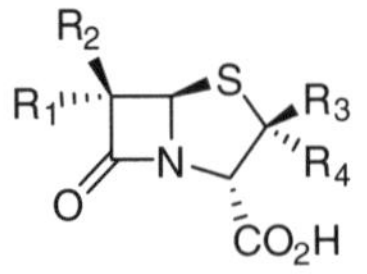

R_1	R_2	R_3	R_4	Reference
H	Br	CH_2X $X = F, N_3, OAc$	Me	[1242]
H	$(CF_3SO_2)_2N$	OMe, SCN	Me	[1243]
H	$HOSO_2NH$	Me	Me	[1244]
H	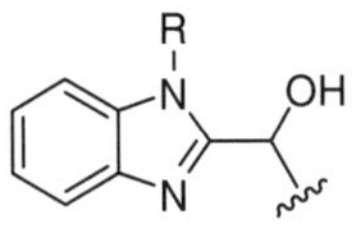	Me	Me	[1245]
	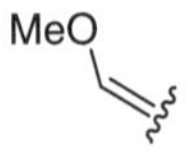	Me	Me	[1246]
	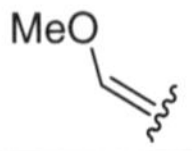	Me	Me	[1247]

β-Lactamase inhibitory properties have been reported for a large number of other β-lactam-containing structures including cephems and monocyclic β-lactams [1142,1248]. Among the more recent reports are those of activity for 7α-(1-hydroxyethyl)-cephems (including the sulfoxides and sulfones) and oxacephems (**447**) bearing electron-withdrawing groups at the 3-position [1249]. Activity has also been reported for other cephems bearing nonclassical 7-substituents such as the 7-allenylidene (**448**) and alkylidene (**449**) cephems [1250].

Buynak et al. have evaluated the fusion of the 6-methylidenepenam and penam sulfone β-lactamase inhibitor structural motifs. These structures (**450**), (**451**), and (**452**) represent potent, broad-spectrum β-lactamase inhibitors at the nanomolar level against all three (A, C, and D) serine β-lactamase classes [1146].

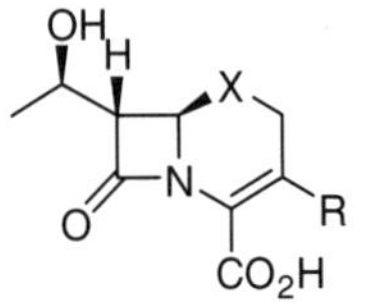

(**447**) X = S, SO, SO$_2$, O
R = electron withdrawing group

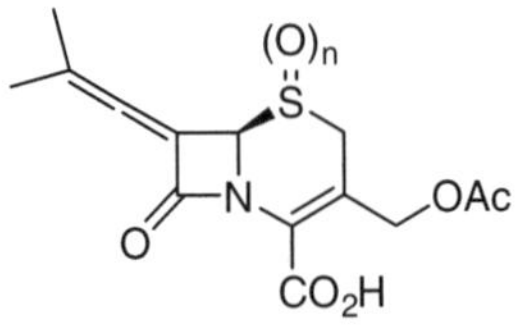

(**448**) n = 0, 2

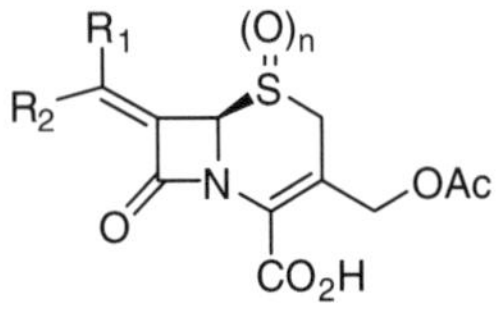

(**449**) n = 0, 2

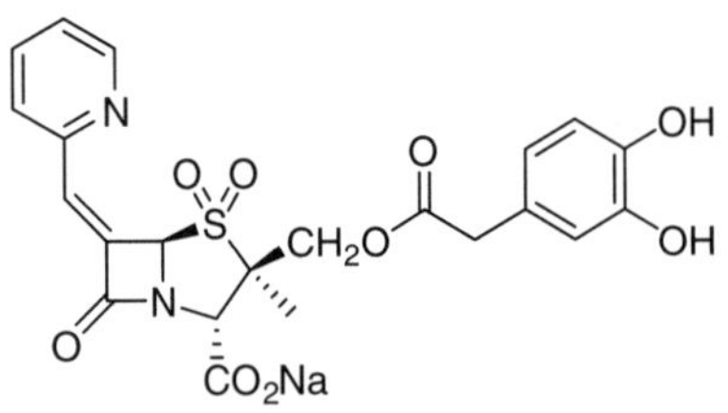

(**450**) LN-1-255

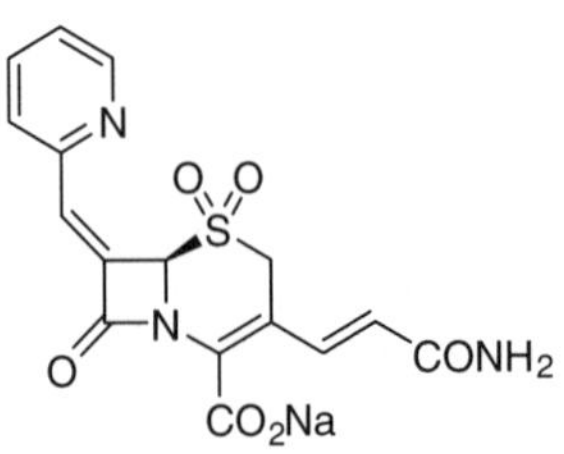

(**451**)

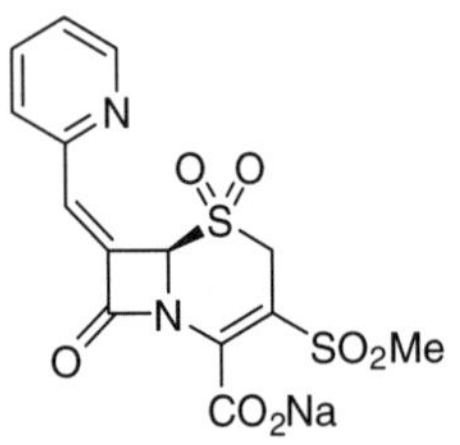

(**452**)

Table 18. Penam Sulfone Inhibitors of β-Lactamases

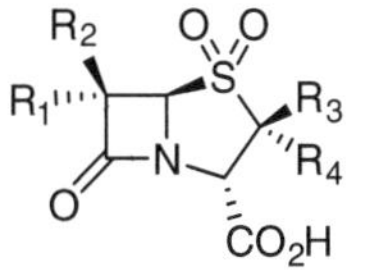

R_1	R_2	R_3	R_4	Reference(s)
H	H	CH$_2$Cl	Me	[1251]
H	CF$_3$SO$_2$NH	Me	Me	[1252]
H	PhCH(OH)	Me	Me	[1253]
H	X = F, OH, OAc 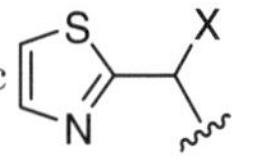 (thiazole with CH(X))	Me	Me	[1254]
H	H	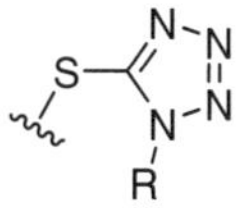 S-triazole R = Me, Ph	Me	[1255]
H	H	CH$_2$SCN	Me	[1255]
H	H	 (CH=CH-CN)	Me	[1256]
H	RCOCH$_2$ R = Me, CH$_2$OPh, CN, CO$_2$Et	Me	Me	[1257]
	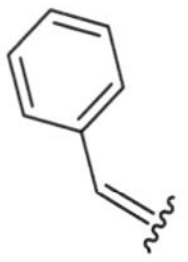 (styryl)	Me	Me	[1258]
	Heterocyle 	Me	Me	[1254,1259]
	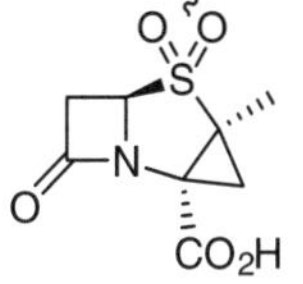 (spiro penam sulfone)			[1260,1261]

Buynak also described 6-(mercaptomethyl) penicillinate the synthesis and β-lactamase inhibitory activity of four (**453**), (**454**), (**455**), and (**456**). These penicillins include both C-6 stereoisomers as well as the sulfide and sulfone oxidation states of the penam thiazolidine sulfur. These (mercaptomethyl) penicillinates are shown to inactivate both metallo- and serine-β-lactamases and to

display synergism with piperacillin against β-lactamase producing strains, including a strain of *P. aeruginosa* [1262]. LN-1-255 (**450**) is a methylidene penam sulfone having a 2′-catechol (siderophore-like) substituent. LN-1-255 synergizes piperacillin against SHV class A IRT and ESBL β-lactamases, and synergizes both ceftazidime (**96**) and cefpirome (**105**) against cephalosporin ESBL and SME-1 carbapenemase-expressing bacteria. The structure of the SHV-inhibited β-lactamase shows movement of the acyl-enzyme carbonyl out of the oxyanion hole [1263].

Ro 48-1220 (**457**) is a potent inhibitor of group 2b and 2be β-lactamases. Its inhibitory activity against TEM-type enzymes was comparable to that of clavulanic acid and tazobactam but was less potent against SHV-type β-lactamases. Ro 48-1220 protected ceftriaxone and ceftazidime from the hydrolytic activity of the group 2be plasmid-mediated β-lactamases [1256,1264]. Ro 48-1220 was at least 15 times more effective than tazobactam against the class C enzymes.

In another report, two new series of C-3 modified penicillin sulfones, having either a simple methylene group (i.e., a homolog) or an exocyclic unsaturation between the thiazolidine ring and the C-3 carboxylate. Homolog (**458**) is 10-fold more active against a class C β-lactamase than sulbactam. By contrast, the exocyclic C-3 unsaturated compound (**459**) is less active [1192].

Class A-class C mechanism-based β-lactamase inhibitors were designed on the basis of the intermediacy of an oxacarbenium species with the potential to cross-linking with amino acids residues in the active site. The spirocyclopropylpenam sulfones (**460a**) and (**460b**) were potent inhibitors of TEM-1 and AmpC enzymes with good MIC_{50} in combination with cefotaxime and piper-acillin [1265].

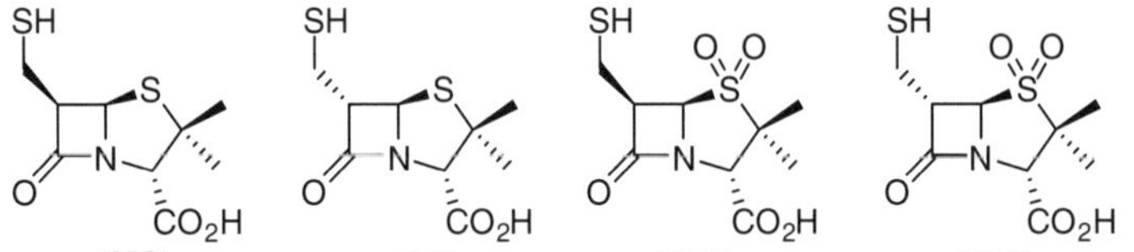

(**453**)   (**454**)   (**455**)   (**456**)

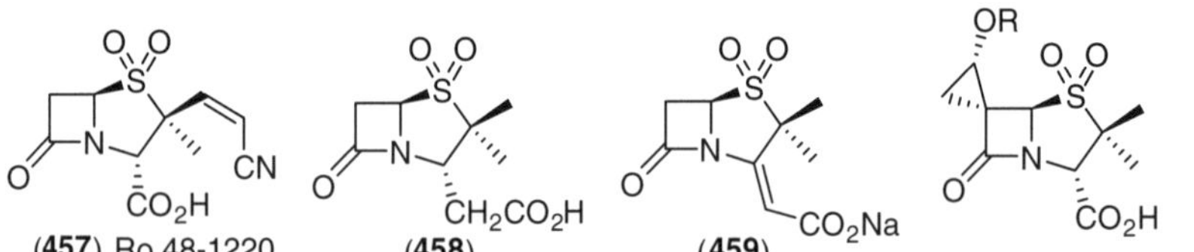

(**457**) Ro 48-1220   (**458**)   (**459**)

(**460a**) R = TBDMS
(**460b**) R = Cyclohexyl

5.6.7. Structurally Modified Oxapenems

The oxapenems AM-112 (**461**) and AM-113 (**462**) have high *in vitro* activity against penicillin and methicillin-resistant bacteria, including a favorable MIC for AM-113 against MRSA, *Enterococctts* sp., *Klebsiella* and anaerobes. Class C and D enzymes were very susceptible to inhibition by AM-112 [1266]. Two other oxapenems, AM-114 (**463**) and AM-115 (**464**) displayed potent activity—comparable to clavulanate—against class A enzymes. Activity against the class C and class D enzymes was similar to that of AM-112 (**461**) and AM-113 (**462**), and again was superior to clavulanate [1267].

Stabilization of the oxapenem ring system by the introduction of bulky 2-substituents has allowed the demonstration of β-lactamase inhibition for members of this highly ring strained class of β-lactam derivatives. Activity has been demonstrated for the 2-*tert*-butyloxapenems (**465**) [1268] and (**466**) [1269], and the 2-isopropyloxapenem (**467**) [1270]. Oxapenem (**467**) is a potent inhibitor of the class C enzymes.

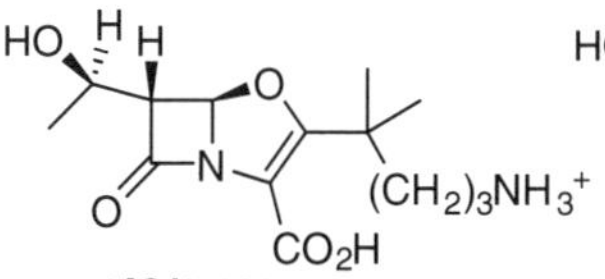

(461) AM-112 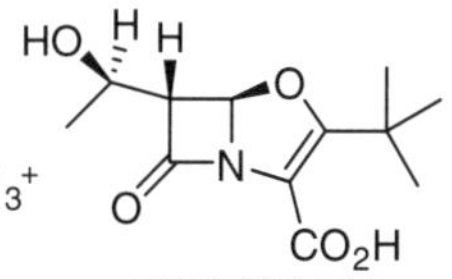   (462) AM-113 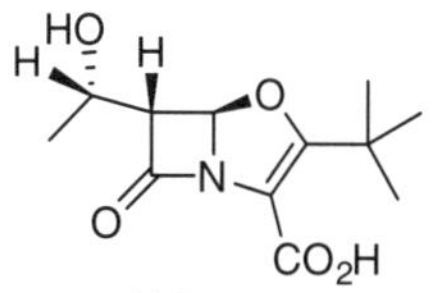   (463) AM-114

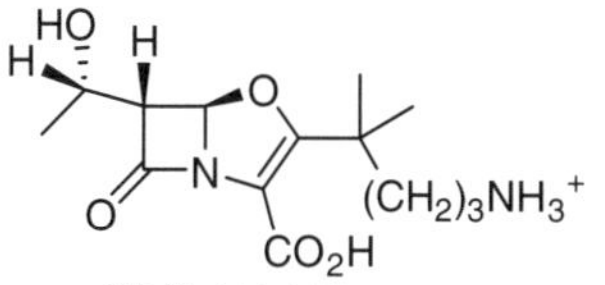

(464) AM-115 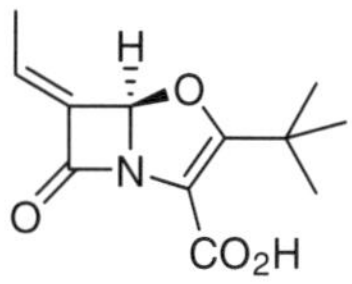   (465) 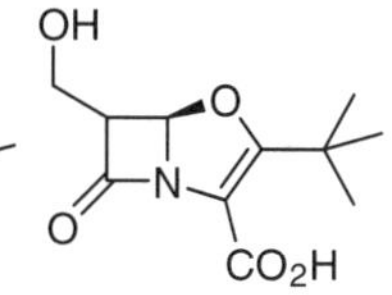   (466)

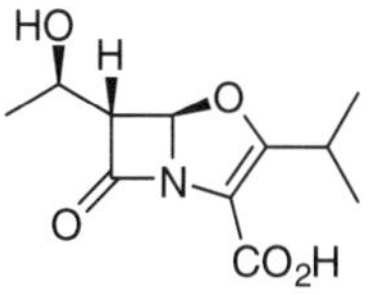

(467) 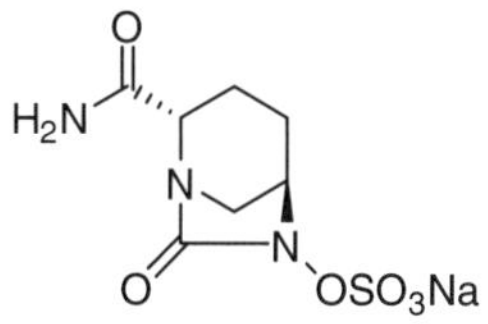   (468) NXL104 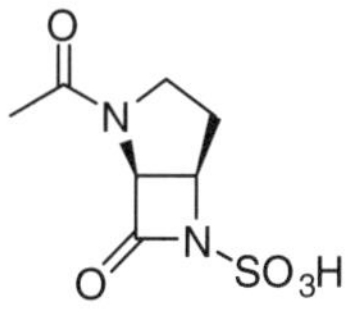   (469)

5.6.8. A Bicyclic Lactam Inhibitor of the β-Lactamases The non-β-lactam inhibitor NXL104 (**468**, formerly AVE1330A) is in clinical evaluation as a β-lactamase inhibitor against class A and class C enzymes, including ESBL. NXL104 (**468**) is a bridged diazabicyclo [3.2.1]bicyclooctanone that inhibits β-lactamases through formation of a stable covalent carbamoyl linkage [1271]. When tested in combination with ceftazidime and cefotaxime against Enterobacteriaceae with CTX-M ESBL, it showed a 4–8000-fold potentiation, reducing the MIC values for these cephalosporins to ≤1 mg/L for all organisms, irrespective of CTX-M type [1272]. Against P99, NXL104 showed stronger inhibition than tazobactam, with an $IC_{50} > 60$-fold lower than that of tazobactam, while clavulanic acid was inactive. The combination of NXL-104 (**468**) with an oxyimino cephalosporin may represent a powerful combination against ESBL-producing and carbapenemase-producing Enterobacteriaceae, bacteria that are not within the oxyimino cephalosporin *in vitro* spectrum of activity for this cephalosporin [1273].

5.6.9. Monobactam Inhibitors of the β-Lactamases The monobactam structure offers relative stability toward both serine (especially

Class C) and metallo-β-lactamases [867]. Selective and potent inhibitors of class C enzymes have been reported for a series of bridged monobactams (**469**). These bridged monobactams yield stable acyl-enzyme intermediates with the Class C β-lactamases, as a result of displacement of the hydrolytic water from the active site [1274,1275]. A second monobactam (Syn2190, having a 1,5-dihydroxy-4-pyridinone side chain) was also reported as a Class C inhibitor that showed excellent synergy with antibacterial β-lactams [1276]. While occasional mechanistic studies have followed up on these reports [1277], there is no evidence of interest in taking these structures forward as clinical β-lactamase inhibitors. These may have, however, value in *in vitro* AmpC ESBL detection [1278].

The stability of the monobactam structure toward metallo-β-lactamase-catalyzed hydrolysis is a consequence of nonproductive binding within the active site [1279]. Bulgecin, a sulfonylated GlcNAc derivative, inhibits the two-zinc (but not one-zinc) form of the BceII MBL. It is not an inhibitor of the single zinc ImiS enzyme, and is a noncompetitive inhibitor of the L1 MBL [1280]. The outcome for these three MBLs is interpreted in terms of the coordination structure of the zinc-sulfonate complex [1280].

5.6.10. Nonlactam Inhibitors of the β-Lactamases

Three well-known classes of non-β-lactam inhibitors are known [257,1145]. The first of these classes use a boronate functional group [1281] as a mimetic for the deacylation transition state of the serine acyl-enzyme [255,1282,1283]. A series of acyl phosph(on)ates behave similarly, although some of these do engage the active site serine in covalent chemistry [1284–1286]. While these two classes have proven value to the understanding of serine β-lactamase mechanism, neither has the drug-likeness nor has the potency for clinical efficacy.

The third class is thiol inhibition of the metallo-β-lactamases. The sensitivity of the zinc active site of the MBLs is long recognized [1144]. With the mobilization of MBLs to plasmids, first observed twenty years ago, the increased distribution and catalytic ability of the MBLs have made the MBL resistance mechanism a particular concern in relation to future antimicrobial chemotherapy [1287]. Despite the shortcomings of the thiol, extensive efforts to incorporate a zinc-interacting thiol for the purpose of MBL inhibition have been described [1288–1292], including thiol incorporation into a penicillin core to attain pan-class β-lactamase inhibition [1262,1293]. The mechanism for thiolate inhibition of the MBL can be surprisingly complex [1294]. Several structures of thiol-inhibited MBLs are available [1295], including in some cases evidence that some thiol inhibitors do not interact directly with the zinc [1296]. The driving force behind these efforts is the expectation that the union of detailed mechanistic [1134,1135] and structural study will enable the structure-based design of efficacious thiol inhibitors. The complementary strategy of dynamic combinatorial assessment of thiol strategy also has notable promise [1296,1297]. Recognizing the stability limitation of the thiol, efforts toward identifying alternative functionalities (such as the 2,4-pyridinedicarboxylate) have been reported [1298].

6. THE β-LACTAM FUTURE

Over eighty years have elapsed since Fleming's inference of the existence of potent antimicrobial natural products. The innovative discoveries in microbiology, biochemistry, and chemistry that have followed his observation have yielded generations of β-lactam structures, each as life-saving chemotherapy. Revelation of the β-lactam subclasses over time has occurred in stages. The discovery of the cephalosporins followed the discovery of the penicillins, and were in turn followed by a paroxysm of β-lactam discovery: the nearly simultaneous appearance, some thirty-five years ago, of the cephamycin, carbapenem, monobactam, and clavulanate classes. These natural products were complemented by chemical ingenuity. The penem class as a hybrid structure, imbuing both penicillin and cephalosporin substructure, is one example. Yet the genius of the penems is not merely the conception of their structure, but no less the ability to realize these structures (as well as other antibiotics) through the power of organic synthesis [1299]. Other examples of spectacular innovation in the medicinal chemistry of the β-lactams include the discovery of the penam sulfones as clavulanate mimetics, the discovery of the oxyimino side chain for the cephalosporins, and the process-scale asymmetric synthesis of the carbapenems. The recent history of the medicinal chemistry of the β-lactams has been the creative interchange of the structural concepts that have emerged from Nature, and from the mind of the medicinal chemist, among all of these β-lactam subclasses. These efforts have yielded successive generations of β-lactam structure, preserving the place of the β-lactams as antibacterials of exquisite potency and efficacy.

Nonetheless, as is evident from the analyses of the individual β-lactam subclasses presented in this chapter, essentially all of the obvious interchanges have now been made. The evolutionary history of some β-lactam subclasses may be argued as nearly complete. If this conclusion concerning evolutionary history were also true of the bacteria that are human pathogens, the possible passing of the β-lactam era would be of small concern. But this is certainly not the case. Bacteria have adapted with alacrity to successive β-lactam structure (and to the structures of other antibacterial classes) with an array of effective resistance mechanisms, and as a result the future of antibacterial chemotherapy may be a future of crisis [1300]. Does sufficient vitality remain within the β-lactam structure to forestall this event?

The introduction to this chapter claimed the history of the β-lactams as a history of sustained accomplishment, engendering sustained optimism for their continued central place in the chemotherapy of bacterial infection. We reiterate this belief, while recognizing that its realization will require both sustained investment in the basic research and sustained perspicacity in applied research toward new β-lactam structures. The essential interconnection of these two enterprises cannot be overemphasized [1301,1302]. We know astonishingly little, for example, of the detailed molecular mechanisms involved in sensing β-lactam structure leading to resistance mechanism expression, nor of the basis by which the β-lactam-inhibited PBP initiates bacteriocidal events. We are just beginning to understand the structure and regulation of the protein hyperstructures of bacterial growth and cell division. While design within the framework of existing β-lactam structure may not coincide with substantial improvement relative to these opportunities (the optimization of substructure to minimize β-lactamase induction in Gram-negative pathogens is already an important empirical design criterion), better understanding of these pathways may identify drug targets synergistic with PBP inhibition by the β-lactams. The use of the expansive breadth of β-lactam structure already in existence, for the purpose of nuanced revelation of the role(s) of particular proteins and enzymes sensitive to the β-lactams, has hardly begun [1303].

Nor should the absence of discovery of new β-lactam structure from Nature over the past 35 years be interpreted as indicating that all of the β-lactam antibiotic classes are already discovered. We are only now unraveling the organization and regulation of the gene clusters expressing the synthases of secondary metabolite biosynthesis [1304,1305]. There is every likelihood that the genetic reprogramming of these clusters, or the epigenetic control of gene expression within these clus-

ters [1306,1307] will yield new β-lactam scaffolds. Successful medicinal chemistry is always the story of perseverance despite setback, and the story of unwavering focus on unmet medical needs. The β-lactams were central to the antibacterial chemotherapy of the past. We can be certain of the continuing medical need for antibacterial discovery, and certain (if neither perseverance nor focus is lost) that the β-lactams will remain central to this need in the future.

REFERENCES

1. Fleming A. Br J Exp Pathol 1929;10:226.
2. Wainwright M. Perspect Biol Med 2002; 45:529–538.
3. Moberg CL. Science 1991;253:734–735.
4. Hamilton-Miller JM. J Antimicrob Chemother 2004;53:691–692.
5. Lax E. The Mold in Dr. Florey's Coat New York: Henry Holt & Co; 2004. p 307.
6. Sneader W. Drug Discovery: A History. Chichester: John Wiley & Sons; 2006. p 468.
7. Bud R. Penicill: Triumph Tragedy Oxford: Oxford University Press; 2007. p 330.
8. Abraham EP. Nat Prod Rep 1987;4:41–46.
9. Bentley R. J Chem Educ 2007;81:1462–1470.
10. Hodgkin DC. Science 1965;150:979–988.
11. Sheehan JC. The Enchanted Ring: The Untold Story of Penicillin. MIT Press; 1984. p 248.
12. Proctor P, Gensmantel NP, Page MI J Chem Soc Perkin Trans 2 1982; 1185–1192.
13. Page MI. Curr Pharm Des 1999;5:895–913.
14. Llinas A, Page MI. Org Biomol Chem 2004; 2:651–654.
15. Abraham EP. Drugs 1987;34(Suppl 2): 1–14.
16. Martin JF, Ullan RV, Casqueiro J. Adv Biochem Eng Biotechnol 2004;88:91–109.
17. Lee HJ, Lloyd MD, Harlos K, Clifton IJ, Baldwin JE, Schofield CJ. J Mol Biol 2001;308:937–948.
18. Lloyd MD, Lipscomb SJ, Hewitson KS, Hensgens CM, Baldwin JE, Schofield CJ. J Biol Chem 2004;279:15420–15426.
19. Wei CL, Yang YB, Deng CH, Liu WC, Hsu JS, Lin YC, Liaw SH. et al. Appl Environ Microbiol 2005;71:8873–8880.
20. Lejon S, Ellis J, Valegard K. J Mol Biol 2008;377:935–944.
21. Beveridge TJ. J Histotechnol 2002;25:55–60.

22. Matias VR, Beveridge TJ. Mol Microbiol 2005;56:240–251.

23. Matias VRF, Beveridge TJ. J Bacteriol 2006;188:1011–1021.

24. Matias VR, Beveridge TJ. Mol Microbiol 2007;64:195–206.

25. Matias VR, Al-Amoudi A, Dubochet J, Beveridge TJ. J Bacteriol 2003;185:6112–6118.

26. Ehrmann M. The Periplasm. Washington, DC: ASM Press; 2006. p 462.

27. Jensen GJ, Briegel A. Curr Opin Struct Biol 2007;17:260–267.

28. Marko M, Hsieh C, Schalek R, Frank J, Mannella C. Nat Methods 2007;4:215–217.

29. Zhang P, Khursigara CM, Hartnell LM, Subramaniam S. Proc Natl Acad Sci USA 2007;104:3777–3781.

30. Borgnia MJ, Subramaniam S, Milne JL. J Bacteriol 2008;190:2588–2596.

31. Meyer P, Dworkin J. Res Microbiol 2007;158:187–194.

32. Leevy WM, Gammon ST, Jiang H, Johnson JR, Maxwell DJ, Jackson EN, Marquez M. et al. J Am Chem Soc 2006;128:16476–16477.

33. Scheffers DJ, Jones LJ, Errington J. Mol Microbiol 2004;51:749–764.

34. Mullineaux CW, Nenninger A, Ray N, Robinson C. J Bacteriol 2006;188:3442–3448.

35. Schouten JA, Bagga S, Lloyd AJ, de Pascale G, Dowson CG, Roper DI, Bugg TD. Mol Biosyst 2006;2:484–491.

36. Wilks JC, Slonczewski JL. J Bacteriol 2007;189:5601–5607.

37. Tiyanont K, Doan T, Lazarus MB, Fang X, Rudner DZ, Walker S. Proc Natl Acad Sci USA 2006;103:11033–11038.

38. Goffin C, Ghuysen JM. Microbiol Mol Biol Rev 1998;62:1079–1093.

39. Barreteau H, Kovac A, Boniface A, Sova M, Gobec S, Blanot D. FEMS Microbiol Rev 2008;32:168–172.

40. Bouhss A, Trunkfield AE, Bugg TD, Mengin-Lecreulx D. FEMS Microbiol Rev 2008;32:208–233.

41. van Dam V, Sijbrandi R, Kol M, Swiezewska E, de Kruijff B, Breukink E. Mol Microbiol 2007;64:1105–1114.

42. Ruiz N. Proc Natl Acad Sci USA 2008;105:15553–15557.

43. Macheboeuf P, Contreras-Martel C, Job V, Dideberg O, Dessen A. FEMS Microbiol Rev 2006;30:673–691.

44. Yuan Y, Barrett D, Zhang Y, Kahne D, Sliz P, Walker S. Proc Natl Acad Sci USA 2007;104:5348–5353.

45. Lovering AL, de Castro LH, Lim D, Strynadka NC. Science 2007;315:1402–1405.

46. Lovering AL, De Castro L, Strynadka NC. J Mol Biol 2008;383:167–177.

47. Perlstein DL, Zhang Y, Wang TS, Kahne DE, Walker S. J Am Chem Soc 2007;129:12674–12675.

48. Morlot C, Pernot L, Le Gouellec A, Di Guilmi AM, Vernet T, Dideberg O, Dessen A. J Biol Chem 2005;280:15984–15991.

49. Sauvage E, Kerff F, Terrak M, Ayala JA, Charlier P. FEMS Microbiol Rev 2008;32:234–258.

50. Ghosh AS, Chowdhury C, Nelson DE. Trends Microbiol 2008;16:309–317.

51. Popham DL, Young KD. Curr Opin Microbiol 2003;6:594–599.

52. Young KD. Microbiol Mol Biol Rev 2006;70:660–703.

53. Priyadarshini R, Popham DL, Young KD. J Bacteriol 2006;188:5345–5355.

54. Nelson DE, Young KD. J Bacteriol 2000;182:1714–1721.

55. Nelson DE, Young KD. J Bacteriol 2001;183:3055–3064.

56. Schurek KN, Wiebe R, Karlowsky JA, Rubinstein E, Hoban DJ, Zhanel GG. Expert Rev Anti-Infect Ther 2007;5:185–198.

57. Wiedemann B, Pfeifle D, Wiegand I, Janas E. Drug Resist Updat 1998;1:223–226.

58. Pfeifle D, Janas E, Wiedemann B. Antimicrob Agents Chemother 2000;44:169–172.

59. Kresge N, Simoni RD, Hill RL. J Biol Chem 2007;282:e25–e27.

60. Waxman DJ, Yocum RR, Strominger JL. Phil Trans R Soc Lond B Biol Sci 1980;289:257–271.

61. Yocum RR, Amanuma H, O'Brien TA, Waxman DJ, Strominger JL. J Bacteriol 1982;149:1150–1153.

62. Waxman DJ, Strominger JL. Annu Rev Biochem 1983;52:825–869.

63. Lee B. J Mol Biol 1971;61:463–469.

64. Sweet RM.In: Flynn EH, editor. Cephalosporins and Penicillins: Chemistry and Biology. New York: Academic Press; 1972. p 280–309.

65. Pratt RF. J Chem Soc Perkin Trans 2002;2:851–861.

66. Pratt RF. Cell Mol Life Sci 2008;65:2138–2155.

67. van Heijenoort J. Microbiol Mol Biol Rev 2007;71:620–635.

68. Holtje JV.In: Schaechter M, editor. The Desk Encyclopedia of Microbiology (Cell Walls, Bacterial) San Diego, CA: Elsevier Academic Press; 2003. p 239–250.

69. Suvorov M, Fisher JF, Mobashery S.In: Westbury L, editor. The Practical Handbook of Microbiology (Bacterial Cell Wall: Morphology and Biochemistry) Boca Raton FL: CRC Press; 2008. p 159–190.

70. Vollmer W. FEMS Microbiol Rev 2008;32: 287–306.

71. Vollmer W, Bertsche U. Biochim Biophys Acta 2008;1778:1714–1734.

72. Vollmer W, Blanot D, de Pedro MA. FEMS Microbiol Rev 2008;32:149–167.

73. Scheurwater E, Reid CW, Clarke AJ. Int J Biochem Cell Biol 2008;40:586–591.

74. Magnet S, Bellais S, Dubost L, Fourgeaud M, Mainardi JL, Petit-Frere S, Marie A. et al. J Bacteriol 2007;189:3927–3931.

75. Magnet S, Dubost L, Marie A, Arthur M, Gutmann L. J Bacteriol 2008;190:4782–4785.

76. Dramsi S, Magnet S, Davison S, Arthur M. FEMS Microbiol Rev 2008;32:307–320.

77. Schleifer KH, Kandler O. Bacteriol Rev 1972;36:407–477.

78. Heidrich C, Templin MF, Ursinus A, Merdanovic M, Berger J, Schwarz H, de Pedro MA. et al. Mol Microbiol 2001;41:167–178.

79. Meisel U, Holtje JV, Vollmer W. J Bacteriol 2003;185:5342–5348.

80. Holtje JV, Tuomanen EI. J Gen Microbiol 1991;137:441–454.

81. Doyle RJ, Chaloupka J, Vinter V. Microbiol Rev 1988;52:554–567.

82. Holtje JV, Heidrich C. Biochimie 2001;83:103–108.

83. Fukushima T, Afkham A, Kurosawa S, Tanabe T, Yamamoto H, Sekiguchi J. J Bacteriol 2006;188:5541–5550.

84. Mesnage S, Chau F, Dubost L, Arthur M. J Biol Chem 2008;283:19845–19853.

85. Viollier PH, Shapiro L. Mol Microbiol 2003;49:331–345.

86. Kojima S, Shinohara A, Terashima H, Yakushi T, Sakuma M, Homma M, Namba K. et al. Proc Natl Acad Sci USA 2008;105:7696–7701.

87. Roujeinikova A. Proc Natl Acad Sci USA 2008;105:10348–10353.

88. Paradis-Bleau C, Cloutier I, Lemieux L, Sanschagrin F, Laroche J, Auger M, Garnier A. et al. FEMS Microbiol Lett 2007;266: 201–209.

89. Rashel M, Uchiyama J, Takemura I, Hoshiba H, Ujihara T, Takatsuji H, Honke K. et al. FEMS Microbiol Lett 2008;284:9–16.

90. Edgar R, Rokney A, Feeney M, Semsey S, Kessel M, Goldberg MB, Adhya S. et al. Mol Microbiol 2008;68:1107–1116.

91. Antignac A, Sieradzki K, Tomasz A. J Bacteriol 2007;189:7573–7580.

92. Kohanski MA, Dwyer DJ, Hayete B, Lawrence CA, Collins JJ. Cell 2007;130:797–810.

93. Kohanski MA, Dwyer DJ, Wierzbowski J, Cottarel G, Collins JJ. Cell 2008;135: 679–690.

94. Wright GD. Cell 2007;130:781–783.

95. Hassett DJ, Imlay JA. ACS Chem Biol 2007;2:708–710.

96. Walsh C. Antibiotics: Actions, Origins, Resistance. Washington, DC: ASM Press; 2003. p 335.

97. Poole K. Cell Mol Life Sci 2004;61:2200–2223.

98. Fisher JF, Meroueh SO, Mobashery S. Chem Rev 2005;105:395–424.

99. Stefanova ME, Tomberg J, Olesky M, Holtje JV, Gutheil WG, Nicholas RA. Biochemistry 2003;42:14614–14625.

100. Zapun A, Contreras-Martel C, Vernet T. FEMS Microbiol Rev 2008;32:361–385.

101. Meberg BM, Paulson AL, Priyadarshini R, Young KD. J Bacteriol 2004;186: 8326–8336.

102. Young KD. Curr Opin Microbiol 2007;10: 596–600.

103. Zapun A, Vernet T, Pinho MG. FEMS Microbiol Rev 2008;32:345–360.

104. Scheffers DJ, Pinho MG. Microbiol Mol Biol Rev 2005;69:585–607.

105. Norris V, den Blaauwen T, Doi RH, Harshey RM, Janniere L, Jimenez-Sanchez A, Jin DJ. et al. Annu Rev Microbiol 2007;61: 309–329.

106. Norris V, den Blaauwen T, Cabin-Flaman A, Doi RH, Harshey R, Janniere L, Jimenez-Sanchez A. et al. Microbiol Mol Biol Rev 2007;71:230–253.

107. den Blaauwen T, de Pedro MA, Nguyen-Distèche M, Ayala JA. FEMS Microbiol Rev 2008;32:321–344.

108. Hakenbeck R, Tarpay M, Tomasz A. Antimicrob Agents Chemother 1980;17:364–371.

109. Handwerger S, Tomasz A. Antimicrob Agents Chemother 1986;30:57–63.

110. Dowson CG, Coffey TJ, Kell C, Whiley RA. Mol Microbiol 1993;9:635–643.

111. Dowson CG, Hutchison A, Woodford N, Johnson AP, George RC, Spratt BG. Proc Natl Acad Sci USA 1990;87:5858–5862.

112. Olesky M, Zhao S, Rosenberg RL, Nicholas RA. J Bacteriol 2006;188:2300–2308.

113. Takahata S, Senju N, Osaki Y, Yoshida T, Ida T. Antimicrob Agents Chemother 2006;50: 3638–3645.

114. Taha MK, Vazquez JA, Hong E, Bennett DE, Bertrand S, Bukovski S, Cafferkey MT. et al. Antimicrob Agents Chemother 2007;51: 2784–2792.

115. Ochiai S, Sekiguchi S, Hayashi A, Shimadzu M, Ishiko H, Matsushima-Nishiwaki R, Kozawa O. et al. J Antimicrob Chemother 2007;60:54–60.

116. Powell AJ, Tomberg J, Deacon AM, Nicholas RA, Davies C. J Biol Chem 2009;284: 1202–1212.

117. Parr TR Jr, Bryan LE. Antimicrob Agents Chemother 1984;25:747–753.

118. Yamada M, Watanabe T, Miyara T, Baba N, Saito J, Takeuchi Y, Ohsawa F. Antimicrob Agents Chemother 2007;51:3902–3907.

119. Takahata S, Ida T, Senju N, Sanbongi Y, Miyata A, Maebashi K, Hoshiko S. Antimicrob Agents Chemother 2007;51:1589–1595.

120. Tristram S, Jacobs MR, Appelbaum PC. Clin Microbiol Rev 2007;20:368–389.

121. Russo TA, MacDonald U, Beanan JM, Olson R, MacDonald IJ, Sauberan SL, Luke NR. et al. J Infect Dis 2009;199:513–521.

122. Giamarellou H, Antoniadou A, Kanellakopoulou K. Int J Antimicrob Agents 2008;32: 106–119.

123. Peleg AY, Seifert H, Paterson DL. Clin Microbiol Rev 2008;21:538–582.

124. Georgopapadakou NH. Antimicrob Agents Chemother 1993;37:2045–2053.

125. Tomasz A, Drugeon HB, de Lencastre HM, Jabes D, McDougall L, Bille J. Antimicrob Agents Chemother 1989;33:1869–1874.

126. Spratt BG. Science 1994;264:388–393.

127. Bowler LD, Zhang QY, Riou JY, Spratt BG. J Bacteriol 1994;176:333–337.

128. Spratt BG, Bowler LD, Zhang QY, Zhou J, Smith JM. J Mol Evol 1992;34:115–125.

129. Spratt BG. Nature 1988;332:173–176.

130. Dougherty TJ, Koller AE, Tomasz A. Antimicrob Agents Chemother 1980;18:730–737.

131. Dougherty TJ. Antimicrob Agents Chemother 1986;30:649–652.

132. Pan W, Spratt BG. Mol Microbiol 1994;11:769–775.

133. Zighelboim S, Tomasz A. Antimicrob Agents Chemother 1980;17:434–442.

134. Markiewicz Z, Tomasz A. J Clin Microbiol 1989;27:405–410.

135. Laible G, Spratt BG, Hakenbeck R. Mol Microbiol 1991;5:1993–2002.

136. Jamin M, Hakenbeck R, Frere JM. FEBS Lett 1993;331:101–104.

137. Jamin M, Damblon C, Millier S, Hakenbeck R, Frere JM. Biochem J 1993;292:735–741.

138. Chi F, Nolte O, Bergmann C, Ip M, Hakenbeck R. Int J Med Microbiol 2007;297:503–512.

139. Kilian M, Poulsen K, Blomqvist T, Havarstein LS, Bek-Thomsen M, Tettelin H, Sorensen UB. PLoS ONE 2008;3:e2683.

140. Soriano F, Cafini F, Aguilar L, Tarrago D, Alou L, Gimenez MJ, Gracia M. et al. J Antimicrob Chemother 2008;62:1234–1240.

141. Serfass DA, Mendelman PM, Chaffin DO, Needham CA. J Gen Microbiol 1986;132: 2855–2861.

142. Mendelman PM, Chaffin DO, Kalaitzoglou G. J Antimicrob Chemother 1990;25:525–534.

143. Powell M, Livermore DM. J Antimicrob Chemother 1990;26:741–747.

144. Arbeloa A, Hugonnet JE, Sentilhes AC, Josseaume N, Dubost L, Monsempes C, Blanot D. et al. J Biol Chem 2004;279:41546–41556.

145. Mainardi JL, Villet R, Bugg TD, Mayer C, Arthur M. FEMS Microbiol Rev 2008;32: 386–408.

146. Vernel-Pauillac F, Merien F. Clin Chem 2006;52:2294–2296.

147. Lindberg R, Fredlund H, Nicholas R, Unemo M. Antimicrob Agents Chemother 2007;51: 2117–2122.

148. Zhao S, Tobiason DM, Hu M, Seifert HS, Nicholas RA. Mol Microbiol 2005;57:1238–1251.

149. Shafer WM, Folster JP. J Bacteriol 2006;188: 2297–2299.

150. Ropp PA, Hu M, Olesky M, Nicholas RA. Antimicrob Agents Chemother 2002;46:769–777.

151. Ameyama S, Onodera S, Takahata M, Minami S, Maki N, Endo K, Goto H. et al. Antimicrob Agents Chemother 2002;46:3744–3749.

152. Ito M, Deguchi T, Mizutani KS, Yasuda M, Yokoi S, Ito S, Takahashi Y. et al. Antimicrob Agents Chemother 2005;49:137–143.

153. de Lencastre H, de Jonge BL, Matthews PR, Tomasz A. J Antimicrob Chemother 1994;33: 7–24.

154. Oliveira DC, Tomasz A, de H, Lencastre Lancet Infect Dis 2002;2:180–189.

155. Tenover FC, Pearson ML. Emerg Infect Dis 2004;10:2052–2053.

156. Chambers HF. N Engl J Med 2005;352: 1485–1487.

157. Furuya EY, Lowy FD. Nat Rev Microbiol 2006;4:36–45.

158. Livermore DM. Clin Microbiol Infect 2006;12 (Suppl 2): 11–16.

159. de Lencastre H, Oliveira D, Tomasz A. Curr Opin Microbiol 2007;10:428–435.

160. Kajita E, Okano JT, Bodine EN, Layne SP, Blower S. Nat Rev Microbiol 2007;5:700–709.

161. Sieradzki K, Chung M, Tomasz A. Antimicrob Agents Chemother 2008;52:505–512.

162. Kennedy AD, Otto M, Braughton KR, Whitney AR, Chen L, Mathema B, Mediavilla JR. et al. Proc Natl Acad Sci USA 2008;105:1327–1332.

163. Deurenberg RH, Stobberingh EE. Infect Genet Evol 2008;8:747–763.

164. Chambers HF, Sachdeva MJ, Hackbarth CJ. Biochem J 1994;301:139–144.

165. Fuda CC, Fisher JF, Mobashery S. Cell Mol Life Sci 2005;62:2617–2633.

166. Hartman BJ, Tomasz A. J Bacteriol 1984;158:513–516.

167. Reynolds PE, Brown DF. FEBS Lett 1985;192:28–32.

168. Ubukata K, Yamashita N, Konno M. Antimicrob Agents Chemother 1985;27:851–857.

169. Wielders CL, Fluit AC, Brisse S, Verhoef J, Schmitz FJ. J Clin Microbiol 2002;40: 3970–3975.

170. Pinho MG, de Lencastre H, Tomasz A. Proc Natl Acad Sci USA 2001;98:10886–10891.

171. de Jonge BL, Chang YS, Gage D, Tomasz A. J Biol Chem 1992;267:11248–11254.

172. de Jonge BL, Chang YS, Gage D, Tomasz A. J Biol Chem 1992;267:11255–11259.

173. de Jonge BL, Tomasz A. Antimicrob Agents Chemother 1993;37:342–346.

174. Thomas CM, Nielsen KM. Nat Rev Microbiol 2005;3:711–721.

175. Severin A, Wu SW, Tabei K, Tomasz A. J Bacteriol 2005;187:6651–6658.

176. Fuda C, Suvorov M, Shi Q, Hesek D, Lee M, Mobashery S. Biochemistry 2007;46: 8050–8057.

177. Zhou Y, Antignac A, Wu SW, Tomasz A. J Bacteriol 2008;190:508–514.

178. Antignac A, Tomasz A. Antimicrob Agents Chemother 2009;53:435–431.

179. Noto MJ, Kreiswirth BN, Monk AB, Archer GL. J Bacteriol 2008;190:1276–1283.

180. Llarrull LI, Fisher JF, Mobashery S. Antimicrob Agents Chemother 2009;53: 4051–4063.

181. Lee SM, Ender M, Adhikari R, Smith JM, Berger-Bachi B, Cook GM. Antimicrob Agents Chemother 2007;51:1497–1499.

182. Laplana LM, Cepero MA, Ruiz J, Zolezzi PC, Calvo MA, Erazo MC, Gomez-Lus R. Int J Antimicrob Agents 2007;30:505–513.

183. Haenni M, Moreillon P. Antimicrob Agents Chemother 2008;52:337–339.

184. Veguilla W, Peak KK, Luna VA, Roberts JC, Davis CR, Cannons AC, Amuso P. et al. J Clin Microbiol 2008;46:3494–3497.

185. Suzuki E, Hiramatsu K, Yokota T. Antimicrob Agents Chemother 1992;36:429–434.

186. Hanssen AM, Kjeldsen G, Sollid JU. Antimicrob Agents Chemother 2004;48:285–296.

187. Berglund C, Soderquist B. Clin Microbiol Infect 2008;14:1048–1056.

188. Maidhof H, Reinicke B, Blumel P, Berger-Bachi B, Labischinski H. J Bacteriol 1991;173:3507–3513.

189. Rohrer S, Berger-Bachi B. Microbiology 2003;149:2733–2738.

190. Heath LS, Gargis SR, Smithberg SR, Johnson HP, Heath HE, Leblanc PA, Sloan GL. FEMS Microbiol Lett 2005;249:227–231.

191. Weber B, Ehlert K, Diehl A, Reichmann P, Labischinski H, Hakenbeck R. FEMS Microbiol Lett 2000;188:81–85.

192. Ryffel C, Strassle A, Kayser FH, Berger-Bachi B. Antimicrob Agents Chemother 1994;38: 724–728.

193. Boyce JM, Medeiros AA. Antimicrob Agents Chemother 1987;31:1426–1428.

194. Katayama Y, Zhang HZ, Hong D, Chambers HF. J Bacteriol 2003;185:5465–5472.

195. Chambers HF, Hackbarth CJ. Antimicrob Agents Chemother 1987;31:1982–1988.

196. Inglis B, Matthews PR, Stewart PR. J Gen Microbiol 1988;134:1465–1469.

197. Plipat N, Livni G, Bertram H, Thomson RBJ. J Clin Microbiol 2005;43:2494–2496.

198. Deresinski S. Expert Rev Anti Infect Ther 2007;5:393–401.

199. Falagas ME, Makris GC, Dimopoulos G, Matthaiou DK. Clin Microbiol Infect 2008;14: 101–104.

200. Lim D, Strynadka NC. Nat Struct Biol 2002;9:870–876.

201. Fuda C, Suvorov M, Vakulenko SB, Mobashery S. J Biol Chem 2004;279:40802–40806.

202. Fuda C, Hesek D, Lee M, Morio K, Nowak T, Mobashery S. J Am Chem Soc 2005;127: 2056–2057.

203. Fuda C, Hesek D, Lee M, Heilmayer W, Novak R, Vakulenko SB, Mobashery S. J Biol Chem 2006;281:10035–10041.

204. Villegas-Estrada A, Lee M, Hesek D, Vakulenko SB, Mobashery S. J Am Chem Soc 2008;130:9212–9213.

205. Lemaire S, Fuda C, Van Bambeke F, Tulkens PM, Mobashery S. J Biol Chem 2008;283: 12769–12776.

206. Lemaire S, Van Bambeke F, Mingeot-Leclercq MP, Glupczynski Y, Tulkens PM. Antimicrob Agents Chemother 2007;51:1627–1632.

207. Fontana R, Cerini R, Longoni P, Grossato A, Canepari P. J Bacteriol 1983;155:1343–1350.

208. Canepari P, Lleo MM, Cornaglia G, Fontana R, Satta G. J Gen Microbiol 1986;132:625–631.

209. Fontana R, Aldegheri M, Ligozzi M, Lopez H, Sucari A, Satta G. Antimicrob Agents Chemother 1994;38:1980–1983.

210. Grayson ML, Eliopoulos GM, Wennersten CB, Ruoff KL, De Girolami PC, Ferraro MJ, Moellering RCJ. Antimicrob Agents Chemother 1991;35:2180–2184.

211. Rice LB, Bellais S, Carias LL, Hutton-Thomas R, Bonomo RA, Caspers P, Page MG. et al. Antimicrob Agents Chemother 2004;48: 3028–3032.

212. Sauvage E, Kerff F, Fonze E, Herman R, Schoot B, Marquette JP, Taburet Y. et al. Cell Mol Life Sci 2002;59:1223–1232.

213. Hujer AM, Kania M, Gerken T, Anderson VE, Buynak JD, Ge X, Caspers P. et al. Antimicrob Agents Chemother 2005;49:612–618.

214. Chesnel L, Carapito R, Croize J, Dideberg O, Vernet T, Zapun A. Antimicrob Agents Chemother 2005;49:2895–2902.

215. Smith AM, Klugman KP. Antimicrob Agents Chemother 2005;49:4622–4627.

216. Dahesh S, Hensler ME, Van Sorge NM, Gertz REJ, Schrag S, Nizet V, Beall BW. Antimicrob Agents Chemother 2008;52:2915–2918.

217. Nagano N, Nagano Y, Kimura K, Tamai K, Yanagisawa H, Arakawa Y. Antimicrob Agents Chemother 2008;52:4258–4267.

218. Pares S, Mouz N, Petillot Y, Hakenbeck R, Dideberg O. Nat Struct Biol 1996;3:284–289.

219. Gordon E, Mouz N, Duee E, Dideberg O. J Mol Biol 2000;299:477–485.

220. Yamada M, Watanabe T, Baba N, Takeuchi Y, Ohsawa F, Gomi S. Antimicrob Agents Chemother 2008;52:2053–2060.

221. Chesnel L, Pernot L, Lemaire D, Champelovier D, Croize J, Dideberg O, Vernet T. et al. J Biol Chem 2003;278:44448–44456.

222. Pernot L, Chesnel L, Le Gouellec A, Croize J, Vernet T, Dideberg O, Dessen A. J Biol Chem 2004;279:16463–16470.

223. Carapito R, Chesnel L, Vernet T, Zapun A. J Biol Chem 2006;281:1771–1777.

224. Maurer P, Koch B, Zerfass I, Krauss J, van der Linden M, Frere JM, Contreras-Martel C. et al. J Mol Biol 2008;376:1403–1416.

225. Josephine HR, Charlier P, Davies C, Nicholas RA, Pratt RF. Biochemistry 2006;45: 15873-1 Antimicrob Agents Chemother 5883.

226. Massova I, Mobashery S. Curr Pharm Des 1999;5:929–937.

227. Meroueh SO, Minasov G, Lee W, Shoichet BK, Mobashery S. J Am Chem Soc 2003;125: 9612–9618.

228. Hall BG, Barlow M. Drug Resist Updat 2004;7:111–123.

229. Fevre C, Jbel M, Passet V, Weill FX, Grimont PA, Brisse S. Antimicrob Agents Chemother 2005;49:3453–3462.

230. Urbach C, Fastrez J, Soumillion P. J Biol Chem 2008;283:32516–32526.

231. Bebrone C. Biochem Pharmacol 2007;74:1686–1701.

232. Hall BG, Salipante SJ, Barlow M. J Mol Evol 2004;59:133–141.

233. Hall BG, Salipante SJ, Barlow M. J Mol Evol 2003;57:249–254.

234. Garau G, Di Guilmi AM, Hall BG. Antimicrob Agents Chemother 2005;49:2778–2784.

235. Peitsaro N, Polianskyte Z, Tuimala J, PornAres I, Liobikas J, Speer O, Lindholm D. et al. BMC Evol Biol 2008;8:26.

236. Smith TS, Southan C, Ellington K, Campbell D, Tew DG, Debouck C. Genomics 2001;78:12–14.

237. Chen Y, Zhu J, Lum PY, Yang X, Pinto S, MacNeil DJ, Zhang C. et al. Nature 2008;452:429–435.

238. Meroueh SO, Roblin P, Golemi D, Maveyraud L, Vakulenko SB, Zhang Y, Samama JP. et al. J Am Chem Soc 2002;124:9422–9430.

239. Wang X, Minasov G, Shoichet BK. J Biol Chem 2002;277:32149–32156.

240. Barlow M, Hall BG. Genetics 2002;160: 823–832.

241. Babic M, Hujer AM, Bonomo RA. Drug Resist Updat 2006;9:142–156.

242. Perez F, Endimiani A, Hujer KM, Bonomo RA. Curr Opin Pharmacol 2007;7:459–469.

243. Hawkey PM. Br J Pharmacol 2008;153: S406–S413.

244. Gniadkowski M. Clin Microbiol Infect 2008;14 (Suppl 1): 11–32.

245. Richmond MH, Sykes RB. Adv Microb Physiol 1973;9:31–88.

246. Matthew M. J Antimicrob Chemother 1979;5: 349–358.

247. Jacoby GA. Antimicrob Agents Chemother 2006;50:1123–1129.

248. Bush K. Antimicrob Agents Chemother 1989;33:259–263.

249. Bush K, Jacoby GA, Medeiros AA. Antimicrob Agents Chemother 1995;39:1211–1233.

250. Ambler RP. Philos Trans R Soc Lond B Biol Sci 1980;289:321–331.

251. Bos F, Pleiss J. Antimicrob Agents Chemother 2008;52:1072–1079.

252. Meroueh SO, Fisher JF, Schlegel HB, Mobashery S. J Am Chem Soc 2005;127:15397–15407.

253. Chen Y, Bonnet R, Shoichet BK. J Am Chem Soc 2007;129:5378–5380.

254. Bulychev A, Massova I, Miyashita K, Mobashery S. J Am Chem Soc 1997;119:7619–7625.

255. Chen Y, Minasov G, Roth TA, Prati F, Shoichet BK. J Am Chem Soc 2006;128: 2970–2976.

256. Maveyraud L, Golemi-Kotra D, Ishiwata A, Meroueh O, Mobashery S, Samama JP. J Am Chem Soc 2002;124:2461–2465.

257. Mansour TS, Bradford PA, Venkatesan A. Annu Rep Med Chem 2008;43:247–267.

258. Hall BG, Barlow M. J Antimicrob Chemother 2005;55:1050–1051.

259. Frere JM, Galleni M, Bush K, Dideberg O. J Antimicrob Chemother 2005;55: 1051–1053.

260. Jacoby GA, Bush K. J Clin Microbiol 2005;43:6220.

261. Ghuysen JM. Annu Rev Microbiol 1991;45: 37–67.

262. Canton R, Morosini MI, de la Maza OM, de la Pedrosa EG, Clin Microbiol Infect 2008;14 (Suppl 1): 53–62.

263. Sulton D, Pagan-Rodriguez D, Zhou X, Liu Y, Hujer AM, Bethel CR, Helfand MS. et al. J Biol Chem 2005;280:35528–35536.

264. Thomas VL, Golemi-Kotra D, Kim C, Vakulenko SB, Mobashery S, Shoichet BK. Biochemistry 2005;44:9330–9338.

265. Tristram SG, Burdach JG. J Antimicrob Chemother 2007;60:1151–1154.

266. Helfand MS, Taracila MA, Totir MA, Bonomo RA, Buynak JD, Akker FV, Carey PR. Biochemistry 2007;46:8689–8699.

267. Thomson JM, Distler AM, Bonomo RA. Biochemistry 2007;46:11361–11368.

268. Perez-Llarena FJ, Cartelle M, Mallo S, Beceiro A, Perez A, Villanueva R, Romero A. et al. J Antimicrob Chemother 2008;61: 792–797.

269. Mroczkowska JE, Barlow M. Antimicrob Agents Chemother 2008;52:2340–2345.

270. De Wals PY, Doucet N, Pelletier JN. Protein Sci 2009;18:147–160.

271. Le Turnier S, Nordmann P, Eb F, Mammeri H. J Antimicrob Chemother 2009;63:216–218.

272. Helfand MS, Bonomo RA. Curr Opin Pharmacol 2005;5:452–458.

273. Paterson DL, Bonomo RA. Clin Microbiol Rev 2005;18:657–686.

274. Helfand MS, Bonomo RA. Clin Infect Dis 2006;43:1415–1416.

275. Livermore DM. Clin Microbiol Infect 2008;14 (Suppl 1): 3–10.

276. Livermore DM, Canton R, Gniadkowski M, Nordmann P, Rossolini GM, Arlet G, Ayala J. et al. J Antimicrob Chemother 2007;59: 165–174.

277. Mammeri H, Poirel L, Nordmann P. J Antimicrob Chemother 2007;60:490–494.

278. Jacoby GA. Clin Microbiol Rev 2009;22: 161–182.

279. Nordmann P, Poirel L. Clin Microbiol Infect 2002;8:321–331.

280. Livermore DM, Woodford N. Trends Microbiol 2006;14:413–420.

281. Queenan AM, Bush K. Clin Microbiol Rev 2007;20:440–458.

282. Walther-Rasmussen J, Hoiby N. J Antimicrob Chemother 2007;60:470–482.

283. Walther-Rasmussen J, Hoiby N. J Antimicrob Chemother 2006;57:373–383.

284. Schwaber MJ, Carmeli Y. JAMA 2008;300: 2911–2913.

285. Giske CG, Sundsfjord AS, Kahlmeter G, Woodford N, Nordmann P, Paterson DL, Canton R. et al. J Antimicrob Chemother 2009;63:1–4.

286. Rolain JM, Francois P, Hernandez D, Bittar F, Richet H, Fournous G, Mattenberger Y. et al. Biol Direct 2009;4:1.

287. Nikaido H. Microbiol Mol Biol Rev 2003;67:593–656.

288. Pages JM, James CE, Winterhalter M. Nat Rev Microbiol 2008;6:893–903.

289. Nikaido H, Normark S. Mol Microbiol 1987;1:29–36.

290. Raimondi A, Traverso A, Nikaido H. Antimicrob Agents Chemother 1991;35: 1174–1180.

291. Jaffe A, Chabbert YA, Semonin O. Antimicrob Agents Chemother 1982;22:942–948.

292. Jaffe A, Chabbert YA, Derlot E. Antimicrob Agents Chemother 1983;23:622–625.

293. Nikaido H. Antimicrob Agents Chemother 1989;33:1831–1836.

294. Martinez-Martinez L, Hernandez-Alles S, Alberti S, Tomas JM, Benedi VJ, Jacoby GA. Antimicrob Agents Chemother 1996;40: 342–348.

295. Pangon B, Bizet C, Bure A, Pichon F, Philippon A, Regnier B, Gutmann L. J Infect Dis 1989;159:1005 1006.

296. Martinez-Martinez L, Pascual A, Hernandez-Alles S, Alvarez-Diaz D, Suarez AI, Tran J, Benedi VJ. et al. Antimicrob Agents Chemother 1999;43:1669–1673.

297. Cao VT, Arlet G, Ericsson BM, Tammelin A, Courvalin P, Lambert T. J Antimicrob Chemother 2000;46:895–900.

298. Jacoby GA, Mills DM, Chow N. Antimicrob Agents Chemother 2004;48:3203–3206.

299. Kaczmarek FM, Dib-Hajj F, Shang W, Gootz TD. Antimicrob Agents Chemother 2006;50: 3396–3406.

300. Martinez-Martinez L. Clin Microbiol Infect 2008;14(Suppl 1): 82–89.

301. Lee EH, Nicolas MH, Kitzis MD, Pialoux G, Collatz E, Gutmann L. Antimicrob Agents Chemother 1991;35:1093–1098.

302. Szabo D, Silveira F, Hujer AM, Bonomo RA, Hujer KM, Marsh JW, Bethel CR. et al. Antimicrob Agents Chemother 2006;50: 2833–2835.

303. Armand-Lefevre L, Leflon-Guibout V, Bredin J, Barguellil F, Amor A, Pages JM, Nicolas-Chanoine MH. Antimicrob Agents Chemother 2003;47:1165–1168.

304. Weber DA, Sanders CC, Bakken JS, Quinn JP. J Infect Dis 1990;162:460–465.

305. Boucher HW, Talbot GH, Bradley JS, Edwards JE, Gilbert D, Rice LB, Scheld M. et al. Clin Infect Dis 2009;48:1–12.

306. Nordmann P, Naas T, Fortineau N, Poirel L. Curr Opin Microbiol 2007;10:436–440.

307. Grossi P, Dalla D, Gasperina Expert Rev Anti Infect Ther 2006;4:639–662.

308. Gomez MI, Prince A. Curr Opin Pharmacol 2007;7:244–251.

309. Hocquet D, Berthelot P, Roussel-Delvallez M, Favre R, Jeannot K, Bajolet O, Marty N. et al. Antimicrob Agents Chemother 2007;51: 3531–3536.

310. Wolter DJ, Acquazzino D, Goering RV, Sammut P, Khalaf N, Hanson ND. Clin Infect Dis 2008;46:e137–41.

311. Walsh F, Amyes SG. J Chemother 2007;19: 376–381.

312. Quale J, Bratu S, Gupta J, Landman D. Antimicrob Agents Chemother 2006;50: 1633–1641.

313. Maniati M, Ikonomidis A, Mantzana P, Daponte A, Maniatis AN, Pournaras S. J Antimicrob Chemother 2007;60:132–135.

314. Bratu S, Landman D, Gupta J, Quale J. J Med Microbiol 2007;56:809–814.

315. Ikonomidis A, Tsakris A, Kantzanou M, Spanakis N, Maniatis AN, Pournaras S. FEMS Microbiol Lett 2008;279:36–39.

316. Giske CG, Buaro L, Sundsfjord A, Wretlind B. Microb Drug Resist 2008;14:23–30.

317. Trias J, Dufresne J, Levesque RC, Nikaido H. Antimicrob Agents Chemother 1989;33: 1202–1206.

318. Livermore DM, Yang YJ. J Antimicrob Chemother 1989;24(Suppl A): 149–159.

319. Livermore DM. Antimicrob Agents Chemother 1992;36:2046–2048.

320. Yang YJ, Livermore DM. J Antimicrob Chemother 1989;24(Suppl A): 207–217.

321. Chen H, Hu J, Chen PR, Lan L, Li Z, Hicks LM, Dinner AR. et al. Proc Natl Acad Sci USA 2008;105:13586–13591.

322. Alibert-Franco S, Pradines B, Mahamoud A, Davin-Regli A, Pages JM. Curr Med Chem 2009;16:301–317.

323. Sader HS, Jacobs MR, Fritsche TR. Diagn Microbiol Infect Dis 2007;57(Suppl 3): 5S–12S.

324. Humbert G, Fillastre JP, Leroy A, Godin M, Van Winzum C, Rev Infect Dis 1979;1: 118–126.

325. Noel GJ. Clin Microbiol Infect 2007;13(Suppl 2): 25–29.

326. Schmitt-Hoffmann A, Roos B, Schleimer M, Sauer J, Man A, Nashed N, Brown T. et al. Antimicrob Agents Chemother 2004;48: 2570–2575.

327. Schmitt-Hoffmann A, Nyman L, Roos B, Schleimer M, Sauer J, Nashed N, Brown T. et al. Antimicrob Agents Chemother 2004;48: 2576–2580.

328. Murthy B, Schmitt-Hoffmann A. Clin Pharmacokinet 2008;47:21–33.

329. Lodise TP Jr, Pypstra R, Kahn JB, Murthy BP, Kimko HC, Bush K, Noel GJ. et al. Antimicrob Agents Chemother 2007;51:2378–2387.

330. Kimko H, Murthy B, Xu X, Nandy P, Strauss R, Noel GJ. Antimicrob Agents Chemother 2009;53:1228–1230.

331. Chambers HF, Neu HC.In: Mandell GL, Bennett JB, Dolin R, editors. Principles and Practice of Infectious Diseases. 4th ed. New York: Churchill Livingstone; 1995. p 233–246.

332. Chambers HF, Neu HC.In: Mandell GL, Bennett JB, Dolin R, editors. Principles and Practice of Infectious Diseases. 4th ed. New York: Churchill Livingstone; 1995. p 264–272.

333. Karchmer AW.In: Mandell GL, Bennett JB, Dolin R, editors. Principles and Practice of Infectious Diseases. 4th ed. New York: Churchill Livingstone; 1995. p 247–264.

334. Lamb HM, Ormrod D, Scott LJ, Figgitt DP. Drugs 2002;62:1041–1089.

335. Rice LB, Hutton-Thomas R, Lakticova V, Helfand MS, Donskey CJ. J Infect Dis 2004;189:1113–1118.

336. Norrby SR. Med Clin North Am 1995;79:745–759.

337. Bonfiglio G, Russo G, Nicoletti G. Expert Opin Investig Drugs 2002;11:529–544.

338. Wong BK, Sahly Y, Mistry G, Waldman S, Musson D, Majumdar A, Xu X. et al. Xenobiotica 2004;34:379–389.

339. Mandell GL, Sande MA.In: Gilman AG, Goodman LS, Gilman A, editors. The Pharmacologic Basis of Therapeutics New York: Macmillan; 1980. p 1126.

340. Svedhem A, Alestig K, Jertborn M. Antimicrob Agents Chemother 1980;18:349–352.

341. Carrizosa J, Levison ME, Kaye D. Antimicrob Agents Chemother 1973;3:306–307.

342. Berger S, Ernst EC, Barza M. Antimicrob Agents Chemother 1976;9:575–579.

343. Trollfors B, Alestig K, Norrby R. Scand J Infect Dis 1979;11:315–316.

344. Owens RC Jr, Tessier P, Nightingale CH, Ambrose PG, Quintiliani R, Nicolau DP. Int J Antimicrob Agents 2001;17:483–489.

345. Esposito S. Drugs 2000;59(Suppl 3): 47–9 19-28; discussion.

346. Bergan T. Infection 1979;7(Suppl 5): S507–S512.

347. Dancer SJ. J Antimicrob Chemother 2001;48:463–478.

348. Paterson DL. Clin Infect Dis 2004;38(Suppl 4): S341–S345.

349. Bloomfield SF, Cookson B, Falkiner F, Griffith C, Cleary V. Am J Infect Control 2007;35:86–88.

350. Thomas C, Riley TV. Commun Dis Intell 2003;27(Suppl): S28–31.

351. Safdar N, Maki DG. Ann Intern Med 2002;136:834–844.

352. Baines SD, Freeman J, Wilcox MH. J Antimicrob Chemother 2005;55:974–982.

353. Stiefel U, Pultz NJ, Harmoinen J, Koski P, Lindevall K, Helfand MS, Donskey CJ. J Infect Dis 2003;188:1605–1609.

354. Stiefel U, Nerandzic MM, Koski P, Donskey CJ. J Antimicrob Chemother 2008;62: 1105–1108.

355. Harmoinen J, Mentula S, Heikkila M, van der Rest M, Rajala-Schultz PJ, Donskey CJ, Frias R. et al. Antimicrob Agents Chemother 2004;48:75–79.

356. Hoffman A, Horwitz E, Hess S, Cohen-Poradosu R, Kleinberg L, Edelberg A, Shapiro M. Pharm Res 2008;25:667–671.

357. Bourgeois S, Tsapis N, Honnas H, Andremont A, Shakweh M, Besnard M, Fattal E. J Pharm Sci 2008;97:1853–1863.

358. Rodriguez-Pena R, Antunez C, Martin E, Blanca-Lopez N, Mayorga C, Torres MJ. Expert Opin Drug Saf 2006;5:31–48.

359. Stewart GT. Annu Rev Pharmacol 1973;13:309–324.

360. Petz. LD. J Infect Dis 1978;137(Suppl): S74–S79.

361. Solensky R. Clin Rev Allergy Immunol 2003;24:201–220.

362. Porter J, Jick H. Lancet 1977;1:587–588.

363. Levine BB, Zolov DM. J Allergy 1969;43: 231–244.

364. van Winzum C, J Antimicrob Chemother 1978;4:91–104.

365. Ahlstedt S, Ekstrom B, Svard PO, Sjoberg B, Kristofferson A, Ortengren B. Crit Rev Toxicol 1980;7:219–277.

366. Parmar JS, Nasser S. Thorax 2005;60: 517–520.

367. Burrows JA, Nissen LM, Kirkpatrick CM, Bell SC. J Cyst Fibros 2007;6:297–303.

368. Patriarca G, Schiavino D, Lombardo C, Altomonte G, De Cinti M, Buonomo A, Nucera E. Int J Immunopathol Pharmacol 2008;21: 375–379.

369. Johannes CB, Ziyadeh N, Seeger JD, Tucker E, Reiter C, Faich G. Drug Saf 2007;30:705–713.

370. Yates AB. Am J Med 2008;121:572–576.

371. DePestel DD, Benninger MS, Danziger L, LaPlante KL, May C, Luskin A, Pichichero M. et al. J Am Pharm Assoc 2008;48: 530–540.

372. Cunha BA. Med Clin North Am 2006;90: 1257–1264.

373. Schafer JA, Mateo N, Parlier GL, Rotschafer JC. Pharmacotherapy 2007;27:542–545.

374. Romano A, Gueant-Rodriguez RM, Viola M, Pettinato R, Gueant JL. Ann Intern Med 2004;141:16–22.

375. Bousquet PJ, Pipet A, Bousquet-Rouanet L, Demoly P. Clin Exp Allergy 2008;38:185–190.

376. Cunha BA, Hamid NS, Krol V, Eisenstein L. J Chemother 2008;20:233–237.

377. De Sarro A, Ammendola D, Zappala M, Grasso S, De Sarro GB, Antimicrob Agents Chemother 1995;39:232–237.

378. Norrby SR. Drug Saf 1996;15:87–90.

379. Chow KM, Hui AC, Szeto CC. Eur J Clin Microbiol Infect Dis 2005;24:649–653.

380. Owens RC Jr. Crit Care 2008;12(Suppl 4): S3.

381. Norrby SR. J Antimicrob Chemother 2000;45:5–7.

382. Cottagnoud P. Cell Mol Life Sci 2002;59: 1928–1933.

383. Horiuchi M, Kimura M, Tokumura M, Hasebe N, Arai T, Abe K. Toxicology 2006;222:114–124.

384. Linden P. Drug Saf 2007;30:657–668.

385. Rothstein JD, Patel S, Regan MR, Haenggeli C, Huang YH, Bergles DE, Jin L. et al. Nature 2005;433:73–77.

386. Rumbaugh JA, Li G, Rothstein J, Nath A. J Neurovirol 2007;13:168–172.

387. Melzer N, Meuth SG, Torres-Salazar D, Bittner S, Zozulya AL, Weidenfeller C, Kotsiari A. et al. PLoS ONE 2008;3:e3149.

388. Miller BR, Dorner JL, Shou M, Sari Y, Barton SJ, Sengelaub DR, Kennedy RT. et al. Neuroscience 2008;153:329–337.

389. Thone-Reineke C, Neumann C, Namsolleck P, Schmerbach K, Krikov M, Schefe JH, Lucht K. et al. J Hypertens 2008;26:2426–2435.

390. Hota SK, Barhwal K, Ray K, Singh SB, Ilavazhagan G. Neurobiol Learn Mem 2008;89:522–532.

391. Rawls SM, Tallarida R, Robinson W, Amin M. Br J Pharmacol 2007;151:1095–1102.

392. Rawls SM, Cavallo F, Capasso A, Ding Z, Raffa RB. Eur J Pharmacol 2008;584:278–284.

393. Rawls SM, Robinson W, Patel S, Baron A. Neuropharmacology 2008;55:865–870.

394. Lee SG, Su ZZ, Emdad L, Gupta P, Sarkar D, Borjabad A, Volsky DJ. et al. J Biol Chem 2008;283:13116–13123.

395. Ci X, Song Y, Zeng F, Zhang X, Li H, Wang X, Cui J. et al. Biochem Biophys Res Commun 2008;372:73–77.

396. Ci X, Li H, Song Y, An N, Yu Q, Zeng F, Deng X. Inflammation 2008;31:422–427.

397. Rice LB. J Infect Dis 2008;197:1079–1081.

398. Owens RC Jr, Ambrose PG. Diagn Microbiol Infect Dis 2007;57(Suppl 3): 77S–83S.

399. Dellit TH, Owens RC, McGowan JEJ, Gerding DN, Weinstein RA, Burke JP, Huskins WC. et al. Clin Infect Dis 2007;44:159–177.

400. Rice LB. Clin Infect Dis 2008;46:491–496.

401. Nicolau DP. Crit Care 2008;12(Suppl 4): S2.

402. Paterson DL. Clin Infect Dis 2008;47(Suppl 1): S14–20.

403. Gupta K, Macintyre A, Vanasse G, Dembry LM. J Clin Microbiol 2007;45:3930–3934.

404. Avdic E, Cosgrove SE. Expert Opin Pharmacother 2008;9:1463–1479.

405. Kale-Pradhan P, Johnson LB. Expert Rev Anti Infect Ther 2008;6:909–915.

406. Hadley JA, Pfaller MA. Diagn Microbiol Infect Dis 2007;57(Suppl 3): 47S–54S.

407. Peterson LR. Clin Infect Dis 2006;42:224–233.

408. Aspa J, Rajas O, de Castro FR, Expert Opin Pharmacother 2008;9:229–241.

409. Giamarellou H. Med Clin North Am 1995;79:559–580.

410. Hughes WT, Armstrong D, Bodey GP, Brown AE, Edwards JE, Feld R, Pizzo P. et al. Clin Infect Dis 1997;25:551–573.

411. Paul M, Yahav D, Fraser A, Leibovici L. J Antimicrob Chemother 2006;57:176–189.

412. Neuburger S, Maschmeyer G. Ann Hematol 2006;85:345–356.

413. Bodey GP. Clin Infect Dis 1993;17(Suppl 2): S378–S384.

414. Pizzo PA. N Engl J Med 1993;328:1323–1332.

415. Rossini F, Pioltelli P, Bolis S, Borin L, Casaroli I, Lanzi E, Maffe P. et al. Clin Drug Investig 1998;15:425–433.

416. Borbolla JR, Lopez-Hernandez MA, Gonzalez-Avante M, DeDiego J, Trueba E, Alvarado ML, Jimenez RM. Chemotherapy 2001;47: 381–384.

417. Sanders JW, Powe NR, Moore RD. J Infect Dis 1991;164:907–916.

418. Chernobelski P, Lavrenkov K, Rimar D, Riesenberg K, Schlaeffer F, Ariad S, Mermershtain W. Chemotherapy 2006;52:185–189.

419. Gorschluter M, Hahn C, Fixson A, Mey U, Ziske C, Molitor E, Horre R. et al. Support Care Cancer 2003;11:362–370.

420. Viscoli C, Cometta A, Kern WV, Bock R, Paesmans M, Crokaert F, Glauser MP. et al. Clin Microbiol Infect 2006;12:212–216.

421. Fleischhack G, Hartmann C, Simon A, Wulff B, Havers W, Marklein G, Hasan C. et al. J Antimicrob Chemother 2001;47:841–853.

422. Ariffin H, Arasu A, Mahfuzah M, Ariffin WA, Chan LL, Lin HP. J Paediatr Child Health 2001;37:38–43.

423. Ariffin H, Ai CL, Lee CL, Abdullah WA. J Paediatr Child Health 2006;42:781–784.

424. Chain E, Florey HW, Gardner AD, Heatley NG, Jennings MA, Orr-Ewing J, Sanders AG. Lancet 1940;2:226.

425. Clarke HT, Johnson JR, Robinson R. The Chemistry of Penicillin. Princeton, NJ: Princeton University Press; 1949.

426. Abraham EP, Chain E, Gardner AD, Heatley NG, Jennings MA, Florey HW. Lancet 1941;2:177.

427. Crowfoot-Hodgkin D, Bunn CW, Rogers-Low BW, Turner-Jones A.In: Clarke HT, Johnson JR, Robinson R, editors. The Chemistry of Penicillin. Princeton, NJ: Princeton University Press; 1949. p 310–367.

428. Thorn JA, Johnson MJ. J Am Chem Soc 1950;72:2052.

429. Mortimer DC, Johnson MJ. J Am Chem Soc 1952;74:4098.

430. Behrens OK, Corse JJ, Jones RG, Mann MJ, Soper QF, Van Abeel FR, Chiang MC. J Biol Chem 1948;175:771.

431. Abraham EP, Newton GGF. Biochem J 1954;58:94.

432. Flynn EH, McCormick MH, Stamper MC, De Valeria H, Godzeski CW. J Am Chem Soc 1962;84:4594.

433. Soper QF, Whitehead CW, Behrens OK, Corse JJ, Jones RG. J Am Chem Soc 1948;70:2849.

434. Tosoni AL, Glass DG, Goldsmith L. Biochem J 1958;69:476.

435. Rolinson GN, Geddes AM. Int J Antimicrob Agents 2007;29:3–8.

436. Batchelor FR, Doyle FP, Nayler JH, Rolinson GN. Nature 1959;183:257–258.

437. Sheehan JC, Henery-Logan KR. J Am Chem Soc 1957;79:1262.

438. Sheehan JC, Henery-Logan KR. J Am Chem Soc 1959;81:3089.

439. Sheehan JC, Henery-Logan KR. J Am Chem Soc 1959;81:2912.

440. Sheehan JC, Henery-Logan KR. J Am Chem Soc 1962;84:2983.

441. Bose AK, Spiegelman G, Manhas MS. J Am Chem Soc 1968;90:4506.

442. Firestone RA, Maciejewicz NS, Ratcliffe BG, Christensen BG. J Org Chem 1974;39:437.

443. Baldwin JE, Christie MA, Haber SB, Kruse LI. J Am Chem Soc 1976;98:3045.

444. Ponsford RJ. The penicillins. In: Kirk–Othmer Encyclopedia of Chemical Technology 4th ed. Vol, 3,New York: John Wiley Sons; 1992. p 129–158.

445. Williamson GM, Morrison JK, Stevens KJ, Lancet 1961;1:847–850.

446. Ridley M, Lynn R, Barrie D, Stead KC. Lancet 1970;1:230–233.

447. Doyle FP, Hardy KD, Nayler JHC, Soulal MJ, Stove ER, Waddington HRJ. J Chem Soc 1962; 1453.

448. Yurchenco JA, Hopper MW, Warren GH. Antibiot Chemother 1962;12:534–544.

449. Doyle FP, Long AA, Nayler JH, Stove ER. Nature 1961;192:1183–1184.

450. Nayler JHC, Long AAW, Brown DM, Acred P, Rolinson GN, Batchelor FR, Stevens S. et al. Nature 1962;195:1264–1267.

451. Bennett JV, Gravenkemper CF, Brodie JL, Kirby WM. Antimicrob Agents Chemother 1964;10:257–262.

452. Sutherland R, Croydon EA, Rolinson GN. Br Med J 1970;4:455–460.

453. Rolinson GN, Stevens S. Br Med J 1961;2:191–196.

454. Dolfini JE, Applegate HE, Bach G, Basch H, Bernstein J, Schwartz J, Weisenborn FL. J Med Chem 1971;14:117–119.

455. Brogden RN, Speight TM, Avery GS. Drugs 1974;7:326–336.

456. Brogden RN, Heel RC, Speight TM, Avery GS. Drugs 1979;18:169–184.

457. Roseman SB, Weber LS, Owen G, Warren GH. Antimicrob Agents Chemother 1967;7: 590–596.

458. Clayton JP, Cole M, Elson SW, Ferres H. Antimicrob Agents Chemother 1974;5:670–671.

459. Bodin NO, Ekstrom B, Forsgren U, Jalar LP, Magni L, Ramsay CH, Sjoberg B. Antimicrob Agents Chemother 1975;8:518–525.

460. Foltz EL, West JW, Breslow IH, Wallick H. Antimicrob Agents Chemother 1970;10: 442–454.

461. Sakamoto F, Ikeda S, Tsukamoto G. Chem Pharm Bull 1984;32:2241.

462. Acred P, Brown DM, Knudsen ET, Rolinson GN, Sutherland R. Nature 1967;215:25–30.

463. Sutherland R, Burnett J, Rolinson GN. Antimicrob Agents Chemother 1970;10: 390–395.

464. Morimoto S, Nomura H, Fugono T, Azuma T, Minami J. J Med Chem 1972;15:1108–1111.

465. Lund FJ.In: Elks J, editors. Recent Advances in the Chemistry of β-Lactam Antibiotics. London: Royal Society of Chemistry; 1977. p 25–45.

466. Roholt K. J Antimicrob Chemother 1977;3 (Suppl B): 71–81.

467. Josefsson K, Bergan T, Magni L, Pring BG, Westerlund D. Eur J Clin Pharmacol 1982;23:249–252.

468. Brown P, Calvert SH, Chapman PCA, Cosham SC, Eglington AJ, Elliot RL, Harriss MA. et al. J Chem Soc Perkin Trans 1991;1:881.

469. Mizen L, Berry V, Woodnutt G. J Pharm Pharmacol 1995;47:725–730.

470. Rolinson GN. J Antimicrob Chemother 1986;17:5–36.

471. Lorian V, editor. Antibiotics in Laboratory Medicine. 2nd ed. Baltimore MD: Williams & Wilkins; 1986.

472. Wright AJ. Mayo Clin Proc 1999;74:290–307.

473. Strominger JL, Tipper DJ. Am J Med 1965;39:708–721.

474. Tipper DJ.In: Tipper DJ, editor. Mode of Action of β-Lactam Antibiotics: Antibiotic Inhibitors of Bacterial Cell Wall Biosynthesis. Elmsford, NY: Pergamon; 1987. p 133–170.

475. Bohme EHW, Applegate HE, Teoplitz B, Gougoutas JZ. J Am Chem Soc 1971;93:4324.

476. Firestone RA, Schelechow N, Johnson DBR, Christensen BG. Tetrahedron Lett 1972;13:375.

477. Gordon EM, Sykes RB.In: Morin RB Gorman Meditros. Chemistry Biology of β-Lactam Antibiotics Vol, 1,New York: Academic Press; 1982. p 199–370.

478. Baldwin JE, Urban FJ, Cooper RDG, Jose FL. J Am Chem Soc 1973;95:2401.

479. Koppel GA, Koehler RE. J Am Chem Soc 1973;95:2403.

480. Slusarchyk WA, Applegate HE, Funke P, Koster W, Puar MS, Young M, Dolfini JE. J Org Chem 1973;38:943.

481. Jen T, Frazee J, Hoover RE. J Org Chem 1973;38:2857.

482. Cama LD, Leanza WJ, Beattie TR, Christensen BG. J Am Chem Soc 1972;94: 1408–1410.

483. Bentley PH, Clayton JP. J Chem Soc Chem Commun 1974; 278.

484. Taylor AW, Burton G. Tetrahedron Lett 1977;18:3831.

485. Gordon EM, Chang HW, Cimarusti CM. J Am Chem Soc 1977;99(16): 5504–5505.

486. Yanagisawa H, Fukushima M, Ando A, Nakao H. J Antibiot 1976;29:969–972.

487. Ponsford RJ, Basker MJ, Burton G, Guest AW, Harrington FP, Milner PH, Pearson MJ. et al. In: Brown AJ, Roberts SM, editors. Recent Advances in the Chemistry of β-Lactam Antibiotics. London: Royal Society of Chemistry; 1985. 32–57.

488. Milner PH, Guest AW, Harrington FP, Ponsford RJ, Smale TC, Stachulski AV. J Chem Soc Chem Commun 1984; 1335.

489. Branch CL, Pearson MJ, Smale TC. J Chem Soc Perkin Trans 1: 2865;1988:.

490. Kaura AC, Pearson MJ. Tetrahedron Lett 1985;26:2597.

491. Slocombe B, Basker MJ, Bentley PH, Clayton JP, Cole M, Comber KR, Dixon RA. et al. Antimicrob Agents Chemother 1981;20:38–46.

492. Spencer RC. J Antimicrob Chemother 1990;26:735–737.

493. Rodriguez-Villalobos H, Malaviolle V, Frankard J, de Mendonca R, Nonhoff C, Struelens MJ. J Antimicrob Chemother 2006;57:771–774.

494. Livermore DM, Hope R, Fagan EJ, Warner M, Woodford N, Potz. N. J Antimicrob Chemother 2006;57:1012–1014.

495. Giamarellou H. Clin Microbiol Infect 2008;14 (Suppl 1): 194–197.

496. Livermore DM, Tulkens PM. J Antimicrob Chemother 2009;63:243–245.

497. Burton G, Best DJ, Dixon RA, Kenyon RF, Lashford AG. J Antibiot 1986;39:1419–1429.

498. Guest AW, Harrington FP, Milner PH, Ponsford RJ, Smale TC, Stachulski AV, Basker MJ. et al. J Antibiot 1986;39:1498–1501.

499. Basker MJ, Edmondson RA, Knott SJ, Ponsford RJ, Slocombe B, White SJ. Antimicrob Agents Chemother 1984;26:734–740.

500. Best DJ, Burton G, Davies DT, Elder JS, Smale TC, Southgate R, Stachulski AV. et al. J Antibiot 1990;43:574–577.

501. Watanabe Y, Minami S, Hayashi T, Araki H, Kitayama R, Ochiai H. Antimicrob Agents Chemother 1995;39:2787–2791.

502. Matsumura N, Minami S, Mitsuhashi S. J Antimicrob Chemother 1997;39:31–34.

503. Fawcett PA, Usher JJ, Huddleston JA, Bleaney RC, Nisbet JJ, Abraham EP. Biochem J 1976;157:651–660.

504. O'Sullivan J, Bleaney RC, Huddleston JA, Abraham EP. Biochem J 1979;184:421–426.

505. van Liempt H, von Dohren H, Kleinkauf H. J Biol Chem 1989;264:3680–3684.

506. MacCabe AP, van Liempt H, Palissa H, Unkles SE, Riach MB, Pfeifer E, von Dohren H. et al. J Biol Chem 1991;266:12646–12654.

507. Shiau CY, Baldwin JE, Byford MF, Sobey WJ, Schofield CJ. FEBS Lett 1995;358:97–100.

508. Kallow W, Neuhof T, Arezi B, Jungblut P, von Dohren H, FEBS Lett 1997;414:74–78.

509. Demain AL. J Antibiot 2000;53:995–1002.

510. Roach PL, Clifton IJ, Hensgens CM, Shibata N, Schofield CJ, Hajdu J, Baldwin JE. Nature 1997;387:827–830.

511. Burzlaff NI, Rutledge PJ, Clifton IJ, Hensgens CM, Pickford M, Adlington RM, Roach PL. et al. Nature 1999;401:721–724.

512. Miller MT, Bachmann BO, Townsend CA, Rosenzweig AC. Nat Struct Biol 2001;8:684–689.

513. Elkins JM, Rutledge PJ, Burzlaff NI, Clifton IJ, Adlington RM, Roach PL, Baldwin JE. Org Biomol Chem 2003;1:1455–1460.

514. Long AJ, Clifton IJ, Roach PL, Baldwin JE, Rutledge PJ, Schofield CJ. Biochemistry 2005;44:6619–6628.

515. Howard-Jones AR, Rutledge PJ, Clifton IJ, Adlington RM, Baldwin JE. Biochem Biophys Res Commun 2005;336:702–708.

516. Howard-Jones AR, Elkins JM, Clifton IJ, Roach PL, Adlington RM, Baldwin JE, Rutledge PJ. Biochemistry 2007;46:4755–4762.

517. Nolan EM, Walsh CT. ChemBioChem 2009;10:34–53.

518. Lundberg M, Siegbahn PE, Morokuma K. Biochemistry 2008;47:1031–1042.

519. Valegard K, van Scheltinga AC, Lloyd MD, Hara T, Ramaswamy S, Perrakis A, Thompson A. et al. Nature 1998;394: 805–809.

520. Bachmann BO, Li R, Townsend CA. Proc Natl Acad Sci USA 1998;95:9082–9086.

521. Tahlan K, Anders C, Wong A, Mosher RH, Beatty PH, Brumlik MJ, Griffin A. et al. Chem Biol 2007;14:131–142.

522. Zelyas NJ, Cai H, Kwong T, Jensen SE. J Bacteriol 2008;190:7957–7965.

523. Sprote P, Hynes MJ, Hortschansky P, Shelesty E, Scharf DH, Wolke SM, Brakhage AA. Mol Microbiol 2008;70:445–461.

524. Newton GG, Abraham EP. Nature 1955;175:548.

525. Newton GG, Abraham EP. Biochem J 1956;62:651–658.

526. Abraham EP, Newton GG. Biochem J 1956;62:658–665.

527. Abraham EP, Newton GG. Biochem J 1961;79:377–393.

528. Hodgkin DC, Maslen EN. Biochem J 1961;79:393–402.

529. Abraham EP, Loder PB.In: Flynn EH, editor. Cephalosporins and Penicillins: Chemistry and Biology. New York: Academic Press; 1972. p 1–26.

530. Elks J. Drugs 1987;34(Suppl 2): 240–246.

531. Nagarajan R, Boeck LD, Gorman M, Hamill RL, Higgens CE, Hoehn MM, Stark WM. et al. J Am Chem Soc 1971;93:2308–2310.

532. Christensen BG, Ruswinkle LJ, Cama LD. Rev Infect Dis 1979;1:64–72.

533. Tsubotani S, Hida T, Kasahara F, Wada Y, Harada S. J Antibiot 1984;37:1546–1554.

534. Dolfini JE, Schwartz J, Weisenborn F. J Org Chem 1969;34:1582–1586.

535. Neidleman SL, Pan SC, Last JA, Dolfini JE. J Med Chem 1970;13:386–388.

536. Ratcliffe RW, Christensen BG. Tetrahedron Lett 1973;14:4645.

537. Ratcliffe RW, Christensen BG. Tetrahedron Lett 1973;14:4649.

538. Ratcliffe RW, Christensen BG. Tetrahedron Lett 1973;14:4653.

539. Woodward RB. Science 1966;153:487.

540. Woodward RB, Heusler K, Gosteli J, Naegeli P, Oppolzer W, Ramage R, Ranganathan S. et al. J Am Chem Soc 1966;88:852.

541. Morin RB, Jackson BG, Mueller RA, Lavagnino ER, Scanlon WB, Andrews SL. J Am Chem Soc 1963;85:1896.

542. Chou TS, Burgtorf JR, Ellis AL, Lammert SR, Kukolja SP. J Am Chem Soc 1974;96: 1609–1610.

543. Cooper RDG, Spry DO.In: Flynn EH, editor. Cephalosporins Penicillins: Chemistry Biology New York: Academic Press; 1972. p 183–254.

544. Cooper RDG, Hatfield LD, Spry DO. Acc Chem Res 1973;6:32.

545. Preston DA, Turik M. J Chemother 1998;10: 195–202.

546. Chauvette RR, Pennington PA, Ryan CW, Cooper RD, Jose FL, Wright IG, Van Heyningen EM. et al. J Org Chem 1971;36:1259–1267.

547. Kukolja S, Lammert SR, Gleissner MR, Ellis AI. J Am Chem Soc 1976;98:5040–5041.

548. Kukolja S, Chauvette RR.In: Morin RB, Gorman M, editors. Chemistry and Biology of β-Lactam Antibiotics. Vol. 1.New York: Academic Press; 1982. p 93–198.

549. Torii S, Tanaka H, Saitoh N, Siroi T, Sasaoka H, Nokami J. Tetrahedron Lett 1982;23:2187.

550. Tanaka H, Taniguchi M, Kameyama Y, Monnin M, Sasaoka H, Shiroi T, Nagao S. et al. Chem Lett 1990 1867.

551. Huber FM, Baltz RH, Caltrider PG. Appl Microbiol 1968;16:1011–1014.

552. Higgins CE, Hamill RL, Sands TH, Hoehn MM, Davis NE, Nagarajan R, Boeck LD. J Antibio 1974;27:298.

553. Traxler P, Treichler HJ, Nuesch J. J Antibiot 1975;28:605–606.

554. Kaznaki T, Fukita T, Kitano K, Katamoto K, Nara K, Nakao Y. J Ferment Technol 1976;54:712.

555. Kitano K, Fujusawa Y, Katamoto K, Nara K, Nakao Y. J Ferment Technol 1976;54:712.

556. Kitano K, Fujusawa Y, Katamoto K, Nara K, Nakao Y. J Ferment Technol 1976;54:720.

557. Shoji J, Sakazaki R, Matsumoto K, Tanimoto T, Terui Y, Kozuki S, Kondo E. J Antibiot 1983;36:167–169.

558. Alvi KA, Reeves CD, Peterson J, Lein J. J Antibiot 1995;48:338–340.

559. Hatfield LD, Lunn WH, Jackson BG, Peters LR, Blaszczac LC, Fisher JW, Gardiner JP. et al. In: Gregory GI, editor. Recent Advances in the Chemistry of β-Lactam Antibiotics. London: Royal Society of Chemistry; 1981; p 109–124.

560. Roberts J, editor. The cephalosporins. In: Kirk–Othmer Encyclopedia of Chemical Technology 4th ed.Vol, 3,New York: John Wiley Sons; 1992. p 28–82.

561. Murray CF, Webber JA.In: Flynn EH, editor. Cephalosporins and Penicillins, Chemistry & Biology. London; Academic Press; 1972. p 134–182.

562. Hatfield LD, Fisher JW, Dunigan JM, Burchfield RW, Greene JM, Webber JA, Vasileff RT. et al. Philos Trans R Soc Lond B Biol Sci 1980;289:173–179.

563. Stedman RJ, Swered K, Hoover JR. J Med Chem 1964;7:117–119.

564. Takaya T, Takasugi H, Murakawa T, Nakano H. J Antibiot 1981;34:1300–1310.

565. Wilson EM. Chem Ind 1984; 217.

566. Koppel GA, Kinnick MD, Nummy LJ. J Am Chem Soc 1977;99:2822–2823.

567. Elks J. Drugs 1987;34(Suppl 2): 247–252.

568. Newall CH, Hallam PD.In: Sammes PG, Taylor JB, editors. Comprehensive Medicinal Chemistry. Vol. 2.Elmsford, NY: Pergamon; 1990. p 609–653.

569. Durkheimer W, Adam F, Fisher G, Kirrstetter R. Adv Drug Res 1988;17:61–234.

570. Klein NC, Cunha BA. Adv Ther 1995;12:83–101.

571. Ryan CW, Simon RL, Van EM, Heyningen J Med Chem 1969;12:310–313.

572. Chauvette RR, Jackson BG, Lavagnino ER, Morin RB, Mueller RA, Pioch RP, Roeske RW. et al. J Am Chem Soc 1962;84:3401.

573. Adams HG, Stilwell GA, Turck M. Antimicrob Agents Chemother 1976;9:1019–1024.

574. Brogden RN, Heel RC, Speight TM, Avery GS. Drugs 1979;17:233–266.

575. Neu HC, Fu KP. Antimicrob Agents Chemother 1978;13:584–588.

576. Klein NC, Cunha BA. Med Clin North Am 1995;79:705–719.

577. Adu A, Armour CL. Drugs 1995;50:423–439.

578. Muytjens HL, van der Ros-van de Repe J. Antimicrob Agents Chemother 1982;21:925–934.

579. Todd PA, Brogden RN. Drugs 1990; 40:608–651.

580. Neu HC. Infection 1991;19(Suppl 6): S309–S315.

581. Lode H. Diagn Microbiol Infect Dis 1995;22:1–3.

582. Richards DM, Heel RC, Brogden RN, Speight TM, Avery GS. Drugs 1984;27:469–527.

583. Brogden RN, Campoli-Richards DM. Drugs 1989;38:524–550.

584. Brogden RN, Carmine A, Heel RC, Morley PA, Speight TM, Avery GS. Drugs 1981;22:423–460.

585. Richards DM, Brogden RN. Drugs 1985;29: 105–161.

586. Tsuchiya K, Kondo M, Nagatomo H. Antimicrob Agents Chemother 1978;13:137–145.

587. Kessler RE, Bies M, Buck RE, Chisholm DR, Pursiano TA, Tsai YH, Misiek M. et al. Antimicrob Agents Chemother 1985;27: 207–216.

588. Wynd MA, Paladino JA. Ann Pharmacother 1996;30:1414–1424.

589. Endimiani A, Perez F, Bonomo RA. Expert Rev Anti Infect Ther 2008;6:805–824.

590. Wiseman LR, Lamb HM. Drugs 1997;54: 117–140.

591. Numata M, Minamida I, Yamaoka M, Shiraishi M, Miyawaki T, Akimoto H, Naito K. et al. J Antibiot 1978;31:1262–1271.

592. Cherry PC, Cook MC, Foxton MW, Gregson M, Gregory GI, Webb GB.In: Elks J, editor. Recent Advances in the Chemistry of β-Lactam Antibiotics. London: Royal Society of Chemistry; 1977. p 145–152.

593. Kant J, Farina V. Tetrahedron Lett 1992;33:3563.

594. Kant J, Roth JA, Fuller CE, Walker DG, Benigni DA, Farina V. J Org Chem 1994;59:4956.

595. Martinez JL, Delgado-Iribarren A, Baquero F. FEMS Microbiol Rev 1990;6:45–56.

596. Miller MJ, Maouin F. Acc. Chem. Res. 1993;26:241.

597. Mochizuki H, Oikawa Y, Yamada H, Kusakabe S, Shiihara T, Murakami K, Kato K. et al. J Antibiot 1988;41:377–391.

598. Okita T, Imae K, Hasegawa T, Iimura S, Masuyoshi S, Kamachi H, Kamei H. J Antibiot 1993;46:833–839.

599. Adams RG, Brain EG, Branch CL, Guest AW, Harrington FP, Mizen L, Neale JE. et al. J Antibiot 1995;48:417–424.

600. Watanabe NA, Nagasu T, Katsu K, Kitoh K. Antimicrob Agents Chemother 1987;31: 497–504.

601. Critchley IA, Basker MJ, Edmondson RA, Knott SJ. J Antimicrob Chemother 1991;28: 377–388.

602. Silley P, Griffiths JW, Monsey D, Harris AM. Antimicrob Agents Chemother 1990;34: 1806–1808.

603. Tatsumi Y, Maejima T, Mitsuhashi S. Antimicrob Agents Chemother 1995;39:613–619.

604. Southgate R, Elson S, editors. Progress in the Chemistry of Organic Natural Products. New York: Springer-Verlag; 1985. p 1–106.

605. Nozaki Y, Katayama N, Tsubotani S, Ono H, Okazaki H. J Antibiot 1985;38:1141–1151.

606. Singh PD, Young MG, Johnson JH, Cimarusti CM, Sykes RB. J Antibiot 1984;37:773–780.

607. Shoji J, Kato T, Sakazaki R, Nagata W, Terui Y, Nakagawa Y, Shiro M. et al. J Antibiot 1984;37:1486–1490.

608. Shoji J, Sakazaki R, Kato T, Terui Y, Matsumoto K, Tanimoto T, Hattori T. et al. J Antibiot 1985;38:538–540.

609. Karady S, Pines SH, Weinstock LM, Roberts FE, Brenner GS, Hoinowski AM, Cheng TY. et al. J Am Chem Soc 1972;94:1410–1411.

610. Lunn WH, Burchfield RW, Elzey TK, Mason EV. Tetrahedron Lett 1974;15:1307.

611. Karady S, Amato JS, Weinstock LM, Sletzinger M. Tetrahedron Lett 1978;19:407.

612. Applegate HE, Cimarusti CM, Slusarchyk WA. J Chem Soc Chem Commun 1980; 293.

613. Shiokazi M, Ishida N, Iino K, Hiraoka T. Tetrahedron 1980;36:2735.

614. Stapley EO, Birnbaum J, Miller KA, Hyman W, Endlin D, Woodruff B. Rev Infect Dis 1979;1:73.

615. Okonogi K, Sugiura A, Kuno M, Ono H, Harada S, Higashide E. J Antibiot 1985;38: 1555–1563.

616. Koppel GA, Koehler RE. J Am Chem Soc 1980;102:1690.

617. Saito T, Sugimura Y, Iwano Y, Iino K, Hiraoka T. Tetrahedron Lett 1976;17:1310.

618. Yanagisawa H, Fukushima M, Ando A, Nakao H. Tetrahedron Lett 1975;16:2705.

619. Nakao H, Yanagisawa H, Shimizu B, Kaneko M, Nagano M. J Antibiot 1976;29:554–558.

620. Applegate HE, Cimarusti CM, Dolfini JE, Funke P, Koster WH, Puar MS, Slusarchyk WA. et al. J Org Chem 1979;44:811.

621. Nakatsuka SI, Tanino H, Kishi Y. J Am Chem Soc 1975;97:5008–5010.

622. Nakatsuka SI, Tanino H, Kishi Y. J Am Chem Soc 1975;97:5010–5012.

623. Brogden RN, Heel RC, Speight TM, Avery GS. Drugs 1979;17:1–37.

624. Benlloch M, Torres A, Soriano F. J Antimicrob Chemother 1982;10:347–350.

625. Jones RN. Am J Surg 1988;155:16–23.

626. Guest AW, Branch CL, Finch SC, Kaura AC, Milner PH, Pearson MJ, Ponsford RJ. et al. J Chem Soc Perkin Trans 1 1987; 45.

627. Berry PD, Brown AG, Hanson JC, Kaura AC, Milner PH, Moores CJ, Quick K et al. Tetrahedron Lett 1991;32:2683.

628. Basker MJ, Branch CL, Finch SC, Guest AW, Milner PH, Pearson MJ, Ponsford RJ. et al. J Antibiot 1986;39:1788–1791.

629. Branch CL, Basker MJ, Finch SC, Guest AW, Harrington FP, Kaura AC, Knott SJ. et al. J Antibiot 1987;40:646–651.

630. Gensberg K, Doyle EJ, Perry DJ, Smith AW. J Antimicrob Chemother 1994;34:697–705.

631. Southgate R, Branch CL, Coulton S, Hunt E. In: Lukacs G, Ohno M, editors. Recent Progress in the Chemical Synthesis of Antibiotics. New York: Springer-Verlag; 1993. p 622–675.

632. Cama LD, Christensen BG. J Am Chem Soc 1974;96:7582–7584.

633. Firestone RA, Fahey JL, Maciejewicz NS, Patel GS, Christensen BG. J Med Chem 1977;20:551–556.

634. Narisada M, Onoue M, Nagata H. Heterocycles 1977;7:839.

635. Branch CL, Pearson MJ. J Chem Soc Perkin Trans 1979;1:2268.

636. Narisada M, Yoshida T, Onoue M, Ohtani M, Okada T, Tsuji T, Kikkawa I. et al. J Med Chem 1979;22:757–759.

637. Carmine AA, Brogden RN, Heel RC, Romankiewicz JA, Speight TM, Avery GS. Drugs 1983;26:279–333.

638. Lipsky JJ, Lewis JC, Novick WJ Jr. Antimicrob Agents Chemother 1984;25:380–381.

639. Narisada M, Tsuji T.In: Lukacs G, Ohno M, editors. Recent Progress in the Chemical Synthesis of Antibiotics. New York: Springer-Verlag; 1990. p 705–725.

640. Tsuji T, Satoh H, Narisada M, Hamashima Y, Yoshida T. J Antibiot 1985;38:466–476.

641. Cazzola M, Brancaccio V, De Giglio C, Paterno E, Matera MG, Rossi F. Int J Clin Pharmacol Ther Toxicol 1993;31:148–152.

642. Nagata W. Philos Trans R Soc Lond B Biol Sci 1980;289:225–230.

643. Nagata W. Pure Appl Chem 1989;61:325.

644. Okonogi T, Shibahara S, Murai Y, Yoshida T, Inouye S, Kondo S, Christensen BG. J Antibiot 1990;43:357–371.

645. Kamachi H, Okita T, Yamasaki T, Naito T. J Antibiot 1990;43:820–829.

646. Branch CL, Basker MJ, Pearson MJ. J Antibiot 1986;39:1792–1795.

647. Cooper RDG.In: Page MI, editor. The Chemistry of β-Lactams. London: Chapman & Hall; 1992. p 272–303.

648. Neu HC.In: Page MI, editor. The Chemistry of, β-Lactams London: Chapman, Hall; 1992. p 118.

649. Cook GK, McDonald JH 3rd Alborn W Jr, Boyd DB, Eudaly JA, Indelicato JM, Johnson R. et al. J Med Chem 1989;32:2442–2450.

650. Tune BM, Hsu CY, Fravert D. Biochem Pharmacol 1996;51:557–561.

651. Ternansky RJ, Draheim SE, Pike AJ, Bell FW, West SJ, Jordan CL, Wu CY. et al. J Med Chem 1993;36:1971–1976.

652. Ternansky RJ, Jordan CL, Eudaly JA, Kasher JS. J Med Chem 1993;36:2332–2334.

653. Ruano G, Martianez J, Grande M, Anaya J. J Org Chem 2003;68:2024–2027.

654. Hakimelahi GH, Li PC, Moosavi-Movahedi AA, Chamani J, Khodarahmi GA, Ly TW, Valiyev F. et al. Org Biomol Chem 2003;1:2461–2467.

655. Page MG. Expert Opin Investig Drugs 2004;13:973–985.

656. Page MG. Expert Opin Emerg Drugs 2007;12:511–524.

657. Huang V, Brown WJ, Rybak MJ. Antimicrob Agents Chemother 2004;48:2719–2723.

658. Miller K, Storey C, Stubbings WJ, Hoyle AM, Hobbs JK, Chopra I. J Antimicrob Chemother 2005;55:579–582.

659. Page MG. Curr Opin Pharmacol 2006; 6:480–485.

660. Toda A, Ohki H, Yamanaka T, Murano K, Okuda S, Kawabata K, Hatano K. et al. Bioorg Med Chem Lett 2008;18:4849–4852.

661. Takeda S, Nakai T, Wakai Y, Ikeda F, Hatano K. Antimicrob Agents Chemother 2007; 51:826–830.

662. Takeda S, Ishii Y, Hatano K, Tateda K, Yamaguchi K. Int J Antimicrob Agents 2007;30:443–445.

663. Vouillamoz J, Entenza JM, Hohl P, Moreillon P. Antimicrob Agents Chemother 2004;48: 4322–4327.

664. Sader HS, Johnson DM, Jones RN. Antimicrob Agents Chemother 2004;48:53–62.

665. Lee VJ, Hecker SJ. Med Res Rev 1999; 19:521–542.

666. Hecker SJ, Glinka TW, Cho A, Zhang ZJ, Price ME, Chamberland S, Griffith D. et al. J Antibiot 2000;53:1272–1281.

667. Cho A, Glinka TW, Ludwikow M, Fan AT, Wang M, Hecker SJ. Bioorg Med Chem Lett 2001;11:137–140.

668. Hoellman DB, Kelly LM, Jacobs MR, Appelbaum PC. Clin Microbiol Infect 2002;8: 814–822.

669. Johnson AP, Warner M, Carter M, Livermore DM. Antimicrob Agents Chemother 2002;46: 321–326.

670. Swenson JM, Tenover FC. J Antimicrob Chemother 2002;49:845–850.

671. Malouin F, Blais J, Chamberland S, Hoang M, Park C, Chan C, Mathias K. et al. Antimicrob Agents Chemother 2003;47:658–664.

672. Chamberland S, Blais J, Hoang M, Dinh C, Cotter D, Bond E, Gannon C. et al. Antimicrob Agents Chemother 2001;45:1422–1430.

673. Griffith DC, Harford L, Williams R, Lee VJ, Dudley MN. Antimicrob Agents Chemother 2003;47:43–47.

674. Griffith DC, Rodriguez D, Corcoran E, Dudley MN. Antimicrob Agents Chemother 2008;52: 244–247.

675. Yoshizawa H, Itani H, Ishikura K, Irie T, Yokoo K, Kubota T, Minami K. et al. J Antibiot 2002;55:975–992.

676. Yoshizawa H, Kubota T, Itani H, Ishitobi H, Miwa H, Nishitani Y. Bioorg Med Chem 2004;12:4211–4219.

677. Fujimura T, Yamano Y, Yoshida I, Shimada J, Kuwahara S. Antimicrob Agents Chemother 2003;47:923–931.

678. Miyazaki S, Okazaki K, Tsuji M, Yamaguchi K. Antimicrob Agents Chemother 2004;48:378–383.

679. Tsuji M, Takema M, Miwa H, Shimada J, Kuwahara S. Antimicrob Agents Chemother 2003;47:2507–2512.

680. Barbachyn MR. Annu Rep Med Chem 2008;43:281–290.

681. Long DD, Aggen JB, Christensen BG, Judice JK, Hegde SS, Kaniga K, Krause KM. et al. J Antibiot 2008;61:595–602.

682. Long DD, Aggen J, Chinn J, Choi S-K, Christensen BG, Fatheree P, Green D. et al. 47th ICCAC Meeting; Chicago 2007, Poster F1 (2109).

683. Long DD, Aggen JB, Chinn J, Choi SK, Christensen BG, Fatheree PR, Green D. et al. J Antibiot 2008;61:603–614.

684. Krause KM, Difuntorum S, Blais J, Turner SD, Marquess D. 47th ICCAC Meeting; Chicago IL; 2007, Poster E(1626).

685. Blais J, Difuntorum S, Krause KM, Debabov DV, Benton BM, Turner SD, Marquess D. 47th ICCAC Meeting; Chicago IL; 2007, Poster C1 (1475).

686. Difuntorum S, Blais J, Hedge SS, Skinner R, Reyes N, Trumbull J, Turner SD. et al. 47th ICCAC Meeting; Chicago IL; 2007. Poster F1 (2110).

687. Ishikawa T, Matsunaga N, Tawada H, Kuroda N, Nakayama Y, Ishibashi Y, Tomimoto M. et al. Bioorg Med Chem 2003;11:2427–2437.

688. Iizawa Y, Nagai J, Ishikawa T, Hashiguchi S, Nakao M, Miyake A, Okonogi K. J Infect Chemother 2004;10:146–156.

689. Parish D. Scheinfeld N. Curr Opin Investig Drugs 2008;9201–209.

690. Wang Y, Serradell N, Rosa E, Bolos J. Drugs Fut 2008;33:302.

691. Sader HS, Fritsche TR, Kaniga K, Ge Y, Jones RN. Antimicrob Agents Chemother 2005;49: 3501–3512.

692. Mushtaq S, Warner M, Ge Y, Kaniga K, Livermore DM. J Antimicrob Chemother 2007;60:300–311.

693. Sader HS, Fritsche TR, Jones RN. Antimicrob Agents Chemother 2008;52:1153–1155.

694. Fenoll A, Aguilar L, Robledo O, Gimenez MJ, Granizo JJ, Biek D, Tarrago D. Antimicrob Agents Chemother 2008;52:4209–4210.

695. McGee L, Biek D, Ge Y, Klugman M, du Plessis M, Smith AM, Beall B. et al. Antimicrob Agents Chemother 2009;53:552–556.

696. Ge Y, Biek D, Talbot GH, Sahm DF. Antimicrob Agents Chemother 2008;52:3398–3407.

697. Brown SD, Traczewski MM. Antimicrob Agents Chemother 2009;53:1271–1274.

698. Jacqueline C, Caillon J, Le Mabecque V, Miegeville AF, Hamel A, Bugnon D, Ge JY. et al. Antimicrob Agents Chemother 2007;51: 3397–3400.

699. Talbot GH, Thye D, Das A, Ge Y. Antimicrob Agents Chemother 2007;51:3612–3616.

700. Abbanat D, Morrow B, Bush K. Curr Opin Pharmacol 2008;8:582–592.

701. Bush K, Heep M, Macielag MJ, Noel GJ. Expert Opin Investig Drugs 2007;16:419–429.

702. Anderson SD, Gums JG. Ann Pharmacother 2008;42:806–816.

703. Deresinski SC. Diagn Microbiol Infect Dis 2008;61:82–85.

704. Zhanel GG, Lam A, Schweizer F, Thomson K, Walkty A, Rubinstein E, Gin AS. et al. Am J Clin Dermatol 2008;9:245–254.

705. Sorbera LA, Castaner J, Castaner RM. Drugs Fut 2005;30:11–22.

706. Zbinden R, Punter V, von Graevenitz A, Antimicrob Agents Chemother 2002;46:871–874.

707. Jones RN, Deshpande LM, Mutnick AH, Biedenbach DJ. J Antimicrob Chemother 2002;50:915–932.

708. Deshpande LM, Jones RN. Clin Microbiol Infect 2003;9:1120–1124.

709. Issa NC, Rouse MS, Piper KE, Wilson WR, Steckelberg JM, Patel R. Diagn Microbiol Infect Dis 2004;48:73–75.

710. Deshpande L, Rhomberg PR, Fritsche TR, Sader HS, Jones RN. Diagn Microbiol Infect Dis 2004;50:73–75.

711. Bogdanovich T, Ednie LM, Shapiro S, Appelbaum PC. Antimicrob Agents Chemother 2005;49:4210–4219.

712. Kosowska K, Hoellman DB, Lin G, Clark C, Credito K, McGhee P, Dewasse B. et al. Antimicrob Agents Chemother 2005;49:1932–1942.

713. Jones ME. Clin Microbiol Infect 2007; 13 (Suppl 2): 17–24.

714. Fritsche TR, Sader HS, Jones RN. Diagn Microbiol Infect Dis 2008;61:86–95.

715. Chung M, Antignac A, Kim C, Tomasz A. Antimicrob Agents Chemother 2008;52:2709–2717.

716. Hebeisen P, Heinze-Krauss I, Angehrn P, Hohl P, Page MG, Then RL. Antimicrob Agents Chemother 2001;45:825–836.

717. Banerjee R, Gretes M, Basuino L, Strynadka N, Chambers HF. Antimicrob Agents Chemother 2008;52:2089–2096.

718. Davies TA, Page MG, Shang W, Andrew T, Kania M, Bush K. Antimicrob Agents Chemother 2007;51:2621–2624.

719. Queenan AM, Shang W, Kania M, Page MG, Bush K. Antimicrob Agents Chemother 2007;51:3089–3095.

720. Arias CA, Singh KV, Panesso D, Murray BE. J Antimicrob Chemother 2007;60:594–598.

721. Laohavaleeson S, Tessier PR, Nicolau DP. Antimicrob Agents Chemother 2008;52:2389–2394.

722. Craig WA, Andes DR. Antimicrob Agents Chemother 2008;52:3492–3496.

723. Lodise TP, Patel N, Renaud-Mutart A, Gorodecky E, Fritsche TR, Jones RN. Diagn Microbiol Infect Dis 2008;61:96–102.

724. Chambers HF. Clin Microbiol Infect 2006;12 (Suppl 2): 17–22.

725. Deresinski SC. Diagn Microbiol Infect Dis 2008;61:103–109.

726. Noel GJ, Bush K, Bagchi P, Ianus J, Strauss RS. Clin Infect Dis 2008;46:647–655.

727. Woodward RB.In: Elks J, editor. Recent Advances in the Chemistry of β-Lactam Antibiotics. London: Royal Society of Chemistry; 1977. p 167–180.

728. Woodward RB. Philos. Trans. R. Soc. Lond. B Biol. Sci. 1980;289:239–250.

729. Dalhoff A, Thomson CJ. Chemotherapy 2003;49:105–120.

730. Hamilton-Miller JM. Pharmacotherapy 2003;23:1497–1507.

731. Dalhoff A, Janjic N, Echols R. Biochem Pharmacol 2006;71:1085–1095.

732. Ernest I, Gosteli J, Greengass CW, Holick W, Jackman DE, Pfaendler HR, Woodward RB. J Am Chem Soc 1978;100:8214.

733. Claues K, Grimm D, Prossel G. Liebig's Ann Chem 1974; 539.

734. Lang M, Prasad K, Holick W, Gosteli J, Ernest I, Woodward RB. J Am Chem Soc 1979;101:6296.

735. Lang M, Prasad K, Gosteli J, Woodward RB. Helv Chim Acta 1980;63:1093.

736. McCombie S, Ganguly AK, Girijavallabhan VM, Jeffrey PD, Lin S, Pinto P, McPhail AT. Tetrahedron Lett 1981;22:3489.

737. Pfaendler HR, Gosteli J, Woodward RB. J Am Chem Soc 1979;101:6306.

738. DiNinno F, Beattie TR, Christensen BG. J Org Chem 1977;42:2960.

739. Girijavallabhan VM, Ganguly AK, McCombie S, Pinto P, Rizi R. Tetrahedron Lett 1981;22:3485.

740. Yoshida A, Hayashi T, Takeda N, Oida S, Ohki E. Chem Pharm Bull 1981;29:1854–1861.

741. Hayashi T, Yoshida A, Takeda N, Oida S, Sugawara S, Ohki E. Chem Pharm Bull 1981;29:3158–3172.

742. Alpegiani M, Bedeschi A, Giudici F, Perrone E, Franceschi G. J Am Chem Soc 1985;107:6398.

743. Foglio M, Battistini C, Zarini F, Scarafile C, Franceschi G. Heterocycles 1983;20:1491.

744. Alpegiani M, Bedeschi A, Foglio M, Giudici F, Perrone E. Tetrahedron Lett. 1983; 24:1627.

745. Marchand-Brynaert J, Vekemans J, Bogdan S, Cossement M, Ghosez L.In: Gregory GI, editor. Recent Advances in the Chemistry of β-Lactam Antibiotics. London: Royal Society of Chemistry; 1981. p 269–280.

746. Battistini C, Scarafile C, Foglio M, Franceschi G. Tetrahedron Lett 1984;25:2395.

747. Alfonso A, Hon F, Weinstein J, Ganguly AK. J Am Chem Soc 1982;104:6138.

748. Akira Y, Teruo H, Noriko T, Sadao O, Eiji O. Chem Pharm Bull 1983;31:768–771.

749. Perrone E, Alpegiani M, Bedeschi A, Giudici F, Franceschi G. Tetrahedron Lett 1984; 25:2399.

750. Yoshida A, Hayashi T, Takeda N, Oida S, Ohki E. Chem Pharm Bull 1983;31:768.

751. Baker AJ, Campbell MM, Jenkins MJ. Tetrahedron Lett 1990;30:4359.

752. Cooke MD, Moore KW, Ross BC, Turner SE. J Chem Soc Chem Commun 1983 1005.

753. Franceschi G, Perrone E, Alpegiani M, Bedeschi A, Della Bruna C, Zarini F, Bentley PH.In: Southgate R, editor. Recent Advances in the Chemistry of β-Lactam Antibiotics. London: Royal Society of Chemistry; 1988. p 222–246.

754. DiNinno F, Muthard DA, Ratcliffe RW, Christensen BG. Tetrahedron Lett 1982;23:3535.

755. Baker AJ, Teall MR, Johnson G. Tetrahedron Lett 1987;28:2283.

756. Phillips D, O'Neil BT. Tetrahedron Lett. 1990;31:3291.

757. Banville J, Lapointe P, Belleau B, Menard M. Can J Chem 1980;66:1390.

758. Gosteli J, Holick W, Lang M, Woodward RB.In: Gregory GI, editor. Recent Advances in the Chemistry of β-Lactam Antibiotics. London: Royal Society of Chemistry; 1981. p 359–367.

759. Menard M. Martel A.Br Patent Appl 2042515A. 1980; U.K.

760. Zak O, Lang M, Cozens R, Konopka EA, Mett H, Schneider P, Tosch W. et al. J Clin Pharmacol 1988;28:128–135.

761. Saitoh H, Sawazaki R, Oda M, Kobayashi M. Int J Antimicrob Agents 2008;32:267–271.

762. Gettig JP, Crank CW, Philbrick AH. Ann Pharmacother 2008;42:80–90.

763. Sorbera LA, Del Fresno M, Castaner RM, Rabasseda X. Drugs Future 2002;27:223–233.

764. Tanaka R, Oyama Y, Imajo S, Matsuki S, Ishiguro M. Bioorg Med Chem 1997;5: 1389–1399.

765. Woodcock JM, Andrews JM, Brenwald NP, Ashby JP, Wise R. J Antimicrob Chemother 1997;39:35–43.

766. Mushtaq S, Hope R, Warner M, Livermore DM. J Antimicrob Chemother 2007;59: 1025–1030.

767. Dalhoff A, Nasu T, Okamoto K. Chemotherapy 2003;49:229–236.

768. Hadley JA, Tillotson GS, Tosiello R, Echols RM. Expert Rev Anti Infect Ther 2006;4:923–937.

769. Stone KC, Dagan R, Arguedas A, Leibovitz E, Wang E, Echols RM, Janjic N. et al. Antimicrob Agents Chemother 2007;51:2230–2235.

770. Boswell FJ, Ashby JP, Andrews JM, Wise R. J Antimicrob Chemother 2002;50:525–532.

771. Gustafsson I, Cars O. Clin Microbiol Infect 2004;10:934–937.

772. MacGowan A, Bowker K. J Chemother 2004;16:23–29.

773. Gootz TD, Retsema J, Girard A, Hamanaka E, Anderson M, Sokolowski S. Antimicrob Agents Chemother 1989;33:1160–1166.

774. Chandra RH, Skogerboe T, Labadie RK, Soma D, Dunne M. 48th ICAAC; Washington DC; 2008, Poster F1(353).

775. Butler MS. Nat Prod Rep 2008;25:475–516.

776. Huband MD, Gootz T, Mullins LM, McCurdy SP, Brennan LA, Penzien JB, Buignan JM. et al. 48th ICAAC Washington DC; 2008, Poster F1(344).

777. Aoki H, Sakai H, Kohsaka M, Konomi T. J. Hosoda. J Antibiot 1976;29:492–500.

778. Kurita M, Jomon K, Komori T, Miyairi N, Aoki H. J Antibiot 1976;29:1243–1245.

779. Imada A, Kitano K, Kintaka K, Muroi M, Asai M. Nature 1981;289:590–591.

780. Sykes RB, Cimarusti CM, Bonner DP, Bush K, Floyd DM, Georgopapadakou NH, Koster WM. et al. Nature 1981;291:489–491.

781. Thomas RC.In: Lukacs G, Ohno MH,editros. Recent Progress in the Chemical Synthesis of Antibiotics Berlin: Springer-Verlag; 1990. p 533–564.

782. Hashimoto M, Komori T, Kamiya T. J Antibiot 1976;29:890–901.

783. Hashimoto M, Komori TA, Kamiya T. J Am Chem Soc 1976;98:3023–3025.

784. Nisbet LJ, Mehta RJ, Oh Y, Pan CH, Phelen CG, Polansky MJ, Shearer MC. et al. J Antibiot 1985;38:133–138.

785. Kamiya T, Aoki H, Mino Y.In: Morin RB, Gorman M, editors. Chemistry and Biology of β-Lactam Antibiotics. Vol. 2.New York: Academic Press; 1982. p 166–226.

786. Komori T, Kunigita K, Nakahara K, Aoki H, Imanaka H. Agric Biol Chem 1978;42:1439.

787. Kamiya T.In: Elks J, editor. Recent Advances in the Chemistry of β-Lactam Antibiotics. London: Royal Society of Chemistry; 1977. p 281–294.

788. Foglio M, Franceshi G, Lombardi P, Scarafile C, Arcamone F. J Chem Soc Chem Commun 1978; 1101.

789. Shaffner-Sabba K, Muller BW, Scartazzini R, Wehrli H. Helv Chim Acta 1980;63:321.

790. Kamiya T, Hashimoto M, Nakaguchi O, Oku T. Tetrahedron 1979;35:323.

791. Koppel GA, McShane L, Jose F, Cooper RDG. J Am Chem Soc 1978;100:3933.

792. Miller MJ. Acct Chem Res 1986;19:49.

793. Mattingley PG, Miller MJ. J Org Chem 1980;45:410.

794. Mattingley PG, Miller MJ. J Org Chem 1981;46:1557.

795. Salituro GM, Townsend CA. J Am Chem Soc 1990;112:760.

796. Kelly WL, Townsend CA. J Am Chem Soc 2002;124:8186–8187.

797. Gunsior M, Breazeale SD, Lind AJ, Ravel J, Janc JW, Townsend CA. Chem Biol 2004;11:927–938.

798. Kelly WL, Townsend CA. J Biol Chem 2004;279:38220–38227.

799. Kelly WL, Townsend CA. J Bacteriol 2005;187:739–746.

800. Chiba K, Mori M, Ban Y. Tetrahedron 1985;41:387.

801. Wasserman HH, Hlasta DJ, Tremper AW, Wu JS. J Org Chem 1981;46:2999.

802. van der Steen FH, van G, Koten Tetrahedron 1991;47:7503.

803. Nishida M, Mine Y, Nonoyama S, Kojo H. J Antibiot 1977;30:917–925.

804. Kojo H, Mine Y, Nishida M. J Antibiot 1977;30:926–931.

805. Georg GI. Bioorg Med Chem Lett 1993;3:2157.

806. Katayama N, Nozaki Y, Okonogi K, Ono H, Harada S, Okazaki H. J Antibiot 1985;38:1117–1127.

807. Hida T, Tsubotani S, Katayama N, Okazaki H, Harada S. J Antibiot 1985;38:1128–1140.

808. Koster WH, Cimarusti CM, Sykes RB.In: Morin RB, Gorman M, editors. Chemistry and Biology of β-Lactam Antibiotics. Vol. 2:New York: Academic Press; 1982. p 339–375.

809. Parker WL, O'Sullivan J, Sykes RB. Adv Appl Microbiol 1986;31:181–205.

810. Parker WL, Koster WH, Cimarusti CM, Floyd DM, Liu WC, Rathnum ML. J Antibiot 1982;35:189–195.

811. Asai M, Haibara K, Muroi M, Kintaka K, Kishi T. J Antibiot 1981;34:621–627.

812. Kintaka K, Haibara K, Asai M, Imada A. J Antibiot 1981;34:1081–1089.

813. Parker WL, Rathnum ML. J Antibiot 1982;35:300–305.

814. Singh PD, Johnson JH, Ward PC, Wells JS, Trejo WH, Sykes RB. J Antibiot 1983;36:1245–1251.

815. Cooper R, Bush K, Principe PA, Trejo WH, Wells JS, Sykes RB. J Antibiot 1983; 36:1252–1257.

816. Kato T, Hinoo H, Terui Y, Nishikawa J, Nakagawa Y, Ikenishi Y, Shoji J. J Antibiot 1987;40:139–144.

817. Box SJ, Brown AG, Gilpin ML, Gwynn MN, Spear SR. J Antibiot 1988;41:7–12.

818. Kamiya K, Takamoto M, Wada Y, Asai M. Acta Crystallogr B37 1981; 1626.

819. Cimarusti CM, Applegate HE, Chang HW, Floyd DM, Koster WM, Slusarchyk WA, Young MG. J Org Chem 1982;47:179.

820. Floyd DM, Fritz AW, Cimarusti CM. J Org Chem 1982;47:176.

821. Linder KR, Bonner DP, Koster WH, editors. Kirk–Othmer Encyclopedia of Chemical Technology. 4th ed. Vol. 3.New York: John Wiley & Sons; 1992. p 107–129.

822. Georgopapadakou NH, Smith SA, Cimarusti CM, Sykes RB. Antimicrob Agents Chemother 1983;23:98–104.

823. Boucher BA. Am J Surg 2000;179:45–50.

824. Georgopapadakou NH, Smith SA, Sykes RB. Antimicrob Agents Chemother 1982;21: 950–956.

825. Liao X, Hancock RE. Antimicrob Agents Chemother 1997;41:1158–1161.

826. Denome SA, Elf PK, Henderson TA, Nelson DE, Young KD. J Bacteriol 1999;181: 3981–3993.

827. Den Blaauwen T, Aarsman ME, Vischer NO, Nanning N. Mol Microbiol 2003;47:539–547.

828. Eberhardt C, Kuerschner L, Weiss DS. J Bacteriol 2003;185:3726–3734.

829. Bonner DP, Sykes RB. J Antimicrob Chemother 1984;14:313–327.

830. Sykes RB, Bonner DP. Am J Med 1985;78 (Suppl 2A): 2–10.

831. Westley-Horton E, Koestner JA. Am J Med Sci 1991;302:46–49.

832. Cunha BA. Urology 1993;41:249–258.

833. Angehrn P. Chemotherapy 1985;31:440–450.

834. Imada A, Kondo M, Okonogi K, Yukishige K, Kuno M. Antimicrob Agents Chemother 1985;27:821–827.

835. Manchand PS, Luk KC, Belica PS, Choudhry SC, Wei CC, Soukup M. J Org Chem 1988;53:5507–5512.

836. Woulfe SR, Miller MJ. J Med Chem 1985;28:1447–1453.

837. Perez F, Hujer AM, Hujer KM, Decker BK, Rather PN, Bonomo RA. Antimicrob Agents Chemother 2007;51:3471–3484.

838. Gilad J, Carmeli Y. Drugs 2008;68:165–189.

839. Maragakis LL, Perl TM. Clin Infect Dis 2008;46:1254–1263.

840. Martinez-Solano L, Macia MD, Fajardo A, Oliver A, Martinez JL. Clin Infect Dis 2008;47:1526–1533.

841. Dudley MN, Loutit J, Griffith DC. Curr Opin Biotechnol 2008;19:637–643.

842. Retsch-Bogart GZ, Burns JL, Otto KL, Liou TG, McCoy K, Oermann C, Gibson RL. Pediatr Pulmonol 2008;43:47–58.

843. McCoy KS, Quittner AL, Oermann CM, Gibson RL, Retsch-Bogart GZ, Montgomery AB. Am J Respir Crit Care Med. 2008;178: 921–928.

844. Hofer B, Müller C, Desabre E, Page MGP. 48th ICAAC; Washington DC; 2008, Poster F1 (1175).

845. Dantier C, Desabre E, Page MGP. 48th ICAAC; Washington DC; 2008, Poster F1 (1173).

846. Hujer AM, Hujer KM, Desabre E, Endimiani A, Page MGP, Bonomo RA. 48th ICAAC; Washington DC; 2008, Poster F1(1165).

847. Hermesh O, Page MGP, Schmitt-Hoffmann A, Carmeli Y, Navon-Venezia S. 48th ICAAC; Washington DC; 2008, Poster F1(1166).

848. Mushtaq S, Warner M, Livermore D. 48th ICAAC; Washington DC; 2008, Poster F1 (1167).

849. Bartolone JB, Hite GJ, Kelley JA, Knox JR.In: Brown AG, Roberts SM, editors. Recent Advances in the Chemistry of β-Lactam Antibiotics. London: Royal Society of Chemistry; 1985. p 327–337.

850. Chin NX, Neu HC. Antimicrob Agents Chemother 1988;32:84–91.

851. van Ogtrop ML, Mattie H, Guiot HF, van Strijen E, Sekh BR, van Furth R, Antimicrob Agents Chemother 1991;35:417–422.

852. Boyd DB, Eigenbrot C, Indelicato JM, Miller MJ, Pasini CE, Woulfe SR. J Med Chem 1987;30:528–536.

853. McKee JA, Sharma SK, Miller MJ. Bioconjug Chem 1991;2:281–291.

854. Dolence EK, Minnick AA, Lin CE, Miller MJ, Payne SM. J Med Chem 1991;34:968–978.

855. Nikaido H, Rosenberg EY. J Bacteriol 1990;172:1361–1367.

856. Chantot JF, Klich M, Teutsch G, Bryskier A, Collette P, Markus A, Seibert G. Antimicrob Agents Chemother 1992;36:1756–1763.

857. Obi K, Ito Y, Terashima S. Chem Pharm Bull 1990;38:917.

858. Brickner SJ, Gaikema JJ, Greenfield LJ, Zurenko GE, Manninen PR. Bioorg Med Chem Lett 1993;3:2241–2246.

859. Turos E, Long TE, Heldreth B, Leslie JM, Reddy GS, Wang Y, Coates C. et al. Bioorg Med Chem Lett 2006;16:2084–2090.

860. Heldreth B, Long TE, Jang S, Reddy GS, Turos E, Dickey S, Lim DV. Bioorg Med Chem 2006;14:3775–3784.

861. Turos E, Revell KD, Ramaraju P, Gergeres DA, Greenhalgh K, Young A, Sathyanarayan N. et al. Bioorg Med Chem 2008;16: 6501–6508.

862. Revell KD, Heldreth B, Long TE, Jang S, Turos E. Bioorg Med Chem 2007;15:2453–2467.

863. O'Driscoll M, Greenhalgh K, Young A, Turos E, Dickey S, Lim DV. Bioorg Med Chem 2008;16:7832–7837.

864. Chen D, Falsetti SC, Frezza M, Milacic V, Kazi A, Cui QC, Long TE. et al. Cancer Lett 2008;268:63–69.

865. Turos E, Coates C, Shim JY, Wang Y, Leslie JM, Long TE, Reddy GS. et al. Bioorg Med Chem 2005;13:6289–6308.

866. Mulchande J, Martins L, Moreira R, Archer M, Oliveira TF, Iley J. Org Biomol Chem 2007;5:2617–2626.

867. Singh R, Micetich RG. IDrugs 2000;3:512–517.

868. Veinberg G, Vorona M, Shestakova I, Kanepe I, Lukevics E. Curr Med Chem 2003;10: 1741–1757.

869. Alcaide B, Almendros P. Curr Med Chem 2004;11:1921–1949.

870. Laborde MA, Mata EG. Mini Rev Med Chem 2006;6:109–120.

871. Moreira R, Santana AB, Iley J, Neres J, Douglas KT, Horton PN, Hursthouse MB. J Med Chem 2005;48:4861–4870.

872. Dell'Aica I, Sartor L, Galletti P, Giacomini D, Quintavalla A, Calabrese F, Giacometti C. et al. J Pharmacol Exp Ther 2006;316: 539–546.

873. Singh P, Williams SA, Shah MH, Lectka T, Pritchard GJ, Isaacs JT, Denmeade SR. Proteins 2008;70:1416–1428.

874. Burnett DA. Curr Med Chem 2004;11: 1873–1887.

875. Sweeney ME, Johnson RR. Expert Opin Drug Metab Toxicol 2007;3:441–450.

876. Yamanashi Y, Takada T, Suzuki H. J Pharmacol Exp Ther 2007;320:559–564.

877. Telford DE, Sutherland BG, Edwards JY, Andrews JD, Barrett PH, Huff MW. J Lipid Res 2007;48:699–708.

878. Ge L, Wang J, Qi W, Miao HH, Cao J, Qu YX, Li BL. et al. Cell Metab 2008;7:508–519.

879. Weinglass AB, Kohler M, Schulte U, Liu J, Nketiah EO, Thomas A, Schmalhofer W. et al. Proc Natl Acad Sci USA 2008;105: 11140–11145.

880. Singh GS. Mini Rev Med Chem 2004;4:69–92.

881. Coulton S, Hunt E. Prog Med Chem 1996;33:99–145.

882. Sader HS, Gales AC. Drugs 2001;61:553–564.

883. Zhanel GG, Wiebe R, Dilay L, Thomson K, Rubinstein E, Hoban DJ, Noreddin AM. et al. Drugs 2007;67:1027–1052.

884. Nicolau DP. Expert Opin Pharmacother 2008;9:23–37.

885. Shah PM. Clin Microbiol Infcct 2008;14: 175–180.

886. Kattan JN, Villegas MV, Quinn JP. Clin Microbiol Infect 2008;14:1102–1111.

887. Kahan JS, Kahan FM, Goegelman R, Currie SA, Jackson M, Stapley EO, Miller TW. et al. J Antibiot 1979;32:1–12.

888. Butterworth D, Cole M, Hanscomb G, Rolinson GN. J Antibiot 1979;32:295–304.

889. Hood JD, Box SJ, Verrall MS. J Antibiot 1979;32:295–304.

890. Parker WL, Rathnum ML, Wells JSJ, Trejo WH, Principe PA, Sykes RB. J Antibiot 1982;35:653–660.

891. Southgate R, Elson S. Prog Chem Org Nat Prod 1985;47:1–106.

892. Southgate R, Osborne NF. Carbapenems and penems. In: Kirk–Othmer Encyclopedia of Chemical Technology. 4th ed. Vol. 3. New York: John Wiley, Sons; 1992 1–27.

893. Brown AG, Corbett DF, Eglington AJ, Howarth TT. J Chem Soc Chem Commun 1977; 523.

894. Okamura K, Hirata S, Okumura Y, Fukagawa Y, Shimauchi Y, Kouno K, Ishikura T. J Antibiot 1978;31:480–482.

895. Nakayama M, Iwasaki A, Kimura S, Mizoguchi T, Tanabe S, Murakami A, Watanabe I. et al. J Antibiot 1980;33:1388–1390.

896. Tanaka K, Shoji J, Terui Y, Tsuji N, Kondo E, Mayama M, Kawamura Y. et al. J Antibiot 1981;34:909–911.

897. Tsuji N, Nagashima K, Kobayashi M, Terui Y, Matsumoto K, Kondo E. J Antibiot 1982;35: 536–540.

898. Butterworth D, Hood JD, Verrall MS. In: Mizrahi A, editors. Advances in Biotechnological Progress. New York: A. R. Liss; 1982. p 252–282.

899. Albers-Schonberg G, Arison BH, Hensens TO, Hirshfield K, Ratcliffe RW, Walton E, Rushwinkle LJ. et al. J Am Chem Soc 1978;100:6491.

900. Ratcliffe RW, Albers-Schonberg G. In: Morin RB, Gorman M, editors. Chemistry and Biology of β-Lactam Antibiotics. Vol. 2: New York: Academic Press; 1982. p 227–313.

901. Corbett DF, Eglington AJ, Howarth TT. J Chem Soc Chem Commun 1977; 953.

902. Box SJ, Hood JD, Spear SR. J Antibiot 1979;32:1239–1247.

903. Brown AG. In: Kirk–Othmer Encyclopedia of Chemical Technology 3rd ed, New York: John Wiley Sons; 1984. p 83–131.

904. Brown AG, Corbett DF, Eglington AJ, Howarth TT. J Antibiot 1979;32:961–963.

905. Brown AG, Corbett DF, Eglington AJ, Howarth TT. Tetrahedron 1983;39:2551.

906. Yamamoto K, Yoshioka T, Kato Y, Shibamoto N, Okamura K, Shimauchi Y, Ishikura T. J Antibiot 1980;33:796–803.

907. Nakayama M, Kimura S, Tanabe S, Mizoguchi T, Watanabe I, Mori T, Miyahara K. et al. J Antibiot 1981;34:818–823.

908. Tsuji N, Nagashima K, Kobayashi M, Shoji J, Kato T, Terui Y, Nakai H. et al. J Antibiot 1982;35:24–31.

909. Leanza WJ, Wildonger KJ, Hannah J, Shih DH, Ratcliffe RW, Barash L, Walton E. et al. In: Gregory GI, editor. Recent Advances in the Chemistry of β-Lactam Antibiotics. London: Royal Society of Chemistry; 1981. p 240–245.

910. Leanza WJ, Wildonger KJ, Miller TW, Christensen BG. J Med Chem 1979;22:1435–1436.

911. Graham DW, Ashton WT, Barash L, Brown JE, Brown RD, Canning LF, Chen A. et al. J Med Chem 1987;30:1074–1090.

912. Brown AG, Corbett DF, Eglington AJ, Howarth TT. In: Gregory GI, editor. Recent Advances in the Chemistry of β-Lactam Antibiotics. London: Royal Society of Chemistry; 1981. p 255–268.

913. Corbett DF. J Chem Soc Chem Commun 1981; 803.

914. Yamamoto K, Yoshioka T, Kato Y, Ishiki K, Nishino M, Nakamura F, Shimauchi Y. et al. Tetrahedron Lett 1982;23:897.

915. Southgate R, Branch C, Coulton S, Hunt E, Lukacs G, Ohno M, editors. Progress in the Chemical Synthesis of Antibiotics. New York: Springer-Verlag; 1990. p 622–675.

916. Kametani T, Fukumoto K, Ihara M. Heterocycles 1982;17:463.

917. Durkeheimer W, Blumbach J, Lattrell R, Scheunemann KH. Angew Chem Int Ed Engl 1985;24:180.

918. Berks AH. Tetrahedron 1996;52:331.

919. Nagahara T, Kametani T. Heterocycles 1987;25:729.

920. Palomo C, Lukacs G, Ohno M, editors. Recent Progress in the Chemical Synthesis of Antibiotics. New York: Springer-Verlag; 1990. p 562–612.

921. Sasaki A, Sunagawa M. Chem Heterocycl Compd 1999;34:1249.

922. Sunagawa M, Sasaki A. Heterocycles 2001;54:497.

923. Nunez LE, Mendez C, Brana AF, Blanco G, Salas JA. Chem Biol 2003;10:301–311.

924. Wei JR, Lai HC. Int J Med Microbiol 2006;296:117–124.

925. Corre C, Song L, O'Rourke S, Chater KF, Challis GL. Proc Natl Acad Sci USA 2008;105:17510–17515.

926. McGowan SJ, Barnard AM, Bosgelmez G, Sebaihia M, Simpson NJ, Thomson NR, Todd DE. et al. Mol Microbiol 2005;55:526–545.

927. Coulthurst SJ, Barnard AM, Salmond GP. Nat Rev Microbiol 2005;3:295–306.

928. Demain AL, Vaishnav P. Crit Rev Biotechnol 2006;26:67–82.

929. Sleeman MC, Sorensen JL, Batchelar ET, McDonough MA, Schofield CJ. J Biol Chem 2005;280:34956–34965.

930. Batchelar ET, Hamed RB, Ducho C, Claridge TD, Edelmann MJ, Kessler B, Schofield CJ. Angew Chem Int Ed 2008;47:9322–9325.

931. Arnett SO, Gerratana B, Townsend CA. Biochemistry 2007;46:9337–9345.

932. Clifton IJ, Doan LX, Sleeman MC, Topf M, Suzuki H, Wilmouth RC, Schofield CJ. J Biol Chem 2003;278:20843–20850.

933. Sleeman MC, Smith P, Kellam B, Chhabra SR, Bycroft BW, Schofield CJ. Chembiochem 2004;5:879–882.

934. Stapon A, Li R, Townsend CA. J Am Chem Soc 2003;125:8486–8493.

935. Kershaw NJ, Caines ME, Sleeman MC, Schofield CJ. Chem Commun 2005; 4251–4263.

936. Borowski T, Broclawik E, Schofield CJ, Siegbahn PE. J Comput Chem 2006;27:740–748.

937. Williamson JM. Crit Rev Biotechnol 1986;4:111–131.

938. Chen TS, Arison BH, Ruby CL, Dombrowski AW, Inamine ES. J Ind Microbiol 1993;12:66–67.

939. Freeman MF, Moshos KA, Bodner MJ, Li R, Townsend CA. Proc Natl Acad Sci USA 2008.105:11128–11133.

940. Johnston DBR, Schmitt SM, Bouffard FA, Christensen BG. J Am Chem Soc 1978;100:313.

941. Ratcliffe RW, Salzmann TN, Christensen BG. Tetrahedron Lett 1980;21:2783.

942. Melillo DG, Shinkai I, Liu T, Ryan KM, Sletzinger M. Tetrahedron Lett 1980;21:2783.

943. Cama LD, Christensen BG. J Am Chem Soc 1978;100:8006.

944. Baxter AJG, Dickinson KH, Roberts PM, Smale TC, Southgate R. J Chem Soc Chem Commun 1979; 236.

945. Bateson JH, Baxter AJG, Roberts PM, Smale TC, Southgate R. J Chem Soc Perkin Trans 1981;1:3242.

946. Pfaendler HR, Gosteli J, Woodward RB, Rihs G. J Am Chem Soc 1981;103:4526.

947. Southgate R. Contemp Org Synth 1994;1:417.

948. Schmitt SM, Johnston DBR, Christensen BG. J Org Chem 1980;45:1142.

949. Salzmann TN, Ratcliffe RW, Christensen BG, Bouffard FA. J Am Chem Soc 1980;102:6161.

950. Shinkai I, Reamer RA, Hartner FW, Liu T, Sletzinger M. Tetrahedron Lett 1982;23:4903.

951. Baxter AJG, Davis P, Ponsford RJ, Southgate R. Tetrahedron Lett 1980;21:5071.

952. Hannah J, Johnson CR, Wagner AF, Walton E. J Med Chem 1982;25:457–469.

953. Cama LD, Wildonger KJ, Guthikonda RN, Ratcliffe RW, Christensen BG. Tetrahedron 1983;39:2531.

954. Melillo DG, Cuetovich RJ, Ryan KM, Sletzinger M. J Org Chem 1986;51:1498.

955. Karady S, Amato JS, Reamer RA, Weinstock LM. J Am Chem Soc 1981;103:6745.

956. Reader PJ, Grabowski EJ. Tetrahedron Lett 1982;23:2293.

957. George GI, Kant J, Gill HS. J Am Chem Soc 1987;109:1129.

958. Ito Y, Kobayashi Y, Kawabata T, Takase M, Terashima S. Tetrahedron 1989;45:5767.

959. Maruyama H, Hiraoka T. J Org Chem 1986;51:399.

960. Quallich GJ, Bordner J, Elliot ML, Morrisey P, Volkmann RA, Wroblesoska-Adam MM. J Org Chem 1990;55:367.

961. Miyashita M, Chida MN, Yoshikoshi A. J Chem Soc Chem Commun 1982; 1454.

962. Knierzinger A, Vasella A. J Chem Soc Chem Commun 1985; 9.

963. Maruyama H, Shiozaki M, Hiraoka T. Bull Chim Soc 1985;58:3264.

964. Shiozaki M, Ishida N, Maruyama H, Hiraoka T. Tetrahedron 1983;39:2399.

965. Kamata T, Nagahara T, Honda T. J Org Chem 1985;50:2327.

966. Hodgson ST, Hollinshead DM, Ley SV. Tetrahedron 1985;41:5871.

967. Pattenden G, Reynolds SJ. J Chem Soc Perkin Trans 1994;1:379.

968. Meyers AI, Sowin TJ, Sholz S, Ueda Y. Tetrahedron Lett 1987;28:5103.

969. Hanessian S, Desilets D, Bennani YL. J Org Chem 1990;55:3098.

970. Ponsford RJ, Southgate R. J Chem Soc Chem Commun 1990 1085.

971. Bateson JH, Baxter AJG, Dickinson KH, Hickling RI, Ponsford RJ, Roberts PM, Smale TC. et al. In: Gregory GI, editor. Recent Advances in the Chemistry of β-Lactam Antibiotics. London: Royal Society of Chemistry; 1981. p 291–313.

972. Bateson JH, Roberts PM, Smale TC, Southgate R. J Chem Soc Perkin Trans 1990;1:1541.

973. Bateson JH, Hickling RI, Smale TC, Southgate R. J Chem Soc Perkin Trans 1: 1793;1990:.

974. Shibasaki M, Ishida Y, Okabe N. Tetrahedron Lett 1985;26:2217.

975. Shih DH, Baker F, Cama LD, Christensen BG. Heterocycles 1984;21:29.

976. Deziel R, Faureau D. Tetrahedron Lett 1986;27:5687.

977. Fuentes LM, Shinkai I, Salzmann TN. J Am Chem Soc 1986;108:4675.

978. Shirai F, Nakai H. Chem Lett 1989; 445.

979. Ihara M, Takahashi M, Fukumoto M, Kametani T. J Chem Soc Perkin Trans 1989;1:2215.

980. Kitumuro M, Nagai K, Hsiao Y, Noyori R. Tetrahedron Lett 1990;31:5686.

981. Choi WB, Churchill HRO, Lynch JE, Thompson AS, Humphrey CR, Volante RP, Raider RP. et al. Tetrahedron Lett 1994;35:2275.

982. Kaga H, Kobayashi S, Ohno M. Tetrahedron Lett 1989;30:113.

983. Guthikonda RN, Cama LD, Quesada M, Woods MF, Salzmann TN, Christensen BG. J Med Chem 1987;30:871–880.

984. Schmitt SM, Salzmann TN, Shih DH, Christensen BG. J Antibiot 1988;41:780–787.

985. Kim CU, Luh BY, Misco PF, Hitchcock JM. J Med Chem 1989;32:601–604.

986. Shibata T, Sugimura Y. J Antibiot 1989;42:374–381.

987. Haruta J, Nishi K, Kikuchi K, Matsuda S, Tamura Y, Kita Y. Chem Pharm Bull 1989;37:2338.

988. Andrus A, Baker F, Bouffard FA, Cama LD, Christensen BG, Guthikonda RN, Heck JV. et al. In: Brown AG, Roberts SM, editors. Recent Advances in the Chemistry of β-Lactam Antibiotics. London: Royal Society of Chemistry; 1985. p 86–99.

989. Kim CU, Misco PF, Luh BY. Heterocycles 1987;26:1193.

990. Shibata T, Iino K, Tanaka T, Hashimoto T, Kameyama Y, Sugimura Y. Tetrahedron Lett 1985;26:4739.

991. Nagao Y, Abe T, Shimizu H, Kumagai T, Inoue Y. J Chem Soc Chem Commun 1989; 821.

992. Rosati RL, Kapili LV, Morrissey P, Retsema JA. J Med Chem 1990;33:291–297.

993. Shah NV, Cama LD. Heterocycles 1987;25:221.

994. Menard M, Banville J, Martel A, Desiderio J, Fung-Tomc J, Partyka RA.In: Bentley PH, Ponsford, RJ, editors. Recent Advances in the Chemistry of Anti-Infective Agents. London: Royal Society of Chemistry; 1993. p 3–20.

995. Fung-Tomc JC, Huczko E, Banville J, Menard M, Kolek B, Gradelski E, Kessler RE. et al. Antimicrob Agents Chemother 1995;39: 394–399.

996. Rao VS, Remillard R, Menard M. Heteroat Chem 1992;3:25.

997. Ruediger EH, Solomon C. J Org Chem 1991;56:3183.

998. Mastalerz H, Menard M. Heterocycles 1991;32:93.

999. Mastalerz H, Menard M, Ruediger E, Fung-Tomc J. J Med Chem 1992;35:953–958.

1000. Bouthillier G, Mastalerz H, Menard M, Fung-Tomc J, Gradelski E. J Antibiot 1992;45:240–245.

1001. Nagao Y, Abe T, Shimizu H, Kumagai T, Inoue Y. Heterocycles 1992;33:523.

1002. Sunagawa M, Matsumura H, Inoue T, Fukasawa M, Kato M. J Antibiot 1990;43:519–532.

1003. Sunagawa M, Matsumura H, Inoue T, Fukasawa M, Kato M. J Antibiot 1991;44: 459–462.

1004. Sunagawa M, Matsumura H, Inoue T, Yamaga H, Fukasawa M. J Antibiot 1992;45: 971–976.

1005. Sunagawa M, Matsumura H, Inoue T, Fukasawa M. J Antibiot 1992;45:500–504.

1006. Oh CH, Cho JH. J Antibiot 1994;47:126–128.

1007. Sundelof JG, Hajdu R, Gill CJ, Thompson R, Rosen H, Kropp H. Antimicrob Agents Chemother 1997;41:1743–1748.

1008. Gill CJ, Jackson JJ, Gerckens LS, Pelak BA, Thompson RK, Sundelof JG, Kropp H. et al. Antimicrob Agents Chemother 1998;42: 1996–2001.

1009. Odenholt I, Lowdin E, Cars O. Antimicrob Agents Chemother 1998;42:2365–2370.

1010. Sunagawa M, Sasaki A, Yamaga H, Shinagawa H, Fukasawa M, Sumita Y. J Antibiot 1994;47:1354–1358.

1011. Nagano R, Shibata K, Adachi Y, Imamura H, Hashizume T, Morishima H. Antimicrob Agents Chemother 2000;44:489–495.

1012. Perboni A, Tamburini B, Rossi T, Donati D, Tarzia G, Gaviraghi G.In: Bentley PH, Ponsford RJ, Recent Advances in the Chemistry of Anti-Infective Agents. London: Royal Society of Chemistry; 1993. p 21–35.

1013. Di Modugno E, Erbetti I, Ferrari L, Galassi G, Hammond SM, Xerri L. Antimicrob Agents Chemother 1994;38:2362–2368.

1014. Wise R, Andrews JM, Brenwald N. Antimicrob Agents Chemother 1996;40:1248–1253.

1015. Ngo J, Castaner J. Drugs Future 1996;21: 1238.

1016. Tamura S, Miyazaki S, Tateda K, Ohno A, Ishii Y, Matsumoto T, Furuya N. et al. Antimicrob Agents Chemother 1998;42: 1858–1861.

1017. Gaviraghi G. Eur J Med Chem 1995;30:S467.

1018. Rossi T, Biondi S, Contini S, Thomas RJ, Marchioro C. J Am Chem Soc 1995;117:9604.

1019. Biondi S, Gaviraghi G, Rossi T. Bioorg Med Chem Lett 1996;6:525.

1020. Ghiron C, Piga E, Rossi T, Thomas RJ. Tetrahedron Lett 1996;37:3891.

1021. Kennedy G, Rossi T, Tamburini B. Tetrahedron Lett 1996;37:7441.

1022. Matsumoto T, Murayama T, Mitsuhashi S, Miura T. Tetrahedron Lett 1999;40:5043.

1023. Stead P, Marley H, Mahmoudian M, Webb G, Noble D, Yam IP, Piga E. et al. Tetrahedron: Asymmetry 1996;7:2247.

1024. Fuganti C, Grasselli P, Mendozza M, Servi S, Zucchi G. Tetrahedron 1997;53:2617.

1025. Hanessian S, Rozema MJ. J Am Chem Soc 1996;118:9884.

1026. Gehanne S, Piga E, Andreotti D, Biondi S, Pizzi DA. Bioorg Med Chem Lett 1996;6: 2791.

1027. Di Modugno E, Broggio R, Erbetti I, Lowther J. Antimicrob Agents Chemother 1997;41:2742–2748.

1028. Wollmann T, Gerlach U, Horlein R, Krass N, Lattrell R, Limbert M, Markus A.In: Bentley PH, Ponsford RJ, editors. Recent Advances in the Chemistry of Anti-Infective Agents. London: Royal Society of Chemistry; 1993. p 50–66.

1029. Schmidt G, Schrock W, Endermann R. Bioorg Med Chem Lett 1993;3:2193–2198.

1030. Kanno O, Kawamoto I. Tetrahedron 2000;56: 5639.

1031. Kanno O, Shimoji Y, Ohya S, Kawamoto I. J Antibiot 2000;53:404–414.

1032. Andreotti D, Biondi S, Donati D, Lociuro S, Pain G. Can J Chem 2000;78:772.

1033. Andreotti D, Biondi S. Curr Opin Anti Infect Invest Drugs 2000;2:133.

1034. Basker MJ, Boon RJ, Hunter PA. J Antibiot 1980;33:878–884.

1035. Basker MJ, Bateson JH, Baxter AJ, Ponsford RJ, Roberts PM, Southgate R, Smale TC. et al. J Antibiot 1981;34:1224–1226.

1036. Miyashita K, Massova I, Mobashery S. Bioorg Med Chem Lett 1996;6:319–322.

1037. Spratt BG, Jobanputra V, Zimmermann W. Antimicrob Agents Chemother 1977;12: 406–409.

1038. Kropp H, Sundelof JG, Kahan JS, Kahan FM, Birnbaum J. Antimicrob Agents Chemother 1980;17:993–1000.

1039. Neu HC, Labthavikul P. Antimicrob Agents Chemother 1982;21:180–187.

1040. Norrby SR, Alestig K, Bjornegard B, Burman LA, Ferber F, Huber JL, Jones KH. et al. Antimicrob Agents Chemother 1983;23:300–307.

1041. Kropp H, Sundelof JG, Hajdu R, Kahan FM. Antimicrob Agents Chemother 1982;22: 62–70.

1042. Kahan FM, Kropp H, Sundelof JG, Birnbaum J. J Antimicrob Chemother 1983;12(Suppl D): 1–35.

1043. Goa KL, Noble S. Drugs 2003;63:913–925.

1044. Greenlee ML, DiNinno F, Herrmann JJ, Jaworsky C, Muthard DA, Salzmann TN. Bioorg Med Chem Lett 1999;9:2893–2896.

1045. Greenlee ML, Laub JB, Rouen GP, DiNinno F, Hammond ML, Huber JL, Sundelof JG. et al. Bioorg Med Chem Lett 1999;9:3225–3230.

1046. Biondi S.In: Bentley PH, Ponsford RJ, editors. Recent Advances in the Chemistry of Anti-Infective Agents. London: Royal Society of Chemistry; 1993. p 86–100.

1047. Biondi S, Pecunioso A, Busi F, Contini SA, Donati D, Maffeis M, Pizzi DA. et al. Tetrahedron 2000;56:5649.

1048. Magnet S, Arbeloa A, Mainardi JL, Hugonnet JE, Fourgeaud M, Dubost L, Marie A. et al. J Biol Chem 2007;282:13151–13159.

1049. Mainardi JL, Hugonnet JE, Rusconi F, Fourgeaud M, Dubost L, Moumi AN, Delfosse V. et al. J Biol Chem 2007;282:30414–30422.

1050. Lavollay M, Arthur M, Fourgeaud M, Dubost L, Marie A, Veziris N, Blanot D. et al. J Bacteriol 2008;190:4360–4366.

1051. Hakimelahi GH, Moosavi-Movahedi AA, Saboury AA, Osetrov V, Khodarahmi GA, Shia KS. Eur J Med Chem 2005;40:339–349.

1052. Maruyama T, Yamamoto Y, Kano Y, Kurazono M, Matsuhisa E, Takata H, Takata T. et al. Bioorg Med Chem 2007;15:6379–6387.

1053. Baldwin CM, Lyseng-Williamson KA, Keam SJ. Drugs 2008;68:803–838.

1054. Odenholt I. Expert Opin Investig Drugs 2001;10:1157–1166.

1055. Cunha BA. Drugs Today 2002;38:195–213.

1056. Livermore DM, Sefton AM, Scott GM. J Antimicrob Chemother 2003;52:331–344.

1057. Shah PM, Isaacs RD. J Antimicrob Chemother 2003;52:538–542.

1058. Tice AD. J Antimicrob Chemother 2004;53 (Suppl. 2): ii83–6.

1059. Hammond ML. J Antimicrob Chemother 2004;53(Suppl. 2): ii7–ii9.

1060. Zhanel GG, Johanson C, Embil JM, Noreddin A, Gin A, Vercaigne L, Hoban DJ. Expert Rev Anti Infect Ther 2005;3:23–39.

1061. Keating GM, Perry CM. Drugs 2005;65: 2151–2178.

1062. Burkhardt O, Derendorf H, Welte T. Expert Opin Pharmacother 2007;8:237–256.

1063. Nix DE, Matthias KR, Ferguson EC. Antimicrob Agents Chemother 2004;48:3419–3424.

1064. Nix DE, Majumdar AK, DiNubile MJ. J Antimicrob Chemother 2004;53(Suppl 2): ii23–ii28.

1065. Zajac M, Cielecka-Piontek J, Jelinska A. J Pharm Biomed Anal 2007;43:445–449.

1066. Lartigue MF, Poirel L, Poyart C, Reglier-Poupet H, Nordmann P. Emerg Infect Dis 2007;13:315–317.

1067. Celenza G, Luzi C, Aschi M, Segatore B, Setacci D, Pellegrini C, Forcella C. et al. J Antimicrob Chemother 2008;62:991–997.

1068. Jones RN. J Chemother 2001;13:363–376.

1069. Perry CM, Ibbotson T. Drugs 2002;62: 2221–2234.

1070. Shah PM. Clin Microbiol Infect 2008;14 (Suppl 1): 175–180.

1071. Xu D, Xie D, Guo. H. J Biol Chem 2006;281:8740–8747.

1072. Simona F, Magistrato A, Vera DM, Garau G, Vila AJ, Carloni P. Proteins 2007;69:595–605.

1073. Garau G, Bebrone C, Anne C, Galleni M, Frere JM, Dideberg O. J Mol Biol 2005;345:785–795.

1074. Bebrone C, Anne C, Kerff F, Garau G, De Vriendt K, Lantin R, Devreese B. et al. Biochem J 2008;414:151–159.

1075. Okamoto K, Gotoh N, Nishino T. J Infect Chemother 2002;8:371–373.

1076. Hikida M, Masukawa Y, Nishiki K, Inomata N. Antimicrob Agents Chemother 1993;37: 199–202.

1077. Iso Y, Irie T, Nishino Y, Motokawa K, Nishitani Y. J Antibiot 1996;49:199–209.

1078. Iso Y, Irie T, Iwaki T, Kii M, Sendo Y, Motokawa K, Nishitani Y. J Antibiot 1996;49:478–484.

1079. Nishino Y, Kobayashi M, Shinno T, Izumi K, Yonezawa H, Masui Y, Takahitrra M. Org Process Res Dev 2003;7:846–850.

1080. Lister PD. Expert Rev Anti Infect Ther 2007;5:793–809.

1081. Keam SJ. Drugs 2008;68:2021–2057.

1082. Poulakou G, Giamarellou H. Expert Opin Investig Drugs 2008;17:749–771.

1083. Tsuji M, Ishii Y, Ohno A, Miyazaki S, Yamaguchi K. Antimicrob Agents Chemother 1998;42:94–99.

1084. Fritsche TR, Stilwell MG, Jones RN. Clin Microbiol Infect 2005;11:974–984.

1085. Jones RN, Huynh HK, Biedenbach DJ, Fritsche TR, Sader HS. J Antimicrob Chemother 2004;54:144–154.

1086. Jones RN, Huynh HK, Biedenbach DJ. Antimicrob Agents Chemother 2004;48: 3136–3140.

1087. Ge Y, Wikler MA, Sahm DF, Blosser-Middleton RS, Karlowsky JA. Antimicrob Agents Chemother 2004;48:1384–1396.

1088. Mushtaq S, Ge Y, Livermore DM. Antimicrob Agents Chemother 2004;48:1313–1319.

1089. Traczewski MM, Brown SD. Antimicrob Agents Chemother 2006;50:819–821.

1090. Marti S, Sanchez-Cespedes J, Alba V, Vila J. Int J Antimicrob Agents 2008.

1091. Davies TA, Shang W, Bush K, Flamm RK. Antimicrob Agents Chemother 2008;52: 1510–1512.

1092. Sakyo S, Tomita H, Tanimoto K, Fujimoto S, Ike Y. J Antibiot 2006;59:220–228.

1093. Huynh HK, Biedenbach DJ, Jones RN. Diagn Microbiol Infect Dis 2006;55:241–243.

1094. Hagerman JK, Knechtel SA, Klepser ME. Formulary 2007;42:676–688.

1095. Cirillo I, Mannens G, Janssen C, Vermeir M, Cuyckens F, Desai-Krieger D, Vaccaro N. et al. Antimicrob Agents Chemother 2008;52: 3478–3483.

1096. Lucasti C, Jasovich A, Umeh O, Jiang J, Kaniga K, Friedland I. Clin Ther 2008;30: 868–883.

1097. Rea-Neto A, Niederman M, Lobo SM, Schroeder E, Lee M, Kaniga K, Ketter N. et al. Curr Med Res Opin 2008;24:2113–2126.

1098. Kawamoto I, Shimoji Y, Kanno O, Kojima K, Ishikawa K, Matsuyama E, Ashida Y. et al. J Antibiot 2003;56:565–579.

1099. Koga T, Abe T, Inoue H, Takenouchi T, Kitayama A, Yoshida T, Masuda N. et al. Antimicrob Agents Chemother 2005;49:3239–3250.

1100. MacGowan AP, Bowker KE, Noel AR. Antimicrob Agents Chemother 2008;52: 1401–1406.

1101. Lo T.S. Welch J.M. Alonto A.M. Vicaldo-Alonto E.A. Recent Patents Anti Infect Drug Disc 2008;3:123–131.

1102. Tanaka K, Mikamo H, Nakao K, Ichiishi T, Goto T, Yamagishi Y, Watanabe K. Antimicrob Agents Chemother 2009;53:319–322.

1103. Koga T, Masuda N, Kakuta M, Namba E, Sugihara C, Fukuoka T. Antimicrob Agents Chemother 2008;52:2849–2854.

1104. Thomson KS, Moland ES. J Antimicrob Chemother 2004;54:557–562.

1105. Morinaga Y, Yanagihara K, Nakamura S, Yamamoto K, Izumikawa K, Seki M, Kakeya H. et al. J Antimicrob Chemother 2008;62: 1326–1331.

1106. Shibayama T, Matsushita Y, Hirota T, Ikeda T, Kuwahara S. Antimicrob Agents Chemother 2006;50:4186–4188.

1107. Shibayama T, Yamamura N, Matsushita Y, Tokui T, Hirota T, Ikeda T. Xenobiotica 2006;36:1273–1287.

1108. Shibayama T, Matsushita Y, Kawai K, Hirota T, Ikeda T, Kuwahara S. Antimicrob Agents Chemother 2007;51:257–263.

1109. Shibayama T, Matsushita Y, Kurihara A, Hirota T, Ikeda T. Xenobiotica 2007;37: 91–102.

1110. Shibayama T, Sugiyama D, Kamiyama E, Tokui T, Hirota T, Ikeda T. Drug Metab Pharmacokinet 2007;22:41–47.

1111. Mallalieu NL, Lennon S, Liu M, Kirkpatrick C, Robson R, Luedin E, Davies BE. Antimicrob Agents Chemother 2008;52:2360–2366.

1112. Sunagawa M, Itoh M, Kubota K, Sasaki A, Ueda Y, Angehrn P, Bourson A. et al. J Antibiot 2002;55:722–757.

1113. Ueda Y, Sunagawa M. Antimicrob Agents Chemother 2003;47:2471–2480.

1114. Ueda Y, Itoh M, Sasaki A, Sunagawa M. J Antibiot 2005;58:118–140.

1115. Ueda Y, Kanazawa K, Eguchi K, Takemoto K, Eriguchi Y, Sunagawa M. Antimicrob Agents Chemother 2005;49:4185–4196.

1116. Eguchi K, Ueda Y, Kanazawa K, Sunagawa M, Gotoh N. J Antibiot 2007;60:129–135.

1117. Kihara R, Yanagihara K, Morinaga Y, Araki N, Nakamura S, Seki M, Izumikawa K. et al. Antimicrob Agents Chemother 2008;52:2163–2168.

1118. Kurazono M, Ida T, Yamada K, Hirai Y, Maruyama T, Shitara E, Yonezawa M. Antimicrob Agents Chemother 2004;48: 2831–2837.

1119. Maeda K, Ida T, Sanbongi Y, Suzuki T, Fukushima T, Kurazono M, Yonezawa M. et al. J Infect Chemother 2005;11:107–111.

1120. Maruyama T, Kano Y, Yamamoto Y, Kurazono M, Iwamatsu K, Atsumi K, Shitara E. Bioorg Med Chem 2007;15:392–402.

1121. Fenoll A, Aguilar L, Robledo O, Gimenez MJ, Granizo JJ, Biek D, Tarrago D. J Antimicrob Chemother 2008;62:1156–1158.

1122. Nagura J, Kijima K, Kurazono M, Takahata S, Sugano T, Tanaka Y, Hirai Y. et al. Antimicrob Agents Chemother 2005;49: 3526–3528.

1123. Yanagihara K, Ohnishi Y, Morinaga Y, Nakamura S, Kurihara S, Seki M, Izumikawa K. et al. Int J Antimicrob Agents 2008;32: 401–404.

1124. Wang Y, Bolos J, Serradell N. Drugs Future 2006;31:676–681.

1125. Isoda T, Yamamura I, Tamai S, Kumagai T, Nagao Y. Chem Pharm Bull 2006;54: 1408–1411.

1126. Isoda T, Ushirogochi H, Satoh K, Takasaki T, Yamamura I, Sato C, Mihira A. et al. J Antibiot 2006;59:241–247.

1127. Kobayashi R, Konomi M, Hasegawa K, Morozumi M, Sunakawa K, Ubukata K. Antimicrob Agents Chemother 2005;49:889–894.

1128. Hikida M, Itahashi K, Igarashi A, Shiba T, Kitamura M. Antimicrob Agents Chemother 1999;43:2010–2016.

1129. Hotomi M, Suzumoto M, Itahashi K, Nagura J, Fukushima T, Shimada J, Billal DS. et al. Vaccine 2007;25:2478–2484.

1130. Abraham E. Bioessays 1990;12:601–606.

1131. Massova I, Mobashery S. Antimicrob Agents Chemother 1998;42:1–17.

1132. Hu Z, Periyannan G, Bennett B, Crowder MW. J Am Chem Soc 2008;130:14207–14216.

1133. Gonzalez JM, Medrano Martin FJ, Costello AL, Tierney DL, Vila AJ. J Mol Biol 2007;373:1141–1156.

1134. Llarrull LI, Tioni MF, Vila AJ. J Am Chem Soc 2008;130:15842–15851.

1135. Tioni MF, Llarrull LI, Poeylaut-Palena AA, Marti MA, Saggu M, Periyannan GR, Mata EG. et al. J Am Chem Soc 2008;130: 15852–15863.

1136. Levy SB. Adv. Drug Deliver Rev 2005;57: 1446.

1137. Wright GD. Nat Rev Microbiol 2007;5: 175–186.

1138. Bush K, Mobashery S. Adv Exp Med Biol 1998;456:71–98.

1139. Piddock LJ. Clin Microbiol Rev 2006;19: 382–402.

1140. Piddock LJ. Nat Rev Microbiol 2006;4: 629–636.

1141. Park JT, Uehara T. Microbiol Mol Biol Rev 2008;72:211–227.

1142. Cartwright SJ, Waley SG. Med Res Rev 1983;3:341–382.

1143. Maiti SN, Phillips OA, Micetich RG, Livermore DM. Curr Med Chem 1998;5:441–456.

1144. Page MI, Laws, AP. Chem Commun 1998; 1609–1617.

1145. Sandanayaka VP, Prashad AS. Curr Med Chem 2002;9:1145–1165.

1146. Buynak JD. Curr Med Chem 2004;11: 1951–1964.

1147. Buynak JD. Biochem Pharmacol 2006;71: 930–940.

1148. Howarth TT, Brown AG, King J. J Chem Soc Chem Commun 1976; 266.

1149. Brown AG, Butterworth D, Cole M, Hanscomb G, Hood JD, Reading C, Rolinson GN. J Antibiot 1976;29:668–669.

1150. Li R, Townsend CA. Metab Eng 2006;8: 240–252.

1151. Merski M, Townsend CA. J Am Chem Soc 2007;129:15750–15751.

1152. MacKenzie AK, Kershaw NJ, Hernandez H, Robinson CV, Schofield CJ, Andersson I. Biochemistry 2007;46:1523–1533.

1153. Raber ML, Freeman MF, Townsend CA. J Biol Chem 2009;284:207–217.

1154. Song JY, Kim ES, Kim DW, Jensen SE, Lee KJ. J Ind Microbiol Biotechnol 2008;18: 417–426.

1155. Reading C, Cole M. Antimicrob Agents Chemother 1977;11:852–857.

1156. Coleman K, Griffin DR, Page JW, Upshon PA. Antimicrob Agents Chemother 1989;33: 1580–1587.

1157. Hunter PA, Coleman K, Fisher J, Taylor D. J Antimicrob Chemother 1980;6:455–470.

1158. Bennett IS, Brooks G, Broom NJ, Calvert SH, Coleman K, Francois I. J Antibiot 1991;44:969–978.

1159. White AR, Kaye C, Poupard J, Pypstra R, Woodnutt G, Wynne B. J Antimicrob Chemother 2004;53:i3–i20.

1160. Geddes AM, Klugman KP, Rolinson GN. Int J Antimicrob Agents 2007;30(Suppl 2): S109–S112.

1161. Ball P, Int J Antimicrob Agents 2007;30: S113–S117.

1162. Ball P. Int J Antimicrob Agents 2007;30: S139–S141.

1163. Neu HC, Wilson AP, Gruneberg RN. J Chemother 1993;5:67–93.

1164. Rolinson GN. J Chemother 1994;6:283–318.

1165. Ball P, Geddes A, Rolinson G. J Chemother 1997;9:167–198.

1166. Sun T, Bethel CR, Bonomo RA, Knox JR. Biochemistry 2004;43:14111–14117.

1167. Helfand MS, Totir MA, Carey MP, Hujer AM, Bonomo RA, Carey PR. Biochemistry 2003;42:13386–13392.

1168. Padayatti PS, Helfand MS, Totir MA, Carey MP, Carey PR, Bonomo RA, van den Akker F, J Biol Chem 2005;280:34900–34907.

1169. Totir MA, Padayatti PS, Helfand MS, Carey MP, Bonomo RA, Carey PR, van den Akker F, Biochemistry 2006;45:11895–11904.

1170. Livermore DM, Hope R, Mushtaq S, Warner M. Clin Microbiol Infect 2008;14(Suppl 1): 189–193.

1171. Wang F, Cassidy C, Sacchettini JC. Antimicrob Agents Chemother 2006;50:2762–2771.

1172. Hugonnet JE, Blanchard JS. Biochemistry 2007;46:11998–12004.

1173. Tremblay LW, Hugonnet JE, Blanchard JS. Biochemistry 2008;47:5312–5316.

1174. Docobo-Perez F, Fernandez-Cuenca F, Pachon-Ibanez ME, Pascual A, Pichardo C, Martinez-Martinez L, Pachon J. Clin Microbiol Infect 2008;14:582–587.

1175. English AR, Retsema JA, Girard AE, Lynch JE, Barth WE. Antimicrob Agents Chemother 1978;14:414–419.

1176. Retsema JA, English AR, Girard AE. Antimicrob Agents Chemother 1980;17: 615–622.

1177. Volkman RA, Carroll RD, Drolet R, Elliot ML, Moore BS. J Org Chem 1982;47:3344.

1178. Imtiaz U, Billings EM, Knox JR, Mobashery S. Biochemistry 1994;33:5728–5738.

1179. Totir MA, Helfand MS, Carey MP, Sheri A, Buynak JD, Bonomo RA, Carey PR. Biochemistry 2007;46:8980–8987.

1180. Retsema JA, English AR, Girard A, Lynch JE, Anderson M, Brennan L, Cimochowski C. et al. Rev Infect Dis 1986;8(Suppl 5): S528–S534.

1181. English AR, Girard D, Cimochowski C, Faiella J, Retsema JA, Lynch JE. Rev Infect Dis 1986;8(Suppl 5): S535–42.

1182. English AR, Girard D, Haskell SL. Antimicrob Agents Chemother 1984;25:599–602.

1183. English AR, Girard D, Jasys VJ, Martingano RJ, Kellogg MS. J Med Chem 1990;33:344–347.

1184. Akova M. Clin Microbiol Infect 2008;14 (Suppl 1): 185–188.

1185. Lode HM. Int J Antimicrob Agents 2008;32:10–28.

1186. Higgins PG, Wisplinghoff H, Stefanik D, Seifert H. Antimicrob Agents Chemother 2004;48:1586–1592.

1187. Gootz TD, Marra A. Expert Rev Anti Infect Ther 2008;6:309–325.

1188. Karageorgopoulos DE, Falagas ME. Lancet Infect Dis 2008;8:751–762.

1189. Wang FD, Lin ML, Lee WS, Liu CY, Int J Antimicrob Agents 2004;23:590–595.

1190. Farmer TH, Degnan BA, Payne DJ. FEMS Microbiol Lett 1999;176:11–15.

1191. Phillips OA, Reddy AV, Setti EL, Spevak P, Czajkowski DP, Atwal H, Salama S. et al. Bioorg Med Chem 2005;13:2847–2858.

1192. Buynak JD, Ghadachanda VR, Vogeti L, Zhang H, Chen H. J Org Chem 2005; 4510–4513.

1193. Bryson HM. R. N. Brogden. Drugs 1994;47:506–535.

1194. Gin A, Dilay L, Karlowsky JA, Walkty A, Rubinstein E, Zhanel GG. Expert Rev Anti Infect Ther 2007;5:365–383.

1195. Marunaka T, Matsushima E, Minami Y, Yoshida K, Azuma R. Chem Pharm Bull 1988;36:4478–4487.

1196. Padayatti PS, Helfand MS, Totir MA, Carey MP, Hujer AM, Carey PR, Bonomo RA. et al. Biochemistry 2004;43:843–848.

1197. Totir MA, Cha J, Ishiwata A, Wang B, Sheri A, Anderson VE, Buynak J. et al. Biochemistry 2008;47:4094–4101.

1198. Higashitani F, Hyodo A, Ishida N, Inoue M, Mitsuhashi S. J Antimicrob Chemother 1990;25:567–574.

1199. Basker MJ, Osborne NF. J Antibiot 1990;43:70–75.

1200. Broom NJP, Farmer TH, Osborne NF, Walker G. J Chem Soc Chem Commun 1992; 1663–1664.

1201. Osborne NF, Atkins RJ, Broom NJ, Coulton S, Harbridge JB, Harris MA, Stirling-Francois I. et al. J Chem Soc Perkin Trans 1994;1:179.

1202. Abe T, Sato C, Ushirogochi H, Sato K, Takasaki T, Isoda T, Mihira A. et al. J Org Chem 2004;69:5850–5860.

1203. Pechere JC, Letarte R, Guay R, Asselin C, Morin C. J Antimicrob Chemother 1982;9 (Suppl. sC): 123–132.

1204. Broom NJ, Coulton S, Francois I, Harbridge JB, J. Nayler HC, Osborne NF.In: Bentley H, Southgate R, editors. Recent Advances in the Chemistry of β-Lactam Antibiotics. London: Royal Society of Chemistry; 1989. p 247–258.

1205. Zhou XY, Kitzis MD, Acar JF, Gutmann L. J Antimicrob Chemother 1993;31:473–480.

1206. Qadri SM, Ueno Y, Burdette M, Kroschinsky R, Almodovar E. Chemotherapy 1991;37:398–404.

1207. Matagne A, Ledent P, Monnaie D, Felici A, Jamin M, Raquet X, Galleni M. et al. Antimicrob Agents Chemother 1995;39:227–231.

1208. Coleman K, Griffin DR, Upshon PA. Antimicrob Agents Chemother 1991;35:1748–1752.

1209. Farmer TH, Page JW, Payne DJ, Knowles DJ. Biochem J 1994;303:825–830.

1210. Bulychev A, Massova I, Lerner SA, Mobashery S. J Am Chem Soc 1995;117:4797.

1211. Nukaga M, Abe T, Venkatesan AM, Mansour TS, Bonomo RA, Knox JR. Biochemistry 2003;42:13152–13159.

1212. Venkatesan AM, Gu Y, Dos Santos O, Abe T, Agarwal A, Yang Y, Petersen PJ. et al. J Med Chem 2004;47:6556–6568.

1213. Tabei K, Feng X, Venkatesan AM, Abe T, Hideki U, Mansour TS, Siegel MM. J Med Chem 2004;47:3674–3688.

1214. Michaux C, Charlier P, Frere JM, Wouters J. J Am Chem Soc 2005;127:3262–3263.

1215. Venkatesan AM, Agarwal A, Abe T, Ushirogochi H, Yamamura I, Kumagai T, Petersen PJ. et al. Bioorg Med Chem 2004;12:5807–5817.

1216. Weiss WJ, Petersen PJ, Murphy TM, Tardio L, Yang Y, Bradford PA, Venkatesan AM. et al. Antimicrob Agents Chemother 2004;48:4589–4596.

1217. Bethel CR, Distler AM, Ruszczycky MW, Carey MP, Carey PR, Hujer AM, Taracila M. et al. Antimicrob Agents Chemother 2008;52:3135–3143.

1218. Petersen PJ, Jones CH, Venkatesan AM, Mansour TS, Projan SJ, Bradford PA. Antimicrob Agents Chemother 2009;53:370–384.

1219. Venkatesan AM, Agarwal A, Abe T, Ushirogochi H, Ado M, Tsuyoshi T, Dos Santos O. et al. Bioorg Med Chem 2008;16:1890–1902.

1220. Venkatesan A, Agarwal A, Abe T, Ushirogochi H, Takasaki T, Mihira A, Mansour TS. ChemMedChem 2008;3:1658–1661.

1221. Kohler J, Dorso KL, Young K, Hammond GG, Rosen H, Kropp H, Silver LL. Antimicrob Agents Chemother 1999;43:1170–1176.

1222. Maveyraud L, Massova I, Birck C, Miyashita K, Samama JP, Mobashery S. J Am Chem Soc 1996;118:7435–7440.

1223. Golemi D, Maveyraud L, Ishiwata A, Tranier S, Miyashita K, Nagase T, Massova I. et al. J Antibiot 2000;53:1022–1027.

1224. Pernot L, Frenois F, Rybkine T, L'Hermite G, Petrella S, Delettre J, Jarlier V. et al. J Mol Biol 2001;310:859–874.

1225. Nagase T, Golemi D, Ishiwata A, Mobashery S. Bioorg Chem 2001;29:140–145.

1226. Knowles JR. Acct Chem Res 1985;18:97.

1227. Taibi P, Mobashery S. J Am Chem Soc 1995;117:7600.

1228. Maveyraud L, Mourey L, Kotra LP, Pedelacq J-D, Guillet V, Mobashery S, Samana JP. J Am Chem Soc 1998;120:9748.

1229. Nukaga M, Bethel CR, Thomson JM, Hujer AM, Distler A, Anderson VE, Knox JR. et al. J Am Chem Soc 2008;130:12656–12662.

1230. Santillana E, Beceiro A, Bou G, Romero A. Proc Natl Acad Sci USA 2007;104:5354–5359.

1231. Plantan I, Selic L, Mesar T, Anderluh PS, Oblak M, Prezelj A, Hesse L. et al. J Med Chem 2007;50:4113–4121.

1232. Pratt RF, Loosemore MJ. Proc Natl Acad Sci USA 1978;75:4145–4149.

1233. Knott-Hunziker V, Orlek BS, Sammes PG, Waley SG. Biochem J 1979;177:365–367.

1234. Loosemore MJ, Cohen SA, Pratt RF. Biochemistry 1980;19:3990–3995.

1235. Cohen SA, Pratt RF. Biochemistry 1980;19:3996–4003.

1236. Orlek BS, Sammes PG, Knott-Hunziker V, Waley SG. J Chem Soc Perkin Trans 1980;1:2322–2329.

1237. Wise R, O'Sullivan N, Johnson J, Andrews JM. Antimicrob Agents Chemother 1992;36:1002–1004.

1238. Wise R, Andrews JM, Patel N. J Antimicrob Chemother 1981;7:531–536.

1239. Moore BA, Brammer KW. Antimicrob Agents Chemother 1981;20:327–331.

1240. Frere JM, Dormans C, Duyckaerts C, De Graeve J, Biochem J 1982;207:437–444.

1241. von Daehne W, J Antibiot 33(4): 1980; 451–452.

1242. von Daehne W, Hansen ET, Rastrup-Anderson N.In: Brown AG, Roberts SM, editors. Recent Advances in the Chemistry of β-Lactam Antibiotics. London: Royal Society of Chemistry; 1985. p 375–380.

1243. Mezes PFS, Frieson RW, Viswanatha T, Dmitrienko GI. Heterocycles 1982;19:1207.

1244. Yamashita M, Hashimoto S, Ezaki M, Iwami M, Komori T, Kohsaka M, Imanaka H. J Antibiot 1983;36:1774–1776.

1245. Chen YL, Hedberg K, Guarino K, Retsema JA, Anderson M, Manousos M, Barrett J. J Antibiot 1991;44:870–884.

1246. Chin NX, McElrath MJ, Neu HC. Chemotherapy 1988;34:318–325.

1247. Brenner DG, Knowles JR. Biochemistry 1984;23:5839–5846.

1248. Cole M. Drugs Fut. 1981;6:697.

1249. Nishimura S, Yasuda N, Sasaki H, Matsumoto Y, Kamimura T, Sakane K, Takaya T. J Antibiot 1990;43:114–117.

1250. Buynak JD, Wu K, Bachmann B, Khasnis D, Hua L, Nguyen HK, Carver CL. J Med Chem 1995;38:1022–1034.

1251. Gottstein WJ, Crast LBJ, Graham RG, Haynes UJ, McGregor DN. J Med Chem 1981;24:1531–1534.

1252. Dmitrienko GI, Copeland CR, Arnold L, Savard ME, Clarke AJ, Viswanatha T. Bioorg Chem 1985;13:34.

1253. Knight GC, Waley SG. Biochem J 1985;225:435–439.

1254. Chen YL, Hedberg K, Barrett JF, Retsema JA. J Antibiot 1988;41:134–138.

1255. Tanaka H, Tanaka M, Nakai A, Yamada S, Ishida N, Otani T, Torii S. J Antibiot 1988;41:579–582.

1256. Richter HG, Angehrn P, Hubschwerlen C, Kania M, Page MG, Specklin JL, Winkler FK. J Med Chem 1996;39:3712–3722.

1257. Adam S, Then R, Angehrn P. J Antibiot 1993;46:641–646.

1258. Foulds CD, Kosmirak M, Sammes PG. J Chem Soc Perkin Trans 1985;1:963–968.

1259. Im C, Maiti SN, Micetich RG, Daneshtalab M, Atchison K, Phillips OA, Kunugita C. J Antibiot 1994;47:1030–1040.

1260. Keith DD, Tengi J, Rossman P, Todaro L, Weigele M. Tetrahedron 1983;39:2445–2458.

1261. Wei CC, Christenson JG, Corraz AJ, Keith DD. Bioorg Med Chem Lett 1991;1:43–46.

1262. Buynak JD, Chen H, Vogeti L, Gadhachanda VR, Buchanan CA, Palzkill T, Shaw RW. et al. Bioorg Med Chem Lett 2004;14:1299–1304.

1263. Pattanaik P, Bethel CR, Hujer AM, Hujer KM, Distler AM, Taracila M, Anderson VE. et al. J Biol Chem 2009;284:945–953.

1264. Tzouvelekis LS, Gazouli M, Prinarakis EE, Tzelepi E, Legakis NJ. Antimicrob Agents Chemother 1997;41:475–477.

1265. Sandanayaka VP, Prashad AS, Yang Y, Williamson RT, Lin YI, Mansour TS. J Med Chem 2003;46:2569–2571.

1266. Jamieson CE, Lambert PA, Simpson IN. Antimicrob Agents Chemother 2003;47:1652–1657.

1267. Jamieson CE, Lambert PA, Simpson IN. Antimicrob Agents Chemother 2003;47:2615–2618.

1268. Wild H, Hartwig W. Synthesis 1992;1099–1103.

1269. Pfaendler HR, Neumann T, Bartsch R. Synthesis 1992; 1179–1184.

1270. Murakami M, Aoki T, Matsuura M, Nagata W. J Antibiot 1990;43:1441–1449.

1271. Bonnefoy A, Dupuis-Hamelin C, Steier V, Delachaume C, Seys C, Stachyra T, Fairley M. et al. J Antimicrob Chemother 2004;54:410–417.

1272. Mushtaq S, Warner M, Miossec C, Woodford N, Livermore DM. 47th Interscience Conference on Antimicrobial Agents and Chemotherapy; 2007, Abstract F1(319).

1273. Livermore DM, Mushtaq S, Warner M, Miossec C, Woodford N. J Antimicrob Chemother 2008;62:1053–1056.

1274. Heinze-Krauss I, Angehrn P, Charnas RL, Gubernator K, Gutknecht EM, Hubschwerlen C, Kania M. et al. J Med Chem 1998;41:3961–3971.

1275. Mourey L, Kotra LP, Bellettini J, Bulychev A, O'Brien M, Miller MJ, Mobashery S. et al. J Biol Chem 1999;274:25260–25265.

1276. Nishida K, Kunugita C, Uji T, Higashitani F, Hyodo A, Unemi N, Maiti SN. et al. Antimicrob Agents Chemother 1999;43:1895–1900.

1277. Adediran SA, Lohier JF, Cabaret D, Wakselman M, Pratt RF. Bioorg Med Chem Lett 2006;16:869–871.

1278. Netzel TC, Jindani I, Hanson N, Turner BM, Smith L, Rand KH. Diagn Microbiol Infect Dis 2007;58:345–348.

1279. Poeylaut-Palena AA, Tomatis PE, Karsisiotis AI, Damblon C, Mata EG, Vila AJ. Bioorg Med Chem Lett 2007;17:5171–5174.

1280. Simm AM, Loveridge EJ, Crosby J, Avison MB, Walsh TR, Bennett PM. Biochem J 2005;387:585–590.

1281. Pazhanisamy S, Pratt RF. Biochemistry 1989;28:6875–6882.

1282. Strynadka NC, Martin R, Jensen SE, Gold M, Jones JB. Nat Struct Biol 1996;3:688–695.

1283. Morandi S, Morandi F, Caselli E, Shoichet BK, Prati F. Bioorg Med Chem 2008;16: 1195–1205.

1284. Kaur K, Pratt RF. Biochemistry 2001;40: 4610–4621.

1285. Kaur K, Lan MJ, Pratt RF. J Am Chem Soc 2001;123:10436–10443.

1286. Kaur K, Adediran SA, Lan MJ, Pratt RF. Biochemistry 2003;42:1529–1536.

1287. Crowder MW, Spencer J, Vila AJ. Acc Chem Res 2006;39:721–728.

1288. Payne DJ, Bateson JH, Gasson BC, Khushi T, Proctor D, Pearson SC, Reid R. FEMS Microbiol Lett 1997;157:171–175.

1289. Payne DJ, Bateson JH, Gasson BC, Proctor D, Khushi T, Farmer TH, Tolson DA. et al. Antimicrob Agents Chemother 1997;41: 135–140.

1290. Hammond GG, Huber JL, Greenlee ML, Laub JB, Young K, Silver LL, Balkovec JM. et al. FEMS Microbiol Lett 1999;179: 289–296.

1291. Greenlee ML, Laub JB, Balkovec JM, Hammond ML, Hammond GG, Pompliano DL, Epstein-Toney JH. Bioorg Med Chem Lett 1999;9:2549–2554.

1292. Mollard C, Moali C, Papamicael C, Damblon C, Vessilier S, Amicosante G, Schofield CJ. et al. J Biol Chem 2001;276:45015–45023.

1293. Beharry Z, Chen H, Gadhachanda VR, Buynak JD, Palzkill T. Biochem Biophys Res Commun 2004;313:541–545.

1294. Siemann S, Clarke AJ, Viswanatha T, Dmitrienko GI. Biochemistry 2003;42: 1673–1683.

1295. Yamaguchi Y, Jin W, Matsunaga K, Ikemizu S, Yamagata Y, Wachino J, Shibata N. et al. J Med Chem 2007;50:6647–6653.

1296. Lienard BM, Garau G, Horsfall L, Karsisiotis AI, Damblon C, Lassaux P, Papamicael C. et al. Org Biomol Chem 2008;6:2282–2294.

1297. Lienard BM, Huting R, Lassaux P, Galleni M, Frere JM, Schofield CJ. J Med Chem 2008;51:684–688.

1298. Horsfall LE, Garau G, Lienard BM, Dideberg O, Schofield CJ, Frere JM, Galleni M. Antimicrob Agents Chemother 2007;51:2136–2142.

1299. Wilson RM, Danishefsky SJ. Chem Soc Rev 2007;36:1207–1226.

1300. Vicente M, Hodgson J, Massidda O, Tonjum T, Henriques-Normark B, Ron EZ. FEMS Microbiol Rev 2006;30:841–852.

1301. Payne DJ, Gwynn MN, Holmes DJ, Pompliano DL. Nat Rev Drug Discov 2007;6:29–40.

1302. Martinez JL, Fajardo A, Garmendia L, Hernandez A, Linares JF, Martinez-Solano L, Sanchez MB. FEMS Microbiol Rev 2009;33: 44–65.

1303. Staub I, Sieber SA. J Am Chem Soc 2008;130:13400–13409.

1304. Walsh CT. Acc Chem Res 2008;41:4–10.

1305. Lian W, Jayapal KP, Charaniya S, Mehra S, Glod F, Kyung YS, Sherman DH. et al. BMC Genomics 2008;9:56.

1306. Williams RB, Henrikson JC, Hoover AR, Lee AE, Cichewicz RH. Org Biomol Chem 2008;6:1895–1897.

1307. Henrikson JC, Hoover AR, Joyner PM, Cichewicz RH. Org Biomol Chem 2009;7: 435–438.

TETRACYCLINE, AMINOGLYCOSIDE, MACROLIDE, AND MISCELLANEOUS ANTIBIOTICS

Lester A. Mitscher
Department of Medicinal
Chemistry, Kansas
University, Lawrence, KS

1. INTRODUCTION

Despite enormous advances in the last century, infectious diseases continue to cause great suffering and death worldwide. The widespread emergence of bacterial resistance to chemotherapy in recent years has largely replaced earlier euphoria with gathering concern that we are starting to loose the battle against infectious disease.

The antibiotic families covered in this chapter were established in the 1940s and 1950s as mainstays in antibacterial chemotherapy and have remained important weapons. Newer members emerged at first through directed screening programs examining the fermentation products of soil microorganisms and subsequently through semisynthesis. The enormous research effort that went into this was quite productive but has reached the stage of diminishing returns with progressively fewer agents entering into medical practice. Semisynthesis of newer agents is however intensively pursued today.

It is interesting to note that the once widely held belief that evolutionary factors would inevitably have led to structural optimization of natural antibiotics now seems quaint. The most widely utilized tetracyclines are doxycycline, minocycline, and tigecycline. None of these are of natural provenance. The ketolide members of the macrolide family as well as the very important semisynthetic analogs azithromycin and clarithromycin also challenge this cliché. One can only speculate as to why this should not be a tenable belief. The most convincing argument is that it takes energy to generate and maintain a metabolic product. If energy is not inexhaustible, then one must spare some for other purposes as well. It is further clear that soil microorganisms have not had to worry about ADME and toxicity concerns of humans. The medicinal chemist's motto (good enough soon enough) may well serve soil microorganisms as well.

Nonetheless, the antibiotic drugs covered in this chapter are all natural products or are derived from natural products. The tetracyclines are polyketide based as are the macrolides. The aminoglycosides are carbohydrate derived. All three groups inhibit bacteria by inhibiting protein biosynthesis after binding to specific rRNA segments. It was believed for a long time that their cellular targets were proteins. This turned out not to be so. The actual target in the bacterial cell is the ribosomal RNA. Their selectivity derives from structural differences from hrRNA that makes human ribosomes comparatively less sensitive to their action. Resistance to these drugs takes many forms ranging from inactivating enzymic attack on their structures to accumulation barriers and alterations in target structure. The newest agents have been designed to overcome bacterial resistance and to provide enhanced pharmacokinetic features. This has often been accomplished by finding another binding site that is not utilized by the products of nature. The additional strength in these host–guest relationships is often sufficient to overcome resistance.

A landmark achievement in the years since the previous chapter on these agents in this series has been the X-ray determination of the structure of the bacterial ribosome and, as a consequence, the elucidation of the specific binding sites for these antibiotics. Fortunately this largely confirmed inferences about the structure and functional aspects of the ribosome gained by many lines of earlier evidence. A bit of caution is however required in making these conclusions. The X-ray data utilizes ribosomes from nonpathogenic *Deinococcus radiodurans* [1–3] and *Haloarcula mortismortui* [4–6]. The data have been interpreted as though it came from *Escherichia coli* and it may well be applicable to it. Nonetheless, as politicians have learned to their cost, an excessive reliance on models can lead to serious trouble.

The fascinating and complex operation of the ribosome is beyond the scope of this chapter but can be briefly synopsized. Ribosomes are assembled as needed from their many parts. There are two component particles, the large 50S unit comprised of 31 proteins, and two segments of rRNA (the 23S and 5S units) and the small 30S subunit comprised of 21 proteins and a segment of rRNA (the 16S unit). These are joined by a series of initiating and elongation protein factors. The functional portions of the completed ribosome are essentially three. These consist of an A-site where specific rRNAs each carrying specific amino acids bind to their complementary codon segments at the same time as GTP is hydrolyzed. Next peptide bond formation occurs between the amino group of the amino acid at the A-site and the activated ester carbonyl of a growing peptide chain attached to the adjacent P-site. Thus, the peptide grows by one amino acid residue at a time. The freed tRNA migrates from the P-site to the E-site from which it dissociates. The now longer by one peptide attached to the tRNA migrates from the A-site to the P-site. The ribosome is now ready to repeat the process utilizing the newly available codon triad at the A-site when its cognate amino acid laden tRNA molecule binds. The growing peptide chain is progressively extruded through a tunnel-like portion of the ribosome structure and receives its final conformation (folding) following completion. This intimately coordinated sequence of events is rigorously conserved such that binding of antibiotics in the vicinity of these events prevents proper functioning and bacterial are generally unable to alter this process so as to escape. The consequence is inhibition of growth and or death, depending upon the achievable concentration of drug.

Much fascinating detail has had to be glossed over or omitted due to space limitations but excellent treatments exist in contemporary biochemistry text books for the interested reader to consult for more detailed information. At least a general understanding of the overall process is necessary however for much of the following treatment to make sense to the reader new to the topic.

2. TETRACYCLINES

2.1. Clinical Use of Tetracycline Antibiotics and Currently Used Drugs

The tetracycline antibiotics (Table 1) have been used for nearly 60 years in clinical medicine. Because of their general safety, oral activity, and breadth of spectrum they dominated office practice for many years but the appearance of significant bacterial resistance and availability of alternate therapeutic choices has led to a general decline in their use so that they are no longer the empirical drugs of first choice for many common community-acquired infections. The intrinsic antibacterial spectrum of the tetracyclines is very broad including tetracycline-sensitive strains of Gram-positive and Gram-negative aerobes and anaerobes as well as many more unusual microbes such as *Rickettsia*, *Chlamydia*, *Borrelia*, *Brucella*, *Propionibacterium*, *Helicobacter* (where they are used in "cocktails" with other drugs), *Vibrio*, and so on. Their ease of administration and freedom from serious side effects is now countered by uncertainty of efficacy due to resistance so their popularity has declined substantially. The newest member, tigecycline, is active against many tetracycline resistant strains and against bacteria resistant to many other antibiotic types so its appearance has been welcomed. It is, however, available only for IV administration that diminishes the extent of its use.

A number of years lapsed between the appearance of semisynthetic doxycycline and

Table 1. Tetracycline Antibiotics in Use in 2008

Generic Name	Common Name	Structure	Administration Route	Usual Dose
Tetracycline	Achromycin	2	Oral	250 mg, qid
Demethylchlortetracycline	Demeclomycin	3	Oral	150 mg, qid
Minocycline	Minocin	4	Oral	100 mg, bid
Doxycycline	Vibramycin	7	Oral	50–100 mg, bid
Tigecycline	Tygacil	8	IV	50–100 mg

minocycline and the appearance of the most recent member of this class, tigecycline. A survey of the relative rankings of the most frequently prescribed office practice medications in the year 2005 listed doxycycline (#68), minocycline (#149), and tetracycline (#242)

and by the year 2007, the list contained only doxycycline (#112). Previously utilized tetracyclines (chlortetracycline, demethylchlortetracycline, oxytetracycline, and rondomycin) have already been retired or see comparatively little use.

The Tetracycline Group[1]

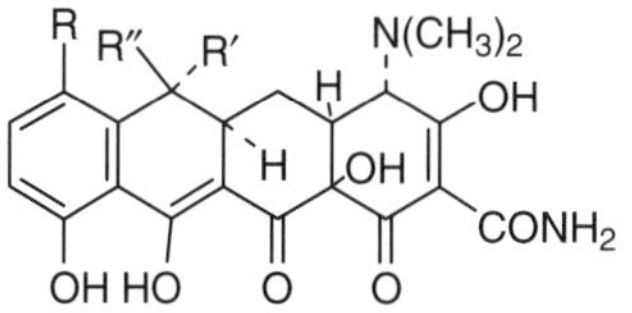

(**1**) Chlortetracycline, R = Cl, R″ = OH, R′ = Me
(**2**) Tetracycline, R = H, R″ = OH, R′ = Me
(**3**) Demethylchlortetracycline, R = Cl, R″ = OH, R′ = H
(**4**) Minocycline, R = N(Me)$_2$, R′ = R″ = H

The Oxytetracycline Group[1]

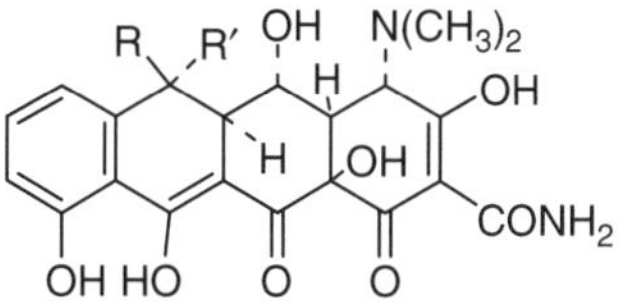

(**5**) Oxytetracycline, R = OH, R′ = Me
(**6**) Rondomycin, R = R′ = CH$_2$
(**7**) Doxycycline, R = H, R′ = Me

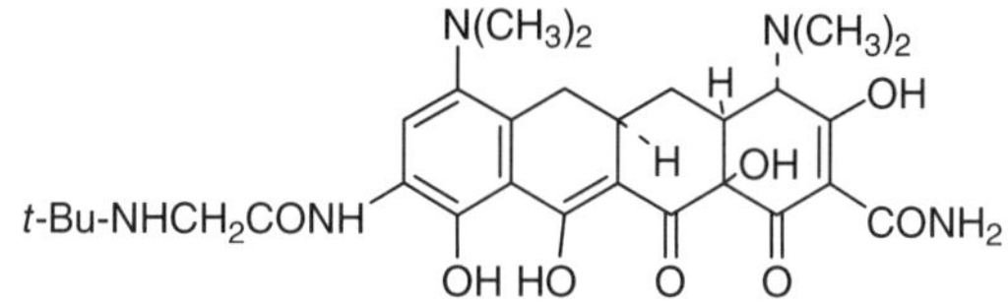

(**8**) Tigecycline

As can be inferred from their structures, the tetracycline family is named for its partially reduced naphthacene nucleus. Its rings are labeled A–D from right to left and its carbons are numbered counterclockwise as shown in Fig. 1.

The pharmacophoric region of the tetracyclines includes the intact ring system and

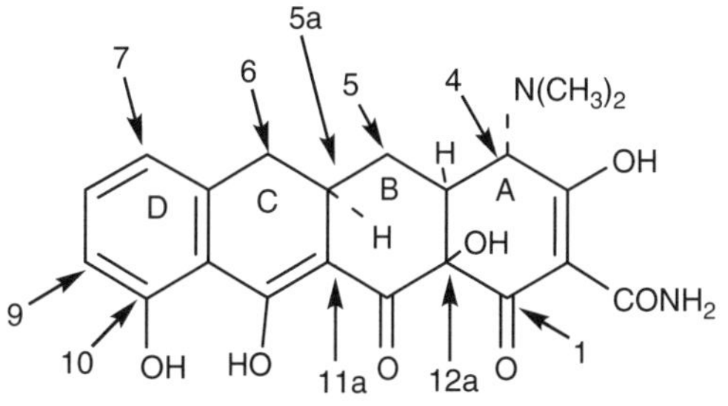

Figure 1. The numbering and lettering system for the tetracycline antibiotics.

[1]The reader of course knows that the 1,3-dicarbonyl systems of the antibiotic tetracyclines can be represented in a number of different enolic forms. The formulations used above are but one of the conventional depictions.

the region extending to the right from carbons 10-4 with all of the substituents and their stereochemistry required to be as indicated as shown in structures 1–8. The nonpharmacophoric region extends to the left from carbons 4a-9. Significant structural variation is tolerated in the nonpharmacophoric region. This allows for significant variations in stability, potency, antimicrobial spectrum and pharmacokinetics. The fermentation-derived tetracyclines are produced by various *Streptomyces* sp. and include chlortetracycline (**1**), tetracycline (**2**), demethylchlortetracycline (**3**), and oxytetracycline (**4**). The semisynthetic tetracyclines are derived from these by chemical transformations and include minocycline (**4**), rondomycin (**6**), doxycycline (**7**), and tigecycline (**8**).

2.2. Chemical Stability, Side Effects, Toxicity, and Contraindications of Tetracycline Antibiotics

Being polyketides, the tetracyclines are rich in β-diketo residues and are accordingly unstable in basic solutions. They are, on the other hand mostly remarkably stable to acid allowing for convenient electrophilic substitution reactions. The exceptions are those tetracyclines bearing a hydroxyl group attached to carbon 6. This is axial, benzylic, and trans periplanar to the hydrogen at carbon 5a so that in acidic solutions these derivatives have a pronounced tendency to dehydrate irreversibly forming a naphthaleneoid structure.

These anhydrotetracyclines (**10**) are antimicrobially inactive. To prevent this degradation various reductive reactions have been employed to produce the much more stable 6-deoxy analogs such as minocycline (**4**), tigecycline (**8**), rondomycin (**6**), and doxycycline (**7**). In addition to their greater acid stability, these agents are less polar so are better absorbed and distributed into tissues.

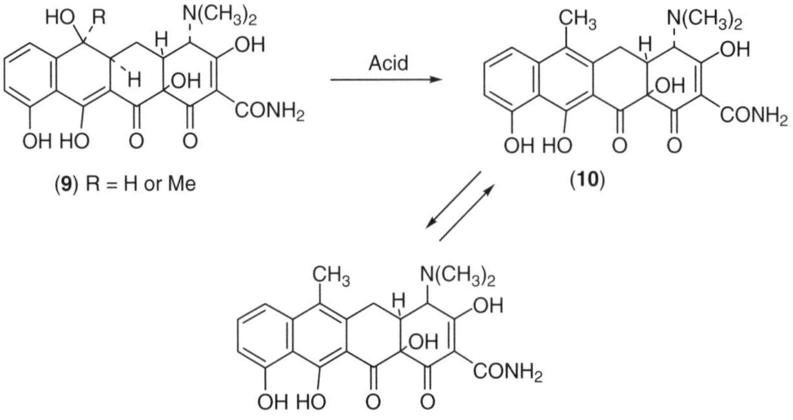

(**9**) R = H or Me → Acid → (**10**)

(**11**)

Other chemical aspects of note include the tendency of tetracyclines to be configurationally unstable through epimerization at C-4. The resulting 4-epitetracyclines are essentially inactive as antibiotics so this feature is carefully controlled in products that reach the public. The optimum pH range for the epimerization is about 4–6 and the equilibrium point is close to 1:1. If activity is to be retained the presence of a α-dimethylamino function at C-4 cannot be avoided. Epimerization could in principal be prevented by alkylation at C-4 with retention of configuration, but no one has yet succeeded in doing this. Rather more worrisome is the tendency of anhydrotetracyclines to epimerize. The 4-epianhydrotetracyclines (**11**) are significantly toxic so their formation is carefully guarded against. One notes that those tetracyclines without a C-6 hydroxyl group cannot form these degradation products.

Tetracyclines are excellent chelating agents forming quite water insoluble magnesium, calcium, ferrous, and aluminum complexes at neutral pHs. These complexes are also poorly absorbed from the GI tract so chelate formation

leads to drug–drug incompatibilities with ion rich foods (milk, cheese) and drugs (antacids, hematinics) so coadministration with these agents is to be avoided. The structural region generally associated with chelate formation is the lower periphery of the B-D rings extending from C-10 to C-12. Since this portion of the molecule cannot be changed without loss of antimicrobial activity, chemical transformations cannot solve this problem. Another consequence of chelation is the significant tendency of tetracyclines to form insoluble yellow complexes in ion rich body structures such as bones. This is not generally associated with toxicity however staining of the teeth (the bones that one sees) is cosmetically unattractive. Consequently tetracyclines are only given following careful consideration to children when their permanent teeth are being formed (generally from about 6 to 12 years of age).

Tetracyclines are painful on injection. This is often attributed to the formation of insoluble calcium chelates at or near the site of injection. Thus, injection of tetracyclines is not a favored route of administration. Tigecycline is injected intravenously but must be given by slow IV drip over a period of a half hour or so to avoid thrombophlebitis.

Tetracyclines, especially those with chlorine atoms at C-7, are photolytically unstable readily generating free radicals that can trigger an inflammatory response. Thus, some tetracyclines are phototoxic to some patients. Tetracyclines have a tendency to be transported to the skin following oral administration helping to rationalize this effect. Exposure to strong sunlight following administration thus can lead to severe sunburns so patients are warned to avoid this while taking the first couple of days of treatment. If no unusual sensitivity to sunlight develops during this time then this precaution can be lifted. The newer tetracyclines do not seem to possess this characteristic to the same extent but the patient is warned anyhow in case they should be hyper sensitive.

Minocycline is somewhat unstable to oxidation leading to highly colored materials that are believed to be quinones or quinoneimines. This seems not to have significant clinical implications. Injection under the skin, however, can lead to a dark blue tattoo-like circle but since minocycline is rarely used this way this seems not to be a significant problem.

Minocycline is also associated with an unusually frequent, for tetracyclines, incidence of dizziness, and light headedness. Since it is quite lipophilic compared to other tetracyclines, it is thought to penetrate more into the CNS helping to rationalize this effect.

As with virtually all antimicrobial agents of significant breadth of spectrum, tetracyclines are also associated with some gastrointestinal discomfort and with Candida overgrowth. Less commonly and in high doses, some hepatotoxicity has also been observed in some patients.

In sum, the tetracyclines possess a significant number of fairly mild side effects but are on the whole quite safe and well tolerated.

2.3. Pharmacology and Mode of Action of Tetracycline Antibiotics

Tetracyclines, particularly the newer ones that are more lipophilic, are well absorbed from the gastrointestinal tract and distributed efficiently into tissues. Minocycline and doxycycline, for example, are nearly completely absorbed following oral administration. As indicated above the presence of significant amounts of multivalent metallic ions in the gut decreases absorption due to the insolubility of these complexes at physiological pH values. They cross the placental barrier so a fetus is exposed to the mother's medication as are suckling newborns.

Excretion of the tetracyclines is primarily in active form in the urine (allowing for treatment of urinary tract infections caused by susceptible bacteria) with the exception of tigecycline and doxycycline in which case significant billiary and therefore fecal excretion takes place.

Metabolic transformation of tetracyclines is minimal. Serum protein binding varies from 20 to 90% depending on the lipophilicity of the particular tetracycline and serum half-lives likewise vary from 6 to more than 20 h. The doses commonly employed are set forth in Table 1 above.

Tetracyclines are primarily bacteriostatic in doses realistically achievable orally in patients. Uptake into cells is primarily passive so is diffusion controlled. On contact with bacterial ribosomes tetracyclines bind primarily but not exclusively to the 30S subunit with high affinity for the A (acceptor) site. This stops translation and thus deprives the cell of its proteins. An X-ray crystal structure of tetracycline soaked into the 30 S ribosomal subparticle of Thermus thermophilus has been published and is illustrated in Fig. 2 [7–9]. Two sites were identified but the more likely relevant site is near the A site. This agrees with the findings of many previous studies. In contrast to long held belief that tetracyclines bound to ribosomal proteins, it has been found that it does not. It rather binds to the 16S rRNA molecules in a pocket just above the aminoacyl tRNA binding pocket. Modeling studies suggest that this results in a steric clash between bound tetracycline and approaching tRNA rationalizing the molecular mode of action. An additional action mode has been proposed involving catalyzed hydrolysis of GTP associated with the interaction of tRNA with EF-Tu thus depleting the pool of GTP in the cell [10]. Magnesium ion as well as backbone phosphate residues and some base interactions are observed such that the A–D

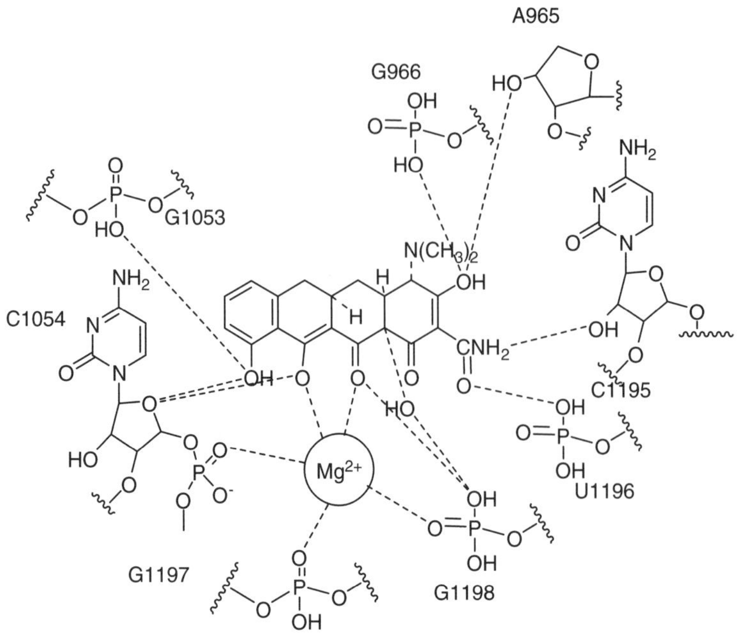

Figure 2. Schematic of the attraction between 6-demethyl-6-deoxytetracycline and the bacterial 30S ribosomal subunit. The bases are numbered as though they were from *E. coli* although the above interactions are with *T. thermophilus* ribosomes.

ring pharmacophoric region is fully engaged as empirical SAR studies have suggested should be the case. This tetracycline binding site differs somewhat from that present in eukaryotic animals (including humans) rationalizing the observed selective toxicity. Significant space is available along the upper and left hand peripheries of the molecules to allow for the variation in substitution patterns that have been performed successfully. A discordant feature is that the X-ray structure reveals no role for the C-4 dimethylamino moiety. Since epimerization at this center results in inactivity, this X-ray picture cannot be the entire story. Perhaps a cocrystallization study will resolve this remaining issue. One also cautions that such an X-ray determination inevitably is a stop-frame photograph. The ribosome undergoes substantial conformational movement while performing protein biosynthesis and the X-ray picture of tetracycline soaked into the ribosome presently in hand may not have captured the key moment in the inhibition.

X-ray studies with tigecycline allow a rationalization of its strong antimicrobial potency

and possibly also its activity against resistant strains [11,12]. Tigecycline possesses an additional interaction with rRNA that the other tetracyclines lack. The glycine amide NH and the secondary NH of the glycyl unit both hydrogen bond to the carbonyl oxygen of C1054. This provides a credible explanation for tigecycline's 3 times greater inhibition of protein biosynthesis than minocycline's and its 20 times greater inhibition than tetracycline.

2.4. History and Biosynthesis of the Tetracycline Antibiotics

The year 1948 began the tetracycline saga with the isolation of chlortetracycline (**1**) from *Streptomyces aureofaciens* and of oxytetracycline (**5**) from *Streptomyces rimosus*. Tetracycline (**2**) itself was shortly thereafter (1952) isolated from several streptomycetes and was also prepared by hydrogenolysis of tetracycline. Demethylchlortetracycline (**3**) was later isolated from a mutant culture prepared in attempts to enhance fermentation yields of tetracyclines. Chemical transformations of these agents led to minocycline (**4**) and rondomycin (**6**) and doxycycline (**7**) (which was made from rondomycin). Tigecycline (**8**) was prepared from a by-product of the synthesis of minocycline.

There are several synthetic routes to minocycline and on to tigecycline. The following is representative and illustrates the stability

to acid once the hydroxyl at C-6 is removed. This opens the way to electrophilic reactions that would otherwise destroy activity because of formation of anhydrotetracyclines (**10** and **11**).

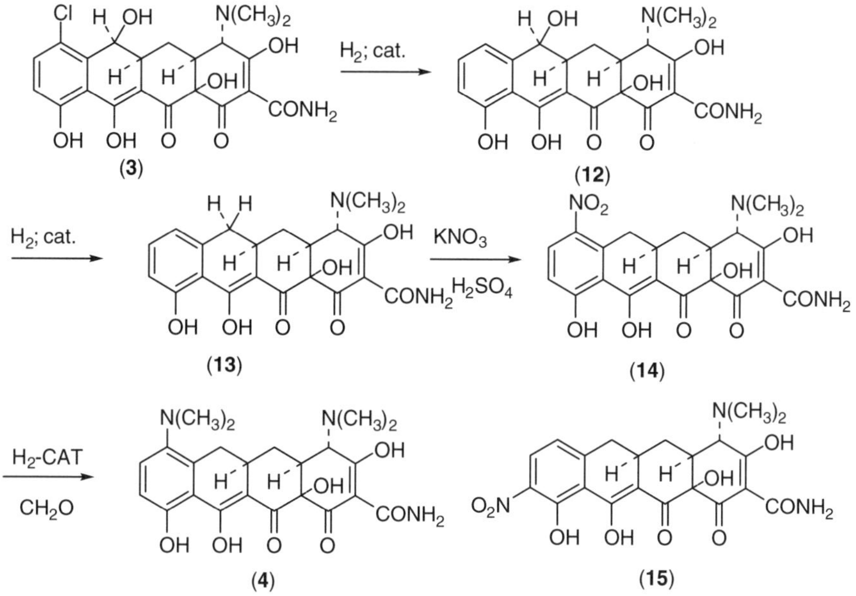

This sequence starts with the hydrogenolysis of the chlorine and the secondary alcohol moieties of demethylchlortetracycline (**3**). Special catalysts allow the simultaneous removal of both functions leading efficiently to sancycline (**13**). Sancycline is sufficiently inert to strong acid that it can be nitrated to a mixture of **14** and **15** by dissolving it in concentrated sulfuric acid and adding potassium nitrate to effect the electrophilic reaction. Various alternatives to this sequence are available that minimize the formation of **15**. A catalytic reductive alkylation completes this synthesis of minocycline (**4**). Many other electrophilic reactions can be performed on **13** leading to a variety of bioactive products but that leading to minocycline has been the most useful. The conversion of **15** to *iso*-minocycline resulted in a less desirable commodity.

Synthesis of tigecycline and its analogs also can be done in a number of ways but the following sequence is representative.

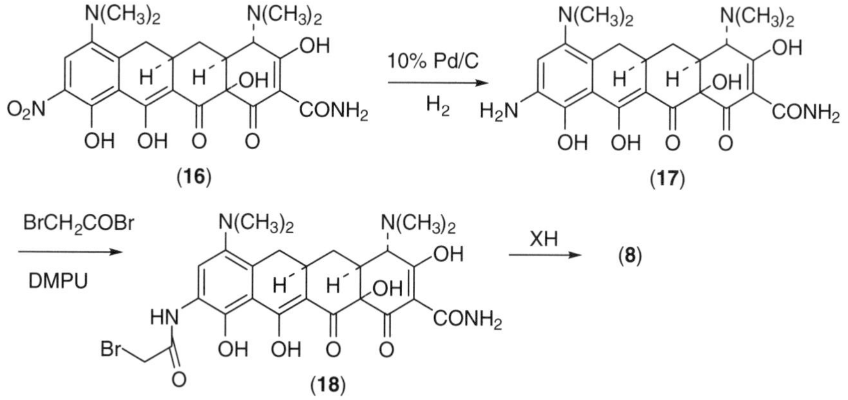

This sequence starts with the nitration of minocycline to produce **16** and continues to the reduction to amine **17**. While bioactive, **17** is too unstable for use as an antibiotic. Acylation stabilizes it but makes it too insoluble for use. Conversion to a wide variety of glycine analogs led to the selection of glycylcycline (**8**) whose properties were vastly superior. Glycylcycline has outstanding activity against a wide range of otherwise tetracycline resistant bacteria and has found very significant clinical use as the most recent of the tetracycline family [13].

The structure determination of oxytetracycline by R.B. Woodward and Pfizer scientists was a landmark achievement since its complex structure was unprecedented. It represents one of the last of the major structures to have been elucidated prior to the availability of X-ray, NMR, and mass spectrometry and is a superb example of the use of classical degradations and deductive logic.

Tetracyclines are typical polyketides being derived from acetate, malonate, methionine, oxygen, and ammonia (see Fig. 3 wherein that path leading to oxytetracycline is laid out). Detailed work with blocked mutants and radioisotopes as well as cloning and sequencing of the genes in the tetracycline biosynthetic clusters have revealed and/or allowed the reasonable postulation of the overall pathway [14–17].

The reduction of the carbonyl of the upper leftmost carbonyl in the condensation phase to an alcohol followed by dehydration to a *cis* olefinic moiety nicely positions the carbons for a series of Dieckmann-like cyclodehydrations leading to the ring system of 6-demethylpretetramid. There follows the stepwise oxidations, transaminations and oxidations leading to the final oxytetracycline molecule. If the starter unit is acetoacetate, this allows for the formation of the known fermentation derived 2-acetyl tetracyclines. The formation of chlorotetracyclines involves a halogenation reaction at the earliest stages. Omission of the 6-methyl group in some mutant species accounts for the formation of the 6-demethyltetracyclines. Starvation by media exclusion of methionine or addition of methionine antagonists allows formation of 4-amino tetracyclines. *S. aureofaciens* lacks the gene for incorporation of the 5-hydroxy group so this feature is lacking in its products. This knowledge led to the combined synthetic and biosynthetic preparation of oxychlortetracycline (**19**) [18]. This otherwise missing link is the most fully elaborated tetracycline and, like the Edsel, proved to be unsuccessful commercially. In the case of oxychlortetracycline the primary reason was the instability of the substance. Biosynthesis of some rarer tetracyclines of no present commercial interest such as the dactylocyclines (**21**) [19–21] and chelocardin (**22**) [22–24] is readily rationalized by modest departures from this overall scheme.

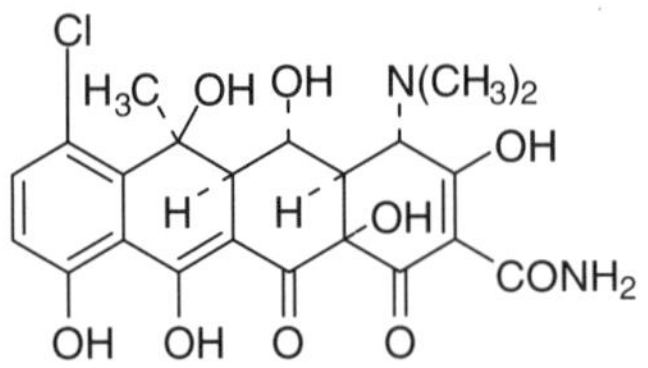

(19)

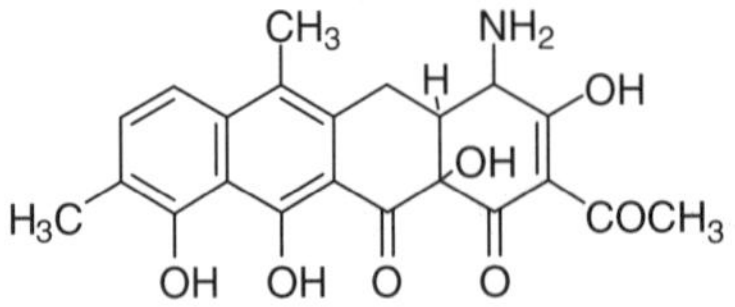

(20)

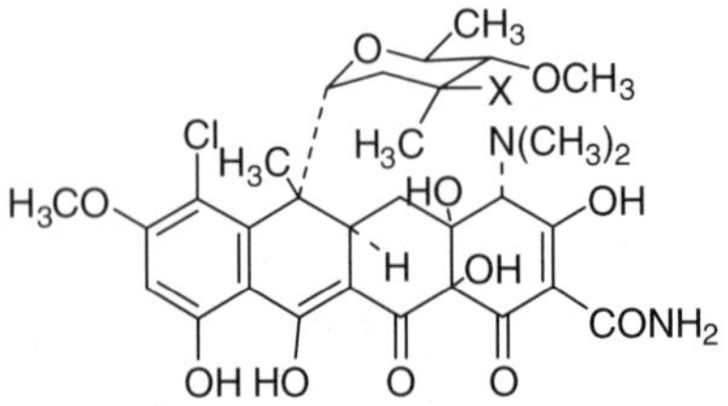

(21) X = NHOH; NO₂; NHAc; OH

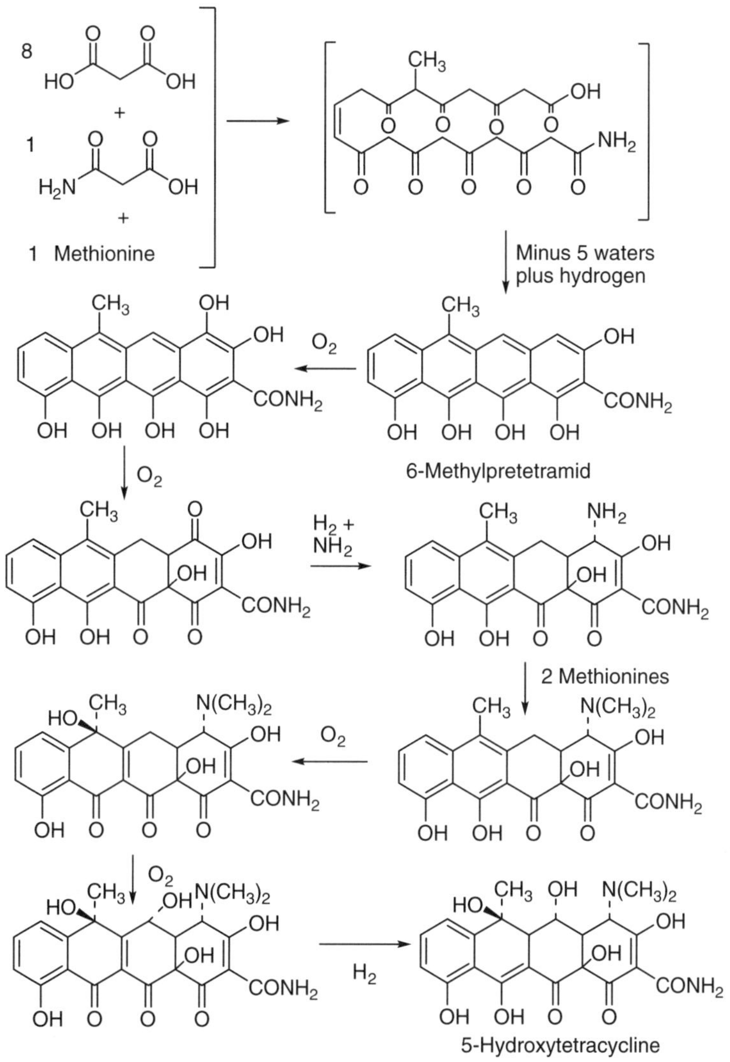

Figure 3. Apparent biosynthetic pathway for 5-hydroxytetracycline.

The increasing ability to direct artificial biosynthesis by mixing, matching, introducing, and inactivating biosynthetic genes suggests that one could in principle develop such a process for production of sancycline (**13**). As this substance is a key intermediate in the production of minocycline and tigecycline, this would probably be a commercially as well as scientifically worthwhile achievement.

2.5. Microbial Resistance to Tetracyclines

Widespread resistance to the tetracyclines has emerged over the years so that empirical use of these antibiotics has drastically diminished. At least 36 genes have been associated with microbial resistance to tetracyclines [25–28]. Resistance of clinical relevance occurs by two main pathways. Many cultures actively exclude these drugs by efflux [29]. Alternatively, a ribosomal protecting protein is also elaborated by many strains that prevents tetracycline from binding to ribosomes [30]. A number of pathogens have been isolated that exhibit both forms of resistance. Other mechanisms have been published in the literature but are not at present found in most tetracycline resistant strains of bacteria [31,32].

The tetracycline efflux proteins belong to a large family of efflux proteins that export small molecules using protonmotive force for energy [33]. They are average sized (ca. 46 kDa) and possess similarities in amino acid sequences [34]. At least six families of tetracycline efflux resistance genes are known: group 1 consists of Tet (A) through (E), Tet (G and (H), and Tet Z; group 2 contains Tet (K) and (L); group 3 contains OtrB and Ter3, group 4 has TetA (P); group 5 has et (V); and group 6 has Tet (AB). These are unevenly distributed throughout the members of the microbial kingdom that have learned how to resist tetracyclines. Strains carrying many of these genes are sensitive to tigecycline accounting for its present popularity [27,35,36]. Structural information about these protein products is limited but the Tet (A) exporter apparently has 12-transmembrane helices surrounding a water filled pore through which apparently the tetracyclines pass on their way out of the cell [37].

The TetR family of transcriptional regulators are found in many bacterial species [38]. Their protein products control the level of antibiotic efflux pumps by binding to DNA and preventing transcription. They are also involved in pathogenicity. The repression of transcription is cytoprotective but can be reversed when tetracycline binds to the protein product producing an allosteric conformational shift that leads to its release from DNA thereby inducing transcription of tetracycline antiport efflux pumps. Thus, tetracycline can induce its own resistance. There are many interactions between tetracycline and its repressor protein making this a difficult target for chemotherapy. Fortunately an X-ray structure of the repressor complex with tetracycline chelate is available from which to work [39].

The ribosomal protecting genes produce somewhat larger proteins (ca. 70 kDa) and at present there are eight of these (Tet(M), Tet(O), Tet(Q), Tet(S), Tet(T)Tet(W), TetP(B), and Otr(A)). Tet(M) and (O) have sequence homologies with elongation factors G and Tu such that it has been proposed that they bind GTP preventing attachment of these elongation factors to the ribosome thus leading to release of tetracycline. Further, X-ray studies indicate that Tet(O) binds to ribosomes in a similar manner as does EF-G but that the binding of Tet(O) does not lead to the conformational changes that follow EF-G binding. This is believed to be important in explaining how the ribosomal protecting proteins interfere with tetracycline inhibition of protein biosynthesis.

Early concerns that resistance to tigecycline would emerge rapidly among bacteria have eased so far as such resistance has so far not been found to a significant extent among clinical isolates. Experience justifies continuing apprehension but the news is good so far [35,36,40–42].

2.6. Recent Developments in the Tetracycline Field

Tigecycline, discussed above, is the most recent tetracycline to reach the clinic. Its utility is based upon its significant superiority to precedent tetracyclines in inhibiting tetracycline-resistant microorganisms. Its breadth of spectrum is illustrated in the murine ED_{50} values in Table 2 [43,44].

In addition to numerous analogs produced collaterally with the tigecycline campaign, PTK-0796/BAY 73-6944 (*), a broad-spectrum analog intended for oral and parenteral use, is now in phase II clinical trials. This agent is active against many tetracycline-resistant strains. The mode of action of **22** has been shown to be essentially the same as that of the other tetracyclines.

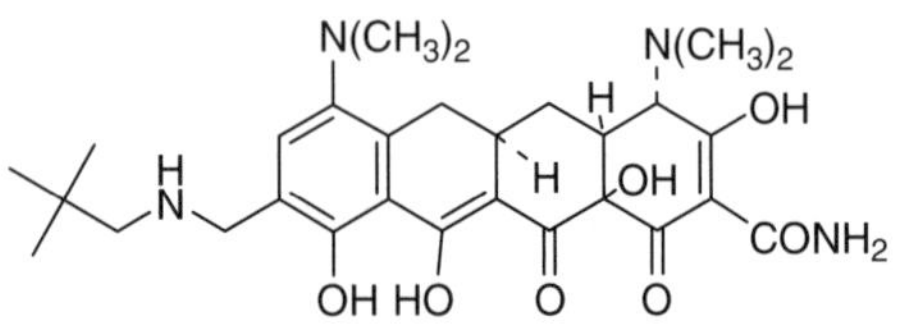

(22)

Table 2. Comparative *In Vivo* Potency of Some Tigecycline Analogs

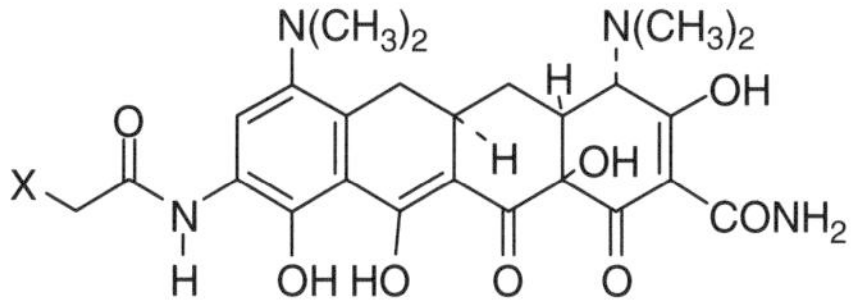

X	Sa	MRSA	SpPenR	Ec	Ec(TetA)	Ec(TetM)
NHtBu*	1.0	0.79	0.61	1.7	1.6	3.5
NMe₂	0.68	0.48	0.53	1.5	4.6	2.1
Minocycline	1.8	0.31	30	3.2	13	>32

*, tigecycline; Sa, *Staphylococcus aureus*; MRSA, methacillin-resistant Sa; SpPenR, penicillin-resistant *Streptococcus pyogenes*; Ec, *Escherichia coli*; Ec(TetA), a reflux exhibiting mutant of Ec; Ec(TetM), a ribosomal protectant exhibiting mutant of Ec.

A number of chemically modified tetracyclines apparently have the ability to block tetracycline efflux pumps (TetA and TetB) reversing resistance. SAR studies indicate that the portion of the tetracycline molecule involved in facilitated export extends along the lower periphery from C-10 to the carboxamide function attached to C-2 [45]. Two isopimerane diterpenes isolated from the higher plant *Lycopus europaeus* weakly decrease the dose of tetracycline needed to overcome the resistance of bacterial strains carrying Tet(K) efflux gene products. It is possible that stronger inhibitors will be found that could have practical value. Various other sesquiterpenes disturb the membranes of *Staphylococcus aureus* and *E. coli* sensitizing the bacteria to the action of tetracyclines by allowing better penetration of the drugs into bacterial cells [46]. Catechins from *Camellia sinensis*, notably epigallocatechin gallate, have been shown *in vitro* to prevent development of resistance to tetracyclines by *S. aureus* apparently by an antimutagenic action [47,48].

Tetracyclines have some prophylactic activity against malaria-causing *Plasmodium falciparum*. This is apparently associated with inhibition of a functioning apicoplast, an organelle of uncertain function, in progeny cells. The cells are still infectious but fail to thrive in newly infected cells [49,50].

Various chemically modified tetracyclines lacking a C-4 dimethylamino group and thus not antibacterial have been found to possess activity in various drug seeking screens suggesting a potentially wider therapeutic application of these compounds may eventually occur [51]. Activity in inhibiting metalloproteinases, [52] antitumor, [53,54] antimetastatic, [53] antifungal, [55] antineurotoxicity, [55–57] anti-inflammatory, [58] and antiarthritic activity, neuroprotection, [59] and activity against septic shock, [60] have been reported.

3. AMINOGLYCOSIDE ANTIBIOTICS

3.1. Clinical Use of Aminoglycoside Antibiotics and Currently Used Drugs

The aminoglycoside antibiotics are broad spectrum against bacteria but generally restricted because of potentially severe toxicities to the treatment of severe infections caused by aerobic Gram-negative microorganisms (*Klebsiella pneumoniae, Pseudomonas aeruginosa, E. coli, Proteus* sp., *Serratia marcescens*), drug-resistant *S. aureus*. To a lesser extent, certain aminoglycoside antibiotics are used against gonorrheal, tubercular, and amoebal infections. Thus, their clinical spectrum encompasses the treatment of life-threatening Gram-negative infections,

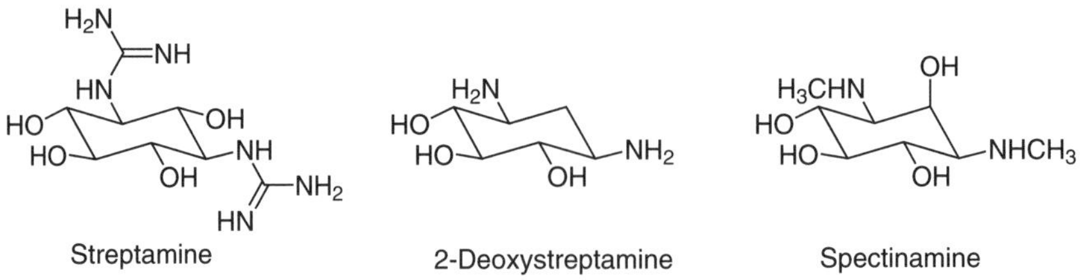

Figure 4. The structures of the amino inositol components of the aminoglycoside antibiotics.

complicated skin, bone and soft tissue infections, complicated urinary tract infections, septicemia, peritonitis, severe pelvic inflammatory disease, endocarditis, and the like. Due to significant toxicities and their primary excretion route through the kidneys, the doses are customarily adjusted downward in patients with kidney damage in order to avoid accumulation of the drugs to unacceptable blood and tissue levels. These factors and the ever increasing level of resistance by bacteria along with the introduction of competing drugs has, until recently, decreased the utilization of these drugs. There has not been a new aminoglycoside antibiotic introduced into the clinic for a generation. Nevertheless, the resistance phenomenon continues to narrow therapeutic options for particular patients so that some resurgence in utilization has taken place of late.

Since they are carbohydrate-based and contain numerous amino groups they are positively charged in physiological fluids. Thus, antibiotic utility by oral administration is limited to applications in the GI tract since they are very poorly absorbed. Nevertheless, some oral use for preoperative bowel disinfection or (with paromomycin (**25**)) for treatment of intestinal amoebiasis takes place. Topical use for eye infections and in treatment of burn patients is also done. Tobramycin (**29**) is also used in the form of a spray into the lungs for treatment of *P. aeruginosa* infections especially for cystic fibrosis sufferers. As a consequence they are mostly used by intramuscular injection or intravenous drip. Because of this, most of the utilization of these agents is in an institutional setting under the control of health professionals raising the cost of ther-

apy. Thus, none of these agents are listed among the 200 most frequently prescribed office practice drugs in the United States.

The first member of this antibiotic family was streptomycin (**23**). Discovered in 1943 it was the first really useful drug effective against *Mycobacterium tuberculosis* and Selmon Waksman received a Nobel prize for it shortly thereafter. Due to resistance it is now a minor drug for this indication and when used is usually a member of a cocktail of antitubercular agents. It can also be used for treatment of tularemia, plague, and leprosy.

Chemically these agents are glycosides of amino inositol moieties (Fig. 4). The pharmacophoric amino inositol units leads many to term these agents as aminocyclitol antibiotics or aminoglycoside-aminocyclitol drugs. They can be subdivided into subgroups based upon the specific amino inositol group contained. Streptomycin (**23**) contains streptamine; the 2-deoxystreptamine-containing group consists of the neomycin mixture (**24** = isomer C) and paromomycin (**25**) wherein sugars are attached to the 4 and 5 positions and of the gentamicin mixture (**26** = isomer C-2), amikacin (**28**), tobramycin (**29**), and netilmicin (**27**) in which the sugars are attached to the 4 and 6 positions; and of spectinomycin (**31**) in which the sugar is annulated into a tricyclic structure. The main group consists of the 2-deoxystreptamine class whereas the outlying groups containing the spectinamine and streptamine moieties are used differently in the clinic largely as the result of significant differences in their molecular modes of action leading to a different antimicrobial spectrum. The commercial forms of the aminoglycosides are usually as the sulfate salts (Table 3).

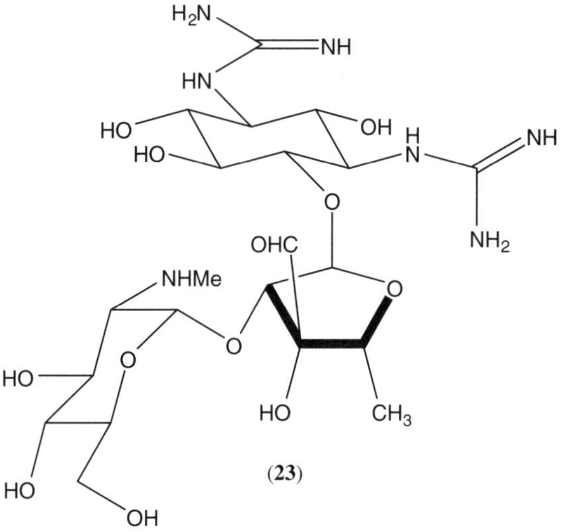

(23)

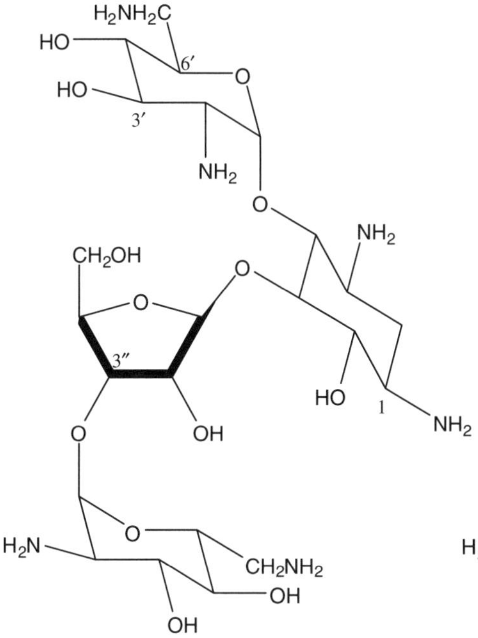

(24)

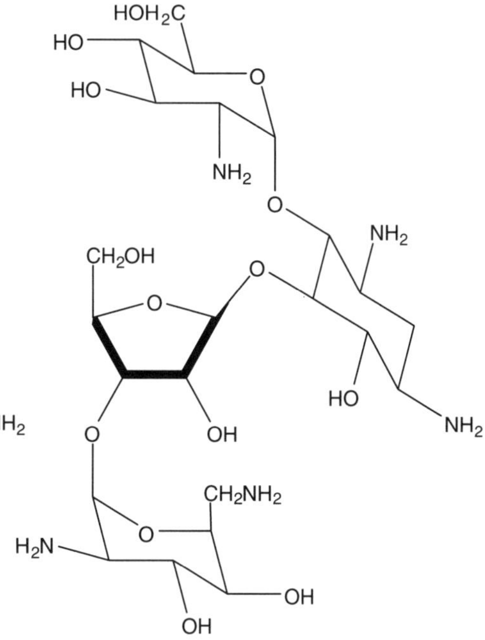

(25)

(32), C-3″ = OH instead.
(33), C-1 = NHCOCHOH(CH$_2$)$_2$NH$_2$,
    C-3″ = OH instead
(34), C-3″ = OH, C-6′ = CH2OH,
    C-3″ =

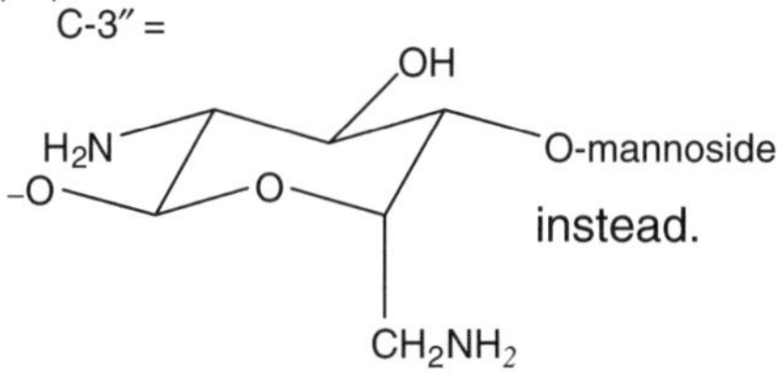

instead.

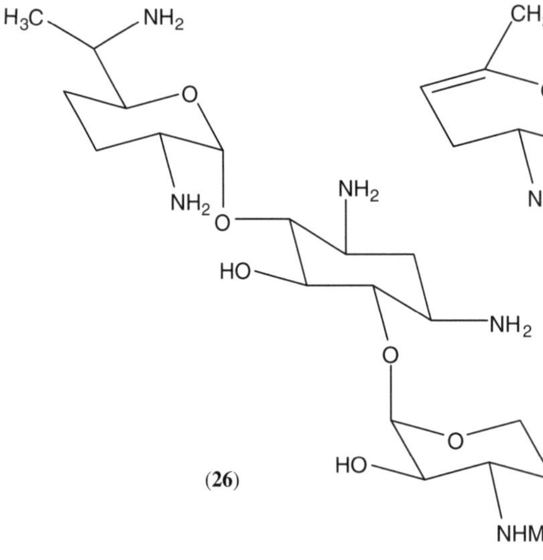

(26)

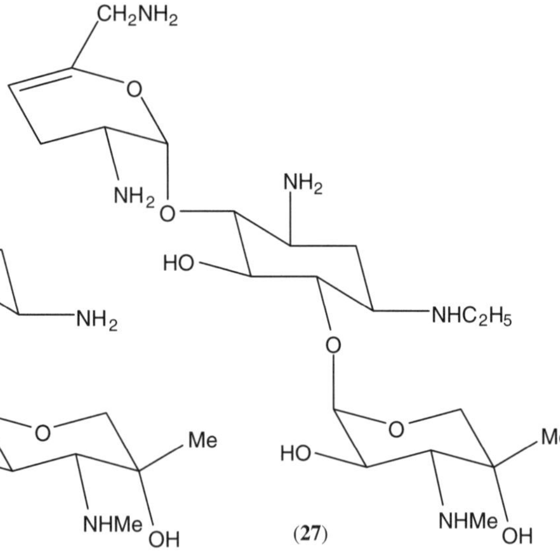

(27)

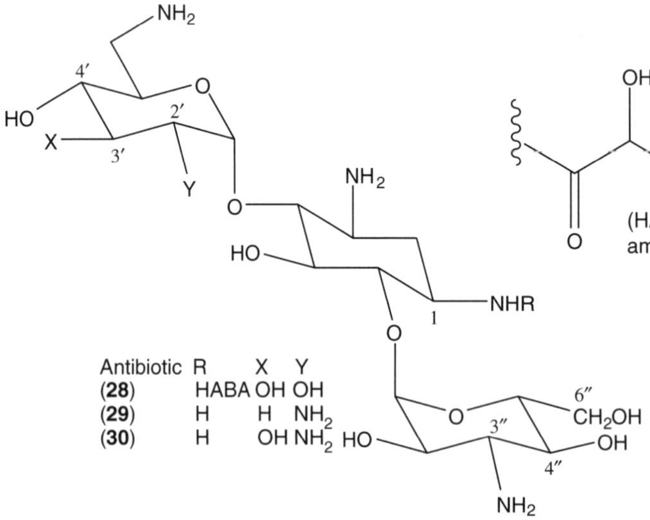

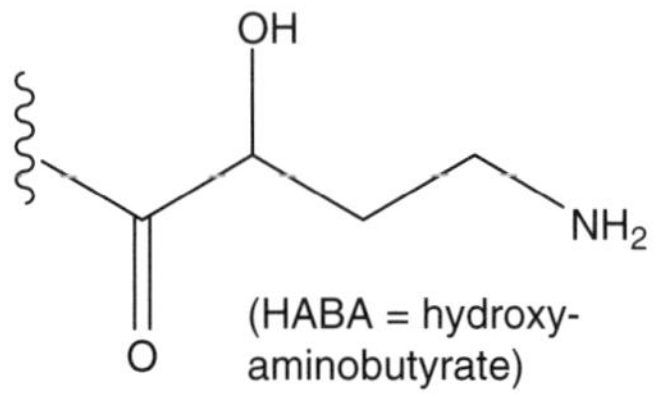

(HABA = hydroxy-
aminobutyrate)

Antibiotic	R	X	Y
(28)	HABA	OH	OH
(29)	H	H	NH$_2$
(30)	H	OH	NH$_2$

(35) C-1 = NH$_2$, C-2′ = NH$_2$, C-3′ = H, C-4′ = H instead.
(36) C-1 = R = H, C-2′ = NH$_2$, C-3′ = H, C-4′ = H, C-3″ = NHCH$_3$,
C-4″ = aOH, bCH$_3$, C-6″ = H instead.
(37) C-1 = NH(HABA), C-2′ = OH, C-3′ = OH, C-3″ = NHCH$_3$,
C-4″ = aOH, bCH$_3$, C-6″ = H instead.
(38) C-1 = NH(HABA), C-2′ = NH$_2$, C-3′ = H, C-4′ = H, C-3″ = NH$_2$ instead.

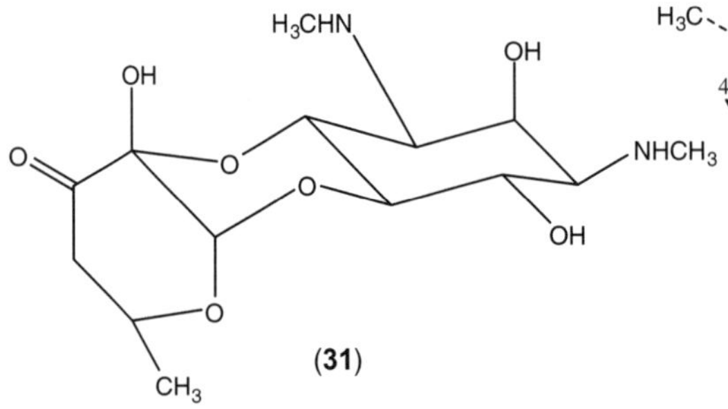

(31)

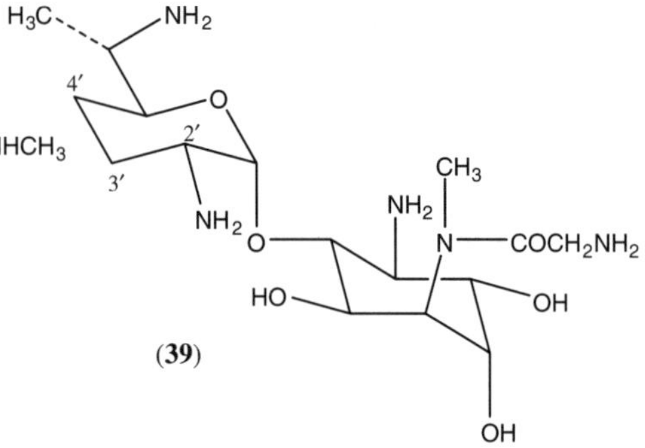

(39)

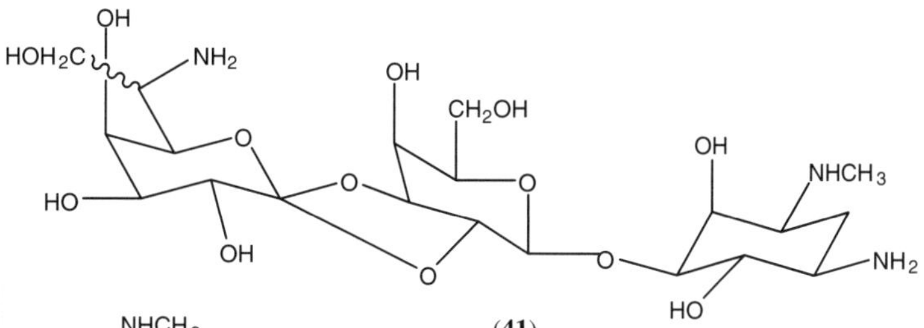

Also depicted are the structures of a number of aminoglycoside antibiotics that are not in present use in the United States but which are used elsewhere or are of historic or structural interest. These are ribostamycin (**32**), butirosin (**33**), lividomycin (**34**), dibekacin (**35**), sisomicin (**36**), ispemicin (**37**), arbekacin (**38**), fortimicin A (**39**), apramycin (**40**), and hygromycin B (**41**).

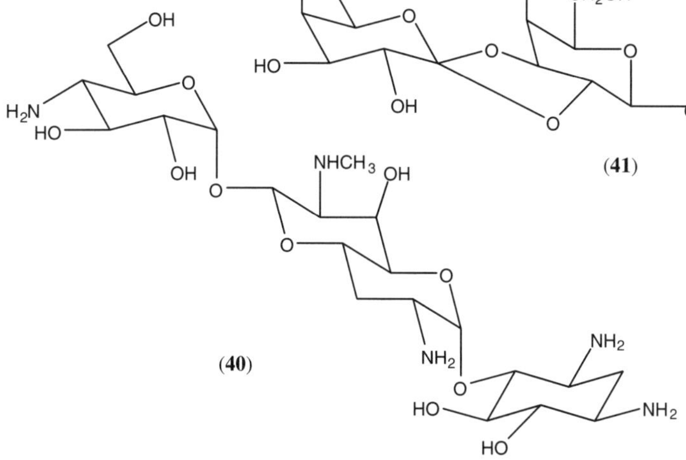

Those antibiotics ending in the suffix mycin are derived from *Streptomyces* sp. while those ending in micin are derived from *Micromonospora* or other species.

3.2. Side Effects, Toxicity, and Contraindications of the Aminoglycoside Antibiotics

The aminoglycoside antibiotics, with the exception of spectinomycin (**31**), produce ototoxicity (hearing loss and/or vertigo) and nephrotoxicity at higher than recommended doses or in patients with impaired renal function. To minimize the risk of kidney damage, doses are reduced to match the patient's renal function. Coadministration with other drugs that are capable also of damaging kidney function (cephalosporins and diuretics) is not advised. The ototoxicity is attributed to drug-related damage to the eighth cranial nerve and damage to the sensory hairs of the inner ear. Aminoglycosides have affinity for phosphatidylinositol-4,5-bisphosphate and inhibit ornithine decarboxylase [61,62]. The damage appears to be due to caspace-mediated apoptosis, can be delayed for a significant time after drug administration and is not reversible [63–67]. The nephrotoxicity, on the other hand, results from accumulation of the aminoglycoside in the proximal renal tubule lysosomes. This

Table 3. Aminoglycoside Antibiotics In Use in 2008

Generic Name	Structure	Administration Route	Usual IM Dose (mg/kg/day)
Streptomycin	**23**	Parenteral	15
Neomycin	**24**	Oral	—
Paromomycin	**25**	Oral	—
Gentamicin	**26**	Parenteral	3–5
Netilmicin	**27**	Parenteral	3–6.5
Amikacin	**28**	Parenteral	15
Tobramycin	**29**	Parenteral/nebulizer	3–5
Kanamycin	**30**	Parenteral/oral	15
Spectinomycin	**31**	Parenteral	A single dose of 2–4 g

leads to formation of reactive oxygen species, inhibition of phospholipases, inhibition of the sodium potassium pump, increases in the biosynthesis of thromboxanes, and so on [63,68–72]. The generation of free radicals is possibly associated with iron chelate formation [63].

In addition to these problems, rapid IV administration of these drugs and coadministration with muscle relaxants must be avoided in order to prevent the possibility of neuromuscular blockade [73–75].

Clearly the development of a broad-spectrum aminoglycoside antibiotic that lacked these problems would be a very welcome event.

3.3. Pharmacology and Mode of Action of the Aminoglycoside Antibiotics

As noted previously, these agents are mostly used parenterally. Except in cases of renal insufficiency, these agents are cleared fairly rapidly from the blood by glomerular filtration and kidney excretion. Their serum half-lives are generally on the order of a couple of hours although this varies substantially. There is very little metabolism of these agents and serum protein binding is minimal. Reports of metabolites of gentamicin and other aminoglycoside antibiotics causing ototoxicity have appeared but the structure of the putative metabolites are unknown [76]. It seems quite possible in light of the reports that these drugs induce the formation of reactive oxygen species that the toxicity observed is not due to the aminoglycosides themselves but is secondary to some of the biological effects that their use induces.

The difference between a bacteriostatic and a bactericidal dose of aminoglycosides is narrow so they are considered to be bactericidal in the clinic. The general consensus is that their target is the 16S rRNA within the mRNA decoding A-site and recent work has clarified much of the nature of the interaction [77–92].

The 30S ribosomal subunit is critical to successful protein biosynthesis. The overall process of protein biosynthesis is now well known and clear explanations are found in most contemporary biochemistry textbooks so the following treatment will be restricted to that part particularly relevant to the action of aminoglycoside antibiotics. The 30S–50S ribosomal unit must dictate precisely the codon–anticodon interactions so that only the proper amino acids are inserted in their intended place in the growing peptide chain and the 30S subunit must also cooperate with the 50S ribosomal subparticle in moving the tRNA/mRNA pairs along by exactly one codon so that the intended sequence of amino acids is precise and unbroken. It is known that the strictly conserved A1493 unit of 16S rRNA monitors the correctness of base pairing between the first two bases of codon and the anticodon so that only the correct tRNA molecule is put in place [93]. As might be expected a network of hydrogen and electrostatic bonds is involved in this intricate process [94]. A brief interval before the addition of the next amino acid allows time for this to take place [95]. There is no such "check" mechanism for the third base in the codon triad so alternative codon–anticodon base pairings are possible. This is believed to be responsible for the degeneracy in the genetic code that leads to more than one triad encoding for a given amino acid. This is the structural basis for the well-known "wobble" base phenomenon. Binding of aminoglycosides distorts the codon so that the codon/anticodon relationship in the first two bases is also blurred and thus mistranslation in the sense of selecting "wrong" tRNAs occurs. Aminoglycoside antibiotics are excellent hydrogen bonding molecules enhancing their ability to bind in the A region thus leading to this problem [96].

It is, however, generally agreed that this binding is not the whole story. Subsequent sequential penetration of many additional aminoglycoside molecules into bacterial cells plays an important role leading to even more dramatic conformational aberrations sufficient to stop protein biosynthesis entirely. Initially aminoglycosides do not penetrate well into naïve cells. With their positive charges (due to protonation) these drugs are attracted to the negatively charged bacterial cells but penetration requires expenditure of significant energy [97–99]. The initial concentration of drug that enters is, however, sufficient to cause mistranslation to occur. The cell begins to contain significant amounts of "nonsense proteins" that compromise the ability of the cell to control trafficking through its cell wall, possibly by formation of abnormal membrane channels. Consequently larger quantities of aminoglycosides then gain access and protein biosynthesis shuts down killing the cell [100,101]. The triggering effect in this complicated scenario is believed to be the mistranslation.

The specifics of the molecular interaction between various aminoglycoside antibiotics and the A-site of bacterial ribosomes have been studied in detail by several X-ray experiments. Rationalization of this information has led to a significant understanding of the specific manner in which these drugs kill

bacteria [85,88,90–92,102–107]. Although chemically related, it is interesting to note that the specific interactions of individual types of aminoglycoside antibiotics with ribosomes differ in fine detail. The differences appear to rationalize differences in their antimicrobial utility.

The main group (the 2-deoxystreptamine-based group) bind as illustrated by the case of paromomycin in Fig. 5. The drug interacts with five different base fragments primarily through hydrogen bonds [92] also involving in part participation by structural waters [90]. This binding site is in a pocket in the tRNA acceptor. It is especially important to note that the binding to bases A1492 and A1493

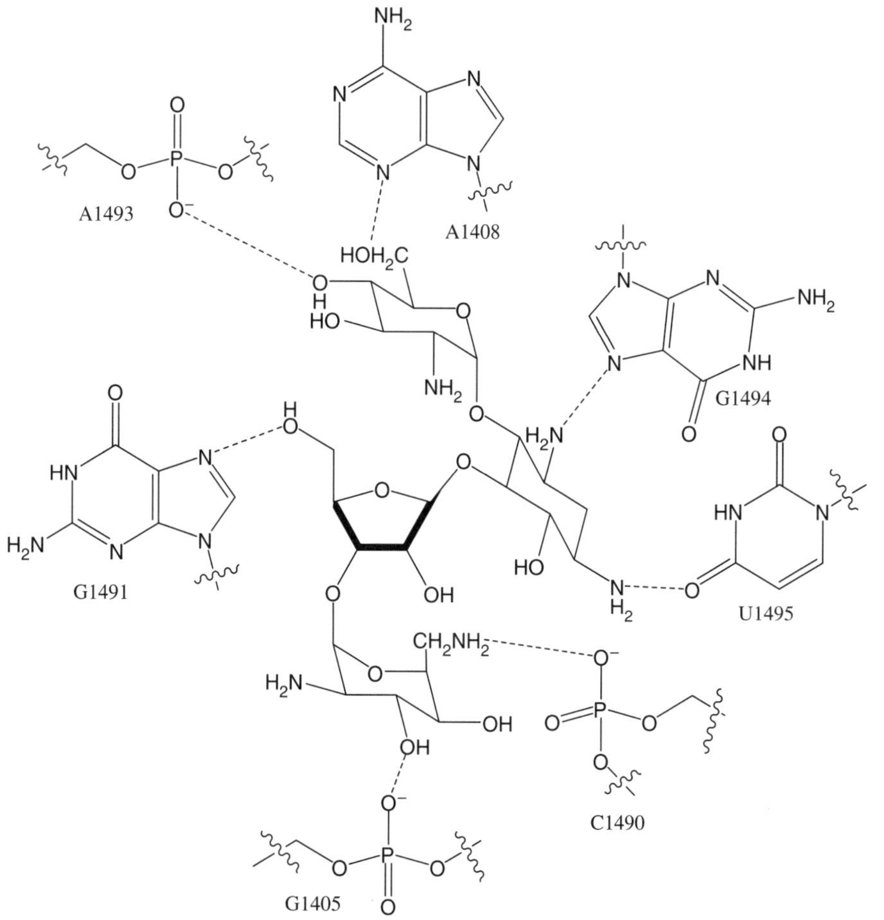

Figure 5. Schematic of the interaction of paromomycin, a representative of the 2-deoxystreptamine subclass of aminoglycoside antibiotics, with the bacterial ribosome 30S subunit. The base numbering is that of *E. coli*.

requires them to rotate outward in the direction of the binding region. In the absence of a cognate tRNA ligand, this conformational shift is rationalized as being significant to cause the observed miscoding that attends the binding of these drugs to the ribosomal A-site [91]. This feature is present in the interactions of several aminoglycosides as shown by X-ray [85] and NMR studies [88]. These interactions also are quite consistent with the structure–activity relationships in this class gained laboriously over the years by empiric analoging. In this context a significant beginning has been made in understanding the specific influence on potency of individual functional group changes on potency [104]. One finding of particular interest is that changes brought about by alterations at a particular site can be counterbalanced by substituents at distant locations in the molecules. This lore is beginning to allow rational analog design.

A related X-ray investigation of the interaction of amikacin (**28**) as compared with its

precursor kanamycin (**30**) shows that the added hydroxyaminobutyrate (HABA) residue results in two new interactions (with C1496 and G1497) rationalizing amikacin's higher affinity for the A-site [83]. This is another example (added to that of tigecycline above and the ketocyclines in the macrolide section) where addition of a new moiety to a natural product can introduce new receptor interactions that result in greater bioactivity as well as leading to decreased resistance.

The binding of streptomycin (**23**) to 16S ribosomal subparticles is overall similar but most of the specific interactions are different (Fig. 6). These binding differences can perhaps rationalize the different antibacterial spectrum of streptomycin. Binding also results in mistranslation. There is however a significant difference. Streptomycin has an additional hydrogen bonding interaction between the two adjacent hydroxyl groups in the streptamine portion. These interact with the side-chain amino function of lysine-45 in ribosomal

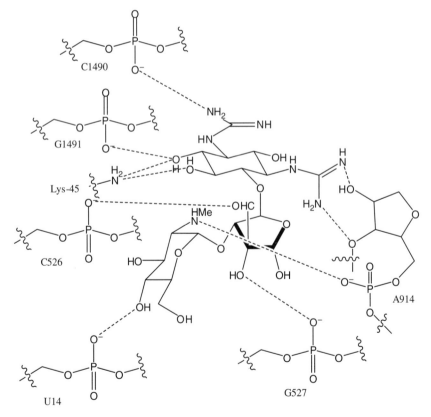

Figure 6. Schematic of the interactions between streptomycin (**23**) and bacterial 16S rRNA.

protein S12. Collectively these stabilize the ribosome in a conformation that is strongly associated with translational ambiguity thus enhancing cell death [92].

Spectinomycin (31) differs substantially both in structure and in biological actions. It is bacteriostatic and does not cause misreading of the genetic code. Thus, it is not surprising to note that its binding to 16S rRNA is also different. It binds to G1064 and C1192 so that it lies between helices H34 and H35 preventing movement or conformational shift with the result that movement of the tRNA from the A-site to the P-site is blocked [92]. Growth of a peptide chain is thus prevented. Some recent work elucidates some of the molecular details of this interference [108].

3.4. History and Biosynthesis of the Aminoglycoside Antibiotics

Selman Waksman and his group at Rutgers pioneered the screening of soil microorganisms for antibiotic activity as a consequence of which streptomycin and neomycin were discovered in 1944 and 1949, respectively. Waksman was ultimately to receive a Nobel prize for this effort. Others did related work and Umezawa in Tokyo discovered kanamycin (30) in 1957. Gentamicin (26) (1963) and sisomicin (36) (1970) were introduced by Schering Laboratories in New Jersey. Later tobramycin (29) was introduced by Eli Lilly and Co. Many additional but less prominent antibiotics were also discovered by screening of soil microorganisms.

In the 1970s, chemists reported semisynthetic alterations that produced clinically useful products. Guided by the presence of a HABA group in the unmarketed antibiotic butirosin (33), this group was added to kana-

mycin resulting in the discovery of amikacin (28). Netilmicin (27) was prepared by introducing an N-1 ethyl moiety into sisomicin.

Interest in the aminoglycoside antibiotics declined subsequently largely because of the introduction of third- and fourth-generation cephalosporins and the fluoroquinolones coupled with increasing resistance to aminoglycosides and failure to solve the toxicity problems associated with these drugs. No new aminoglycoside antibiotic has been introduced into the clinic in the United States since 1980.

The naturally occurring aminoglycoside antibiotics are produced by fermentation of several genera (for examples, *Streptomyces*, *Micromonospora*, and *Saccharopolyspora*) and from bacteria (*Bacillus* and *Pseudomonas*). The biosynthesis of these drugs has been reviewed thoroughly recently [109]. The amino inositol moieties that characterize this class of antibiotics are derived from glucose-6-phosphate (42), which is, therefore, the gatekeeper for the whole process. The biosynthesis of streptamine, fortimine, and spectinamine passes through *myo*-inositol (as its 1-phosphate) to 43 to which is added other glucose-derived sugars [110–113] whereas the biosynthesis of 2-deoxystreptamine passes through the related 2-deoxy-*Scyllo*-inositol analog to 44 (also as its phosphate ester) with the addition of various glucose-derived sugars [114–128]. The specific pathways leading to the various antibiotics are complex and, since the gene sequences are known, progress is being made toward the rational prediction of analogs that might yet be found in nature and toward formation of novel unnatural analogs by gene manipulations.

The formation of the amino inositol centroids is followed by addition of the characteristic sugars. These may be modified either before or after addition to the amino inositol portion of the antibiotics. The amino groups of **43** and **44** and the second amino group that is added later follow oxidation of the appropriate hydroxyl group followed by a stereospecific reductive transamination reaction. The prime and double prime sugars also contain amino groups that are installed by the same Borch-like reductive amination reactions. The presence of keto or aldehyde intermediates also provides opportunities for epimerizations. Deoxygenations appear to result from dehydrations followed by addition of hydrogen. The gentamicin group is characterized by an unusual incidence of C and N methylations involving methionine donations. A remarkable range of sugar types are the result of the operation of these comparatively few biochemical transformations. The known information about all this, including specific intermediate sequences, is collected in an excellent recent review for the interested reader [109].

In a number of cases, the gene clusters for biosynthesis of specific aminoglycoside antibiotics have been isolated [119–121].

One wonders how a soil microorganism can survive the biosynthesis of such a devastating product. A clue in the aminoglycoside class comes from information that streptomycin is produced inside cells in the form of its inactive 6-phosphate. This is extruded from the cell and hydrolyzed to active streptomycin by extracellular 6-phosphostreptamycin phosphatase [129]. Given that one of the modes of resistance (covered in the next section) is phosphorylation of aminoglycosides, this may also provide a clue as to the origin of bacterial resistance enzymes that work by phosphorylation of aminoglycosides.

Figure 7 outlines the current thoughts about aminoglycoside biosynthesis pathways by proposing how gentamicin C2 might be formed [109].

3.5. Aminoglycoside Antibiotic Resistance

Bacterial resistance to aminoglycoside antibiotics takes at least three forms: failure to accumulate, modification of target and enzy-

matic modification of the drugs. Target modification is most relevant with *M. tuberculosis* [130] whereas enzymatic modification is most common for most other pathogens [86]. Distressingly, there are more than 50 aminoglycoside modifying enzymes now recorded and more appear regularly in the literature. Self-methylation of ribosomes is emerging but is not common as yet [131,132].

Altered accumulation due to aminoglycoside efflux is not as yet regarded as a significant clinical problem but the phenomenon has been observed and is probably spreading [133–135]. This mechanism is associated with magnesium ion starvation. Conversely, magnesium ion excess can lead to decreased potency of aminoglycosides. This phenomenon has been known to laboratory scientists for a long time. There is gathering evidence that "junk" peptides generated in response to aminoglycoside binding to rRNA are cleared from the cell by chromosomally encoded multiple RND pumps (resistance-nodulation-division family), especially in Gram negatives. Their regulation is independent of antibiotic exposure leading to the reasonable belief that the antibiotics are not their normal clients [136].

Point mutations of bacterial ribosome structures to convey resistance have been noted [137–139] as has self-methylation of particular bases dependent upon *S*-adenosylmethionine [132,140–142]. The methylation process is especially worrisome as it appears to be encoded on a transferable plasmid [140]. Resistance by point mutations is not surprising given the knowledge that aminoglycosides hydrogen bond to particular ribosomal bases (see previous section).

Rather more common than these problems is enzymatic deactivation by bacterial enzymes. These transformations interestingly do not involve cleavage but rather involve addition of blocking groups to specific hydroxyl and amino groups. Presumably addition of these blocking groups prevents the normal association between aminoglycosides and rRNA that is necessary for their antibacterial action. These enzymes are located within bacterial cells so they are particularly effective.

There are many such enzymes and they are classified as to reaction type (APH for amino-

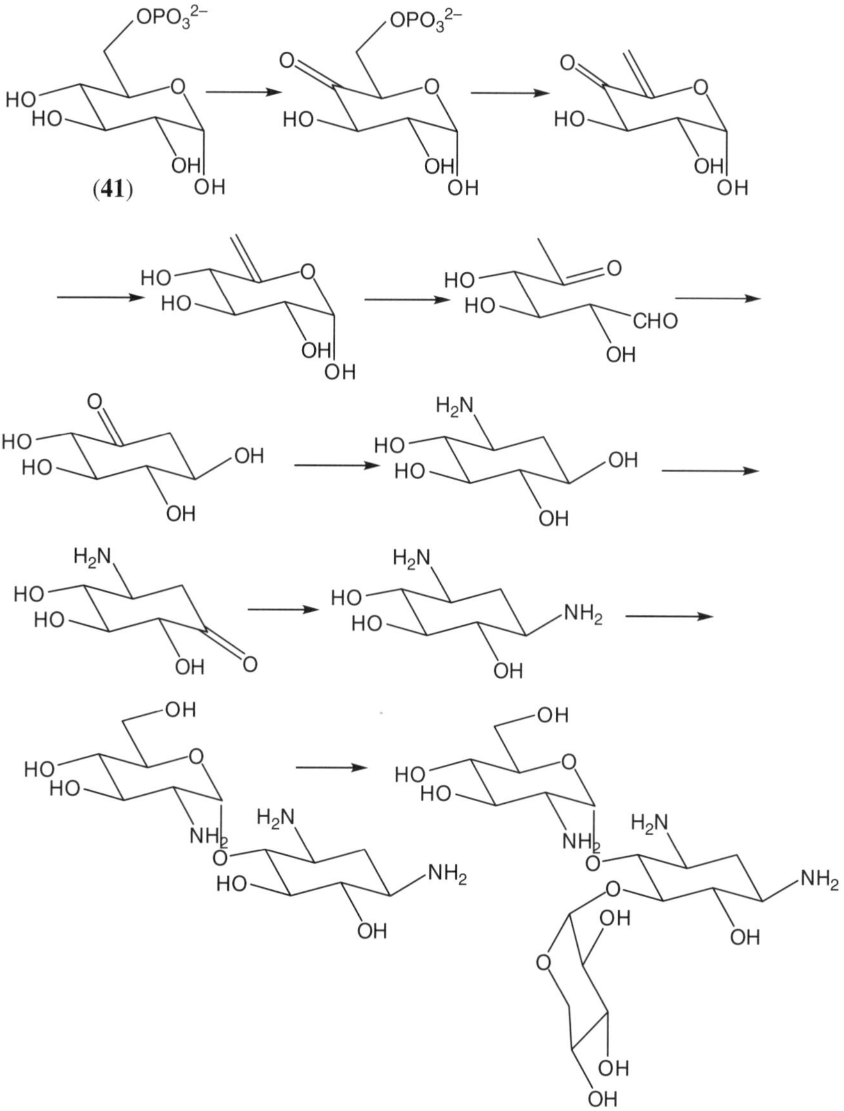

Figure 7. Putative biosynthetic pathway from glucose-6-phosphate to gentamicin C2. This sequence is adapted from a recent comprehensive review [109].

glycoside phosphotransferase, ANT for aminoglycoside adenyltransferase, and AAC for aminoglycoside acetyltransferase). The specific location on the aminoglycoside where this reaction takes place is indicated by number (3, 3′, or 3″). A Roman numeral follows designating the specific source (I, II, III), and a lower case letter designates its temporal sequence of identification (a, b, c) [143]. As an example, AAC(6′)-Ic is an aminoglycoside acetyltrans-

ferase that acylates kanamycin, tobramycin, amikacin, and neomycin (I) at position 6′ and the gene was the third cloned from *S. marcescens*. This is a convenient way of designating the enzyme and what it does. An alternative means of keeping interrelationships straight focuses on the antibiotic instead and points out the positions available for attack by which enzymes. This is illustrated with gentamicin C2 in Fig. 8.

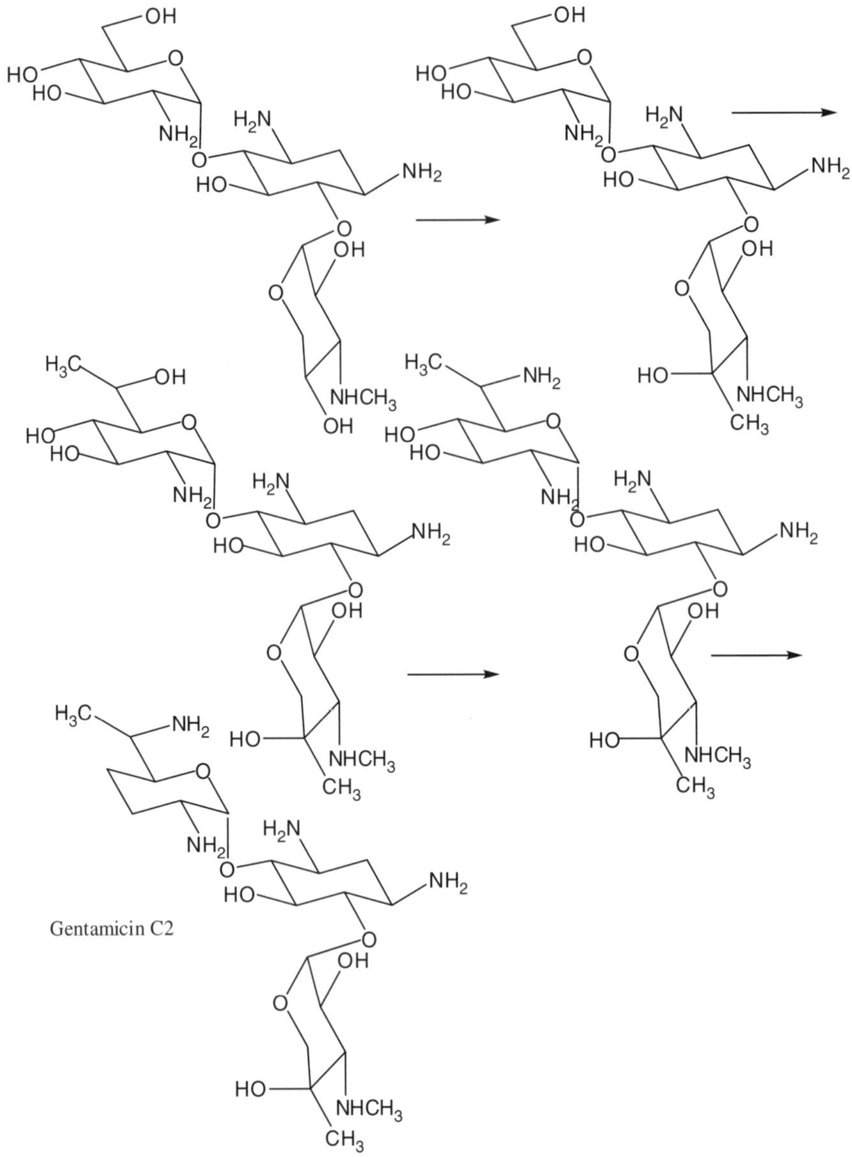

Gentamicin C2

Figure 7. (*Continued*).

An interesting consequence of the specificity of position of attack on functional groups is that these enzymes are not broad in their attack spectrum. For example, a resistant bacterium carrying an enzyme that attacks the C-3′ position of kanamycin (**30**) will probably still be sensitive to tobramycin (**29**) since this has only a methylene at this position and this position is not essential for antibacterial action. This circumstance has created a vogue among medicinal chemists for specific molecular simplification of aminoglycoside structures.

The aminoglycoside phosphotransferases require ATP and transfer the distal phosphate group to specific drug hydroxyl

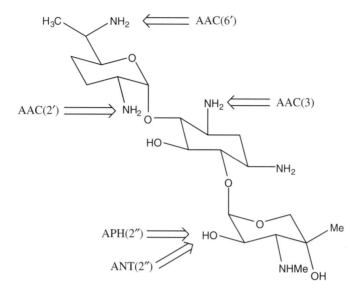

Figure 8. Some sites of resistance-enzyme attack on the molecule of gentamicin C2.

groups producing ADP as a by-product in the process [144]. An exception is aminoglycoside 2″-phosphotransferase that unexpectedly shows a strong preference for guanosine triphosphate over adenosine triphosphate [145]. They are rather typical kinases resembling the better-known protein kinases. The complete X-ray structure for an APH is known [146,147]. The molecular interactions revealed by this X-ray show that the binding surface of the enzyme is quite acidic thus possessing a substantial attraction for the aminoglycosides. Jocularly in some circles this is called a vacuum cleaner for aminoglycosides. It has been pointed out that APH activity significantly depletes the ATP present in a bacterial cell so its maintenance of this activity exerts a significant cost on the producing microorganism [148]. This would suggest that the absence of selecting pressure by the antibiotic could result in gradual loss of this drug destroying activity.

The aminoglycoside adenyltransferases also require ATP and transfer the adenosyldiphosphate residue to a particular aminoglycoside hydroxyl. These enzymes cause resistance in particularly important bacterial pathogens. An X-ray structure of one of these enzymes is available [149–152].

The aminoglycoside acetyltransferases make up the largest family of aminoglycoside-modifying enzymes. These enzymes transfer the activated acetyl group of acetyl coenzyme A to specific amino groups in these drugs. The structure of some of these enzymes is also known [153,154].

Some idea of the decreases in potency due to the action of these enzymes can be gathered from the work of Llano-Sotello et al. [155] The K_d value for an unaltered drug fragment was $1.1\,\mu\text{M}$ whereas phosphorylation at C-3-OH reduced this to 1300 and acetylation at the C-6′ amino group reduced it to 600. These effects are rather dramatic.

One could imagine that specific inhibitors of these enzymes could be developed to use in combination therapy and some work has been done in this direction. For example the streptomycete fermentation product 7-hydroxytropolone inhibits ANT(2′)-I by competitive inhibition of ATP. When added to tobramycin, a substrate for this enzyme, potency was enhanced *in vitro*.

3.6. Some Recent Developments in the Aminoglycoside Antibiotic Field

Despite the lack of introduction into the clinic of novel members of this antibiotic class, in the intervening 7 years since the previous review of aminoglycosides in this series, there have been published nearly 8000 papers retrievable from PubMed under the rubric aminoglycoside antibiotic 200[*]. Clearly interest remains high. Substantial progress has been made in dealing with their resistance. A great deal is now known about the genetics and the details of their biosynthesis. Much less has been accomplished in dealing with toxicity.

The diversity of sugar attachments to the aminocyclitol portion of these drugs makes a systematic presentation of the current understanding of the SAR of this antibiotic family hard to accomplish concisely. The original approach was to find new members of the family and to blend their salient structural features into other molecules. This was laborious and not very intellectually satisfying. The general strategy in present use is to simplify the structures of the natural products in order to ascertain the minimum structure necessary for significant biological activity. This is essentially a pharmacophore search. Once this is in hand, then one builds out from this core again in attempts to make active molecules that are easier to construct and that have enhanced biological activity and, in particular, activity against microorganisms resistant to the existing agents. At the same time, since much is now known about the specifics of the host–guest relationships extant in the aminoglycoside family, attempts are made to design novel molecules that take advantage of this lore. These approaches are not restricted to aminoglycosides but are widely used in most drug families.

It is clear that the aminocyclitol ring itself is essential for activity. Its relative rigidity and the functional groups attached are its key features. Alicyclic replacements for the aminocyclitol ring have proven disappointing. The prime-numbered sugar needs to be attached with an α-anomeric bond and addition of flat aromatic residues capable of intercalative interaction with rRNA molecules often produces significantly enhanced bioactivity.

The structural arrangement found in neamine has emerged as superior. Adding a hydroxyaminobutyrate moiety to the deoxy-streptamine proportion enhances potency and activity against otherwise resistant bacteria. Modifications and substitutes for the double prime-numbered ring are enhanced when C-4″ bears an amino group and C-6″ is a methyl whereas activity is diminished when the C-3″ OH is replaced by a primary amino group.

As indicated below, dimerization has proven useful providing the two groups are separated by a satisfactory linker arm. Preparation of aminoglycosides conformationally constrained by annulation has been employed in attempts to divine the optimal conformational state of these molecules. Occasionally this has produced analogs with enhanced activity against specific resistant microorganisms.

Wong and his colleagues have begun a systematic SAR study of aminoglycosides. The pharmacophore of this drug family appears to be the deoxystreptamine portion when the prime numbered ring is attached to it at   C-4. Wong's group found that the presence of only a single amino group in this sugar ring leads to poor activity. When two amino groups are present, the arrangement found in neamine (at C-2′ and C-6′) is optimal [156]. Exploitation of this information using combinatorial methodologies led to some interestingly simplified compounds building out from the prime numbered sugar using hydroxylamine arms [157]. Clearly simpler molecules can be constructed that retain activity although at the price of diminished potency. This is probably due to their increased flexibility and decreased ability of the overall molecule to form productive hydrogen bonds to rRNA. Much follow-on and similar work has been published and is available for inspection in a thorough review by Zhou et al [158].

Analogous SAR work has been carried out on the various other sugars of the aminoglycosides helping to clarify the specific role that various substituents play in their activity. While this information has proved interesting, it has not as yet led to hot new leads [158].

Mobashery and his colleagues have designed and prepared novel, structurally simplified, aminoglycoside analogs in which the pharmacophoric neamine residue has been modified by addition of a HABA group at N-3 and the double prime sugar has been replaced by a diamine-containing aliphatic arm. The design of these analogs was assisted materially by knowledge of the mode of action of aminoglycosides summarized above. Some of these new derivatives not only have been shown to bind to the paromomycin site on the ribosome but also possess significant antibiotic potency. Since these contain a more flexible surrogate instead of the double prime sugar-containing natural products, it is not perhaps surprising that potency fell off by an order of magnitude, but these novel analogs reveal significant information about the mode of action of aminoglycosides. Helpfully, an X-ray study has revealed specific details of the molecular interaction involving one of these novel analogs (**45**). Most interestingly, these analogs retain their activity in the presence of aminoglycoside transforming bacterial enzymes [106].

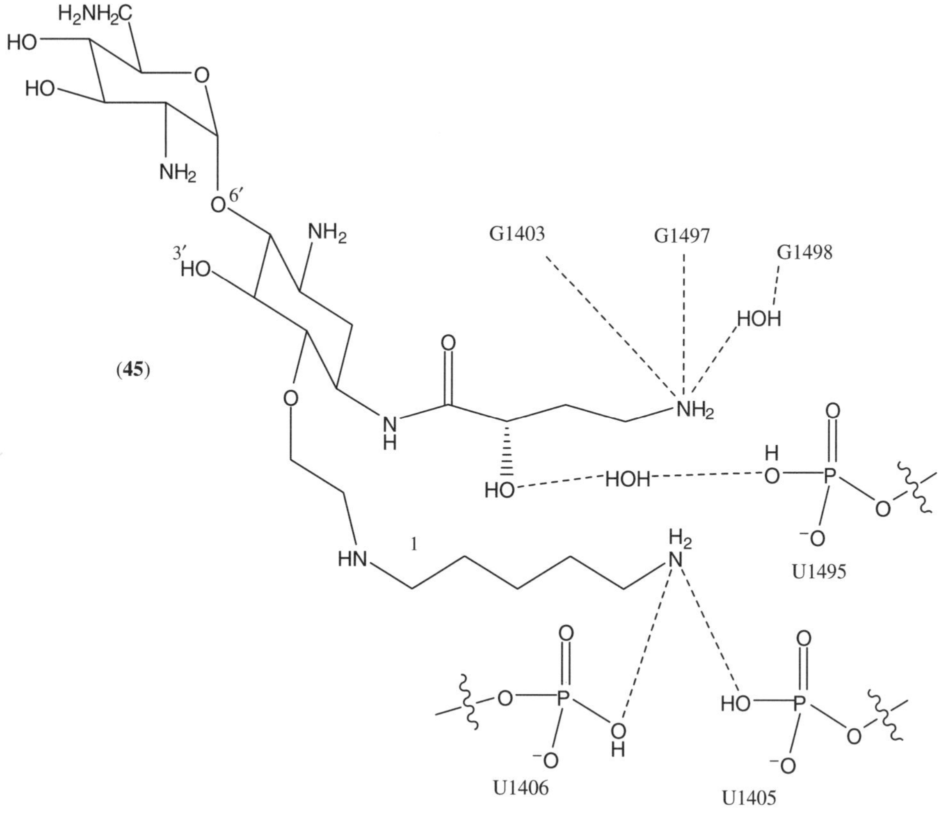

Knowledge of the specifics of drug modification by bacterial enzymes have also been employed by chemists to prepare interesting analogs. The Mobashery group synthesized 4,4-difluoro analogs of kanamycin A. The presence of the fluoro atoms (**46**) of course significantly reduced the nucleophilicity of the adjacent C-3′ hydroxyl group. Since this hydroxyl is the site of phosphorylation of a drug inactivating bacterial enzyme it is interesting to note that this enzyme hardly attacks this hydroxyl. Unfortunately from the standpoint of antibiotic discovery, this agent was also very weak as an antibiotic [159].

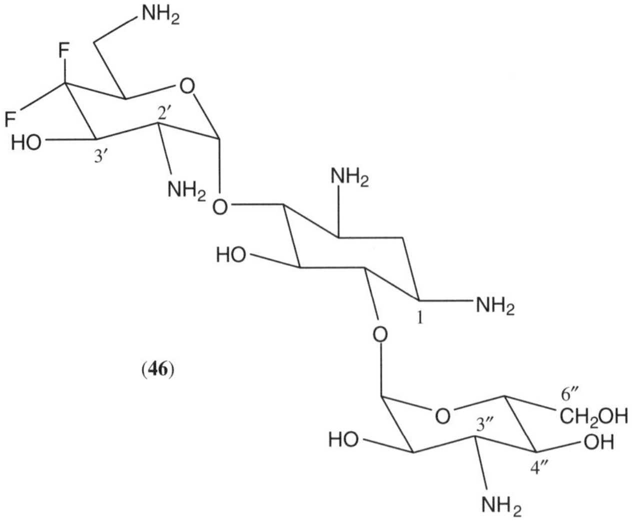

(46)

In another effort, the Mobashery group synthesized the 2′-nitro analog of kanamycin A (47). The presence of the nitro group acidified sufficiently the H attached to the C-2′ carbon so that, following phosphorylation at C-3′ by APH(3′) phosphotransferase, a retro-

Michael reaction took place ejecting the phosphorylated oxygen and producing a Δ-2′,3′ olefinic linkage. This conjugated double bond is capable in principle of reacting with nucleophilic groups on the enzyme thus forming an enzyme inactivating covalent linkage [160].

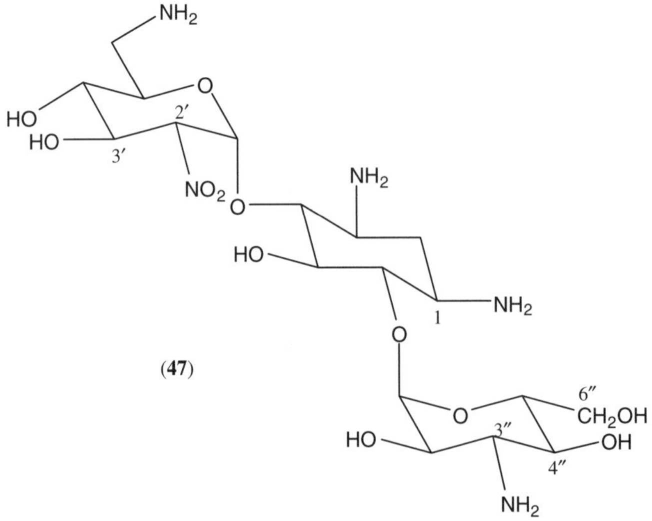

(47)

Another cleaver attempt to circumvent the enzymatic inactivation of aminoglycosides involved formation of 3-ketokanamycin (50). This functional group is hydrated in aqueous solution (48). APH(3′) phosphotransferase at-

taches a phosphoryl group to the equatorial hydroxyl of the hydrated keto moiety (49). This hemiphosphate ester is unstable and reverts to the keto form thereby ejecting the phosphate. Unfortunately compound 48 is only weakly active as an antibiotic. It does, however, serve to protect competitively other

aminoglycoside derivatives from attack by this enzyme [161].

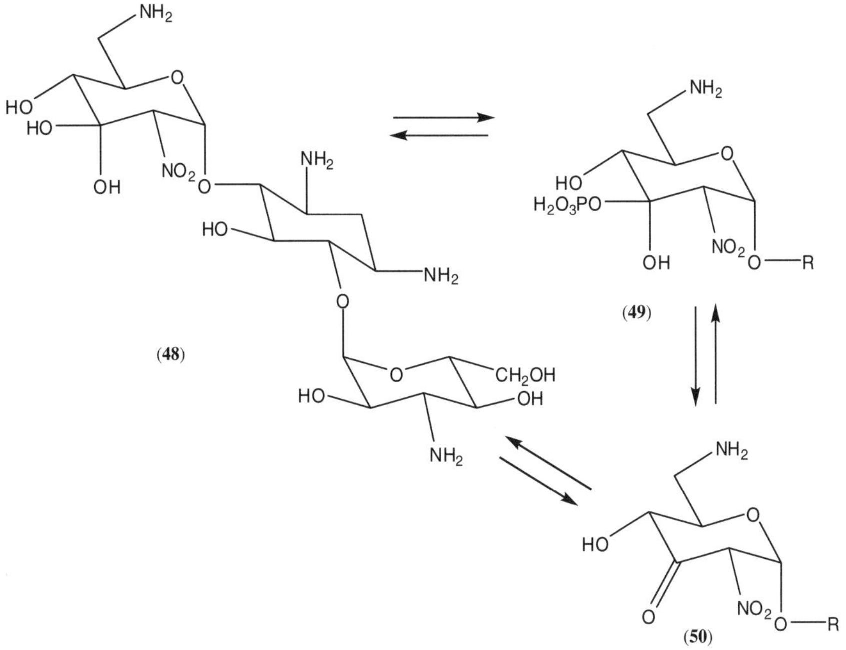

A rather different approach has been utilized by the Wong group. In order to increase the level of attachment of neamine to the ribosome, they tethered two molecules together by a connecting arm. Intriguingly this

analog (50) not only possessed significant, though reduced, *in vitro* antimicrobial activity, but was also significantly resistant to inactivating bacterial enzymes [162].

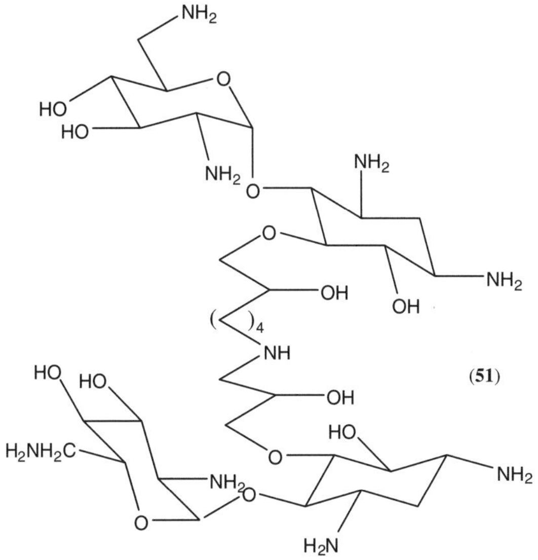

It is reasonable to assume that the connecting arm, with its rich content of hydrogen bonders, is significantly responsible for the activity of compound **51**.

Conformational restriction by adding an intramolecular linker is a significant drug design stratagem providing the linker does not introduce unsuitable bimolecular interactions between the linked agent and its receptor. Application of this design element to aminoglycosides is apt since these agents are otherwise capable of sampling considerable conformational space. Suitable rigidification could be expected in principle to enhance activity by reducing entropy of association between such a guest and its host rRNA. Adding a butyl diamide linker to neamine thus linking amino groups at C-3 and C-6′ produced analog **52** fixing the two original rings nearly orthogonal to each other. There is no biodata available as yet from which to judge the biological success of this interesting drug design approach [163].

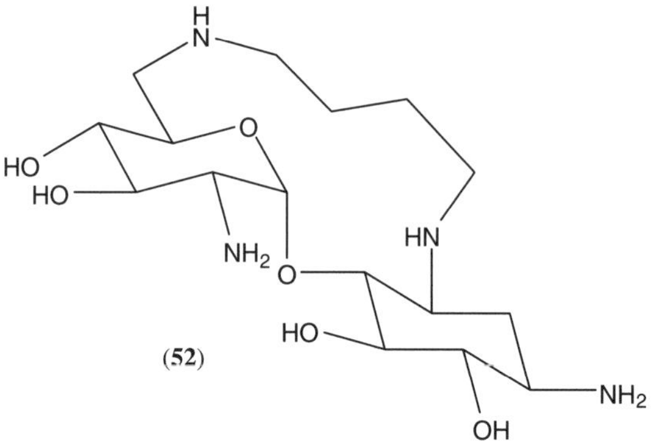

(52)

Bridging between the 2′-nitrogen atom and C-5″ of neomycin also led to conformational restriction [164]. This resulted in a reduction in antibacterial activity suggesting that the C-2′ nitrogen forms an electrostatic contact altering the mobility of bases 1492 and 1493 of the A-site. It is alternatively possible that the steric restraint fixes the molecule in an unsuitable conformation for good activity.

In a more traditional SAR study, Hanessian's group have prepared C-2″ ether analogs of paromomycin in which the ether groups mostly terminate in aliphatic or aromatic amines [165]. These were designed using modern drug design methods so that they would project into space at approximately where the third ring of tobramycin lies and thus form productive bonds with the A-site of rRNA. Encouragingly quite a number of these analogs possessed enhanced activity over paromomycin itself and two of these were shown to protect mice *in vivo* against otherwise lethal *S. aureus* infections. This excellent result suggests that analogous work may well restore interest in this relatively neglected family of antibiotics.

Alteration of the C-5″ to amines, amides, and alkoxyamines of C-6′ deoxyparomomycin by another group, on the other hand, was less successful as it resulted in decreases in potency [166].

It is interesting to note that some potentially useful antiviral activity of aminoglycoside derivatives has been observed [78,158,167–169]. Nothing very striking has yet come of this but it suggests that these agents could play a role in at least antiretrovirus chemotherapy in the future.

It is hoped that chemically engineered novel aminoglycosides will in due course emerge from analogous studies that will be active enough for clinical use and will be exempt from the present resistance mechanisms. For further details of the SAR of recent chemically produced analogs of aminoglycoside antibiotics, a thorough review can be consulted [158].

4. MACROLIDE ANTIBIOTICS

4.1. Clinical Use of the Macrolide Antibiotics and Currently Used Drugs

The macrolide antibiotics received that name based upon their possession of a macrocyclic ring to which was attached one or more sugars via glycosidic bonds. At least one of the sugars commonly has an amino substituent so these compounds form acid addition salts. These agents are chemically rather lipophilic but form acid-addition salts. They are orally active but absorption is in some cases depressed by degradation in stomach acid and by the presence of food. Protein binding is about 75% but the drug is freely released from bonds so this serves more as a transport mechanism than as a site of loss. They are mostly natural products produced by soil microorganisms although some of the presently most popular members of this class are produced by chemical semi-synthesis. The primary classification of the macrolide antibiotics is based upon the macrocyclic ring size (e.g., 12, 14, 15, 16) and care must be taken not to confuse them with the polyene macrolide antifungal antibiotics. The latter not only possess much larger macrocyclic lactone rings but also, more importantly, possess a different molecular mode of action (directed toward sterols in fungal cell walls) so are both chemically and clinically distinct from the antibacterial macrolides.

Macrolide antibiotics with 14-membered rings are more popular in the United States and Europe whereas macrolides with 16-membered rings are frequently used in Japan and the 12-membered ring group is not used medicinally. Tylosin (**62**) is a 16-membered macrolide antibiotic that sees substantial use worldwide as an animal feed supplementary agent.

Members of the macrolide family have been popular worldwide as antibiotics for over half of a century because of their oral efficacy against commonly acquired mild infections and their outstanding safety profile. Erythromycin A itself (**53**) became popular initially because of its utility in the treatment of staphylococcal infections in patients allergic to penicillins and to this day macrolides are often thought of by physicians as antibiotics that

can be used in many clinical applications in place of the early penicillins. These drugs are especially useful in the treatment of upper and lower respiratory tract infections because they accumulate preferentially in cells of the respiratory tract, often achieving concentrations higher by an order of magnitude in these tissues than in the blood stream.

Due mainly to pharmacokinetic problems with the classical fermentation-derived macrolides (fairly low blood levels following oral administration, instability in gastric fluids, comparatively short half-lives, gastrointestinal complaints, unpleasant taste, etc.), a number of successful semisynthetic modifications have been performed leading to drugs that have become very popular recently. Clarithromycin (**58**) and azithromycin (**59**) typify this group. The ketolides, typified by telithromycin (**60**), have been introduced to help deal with resistance problems but they have yet to have the impact of clarithromycin and azithromycin on clinical practice and recent toxicity reports have cooled enthusiasm for them.

The clinical utility of the macrolides includes community-acquired pneumonia (CAP), exacerbation of chronic acute bacterial bronchitis, acute bacterial sinusitis, tonsillitis, pharyngitis, otitis media, skin and soft-tissue infections, and ophthalmic infections. Many common pathogens frequently remain susceptible to macrolides including *S. aureus*, *Staphylococcus epidermidis*, *Streptococcus pyogenes*, *Streptococcus pneumoniae*, *Haemophilus influenzae*, *Moraxella catarrhalis*, *Borrelia burgdorferi*, *Legionella pneumophila*, *Mycobacterium pneumoniae*, *Chlamydia pneumoniae*, *Treponema pallidum*, *Corynebacterium diphtheriae*, and *Bordatella pertussis*. Erythromycin itself is comparatively less effective against *H. influenzae* but clarithromycin and, particularly, azithromycin are more active against H. flu. Gram-negative enterobacteria are only modestly sensitive to macrolides. A list of the macrolides in current use is presented in Table 4.

It should be noted that in depicting macrolide structures, an assumed conformation is drawn and the bonds at stereocenters are drawn α, standing for S, and β, standing for R, as an indication of the absolute stereochemistry. Early on there was little to no conforma-

Table 4. Macrolide Antibiotics in Use in 2008

Generic Name	Structure	Administration Route	Usual Dose
Erythromycin	**53**	Oral	250 mg qid
Erythromycin estolate	**54**	Oral	125–150 mg
Erythromycin ethylsuccinate	**55**	Oral	400 mg ea. 4 h (adult)
Erythromycin lactobionate	**56**	Parenteral	500 mg
Erythromycin stearate	**57**	Oral	250 mg ea. 6 h
Clarithromycin	**58**	Oral	500–1000 mg each day
Azithromycin	**59**	Oral	2000 mg each day
Telithromycin	**60**	Oral	800 mg each day

tional information available so the traditional meaning used in steroid chemistry could not be followed. The 14-membered ring macrolides are sometimes drawn in different ways by different authors and confusion is possible unless the stereochemical convention is followed rigorously. The absolute configuration is (numbering counterclockwise from the lactone carbon): $2R,3S,4S,5R,6R,8R,10R,11R,12S,13R$.

It is also readily apparent from these structures that they are polyketide (propionate) derived and, in the case of erythromycin, the methyl groups attached to the desosamine sugar nitrogen and the cladinose sugar oxygen are derived from methionine. The only unsubstituted ring carbon is at position C-7. Not possessing a substituent there allows to ring to swing somewhat outward so as to avoid unacceptable through-space interactions. Further, in contrast to small carbocyclic rings, substitutents pointing into the lumen of the ring are possible. This would create conformational difficulties. The lactone ring and the keto function are located strategically so that this problem is minimized. If erythromycin were to possess a conformation derived from a perfect diamond lattice, the conformation that would best fit the NMR data would be **63a.** This conformation would however result in a severe through space clash between the C-4 and C-6 methyl groups. This can be relieved by adoption of the presently accepted conformation of erythromycin (**63b**). This conformation is in accord with all of the available data especially including the circular dichroism spectra. A perfect diamond lattice is shown in formula **64**.

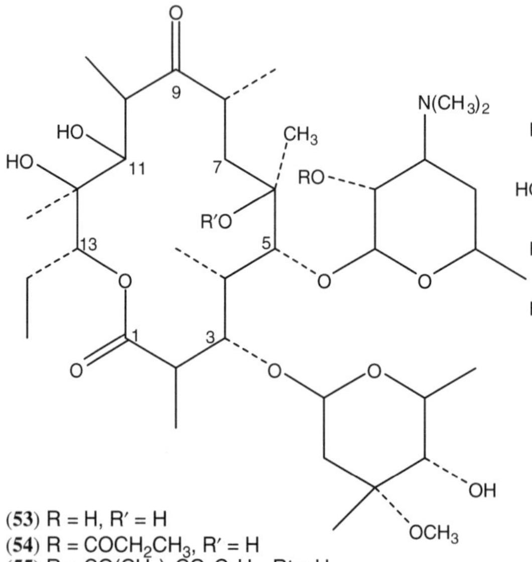

(A)

(53) R = H, R′ = H
(54) R = COCH$_2$CH$_3$, R′ = H
(55) R = CO(CH$_2$)$_2$CO$_2$C$_2$H$_5$, R′ = H
(56) R = R′ = H, A salt.
(57) R = R′ = H, CH$_3$(CH$_2$)$_{16}$CO$_2$H salt.
(58) R = H, R′ = CH$_3$

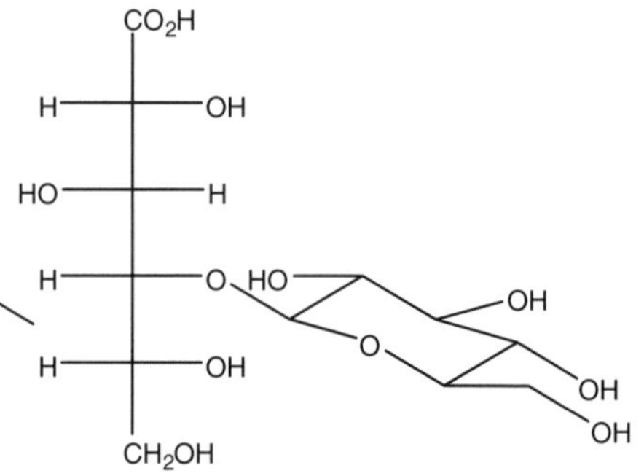

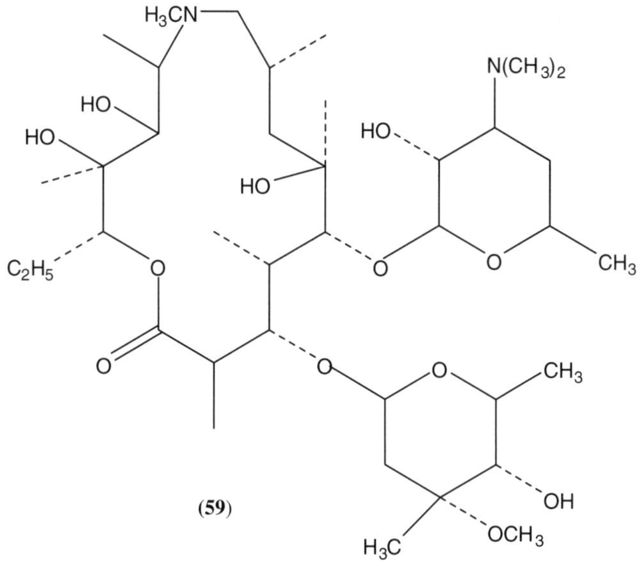

(59)

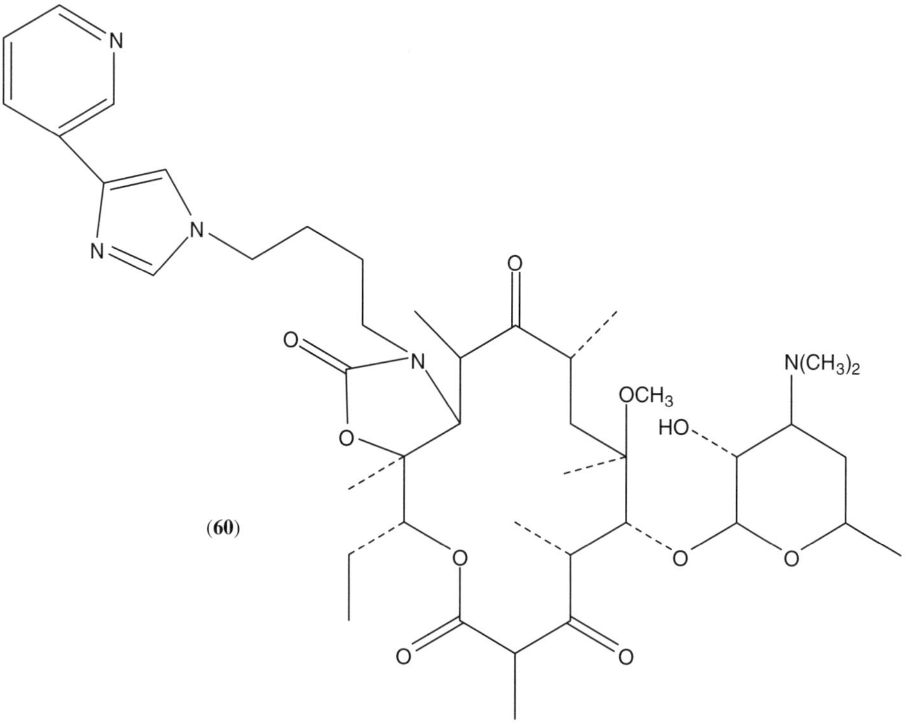

(60)

As will be detailed below, erythromycin in acidic aqueous solutions forms essentially irreversibly an internal ketal that is antibiotically inactive. Thus, it looses considerable potency in stomach contents. The semisynthetic analogs (clarithromycin, azithromycin, and telithromycin) have been chemically altered so that this reaction cannot take place. Thus, these newer agents have superior pharmacokinetic properties compared to the erythromycin family. Following marketing of telithromycin reports have emerged that this compound can cause hepatotoxicity so its use has been somewhat curtailed [170,171].

Historically significant but not of commercial value, methymycin (**61**) is representative of the comparatively small natural group of 12-membered macrolides.

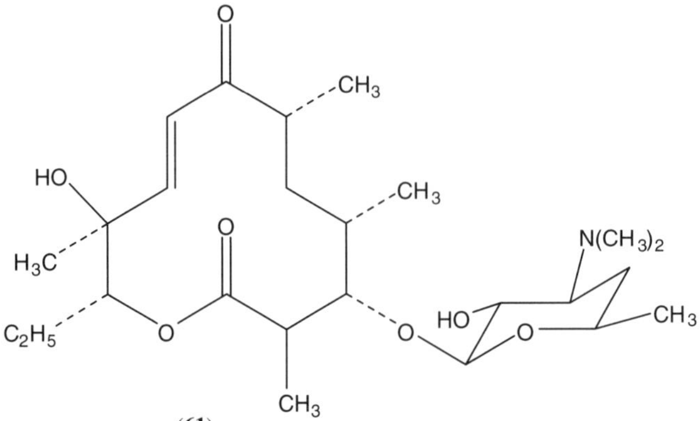

(**61**)

A number of 16-membered lactone ring macrolide antibiotics are popular outside of the United States. The most important commercially available such antibiotics in the United States is tylosin (**62**), which finds significant use as an animal food supplement.

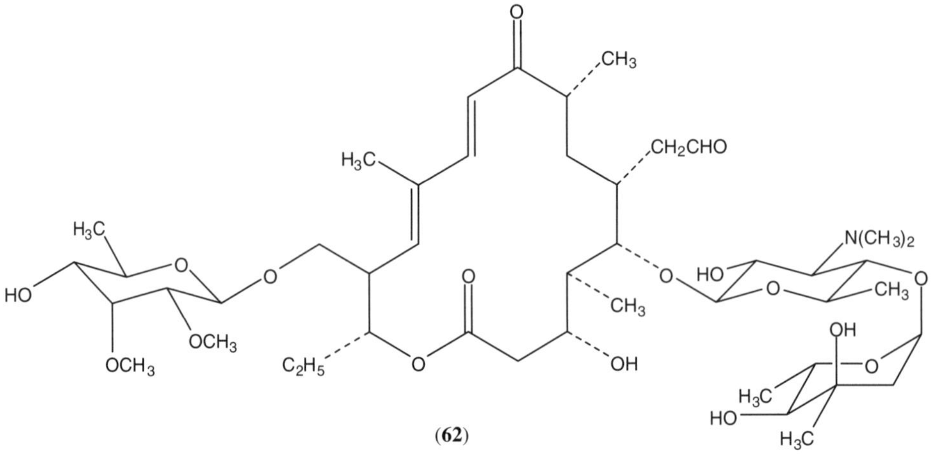

(**62**)

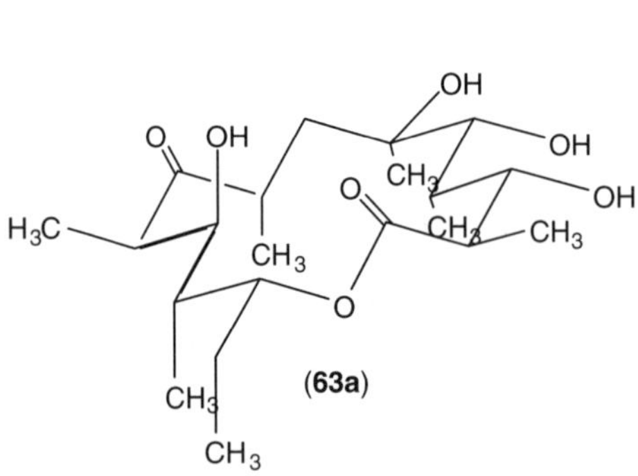

(**63a**) 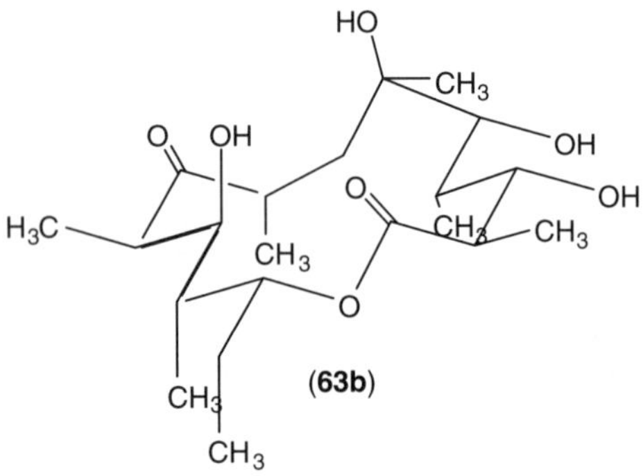   (**63b**)

(64)

(65)

(66)

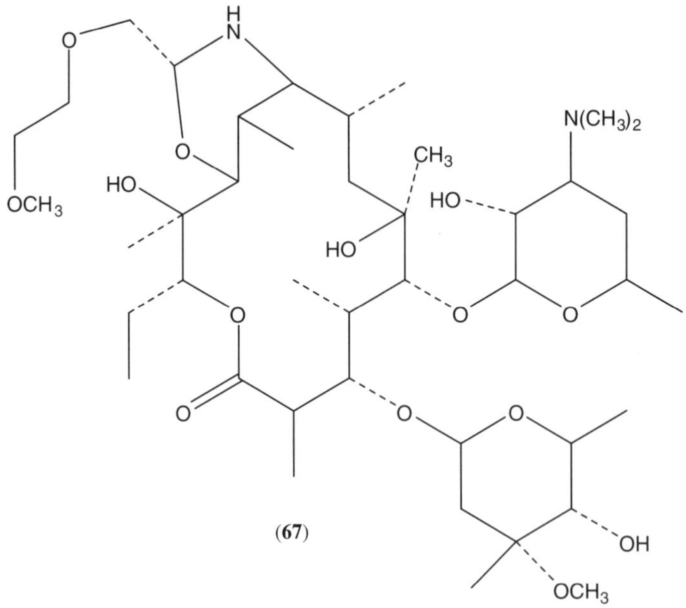

(67)

Some lesser successful but prominent for a while macrolides include flurithromycin (with a C-8 fluoro atom) (65), roxithromycin (with an oximinoether function at C-9) (66), and dirithromycin (a prodrug analog of erythromyclamine) (67).

4.2. Side Effects, Toxicity, and Contraindications of the Macrolide Antibiotics

The majority of the side effects of the macrolides are mild and of short duration. The most often reported complaints are diarrhea, nausea, abnormal taste, dyspepsia, abdominal pain, and headache. Some of these gastrointestinal problems are attributed to degradation to the internal ketal. Since this degradation is chemically impossible with the more recent semisynthetics, there are fewer complaints attendant their use. As with most antibiotics, suppression of the normal gut flora can lead to proliferation of the anaerobic opportunistic pathogen, *Clostridium difficile*, leading to pseudo-membranous colitis. This causes a severe diarrhea that can be comparatively mild to fatal.

The metabolism of erythromycin involves oxidative *N*-demethylation mediated by the liver cytochrome P450 enzyme CYP3A4. This can lead to severe drug–drug interactions with otherwise safe drugs. Such interactions with astemizole, terphenidine, midazolam, theophylline, and so on, leads to abnormally high levels of these drugs sometimes resulting in cardiac arrhythmias that have led to death. Metabolic oxidation of clarithromycin leads to the C-14 hydroxy analog that has an expanded antimicrobial spectrum.

Among the less common side effects is the possibility of QT prolongation leading to cardiac problems [172,173]. Erythromycin itself causes this effect but the potency is so small that it seems of no important clinical significance. This problem seems less commonly associated with clarithromycin, azithromycin, and telithromycin but cases are appearing in the literature and careful monitoring is prudent.

4.3. Pharmacology and Mode of Action of the Macrolide Antibiotics

Macrolide antibiotics are primarily given orally and they are readily but incompletely absorbed from the gastrointestinal tract. Erythromycin itself is acid unstable so produces decreased blood levels compared to the semisynthetic analogs. Consumption with food depresses achievable blood levels of the macrolides.

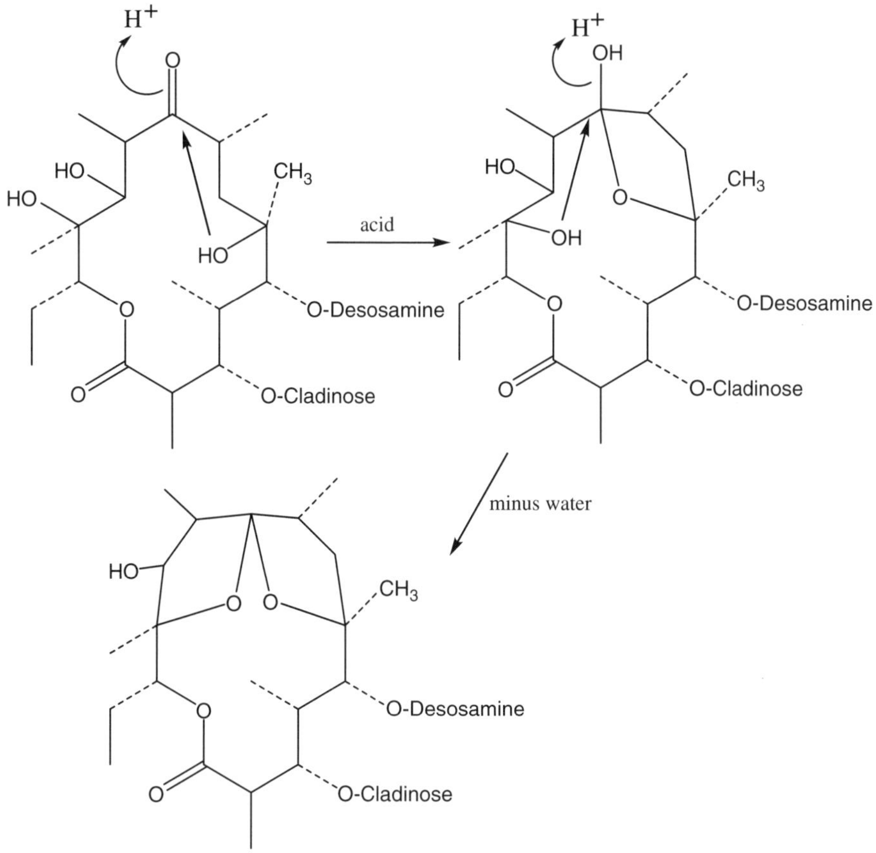

Figure 9. Acid-catalyzed internal ketal formation of C-6 hydroxylated 14-membered macrolides.

The acid degradation of erythromycin involves formation of a cyclic ketal that is antibiotically inactive. Although when drawn as in formula **53** it does not appear so, the C-6 hydroxyl is located just above and near the C-9 keto moiety and rapidly adds to it when the ketone function is protonated. The hemiketal is unstable also to acid and cyclodehydration occurs with the C-12 hydroxyl. Figure 9 illustrates this process. Not only is this reaction essentially irreversible and inactivating but the ketal appears to have propropulsive activity in the GI tract to which is attributed the GI upset that a number of patients experience. It is to avoid this problem that clarithromycin (**44**), azithromycin (**45**), and telithromycin (**46**) were introduced. These antibiotics either lack a free hydroxyl at C-6 (**43** and **45**) or lack a C-9 keto group so are chemically incapable of undergoing this inac-

tivating reaction. Film coating of tablets and the formation of water insoluble prodrug esters and salts are also devices employed with lesser success in avoiding this degradation.

An additional benefit to the patient of avoiding the formation of the internal ketal is that this agent has been found to mimic the pharmacological effects of the hormone motilin that stimulates stomach contractions and can lead to uncomfortable stomach cramps [174–178].

A pharmacokinetic comparison of the newer semisynthetic derivatives with erythromycin is instructive. Erythromycin is about 35% bioavailable orally, is about 84% serum protein bound and has an excretion half-life of 1.6 h. The newer agents are considerably improved in these respects. Clarithromycin is about 55% bioavailable, is 42–50% serum protein bound and has a half-life of 3.3 h. Azithromycin is about 34% bioavailable, is 7–50% serum protein bound and has a half-life of 40 h. It is clear from this that in addition to a more attractive antimicrobial spectrum the pharmacokinetics of the semisynthetic agents are a significant advance in macrolide chemotherapy.

Macrolides concentrate in the cells of the respiratory tract often achieving concentrations 10-fold higher than their blood levels. This contributes strongly to their utility in treating upper and lower respiratory tract infections due to sensitive Gram-positive microorganisms.

Their molecular mode of action takes place by binding to particular segments of 50S rRNA causing a disruption of programmed protein biosynthesis. The binding site interactions for erythromycin A are illustrated in Fig. 10 [4]. From this it will be seen that important contacts occur with the amino su-

gar (desosamine) whereas the neutral sugar (cladinose) makes no important interactions. Likewise the three hydroxyl groups attached to C-6, -11, and -12 also are hydrogen bonding sites. The essential dimethylamino moiety of desosamine (in the 14-membered ring family) or mycaminose (in the 16-membered ring family) form electrostatic contacts that serve to orient the molecule and thus serve as a docking site assisting the hydrogen bonding interactions to form properly. When the host–guest association is complete, the escape tunnel for the growing peptide chain is blocked and peptide biosynthesis ceases. The molecule is oriented in the tunnel with the cladinose residue pointing toward the peptidyltransfer site.

Tunnel blockade results in short, incomplete peptide sequences. These "junk" peptides are secreted, in part, from bacterial cells by RND export pumps (resistance-nodulation-division). This family of export pumps is

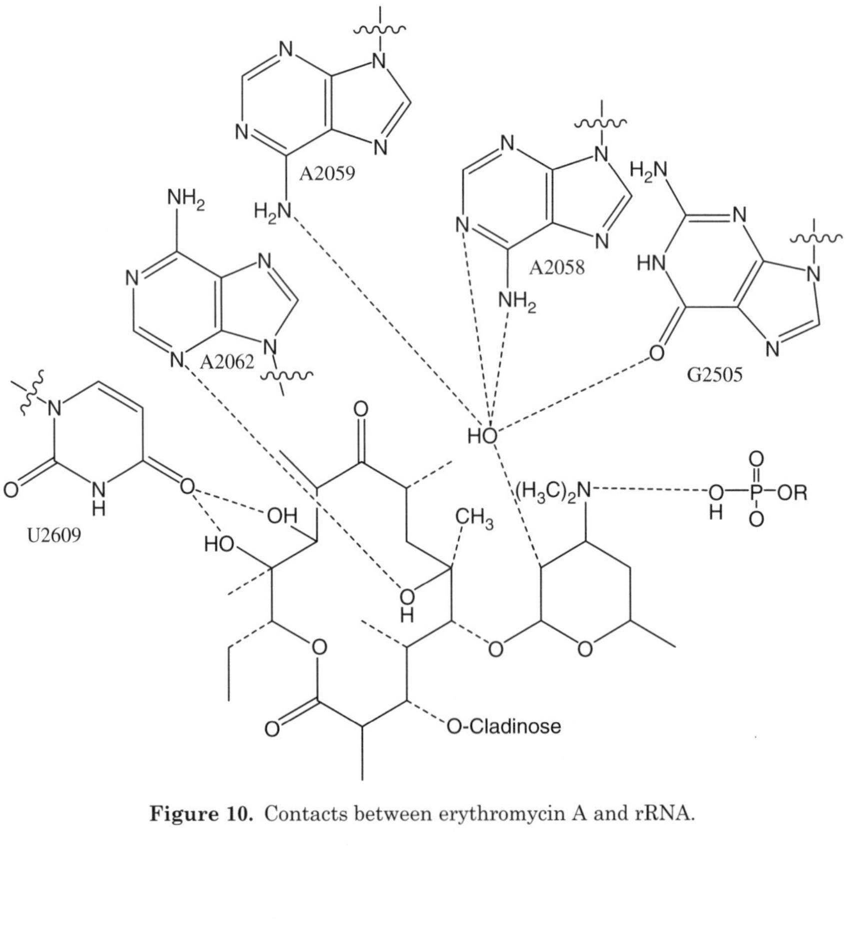

Figure 10. Contacts between erythromycin A and rRNA.

able to export a wide variety of structural types, including antibiotics. It is believed that antibiotic export is likely to be due to collateral damage as the junk peptides are the normal substrates for these pumps [136].

The structural interactions of macrolides with rRNA help rationalize the empirical SAR relationships learned the hard way by empirical chemical transformations. It should be borne in mind, however, that the X-ray structures are freeze frame photos of a dynamic process and many not be revealing the whole story.

Lack of interactions with cladinose is consistent with the activity of telithromycin. Removal of cladinose usually results in lower activity presumably because of the polar hydroxyl group revealed. Conversion of this to a less polar keto group compensates for this. The loss of hydrogen bonding interactions with the C-11 and C-12 hydroxyls is likely made up for by adding the fused heterocyclic ring bridging these two functions. The long functionalized arm projecting from this ring apparently finds another binding site not involved in the binding of erythromycin A itself. Such a binding site can account for the expanded potency and activity against resistant strains that this antibiotic possesses [179].

Lack of contacts with the keto group at C-9 provides a reasonable explanation for the activity of azithromycin and roxithromycin.

The macrolide binding site lies in the lumen of the hollow tunnel through which a growing peptide chain normally escapes from the P-site on the ribosome. This blockade prevents growth of the peptide beyond only a few amino acids in length. A secondary consequence of the blockade is premature ejection of peptidyl tRNA from the ribosome. Interestingly, lincomycin, clindamycin, and chloramphenicol bind in the same region (but not in the same precise manner) so there is cross-resistance between all of these agents. Likewise, the 16-membered macrolides, such as tylosin and dirithromycin bind at an overlapping site in the entrance to the peptide escape tunnel.

In addition to these binding results, there is evidence that macrolides can bind to other components of the 50S ribosomal subunit in such a manner that their assembly into a functional ribosome is impeded. The relative contribution of this phenomenon is not yet clear.

4.4. History, Biosynthesis, and Structure–Activity Relationships of the Macrolide Antibiotics

The first macrolide antibiotic to be isolated from a soil microorganism was pikromycin (in 1950). Erythromycin (**53**), the most important of the first-generation macrolides was isolated from a Phillipino soil sample in 1950–1951 and was launched as a product in 1952. Minor erythromycin analogs have been isolated from fermentation residues. For example, erythromycin B (differing from A in lacking a C-12 hydroxyl), erythromycin C (differing from A in lacking the O-methyl group in the cladinosyl sugar), and erythromycin D (differing from A in lacking both the C-12 hydroxyl and the O-methyl group on the cladinosyl sugar) have been isolated. In the subsequent 60 years, about 50 additional macrolides were isolated in Japan and the United States. The name, macrolide, was coined by R.B. Woodward once the structures of these agents became known (1957) [180]. The 1980s and 1990s were the years of semisynthesis seeing the introduction of the second-generation agents. In 2002, telithromycin was introduced to the clinic ushering in the third generation of macrolides.

The macrolide ring system is a typical polyketide assembled from acetate, butyrate, and propionate in a linear manner reminiscent of the biosynthesis of fatty acids without however removal of most of the oxygen atoms attached to alternating carbons. The sugar components are glucose derived [181].

Determination that the chiral centers of these molecules displayed common absolute configurations at corresponding carbons despite the differences in substitution patterns and ring sizes led to suspicions that they were assembled modularly under the control of similar genes has been borne out by detailed genetic analysis as well as analysis of the results of fermentation of blocked mutants [182,183]. Unusual but structurally related macrolides are frequently isolated by fermentation of less common soil microorganisms. Three stages are recognized: biosynthesis of the macrolide ring, biosynthesis of the sugars and attachment to the ring system, and final modification of functional groups leading to the final products. Understanding of the overall process has led to the ability to alter the biosynthetic pathway so as to produce novel macrolide products not found as yet in nature [181].

The assembly of the lactone ring is carried out by a large polyketide synthase containing several enzymatic centers dictating in an uninterrupted sequence the incorporation of each unit. The synthase is referred to as a module. Erythromycin is biosynthesized by deoxyerythronolide B synthase (DEBS). The domain organization of its polyketide synthase contains three multifunctional proteins (DEBS 1–3) subdivided into a load region and 5 modules consisting of 28 domains all together. These are DEBS 1=AT-ACP(Load)-KS-AT-KR-ACP(module 1)-KS-AT-KR-ACP (module 2)-DEBS 2=KS-AT-ACP(module 3)-KS-AT-DR-ER-KR-ACP(module 4)-DEBS 3=KS-AT-KR-ACP(module 5)-KS-AT-KR-ACP-TE (read from left to right). The biosynthetic process is illustrated schematically in Fig. 11. The overall module is rather similar to the fatty acid type I synthase. Each catalytic center in the module is referred to as a domain. The domains are linked together with intervening spacers. The KS domain encodes for the β-ketoacyl acyl carrier protein (ACP) synthase that catalyzes the condensation between each growing thioester bound acyl unit and the extender unit bound to the acyl carrier protein domain (AT). The AT domain encodes the acyltransferase that is specific for an extender unit, which is bound to it by an ester bond. Each module contains all three of these units (KS, ACP, and AT) thus providing the fundamental backbone and determining by their number the length of the chain. In addition there may be a functional KR (keto reductase) unit that catalyzes the reduction of the β-keto units into hydroxyls. The stereochemistry of the reduction is controlled by the KR domain that utilizes NADPH as the source of the hydrogen for reduction. A DH module (dehydratase) eliminates water from an alcohol function thus producing an α,β-unsaturated olefinic linkage. In macrolides (in contrast to fatty acids) all the double bonds produced are *trans*. An ER module (enoylreductase) reduces these double bonds with NADPH as a hydrogen source so as to produce methylene units. The macrolide synthase modules have a TE unit (thioesterase) at the end of their last module that releases the finished chain from the module. There is also a short-chain thioesterase that functions to remove faulty short-chain units from the module so that it can start over again.

The erythromycin polyketide synthase (6-dEB, so named because the C-6 oxygen is removed) consists of three proteins. DEBS 1 has three modules. The first (loading module) is AT-ACR. It accepts propionate at the AT domain and moves the starter propionic acid moiety to its ACR domain in preparation for condensation. Module 1 contains KS-AT-KR-ACP linked domains that first accept a 2S-methyl malonate unit at its AT site and then transfers it to its ACP site. Next condensation with the propionate unit attached to loading module ACR site is catalyzed by the KS unit and the resultant keto unit is reduced by the KR domain. The controlled dimer is then moved along to the AT site of module 2 in preparation for the addition of the next unit. Module 2 consists of KS-AT-KR-ACP domains that function as before.

Without pause or dissociation, the growing unit moves along into module 3 of DEBS 2 that consists of two modules. Module 3 is made up of KS-AT-ACP. Note the absence of a functional KR domain (due to lack of a NADPH binding site). This lack is responsible for lack of reduction of the carbonyl group so that a keto group remains at C-9 in erythromycin. Module 4 consists of KS-AT-DH-ER-KR-ACP. The presence of DH-ER-KR is responsible for C-7 in the completed lactone ring being present as a methylene.

DEBS 3 contains two more modules. Module 5 consists of KS-AT-KR-ACP and works more or less like modules 1 and 2 of DEBS 1. Module 6 consists of KS-AT-KR-ACP-TE. The first four modules function in the same way as module 5 but contains in addition domain TE that releases the polyketide from the polyketide synthase and catalyzes cyclodehydration to form the lactone ring. By an unknown means the absolute configuration of the methyl groups at C-2, -4, and -11 are inverted along the way.

Subsequent biosynthetic operations introduce the C-6 hydroxyl (by the P450 hydroxylase EryF), mycarose is added at C-3 and then desosamine is added to C-5. The product, erythromycin D, is the first antibiotically active product in the sequence. Blocked mutants produce this compound. Next a P450 enzyme adds the C-12 hydroxyl group (producing er-

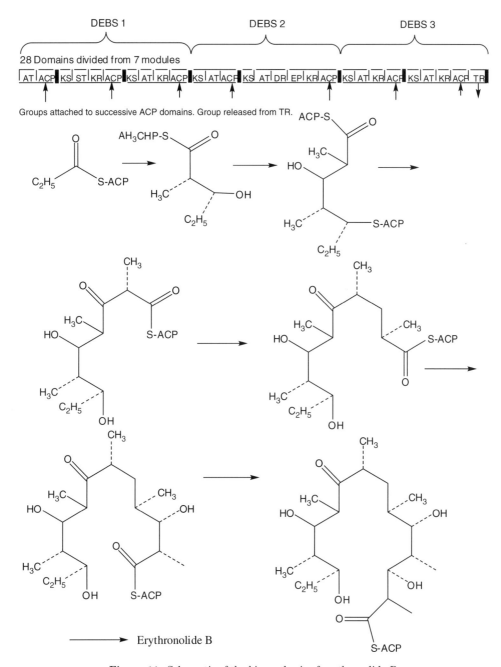

Figure 11. Schematic of the biosynthesis of erythronolide B.

ythromycin C). Finally, an *O*-methyltransferase converts the mycarosyl moiety to cladinose and erythromycin A is complete [181].

The C-12- and C-16-membered macrolides as well as the other C-14-membered ring macrolides are produced by modules quite analogous to these. The similarities in the biosynthetic modules accounts for the absolute stereochemical regularities observed from macrolide to macrolide.

The biosynthesis of the sugar moieties proceeds from glucose-1-phosphate and involves a sequence of dehydrative-hydrogenation deoxygenations, oxidations to keto groups, epimerizations, transaminations, and methylations. These are detailed in an excellent recent review for the interested reader [181].

Many hundreds of analogs of erythromycin A have been prepared by semisynthesis leading to an understanding of its structure–activity relationships. A brief summary of some of this work follows.

Although the keto group at C-9 makes no important direct contacts with rRNA, it does play a significant role in the overall activity of the molecule. As mentioned above, formation of a cyclic ketal with the hydroxyls at C-6 and C-12 abolishes antibiotic activity. Reduction enhances stability, as would be expected, but the potency is decreased. Preparation of an oxime or hydrazone followed by reduction to the 9-(S)-amino analog (erythromyclamine) restores *in vitro* activity but with reduced oral activity. A dicyclic carbonate involving hydroxyls at C-8, -9 and C-11, -12 in the internal cyclic ketal and a C-6 to C-8 cyclic carbonate lacking a C-9 keto group are surprisingly active. Conversion to dirithromycin (**66**) enhances blood levels somewhat. Dirithromycin hydrolyzes nonenzymatically back to erythromyclamine. A variety of ethers can be prepared from the oxime. In this series, the *E* isomers are more active than the *Z* and the most important of these is roxithromycin (**65**). Its antimicrobial spectrum approximates that of erythromycin A but it is somewhat less active *in vitro*. It does not form a cyclic ketal so is more stable in acid solutions.

Formation of azithromycin from the C-9 oxime of erythromycin A via a Beckmann rearrangement and reduction leads to azithromycin, the first of the azalides. The azalides are generally less active against Gram positives but are more active against Gram negatives. More importantly, azithromycin has outstanding pharmacokinetic properties including significant acid stability and excellent distribution into the tissues of the respiratory tract. It is interesting to note that NMR and X-ray studies demonstrate that the alteration in ring size involved in this does not significantly alter the solution conformation. The retention of bioactivity is consistent with this, of course [184,185].

The presence and stereochemical orientation of the hydroxyl and dimethylamino functions in the desosamine moiety are essential for activity of the erythromycin group. Acylation of the hydroxyl is facile and results in prodrugs of which the propionate and ethylsuccinates have reached the market place. The cladinose moiety is not important provided that the hydroxyl group revealed by its removal is made less polar by conversion to a keto group. Likewise, removal of the methyl moiety from C-3″ reveals a free polar hydroxyl and this decreases activity. The C-4″ position can, however, be modified by epimerization or removal without much change in potency. Conversion of C-4″ to an amino or oximino moiety likewise does not increase potency. Acylation of the C-11 ring hydroxyl significantly decreases potency. A C-11 *O*-methyl derivative of erythromycin A is also poorly active. Installation of an α or β-hydroxyl at C-8 significantly decreases potency. Dehydration to produce 10,11-dehydro erythromycin A leads to poor activity. Formation of an α-epoxide between carbons 11 and 12 leads to poor activity. Fluorination at C-8S produces flurithromycin. This substance is quite stable to acid and possesses attractive antimicrobial potency. A cyclic carbonate involving the hydroxyls at C-11 and -12, on the other hand, is significantly active. Further elaboration of a cyclic carbamate at this position is an important feature of the ketolides.

Megalomicins are natural products with megosamine, an amino sugar, at C-6. It has significant antimicrobial activity. *O*-Methylation of the C-6 hydroxyl leads to clarithromycin with its enhanced acid stability and significant potency. Larger alkyl groups on the C-6 oxygen are tolerated but are somewhat less potent. Reduced potency is also seen when an *O*-allyl ether is added to C-6 but this intermediate opens the way to more elaborate substitutions. Some of these, particularly those terminating with aromatic residues, showed significant activity against macrolide resistant bacteria. Extension of this work to the ketolide series has led to molecules (particularly cethromycin) that have entered clinical trials but have yet to be commercialized [170].

4.5. Resistance to Macrolide Antibiotics

Bacterial resistance to macrolide antibiotics has emerged as a significant therapeutic problem.

Such resistance was first reported in 1952—the same year in which erythromycin was released into clinical use! [186] Genes encoding resistance to macrolides have now been found in all Gram-positive bacteria for which these drugs would be otherwise regarded as suitable targets. The soil microorganisms that produce macrolide antibiotics are resistant to these compounds by mechanisms analogous to those found in bacterial pathogens leading to the suspicion that these are the original source of the problem [187–189]. It is understandable that the producing organisms carry resistance to macrolides so that they would not be poisoned as a consequence. Unfortunately the relevant genes have not stayed put!

The two most commonly noted means of macrolide resistance are mono or di self-methylation of the bacterial ribosomes (inducible or constitutive), erm (B) encoded, or by efflux, emf-encoded. Less common means of resistance are also noted. These include enzymatic attack on the structure of macrolides and ribosomal mutations involving RNA and/or proteins. A number of strains carry more than one mode of resistance to macrolides. More details of these forms of resistance have been described in an excellent recent review [181].

Mono or dimethylation of N-6 of adenine A2058 of 23S rRNA by protein Erm methylase results in interference with macrolide binding, probably by disrupting hydrogen bonding to the adjacent C-2' hydroxyl. The genes responsible are ermA, ermB, and ermC. Methylation of 50S or intact ribosomes is not seen with Erm methylase [190]. There are at least 20 different erm genes now recognized. The source of the methyl group(s) is S-adenosyl methionine and some erm enzymes monomethylate and others dimethylate. Although the monomethylated RNA is a substrate for a dimethylating enzyme, it is not yet clear whether dimethylation is stepwise or concerted.

Since the methylation must be enzyme-catalyzed it would seem in principle possible to interfere with this process by developing specific inhibitors for them. Unfortunately, however, practical use of such agents would not appear to be feasible.

Resistance to macrolides due to efflux is becoming increasingly prevalent, especially among strains of S. pyogenes, S. epidermtidis, and S. pneumoniae. S. aureus, on the other hand, does not display this much as yet. The genes responsible for this in streptococci are known as mefA. Interestingly, the 14- and 15-membered macrolides are exported by MefA but the 16-membered macrolides are presently exempt and they do not induce this system. The ketolides also fail to elicit mefA. In staphylococci, efflux is mediated by MsrA that is similar in the resistance pattern that it elicits to various ring sized macrolides as is the case with MefA. Gram-negative bacteria eject macrolides rather well but utilize different gene products. These genes are generally chromosomal and so the resistance mediated by them is intrinsic although not always expressed without a mutational event.

There is increasing evidence that efflux is mediated through a large family of constituative membrane-bound RND export proteins (resistance-nodulation-division) whose normal function in bacterial cells is as yet unknown but appears to be the removal from cells of "junk" proteins produced by ribosome damage due to antibiotic action, reactive oxygen species, bile salts, or other stresses. Their action against antibiotics is seen, in this view, to be due to the wide substrate-accepting capabilities of these pumps and not specifically due to their action against antibiotics. This view is supported by their chromosomal and noninducible nature [136].

In addition to the self-methylation mediated resistance noted above, other mutational events involving ribosomal RNA are also known. Strains of S. pneumoniae can delete A2058 leading to high resistance to macrolides, A2058G or A2058T mutations lead to high levels of broad-spectrum macrolide resistance, C2611T mutation confers resistance to gonorrhea, and so on. The pattern of resistance due to these and other ribosomal mutations is complex and individualized among pathogens. Mutational events involving large subunit ribosomal proteins are also known in clinical strains of H. influenzae, S. aureus, and S. pneumoniae. The proteins involved are located at the opening of the peptide escape tunnel. Binding of erythromycin still takes place but the binding to the altered tunnel does not prevent peptide biosynthesis [191–195].

Enzymatic attack on macrolides has also been noted. There are, for example, esterases in a variety of Gram-negative bacteria that hydrolyze the lactone function destroying the ring [196,197]. Fortunately this form of resistance is not common in clinical strains of Gram positives as yet. Phosphorylation on desosamine (at C-2′) has been reported and appears to be present in erythromycin-producing soil microorganisms [197–199]. Glucosylation at C-2′ has been found in oleandomycin producing *Streptomyces antibioticus* but has not been identified as yet in pathogens [197,200–204].

4.6. Recent Developments in the Macrolide Antibiotic Field

Great progress has been made in understanding the molecular mode of action of macrolide antibiotics. Not very long ago it was believed that they bound to ribosomal proteins and this disrupted some specific vital step in protein biosynthesis. It is now known, as discussed above, that they bind to rRNA at the exit tunnel through which growing peptide chains emerge from the ribosome. This blocks growth and as a secondary effect prevents the completion of peptide chains. Thus, their action has the same effect as through a specific step were being inhibited by macrolide binding. One consequence of this is that the avidity of binding to the receptor site may not be directly proportional to their potency. Detailed under-

standing of the points of interaction with the receptor site has clarified structure–activity effects previously revealed empirically through opportunistic chemical transformations followed by biotesting.

Another area, in which dramatically enhanced understanding has emerged, is the genetics of biosynthesis. Breaking of the genetic code for macrolide biosynthesis revealing its underlying regularities has enabled the deliberate artificial biosynthesis of molecules by recombinant technologies that would be extremely difficult for a chemist to make and unlikely for an undisturbed streptomycete to construct. To do this certain domains can be deleted or novel domains can be introduced. Gene cassettes can even be imported and made functional into bacteria [205]. Provided that the subsequent domains are capable of functioning in the presence of the resulting artificial polyketide units, novel molecules will result. In those cases where the final product is antimicrobially active, the detection of a successful transformation is facilitated [206–209].

An example of a chemobiosynthetic analog is the 15-substituted amidoerythromycins A (**68**) [210].

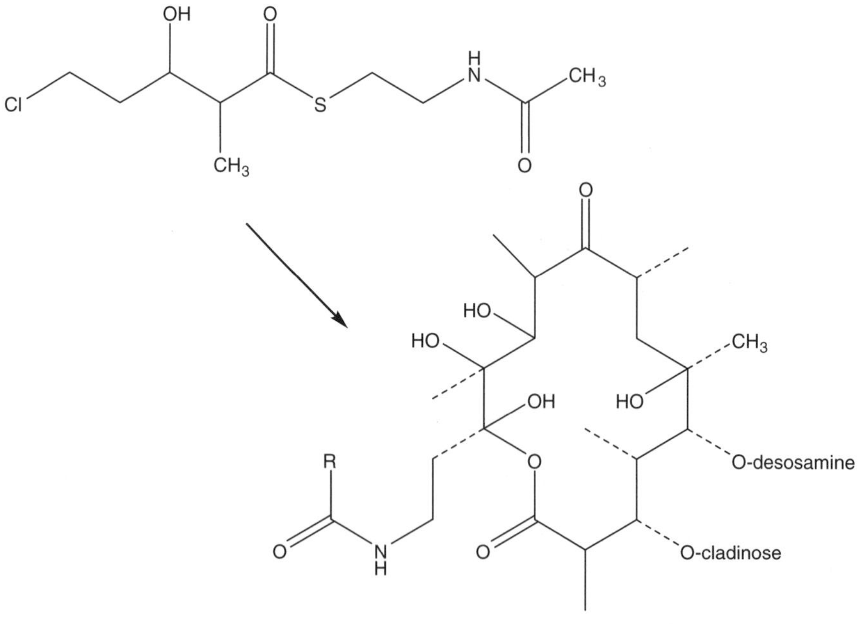

(**68**)

The sugar portions of the macrolides strongly influence their spectrum and potency. Utilization of glycosyltransferases has allowed the formation of several sugar prodrugs in which a variety of sugars have been added onto the 2'-hydroxyl of desosamine in oleandomycin (a largely archaic macrolide). Lesser success was achieved with erythromycin. These novel glycans are most likely prodrugs and one (the galactoside) showed enhanced potency over the parent drug [211].

The most important recent advances in producing superior macrolide antibiotics have been the result of opportunistic following up of opportunities provided by newer chemistry. The ketolides have been the result [181,212].

It has long been known that the neutral sugar could be removed selectively by mild acid treatment provided that the 9-keto moiety was protected so that it could not ketalize. Removal of cladinose resulted in a significant loss of activity so at the time researchers believed that the neutral sugar contributed significantly to receptor binding. When X-ray crystallographic studies demonstrated that this sugar did not make significant contacts with rRNA, this rationalization had to be discarded. Pikromycin, a weakly active natural macrolide, had a C-3 keto group so the possible utility of this transformation was pursued. This transformation, however, led to formation of a cyclic hemiketal with the C-6 hydroxyl and this product was not useful. The discovery of the favorable properties of clarithromycin in which this hemiketalization could not take place (because of methylation of the C-6 hydroxyl) triggered reexamination. It was found that replacement of cladinose by a keto group resulted in molecules that did not induce ribosomal methylation (MLS$_B$) albeit with lessened potency. This encouraged further exploration of these substances n attempts to intensify activity. Reactions made possible by elimination of the C-11 hydroxyl to introduce a Δ10-11 conjugated double bond susceptible to Michael addition reactions led to the ability to annulate novel heterocyclic fused rings to the macrocyclic ring [213]. These derivatives showed very significant potency, especially against certain resistant bacteria of clinical importance. It is suggested that these annulation reactions rigidify the ring system and that

this helps account for improved potency. The ketolides resulted from further elaboration of these rings by adding a projecting arm of an appropriate length terminating in heterocyclic aromatic rings [214]. Telithromycin is a marketed ketolide and cethromycin (ABT-773), [170] EP-13417, CP-544,372, and FMA 0713 are believed to be in various stages of clinical examination. Many other contending ketolides are less far along. The activity of these agents against resistant bacteria appears due to the hetero aromatic ring reaching a binding site not accessible to erythromycin, azithromycin, and clarithromycin. The synthesis of telithromycin from erythromycin requires at least 14 steps making the final product rather costly. Its potency against macrolide resistant S. pneumoniae justifies to some extent the enhanced price. Telithromycin is not ejected by resistance pumps and does not induce bacterial self-methylation of ribosomes.

Unfortunately the clinical use of telithromycin has resulted in a significant incidence of liver toxicity including some deaths. Nasty recriminations about the FDA approval process for this drug have appeared and rebuttals have also been published [215–224]. In any case, the use of telithromycin has sharply decreased as a consequence of hepatotoxicity. Preliminary reports that cethromycin does not cause severe liver damage have encouraged a continued exploration of the ketolide class. Telithromycin has also been involved in a few cases of cardiotoxicity (torsades de pointes—a potentially fatal ventricular arrhythmia characterized by delayed repolarization of heart muscle and prolongation of the QT interval). This effect occurs with most macrolides especially when given in combination with certain other lipophilic drugs and is fortunately rare, [173,200,225,226]

In parallel with the synthesis and evaluation of ketolides, the chemistry leading to clarithromycin was adapted to the addition of C-6 allyl ethers that could themselves serve as the starting point for projecting hetero aromatic rings at the end of suitable arms [227]. These projected heterocyclic substituents apparently access the same binding sites that the ketolides discussed above take advantage of. The synthetic sequence connecting erythromycin to cethromycin is also lengthy making the final product intrinsically expensive. Cethromycin has potency and breadth of spectrum quite similar to that of telithromycin.

Thus, these two initially disparate opportunistic chemical explorations came together at this point. None of the C-6 modified agents have yet been marketed.

An arm that terminated in a variety of heterocyclic rings attached to C-6 produced a series of active ketolide analogs in which the projecting arm modulated only slightly the potency of the final analogs. Of these, a phenylpyrimidine terminus is representative of the best (**69**). Unfortunately oral activity of these agents was not good [228].

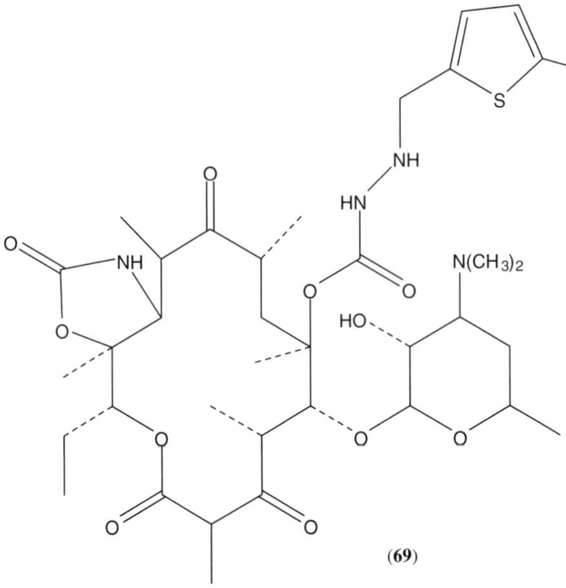

(**69**)

Use of malonate esters as Michael reaction components allowed the production of γ-lactone ring annelated macrolides (in place of the more usual carbamates and imidazolones). Attachment of suitable heterocyclic rings at the end of an arm attached to C-6 produced a series of ketolide analogs with useful *in vitro*

potency but this was significantly reduced in the presence of added mouse serum proteins. Examination of the influence of C-10 methyl stereochemistry demonstrated that the usual β-absolute stereochemistry was superior. These agents are exemplified by (**70**) [229,230].

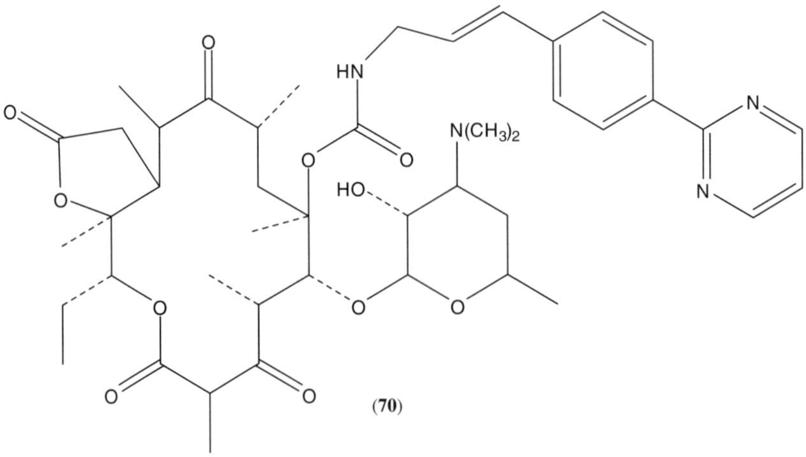

(**70**)

A departure from this structural theme involved esterification of a C-3 hydroxyl with isobutyric acid. The acylide [231,232] so constructed with a C-6 projecting arm terminating in a quinoline ring (71) exemplifies the best of this series. Its potency is roughly equivalent to that of telithromycin. The preparation of this agent takes advantage of the bulk tolerance that cladinose otherwise utilized [233].

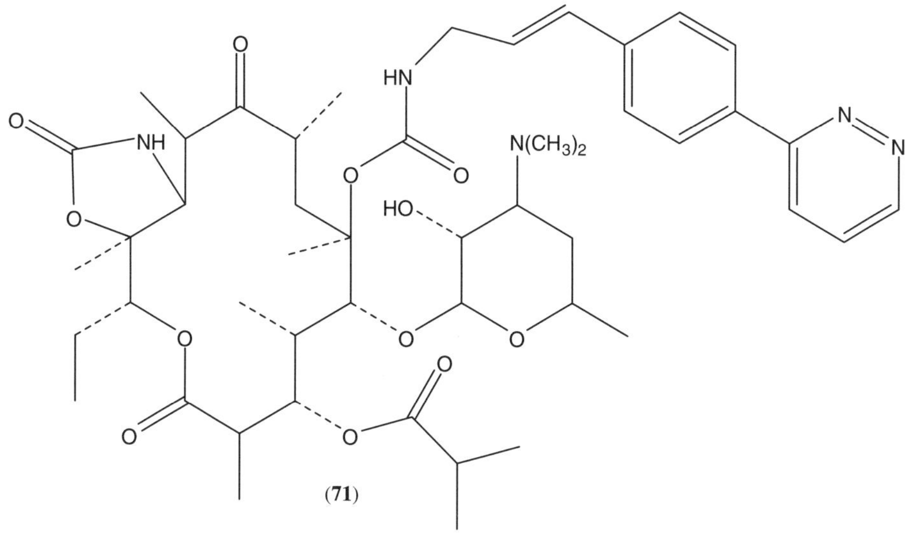

(71)

A ketolide utilizing an oximino ether terminating in a quinoxaline ring projecting from C-9 (72) was the best of another significant set of ketolide analogs. One assumes that the same new binding site accessed by the other ketolides is involved in the favorable properties of this agent. Its activity in animal infection models was roughly equivalent to that of clarithromycin [234].

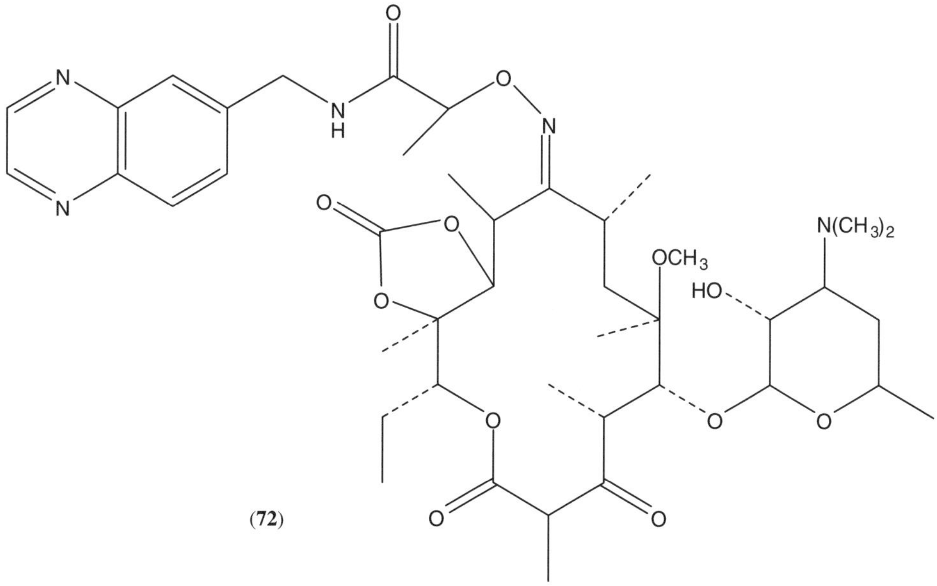

(72)

It has generally been assumed that the methyl groups of these heavily functionalized substances would be difficult to modify other than by genetically engineering microbes. An exception to this resulted from realizing that the Δ10-11 conjugated system activated the C-10 methyl to electrophilic chemistry. Using a lengthy but clever sequence of reactions, a N-benzylamino nitrogen was attached to this methyl group in a ketolide molecular framework (73). No biological properties are reported as yet for this analog [235].

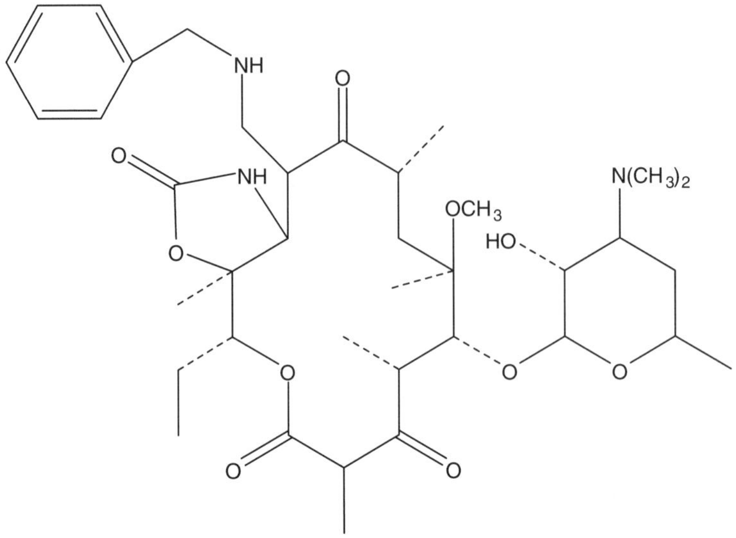

(73)

Substitutions on the nitrogen atom of heterocyclic rings annelated to C-11, -12 are related to telithromycin. Its success has led to a number of analog syntheses. The Kaneko group has made a number of such analogs utilizing either oxazolidinone (74) [236] or imidazolone (75) [237] rings as launching pads.

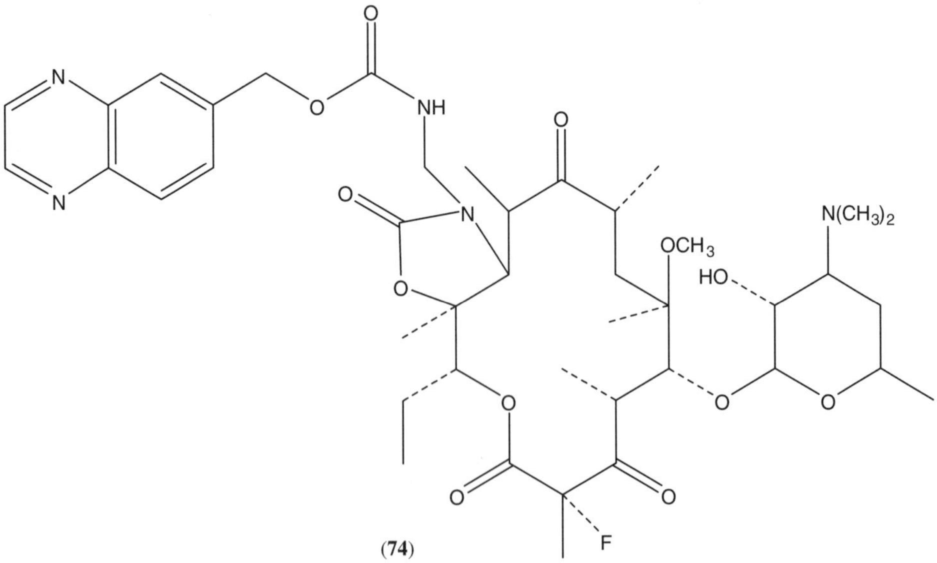

(74)

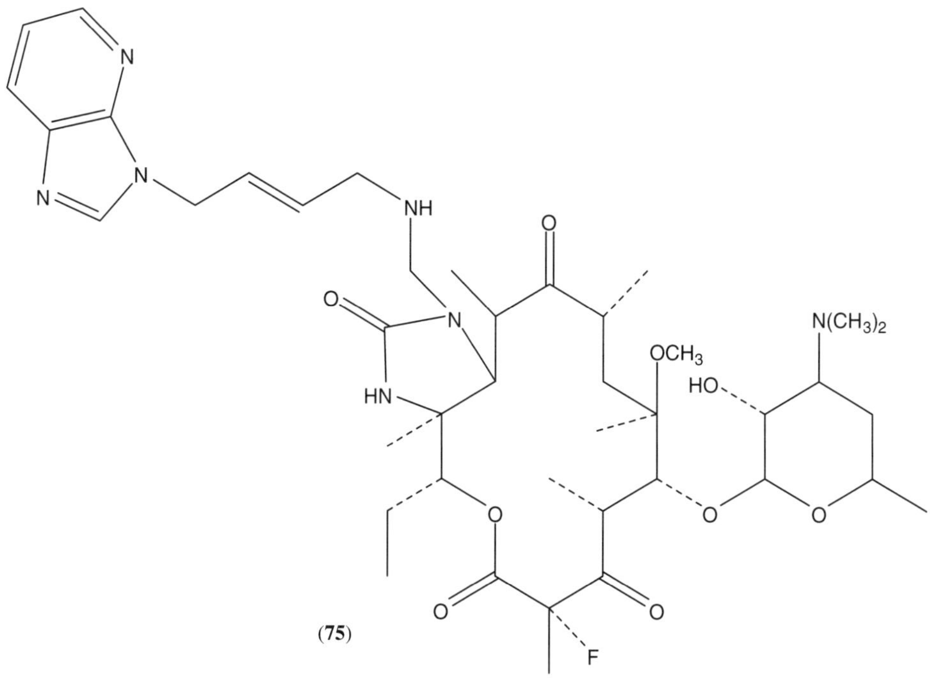

(75)

Departing somewhat from this basic theme, Heggelund et al. used an oxazolidinone ring but also formed an oxazolidinone ring in the *des*-methyl desosamine sugar. The poor activity of this agent (76) is consistent with the X-ray studies indicating that a basic nitrogen is important for ribosome binding [238].

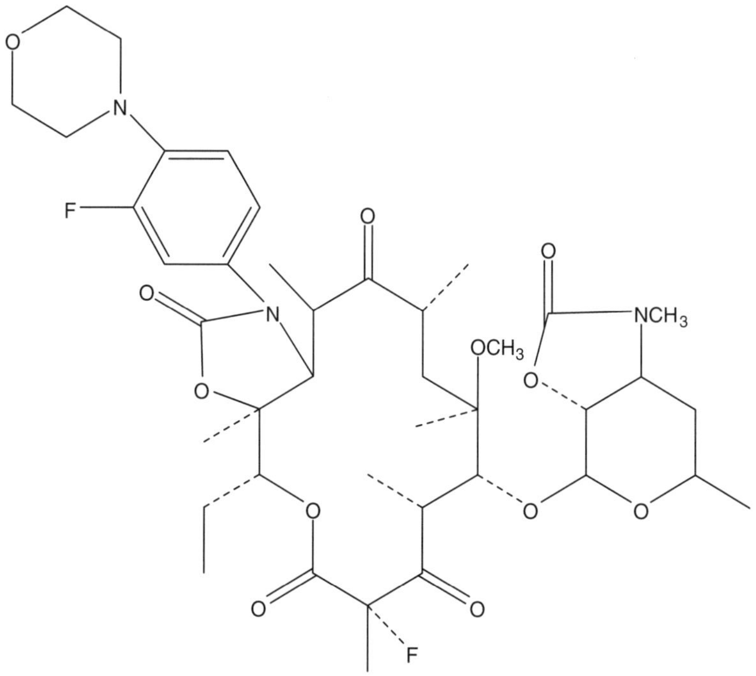

(76)

The Burger group succeeded in preparing an exocyclic C-12 methylene moiety that could then be transformed into ketolides with C-12 ethyl [239] or vinyl [240] analogs in place of the natural methyl. These products were equivalent or less active than clarithromycin/telithromycin in animal models.

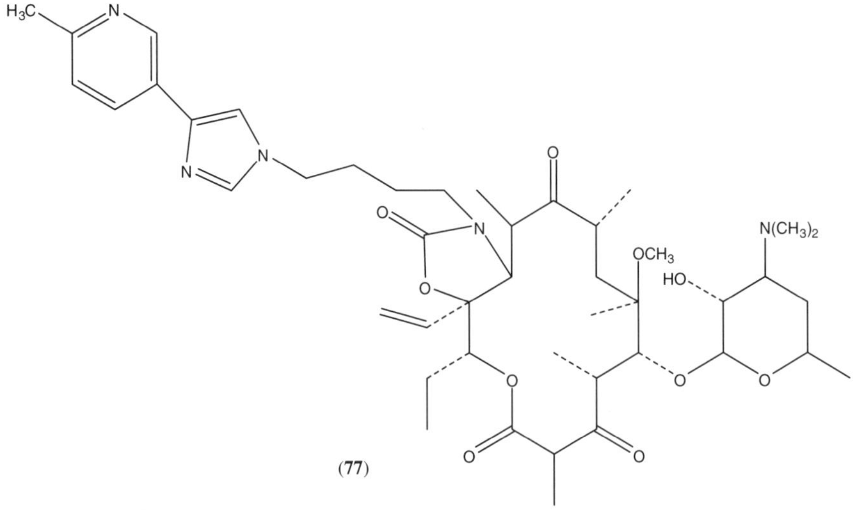

(77)

The presence of the C-3 keto moiety in the ketolides has allowed exploitation of its weakly enolic character. Removal to produce the C-3 methylene analogs gave disappointing potency [241]. Dehydration of the corresponding C-3 alcohols proved difficult but ultimately means to form "anhydrolides" were found [242–244]. The best of these compounds, exemplified by carbazate **77**, were quite active *in vitro*, especially against macrolide resistant microorganisms of the MLS type, but were disappointing *in vivo*.

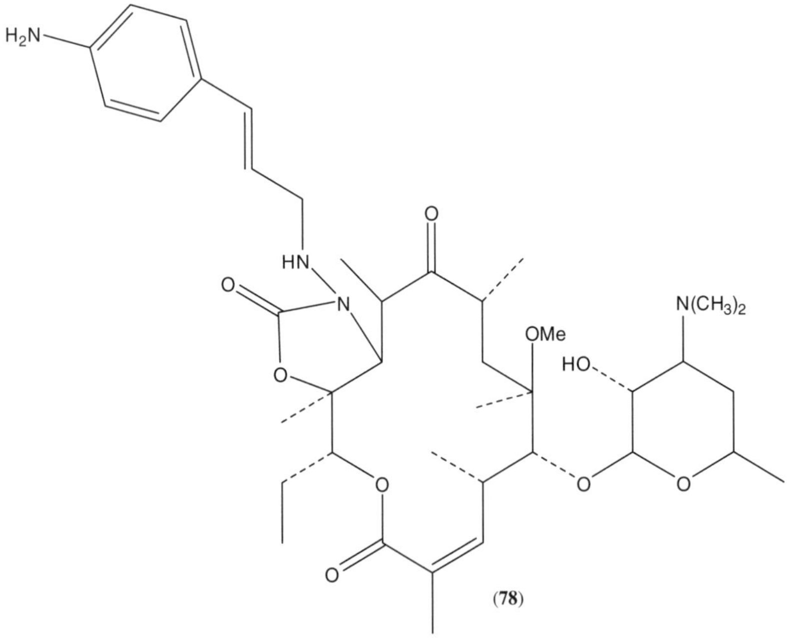

(78)

The most successful chemistry to emerge from manipulating the 3-keto moiety have been the C-2α-fluoro analogs. Fluorination of C-6-O-propargylated ketolides using *N*-fluorobenzene sulfonamide produced a single diastereomer that could be coupled with a variety of heterocycles under Sonogashira conditions and deprotected to produce highly antibiotic active fluorinated ketolide analogs.

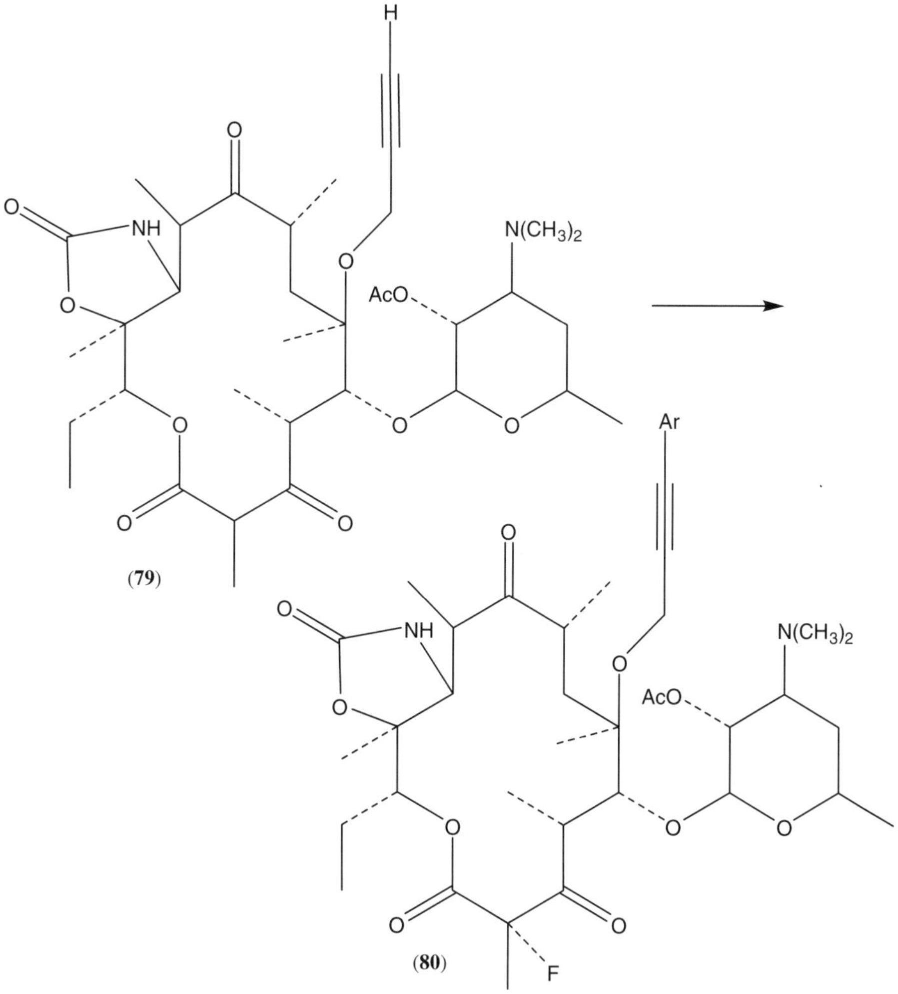

About the same time, another group confirmed the attractive properties of 2-fluoroketolides by conversion of compound **79** to analog **80** [245,246]. In the course of these studies, however, it was found that enol ethers, anhydrous, and C-2 methyl and C-2 chloro analogs were disappointing [246].

Later 2-fluoro analogs were found to be quite active *in vitro* against strep displaying *erm* and *mef* resistance but were significantly protein bound diminishing their *in vivo* performance [247,248]. Compounds **81** and **82** are representative of this group.

(81)

(82)

An extension to ketolides containing unnatural sugars in place of desosamine has been published. The best of products, of which **83** is an example, had excellent *in vitro* potency including resistant strains [249].

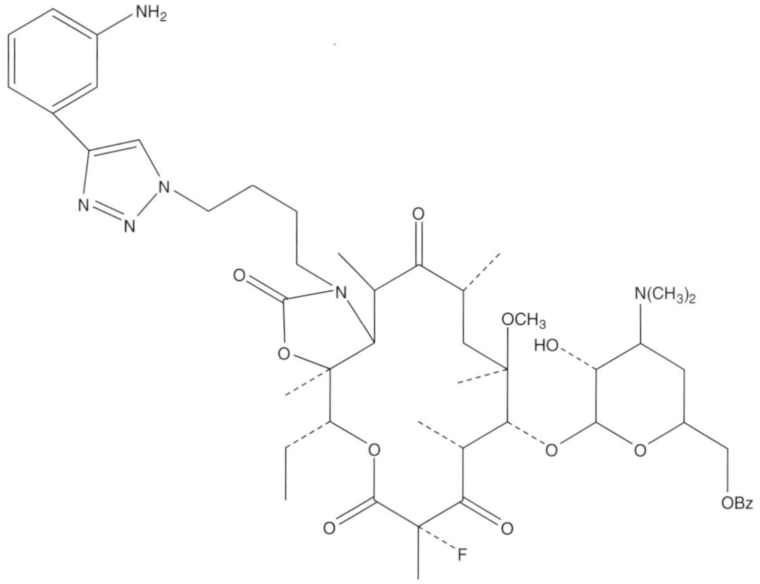

(83)

The usual approach to finding new macrolides of potential clinical interest is to search for agents possessing the broadest possible antimicrobial spectrum. In contrast, OPOT-80 (**84**) is under development (phase III clinical trials are under way) for a very narrow application, namely for the treatment of *C. difficile* infections. This troublesome opportunistic gut pathogen causing pseudomembranous colitis sporulates readily and so survives the action of most anti-infective agents. Suppression of the normal gut flora provides a congenial environment for this anaerobe that resumes growing and proliferates in this depopulated environment. The very severe drug-treatment associated diarrhea is an unfortunate consequence of drug therapy and is increasingly resistant to the usual drugs used to combat it. OPOT-80 is intended to be useful in these cases. Interestingly, OPT-80 is derived from the 16-membered macrolactone group.

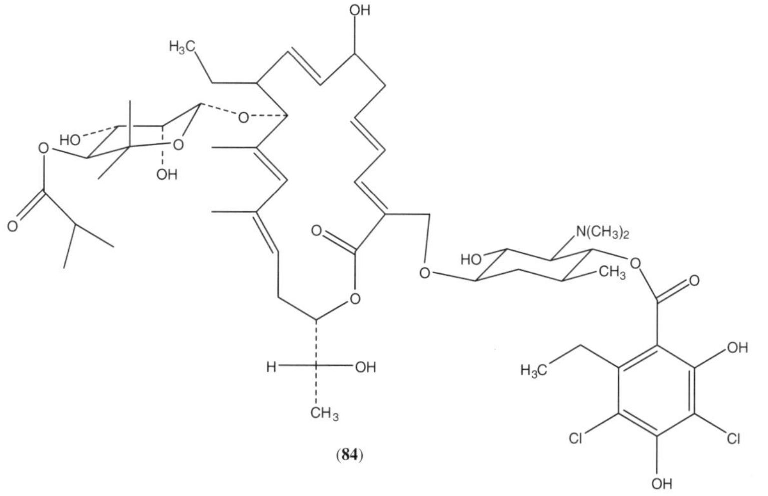

(84)

These studies have produced very interesting selective chemistry in these normally rather fragile molecules but have not as yet resulted in agents that are superior to the second-generation macrolides or to telithromycin. Clearly these compounds represent further examples going to show that revisiting the chemistry of older drugs when newer reagents and reactions become available often produces potentially valuable new agents. Who knows just what the future of macrolide transformations may produce following this operational stratagem.

Nonantibiotic uses for macrolides have been explored of late. Noting the propulsive side effect of the cyclic ketal of erythromycin that is formed in acidic fluids, a synthetic program was instituted to see if this undesirable side effect could be utilized for therapeutic advantage. Mitemcinal (**85**) is one of the results. Mitemcinal has an *O*-12-methoxyl substituent that prevents conversion of this enol ether to a ketal. Other structural changes of interest are the formation of a 11-keto moiety and replacement of one of the *N*-methyl groups with an isopropyl moiety [250,251]. Mitemcinal is an effective laxative. It has the advantage of not inducing diarrhea while shortening the time to first defecation and having a short duration of action [252–256]. Its pharmacological action is caused by stimulation of motilin (a 22-mer peptide that stimulates motor contractions in the upper GI tract between meals). Utility has been demonstrated in a variety of laboratory animals and the compound has progressed into the clinic [256].

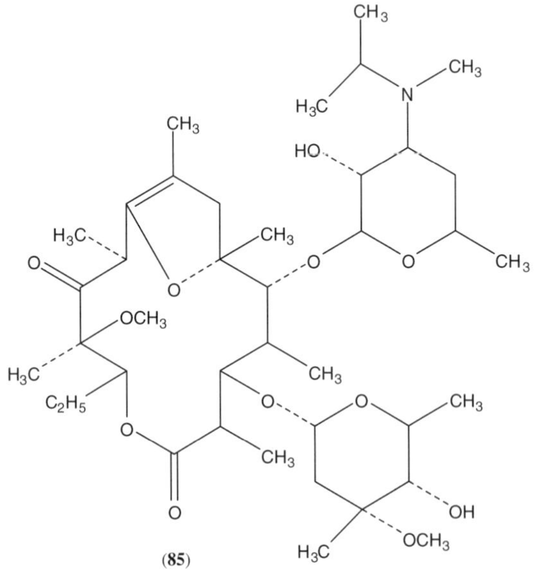

(85)

Also among the nonantibiotic properties of 14-membered ring macrolides that are of medicinal interest, erythromycin, clarithromycin, and roxithromycin have shown immunomodulatory activity in inflammatory skin disorders as well as in chronic airway inflammations [257–259]. This is attributed to inhibition of the effects of inflammatory modulators produced by neutrophils and macrophages [260].

Macrolides have been found to cause QT interval prolongation and torsade de pointes. The clinical meaning of this is unclear since millions of courses of treatment have been administered with these drugs without this problem becoming notable. Under normal circumstances the cardiac depression accompanying use of these agents has no clinical significance. Nonetheless this must be carefully monitored, especially with patients susceptible to TdP who are taking other drugs likely to produce this cardiac problem. It also occurs with clarithromycin, azithromycin, and telithromycin so appears to be a class problem [173,226,261–267].

5. OTHER ANTIBIOTICS THAT TARGET BACTERIAL RIBOSOMES

5.1. Streptogramins

The streptogramins were discovered as fermentation products in the 1950s but were unimpressive so were not pursued at the time for treatment of humans [268]. Virginiamycin, an antibiotic in this class, has been used as an animal feed-supplement for about 20 years. The rapid rise of multiresistant Gram-positive bacterial infections prompted a restudy of this group that produced useful findings. The poor water solubility of the streptogramins was rectified by analoging enabling their use in the treatment of infections due to both Gram-positive bacteria (staphylococci, streptococci, and enterococci) and some Gram negatives (neisseria and legionella). *Enterococcus faecalis* is resistant. Since 1999 the combination of 30:70 quinupristin/dalfopristin has been available for hospital use in the treatment of VREF (vancomycin-resistant *E. fecium*) infections [269].

Streptogramins come in two chemical classes [270]. Class A components are 23-membered ring polyunsaturated polyketide and amino acid derived macrolactones exemplified by pristinamycin-IIA (**86**). Madumycin II is structurally related to pristinamycin [271,272]. Class B components are macrocyclic (19-membered ring) hexadepsipeptides exemplified by pristinamycin-IA (**87**). Virginiamycin S, [273,274] etamycin, [275] patricin A, [276,277] and vernamycin C [278] are structurally related. The quinupristin/dalfopristin-producing streptomycete produces both classes in a 60:40 ratio.

Interestingly, whereas the individual streptogramin types are bacteriostatic, when combined they are synergistic so that their effect is bactericidal [279,280]. The clinically utilized drug synercid resulted from analoging and consists of a 7:3 ratio of dalfopristin (**88**) and quinupristin (**89**). This agent is utilized i. v. for treatment of serious drug-resistant infections. Synercid inhibits the action of P450 3A4 drug metabolizing liver enzymes so caution should be exercised if it is used in combination with other drugs metabolized by this enzyme so that their blood levels do not become excessive.

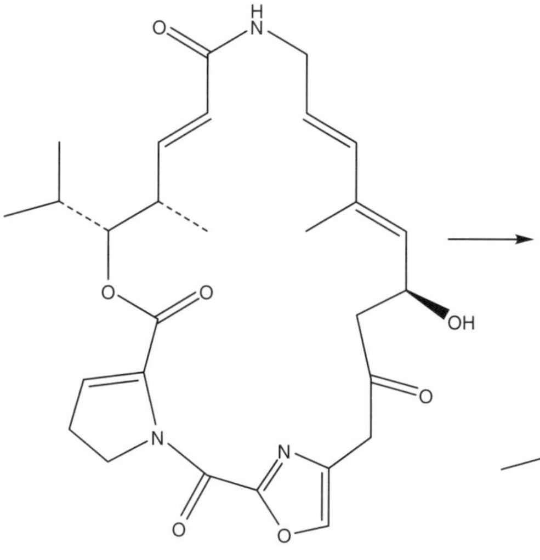

(86)

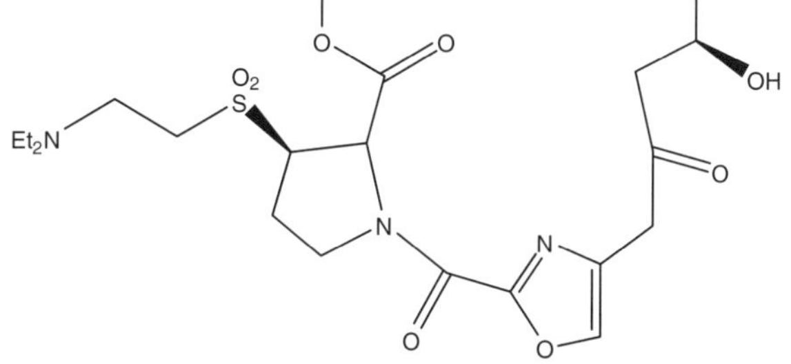

(88)

(87)

(89)

The synercid components both bind to the 50S ribosomal subparticle but at distinct binding sites in the exit tunnel [5]. The bacteriostatic A component binds to the free A and P sites such that it inhibits both the binding of aminoacyl-tRNA and subsequent peptide bond formation. Binding of component A results in a conformational distortion of 50S subunit that facilitates the binding of the B component. This serves to rationalize the synergy attendant to their simultaneous use. By itself, the bacteriostatic component B binds in a site that overlaps with the macrolide binding site so that it consequently is cross-resistant with macrolides. The binding results in incorrect positioning of the tRNA.

A streptogramin (virginiamycin) is used in agriculture as animal feed supplement [281,282]. This use has generated fears that resistant strains that will also infected humans will emerge [283,284]. Mortality from this use is predicted to be low but not zero [285].

Certainly clinical use of streptogramins for the treatment of severe, drug resistant, infections by Gram-positive bacteria has been accompanied by drug resistance and there are scattered reports that at least some of these strains emerged from farm animals [286].

There is a current interest in combining streptogramins with other agents, [287] such as vancomycin [288,289] and rifampin, [290] to extend their spectrum and minimize resistance emergence.

Resistance to streptogramins occurs by a variety of mechanisms [268,291,292]. These include efflux, chemical modification or ribosomal protection. Resistance can take place to either component and the combination has its own resistance mechanism [293,294].

The most important resistance mechanism against the streptogramins is enzymic degradation. Each component is targeted by distinct enzymes. Group A streptogramins are acetylated on their secondary hydroxyl moiety. A variety of acetylases have been isolated that catalyze this transformation [295,296]. Resistance to the group B streptogramins takes a rather different course. The macrolactone ring is opened by a retro-Michael type reaction involving β-elimination of the phenylglycyl ester moiety leaving behind a double bond (**90**) [297,298]. The enzymatic elimination is facilitated by enhanced polarization of the key bond through the participation of a key magnesium ion. Initially the responsible enzyme was thought to be a hydrolase but it is clear that it is more properly termed a ligase.

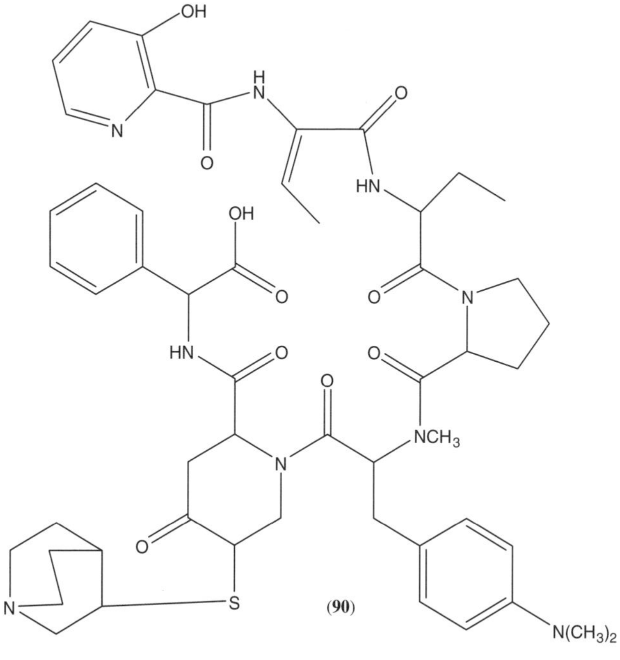

(90)

Efflux resistance can take place with either the A [299] or the B component. That involving the B component is not apparently clinically significant as yet [300,301]. Efflux proteins Vga, MrsA, and Lsa expel group A while MsrB expels group B.

Given the similarity of ribosomal binding site and mechanism, it is not surprising that self-methylation of A2058 of rRNA takes place and that this conveys resistance to group B streptogramin components. Streptogramins, however, do not induce the erm methylase and resistance by this mechanism does not inactivate the mixture as the group A component is not inhibited by this process [302].

A number of point mutations in the rRNA also convey degrees of resistance to streptogramins [301]. A mutation in ribosomal protein L22 has also been observed in drug resistant *S. pneumoniae* [303].

Side effects associated with the use of quinupristin/dalfopristin include anemia, reversible reticulocytopenia, [304] epidermal necrolysis (Lyell's syndrome), [305] and muscle and joint pain [306].

Search for newer members of this antibiotic class has resulted in study of NXL103 [307–313]. This orally active agent is effective against *H. influenzae, Streptococcus influenzae,* and *M. catarrhalis,* frequently associated with community-acquired pneumonia. NXL103 is a 70:30 combination of an A and a B streptogramin type component (**91** and **92**).

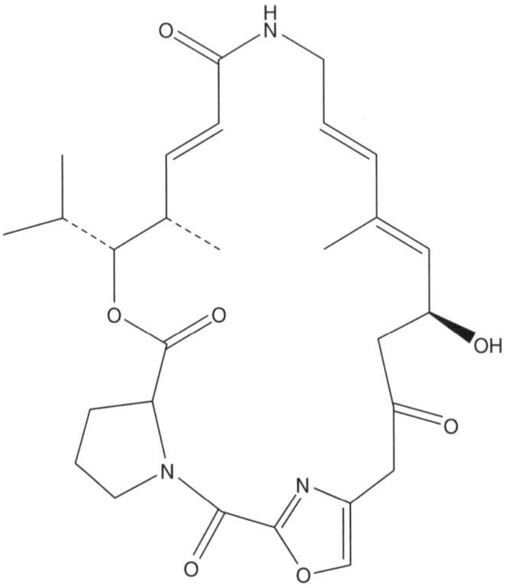

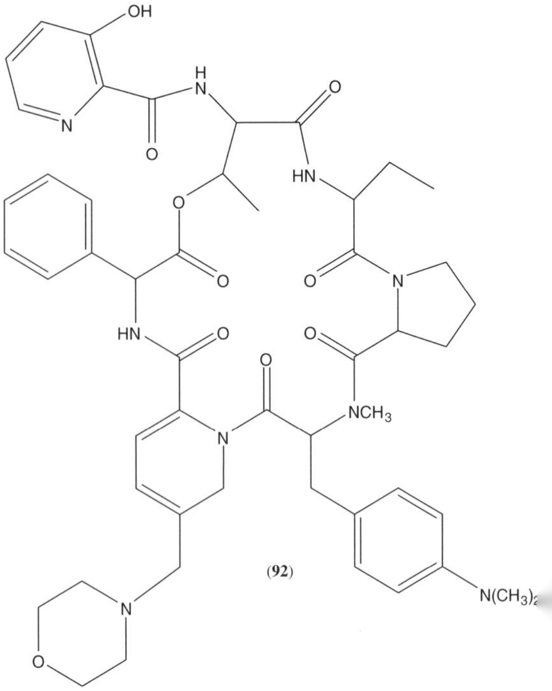

(92)

(91)

5.2. Lincosamides

Lincomycin (**93**) was discovered in 1962 as a fermentation product of *Streptomyces lincolnensis* [314]. Lincomycin consists of a methylthio ether of an amino octose in which the amino group is amidated by a *trans N*-methyl-4-*n*-propylproline moiety. Analoging converted lincomycin into its epichloro analog by an S_N2 reaction. The product, clindamycin (**94**), is better absorbed and more potent than lincomycin and has been much more successful clinically. In addition to the hydrochloride salt, clindamycin is also available in the form of its prodrug C-3-*O*-phosphate ester. This last is specially suited for injection following which it is rapidly cleaved back to clindamycin by alkaline phosphatase. These drugs are used to treat Gram-positive infections and some anaerobic infections (*Bacteroides, Clostridium* but not *C. difficile*). *C. difficile* is an opportunistic gut dwelling anaerobe that proliferates when the normal flora is suppressed. This leads to pseudo-membranous colitis and a life-threatening diarrhea. This condition was originally recog-nized with clindamycin treatment but is now recognized to be a potential problem with a wide variety of antibiotic agents.

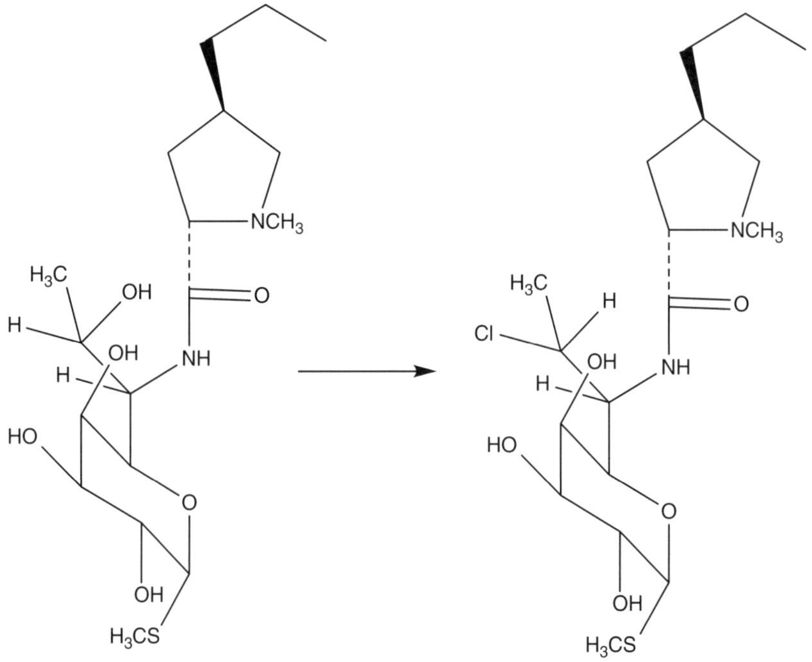

(93)   (94)

The molecular mode of action of the linco-samides is interference with programmed protein biosynthesis following their binding to the peptidyl escape tunnel in the 50S ri-bosomal subparticle. The binding site on 23S rRNA (95) overlaps with that for the macro-lides and chloramphenicol resulting in exten-sive cross-resistance to these otherwise structurally different antibiotic classes. The binding interactions are through hydrogen bonds to specific RNA bases and have been elucidated by X-ray crystal studies [4,315]. It is clear, therefore that a significant mode of resistance to the lincosamides is by mono and di self-methylation of A2058. Resistance can also occur by point mutations at A2058 and A2059 as these are important hydrogen bond-ing partners [316–319]. Resistance has also been noted to take place by O-phosphoryla-tion or adenylation at either the C-3 or the C-4 hydroxyl groups. The C-7 substituent plays a role in this in that some enzymes preferen-tially modify the hydroxyl at C-3 in lincomy-cin while modifying the C-4 hydroxyl in clin-damycin [320–323].

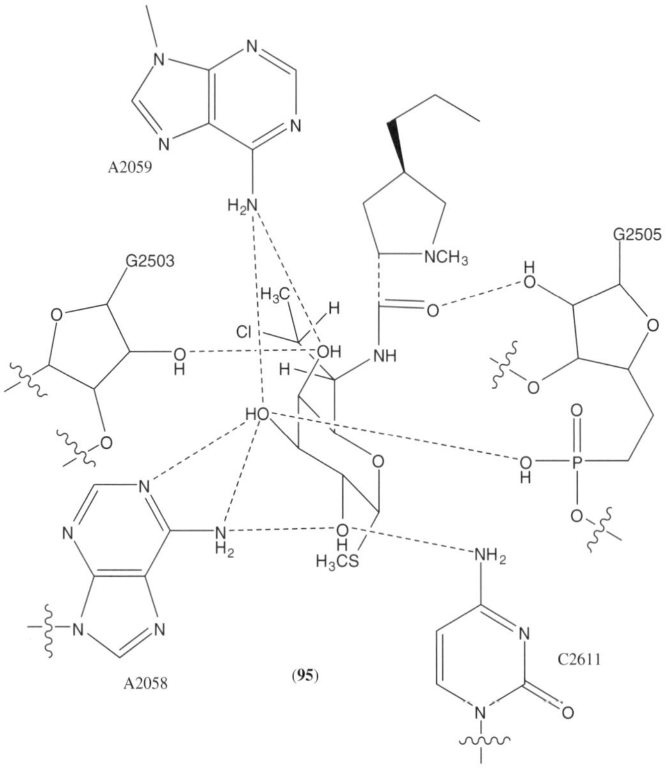

(95)

The modified proline residue of lincomycin is derived biosynthetically from tyrosine [324,325] whereas the octose descends from glucose-1-phosphate and may go through nucleoside sugars [326].

Celesticetin (96) is another member of the lincosaminide family that has not found clinical favor. It differs from lincomycin in its more complex substitution at the anomeric center, lack of the N-propyl group in the prolyl residue, and in etherification of the C-7 hydroxyl [327].

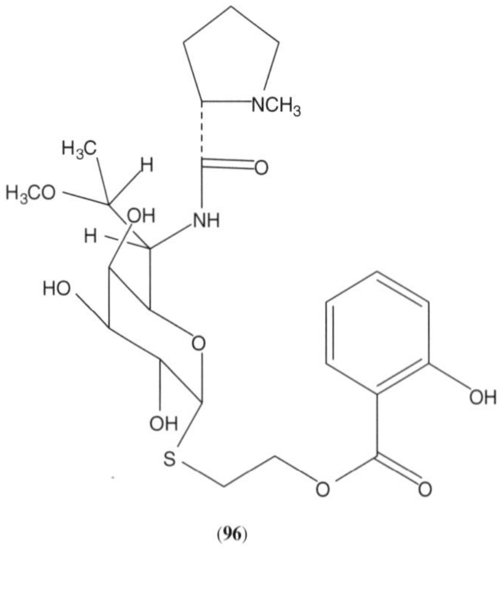

(96)

5.3. Chloramphenicol

Chloramphenicol (97) owns pride of place in being the first orally active broad-spectrum antibiotic introduced in the clinic (1947) [328]. Initially prepared by fermentation of *Streptomyces venezuelae*, because of the comparative simplicity of its structure, chloramphenicol was rapidly synthesized and, following removal of the three less active diastereoisomers, has been commercialized by this route ever since. It is also available in the form of palmitate and succinate prodrug esters. Unfortunate toxicity has limited chloramphenicol's use. This is fortunately rare but involves a risk of fatal irreversible aplastic anemia that occurs regardless of the dose or means of administration [329–335]. In addition, newborn infants have yet to develop efficient drug metabolizing machinery consequently great care must be utilized in treatment to present accumulation of this lipophilic drug. Accumulation to toxic levels can readily lead to the gray-baby syndrome that is characterized by an ashen pallor, vomiting, refusal of food, distended abdomen, and can lead to rapid death [336,337]. Bone marrow suppression leading to anemia, on the other hand, is more common than aplastic anemia and is dose related. It can be controlled or prevented by monitoring the blood levels of chloramphenicol and blood counts [328,338]. Despite these limiting toxicities, chloramphenicol is a valuable drug for the treatment of typhoid fever (*Salmonella typhi*) and is an alternative in the treatment of bacterial meningitis (*H. influenzae*, *S. pneumoniae*, or *Neisseria meningitidis*) when other safer drugs are contraindicated. Use in meningitis is a consequence also of its ease of penetration through the blood–brain barrier.

Since aromatic nitro group containing molecules often undergo metabolism to metabolites that are toxic to bone marrow, it has often been surmised that the hemotoxic characteristics of chloramphenicol are due to the presence of that functional group. Consequently a number of alternate *para*-substituents have been exchanged for the nitro moiety. Thiamphenicol and fluorphenicol are examples [339–343].

Whereas antibiotic activity was preserved, animal data suggests that these agents are also unsafe.

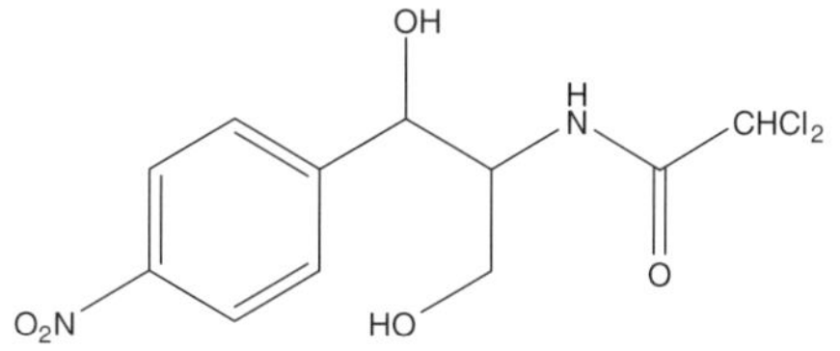

(**97**)

Chloramphenicol is bactericidal following binding in a rRNA site that overlaps with that for macrolides, lincosamides, and streptogramins with which it is cross-resistant. An X-ray crystal determination has revealed the details of chloramphenicol's interactions with rRNA [1,4,344,345]. As with tetracyclines, a magnesium ion is involved in this network of interactions (**98**).

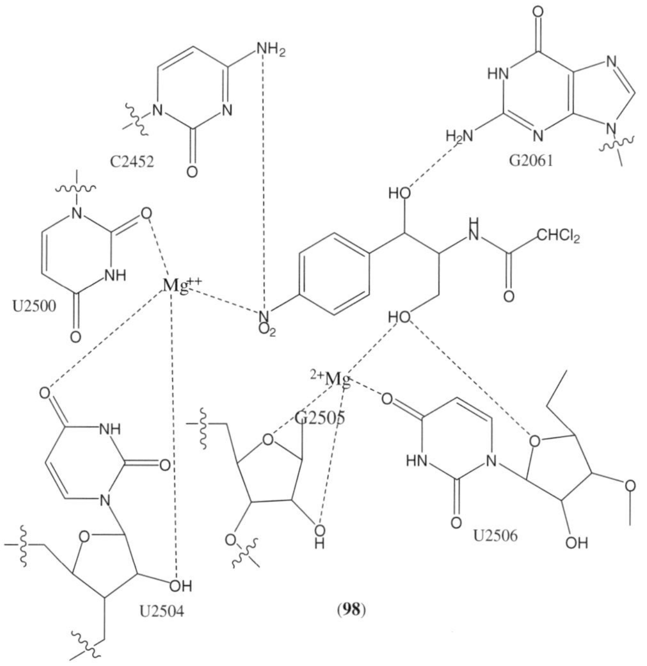

(**98**)

Bacterial resistance to chloramphenicol generally occurs by enzymatic acetylation of the primary hydroxyl group [346–348]. Other modes of chloramphenicol resistance

have also been noted. These include the usual suspects: mutations in 23S rRNA, [349,350] altered permeability, [351] and efflux [352].

5.4. Fusidic Acid

Fusidic acid (**99**) is a steroidal antibiotic produced by fermentation of *Fusidium coccineum*. Its clinical utility is largely restricted to topical ophthalmic and wound infections caused by Gram-positive pathogens such as staphylocci and streptococci. Fusidic acid does not penetrate significantly into Gram-negative bacteria.

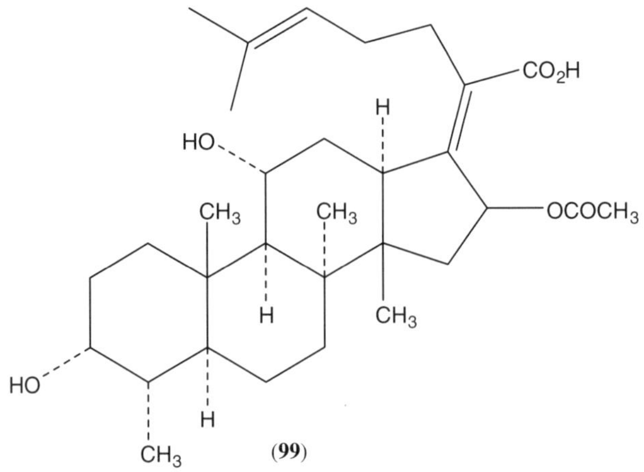

(**99**)

The BC and CD ring juncture geometries differ from that of common mammalian sterols and this altered conformation is likely to be significant in the antibiosis of fusidic acid.

The mechanism of action of fusidic acid is to bind to elongation factor EF-G following GTP hydrolysis [353–357]. The hydrolysis leads to a dramatic conformational shift of EF-G whereupon fusidic acid binds thus stabilizing this altered conformation. The consequence is that EF-G does not dissociate from the ribosome and protein biosynthesis is inhibited.

Resistance to fusidic acid is largely due to mutations in EF-G decreasing affinity for fusidic acid [358–364]. There are indications that binding to chloramphenicol acetyltransferase also plays a role in fusidic acid resistance [363,365,366].

Structurally related fungal sterol antibiotics include helvolic acid [367–372] and cephalosporin P1. Neither of these agents has caught on in therapy.

5.5. Oxazolidinones

The oxazolidinone anti-infective agents are represented by linezolid (**100**). This agent was developed following up on a lead uncovered while exploring the antiweed potential of a series of synthetic agents. Linezolid is bacteriostatic as a consequence of binding to the P-site of 50S ribosomal subparticles. This interferes with binding of initiator fMet-tRNA preventing the formation of a functional initiation complex [373,374]. Strictly speaking, however, linezolid is not an antibiotic so is more properly covered elsewhere.

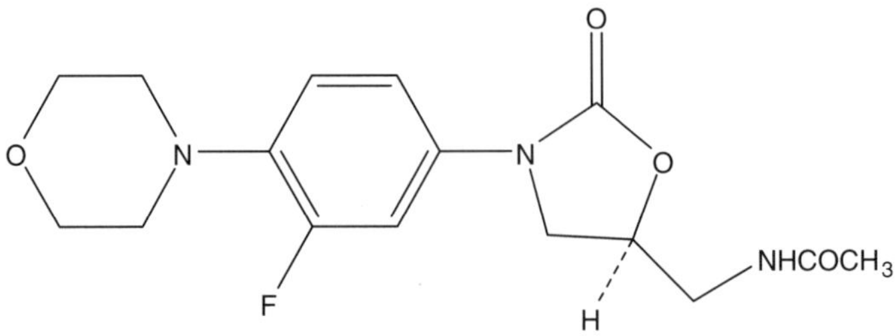

(**100**)

REFERENCES

1. Hansen JL, Moore PB, Steitz TA. Structures of five antibiotics bound at the peptidyltransferase center of the large ribosomal subunit. J Mol Biol. 2003;330(5):1061–1075.

2. Hansen JL, Ippolito JA, Ban N, Nissen P, Moore PB, Steitz TA. The structures of four macrolide antibiotics bound to the large ribosomal subunit. Mol Cell 2002;10(1):117–128.

3. Ban N, Nissen P, Hansen J, Moore PB, Steitz TA. The complete atomic structure of the large ribosomal subunit at 2.4 A resolution. Science 2000;289(5481):905–920.

4. Schlunzen F, Zarivach R, Harms J, Bashan A, Tocilj A, Albrecht R, Yonath A, Franceschi F. Structural basis for the interaction of antibiotics with the peptidyltransferase centre in eubacteria. Nature 2001;413(6858):814–821.

5. Harms JM, Schlunzen F, Fucini P, Bartels H, Yonath A. Alterations at the peptidyltransferase centre of the ribosome induced by the synergistic action of the streptogramins dalfopristin and quinupristin. BMC Biol 2004;2:4.

6. Tocilj A, Schlunzen F, Janell D, Gluhmann M, Hansen HA, Harms J, Bashan A, Bartels H, Agmon I, Franceschi F, Yonath A. The small ribosomal subunit from *Thermus thermophilus* at 4.5 A resolution: pattern fittings and the identification of a functional site. Proc Natl Acad Sci USA 1999;96(25):14252–14257.

7. Brodersen DE, Clemons WM, Jr, Carter AP, Morgan-Warren RJ, Wimberly BT, Ramakrishnan V. The structural basis for the action of the antibiotics tetracycline, pactamycin, and hygromycin B on the 30S ribosomal subunit. Cell 2000;103(7):1143–1154.

8. Anokhina MM, Barta A, Nierhaus KH, Spiridonova VA, Kopylov AM. Mapping of the second tetracycline binding site on the ribosomal small subunit of *E. coli*. Nucleic Acids Res 2004;32(8):2594–2597.

9. Pioletti M, Schlunzen F, Harms J, Zarivach R, Gluhmann M, Avila H, Bashan A, Bartels H, Auerbach T, Jacobi C, Hartsch T, Yonath A, Franceschi F. Crystal structures of complexes of the small ribosomal subunit with tetracycline, edeine and IF3. EMBO J 2001;20(8):1829–1839.

10. Heffron SE, Mui S, Aorora A, Abel K, Bergmann E, Jurnak F. Molecular complementarity between tetracycline and the GTPase active site of elongation factor Tu. Acta Crystallogr D Biol Crystallogr 2006;62(Pt 11):1392–1400.

11. Olson MW, Ruzin A, Feyfant E, Rush TS, 3rd O'Connell J, Bradford PA. Functional, biophysical, and structural bases for antibacterial activity of tigecycline. Antimicrob Agents Chemother 2006;50(6):2156–2166.

12. Bauer G, Berens C, Projan SJ, Hillen W. Comparison of tetracycline and tigecycline binding to ribosomes mapped by dimethylsulphate and drug-directed Fe^{2+} cleavage of 16S rRNA. J Antimicrob Chemother 2004;53(4):592–599.

13. Zhanel GG, Homenuik K, Nichol K, Noreddin A, Vercaigne L, Embil J, Gin A, Karlowsky JA, Hoban DJ. The glycylcyclines: a comparative review with the tetracyclines. Drugs 2004;64(1):63–88.

14. Nakano T, Miyake K, Endo H, Dairi T, Mizukami T, Katsumata R. Identification and cloning of the gene involved in the final step of chlortetracycline biosynthesis in *Streptomyces aureofaciens*. Biosci Biotechnol Biochem 2004;68(6):1345–1352.

15. Dairi T, Nakano T, Mizukami T, Aisaka K, Hasegawa M, Katsumata R. Conserved organization of genes for biosynthesis of chlortetracycline in Streptomyces strains. Biosci Biotechnol Biochem 1995;59(7):1360–1361.

16. Dairi T, Nakano T, Aisaka K, Katsumata R, Hasegawa M. Cloning and nucleotide sequence of the gene responsible for chlorination of tetracycline. Biosci Biotechnol Biochem 1995;59(6):1099–1106.

17. Binnie C, Warren M, Butler MJ. Cloning and heterologous expression in *Streptomyces lividans* of *Streptomyces rimosus* genes involved in oxytetracycline biosynthesis. J Bacteriol 1989;171(2):887–895.

18. Mitscher LA, Martin JH, Miller PA, Shu P, Bohonos N. 5-Hydroxy-7-chlortetracycline. J Am Chem Soc 1966;88:3647–3648.

19. Devasthale PV, Mitscher LA, Telikepalli H, Vander Velde D, Zou JY, Ax HA, Tymiak AA. Dactylocyclines, novel tetracycline derivatives produced by a *Dactylosporangium* sp. III. Absolute stereochemistry of the dactylocyclines. J Antibiot 1992;45(12):1907–1913.

20. Tymiak AA, Ax HA, Bolgar MS, Kahle AD, Porubcan MA, Andersen NH. Dactylocyclines, novel tetracycline derivatives produced by a Dactylosporangium sp. II. Structure elucidation. J Antibiot 1992;45(12):1899–1906.

21. Wells JS, O'Sullivan J, Aklonis C, Ax HA, Tymiak AA, Kirsch DR, Trejo WH, Principe P. Dactylocyclines, novel tetracycline derivatives produced by a Dactylosporangium sp. I.

Taxonomy, production, isolation and biological activity. J Antibiot 1992;45(12):1892–1898.

22. Mitscher LA, Swayze JK, Hogberg T, Khanna I, Rao GS, Theriault RJ, Kohl W, Hanson C, Egan R. Biosynthesis of cetocycline. J Antibiot 1983;36(10):1405–1407.

23. Mitscher LA, Juvarkar JV, Rosenbrook W, Jr, Andres WW, Schenk J, Egan RS. Structure of chelocardin, a novel tetracycline antibiotic. J Am Chem Soc 1970;92(20):6070–6071.

24. Mitscher LA, Rosenbrook W, Jr, Andres WW, Egan RS, Schenck J, Juvarkar JV. Structure of chelocardin, a novel tetracycline antibiotic. Antimicrob Agents Chemother 1970;10: 38–41.

25. van Hoek AH, Mayrhofer S, Domig KJ, Florez AB, Ammor MS, Mayo B, Aarts HJ. Mosaic tetracycline resistance genes and their flanking regions in *Bifidobacterium thermophilum* and *Lactobacillus johnsonii*. Antimicrob Agents Chemother 2008;52(1):248–252.

26. Patterson AJ, Rincon MT, Flint HJ, Scott KP. Mosaic tetracycline resistance genes are widespread in human and animal fecal samples. Antimicrob Agents Chemother 2007;51(3): 1115–1118.

27. Jones CH, Tuckman M, Howe AY, Orlowski M, Mullen S, Chan K, Bradford PA. Diagnostic PCR analysis of the occurrence of methicillin and tetracycline resistance genes among *Staphylococcus aureus* isolates from phase 3 clinical trials of tigecycline for complicated skin and skin structure infections. Antimicrob Agents Chemother 2006;50(2):505–510.

28. Roberts MC. Update on acquired tetracycline resistance genes. FEMS Microbiol Lett 2005;245(2):195–203.

29. Poole K. Efflux-mediated antimicrobial resistance. J Antimicrob Chemother 2005;56 (1):20–51.

30. Aminov RI, Garrigues-Jeanjean N, Mackie RI. Molecular ecology of tetracycline resistance: development and validation of primers for detection of tetracycline resistance genes encoding ribosomal protection proteins. Appl Environ Microbiol 2001;67 (1):22–32.

31. Roberts MC. Tetracycline resistance determinants: mechanisms of action, regulation of expression, genetic mobility, and distribution. FEMS Microbiol Rev 1996;19(1):1–24.

32. Schnappinger D, Hillen W. Tetracyclines: antibiotic action, uptake, and resistance mechanisms. Arch Microbiol 1996;165(6):359–369.

33. Paulsen IT, Brown MH, Skurray RA. Proton-dependent multidrug efflux systems. Microbiol Rev 1996;60(4):575–608.

34. Guillaume G, Ledent V, Moens W, Collard JM. Phylogeny of efflux-mediated tetracycline resistance genes and related proteins revisited. Microb Drug Resist 2004;10(1):11–26.

35. Borbone S, Lupo A, Mezzatesta ML, Campanile F, Santagati M, Stefani S. Evaluation of the *in vitro* activity of tigecycline against multiresistant Gram-positive cocci containing tetracycline resistance determinants. Int J Antimicrob Agents 2008;31(3):209–215.

36. Tuckman M, Petersen PJ, Howe AY, Orlowski M, Mullen S, Chan K, Bradford PA, Jones CH. Occurrence of tetracycline resistance genes among *Escherichia coli* isolates from the phase 3 clinical trials for tigecycline. Antimicrob Agents Chemother 2007;51(9):3205–3211.

37. Sapunaric FM, Levy SB. Substitutions in the interdomain loop of the Tn10 TetA efflux transporter alter tetracycline resistance and substrate specificity. Microbiology 2005;151(Pt 7):2315–2322.

38. Lanig H, Othersen OG, Seidel U, Beierlein FR, Exner TE, Clark T. Structural changes and binding characteristics of the tetracycline-repressor binding site on induction. J Med Chem 2006;49(12):3444–3447.

39. Hinrichs W, Kisker C, Duvel M, Muller A, Tovar K, Hillen W, Saenger W. Structure of the Tet repressor-tetracycline complex and regulation of antibiotic resistance. Science 1994;264(5157):418–420.

40. Izdebski R, Sadowy E, Fiett J, Grzesiowski P, Gniadkowski M, Hryniewicz W. Clonal diversity and resistance mechanisms in tetracycline-nonsusceptible *Streptococcus pneumoniae* isolates in Poland. Antimicrob Agents Chemother 2007;51(4):1155–1163.

41. Jones CH, Tuckman M, Murphy E, Bradford PA. Identification and sequence of a tet(M) tetracycline resistance determinant homologue in clinical isolates of *Escherichia coli*. J Bacteriol 2006;188(20):7151–7164.

42. Felmingham D. Tigecyclin--the first glycylcycline to undergo clinical development: an overview of *in vitro* activity compared to tetracycline. J Chemother 2005;17(Suppl 1):5–11.

43. Barden TC, Buckwalter BL, Testa RT, Petersen PJ, Lee VJ. "Glycylcyclines". 3. 9-Aminodoxycyclinecarboxamides. J Med Chem 1994; 37(20):3205–3211.

44. Sum PE, Lee VJ, Testa RT, Hlavka JJ, Ellestad GA, Bloom JD, Gluzman Y, Tally FP.

Glycylcyclines. 1. A new generation of potent antibacterial agents through modification of 9-aminotetracyclines. J Med Chem 1994;37(1): 184–188.

45. Nelson ML, Park BH, Levy SB. Molecular requirements for the inhibition of the tetracycline antiport protein and the effect of potent inhibitors on the growth of tetracycline-resistant bacteria. J Med Chem 1994;37(9): 1355–1361.

46. Brehm-Stecher BF, Johnson EA. Sensitization of *Staphylococcus aureus* and *Escherichia coli* to antibiotics by the sesquiterpenoids nerolidol, farnesol, bisabolol, and apritone. Antimicrob Agents Chemother 2003;47(10):3357–3360.

47. Sudano Roccaro A, Blanco AR, Giuliano F, Rusciano D, Enea V. Epigallocatechin-gallate enhances the activity of tetracycline in staphylococci by inhibiting its efflux from bacterial cells. Antimicrob Agents Chemother 2004;48 (6):1968–1973.

48. Pillai SP, Pillai CA, Shankel DM, Mitscher LA. The ability of certain antimutagenic agents to prevent development of antibiotic resistance. Mutat Res 2001;496(1–2):61–73.

49. Dahl EL, Shock JL, Shenai BR, Gut J, DeRisi JL, Rosenthal PJ. Tetracyclines specifically target the apicoplast of the malaria parasite *Plasmodium falciparum*. Antimicrob Agents Chemother 2006;50(9):3124–3131.

50. Dahl EL, Rosenthal PJ. Multiple antibiotics exert delayed effects against the Plasmodium falciparum apicoplast. Antimicrob Agents Chemother 2007;51(10):3485–3490.

51. Sapadin AN, Fleischmajer R. Tetracyclines: nonantibiotic properties and their clinical implications. J Am Acad Dermatol 2006;54(2): 258–265.

52. Sorsa T, Ramamurthy NS, Vernillo AT, Zhang X, Konttinen YT, Rifkin BR, Golub LM. Functional sites of chemically modified tetracyclines: inhibition of the oxidative activation of human neutrophil and chicken osteoclast pro-matrix metalloproteinases. J Rheumatol 1998; 25(5):975–982.

53. Lokeshwar BL, Selzer MG, Zhu BQ, Block NL, Golub LM. Inhibition of cell proliferation, invasion, tumor growth and metastasis by an oral non-antimicrobial tetracycline analog (COL-3) in a metastatic prostate cancer model. Int J Cancer 2002;98(2):297–309.

54. Syed S, Takimoto C, Hidalgo M, Rizzo J, Kuhn JG, Hammond LA, Schwartz G, Tolcher A, Patnaik A, Eckhardt SG, Rowinsky EK. A phase I and pharmacokinetic study of Col-3 (Metastat), an oral tetracycline derivative with potent matrix metalloproteinase and antitumor properties. Clin Cancer Res 2004;10 (19):6512–6521.

55. Liu Y, Ryan ME, Lee HM, Simon S, Tortora G, Lauzon C, Leung MK, Golub LM. A chemically modified tetracycline (CMT-3) is a new antifungal agent. Antimicrob Agents Chemother 2002;46(5):1447–1454.

56. Hunter CL, Bachman D, Granholm AC. Minocycline prevents cholinergic loss in a mouse model of Down's syndrome. Ann Neurol 2004;56(5):675–688.

57. Hunter CL, Quintero EM, Gilstrap L, Bhat NR, Granholm AC. Minocycline protects basal forebrain cholinergic neurons from mu p75-saporin immunotoxic lesioning. Eur J Neurosci 2004;19(12):3305–3316.

58. Zernicke RF, Wohl GR, Greenwald RA, Moak SA, Leng W, Golub LM. Administration of systemic matrix metalloproteinase inhibitors maintains bone mechanical integrity in adjuvant arthritis. J Rheumatol 1997;24(7): 1324–1331.

59. Diguet E, Gross CE, Tison F, Bezard E. Rise and fall of minocycline in neuroprotection: need to promote publication of negative results. Exp Neurol 2004;189(1):1–4.

60. Maitra SR, Bhaduri S, Chen E, Shapiro MJ. Role of chemically modified tetracycline on TNF-alpha and mitogen-activated protein kinases in sepsis. Shock 2004;22 (5):478–481.

61. Alexander AM, Gonda I, Harpur ES, Kayes JB. Interaction of aminoglycoside antibiotics with phospholipid liposomes studies by microelectrophoresis. J Antibiot 1979;32(5):504–510.

62. Schacht J, Lodhi S, Weiner ND. Effects of neomycin on polyphosphoinositides in inner ear tissues and monomolecular films. Adv Exp Med Biol 1977;84:191–208.

63. Ali BH. Gentamicin nephrotoxicity in humans and animals: some recent research. Gen Pharmacol 1995;26(7):1477–1487.

64. Seemungal BM, Bronstein AM. Aminoglycoside ototoxicity: vestibular function is also vulnerable. BMJ 2007;335(7627):952.

65. Bitner-Glindzicz M, Rahman S. Ototoxicity caused by aminoglycosides. BMJ 2007;335 (7624):784–785.

66. Rizzi MD, Hirose K. Aminoglycoside ototoxicity. Curr Opin Otolaryngol Head Neck Surg 2007;15(5):352–357.

67. Rybak LP, Ramkumar V. Ototoxicity. Kidney Int 2007;72(8):931–935.

68. Drusano GL, Ambrose PG, Bhavnani SM, Bertino JS, Nafziger AN, Louie A. Back to the future: using aminoglycosides again and how to dose them optimally. Clin Infect Dis 2007;45 (6):753–760.

69. Martinez-Salgado C, Lopez-Hernandez FJ, Lopez-Novoa JM. Glomerular nephrotoxicity of aminoglycosides. Toxicol Appl Pharmacol 2007;223(1):86–98.

70. Nagai J. Molecular mechanisms underlying renal accumulation of aminoglycoside antibiotics and mechanism-based approach for developing nonnephrotoxic aminoglycoside therapy. Yakugaku Zasshi 2006;126(5):327–335.

71. Nagai J, Takano M. Molecular aspects of renal handling of aminoglycosides and strategies for preventing the nephrotoxicity. Drug Metab Pharmacokinet 2004;19(3):159–170.

72. Mingeot-Leclercq MP, Tulkens PM. Aminoglycosides: nephrotoxicity. Antimicrob Agents Chemother 1999;43(5):1003–1012.

73. Manian FA, Stone WJ, Alford RH. Adverse antibiotic effects associated with renal insufficiency. Rev Infect Dis 1990;12(2):236–249.

74. Coleman JW, Yao FY, Jalandoni SR, Artusio JF, McGovern JH. Neomycin-induced neuromuscular blockade. Urology 1981;17(3):265–267.

75. Barrons RW. Drug-induced neuromuscular blockade and myasthenia gravis. Pharmacotherapy 1997;17(6):1220–1232.

76. Crann SA, Schacht J. Activation of aminoglycoside antibiotics to cytotoxins. Audiol Neurootol 1996;1(2):80–85.

77. Moazed D, Noller HF. Interaction of antibiotics with functional sites in 16S ribosomal RNA. Nature 1987;327(6121):389–394.

78. Hermann T, Westhof E. Docking of cationic antibiotics to negatively charged pockets in RNA folds. J Med Chem 1999;42(7): 1250–1261.

79. Leclerc D, Melancon P, Brakier-Gingras L. Mutations in the 915 region of *Escherichia coli* 16S ribosomal RNA reduce the binding of streptomycin to the ribosome. Nucleic Acids Res 1991;19(14):3973–3977.

80. Woodcock J, Moazed D, Cannon M, Davies J, Noller HF. Interaction of antibiotics with A- and P-site-specific bases in 16S ribosomal RNA. EMBO J 1991;10(10):3099–3103.

81. Foster C, Champney WS. Characterization of a 30S ribosomal subunit assembly intermediate found in *Escherichia coli* cells growing with neomycin or paromomycin. Arch Microbiol 2008;189(5):441–449.

82. Yang G, Trylska J, Tor Y, McCammon JA. Binding of aminoglycosidic antibiotics to the oligonucleotide A-site model and 30S ribosomal subunit: Poisson–Boltzmann model, thermal denaturation, and fluorescence studies. J Med Chem 2006;49(18): 5478–5490.

83. Kondo J, Francois B, Russell RJ, Murray JB, Westhof E. Crystal structure of the bacterial ribosomal decoding site complexed with amikacin containing the gamma-amino-alpha-hydroxybutyryl (haba) group. Biochimie 2006;88 (8):1027–1031.

84. Hobbie SN, Pfister P, Bruell C, Sander P, Francois B, Westhof E, Bottger EC. Binding of neomycin-class aminoglycoside antibiotics to mutant ribosomes with alterations in the A site of 16S rRNA. Antimicrob Agents Chemother 2006;50(4):1489–1496.

85. Francois B, Russell RJ, Murray JB, Aboul-ela F, Masquida B, Vicens Q, Westhof E. Crystal structures of complexes between aminoglycosides and decoding A site oligonucleotides: role of the number of rings and positive charges in the specific binding leading to miscoding. Nucleic Acids Res 2005;33(17):5677–5690.

86. Magnet S, Blanchard JS. Molecular insights into aminoglycoside action and resistance. Chem Rev 2005;105(2):477–498.

87. Vicens Q, Westhof E. RNA as a drug target: the case of aminoglycosides. ChemBioChem 2003;4(10):1018–1023.

88. Lynch SR, Gonzalez RL, Puglisi JD. Comparison of X-ray crystal structure of the 30S subunit–antibiotic complex with NMR structure of decoding site oligonucleotide–paromomycin complex. Structure 2003;11(1):43–53.

89. Vicens Q, Westhof E. Crystal structure of a complex between the aminoglycoside tobramycin and an oligonucleotide containing the ribosomal decoding a site. Chem Biol 2002;9(6): 747–755.

90. Vicens Q, Westhof E. Crystal structure of paromomycin docked into the eubacterial ribosomal decoding A site. Structure 2001;9(8): 647–658.

91. Ogle JM, Brodersen DE, Clemons WM, Jr, Tarry MJ, Carter AP, Ramakrishnan V. Recognition of cognate transfer RNA by the 30S ribosomal subunit. Science 2001;292(5518): 897–902.

92. Carter AP, Clemons WM, Brodersen DE, Morgan-Warren RJ, Wimberly BT, Ramakrishnan V. Functional insights from the structure of the 30S ribosomal subunit and its interactions

with antibiotics. Nature 2000;407(6802): 340–348.

93. Ogle JM, Ramakrishnan V. Structural insights into translational fidelity. Annu Rev Biochem 2005;74:129–177.

94. Lim VI, Curran JF. Analysis of codon:anticodon interactions within the ribosome provides new insights into codon reading and the genetic code structure. RNA 2001;7 (7):942–957.

95. Sanbonmatsu KY, Joseph S, Tung CS. Simulating movement of tRNA into the ribosome during decoding. Proc Natl Acad Sci USA 2005;102(44):15854–15859.

96. Meroueh SO, Mobashery S. Conformational transition in the aminoacyl t-RNA site of the bacterial ribosome both in the presence and absence of an aminoglycoside antibiotic. Chem Biol Drug Des 2007;69(5):291–297.

97. Taber HW, Mueller JP, Miller PF, Arrow AS. Bacterial uptake of aminoglycoside antibiotics. Microbiol Rev 1987;51(4):439–457.

98. Gilman S, Saunders VA. Uptake of gentamicin by *Staphylococcus aureus* possessing gentamicin-modifying enzymes: enhancement of uptake by puromycin and *N,N'*-dicyclohexylcarbodiimide. J Antimicrob Chemother 1986;18 (3):301–306.

99. Gilman S, Saunders VA. Accumulation of gentamicin by *Staphylococcus aureus*: the role of the transmembrane electrical potential. J Antimicrob Chemother 1986;17(1):37–44.

100. Davis BD. Mechanism of bactericidal action of aminoglycosides. Microbiol Rev 1987;51 (3):341–350.

101. Tanaka N, Matsunaga K, Yamaki H, Nishimura T. Inhibition of initiation of DNA synthesis by aminoglycoside antibiotics. Biochem Biophys Res Commun 1984;122(1):460–465.

102. Kondo J, Hainrichson M, Nudelman I, Shallom-Shezifi D, Barbieri CM, Pilch DS, Westhof E, Baasov T. Differential selectivity of natural and synthetic aminoglycosides towards the eukaryotic and prokaryotic decoding A sites. ChemBioChem 2007;8(14):1700–1709.

103. Westhof E. Molecular recognition between the ribosomal decoding site and natural or nonnatural aminoglycosides. Nucleic Acids Symp Ser (Oxf) (49): 2005; 59–60.

104. Hobbie SN, Pfister P, Brull C, Westhof E, Bottger EC. Analysis of the contribution of individual substituents in 4,6-aminoglycoside–ribosome interaction. Antimicrob Agents Chemother 2005;49(12):5112–5118.

105. Vicens Q, Westhof E. Molecular recognition of aminoglycoside antibiotics by ribosomal RNA and resistance enzymes: an analysis of X-ray crystal structures. Biopolymers 2003;70 (1):42–57.

106. Russell RJ, Murray JB, Lentzen G, Haddad J, Mobashery S. The complex of a designer antibiotic with a model aminoacyl site of the 30S ribosomal subunit revealed by X-ray crystallography. J Am Chem Soc 2003;125(12): 3410–3411.

107. Davies C, Bussiere DE, Golden BL, Porter SJ, Ramakrishnan V, White SW. Ribosomal proteins S5 and L6: high-resolution crystal structures and roles in protein synthesis and antibiotic resistance. J Mol Biol 1998;279(4): 873–888.

108. Borovinskaya MA, Shoji S, Holton JM, Fredrick K, Cate JH. A steric block in translation caused by the antibiotic spectinomycin. ACS Chem Biol 2007;2(8):545–552.

109. Flatt PM, Mahmud T. Biosynthesis of aminocyclitol-aminoglycoside antibiotics and related compounds. Nat Prod Rep 2007;24(2): 358–392.

110. Walker JB. Enzymatic synthesis of aminocyclitol moieties of aminoglycoside antibiotics from inositol by *Streptomyces* spp.: detection of glutamine-aminocyclitol aminotransferase and diaminocyclitol aminotransferase activities in a spectinomycin producer. J Bacteriol 1995;177(3):818–822.

111. Kniep B, Grisebach H. Biosynthesis of streptomycin. Purification and properties of a dTDP-L-dihydrostreptose: streptidine-6-phosphate dihydrostreptosyltransferase from *Streptomyces griseus*. Eur J Biochem 1980; 105(1):139–144.

112. Walker JB, Skorvaga M. Streptomycin biosynthesis and metabolism. Phosphate transfer from dihydrostreptomycin 6-phosphate to inosamines, streptamine, and 2-deoxystreptamine. J Biol Chem 1973;248(7):2441–2446.

113. Walker MS, Walker JB. Enzymic studies on the biosynthesis of streptomycin. Transamidination of inosamine and streptamine derivatives. J Biol Chem 1966;241(6):1262–1270.

114. Nango E, Kumasaka T, Hirayama T, Tanaka N, Eguchi T. Structure of 2-deoxy-scyllo-inosose synthase, a key enzyme in the biosynthesis of 2-deoxystreptamine-containing aminoglycoside antibiotics, in complex with a mechanism-based inhibitor and NAD$^+$. Proteins 2008;70(2):517–527.

115. Kogure T, Wakisaka N, Takaku H, Takagi M. Efficient production of 2-deoxy-scyllo-inosose

from D-glucose by metabolically engineered recombinant *Escherichia coli*. J Biotechnol 2007;129(3):502–509.

116. Llewellyn NM, Spencer JB. Biosynthesis of 2-deoxystreptamine-containing aminoglycoside antibiotics. Nat Prod Rep 2006;23(6):864–874.

117. Kudo F, Yamamoto Y, Yokoyama K, Eguchi T, Kakinuma K. Biosynthesis of 2-deoxystreptamine by three crucial enzymes in *Streptomyces fradiae* NBRC 12773. J Antibiot 2005;58 (12):766–774.

118. Busscher GF, Rutjes FP, van Delft FL. 2-Deoxystreptamine: central scaffold of aminoglycoside antibiotics. Chem Rev 2005;105(3): 775–791.

119. Huang F, Haydock SF, Mironenko T, Spiteller D, Li Y, Spencer JB. The neomycin biosynthetic gene cluster of *Streptomyces fradiae* NCIMB 8233: characterisation of an aminotransferase involved in the formation of 2-deoxystreptamine. Org Biomol Chem 2005;3 (8):1410–1418.

120. Kharel MK, Basnet DB, Lee HC, Liou K, Woo JS, Kim BG, Sohng JK. Isolation and characterization of the tobramycin biosynthetic gene cluster from *Streptomyces tenebrarius*. FEMS Microbiol Lett 2004;230(2):185–190.

121. Huang F, Li Y, Yu J, Spencer JB. Biosynthesis of aminoglycoside antibiotics: cloning, expression and characterisation of an aminotransferase involved in the pathway to 2-deoxystreptamine. Chem Commun 2002; (23):2860–2861.

122. Kudo F, Hosomi Y, Tamegai H, Kakinuma K. Purification and characterization of 2-deoxyscyllo-inosose synthase derived from *Bacillus circulans*. A crucial carbocyclization enzyme in the biosynthesis of 2-deoxystreptamine-containing aminoglycoside antibiotics. J Antibiot 1999;52(2):81–88.

123. Iwase N, Kudo F, Yamauchi N, Kakinuma K. Substrate specificity of 2-deoxy-scyllo-inosose synthase, the starter enzyme for 2-deoxystreptamine biosynthesis, toward deoxyglucose-6-phosphates and proposed mechanism. Biosci Biotechnol Biochem 1998;62(12):2396–2407.

124. Yamauchi N, Kakinuma K. Biochemical studies on 2-deoxy-scyllo-inosose, an early intermediate in the biosynthesis of 2-deoxystreptamine. IV. A clue to the similarity of 2-deoxyscyllo-inosose synthase to dehydroquinate synthase. J Antibiot 1993;46(12):1916–1918.

125. Goda SK, Akhtar M. Neomycin biosynthesis: the incorporation of D-6-deoxy-glucose derivatives and variously labelled glucose into the 2-deoxystreptamine ring. Postulated involve-ment of 2-deoxyinosose synthase in the biosynthesis. J Antibiot 1992;45(6):984–994.

126. Kakinuma K, Ogawa Y, Sasaki T, Seto H, Otake N. Mechanism and stereochemistry of the biosynthesis of 2-deoxystreptamine and neosamine C. J Antibiot 1989;42(6):926–933.

127. Suzukake K, Tokunaga K, Hayashi H, Hori M, Uehara Y, Ikeda D, Umezawa H. Biosynthesis of 2-deoxystreptamine. J Antibiot 1985;38 (9):1211–1218.

128. Fujiwara T, Kondo E. Biosynthetic pathway of 2-deoxystreptamine. J Antibiot 1981;34(1): 13–15.

129. Mansouri K, Piepersberg W. Genetics of streptomycin production in *Streptomyces griseus*: nucleotide sequence of five genes, strFGHIK, including a phosphatase gene. Mol Gen Genet 1991;228(3):459–469.

130. Jana S, Deb JK. Molecular targets for design of novel inhibitors to circumvent aminoglycoside resistance. Curr Drug Targets 2005;6(3): 353–361.

131. Doi Y, Adams JM, Yamane K, Paterson DL. Identification of 16S rRNA methylase-producing *Acinetobacter baumannii* clinical strains in North America. Antimicrob Agents Chemother 2007;51(11):4209–4210.

132. Doi Y, Arakawa Y. 16S ribosomal RNA methylation: emerging resistance mechanism against aminoglycosides. Clin Infect Dis 2007;45 (1):88–94.

133. Aires JR, Nikaido H. Aminoglycosides are captured from both periplasm and cytoplasm by the AcrD multidrug efflux transporter of *Escherichia coli*. J Bacteriol 2005;187(6): 1923–1929.

134. Westbrock-Wadman S, Sherman DR, Hickey MJ, Coulter SN, Zhu YQ, Warrener P, Nguyen LY, Shawar RM, Folger KR, Stover CK. Characterization of a *Pseudomonas aeruginosa* efflux pump contributing to aminoglycoside impermeability. Antimicrob Agents Chemother 1999;43(12):2975–2983.

135. Aires JR, Kohler T, Nikaido H, Plesiat P. Involvement of an active efflux system in the natural resistance of *Pseudomonas aeruginosa* to aminoglycosides. Antimicrob Agents Chemother 1999;43(11):2624–2628.

136. Poole K. Bacterial multidrug efflux pumps serve other functions. Microbe 2008;3: 179–185.

137. Meier A, Kirschner P, Bange FC, Vogel U, Bottger EC. Genetic alterations in streptomycin-resistant *Mycobacterium tuberculosis*: mapping of mutations conferring resistance.

Antimicrob Agents Chemother 1994;38(2): 228–233.

138. Tracevska T, Jansone I, Nodieva A, Marga O, Skenders G, Baumanis V. Characterisation of rpsL, rrs and embB mutations associated with streptomycin and ethambutol resistance in *Mycobacterium tuberculosis*. Res Microbiol 2004;155(10):830–834.

139. Fukuda M, Koga H, Ohno H, Yang B, Hirakata Y, Maesaki S, Tomono K, Tashiro T, Kohno S. Relationship between genetic alteration of the rpsL gene and streptomycin susceptibility of *Mycobacterium tuberculosis* in Japan. J Antimicrob Chemother 1999;43(2):281–284.

140. Doi Y, Yokoyama K, Yamane K, Wachino J, Shibata N, Yagi T, Shibayama K, Kato H, Arakawa Y. Plasmid-mediated 16S rRNA methylase in *Serratia marcescens* conferring high-level resistance to aminoglycosides. Antimicrob Agents Chemother 2004;48(2): 491–496.

141. Wachino J, Shibayama K, Kurokawa H, Kimura K, Yamane K, Suzuki S, Shibata N, Ike Y, Arakawa Y. Novel plasmid-mediated 16S rRNA m1A1408 methyltransferase, NpmA, found in a clinically isolated *Escherichia coli* strain resistant to structurally diverse aminoglycosides. Antimicrob Agents Chemother 2007;51(12):4401–4409.

142. Perichon B, Courvalin P, Galimand M. Transferable resistance to aminoglycosides by methylation of G1405 in 16S rRNA and to hydrophilic fluoroquinolones by QepA-mediated efflux in *Escherichia coli*. Antimicrob Agents Chemother 2007;51(7):2464–2469.

143. Shaw KJ, Rather PN, Hare RS, Miller GH. Molecular genetics of aminoglycoside resistance genes and familial relationships of the aminoglycoside-modifying enzymes. Microbiol Rev 1993;57(1):138–163.

144. Kim C, Mobashery S. Phosphoryl transfer by aminoglycoside 3'-phosphotransferases and manifestation of antibiotic resistance. Bioorg Chem 2005;33(3):149–158.

145. Badarau A, Shi Q, Chow JW, Zajicek J, Mobashery S, Vakulenko S. Aminoglycoside 2''-phosphotransferase type IIIa from *Enterococcus*. J Biol Chem 2008;283:7638–7647.

146. Popovic B, Tang X, Chirgadze DY, Huang F, Blundell TL, Spencer JB. Crystal structures of the PLP- and PMP-bound forms of BtrR, a dual functional aminotransferase involved in butirosin biosynthesis. Proteins 2006;65(1): 220–230.

147. Burk DL, Hon WC, Leung AK, Berghuis AM. Structural analyses of nucleotide binding to an aminoglycoside phosphotransferase. Biochemistry 2001;40(30):8756–8764.

148. Kim C, Cha JY, Yan H, Vakulenko SB, Mobashery S. Hydrolysis of ATP by aminoglycoside 3'-phosphotransferases: an unexpected cost to bacteria for harboring an antibiotic resistance enzyme. J Biol Chem 2006;281 (11):6964–6969.

149. Benning MM, Kuo JM, Raushel FM, Holden HM. Three-dimensional structure of phosphotriesterase: an enzyme capable of detoxifying organophosphate nerve agents. Biochemistry 1994;33(50):15001–15007.

150. Benning MM, Kuo JM, Raushel FM, Holden HM. Three-dimensional structure of the binuclear metal center of phosphotriesterase. Biochemistry 1995;34(25):7973–7978.

151. Pedersen LC, Benning MM, Holden HM. Structural investigation of the antibiotic and ATP-binding sites in kanamycin nucleotidyltransferase. Biochemistry 1995;34(41): 13305–13311.

152. Raussens V, Narayanaswami V, Goormaghtigh E, Ryan RO, Ruysschaert JM. Alignment of the apolipophorin-III alpha-helices in complex with dimyristoylphosphatidylcholine. A unique spatial orientation. J Biol Chem 1995;270(21):12542–12547.

153. Wybenga-Groot LE, Draker K, Wright GD, Berghuis AM. Crystal structure of an aminoglycoside 6'-*N*-acetyltransferase: defining the GCN5-related *N*-acetyltransferase superfamily fold. Structure 1999;7(5):497–507.

154. Wolf E, Vassilev A, Makino Y, Sali A, Nakatani Y, Burley SK. Crystal structure of a GCN5-related *N*-acetyltransferase: *Serratia marcescens* aminoglycoside 3-*N*-acetyltransferase. Cell 1998;94(4):439–449.

155. Llano-Sotelo B, Azucena EF, Jr, Kotra LP, Mobashery S, Chow CS. Aminoglycosides modified by resistance enzymes display diminished binding to the bacterial ribosomal aminoacyl-tRNA site. Chem Biol 2002;9(4): 455–463.

156. Greenberg WA, Priestley ES, Sears PS, Alper PB, Rosenbohm C, Hendrix M, Hung SC, Wong C-H. Design and synthesis of new aminoglycoside antibiotics containing neamine as an optimal core structure: correlation of antibiotic acitivity with *in vitro* inhibition of translation. *J Am Chem Soc.* 1999;121:6527–6541.

157. Hendrix MA, Alper PB, Priestley ES, Wong C-H. Hydroxyamines as a new motif for the molecular recognition of phosphodiesters: implications for aminoglycoside RNA interactions. Angew Chem Int Ed 1997;36:95–98.

158. Zhou J, Wang G, Zhang LH, Ye XS. Modifications of aminoglycoside antibiotics targeting RNA. Med Res Rev 2007;27(3):279–316.

159. Kim C, Haddad J, Vakulenko SB, Meroueh SO, Wu Y, Yan H, Mobashery S. Fluorinated aminoglycosides and their mechanistic implication for aminoglycoside 3′-phosphotransferases from Gram-negative bacteria. Biochemistry 2004;43(9):2373–2383.

160. Roestamadji J, Grapsas I, Mobashery S. Mechanism-based inactivation of bacterial aminoglycoside 3′-phosphotransferases. J Am Chem Soc 1995;117:80–84.

161. Haddad J, Vakulenko S, Mobashery S. An antibiotic cloaked by its own resistance enzyme. J Am Chem Soc 1999;121:11922–11923.

162. Sucheck SJ, Wong AL, Koeller KM, Boehr DD, Draker K-A, Sears P, Wright GD, Wong C-H. Design of bifunctional antibiotics that target bacterial rRNA and Inhibit resistance-causing enzymes. J Am Chem Soc 2000;122: 5230–5231.

163. Kling D, Hesek D, Shi Q, Mobashery S. Design and synthesis of a structurally constrained aminoglycoside. J Org Chem 2007;72(14): 5450–5453.

164. Barbieri CM, Kaul M, Bozza-Hingos M, Zhao F, Tor Y, Hermann T, Pilch DS. Defining the molecular forces that determine the impact of neomycin on bacterial protein synthesis: importance of the 2′-amino functionality. Antimicrob Agents Chemother 2007;51(5): 1760–1769.

165. Hanessian S, Szychowski J, Adhikari SS, Vasquez G, Kandasamy P, Swayze EE, Migawa MT, Ranken R, Francois B, Wirmer-Bartoschek J, Kondo J, Westhof E. Structure-based design, synthesis, and A-site rRNA co-crystal complexes of functionally novel aminoglycoside antibiotics: C2″ ether analogues of paromomycin. J Med Chem 2007;50(10): 2352–2369.

166. Kudyba I, Fernandez DP, Bottger EC, Vasella A. Synthesis of paromomycin derivatives modified at C(5″) to selectively target bacterial rRNA. Carbohydr Res 2007;342(3–4):499–519.

167. Bernacchi S, Freisz S, Maechling C, Spiess B, Marquet R, Dumas P, Ennifar E. Aminoglycoside binding to the HIV-1 RNA dimerization initiation site: thermodynamics and effect on the kissing-loop to duplex conversion. Nucleic Acids Res 2007;35(21):7128–7139.

168. Kirsebom LA, Virtanen A, Mikkelsen NE. Aminoglycoside interactions with RNAs and nucleases. Handbook Exp Pharmacol 2006; (173):73–96.

169. Riguet E, Desire J, Boden O, Ludwig V, Gobel M, Bailly C, Decout JL. Neamine dimers targeting the HIV-1 TAR RNA. Bioorg Med Chem Lett 2005;15(21):4651–4655.

170. Hammerschlag MR, Sharma R. Use of cethromycin, a new ketolide, for treatment of community-acquired respiratory infections. Exp Opin Investig Drugs 2008;17(3):387–400.

171. Shlaes DM, Moellering RC. Telithromycin and the FDA: implications for the future. Lancet Infect Dis 2008;8(2):83–85.

172. Nattel S, Ranger S, Talajic M, Lemery R, Roy D. Erythromycin-induced long QT syndrome: concordance with quinidine and underlying cellular electrophysiologic mechanism. Am J Med 1990;89(2):235–238.

173. Owens RC, Jr, Nolin TD. Antimicrobial-associated QT interval prolongation: pointes of interest. Clin Infect Dis 2006;43(12): 1603–1611.

174. Kawamura O, Sekiguchi T, Itoh Z, Omura S. Effect of erythromycin derivative EM523L on human interdigestive gastrointestinal tract. Dig Dis Sci 1993;38(6):1026–1031.

175. Kawamura O, Sekiguchi T, Kusano M, Nishioka T, Itoh Z. Effect of erythromycin on interdigestive gastrointestinal contractile activity and plasma motilin concentration in humans. Dig Dis Sci 1993;38(5):870–876.

176. Ohtawa M, Mizumoto A, Hayashi N, Yanagida K, Itoh Z, Omura S. Mechanism of gastroprokinetic effect of EM523, an erythromycin derivative, in dogs. Gastroenterology 1993;104 (5):1320–1327.

177. Omura S, Inatomi N, Itoh Z. Motilide, motilin-like macrolides. Tanpakushitsu Kakusan Koso 1993;38(11):1881–1890.

178. Xu L, Depoortere I, Vertongen P, Waelbroeck M, Robberecht P, Peeters TL. Motilin and erythromycin-A share a common binding site in the third transmembrane segment of the motilin receptor. Biochem Pharmacol 2005;70 (6):879–887.

179. Berisio R, Harms J, Schluenzen F, Zarivach R, Hansen HA, Fucini P, Yonath A. Structural insight into the antibiotic action of telithromycin against resistant mutants. J Bacteriol 2003;185(14):4276–4279.

180. Woodward RB. The structure and biogenesis of the macrolides, a new class of natural products. Angew Chem 1957;69:50–58.

181. Katz L, Ashley GW. Translation and protein synthesis: macrolides. Chem Rev 2005;105 (2):499–528.

182. Celmer WD. Stereochemical problems in macrolide antibiotics. Pure Appl Chem 1971; 28(4):413–453.

183. Celmer WD. Biogenetic, constitutional, and stereochemical unitary principles in macrolide antibiotics. Antimicrob Agents Chemother 1965;5:144–156.

184. Djokic S, Kobrehel G, Lopotar N, Kamenar B, Nagl A, Mrvos D Erythromycin series. Part 13. Synthesis and structure elucidation of 10-dihydro-10-deoxo-11-methyl-11-azaerythromycin A. J Chem Res (S) 1988; 152–153.

185. Barber J. Assignments of the carbon and proton NMR spectra of azithromycin in deuterochloroform. Magn Reson Chem 1991;29: 740–743.

186. Haight TH, Finland M. Resistance of bacteria to erythromycin. Proc Soc Exp Biol Med 1952;81(1):183–188.

187. Webb V, Davies J. Accidental release of antibiotic-resistance genes. Trends Biotechnol 1994;12(3):74–75.

188. Webb V, Davies J. Antibiotic preparations contain DNA: a source of drug resistance genes? Antimicrob Agents Chemother 1993;37 (11):2379–2384.

189. Davies J. Inactivation of antibiotics and the dissemination of resistance genes. Science 1994;264(5157):375–382.

190. Skinner R, Cundliffe E, Schmidt FJ. Site of action of a ribosomal RNA methylase responsible for resistance to erythromycin and other antibiotics. J Biol Chem 1983;258(20): 12702–12706.

191. Davydova N, Streltsov V, Wilce M, Liljas A, Garber M. L22 ribosomal protein and effect of its mutation on ribosome resistance to erythromycin. J Mol Biol 2002;322(3):635–644.

192. Zaman S, Fitzpatrick M, Lindahl L, Zengel J. Novel mutations in ribosomal proteins L4 and L22 that confer erythromycin resistance in Escherichia coli. Mol Microbiol 2007;66(4): 1039–1050.

193. Wolter N, Smith AM, Low DE, Klugman KP. High-level telithromycin resistance in a clinical isolate of Streptococcus pneumoniae. Antimicrob Agents Chemother 2007;51(3): 1092–1095.

194. Tsagkalia A, Leontiadou F, Xaplanteri MA, Papadopoulos G, Kalpaxis DL, Choli-Papadopoulou T. Ribosomes containing mutants of L4 ribosomal protein from Thermus thermophilus display multiple defects in ribosomal functions and sensitivity against erythromycin. RNA 2005;11(11):1633–1639.

195. Hisanaga T, Hoban DJ, Zhanel GG. Mechanisms of resistance to telithromycin in Streptococcus pneumoniae. J Antimicrob Chemother 2005;56(3):447–450.

196. Arthur M, Autissier D, Courvalin P. Analysis of the nucleotide sequence of the ereB gene encoding the erythromycin esterase type II. Nucleic Acids Res 1986;14(12):4987–4999.

197. Matsuoka M, Sasaki T. Inactivation of macrolides by producers and pathogens. Curr Drug Targets Infect Disord 2004;4 (3):217–240.

198. Noguchi N, Takada K, Katayama J, Emura A, Sasatsu M. Regulation of transcription of the mph(A) gene for macrolide 2'-phosphotransferase I in Escherichia coli: characterization of the regulatory gene mphR(A). J Bacteriol 2000;182(18):5052–5058.

199. Chesneau O, Tsvetkova K, Courvalin P. Resistance phenotypes conferred by macrolide phosphotransferases. FEMS Microbiol Lett 2007;269(2):317–322.

200. Bolam DN, Roberts S, Proctor MR, Turkenburg JP, Dodson EJ, Martinez-Fleites C, Yang M, Davis BG, Davies GJ, Gilbert HJ. The crystal structure of two macrolide glycosyltransferases provides a blueprint for host cell antibiotic immunity. Proc Natl Acad Sci USA 2007;104(13):5336–5341.

201. Yazawa K, Mikami Y, Sakamoto T, Ueno Y, Morisaki N, Iwasaki S, Furihata K. Inactivation of the macrolide antibiotics erythromycin, midecamycin, and rokitamycin by pathogenic Nocardia species. Antimicrob Agents Chemother 1994;38(9):2197–2199.

202. Cundliffe E. Glycosylation of macrolide antibiotics in extracts of Streptomyces lividans. Antimicrob Agents Chemother 1992;36(2): 348–352.

203. Vilches C, Hernandez C, Mendez C, Salas JA. Role of glycosylation and deglycosylation in biosynthesis of and resistance to oleandomycin in the producer organism, Streptomyces antibioticus. J Bacteriol 1992;174(1):161–165.

204. Quiros LM, Aguirrezabalaga I, Olano C, Mendez C, Salas JA. Two glycosyltransferases and a glycosidase are involved in oleandomycin modification during its biosynthesis by Streptomyces antibioticus. Mol Microbiol 1998;28 (6):1177–1185.

205. Wang Y, Pfeifer BA. 6-Deoxyerythronolide B production through chromosomal localization of the deoxyerythronolide B synthase genes in E. coli. Metab Eng 2008;10(1):33–38.

206. Katz L, Khosla C. Antibiotic production from the ground up. Nat Biotechnol 2007;25(4): 428–429.

207. Ward SL, Desai RP, Hu Z, Gramajo H, Katz L. Precursor-directed biosynthesis of 6-deoxyer-ythronolide B analogues is improved by removal of the initial catalytic sites of the polyketide synthase. J Ind Microbiol Biotechnol 2007;34(1):9–15.

208. Katz L, McDaniel R. Novel macrolides through genetic engineering. Med Res Rev 1999;19 (6):543–558.

209. Stassi DL, Kakavas SJ, Reynolds KA, Gunawardana G, Swanson S, Zeidner D, Jackson M, Liu H, Buko A, Katz L. Ethyl-substituted erythromycin derivatives produced by directed metabolic engineering. Proc Natl Acad Sci USA 1998;95(13):7305–7309.

210. Shaw SJ, Abbanat. D, Ashley. GW, Bush. K, Foleno B. Macielag M, Zhang, D, Miles DC. 15-Amidoerythromycins: Synthesis and in vitro activity of a new class of macrolide antibiotics. J. Antibiotics 2005; 58(3): 167–177.

211. Yang M, Proctor MR, Bolam DN, Errey JC, Field RA, Gilbert HJ, Davis BG. Probing the breadth of macrolide glycosyltransferases: in vitro remodeling of a polyketide antibiotic creates active bacterial uptake and enhances potency J Am Chem Soc 2005;127(26): 9336–9337.

212. Agouridas C, Denis A, Auger JM, Benedetti Y, Bonnefoy A, Bretin F, Chantot JF, Dussarat A, Fromentin C, D'Ambrieres SG, Lachaud S, Laurin P, Le Martret O, Loyau V, Tessot N. Synthesis and antibacterial activity of ketolides (6-O-methyl-3-oxoerythromycin derivatives): a new class of antibacterials highly potent against macrolide-resistant and -susceptible respiratory pathogens. J Med Chem 1998;41(21):4080–4100.

213. Fernandes PB, Baker WR, Freiberg LA, Hardy DJ, McDonald EJ. New macrolides active against Streptococcus pyogenes with inducible or constitutive type of macrolide-lincosamide-streptogramin B resistance. Antimicrob Agents Chemother 1989;33(1):78–81.

214. Denis A, Agouridas C, Auger JM, Benedetti Y, Bonnefoy A, Bretin F, Chantot JF, Dussarat A, Fromentin C, D'Ambrieres SG, Lachaud S, Laurin P, Le Martret O, Loyau V, Tessot N, Pejac JM, Perron S. Synthesis and antibacterial activity of HMR 3647 a new ketolide highly potent against erythromycin-resistant and susceptible pathogens. Bioorg Med Chem Lett 1999;9(21):3075–3080.

215. Onur O, Guneysel O, Denizbasi A, Celikel C. Acute hepatitis attack after exposure

to telithromycin. Clin Ther 2007;29 (8):1725–1729.

216. Bertino JS. Severe hepatotoxicity of telithromycin. Ann Intern Med 2006;145(6):472; author reply 472.

217. Barie PS. A fine pile of pate: the cautionary tale of telithromycin, hepatic failure, and study 3014. Surg Infect (Larchmt) 2006;7(3): 247–249.

218. Clay KD, Hanson JS, Pope SD, Rissmiller RW, Purdum PP, 3rd Banks PM. Brief communication: severe hepatotoxicity of telithromycin: three case reports and literature review. Ann Intern Med 2006;144(6):415–420.

219. Graham DJ. Telithromycin and acute liver failure. N Engl J Med 2006;355(21): 2260–2261.

220. Ross DB. The FDA and the case of Ketek. N Engl J Med 2007;356(16):1601–1604.

221. Soreth J, Cox E, Kweder S, Jenkins J, Galson S. Ketek—the FDA perspective. N Engl J Med 2007;356(16):1675–1676.

222. Dore DD, DiBello JR, Lapane KL. Telithromycin use and spontaneous reports of hepatotoxicity. Drug Saf 2007;30(8):697–703.

223. Mathews AW. Fraud, errors taint a key study of widely used Sanofi drug; despite some faked results, FDA approves antibiotic; one doctor's cocaine use; company defends safety. Wall St J (East Ed) 2006;A1:A12.

224. Young D. Limit Ketek to pneumonia, experts advise: advisers urge black-box warning. Am J Health Syst Pharm 2007;64(2):124–125.

225. Nenciu LM, Laberge P, Thirion DJ. Telithromycin-induced digoxin toxicity and electrocardiographic changes. Pharmacotherapy 2006; 26(6):872–876.

226. Wisialowski T, Crimin K, Engtrakul J, O'Donnell J, Fermini B, Fossa AA. Differentiation of arrhythmia risk of the antibacterials moxifloxacin, erythromycin, and telithromycin based on analysis of monophasic action potential duration alternans and cardiac instability. J Pharmacol Exp Ther 2006;318(1):352–359.

227. Ma Z, Clark RF, Brazzale A, Wang S, Rupp MJ, Li L, Griesgraber G, Zhang S, Yong H, Phan LT, Nemoto PA, Chu DT, Plattner JJ, Zhang X, Zhong P, Cao Z, Nilius AM, Shortridge VD, Flamm R, Mitten M, Meulbroek J, Ewing P, Alder J, Or YS. Novel erythromycin derivatives with aryl groups tethered to the C-6 position are potent protein synthesis inhibitors and active against multidrug-resistant respiratory pathogens. J Med Chem 2001;44 (24):4137–4156.

228. Tennakoon MA, Henninger TC, Abbanat D, Foleno BD, Hilliard JJ, Bush K, Macielag MJ. Synthesis and antibacterial activity of C6-carbazate ketolides. Bioorg Med Chem Lett 2006;16(24):6231–6235.

229. Andreotti D, Bientinesi I, Biondi S, Donati D, Erbetti I, Lociuro S, Marchioro C, Pozzan A, Ratti E, Terreni S. A novel ketolide class: synthesis and antibacterial activity of a lead compound. Bioorg Med Chem Lett 2007;17 (18):5265–5269.

230. Grant EB, Guiadeen D, Abbanat D, Foleno BD, Bush K, Macielag MJ. Synthesis and antibacterial activity of 6-O-heteroarylcarbamoyl-11,12-lactoketolides. Bioorg Med Chem Lett 2006;16(7):1929–1933.

231. Tanikawa T, Asaka T, Kashimura M, Misawa Y, Suzuki K, Sato M, Kameo K, Morimoto S, Nishida A. Synthesis and antibacterial activity of acylides (3-O-acyl-erythromycin derivatives): a novel class of macrolide antibiotics. J Med Chem 2001;44(24):4027–4030.

232. Tanikawa T, Asaka T, Kashimura M, Suzuki K, Sugiyama H, Sato M, Kameo K, Morimoto S, Nishida A. Synthesis and antibacterial activity of a novel series of acylides: 3-O-(3-pyridyl) acetylerythromycin A derivatives. J Med Chem 2003;46(13):2706–2715.

233. Zhu B, Marinelli BA, Abbanat D, Foleno BD, Henninger TC, Bush K, Macielag MJ. Synthesis and antibacterial activity of 3-O-acyl-6-O-carbamoyl erythromycin A derivatives. Bioorg Med Chem Lett 2006;16(4): 1054–1059.

234. Nomura T, Iwaki T, Narukawa Y, Uotani K, Hori T, Miwa H. A new type of ketolide bearing an N-aryl-alkyl acetamide moiety at the C-9 iminoether: synthesis and structure–activity relationships. Bioorg Med Chem 2006;14 (11):3697–3711.

235. Gunnes S, Undheim K. Chemoselective synthesis of erythromycin A ketolides substituted in the C10-methyl group. Bioorg Med Chem 2007;15(1):119–129.

236. Kaneko T, Romero K, Li B, Buzon R. Novel tethers in ketolide antibiotics. Bioorg Med Chem Lett 2007;17(18):5049–5053.

237. Kaneko T, McMillen W, Lynch MK. Synthesis and antibacterial activity of C11, C12-cyclic urea analogues of ketolides. Bioorg Med Chem Lett 2007;17(18):5013–5018.

238. Heggelund A, Undheim K. Preparation of cyclic 2′,3′-carbamate derivatives of erythromycin macrolide antibiotics. Bioorg Med Chem 2007;15(9):3266–3277.

239. Burger MT, Hiebert C, Seid M, Chu DT, Barker L, Langhorne M, Shawar R, Kidney J, Desai MC, Plattner JJ. Synthesis and antibacterial activity of novel C12 ethyl ketolides. Bioorg Med Chem 2006;14(16):5592–5604.

240. Burger MT, Lin X, Chu DT, Hiebert C, Rico AC, Seid M, Carroll GL, Barker L, Huh K, Langhorne M, Shawar R, Kidney J, Young K, Anderson S, Desai MC, Plattner JJ. Synthesis and antibacterial activity of novel C12 vinyl ketolides. J Med Chem 2006;49(5):1730–1743.

241. Elliott RL, Pireh D, Nilius AM, Johnson PM, Flamm RK, Chu DTW, Plattner JJ, Orr YS. Novel 3-desoxy-3-descladinosyl-6-O-methyl erythromycin A analogues. Synthesis and in vitro activity. Bioorg Med Chem Lett 1997;7:641–646.

242. Chu DT. Recent progress in novel macrolides, quinolones, and 2-pyridones to overcome bacterial resistance. Med Res Rev 1999;19 (6):497–520.

243. Elliott RL, Pireh D, Griesgraber G, Nilius AM, Ewing PJ, Bui MH, Raney PM, Flamm RK, Kim K, Henry RF, Chu DT, Plattner JJ, Or YS. Anhydrolide macrolides. 1. Synthesis and antibacterial activity of 2,3-anhydro-6-O-methyl 11,12-carbamate erythromycin A analogues. J Med Chem 1998;41(10):1651–1659.

244. Griesgraber G, Kramer MJ, Elliott RL, Nilius AM, Ewing PJ, Raney PM, Bui MH, Flamm RK, Chu DT, Plattner JJ, Or YS. Anhydrolide macrolides. 2. Synthesis and antibacterial activity of 2,3-anhydro-6-O-methyl 11,12-carbazate erythromycin A analogues. J Med Chem 1998;41(10):1660–1670.

245. Guitton M, Delachaume C, Le Priol P, Steier V, Bonnefoy A. In vitro and in vivo efficacy of a novel fluoro-ketolide HMR 3562 against enterococci. J Antimicrob Chemother 2001;48 (1):131–135.

246. Denis A, Bretin F, Fromentin C, Bonnet A, Piltan G, Bonnefoy A, Agouridas C. Beta-keto-ester chemistry and ketolides. Synthesis and antibacterial activity of 2-halogeno, 2-methyl and 2,3 enol-ether ketolides. Bioorg Med Chem Lett 2000;10(17):2019–2022.

247. Xu X, Henninger T, Abbanat D, Bush K, Foleno B, Hilliard J, Macielag M. Synthesis and antibacterial activity of C2-fluoro, C6-carbamate ketolides, and their C9-oximes. Bioorg Med Chem Lett 2005;15(4):883–887.

248. Abbanat D, Webb G, Foleno B, Li Y, Macielag M, Montenegro D, Wira E, Bush K. In vitro activities of novel 2-fluoro-naphthyridine-containing ketolides. Antimicrob Agents Chemother 2005;49(1):309–315.

249. Liang CH, Yao S, Chiu YH, Leung PY, Robert N, Seddon J, Sears P, Hwang CK, Ichikawa Y, Romero A. Synthesis and biological activity of new 5-O-sugar modified ketolide and 2-fluoroketolide antibiotics. Bioorg Med Chem Lett 2005;15(5):1307–1310.

250. Koga H, Sato T, Tsuzuki K, Onoda H, Kuboniwa H, Takanashi H. Potent, acid-stable and orally active macrolide-type motilin receptor agonists, GM-611 and the derivatives. Bioorg Med Chem Lett 1994;4:1347–1352.

251. Koga H, Takanashi H, Itoh Z, Omura S. Design, SAR and pharmacology of GM-611, the first acid-stabile non-peptide motilin receptor agonist. Drugs Future 2002;27:255–272.

252. Sudo H, Ozaki K, Muramatsu H, Kamei K, Yogo K, Cynshi O, Koga H, Itoh Z, Omura S, Takanashi H. Mitemcinal (GM-611), an orally active motilin agonist, facilitates defecation in rabbits and dogs without causing loose stools. Neurogastroenterol Motil 2007;19(4):318–326.

253. Onoma M, Yogo K, Ozaki K, Kamei K, Akima M, Koga H, Itoh Z, Omura S, Takanashi H. Oral mitemcinal (GM-611), an erythromycin-derived prokinetic, accelerates normal and experimentally delayed gastric emptying in conscious dogs. Clin Exp Pharmacol Physiol 2008;35(1):35–42.

254. Yogo K, Onoma M, Ozaki K, Koto M, Itoh Z, Omura S, Takanashi H. Effects of oral mitemcinal (GM-611), erythromycin, EM-574 and cisapride on gastric emptying in conscious Rhesus monkeys. Dig Dis Sci 2008;53(4):912–918.

255. McCallum RW, Cynshi O. Clinical trial: effect of mitemcinal (a motilin agonist) on gastric emptying in patients with gastroparesis—a randomized, multicentre, placebo-controlled study. Aliment Pharmacol Ther 2007;26(8): 1121–1130.

256. Peeters TL. GM-611 (Chugai Pharmaceutical). Curr Opin Investig Drugs 2001;2(4):555–557.

257. Zalewska-Kaszubska J, Gorska D. Anti-inflammatory capabilities of macrolides. Pharmacol Res 2001;44(6):451–454.

258. Lotter K, Hocherl K, Bucher M, Kees F. In vivo efficacy of telithromycin on cytokine and nitric oxide formation in lipopolysaccharide-induced acute systemic inflammation in mice. J Antimicrob Chemother 2006;58(3):615–621.

259. Leiva M, Ruiz-Bravo A, Moreno E, Jimenez-Valera M. The anti-inflammatory activity of telithromycin in a mouse model of septic shock. Int J Antimicrob Agents 2007;29(3):364–365.

260. Tsuda T, Ishikawa C, Konishi H, Hayashi Y, Nakagawa N, Matsuki M, Mizutani H, Yamanishi K. Effect of 14-membered-ring macrolides on production of interleukin-8 mediated by protease-activated receptor 2 in human keratinocytes. Antimicrob Agents Chemother 2008;52(4):1538–1541.

261. Huang BH, Wu CH, Hsia CP, Yin Chen C. Azithromycin-induced torsade de pointes. Pacing Clin Electrophysiol 2007;30(12): 1579–1582.

262. Kezerashvili A, Khattak H, Barsky A, Nazari R, Fisher JD. Azithromycin as a cause of QT-interval prolongation and torsade de pointes in the absence of other known precipitating factors. J Interv Card Electrophysiol 2007;18 (3):243–246.

263. Moreno A, Bello H, Guggiana D, Dominguez M, Gonzalez G. Extended-spectrum beta-lactamases belonging to CTX-M group produced by Escherichia coli strains isolated from companion animals treated with enrofloxacin. Vet Microbiol 2008;129(1–2):203–208.

264. Germanakis I, Galanakis E, Parthenakis F, Vardas PE, Kalmanti M. Clarithromycin treatment and QT prolongation in childhood. Acta Paediatr 2006;95(12):1694–1696.

265. Hanada E, Ohtani H, Hirota M, Uemura N, Nakaya H, Kotaki H, Sato H, Yamada Y, Iga T. Inhibitory effect of erythromycin on potassium currents in rat ventricular myocytes in comparison with disopyramide. J Pharm Pharmacol 2003;55(7):995–1002.

266. Iannini PB. Cardiotoxicity of macrolides, ketolides and fluoroquinolones that prolong the QTc interval. Expert Opin Drug Saf 2002;1 (2):121–128.

267. Curtis LH, Ostbye T, Sendersky V, Hutchison S, Allen LaPointe NM, Al-Khatib SM, Usdin Yasuda S, Dans PE, Wright A, Califf RM, Woosley RL, Schulman KA. Prescription of QT-prolonging drugs in a cohort of about 5 million outpatients. Am J Med 2003;114(2):135–141.

268. Mukhtar TA, Wright GD. Streptogramins, oxazolidinones, and other inhibitors of bacterial protein synthesis. Chem Rev 2005;105 (2):529–542.

269. Sander A, Beiderlinden M, Schmid EN, Peters J. Clinical experience with quinupristin-dalfopristin as rescue treatment of critically ill patients infected with methicillin-resistant staphylococci. Intensive Care Med 2002;28 (8):1157–1160.

270. Blondeau JM, Sanche SE. Quinupristin/dalfopristin. Exp Opin Pharmacother 2002;3 (9):1341–1364.

271. Kochetkova GV, Maksimova TS, Il'chenko GB, Ol'khovatova OL. Madumycin biosynthesis by

an actinomadure flava culture under conditions of varying aeration. Antibiotiki 1976;21 (4):296–298.

272. Ghosh AK, Liu W. A convergent, enantioselective total synthesis of streptogramin antibiotic (−)-madumycin II. J Org Chem 1997;62 (23):7908–7909.

273. Yates JD, Schaible PJ. Virginiamycin as an antibiotic for poultry feeds. Nature 1962; 194:183–184.

274. Mortensen MS, Osbourn JM, O'Doherty GA. De novo formal synthesis of (−)-virginiamycin M2 via the asymmetric hydration of dienoates. Org Lett 2007;9(16):3105–3108.

275. Garcia-Mendoza C. Studies on the mode of action of etamycin (viridogrisein). Biochim Biophys Acta 1965;97:394–396.

276. Callens RE, Anteunis MJ. Solution conformation of virginiamycin S. III. Patricin A: a further model for cooperative effects of the Pro ring conformation and backbone. Biochim Biophys Acta 1979;577(2):337–345.

277. Milewski S, Mignini F, Covelli I, Borowski E. Specific inhibition of acid proteinase secretion in Candida albicans by Lys-Nva-FMDP. J Med Vet Mycol 1994;32(1):1–11.

278. Bodanszky M, Ondetti MA. Structures of the vernamycin B group of antibiotics. Antimicrob Agents Chemother 1963;161:360–365.

279. Fuchs PC, Barry AL, Brown SD. In vitro bactericidal activity of daptomycin against staphylococci. J Antimicrob Chemother 2002;49 (3):467–470.

280. Cha R, Brown WJ, Rybak MJ. Bactericidal activities of daptomycin, quinupristin-dalfopristin, and linezolid against vancomycin-resistant Staphylococcus aureus in an in vitro pharmacodynamic model with simulated endocardial vegetations. Antimicrob Agents Chemother 2003;47(12):3960–3963.

281. Kieke AL, Borchardt MA, Kieke BA, Spencer SK, Vandermause MF, Smith KE, Jawahir SL, Belongia EA. Use of streptogramin growth promoters in poultry and isolation of streptogramin-resistant Enterococcus faecium from humans. J Infect Dis 2006;194(9):1200–1208.

282. Voegel LP. Path of drug resistance from farm to clinic. Science 2002;295(5555):625.

283. Pedersen KB. Some growth promoters in animals do confer antimicrobial resistance in humans. BMJ 1999;318(7190):1076.

284. Smith DL, Johnson JA, Harris AD, Furuno JP, Perencevich EN, Morris JG, Jr. Assessing risks for a pre-emergent pathogen: virginia-mycin use and the emergence of streptogramin resistance in Enterococcus faecium. Lancet Infect Dis 2003;3(4):241–249.

285. Cox LA, Jr, Popken DA. Quantifying human health risks from virginiamycin used in chickens. Risk Anal 2004;24(1):271–288.

286. Klare I, Konstabel C, Badstubner D, Werner G, Witte W. Occurrence and spread of antibiotic resistances in Enterococcus faecium. Int J Food Microbiol 2003;88(2–3):269–290.

287. Brown J, Freeman BB, 3rdA Combining quinupristin/dalfopristin with other agents for resistant infections Ann Pharmacother 2004; 38(4):677–685.

288. Scotton PG, Rigoli R, Vaglia A. Combination of quinupristin/dalfopristin and glycopeptide in severe methicillin-resistant staphylococcal infections failing previous glycopeptide regimens. Infection 2002;30(3):161–163.

289. Sgarabotto D, Cusinato R, Narne E, Scano F, Zignol M, Gambino A, Cattelan A, Meneghetti F, Cadrobbi P. Synercid plus vancomycin for the treatment of severe methicillin-resistant Staphylococcus aureus and coagulase-negative staphylococci infections: evaluation of 5 cases. Scand J Infect Dis 2002;34(2):122–126.

290. Saleh-Mghir A, Ameur N, Muller-Serieys C, Ismael F, Lemaitre F, Massias L, Feger C, Bleton R, Cremieux AC. Combination of quinupristin-dalfopristin (Synercid) and rifampin is highly synergistic in experimental Staphylococcus aureus joint prosthesis infection. Antimicrob Agents Chemother 2002;46(4):1122–1124.

291. Hershberger E, Oprea SF, Donabedian SM, Perri M, Bozigar P, Bartlett P, Zervos MJ. Epidemiology of antimicrobial resistance in enterococci of animal origin. J Antimicrob Chemother 2005;55(1):127–130.

292. Kehoe LE, Snidwongse J, Courvalin P, Rafferty JB, Murray IA. Structural basis of Synercid (quinupristin-dalfopristin) resistance in Gram-positive bacterial pathogens. J Biol Chem 2003;278(32):29963–29970.

293. El Solh N, Allignet J. Staphylococcal resistance to streptogramins and related antibiotics. Drug Resist Updat 1998;1(3):169–175.

294. Haroche J, Morvan A, Davi M, Allignet J, Bimet F, El Solh N. Clonal diversity among streptogramin A-resistant Staphylococcus aureus isolates collected in French hospitals. J Clin Microbiol 2003;41(2):586–591.

295. Sugantino M, Roderick SL. Crystal structure of Vat(D): an acetyltransferase that inactivates streptogramin group A antibiotics. Biochemistry 2002;41(7):2209–2216.

296. Rende-Fournier R, Leclercq R, Galimand M, Duval J, Courvalin P. Identification of the satA gene encoding a streptogramin A acetyltransferase in *Enterococcus faecium* BM4145. Antimicrob Agents Chemother 1993;37(10):2119–2125.

297. Mukhtar TA, Koteva KP, Hughes DW, Wright GD. Vgb from *Staphylococcus aureus* inactivates streptogramin B antibiotics by an elimination mechanism not hydrolysis. Biochemistry 2001;40(30):8877–8886.

298. Korczynska M, Mukhtar TA, Wright GD, Berghuis AM. Structural basis for streptogramin B resistance in *Staphylococcus aureus* by virginiamycin B lyase. Proc Natl Acad Sci USA 2007;104(25):10388–10393.

299. Haroche J, Allignet J, El Solh N. Tn5406, a new staphylococcal transposon conferring resistance to streptogramin a and related compounds including dalfopristin. Antimicrob Agents Chemother 2002;46(8):2337–2343.

300. Lee CK, Kamitani Y, Nihira T, Yamada Y. Identification and *in vivo* functional analysis of a virginiamycin S resistance gene (varS) from *Streptomyces virginiae*. J Bacteriol 1999;181(10):3293–3297.

301. Roberts MC. Update on macrolide-lincosamide-streptogramin, ketolide, and oxazolidinone resistance genes. FEMS Microbiol Lett 2008;282(2):147–159.

302. Schmitz FJ, Petridou J, Astfalk N, Kohrer K, Scheuring S, Schwarz S. Molecular analysis of constitutively expressed erm(C) genes selected *in vitro* by incubation in the presence of the noninducers quinupristin, telithromycin, or ABT-773. Microb Drug Resist 2002;8(3):171–177.

303. Cattoir V, Merabet L, Legrand P, Soussy CJ, Leclercq R. Emergence of a *Streptococcus pneumoniae* isolate resistant to streptogramins by mutation in ribosomal protein L22 during pristinamycin therapy of pneumococcal pneumonia. J Antimicrob Chemother 2007;59(5):1010–1012.

304. Evans PC, Almas JP, Criddle FJ, 3rd Anemia and reversible reticulocytopenia associated with extended quinupristin/dalfopristin. Ann Pharmacother 2004;38(4):720–721.

305. Chanques G, Girard C, Pinzani V, Jaber S. Fatal pristinamycin-induced toxic epidermal necrolysis (Lyell's syndrome): difficulties in attributing causal association in the polymedicated intensive care unit patient. Acta Anaesthesiol Scand 2005;49(5):721–722.

306. Gupte G, Jyothi S, Beath SV, Kelly DA. Quinupristin-dalfopristin use in children is associated with arthralgias and myalgias. Pediatr Infect Dis J 2006;25(3):281.

307. Dupuis M, Leclercq R. Activity of a new oral streptogramin, XRP2868, against Gram-positive cocci harboring various mechanisms of resistance to streptogramins. Antimicrob Agents Chemother 2006;50(1):237–242.

308. Eliopoulos GM, Ferraro MJ, Wennersten CB, Moellering RC, Jr. *In vitro* activity of an oral streptogramin antimicrobial, XRP2868, against gram-positive bacteria. Antimicrob Agents Chemother 2005;49(7):3034–3039.

309. Pankuch GA, Hoellman D, Bryskier A, Lowther J, Appelbaum PC. Effects of various media on the activity of NXL103 (formerly XRP 2868), a new oral streptogramin, against *Haemophilus influenzae*. Antimicrob Agents Chemother 2006;50(11):3914–3916.

310. Andes D, Craig WA. Pharmacodynamics of a new streptogramin, XRP 2868, in murine thigh and lung infection models. Antimicrob Agents Chemother 2006;50(1):243–249.

311. Mabe S, Champney WS. A comparison of a new oral streptogramin XRP 2868 with quinupristin-dalfopristin against antibiotic-resistant strains of *Haemophilus influenzae, Staphylococcus aureus,* and *Streptococcus pneumoniae.* Curr Microbiol 2005;51(6):363–366.

312. Goldstein EJ, Citron DM, Merriam CV, Warren YA, Tyrrell KL, Fernandez HT, Bryskier A. Comparative *in vitro* activities of XRP 2868, pristinamycin, quinupristin-dalfopristin, vancomycin, daptomycin, linezolid, clarithromycin, telithromycin, clindamycin, and ampicillin against anaerobic gram-positive species, actinomycetes, and lactobacilli. Antimicrob Agents Chemother 2005;49(1):408–413.

313. Pankuch GA, Kelly LM, Lin G, Bryskier A, Couturier C, Jacobs MR, Appelbaum PC. Activities of a new oral streptogramin, XRP 2868, compared to those of other agents against *Streptococcus pneumoniae* and *Haemophilus species*. Antimicrob Agents Chemother 2003;47(10):3270–3274.

314. Mason DJ, Dietz A, DeBoer C. Lincomycin, a new antibiotic. I. Discovery and biological properties. Antimicrobial Agents Chemother 1962;1962:554–559.

315. Schlunzen F, Pyetan E, Fucini P, Yonath A, Harms JM. Inhibition of peptide bond formation by pleuromutilins: the structure of the 50S ribosomal subunit from *Deinococcus radiodur-*

ans in complex with tiamulin. Mol Microbiol 2004;54(5):1287–1294.

316. Leclercq R, Courvalin P. Intrinsic and unusual resistance to macrolide, lincosamide, and streptogramin antibiotics in bacteria. Antimicrob Agents Chemother 1991;35(7): 1273–1276.

317. Tait-Kamradt A, Davies T, Cronan M, Jacobs MR, Appelbaum PC, Sutcliffe J. Mutations in 23S rRNA and ribosomal protein L4 account for resistance in pneumococcal strains selected *in vitro* by macrolide passage. Antimicrob Agents Chemother 2000;44 (8):2118–2125.

318. Wang G, Taylor DE. Site-specific mutations in the 23S rRNA gene of *Helicobacter pylori* confer two types of resistance to macrolide-lincosamide-streptogramin B antibiotics. Antimicrob Agents Chemother 1998;42(8):1952–1958.

319. Tu D, Blaha G, Moore PB, Steitz TA. Structures of MLSBK antibiotics bound to mutated large ribosomal subunits provide a structural explanation for resistance. Cell 2005;121 (2):257–270.

320. Bozdogan B, Berrezouga L, Kuo MS, Yurek DA, Farley KA, Stockman BJ, Leclercq R. A new resistance gene, linB, conferring resistance to lincosamides by nucleotidylation in *Enterococcus faecium* HM1025. Antimicrob Agents Chemother 1999;43(4):925–929.

321. Bozdogan B, Berrezouga L, Leclercq R. Resistance to lincosamides by nucleotidylation associated with conjugative transfer of a large chromosomal element in *Enterococcus faecium*. Adv Exp Med Biol 1997;418:491–493.

322. Marshall VP, Liggett WF, Cialdella JI. Enzymic inactivation of lincosaminide and macrolide antibiotics: divalent metal cation and coenzyme specificities. J Antibiot 1989;42(5):826–830.

323. Brisson-Noel A, Delrieu P, Samain D, Courvalin P. Inactivation of lincosaminide antibiotics in *Staphylococcus*. Identification of lincosaminide O-nucleotidyltransferases and comparison of the corresponding resistance genes. J Biol Chem 1988;263(31):15880–15887.

324. Neusser D, Schmidt H, Spizek J, Novotna J, Peschke U, Kaschabeck S, Tichy P, Piepersberg W. The genes lmbB1 and lmbB2 of *Streptomyces lincolnensis* encode enzymes involved in the conversion of L-tyrosine to propylproline during the biosynthesis of the antibiotic lincomycin A. Arch Microbiol 1998;169(4):322–332.

325. Witz DF, Hessler EJ, Miller TL. Bioconversion of tyrosine into the propylhygric acid moiety of lincomycin. Biochemistry 1971;10(7): 1128–1133.

326. Peschke U, Schmidt H, Zhang HZ, Piepersberg W. Molecular characterization of the lincomycin-production gene cluster of *Streptomyces lincolnensis* 78-11. Mol Microbiol 1995;16 (6):1137–1156.

327. Hoeksema H. Celesticetin. V. The structure of celesticetin. J Am Chem Soc 1968;90 (3):755–757.

328. Ehrlich J, Bartz QR, Smith RM, Joslyn DA, Burkholder PA. Chloromycetin, a new antibiotic from a soil actinomycete. Science 1947;106:417.

329. Feder HM, Jr. Chloramphenicol: what we have learned in the last decade. South Med J 1986;79(9):1129–1134.

330. Isenberg SJ. The fall and rise of chloramphenicol. J Aapos 2003;7(5):307–308.

331. Rayner SA, Buckley RJ. Ocular chloramphenicol and aplastic anaemia. Is there a link? Drug Saf 1996;14(5):273–276.

332. Cox J, Roderick EM. Is it time to stop using chloramphenicol on the eye? General practitioners would expect to see aplasia roughly once each century. BMJ 1995;311(7002):451; author reply 451.

333. Gordon-Smith EC, Marsh JC, Geary CG. Is it time to stop using chloramphenicol on the eye? Prospective study of aplastic anaemia should give definitive answer. BMJ 1995;311 (7002):451.

334. Hall AV, Das SS, Tabaqchali S. Is it time to stop using chloramphenicol on the eye? Risk is low in short courses. BMJ 1995;311(7002):450-1; author reply 451.

335. Mulla RJ, Barnes E, Rogers TR. Is it time to stop using chloramphenicol on the eye? Fears are based on only six cases. BMJ 1995;311 (7002):450; author reply 451.

336. Krasinski K, Perkin R, Rutledge J. Gray baby syndrome revisited. Clin Pediatr 1982;21 (9):571–572.

337. Knight M. Adverse drug reactions in neonates. J Clin Pharmacol 1994;34(2):128–135.

338. Yunis AA. Chloramphenicol toxicity: 25 years of research. Am J Med 1989;87(3N):44N–48N.

339. Tuttle AD, Papich MG, Wolfe BA. Bone marrow hypoplasia secondary to florfenicol toxicity in a Thomson's gazelle (*Gazella thomsonii*). J Vet Pharmacol Ther 2006;29(4):317–319.

340. Turton JA, Andrews CM, Havard AC, Robinson S, York M, Williams TC, Gibson FM. Haemotoxicity of thiamphenicol in the BALB/c mouse and Wistar Hanover rat. Food Chem Toxicol 2002;40(12):1849–1861.

341. Turton JA, Havard AC, Robinson S, Holt DE, Andrews CM, Fagg R, Williams TC. An assessment of chloramphenicol and thiamphenicol in the induction of aplastic anaemia in the BALB/c mouse. Food Chem Toxicol 2000;38(10): 925–938.

342. Skolimowski IM, Knight RC, Edwards DI. Molecular basis of chloramphenicol and thiamphenicol toxicity to DNA *in vitro*. J Antimicrob Chemother 1983;12(6):535–542.

343. Ryckelynck JP, Potier J, Beuve-Mery P. Bone marrow toxicity of a combination of thiamphenicol and trimethoprim-sulfamethoxazole. Nouv Presse Med 1979;8(46):3829.

344. Johansson D, Jessen CH, Pohlsgaard J, Jensen KB, Vester B, Pedersen EB, Nielsen P. Design, synthesis and ribosome binding of chloramphenicol nucleotide and intercalator conjugates. Bioorg Med Chem Lett 2005;15 (8):2079–2083.

345. Thompson J, Kim DF, O'Connor M, Lieberman KR, Bayfield MA, Gregory ST, Green R, Noller HF, Dahlberg AE. Analysis of mutations at residues A2451 and G2447 of 23S rRNA in the peptidyltransferase active site of the 50S ribosomal subunit. Proc Natl Acad Sci USA 2001;98(16):9002–9007.

346. Gross F, Lewis EA, Piraee M, van Pee KH, Vining LC, White RL. Isolation of 3'-O-acetyl-chloramphenicol: a possible intermediate in chloramphenicol biosynthesis. Bioorg Med Chem Lett 2002;12(3):283–286.

347. Shaw WV. Chemical anatomy of antibiotic resistance: chloramphenicol acetyltransferase. Sci Prog 1992;76(301–302 Pt 3–4): 565–580.

348. Leslie AG. Refined crystal structure of type III chloramphenicol acetyltransferase at 1.75 A resolution. J Mol Biol 1990;213(1):167–186.

349. Douthwaite S. Functional interactions within 23S rRNA involving the peptidyltransferase center. J Bacteriol 1992;174(4):1333–1338.

350. Aagaard C, Rosendahl G, Dam M, Powers T, Douthwaite S. Specific structural probing of plasmid-coded ribosomal RNAs from *Escherichia coli*. Biochimie 1991;73(12):1439–1444.

351. Burns JL, Rubens CE, Mendelman PM, Smith AL. Cloning and expression in *Escherichia coli* of a gene encoding nonenzymatic chloramphenicol resistance from *Pseudomonas aeruginosa*. Antimicrob Agents Chemother 1986;29 (3):445–450.

352. Kieboom J, de Bont J. Identification and molecular characterization of an efflux system involved in *Pseudomonas putida* S12 multi-

drug resistance. Microbiology 2001;147(Pt 1): 43–51.

353. Miller DL. Elongation factors EF Tu and EF G interact at related sites on ribosomes. Proc Natl Acad Sci USA 1972;69(3):752–755.

354. Cabrer B, Vazquez D, Modolell J. Inhibition by elongation factor EF G of aminoacyl-tRNA binding to ribosomes. Proc Natl Acad Sci USA 1972;69(3):733–736.

355. Muhonen J, Vidgren J, Helle A, Yohannes G, Viitala T, Holopainen JM, Wiedmer SK. Interactions of fusidic acid and elongation factor G with lipid membranes. Anal Biochem 2008;374 (1):133–142.

356. Seo HS, Abedin S, Kamp D, Wilson DN, Nierhaus KH, Cooperman BS. EF-G-dependent GTPase on the ribosome. conformational change and fusidic acid inhibition. Biochemistry 2006;45(8):2504–2514.

357. Okura A, Kinoshita T, Tanaka N. Formation of fusidic acid-G factor-GDP-ribosome complex and the relationship to the inhibition of GTP hydrolysis. J Antibiot 1971;24(10):655–661.

358. McLaws F, Chopra I, O'Neill AJ. High prevalence of resistance to fusidic acid in clinical isolates of *Staphylococcus epidermidis*. J Antimicrob Chemother 2008;61(5):1040–1043.

359. Noren T, Akerlund T, Wullt M, Burman LG, Unemo M. Mutations in fusA associated with posttherapy fusidic acid resistance in *Clostridium difficile*. Antimicrob Agents Chemother 2007;51(5):1840–1843.

360. Hansson S, Singh R, Gudkov AT, Liljas A, Logan DT. Structural insights into fusidic acid resistance and sensitivity in EF-G. J Mol Biol 2005;348(4):939–949.

361. Besier S, Ludwig A, Brade V, Wichelhaus TA. Molecular analysis of fusidic acid resistance in *Staphylococcus aureus*. Mol Microbiol 2003;47 (2):463–469.

362. Laurberg M, Kristensen O, Martemyanov K, Gudkov AT, Nagaev I, Hughes D, Liljas A. Structure of a mutant EF-G reveals domain III and possibly the fusidic acid binding site. J Mol Biol 2000;303(4):593–603.

363. Turnidge J, Collignon P. Resistance to fusidic acid. Int J Antimicrob Agents 1999;12(Suppl 2):S35–S44.

364. Richter Dahlfors AA, Kurland CG. Novel mutants of elongation factor G. J Mol Biol 1990;215(4):549–557.

365. Bennett AD, Shaw WV. Resistance to fusidic acid in *Escherichia coli* mediated by the type I variant of chloramphenicol acetyltransferase.

A plasmid-encoded mechanism involving antibiotic binding. Biochem J 1983;215(1):29–38.

366. Proctor GN, McKell J, Rownd RH. Chloramphenicol acetyltransferase may confer resistance to fusidic acid by sequestering the drug. J Bacteriol 1983;155(2):937–939.

367. De Vendittis E, De Paola B, Gogliettino MA, Adinolfi BS, Fiengo A, Duvold T, Bocchini V. Fusidic and helvolic acid inhibition of elongation factor 2 from the archaeon *Sulfolobus solfataricus*. Biochemistry 2002;41(50): 14879–14884.

368. Okuda S, Iwasaki S, Sair MI, Machida Y, Inoue A, Tsuda K. Stereochemistry of helvolic acid. Tetrahedron Lett 1967;24:2295–2302.

369. Okuda S, Nakayama Y, Tsuda K. Studies on microbial products. I. Helvolic acid and related compounds. I. 7-Desacetoxyhelvolic acid and helvolinic acid. Chem Pharm Bull 1966;14 (4):436–441.

370. Okuda S, Iwasaki S, Tsuda K, Sano Y, Hata T, Udagawa S, Nakayama Y, Yamaguchi H. The structure of helvolic acid. Chem Pharm Bull 1964;12:121–124.

371. Burton HS, Abraham EP, Cardwell HM. Cephalosporin P1 and helvolic acid. Biochem J 1956;62(1):171–176.

372. Williams TI. Some chemical properties of helvolic acid. Biochem J 1952;51(4):538–542.

373. Kariv I, Cao H, Marvil PD, Bobkova EV, Bukhtiyarov YE, Yan YP, Patel U, Coudurier L, Chung TD, Oldenburg KR. Identification of inhibitors of bacterial transcription/translation machinery utilizing a miniaturized 1536-well format screen. J Biomol Screen 2001;6(4):233–243.

374. Patel U, Yan YP, Hobbs FW, Jr, Kaczmarczyk J, Slee AM, Pompliano DL, Kurilla MG, Bobkova EV. Oxazolidinones mechanism of action: inhibition of the first peptide bond formation. J Biol Chem 2001;276(40):37199–37205.

SYNTHETIC ANTIBACTERIAL AGENTS

Nitya Anand[1]
William A. Remers[2]
[1] Central Drug Research Institute,
Lucknow, India
[2] AmpliMed Corporation, Tucson, AZ

1. INTRODUCTION

Synthetic antibacterial compounds are divided into two major classes: topical agents and systemic agents. The topical agents are commonly termed disinfectants, antiseptics, and preservatives depending on how they are used. Antiseptics and disinfectants differ from systemic agents in that they show little selective toxicity between the microbes and the host. Furthermore, most of them do not aid wound healing and may even impair it. Nevertheless, there are indispensable uses for disinfectants in hospital sanitation including sterilization of surgical instruments, public health methods, and in the home. Antiseptics have important applications in the preoperative preparation of both surgeons and patients. They also are used in treating local infections caused by microorganisms commonly refractory to systemic antimicrobial agents.

The development of systemic antibacterials had a strong dye–drug connection. Ehrlich in his classic studies on the selective uptake of chemicals by cells and tissues used dyes because they could be followed visually. His efforts on developing selective staining methods for the identification of microorganisms led him to propose that dyes may also have selective toxicities for microbes. In fact, many dyes were found to have antimicrobial activity and some are still used as germicides and disinfectants. This was the backdrop in which Ehrlich coined the term "chemotherapy" for selective killing of pathogenic microbes by chemicals. Discovery of the antibacterial activity of prontosil rubrum, a sulfonamide-azo dye by Domagk in 1928, in a streptococcal infection in mice, was the first effective chemotherapeutic agent employed for the treatment of systemic bacterial infections. The identification of p-aminobenzenesulfona-mide (sulfanilamide) as the active antibacterial molecule, formed as a result of the metabolism of prontosil in the body (p-54), opened up many new vistas in medicinal chemistry. Sulfanilamide, apart from providing the first powerful antibacterial drug, served as an excellent lead for structural modification for development of new antibacterials, and practically every major pharmaceutical company around the world in the 1930s jumped at this opportunity, leading to the introduction of a variety of new sulfonamides, filling different needs of antibacterials. This ushered in the modern era of chemotherapy.

The discovery that sulfonamides acted through folate inhibition, focused attention on folate inhibitors as antibacterials, resulting in the development of dihydrofolate reductase inhibitors (DHFRIs), such as trimethoprin, as another class of antibacterials. As sulfonamides and DHFRIs acted on different steps of the same coenzyme system, using a combination of the two provided a new paradigm in chemotherapy, and currently this combination is used with much benefit.

The availability of these antibacterials, and of antibiotics such as penicillins, discovered almost concurrently with sulfonamides, provided major advances in control of bacterial infections, and created the general impression that the battle against bacterial infections had been won. The interest in the development of new antibacterials waned for some time. However, the rise in bacterial resistance, and the realization that emergence of resistant mutants is a part of the normal multiplication process of microbes, and not necessarily dependant on exposure to the antibacterials, posed a serious challenge in bacterial chemotherapy especially from 1970 onward. It was realized that the only way this challenge could be faced was by constantly developing new classes of drugs, preferably acting by different mechanisms, which revived interest in the development of new classes of antibacterials.

Fluoroquinolones was one such class developed from the early 1980s, with activity against both Gram-positive and Gram-negative bacteria, including those resistant to known agents. Antibacterials of this class have very favorable pharmacokinetic and tissue distribution characteristics, meet special needs, and are widely used. More recently, oxazolidinones have emerged as another important class with especially strong activity against Gram-positive bacteria. There are also some less widely used antibacterials covering some niche needs, such as nitrofurans and methenamine for urinary tract infections (UTIs), and nitrofurans as topical antibacterials for wounds, burns, skin grafts, and for impregnating catheters to prevent catheter's associated UTI.

Systemic antibacterial agents are described at two different places in this volume. The different classes of antimycobacterial agents are discribed elsewhere, whereas other antibacterials: antifolates (sulfonamides, sulfones, and dihydrofolate reductase inhibitors), fluoroquinolones, oxazolidinones, nitrofurans, and metheneamine are described in this chapter.

2. TOPICAL SYNTHETIC ANTIBACTERIALS

Table 1 summarizes the topical synthetic antibacterial agents that are in common use today. These agents possess a wide variety of chemical structures and properties, and they act by many different mechanisms to produce their antibacterial effects. Some of them are extremely toxic, which restricts their use to sterilizing surgical instruments and fumigating structures. Others are powerful agents that are irritating to skin. They are used to disinfect hospital areas, dairy barns, and the like. Less irritating agents are used as surgical scrubs. Still milder agents that possess potent antibacterial activity are used as antiseptics for treating wounds, or as mouthwashes. Very mild and nonirritating compounds may be used to kill bacteria on contact lenses. Thus, there is a broad spectrum of needs for topical antibacterial agents, and a large variety of chemical agents have been developed to meet these needs.

2.1. Terminology

The terms describing topical antibacterial agents are used rather loosely in everyday language, which sometimes creates confusion. Some of these terms have strict definitions by

the U.S. Food and Drug Administration. Perhaps, the two most important terms are disinfectant and antiseptic. A *disinfectant* is defined as a substance that destroys harmful microorganisms, although it may not kill bacterial spores. It is used when referring to agents applied to inanimate objects. Physical agents such as X-rays and ultraviolet light also are considered to disinfect. The term *antiseptic* is used for agents that kill or prevent the growth of microorganisms when used on living tissues. Antiseptics are used in soaps, mouthwashes, douches, and preparations for minor wounds and burns.

The ending "cide" is used to denote killing action. Thus, a bactericide kills bacteria, a fungicide kills fungi, a virucide destroys viruses, a germicide kills various kinds of microorganisms, and a biocide kills all living organisms. Similarly, the ending "stat" is used to describe an agent that prevents the growth of organisms, but does not necessarily kill them. The corresponding terms are bacteriostat, fungistat, and so on.

Other commonly used terms include *antimicrobial*, which refers to an agent that kills or suppresses the growth of microorganisms, and *sanitizer*, which refers to an agent that reduces the number of harmful bacteria to an established safe limit. The criterion for sanitization is killing of 99.999% of specific test bacteria in 30 s and it is commonly applied to eating and drinking implements and dairy equipment [1].

Terms used to describe processes include asepsis, which means the prevention of contamination by microorganisms; decontamination, which refers to the disinfection or sterilization of infected objects; *sterilization*, which refers to killing all forms of life, especially microorganisms; and fumigation, which is the exposure of an area or object to disinfecting fumes.

2.2. Principles of Topical Antimicrobial Activity

2.2.1. Selective Toxicity The ideal disinfectant would exert a rapidly lethal action against every pathogenic microorganism or spore and it would be inexpensive, stable, odorless, and nonstaining. Requirements for

Table 1. Topical Synthetic Antibacterials

Generic Name	Formula	Other Names	Use
Chlorine and chlorophores			
Chlorine	Cl_2		Drinking water disinfection
Sodium chlorite	$NaClO_2$		Germicide
Sodium hypochlorite	$NaOCl$	Dakin's solution	Wound disinfectant
Calcium hypochlorite dihydrate	$Ca(OCl)_2.2H_2O$		Germicide
Lithium hypochlorite	$LiOCl$		Germicide
Chlorinated trisodium phosphate	$NaOCl.4Na_3PO_4$		Germicide
Chloramine T	**1**	Chlorazone, etc.	Germicide
Halazone	**2**	Pantocid	Drinking water disinfection
Dichloromethyl-hydantoin	**3**	Halane, Dactin	Sanitizer
Trichloroisocyanuric acid	**4**	Symcolsine	Disinfect swimming pools
Dichlorocyanuric acid	**5**		Wound disinfectant
Chlorazodin	**6**	Azochloramide	Wound disinfectant
Iodine and related products			
Iodine	$I_2 + KI$	Lugol's solution	Wound disinfectant
Iodine	$I_2 + \text{ethanol}$	Iodine tincture	Wound disinfectant
Povidone-iodine	$I_2 + 7$		Surgical antiseptic
Alcohols			
Ethanol	C_2H_5OH		Antiseptic
Isopropanol	$(CH_3)_2CHOH$		Antiseptic
Benzyl alcohol	$C_6H_5CH_2OH$		Pharmaceutical preservative
Phenethyl alcohol	**8**		Pharmaceutical preservative
Chlorobutanol	**9**	Chloretone, etc.	Bacteriostatic for ophthalmology
Octoxynol	**10**	Triton X, etc.	Lens disinfectant
Phenols			
Phenol	C_6H_5OH	Carbolic acid	Disinfectant
Cresols	$CH_3C_6H_5OH$		Disinfectant
2-n-Amyl-5-methylphenol	**11**		Oral antiseptic
Eugenol	**12**		Mouthwash
2-Benzyl-4-chlorophenol	**13**	Chlorophene	Disinfectant
2-Phenylphenol	**14**	Dowicide 1	Disinfectant
Triclosan	**15**	Irgasan	Disinfectant for cosmetics
Chloroxine	**16**	Capitrol	Antibacterial shampoo

(*Continued*)

485

Table 1 (*Continued*)

Generic Name	Formula	Other Names	Use
Resorcinols			
Resorcinol	17		Keratolytic
Hexylresorcinol	18	Crystoids, etc.	Mouthwash
Parabens	$HOC_6H_4CO_2alkyl$		Pharmaceutical preservative
Bisphenols			
Hexachlorophene	19	PHisohex, etc	Topical antiseptic
Anthralin	20	Anthraderm, etc.	Keratolytic
Epoxides and aldehydes			
Ethylene oxide	21		Sterilization
Propylene oxide	22		Sterilization
Formaldehyde solution	$HCHO$ + water	Formalin	Sterilization
Glutaraldehyde	23		Sterilization
Acids			
Acetic acid	CH_3CO_2H		Irrigation
Benzoic acid	$C_6H_5CO_2H$		Pharmaceutical preservative
Azelaic acid	24		Acne and rosacea
Boric acid	25		Antiseptic
Oxidizing agents			
Hydrogen peroxide	H_2O_2		Sterilization
Urea-hydrogen peroxide	$H_2NCONH_2.H_2O_2$	Hydrogen peroxide carbamide	Sterilization
Benzoyl peroxide	26		Acne
Peracetic acid	CH_3CO_3H		Bactericide
Potassium permanganate	$KMnO_4$		Skin lesions
Heavy metals			
Ammoniated mercuric chloride	$Hg(NH_2)Cl$	Ammoniated mercury	Skin infections
Mercuric oxide	HgO		Eye infections
Nitromersol	27	Metaphen	Bacterial antiseptic
Thiomersol	28		Bacterial antiseptic
Phenylmercuric acetate	29	PMA, etc.	Bacterial antiseptic
Phenylmercuric nitrate	30 + 31	Phermernite	Bacterial antiseptic
Merbromin	32	Mercurichrome	Bacterial antiseptic
Silver salts			
Silver nitrate	$AgNO_3$	Lunar caustic	Burns, opthalmic
Toughened silver nitrate	$AgNO_3$		Wounds
Colloidal silver	Silver preparations	Mild silver protein	Wounds
	Ag + protein		

Name	No.	Synonym/trade name	Use
Silver sulfadiazine	33		Burns
Dyes			
Gentian violet	34	Methylrosaniline chloride, crystal violet, etc.	Topical antiseptic
Methylene blue	35	Urolene blue	Cystitis and urethritis, antiseptic
Diarylureas, amidines, and biguanides			
Triclocarban	36	Solubacter	Soaps and cosmetics
Propamidine	37		Soaps and cosmetics
Dibromopropamidine	38		Soaps and cosmetics
Chlorhexidine digluconate	39	Nolvasan, Sterilon	Wound cleansing, burns, surgical scrub
Polyhexamethylene biguanide	40	Polyaminopropyl biguanide	Contact lenses
Polyquaternium 1	41	Polyquad	Contact lenses
Cationic surfactants			
Benzalkonium chloride	$[C_6H_5CH_2N(CH_3)_2\text{-alkyl}]^+\ Cl^-$	Zephiran chloride, etc.	Skin disinfectant
Benzethonium chloride	42	Quatrachlor, etc.	Skin disinfectant
Methylbenzethonium chloride	43	Diaperine chloride, Hyamine 10X	Diaper rash preventative
Cetylpyridinium chloride	44	Cepachol, etc.	Mouthwash and lozenges
Alkylbenzyldimethyl-ammonium chloride + alkyldimethyl(ethyl-benzyl)ammonium chloride		BTC 2125M, Dual Quat	Biocide
Dimethyldioctyl-ammonium bromide		Deciquam	Food preservative
Polyinones	45	Onamer M	Contact lenses
Anionic surfactants			
Sodium dodecylbenzenesulfonate	46	Conoco C-50, etc.	Dairy disinfectant
Oxychlorosene	46 + HClO		Skin disinfectant
Amphoteric surfactants			
Dodecyl + tetradecyl di(aminoethyl)-glycines + tetradecyl-aminoglycines		Tego 51	Surgical disinfectant

an ideal antiseptic are rapid and sustained lethality to microorganisms, activity in the presence of skin and body fluids, lack of irritation and allergenicity, lack of systemic toxicity when applied to skin and mucous membranes, and no detrimental effect on wound healing. This ideal has not been realized completely [2]. The need for selective toxicity increases from disinfectants, which are used on inanimate objects, through antiseptics, which are applied to skin and mucous membranes, to systemic antimicrobial agents. For antiseptics, a major concern is the *therapeutic index*, which is the ratio of the concentration that produces harmful effects to the concentration that is effective against microorganisms. The harmful effects include local tissue irritation and interference with the wound healing process. Hypersensitivity reactions and systemic toxicity resulting from absorption of the drug can be serious problems, as was the case when infants were commonly washed with hexachlorophene. A high degree of selective toxicity may be associated with a narrow antimicrobial spectrum and the emergence of resistance.

2.2.2. Cellular Targets

Chemical antimicrobial agents have a variety of cellular targets and, in some cases, multiple targets. Although the precise mechanisms of many agents remain unclear, there are a number of known interactions [3]. For aldehydes, the target is the cell wall and the chemical mechanism is interaction with amino groups. The cell wall also is the target of anionic surfactants and the mechanism of action is lysis. Certain chelating agents such as EDTA form chelates with cations in the outer membrane of the cell wall and this process induces the release of lipopolysaccharides.

Phenols, quaternary ammonium compounds, biguanides, parabens, and hexachlorophene cause the leakage of low molecular weight compounds from cells and interfere with the normal proton flux. Phenol produces leakage, possible cell lysis, and proton flux changes; quaternary ammonium compounds cause leakage and protoplast lysis, and they interact with membrane phospholipids; chlorhexidine induces leakage and protoplast and spheroplast lysis; parabens cause leakage, transport inhibition, and selective inhibition of proton flux, and hexachlorophene causes leakage, protoplast lysis, and inhibition of respiration.

A variety of agents interfere with nucleic acid function. They include alkylation of DNA and RNA (and proteins) by ethylene oxide and formaldehyde, DNA intercalation by acridines and certain dyes, and inhibition of bacterial DNA gyrase (Type II topoisomerase) by quinolones.

Metal ions bind with sulfhydryl groups on enzymes or other proteins that may be associated with membranes.

2.2.3. Mechanisms of Bacterial Resistance

The outer membrane of Gram-negative bacteria is composed of lipopolysaccharide, proteins, and lipids [4]. It presents a barrier to many chemical agents including quaternary ammonium compounds and triphenylmethane dyes. In contrast, the cytoplasmic membrane of Gram-positive bacteria, excepting spores and mycobacteria, has greater permeability to most agents [5]. Spores have a special coat and/or cortex that may not be permeable to hydrogen peroxide and chlorine disinfectants. Bacterial cells may also have efflux mechanisms that extrude agents such as quaternary ammonium compounds, dyes, and mercury compounds from their interiors [6].

2.2.4. Kinetics and Other Factors

Antibacterial action follows approximately first-order kinetics. The rate depends on concentration, pH, and the vehicle in which the agent is applied. The kinetics are most important when time is critical. An example of a rapid kinetics is the action of 70% ethanol on skin, which results in a 50% reduction in bacterial count in about 36 s. This ethanol concentration does not afford complete bactericidal action; only about 90% reduction in the bacterial count is obtained. Determination of kinetics is complicated by many factors including diffusion, penetration, binding, and redistribution [7]. Consequently, the rate of action often is not directly related to concentration and there is an optimal concentration. Thus, increasing the concentration of ethanol above 70% does not result in increased antibacterial activity. There is a general correlation of antibacterial activity and thermodynamic activity. The latter is related to the proportional saturation of the drug in the medium. This correlation breaks down when the capacity of the medium for the drug becomes a limiting factor because the amount of agent in the medium becomes depleted rapidly [8]. One way to increase the capacity of water for poorly soluble agents such as iodine or hexachlorophene is to add a surfactant.

2.3. Evaluation of Antimicrobial Activity

2.3.1. Methods of Testing Disinfectants
Disinfectants are required to have rapid and lethal antimicrobial effects, which means that bactericidal rather than bacteriostatic test methods are used. The test methods must be precise and reproducible, use standardized microbial strains, and have clearly defined inoculum and culture conditions. Standard bacterial strains are obtained from the American Type Culture Collection (ATCC), The activity of disinfectants is affected by pH, chelators and other metal ions, macromolecules, other organic matter, and detergent residues. Disinfectant activity depends on concentration and contact time according to the relationship $C^n t = k$, where C is the disinfectant concentration, t is the time required for lethal action, n is the concentration exponent and k is a constant. Disinfectants with high exponents have a poor safety margin and require significantly increased contact time when they are diluted [9].

In the United States, the principal methods for testing disinfectants are published in the sixteenth edition of the *Official Methods of Analysis of the Association of Official Analytical Chemists International*. Detailed outlines may also be found in the fourth edition of *Disinfection, Sterilization, and Preservation* [11]. Other countries have their own compendia of official methods [10]. Three representative test methods are described briefly below. The literature indicated should be consulted for more details and further examples.

The phenol coefficient method compares bacterial activity of a disinfectant with that of phenol by a suspension test. A phenol coefficient number is the ratio of the greatest dilution killing test organisms in 10 min but not in 5 min to the greatest dilution of phenol giving the same result. The assay is run in broth culture at 20°C with contact times of 5, 10, and 15 min. It is used with specific strains of *Salmonella typhi, Staphylococcus aureus, and Pseudomonas aeruginosa.*

Available chlorine in disinfectants is measured by a capacity test in which disinfectant activity of a compound is compared with that of a standard sodium hypochlorite solution. The test organisms are *S. typhi and S. aureus.* Ten additions of inoculum are made at 1.5 min intervals and a subculture is made one minute after each addition.

A carrier test is used for germicidal spray products. Broth cultures of test bacteria are spread on slides and dried 30–40 min at 37°C. The disinfectant is then sprayed onto the slides under standard conditions. After 10 min contact time at room temperature, material is transferred from the slides to subculture broth using suture loops or penicylinders. For a successful test, organisms must be killed in 10 out of 10 trials. The test organisms include *S. aureus, P. aeruginosa, and Salmonella choleraesuis.*

2.3.2. Methods for Testing Antiseptics
The most important tests for antiseptic involve surgical hand scrubs. These tests incorporate the cup scrubbing procedure in which a small area of skin is delineated by a glass cup. A wash solution (1 mL containing Triton X-100 in pH 7.9 phosphate buffer) is added by pipette and the skin area is scrubbed for 1 min. The procedure is repeated and an aliquot of the pooled sample is diluted and plated on agar. The plates are incubated for 48 h at 37°C and colonies are counted [13].

The glove juice test is required by the FDA for surgical hand scrubs. In this test, loose gloves are placed on each hand and a sampling solution containing buffer and surfactant is added to one hand. This hand is massaged for 1 min and sample is removed, plated on agar, and incubated to determine microbial growth. The opposite hand serves as a control and the test involves a group of people and statistical analysis [13].

In the modified Cade procedure, used for antimicrobial soaps, repeated hand washing under standard conditions is made in a series of basins and the bacteria in selected basins are plated on agar and incubated [12,13]. Hands are washed 3 times daily for 10 days for at least 10 consecutive days. Reductions in bacterial counts from baseline to the first basin and to the fourth and/or fifth basin are measured. At least 35 subjects are used in the test. Other surgical scrub tests are described in the literature [11].

2.4. History

As described in the interesting historical review by Block [13], the first disinfectant reported in the literature was in *The Odyssey* by Homer. Upon his return from the Trojan Wars, Odysseus burned sulfur to fumigate his house. The burning of sulfur (to sulfur dioxide) was used during the great plagues of the Middle Ages. Sulfur dioxide is still used as a disinfectant and preservative for fruit, fruit juices, and wine.

In the early 1500s, Paracelsus reformed the Pharmacopoeia and introduced compounds of mercury, lead, arsenic, copper, iron, and sulfur as disinfectants and antiseptics. Acidulated water, an antiseptic preparation containing wine or cider vinegar and cream of tartar was used in the eighteenth century, as was mercuric chloride. Labarraque reported the use of calcium hypochlorite for wound dressings and general sanitation in 1825 [14] and Alcock recommended the use of chlorine to disinfect drinking water in 1827 [15]. Tincture of iodine was admitted to the United States Pharmacopeia as an antiseptic in 1830. Richardson discovered the disinfectant activity of hydrogen peroxide in 1858. In 1887, an emulsion of coal tar creosote and soap was patented. A version of it was sold under the name Lysol.

Following the development of the principle of contagion by Holmes and Semmelweiss [16,17], who independently reported the benefit of physicians washing their hands with calcium hypochlorite before conducting examinations and other procedures, Lister made a great advance in medicine by introducing antiseptic surgery [18]. His techniques included the liberal use of phenol. Pasteur's pioneering studies in microbiology were followed by Koch's conclusive demonstration that bacteria invaded tissue and caused disease. In a comprehensive paper in 1881, he evaluated the ability of many chemicals to kill anthrax spores, reporting that halogens, mercuric chloride, and potassium permanganate were highly effective, but phenol was not [19] effective.

Kronig and Paul established the basis for modern chemical disinfection in 1897 [20]. They reported that chemical agents killed bacteria at a rate determined by concentration of the chemical and the temperature and they noted that disinfectants could only be compared accurately when they are tested under carefully controlled conditions. Rideal and Walker introduced the important phenol coefficient method for comparing disinfectants in 1903 [21]. It is still used in standard assays.

The development of organic chemistry provided the basis for the synthesis of antibacterial agents of increasing potency and selectivity. Bechold and Ehrlich reported the high antibacterial activity of halogenated bisphenols in 1906 [22] and alkylresorcinols appeared in 1921. In 1935, Domagk showed that the addition of long alkyl chains to quaternary ammonium compounds greatly increased their disinfectant activity [23]. Clorhexidine, a biguanide, was developed in 1965 by Rose and Swain through the structural modification of the antimalarial biguanides [24].

2.5. Halogens and Halophores

2.5.1. Chlorine and Chlorophores
Chlorine has been used since 1827 to disinfect drinking water and it remains the leading agent for this purpose because it is cheap and effective. Nevertheless, a variety of chlorine-generating compounds (chlorophores) and related compounds have been used in drinking water. Chlorine dioxide, ClO_2, has been used in recent years for drinking water disinfection and wastewater treatment [25]. This highly reactive compound cannot be manufactured and shipped in bulk, but it is prepared at the site of consumption by treating a sodium chlorite solution with chlorine as indicated (Eq. 1). Inorganic chloramines were used in the 1930s and early 1940s to improve the taste of

drinking water, but their use was largely discontinued because of their inferior disinfectant properties. Combining chlorine and ammonia in water results in a mixture of species including $ClNH_2$, Cl_2NH, and Cl_3N. Approximately 25 times as much of these species is needed as is chlorine and the contact time required is 100 times as long [26]. More recently, the addition of inorganic chloramines to water is being reconsidered because they prevent the formation of carcinogenic trihalomethanes from pollutants [27].

$$Cl_2 + 2NaClO_2 \rightarrow 2ClO_2 + 2NaCl \quad (1)$$

The germicidal species formed in water solutions of chlorine is hypochlorous acid (Eq. 2). Based on this process, a variety of inorganic hypochlorites were introduced as disinfectants. They include sodium hypochlorite, calcium hypochlorite dihydrate, lithium hypochlorite, and chlorinated trisodium phosphate [$NaOCl_4(Na_3PO_4)$]. The water solutions of sodium hypochlorite are available in different concentrations of available chlorine, which include the following: 0.4–0.5% (Dakin's solution used on wounds), 5.25% (Chlorox and related preparations), and 12–15% (liquid bleach).

$$Cl_2 + HOH \rightarrow HOCl + HCl \quad (2)$$

Organic compounds such as amides, sulfonamides, imides, and amidines form reasonably stable N-chloro derivatives that may be produced in bulk quantities by treating appropriate nitrogen compounds with HOCl. In water, they slowly release HOCl and regenerate the parent nitrogen compound (Eq. 3). Among the N-chlorosulfonamides, chloramine T (sodium p-toluenesulfonchloramide, 1) has been used for disinfecting wounds. It is permitted for use as a sanitizer in dairies and restaurants by the U.S. Public Health Service. Halazone (p-dichlorosulfamoylbenzoic acid, 2) is only slightly soluble in water, but its sodium salt is very soluble and has been used to disinfect drinking water [28]. Heterocyclic chloramines include dichlorodimethylhydantoin (halane, 3), which is used in some commercial sanitizing products and trichloroisocyanuric acid (trichloro-s-triazinetrione, 4), which is widely used to disinfect swimming pools. The sodium and potassium salts of dichloroisocyanuric acid (5) are used in laundry bleaches, dish washing compounds, scouring powders, and industrial sanitizing products [29]. Chloroazodin (6), N,N'-dichloroazodicarbonamidine, is used for wound disinfection, packing for cavities, and lavage and irrigation. It has prolonged antiseptic action because of its relatively slow reaction with water.

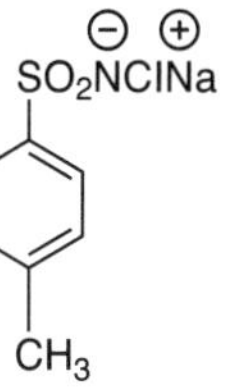

(1) 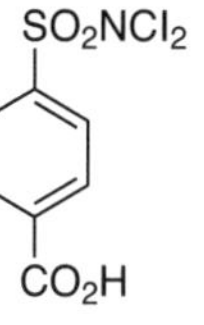   (2) 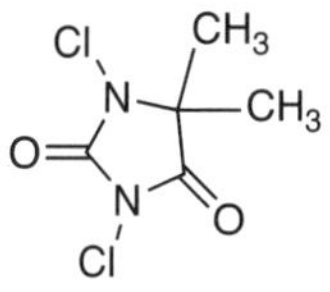   (3)

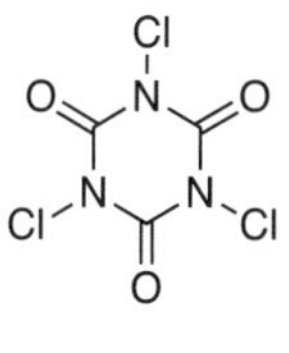

(4) 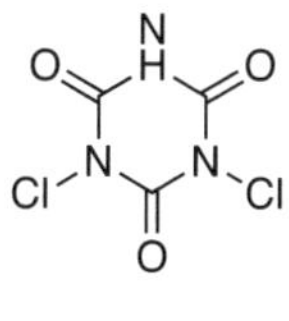   (5) 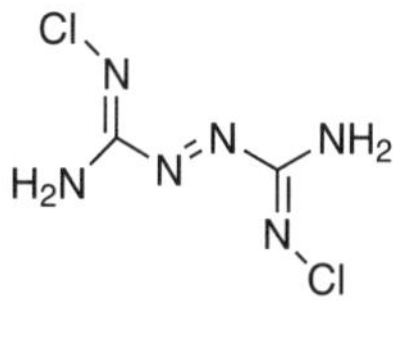   (6)

$$RCONCl_2 + HOH \rightarrow RCONHCl + HOCl \quad (3)$$

Chlorine in minute amounts results in a destructive permeability of bacterial cell walls [30]. Two different mechanisms have been proposed for the germicidal effects of hypochlorous acid. Both of them involve reactions with proteins: one is oxidation of sulfhydryl groups in the proteins and the other is chlorination of amide nitrogens [31]. Although early workers considered that the germicidal action of N-chloramines was caused solely by hydrolysis to HOCl, it was suggested more recently that there is direct transfer of positive chlorine from N-chloramines to receptors in the bacterial cells [32].

2.5.2. Iodine Molecular iodine, I_2, is one of the oldest germicides and is one of the most useful germicides even today. It is highly effective, economical, and minimally toxic at the usual concentrations. Water solutions of iodine are complex systems containing at least seven species, of which I_2 and HIO are considered to be the main disinfectants [33]. Iodine preparations include the tincture (2% solution of I_2 in 50% ethanol containing iodide), Lugol's solution (5% I_2 in water with KI), and iodine solution (2% I_2 in water with NaI). The iodide salts solubilize I_2 and decrease its volatility. Preparations containing iodide ion have triiodide ion, I_3^-, as a major species. This ion is a weak disinfectant compared with I_2. Iodine as I_2 readily penetrates the cell walls of microorganisms. Suggested mechanisms of action include oxidation of the SH groups in proteins, iodination of amino groups, iodination of tyrosine residues, and addition to the double bonds of unsaturated fatty acids [34]. Povidone-iodine is a complex of I_2 with polyvinylpyrrolidone (**7**), a nonionic surfactant polymer. This water-soluble complex contains approximately 10% of available I_2 [35], which it releases slowly. Povidone-iodine is nontoxic, nonirritating, and nonstaining. It is used as an antiseptic before surgery and injections and for treating wounds and lacerations. Its available products include surgical scrubs, aerosols, ointments, antiseptic gauze pads, and mouthwashes.

(**7**)

2.6. Alcohols

Alcohols have desirable properties as disinfectants and antiseptics. They are bactericidal, inexpensive, and relatively nontoxic when used topically; however, they are more active against vegetative forms than spores. Structure–activity relationships among aliphatic alcohols have been established [36]. Bactericidal activity increases as the homologous series of normal alcohols is ascended from methanol through ethanol, propanol, and so on to octanol. The phenol coefficients range from 0.026 for methanol to 21.0 for n-octanol when *S. typhosa* is the organism. Against *P. aeruginosa*, bactericidal activity of alcohols decreased in the order n- primary > i-primary n-secondary > tertiary [37].

Ethanol and isopropanol are the only alcohols used routinely as antiseptics and disinfectants. They are most effective as 60–90% solutions in water and their mode of action is gross protein denaturation. The main use is skin disinfection, and an aerosol preparation is used to disinfect air.

Benzyl alcohol is commonly used as a preservative in vials of injectable drugs in concentrations of 1–4%. Its mild local anesthetic activity also is useful for injection. Further antiseptic uses for benzyl alcohol are in ointments and lotions. Phenylethyl alcohol (**8**) is used primarily in perfumery. Among alcohols, it has the unique property of greater potency against Gram-negative bacteria than Gram-positive bacteria [37]. It has been found to inhibit mRNA synthesis and DNA repair [38]. Chlorobutanol (1,1,1-trichloro-2-methyl-2-propanol, **9**) is used as a bacteriostatic agent for injectable, ophthalmic, and intranasal products.

Ethylene glycol, propylene glycol, and other glycols were used in the past as vapors to disinfect air. Good antimicrobial activity in this use depends on precise control of humidity.

Octoxynol (octylphenoxy polyethoxyethanol, **10**) consists of a mixture of compounds containing 4–14 ethoxy units in addition to the terminal hydroxyethyl residue. Solutions containing this mixture are used to disinfect contact lenses. A single member of this set of compounds, octynol-9 ($n = 8$) is used as a spermicide [39].

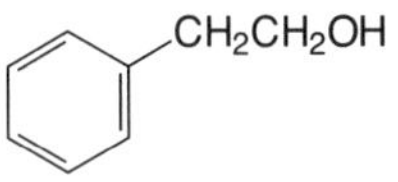

(8) 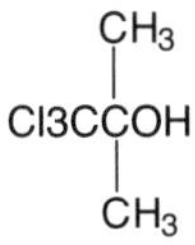   (9) 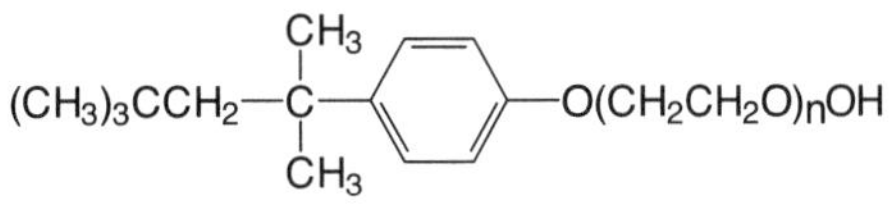   (10)

2.7. Phenols

2.7.1. Monophenols Phenol was introduced by Lister as a surgical anesthetic in 1867. Originally, it was used undiluted and was toxic to tissue; however, it was considered to be less harmful than potential infections. Lister subsequently found that dilutions as low as 1:40 still gave effective antisepsis. The development of substituted phenols and bisphenols with superior antiseptic activity and lower toxicity has led to phenol being replaced as an antiseptic. It has limited use as a preservative for pharmaceuticals and a disinfectant for inanimate objects. Liquefied phenol is phenol containing 10% water. This form is convenient for use in pharmaceutical preparations. Phenol and its derivatives act as gross cellular poisons at higher concentrations, penetrating cells and denaturing proteins. At lower concentrations, they inactivate essential enzymes. In 1% solution, phenol causes a pronounced leak of glutamic acid from cells. This finding suggests that the bactericidal activity of phenol results from physical damage to the permeability barrier in the bacterial cell wall [40].

Mixtures of the three isomeric methylphenols (cresols) are obtained from coal tar or petrolatum by alkaline extraction, acidification, and distillation. Cresol, NF is an inexpensive disinfectant with a phenol coefficient of 2.5. Compound cresol solution contains 50% cresol in saponified linseed or other suitable oil. It is soluble in water and is widely used for disinfecting inanimate objects.

The antibacterial potency of alkylphenols increases with increasing size of the alkyl group, which suggests that lipophilicity may be an important physical property for these compounds. *Para*-substituted alkylphenols increase in potency up to a chain length of six, then potency declines because of poor water solubility. Among the alkylphenols, 2-*n*-amyl-5-methylphenol (**11**) is used as an antiseptic in mouthwashes, gargles, and lozenges [41].

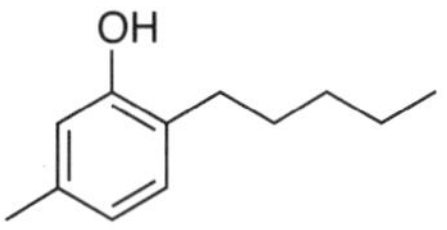

(11) 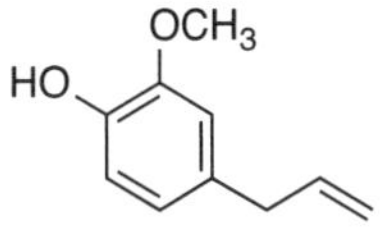   (12)

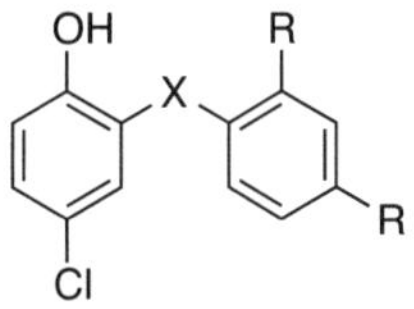

(13) : R = H, X = CH$_2$
(15): R = Cl, X = O

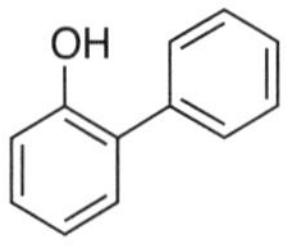

(14)

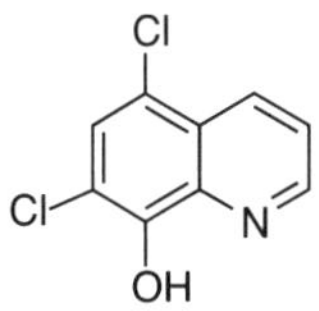

(16)

Eugenol (4-allyl-2-methoxyphenol, **12**) has a phenol coefficient of 14.4. It has local anesthetic activity in addition to antiseptic activity and these properties account for its use in mouthwashes.

The antibacterial potency of phenols is increased by halogenation. *Para*-substituents are more effective than *ortho*-substituents. Addition of alkyl chains further increases potency and straight chains are more effective than branched ones. It is more effective to have the halogen *para* and the alkyl group *ortho* than in the reverse orientation. Increasing the molecular weight of the alkyl group usually increases the antibacterial potency (depending on the species) and decreases the toxicity [42,43]. A free hydroxyl group is required for antibacterial activity. Chloro and alkyl groups enhance potency by increasing lipophilicity and consequently reducing surface tension. Electron-withdrawing groups such as halogens increase the acidity of the phenol. Nitration increases not only the antibacterial potency but also the toxicity to higher species. Nitrophenols uncouple oxidative phosphorylation [44]. The most widely used and effective substituted aryl/alkylphenols are chlorophene (2-benzyl-4-chlorophenol, **13**) and 2-phenylphenol (**14**). They are used against a broad spectrum of Gram-positive and Gram-negative bacteria as environmental disinfectants in places such as hospitals, dairies, barns, poultry houses, and rest rooms. Triclosan (**15**) is a diphenylether substituted with one phenolic hydroxyl group and three chlorines. Its bacteriostatic action on a broad spectrum of organisms makes it a useful disinfectant for cosmetic and detergent preparations.

The methyl, ethyl, propyl, and butyl esters of *p*-hydroxybenzoic acid (parabens) are used as preservatives for liquid dosage forms of pharmaceuticals and in cosmetics and industrial products. They are active against bacteria, yeasts and molds. Parabens are effective in low concentrations (0.1–0.3%) that are devoid of systemic effects, but as constituents of antibacterial ointments they can cause severe contact dermatitis.

Chloroxine, 5,7-dichloro-8-hydroxyquinoline (**16**), present in 2% (w/w) in the antibacterial shampoo, Capitrol, is effective in treatment of dandruff and seborrheic dermatitis. Although the role of microbes in seborrheic dermatitis is unknown, the disease often has increased numbers of *S. aureus* and *Pityrosporon* species. Chloroxine is known to inhibit Gram-positive and some Gram-negative bacteria [45].

2.7.2. Resorcinols The parent compound, resorcinol (**17**), has antibacterial and antifungal activity, but it is less potent than phenol. Nevertheless, its keratolytic properties make it useful in treating conditions such as acne, ringworm, eczema, and psoriasis. Resorcinol monoacetate is a prodrug that slowly liberates resorcinol. It has weaker but more prolonged action. As found with monophenols, the addition of alkyl substituents to bisphenols significantly increases antibacterial potency. Hexylresorcinol (4-*n*-hexylresorcinol, **18**) is an effective bactericidal agent that has a phenol coefficient of 313 against *S. aureus* [46]. It also has local anesthetic activity. Hexylresorcinol is used in 1:1000 water solution or glycerite in mouthwashes or pharyngeal antiseptic preparations.

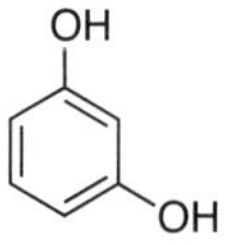

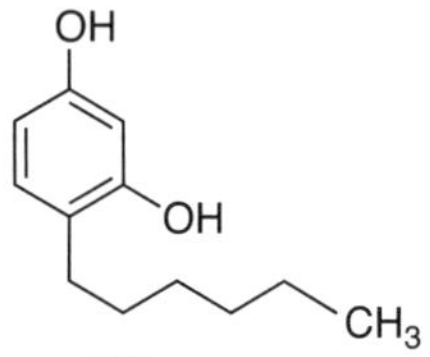

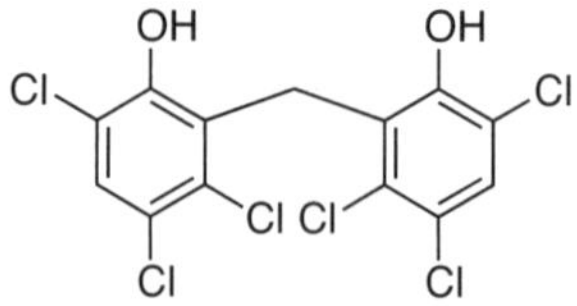

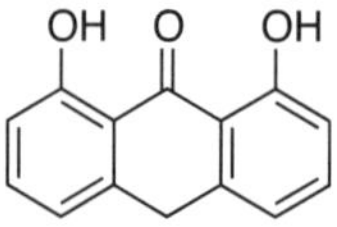

2.7.3. Bisphenols Hexachlorophene is 2,2'-methylenebis(3,4,6-trichlorophenol) (**19**). It was synthesized in 1941 by condensing 2 mol of trichlorophenol with 1 mol of formaldehyde in the presence of sulfuric acid [47]. Hexachlorophene has high bacteriostatic activity, especially against Gram-positive bacteria: a 3% solution kills *S. aureus* in 15–30 s. It is less potent against Gram-negative bacteria and bactericidal activity requires longer contact time (24 h for some Gram-negative bacteria). Single applications of hexachlorophene are not more effective than ordinary soaps, but daily use results in a layer on the skin that confers prolonged bacteriostatic action. This property led to its widespread use as a topical antiseptic and in the late 1950s it successfully combatted virulent *Staphylococcus* infections in hospital nurseries throughout the world. Unfortunately, systemic toxicity can develop from topical use, especially in infants, and more than 30 infants in France died from neurotoxicity resulting from exposure to baby powder containing 6% of hexachlorophene. In 1972, the FDA banned it from all OTC and cosmetic preparations except at preservative levels of 0.1%. Prescription products bear warning labels concerning absorption and potential neurotoxicity [48]. Hexachlorophene is still used for surgical scrubs, hand washing as part of patient care, and control of outbreaks of Gram-positive infections where other procedures have failed.

Anthralin (1,8-dihydroxyanthrone, **20**) is used against psoriasis and other chronic skin conditions because of its antiseptic, irritant, and keratolytic properties.

2.8. Epoxides and Aldehydes

Epoxides and simple aldehydes are highly reactive functionalities that readily alkylate nucleophilic groups such as amino, hydroxyl, and thiol on proteins and nitrogens on nucleic acids. Because of their high toxicity to higher organisms, they are used mainly to disinfect inanimate objects.

2.8.1. Epoxides   Ethylene oxide (oxirane, **21**) is a colorless flammable gas. It readily diffuses through porous materials and destroys all forms of microorganisms at room temperature [49]. Ethylene oxide is very toxic and possibly carcinogenic. In concentrations of 3–80% v/v, it forms explosive mixtures with air. This hazard may be eliminated by mixing it with carbon dioxide or fluorocarbons. For example, the product carboxide has 10% ethylene oxide and 90% carbon dioxide. Ethylene oxide has been used to sterilize temperature-sensitive medical equipment and certain pharmaceuticals that cannot be autoclaved. Propylene oxide (**22**) is a liquid that also has been used as a sterilizing agent [50].

(**21**), R = H
(**22**), R = CH_3

2.8.2. Aldehydes   Formaldehyde is a gas that readily undergoes oxidation to formic acid and polymerization to paraformaldehyde. It usually is used as formalin, an aqueous solution containing not less than 37% formaldehyde and 10–15% methanol to prevent polymerization. Formaldehyde exerts a slow but potent germicidal action thought to involve direct nonspecific alkylation of nucleophilic groups on proteins to form carbinol derivatives (Eq. 4). It is used to disinfect surgical instruments. Formaldehyde is highly allergenic and a cancer suspect agent.

$$Rnu + HCHO \rightarrow RnuCH_2OH \qquad (4)$$

Glutaraldehyde (1,5-pentanedial, **23**) is a reactive dialdehyde that readily undergoes self-condensation to form α,β-unsaturated polymers (Eq. 5). The commercial product is a stabilized solution containing 2% glutaraldehyde buffered to pH 7.5–8.0. Polymerization occurs above pH 8.5 [51]. Glutaraldehyde Disinfectant Solution, NF is used to sterilize instruments and equipment that cannot be autoclaved. One special use is in disinfection of fiber-optic endoscopy equipment, especially to prevent the transmission of *Mycobacterium tuberculosis* between patients [52]. Glutaraldehyde is effective against all microorganisms and its advantages over formaldehyde include less irritation and odor, although it can cause contact dermatitis. The mode of action of glutaraldehyde is based on its strong binding to outer cell layers, especially involving the ε-amino groups of proteins, rendering them impermeable [53]. It may also inactivate cellular enzymes and alkylate nucleic acids [54]. Equation 5 indicates the likely reactive intermediate species involved.

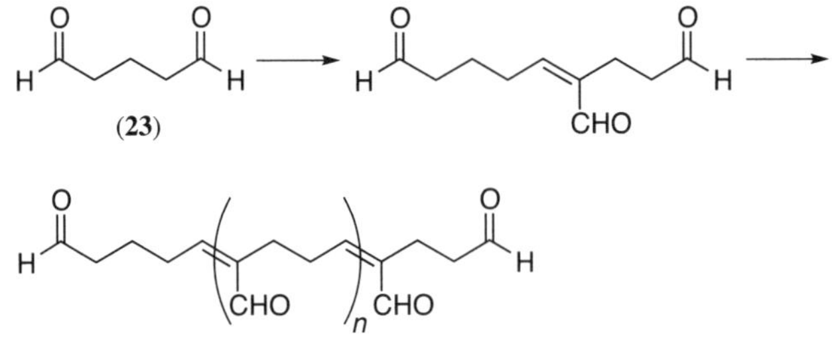

(5)

2.9. Acids

Acetic acid in 1% water solution has been used in surgical dressings as a topical antimicrobial agent. In 0.25–2% solutions, it is useful for infections of the external ear and for irrigation of the lower urinary tract. It is especially effective against *Pseudomonas* and other aerobic Gram-negative bacteria [55]. Benzoic acid is employed externally as an antiseptic in lotions, ointments, and mouthwashes. As a preservative in food and pharmaceuticals, its effect depends on both pK and distribution between phases [56]. It is more active when pH is below its pK_a of 4.2.

Azelaic acid (**24**) is a naturally occurring dicarboxylic acid that reduces the growth of bacteria, especially *Propinibacterium acnes* and *Staphylococcus epidermidis* that occur in follicles. It returns the growth of skin cells lining the follicles to normal, which makes it useful in treating mild to moderate acne. It also is used to treat rosacea because it can reduce skin inflammation. Azelaic acid reduces skin pigmentation and it also has been used as a hair growth stimulant. The usual formulation, 20% in a cream, is nontoxic, but it can be a skin irritant and should be used only when prescribed by a physician [57].

$$HO_2C(CH_2)_7CO_2H$$
(**24**)

Wilhelm Homberg first prepared boric acid (**25**) from borax in the seventeenth century. It is a mild acid used as an antiseptic for minor burns and cuts, or in very dilute solution, as an eyewash. In the form of a vaginal suppository it is used to treat candidiasis, and in powder form it is used to prevent athlete's foot.

Boric acid does not dissociate in water, but it is acidic through an interaction with water molecules to form borate anions and protons (Eq. 6). In the pH range of 7–9 polyborate anions such as tetraborate are formed if the

boron concentration is higher than 0.025 mol/L [58].

$$B(OH)_3 + H_2O \rightarrow B(OH)_4{}^- + H^+$$
(**25**)

$$4B(OH)_4{}^- + 2H \rightarrow B_4O_7{}^= + 9H_2O$$

(6)

2.10. Oxidizing Agents

Hydrogen peroxide, H_2O_2, is stable when it is pure, but small amounts of impurities promote rapid decomposition to water and oxygen. It is stable in 3% water solution if deionized water and clean equipment are used. This solution is used for topical disinfection. Although it has potent activity against bacteria, including anaerobes, it penetrates tissue poorly and the amount that does penetrate is rapidly decomposed by catalase. Thus, its antibacterial action in tissue is weak and brief. Hydrogen peroxide is more effective where living tissue is not present. It finds use in sterilizing milk, hospital water, food containers, and in the ultrasonic disinfection of dental and medical instruments. The lethal effect of hydrogen peroxide on microorganisms is thought to be attack on membrane lipids and DNA. Decomposition to the highly reactive hydroxyl radical may be important in these processes [59]. Concentrations of hydrogen peroxide used in sterilization (3% and higher) overcome the protective effect of catalase in bacterial cells.

Carbamide peroxide is a stable 1:1 complex of urea and hydrogen peroxide, which is provided as a 12.6% solution in anhydrous glycerine. It releases hydrogen peroxide when it is mixed with water.

Benzoyl peroxide (**26**) is chemically unstable and decomposes when heated. Its safety is improved by dilution with 30% water (hydrous benzoyl peroxide, USP). Lotions contain 5–10% of hydrous benzoyl peroxide and they are stabilized by addition of dicalcium phosphate.

Nonstabilized water solutions slowly decompose to hydrogen peroxide and benzoic acid. The main use of benzoyl peroxide is in treatment of acne, where it kills *P. acnes*, decreases production of irritating fatty acids in sebum, and induces cell proliferation by its keratolytic action.

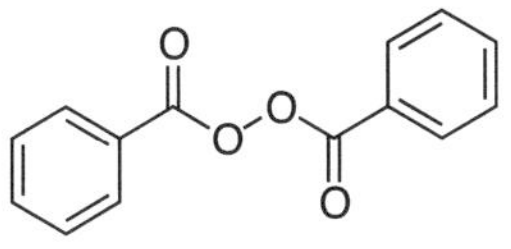

(26)

Peracetic acid is used widely in food processing and beverages. It is bactericidal at 0.001% and has the advantage of decomposing only to oxygen and acetic acid (Eq. 7).

$$2CH_3COOOH \rightarrow 2CH_3COOH + O_2 \quad (7)$$

Potassium permanganate ($KMnO_4$) kills many microorganisms at a dilution of 1:10,000; however, this concentration is irritating to tissues and causes stains. It finds limited use in weeping skin lesions.

2.11. Heavy Metals

2.11.1. Mercury Compounds In the past, mercuric chloride was used widely as an antiseptic, but its present use is limited to disinfecting instruments and occasional application to unabraided skin. The most significant inorganic mercury compound is ammoniated mercury [$Hg(NH_2)Cl$], which is used for skin infections such as impetigo. It is formulated as ammoniated mercury ointment, which contains 5% or 10% of the compound in liquid petrolatum and white ointment. Mercuric oxide (HgO) is used sometimes for inflammation of the eye.

There are two basic types of organomercurials: those in which the mercury is covalently bonded to carbon and those in which the mercury is bonded to a heteroatom such as oxygen, sulfur, or nitrogen. The latter type dissociate more readily than the former. Organomercurials are more bacteriostatic, less toxic, and less irritating than inorganic mercury compounds [60]. Their mechanism of action is thought to result from binding with thiols in enzymes and other proteins. Thiols such as cysteine reverse their toxicity. Organomercurials are bacteriostatic and their potency is reduced substan-

tially in serum because of the proteins present. They are not effective against spores. Among many organomercurials, nitromersol (**27**, designated as the anhydride of 4-nitro-3-mercuri-2-methylphenol by the USP), thiomerosal merthiolate (**28**), and phenylmercuric acetate (**29**), and phenylmercuric nitrate (a mixture of phenylmercuric nitrate, **30** and phenylmercuric hydroxide, **31**) are marketed in many liquid and solid forms as bacteriostatic antiseptics. They also are used in biological products to prevent contamination [61]. Merbromin (mercurochrome, **32**) is used despite its very weak bacteriostatic action. Its brilliant red color may account for its popularity.

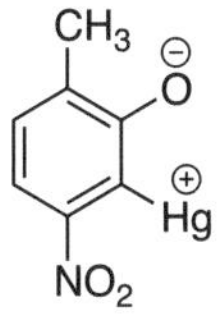

(27)

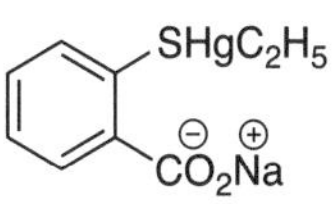

(28)

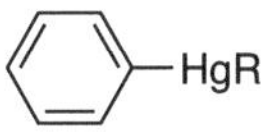

(29), R = OCOCH$_3$
(30), R = ONO$_2$
(31), R = OH

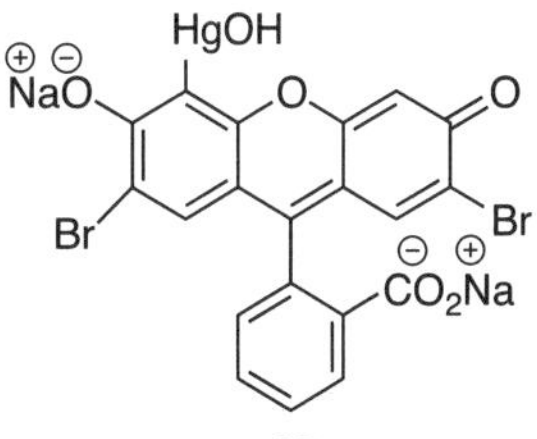

(32)

2.11.2. Silver Salts Silver ions bind readily with biologically important functional groups including thiol, amine, phosphate, and carboxylate. Some of these interactions can alter the properties of bacterial proteins and cause them to precipitate. Other interactions may cause alterations in the bacterial cell wall and cytoplasmic membrane. These drastic changes result in an immediate bactericidal effect and small amounts of silver ions subsequently liberated from silver–protein complexes provide sustained bacteriostatic action [59]. Silver nitrate ($AgNO_3$) solutions are highly germicidal, destroying most microorganisms at 0.1% concentration. Lower concentrations are bacteriostatic. Silver nitrate is particularly effective against *gonococci* and 1% solutions are used for the prophylaxis of *Ophthalmia neonatorum*. In 5% solutions, silver nitrate is used, usually in conjunction with antibiotics, to treat extensive burns.

A solid form of silver nitrate known as lunar caustic (toughened silver nitrate, USP) has been used to cauterize wounds.

Colloidal silver preparations retain substantial antibacterial activity and they are less injurious to tissues. One of these preparations, mild silver protein, contains about 20% of elemental silver.

Silver sulfadiazine (**33**) is used in the topical treatment of extensive burns. It readily penetrates the eschar and the solubility is low enough that insufficient silver is released to precipitate proteins or chloride ions [62]. It is effective against *P. aeruginosa*.

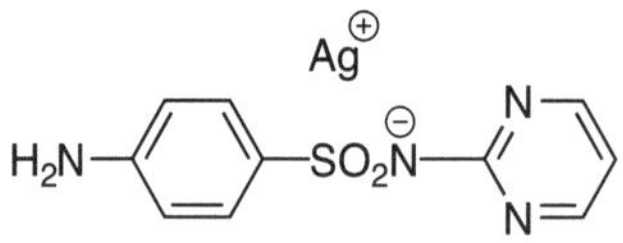

(**33**)

2.12. Dyes

Organic dyes were used extensively as antimicrobial agents before the development of sulfonamides and antibiotics. Now, only a few dyes such as gentian violet and methylene blue are used. Gentian violet (hexamethyl-*p*-rosaniline chloride, **34**) is a triphenylmethane dye that is converted into a colorless form (leucobase) in alkaline solution (Eq. 8). Cationic dyes such as gentian violet generally are active against Gram-positive bacteria and fungi; however, acid-fast and Gram-negative bacteria are resistant. Gentian violet has been used as a topical antibacterial agent, but its main use is as a topical agent for fungal infections. Gentian violet topical solution contains 1% of the agent and 10% of ethanol. Methylene blue (**35**) is a bacteriostatic agent that has been used for cystitis and urethritis, infections associated with *Escherichia coli and Neisseria gonorrhoeae*, respectively.

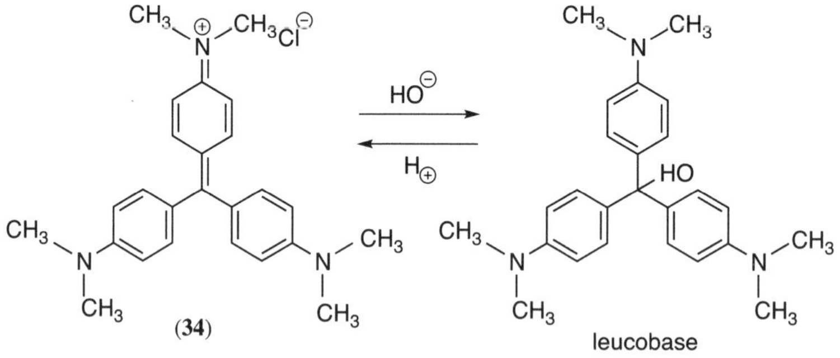

(**34**)

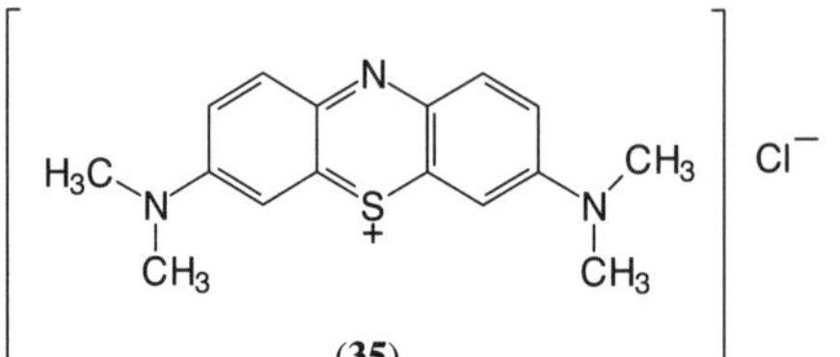

leucobase

(**35**)

2.13. Diarylureas, Amidines, and Biguanides

Diarylureas (carbanilides) are potent antibacterial agents [63]. Among a large number of these compounds, triclocarban (**36**) was chosen for commercial development. It is used mainly in detergents, toilet soaps, and medicated cosmetics. Propamidine (**37**) and dibromopropamidine (**38**) are diamidines with activity against Gram-positive bacteria [64,65]. Their mode of action is not known.

The antibacterial properties of biguanides were discovered by structural manipulation of the earlier biguanides with antimalarial activity [24]. They are strongly basic compounds that exist as dications at physiological pH. Their physical and antimicrobial properties resemble those of cationic surfactants, but they are not inactivated by anionic detergents unless the counter ions cause precipitation. The most important antibacterial biguanide is chlorhexidine (**39**), which is active against a broad spectrum of bacteria, except acid-fast bacteria and spores. It is not absorbed through skin or mucous membranes and it has no systemic toxicity or teratogenicity [66]. The commercial product is chlorhexidine digluconate, which is highly water soluble. A 4% emulsion of it is used in wound cleansing [67], treatment of burns [68], and surgical scrub preparation of skin [69]. In 0.2% solution, it is used as a mouthwash to combat plaque-inducing bacteria [70].

Chlorhexidine acts by a sequence of events involving attraction to the bacterial cell, strong binding to certain phosphate-containing compounds on the bacterial surface, overcoming bacterial cell wall exclusion mechanisms, attraction to the cytoplasmic membrane, leakage of low molecular weight cytoplasmic components, and complexation with phosphated molecules such as ATP and nucleic acids [71].

Some polymeric biguanides, such as polyhexamethylene biguanides (also called polyaminopropyl biguanide, **40**), wherein the molecular weight is in the range 1000–3000 Da are used in disinfecting contact lenses because they have high antimicrobial potency, low binding to the lenses, and very low ocular toxicity

[72]. Another important polymeric quaternary compound is polyquaternium 1 (Polyquad, **41**), which has 2-butenyl chains separating the quaternary nitrogens, and triethanolammonium groups at the chain ends [73].

2.14. Surface Active Agents

2.14.1. Cationic Surfactants
Cationic surfactants are quaternary ammonium or pyridinium salts that are ionic in water and have surface active properties. These properties are associated with the cationic head, which has high affinity for water, and a long hydrocarbon tail, which has high affinity for lipids. Cationic surfactants show potent activity against Gram-positive bacteria and lower activity against Gram-negative bacteria [74], whereas *Pseudomones* sp. and *M. tuberculosis* are resistant.

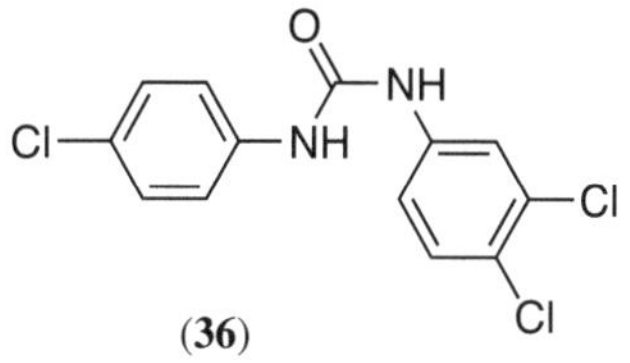

(36)

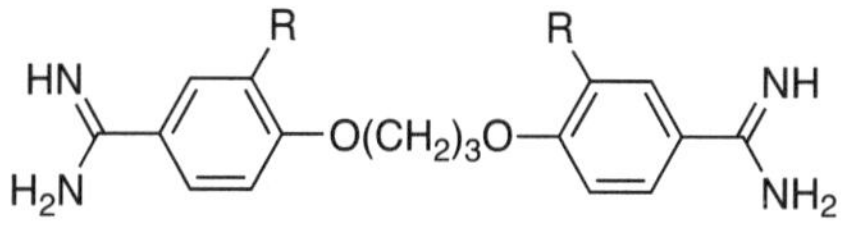

(37), R = H
(38), R = Br

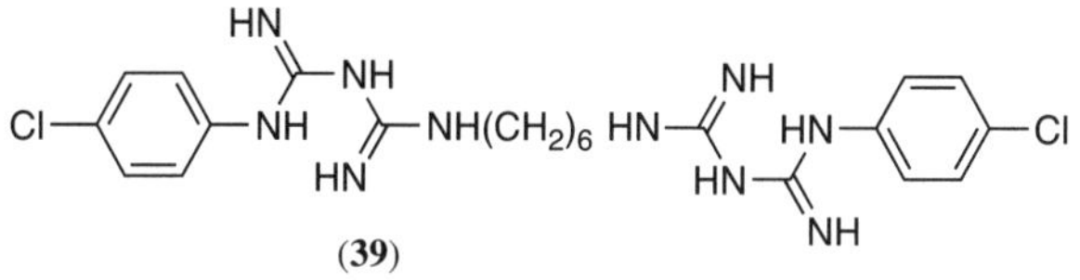

(39)

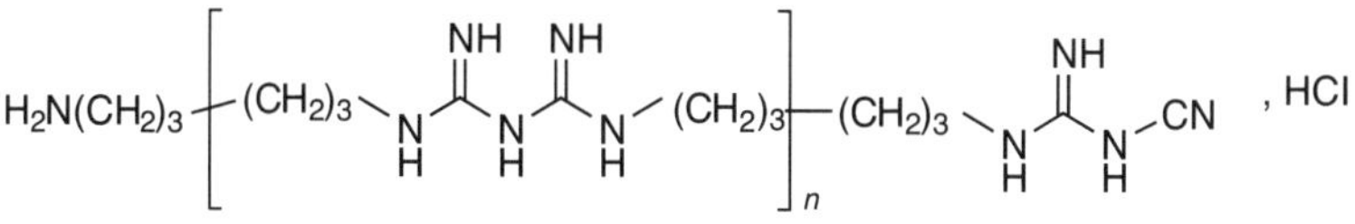

(40)

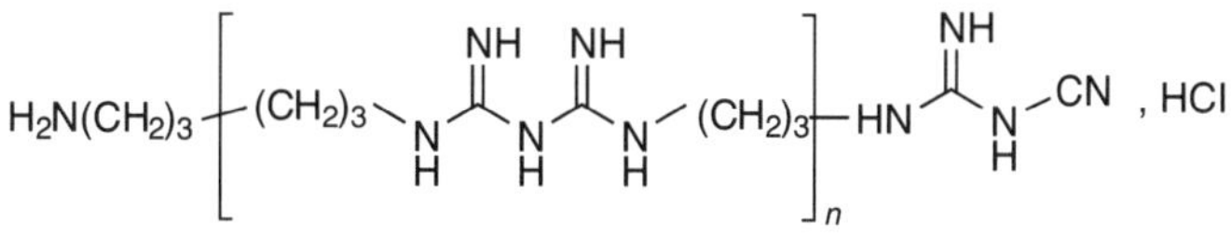

(41)

The mechanism of action of cationic surfactants is association with cell wall protein followed by penetration and disruption of the cell membrane. The resistance of gram-negative bacteria is attributed to difficulty in penetrating the outer membrane [75]. There is no activity against bacterial spores. Desirable features of cationic surfactants include water solubility, low toxicity, relatively good tissue penetration, and freedom from stains and corrosion. Disadvantages include inactivation by anionic surfactants (all traces of soap must be removed from skin), reduced effectiveness in the presence of blood serum and pus, strong adsorption on fibrous material such as cotton, occasional allergic responses on prolonged use, and resistant organisms.

The important surfactants are benzalkonium chloride, benzethonium chloride, methybenzethonium chloride, and cetylpyridinium chloride. Benzalkonium chloride is a mixture of alkylbenzyldimethylammonium chlorides having the general formula $[C_6H_5CH_2N(CH_3)_2R]^+$ Cl^-, where R is a mixture of alkyl groups of which $C_{12}H_{25}$, $C_{14}H_{29}$, and $C_{16}H_{33}$ are the main components. It is used as an antiseptic for skin and mucosa in concentrations of 1:75 to 1:20,000. Other uses include irrigation and disinfection of surgical instruments. Benzethonium chloride (**42**) is also is used as a skin disinfectant and irrigant of mucous membranes. Methylbenzethonium chloride (Diaparene, **43**) is used specifically for control of diaper rash in infants caused by *Bacterium ammoniagenes*, a species that liberates ammonia.

(**42**), R = H
(**43**), R = CH_3

(**44**)

Cetylpyridinium chloride (1-hexadecylpyridinium chloride, **44**) has its positively charged nitrogen as part of a pyridine ring. It finds use as a general anesthetic, irrigant for mucous membranes, and as a component of mouthwashes and lozenges.

Structure–activity relationships have been defined for cationic surfactants. For laurylpyridinium chlorides, antibacterial potency depends on the electronegativity of substituents on the pyridine ring with electron releasing groups affording the highest potencies. There is a linear relationship between potency and partial charge on the pyridine nitrogen [76]. Some highly potent substituted pyridines have not been commercialized because of their potential cost. Octanol–water partition coefficients were measured for a series of alkylbenzyl–dimethylammonium chlorides and used as the independent variable in a correlation with antibacterial potency. The parabolic relationship of the form $\log(1/C) = a + b \log p + c (\log p)^2$ was obtained, wherein p is the partition coefficient, and C is the minimum inhibitory concentration (MIC). Maximum potency was found for the compound with the $C_{14}H_{29}$ side chain. Potency depended on the organism, with the MIC being 10 times as great for Gram-negative bacteria as Gram-positive bacteria [77].

Mixtures of equal proportions of alkylbenzyldimethylammonium chloride and alkyldimethyl(ethylbenzyl)ammonium chloride (alkyl = C_{12} to C_{18}) are known as "dual quats." An example of these mixtures, BTC 2125M, has better biocidal activity than the individual species [78]. Quaternary ammonium compounds having two long alkyl chains were made possible when catalytic amination of long-chain alcohols to give dialkylmethylamines became a commercial process. Quaternization of these compounds with methyl chloride provides products known as "twin chain quats." An example of these compounds, dimethyldioctylammonium bromide (DECIQUAM) is used in the British food industry because of its low toxicity and good antibacterial potency [79]. Polymeric quaternary ammonium compounds, named polyionenes, are milder and safer than monomeric quaternary ammonium salts [80]. Among these compounds, Onamer M (**45**) is used as a preservative for contact lens solutions. It is less irritating than chlorhexidine.

2.14.2. Anionic Surfactants Mixtures of anionic surfactants with acids to lower the pH to

2-3 show rapid germicidal activity [81]. Alkyarylsulfonates such as dodecylbenzene-sulfonic acid (**46**) are the most effective surfactants and phosphoric acid is frequently used in the mixture. Possible modes of action are disorganization of the cellular membrane, denaturation of key enzymes and other proteins, and interruption of cellular transport [82]. Products have been developed for

disinfecting equipment in the food and dairy processing industry.

Oxychlorosene is a complex of sodium dodecylbenzenesulfonate and hypochlorous acid. It has a markedly rapid and complete cidal action against both gram-positive and gram-negative bacteria, fungi, yeasts, molds, viruses, and spores. It is applied as a disinfectant by irrigation, instillation, sprays, soaks, or wet compresses.

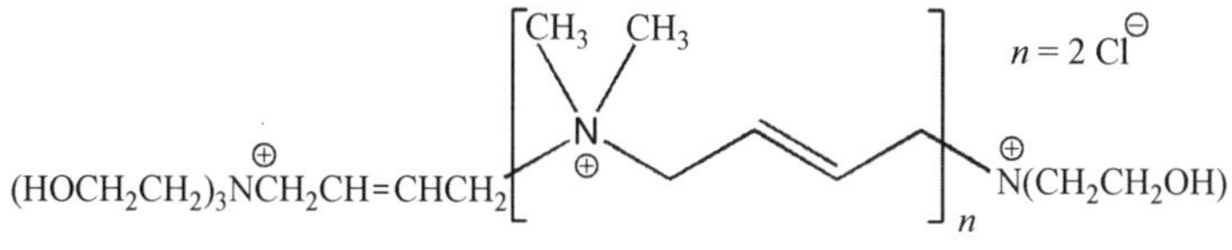

$$(HOCH_2CH_2)_3\overset{\oplus}{N}CH_2CH=CHCH_2\left[\overset{\overset{CH_3\ CH_3}{\underset{\oplus}{N}}}{}\right]_n\overset{\oplus}{N}(CH_2CH_2OH) \qquad n=2\ \overset{\ominus}{Cl}$$

(**45**)

2.14.3. Amphoteric Surfactants

These preparations, known as ampholites, have been used as biocides in Europe for more than 40 years. They are based on mixtures of alkyl-di (aminoethyl)glycines and other diaminoglycine derivatives. For example, Tego 51 contains dodecyl and tetradecyl di(aminoethyl) glycines plus dodecyl and tetradecyl aminoethylglycines [83]. A 1% solution of this product kills many Gram-positive and Gram-negative bacteria within one minute [84]. Specific uses are in hand-disinfection before surgery, disinfection of surgical instruments, and disinfection of rooms in hospitals and food processing facilities.

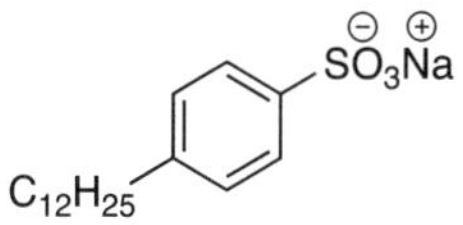

$$C_{12}H_{25}\!\!-\!\!\!\bigcirc\!\!\!-\overset{\ominus\ \oplus}{SO_3Na}$$

(**46**)

3. SYSTEMIC SYNTHETIC ANTIBACTERIALS

3.1. Introduction

The modern era of chemotherapy started with the discovery of sulfonamides as antibacterials in the early 1930s, followed soon by a series of antibiotics. The impact of antibacterial chemotherapy on medicinal science can hardly be exaggerated. These discoveries not only provided the first highly effective antibacterial drugs but also gave the confidence

that the bacterial diseases could be treated and controlled, and the developments that followed led to many of the important concepts and principles of chemotherapy, such as of selective activity/toxicity, of metabolite antagonism as a basis of drug action, of pharmacokinetics and metabolism of drugs as the basis of therapeutics, and gradually some general guidelines for chemotherapy evolved.

3.2. Principles of Antimicrobial Chemotherapy

The outcome of antimicrobial chemotherapy in all different situations is ultimately determined by a set of interactions between the drug, the host, and the infecting microbe, which are broadly discussed below:

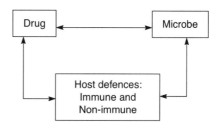

3.2.1. Factors Involved in Chemotherapy

3.2.1.1. The Drug The chemotherapeutic agent has most often a direct selective action on the infecting microbe. In bacterial infections, the drug either reversibly inhibits growth of bacteria, allowing no increase in viable organisms (bacteriostatic) or is irreversibly lethal to them (bactericidal). This distinction is more functional than absolute and is often concentration dependent.

Chemotherapeutic agents, apart from their direct antimicrobial action, also may affect host defenses, acting as biologic response modifiers. Antibacterials can be classified into four categories [85,86]: (a) those that have no effect on host defenses, for example, most β-lactams; (b) those that depress immune functions, for example, tetracyclines; (c) those that display synergy with the immune system, for example, some macrolides and quinolones; and (d) those that enhance the immune function, for example, certain cephalosporins. Since the immune system has an important role to play in the final elimination of the infectious agent, drugs that enhance the immune function are preferred over those that depress this function. The development and availability of drugs that combine antibacterial activity with an ability to restore or enhance the immune function have added a new dimension to the development of antimicrobial agents.

3.2.1.2. The Microbe
Humans exist in consort with a host of microbes, some of which play a very useful role in everyday life, such as in digestion and utilization of food that is consumed. Even among the microbes that cause disease, the outcome depends on the interaction between their intrinsic pathogenic potential or virulence and the defensive measures used by the host to contain or neutralize the infection threat. A distinction is, therefore, often made between infection and disease; infection implies invasion of the host by a pathogen, and the two could coexist, whereas impaired resistance of the host may shift the balance and result in establishing the disease state. In severe impairment of host resistance, organisms normally of low virulence can cause severe disease, and are called opportunistic pathogens. The virulence of a pathogen is thus a relative term. As a result of the increasing use of procedures and drugs causing immunodeficiency, such as cytotoxic use of drugs and radiation in cancer therapy, use of immunosuppressives in transplantation surgery, use of cortiosteroids in inflammatory conditions,

opportunistic infections have assumed a serious dimension and have to be treated expeditiously.

Drug Resistance. The term "drug resistance" refers not to the lack of sensitivity of a microbe species to a particular agent, but to acquired genotypic resistance, with or without exposure to the drug, which it develops during cultivation even in the absence of the drug. Thus, the development of drug-resistant strains is a part of the normal mutations in multiplication, and not dependant on exposure to a drug, which mainly result in selection of resistant mutants. The emergence of resistant bacterial strains is the most serious problem faced in chemotherapy [87].

Development of resistance to drugs by microbes can be by different mechanisms, and more than one mechanism may operate for the same drug, which are well described [88].

Since spontaneous mutation is an inherent characteristic of bacterial multiplication, the origin of mutants, including drug-resistant mutants, cannot be stopped. Sooner or later, microbes will develop resistance to virtually any antimicrobial agent. However, the survival and selection of resistant mutants can be prevented or delayed by using a correct therapeutic regimen, which should be the main concern in chemotherapy. Although there is no general procedure for preventing or overcoming drug resistance, some useful stratagems are available, which are discussed in the sections "Combating Drug Resistance" and "Combination Therapy".

Anaerobic Infections. Anaerobic bacteria require reduced oxygen tension for growth, and are responsible for deep-seated infections in the body. The more common anaerobes include *Clostridium perfringens*, *C. botulinum*, and *C. tetanus*—these organisms produce the most potent bacterial toxins known.

Most anaerobic bacteria exist in the human system as commensals, and anaerobic infections occur when the harmonious relationship between the host and the bacteria is disrupted. Any site in the body is susceptible to infection with these indigenous organisms when mucosal or skin barriers are compromised such as by surgery, trauma, tumor, or situations that reduce local tissue redox potentials, such as ischemia or necrosis. As the sites that are colonized by anaerobic bacteria contain many other species of bacteria and disruption of anatomic barriers causes penetration by many other organisms as well, resulting frequently in mixed infections involving multiple species of these anaerobes with microaerophilic organisms. Such infections include sinusitis, chronic otitis media, Ludwig's angina, periodontal abscesses, brain abscesses, and so on. Thus, abscesses of organs or tissues should first call to mind possible anaerobic infections and need special care and dispensation.

Biofilms. Biofilms [89] are thin films of bacterial colonies formed of multitude of bacterial species, in the aqueous body environment around implants, catheters, teeth, especially dentures, and so on. These colonies create a matrix through which nutrients are distributed and the colony is protected. These biofilms are formed around any site that is not too much disturbed. As these are colonized by multitude of bacterial species, which are protected, they pose a big challenge for chemotherapy and have to be treated by combination chemotherapy.

3.2.1.3. The Host A number of different host factors also have an important influence on the outcome of the efficacy and toxicity of antimicrobial agents. The age, physiological status, especially the renal and hepatic functioning, and the nutritional and genetic factors of the host have a significant effect on the metabolism, pharmacokinetics, and propensity to side effects of drugs. Host defenses, both immune and nonimmune, complement and have an important role in the elimination of the infecting organisms.

Interface with Immunity. Accumulating experience with chemotherapy of recent decades has resulted in a growing realization that the host immune system plays an important role in this outcome. Some of the facts that have enhanced this realization are (a) the increasing incidence of opportunistic infections and increased severity of normal infections in immunocompromised and immunodeficient patients; (b) greater efficacy of chemotherapeutic agents in immune populations. Immu-nomodulation in conjunction with chemotherapy therefore has emerged as a useful means of treating serious infectious diseases. In leprosy it has been shown that a heterologous vaccine can greatly augment the chemotherapy response and hasten bacillary clearance [90]. In experimental filarial infection, it has been shown that muramyl peptides, known immunomodulators, can both prevent infections when given prophylactically and modify their course when given along with DEC [91,92]. It is interesting that, although originally the term chemotherapy was coined by Ehrlich to distinguish it from immune-prophylaxis, after almost 100 years the two are being considered in tandem. An interesting facet of this interface between immunity and chemotherapy is the recent discovery of small molecules that synergize with host immunity by inactivating bacterial counterdefenses [93,94]. Further, Singh et al. [95] have shown that some bicyclic nitroimidazoles kill nonreplicating *M. tuberculosis* bacilli by acting as intracellular NO donors, and augment a killing mechanism intrinsic to the innate immune system. These findings will have special relevance for controlling infections that usually cause immunosuppression.

Genetic Factors. It cannot be sufficiently emphasized that individuals or even whole races show differences in response to identical doses of commonly prescribed drugs, and the answer for this resides largely in differences in genetic makeup. This situation calls for cautious watch when exposing a patient to any new drug that the body has not been exposed to previously. Many drugs are metabolized and deactivated by acetylation controlled by two different acetyl transferases, specified by different genes. These genes occur in different ratios in different individuals/races. Therefore, different people may require different doses of acetylatable drugs to achieve the same blood level of the free drug. These factors have to be considered while initiating new treatment schedules.

Local Tissue Factors. Local tissue factors, especially those resulting from the infections have an important role in the outcome of chemotherapy, and have to be considered while planning for treatment. For example, when bacteria reach a high enough extra cellular population density in a localized tissue site, the surrounding host cells die and suppuration results, forming an abscess. Antibacterial chemotherapy in such areas could become ineffective owing to several factors, such as impairment of circulation in dead tissue. Such abscesses are cured only after surgical drainage, which permits the bacteriostatic pus to be replaced by fresh serous exudate, providing nutrients as well as a wave of new leukocytes and chemotherapeutic drugs. The state and stage of the bacterial infection must also be considered while planning for chemotherapy. Arising out of the foregoing considerations, some general guidelines have emerged for the practice of bacterial chemotherapy, which are described below [96,97].

3.2.2. Guideline For Therapeutics

Initiation and Period of Treatment   The earlier the treatment is begun in an infection episode, the more likely it is to be effective. Some of the special reasons for this are (a) actively metabolizing and multiplying bacteria are more susceptible to the antibacterial action of most drugs, and some bacteria in a stationary phase even become refractory to bactericidal drugs; (b) once suppurative lesions are formed, they require surgical drainage and may cause irreversible tissue damage to vital organs; (c) the number of resistant mutants formed would be proportional to the total number of multiplication cycles bacteria undergo, so the earlier the cycle is interrupted the fewer resistant mutants are likely to be encountered; (d) lesions discovered late are more likely to become superinfected with resistant organisms.

In order to eliminate the last infecting bacterial cell, therapy must be continued for sometime after symptoms have subsided; with bacteriostatic agents, this period may be longer, since most bacteria will have to be eliminated by host defense.

Choice of Drug   Several factors bear directly on the selection of the antimicrobial agent to be used, which include taking into consideration the affected organ/site of infection, the microbe(s) causing the disease, the status of the host physiology, and other drugs being administered to the patient. Therefore, it is important in any infection episode to determine which organ system is affected, identify the offending microbe, and determine the susceptibility of the strain causing the disease to the available drug(s). Based on these findings is decided on the drug to be used and its route and dose of administration so that adequate concentration of the drug is delivered to the site of infection, and concentration above MIC is achieved in the affected tissues.

Host Factors   The age, nutritional and physiologic status of the host have a marked effect on drug disposition and thus on its dosage and side effects. Sulfonamides should not be administered to pregnant women or to newborns because they bind to serum albumin, displacing bilirubin, which may result in kernicterus. Tetracycines should not be administered to pregnant females and to newborn infants or to children less than 8 years of age because these drugs bind to developing bone and tooth structure and cause a permanent brown discoloration of the bones and teeth. Another facet is the affect of age on rate of drug metabolism; with advancing age there is a decreased rate of metabolism and thus an increased half-life of many drugs, such as atendol, and suitable dose adjustment becomes necessary.

Combating Drug Resistance   Development of drug resistance is the most serious problem faced in antimicrobial chemotherapy. Although there is no one general procedure available to overcome drug resistance, various useful stratagems have evolved that help to overcome or delay the development of resistant mutants and treat resistant organisms. Some of these measures are (a) initiating therapy early and with bactericidal drugs; (b) using combination therapy, where indicated, right from the beginning of the treatment; and (c) proper compliance with chemotherapeutic regimens with proper dosage for an adequate period.

Combination Therapy   Although the goal of chemotherapy is to use the most selectively acting drug that produces the least side effects, and most infections can be treated with a single antimicrobial agent, there are definite situations when therapy with a combination of antimicrobial agents is indicated.

The emergence of a rationale for combination therapy has been an important development in antimicrobial chemotherapy. Some situations in which combination therapy is indicated are given below:

(a) *Preventing/Delaying the Emergence of Resistant Organisms*: The most effective combinations are those for which there is a biochemical basis. For example, sulfonamides and dihydrofolate reductase inhibitors block sequential steps on the metabolic pathway to folate coenzymes, and their combination has proved exceptionally effective in preventing emergence of drug resistance.

(b) *Treatment of Polymicrobial Infections*: Some infections, including intra-abdominal, intraperitoneal, and pelvic infections, brain abscesses and biofilms formed around implants or catheters usually are due to a mixture of anaerobic and aerobic flora. Combination therapy is strongly indicated for these situations. Combination therapy is often used to provide optimal effective therapy in life-threatening emergencies.

(c) *Anaerobic Infections*: Because of the time and difficulty involved in the isolation of anaerobic bacteria, diagnosis and treatment of these infections has frequently to be made on an empirical basis. As most of these infections are caused by mixed flora, it is advisable to use combinations of antimicrobials, active against both aerobes and anaerobes, although not necessarily directed against all the organisms. The principle is that chemotherapy, combined with drainage, disrupts any interdependent relationship among the infecting organisms, and that species that may be resistant to the antimicrobial do not survive without the coinfective organisms; only some species such as *Bacteroides fragilis* require specific therapy. Penicillins, cephalosporins, erythromycin, clindamycin, tetracycline, and chloramphenicol are the drugs of choice for most anaerobes of clinical importance, but as their spectrum is confined only to anaerobes, the drug selected must be used in conjunction with an antibacterial active against facultative organisms. Prophylaxis and treatment by active and passive immunization combined with chemotherapy should be advocated where needed, such as for clostridial infections.

Drugs used in combination therapy should preferably be (i) noncross-resistant and act by different mechanisms and (ii) have well matched half-lives to supplement each other and decrease the need for frequent dosing.

Chemoprophylaxis Chemoprophylaxis is a preventive measure and should be used mainly to prevent infection by a specific microorganism or to eradicate an infection soon after it has become established. It has been used effectively in (i) preventing recurrent streptococcal infections in patients with rheumatic fever, (ii) prevention of gonorrhea or syphilis after contact with an infected person, (iii) preventing subacute bacterial endocarditis in patients with valvular heart disease undergoing surgical procedure, (iv) preventing recurrent urinary tract infections caused by *E. coli*, (v) terminating epidemics of meningococcal infections and of shigellosis in closed populations, and (vi) preventing bacterial diseases in neutropenic patients.

Chemoprophylaxis could be used in other similar infections related situations.

Rationale for Use of New Drugs Newly discovered agents should be reserved for cases when there is a lack of sensitivity or resistance to known and commonly used drugs. Otherwise, the new drugs also will become ineffective very quickly. Wherever possible, a sensitivity test of the infecting organism should be carried out and then only those agents should be used for treatments that are effective against that organism. For example, fluoroquinolones should not be the first line of treatment for common urinary tract infections or for gonococcal infections, and should be reserved for situations where other drugs have failed or there is established drug resistance.

The Individual and the Community The problem of drug resistance has highlighted the importance of the patients complying with the prescribed dosage regimens. Inappropriate dosing or faulty compliance of prescribed dosage regimens are most often the cause of the selection of drug-resistant mutants, affecting not only the individual patients but also the spread of resistant organisms in the community. This puts immense public health and civic responsibility on the physician to ensure that the patients comply with and follow the correct drug administration regimens, and on the patients to realize that they have a social responsibility to the community.

3.3. Folate Inhibitors

The discovery of the antibacterial activity of sulfonamides providing agents of unprecedented efficacy ushered in the modern era of chemotherapy. The demonstration that p-aminobenzoic acid (PABA), involved in folate biosynthesis, inhibited the action of sulfonamides, was the first clear demonstration of metabolite antagonism as a mechanism of drug action opening a rational approach to drug discovery. Detailed elucidation of the mechanism of action of sulfonamides showed that the enzymatic steps inhibited by sulfonamides was absent in the human host, highlighting that chemotherapeutic effort could be directed toward designing inhibitors of essential enzymes and pathways present in the pathogens but lacking in the human host. This gave support to the concept that biochemical differences between humans and their parasites could serve as the basis of a rational approach to the design of chemotherapeutic agents. It also highlighted the importance of folate pathway as a suitable target for development of new antibacterials and different classes of compounds started being tested as folate antagonists. This resulted in the discovery of inhibitors of DHFR, another important step in the folate pathway. However, the discovery of DHFRI showed that although this enzymatic step in the folate pathway was present in both the mammalian host and the microbes, there were marked differences in the selectivity of action of some compounds against the same enzyme from different sources. This added another important facet to the concept of biochemical differences between the mammalian host and the parasite as the basis for the design and discovery of antimicrobials.

Thus the discovery of antibacterial activity of sulfonamides (and sulfones) followed by that of dihydrofolate reductase inhibitors put the concept of biochemical differences between the host and their parasites as the basis for a rational approach to the design of chemotherapeutic agents on a very broad and sound footing. These biochemical differences could be either in the absence of the essential enzyme systems in the host as in the case of sulfonamides or in the selectivity of the inhibition of an essential enzyme between the host and the microbe. These concepts, illustrated below in the sections on sulfonamides (and sulfones) and dihydrofolate reductase inhibitors, continue to be the mainstay of drug design and discovery to this day.

3.3.1. Sulfonamides and Sulfones

Introduction   Prontosil rubrum (**47**), a sulfonamido-azo dye, was the first clinically useful systemic antibacterial agent to be discovered. This discovery in the early 1930s and the development of sulfonamides and sulfones as a class of antibacterial agents, which followed, form a fascinating chapter in the annals of medicinal chemistry. Their broad antimicrobial spectrum provided for the first time drugs for the cure and prevention of a variety of bacterial infections; their widespread clinical use brought about a sharp decline in morbidity and mortality of treatable infectious diseases, and thus proved of great medical and public health importance. Recognition of the inhibition of the action of sulfonamides by yeast extracts, which was shown to be due to the presence of PABA, required in folate biosynthesis, was the first clear demonstration of metabolite antagonism as a mechanism of drug action; this provided the long sought after mechanistic basis for drug action.

This led Fildes (1940) to propose his classic theory of "antimetabolites" as an approach to chemotherapy [230]. The development of dihydrofolate reductase inhibitors as antimicrobial agents, and their synergistic use in combination with sulfonamides inhibiting another step in folate biosynthesis, was a direct result of this interest generated in antimetabolites. That sulfanilamide (**48**), formed *in vivo* was responsible for the antibacterial action of prontosil, focused attention on the importance of drug metabolism and blood levels of the active species for drug action. Pharmacokinetic studies thus became an integral part of drug development. Carefully observed side effects in pharmacological and clinical studies of the early sulfonamides revealed new and unanticipated activities; successful exploitation of these leads opened up new areas in chemotherapy such as oral antidiabetics, carbonic anhydrase inhibitors, and diuretics. This also highlighted the importance of side effects of drugs as a source of new leads in drug design, which is used to this day. The rapidity, with which new developments took place between 1933 and 1940, from the discovery of antibacterial activity of prontosil to the enunciation of the theory of antimetabolites by Fildes indicates that the time was just ripe for major developments in drug research and needed only a catalyst, which was provided by the discovery of the antibacterial activity of sulfonamides. The discovery of sulfonamides thus was not only the beginning of the modern era of systemic synthetic antibacterials but also had a strong impact on developments in medicinal chemistry that influenced later work in drug research in general and chemotherapy in particular.

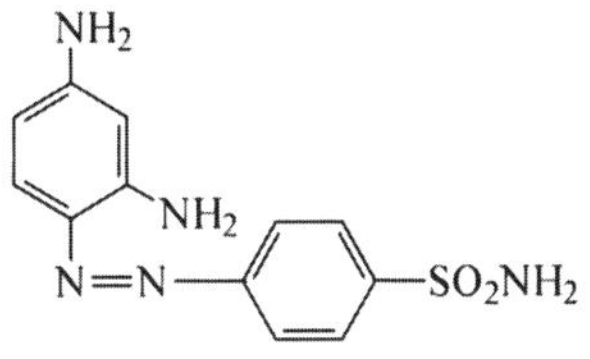

(47) 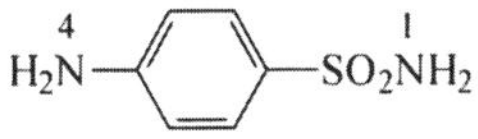   (48)

The interest in sulfonamides and sulfones continues even eight decades after their discovery. Although no major new drug in this class has been added in the last three decades, and the addition of other new classes of antibacterials has diminished the clinical use of the existing sulfonamides/sulfones, they still occupy a distinct place in the therapeutic armamentarium; for some bacterial infections alone or in combination with trimethoprim they are still the drugs of choice. One major recent scientific development around sulfonamides is the elucidation of their mode of action at the molecular level. With the identification of the pterin, PABA, and sulfonamide binding sites on the dihydropteroate synthase (DHPS) of different classes of microbes, the stage is set for the design of new generation of DHPS inhibitors with broad-based antimicrobial activity.

3.3.1.1. Historical Background

The story of sulfonamides goes back to the early years of twentieth century when Orlein, Dressel and Kethe of I.G. Farbenindustrie, Germany [98] found that introduction of a sulfamyl group imparted fastness to acid wool dyes; thus, indicating affinity for protein molecules. However, none of these sulfonamides was investigated for antibacterial activity. The interest in dyes as possible antimicrobials was prompted by Ehrlich's studies on the relationship between selective staining of cells by dyes and their antiprotozoal activity, which led to the testing of azo dyes for antibacterial activity also; some of them indeed showed such activity. In an attempt to improve the antimicrobial activity of quinine derivatives, Heidelberger and Jacobs [99] prepared dyes based on dihydrocupreine, which included p-aminobenzene-sulfonamido-hydrocupreine. Although the latter was reported to have bactericidal activity, it did not arouse much interest because the activity, having been tested in vitro, was of a low order and no further work was published on these compounds. Mietzch and Klarer at I. G. Farbenindustrie synthesized a variety of azo dyes, a continuation of Ehrlich's interest in imparting to azo dyes the property of specific binding to bacterial proteins, comparable to the binding to wool proteins. Mietzsch and Klarer [100] synthesized a group of such dyes containing a sulfonamide group, which included prontosil rubrum [47]. Domagk, at I.G. Farbenindustrie, carried out the antibacterial testing of these dyes. Realizing the lack of correlation between *in vitro* and *in vivo* screening, Domagk decided to do the testing in mice, a very fortunate decision, since otherwise the fate of sulfonamides might have been different. Domagk [101] observed in 1932 that prontosil protected mice against streptococcal infections and rabbits against staphylococcal infections, although it was without action *in vitro* on bacteria. Anecdotal reports say that the first patient to be successfully treated with prontosil was Hildegarde Domagk, the daughter of its discoverer, who had septicemia due to a stitching needle prick. Foerster [102] published the first clinical success with prontosil in a case of staphylococcal septicemia in 1933.

These studies aroused worldwide interest and further developments took place at a very fast rate. One of the earliest systematic investigations on sulfonamides was by Trefouel, Nitti, and Bovet [103] working at the Pasteur Institute in Paris. Under a program of structural modification of this class of compounds, they prepared a series of azo dyes by coupling diazotized sulfanilamides with phenols, with or without amino or alkyl groups. They observed that variation in the structure of the phenolic moiety had very little effect on antibacterial activity, whereas even small changes in the sulfanilamide component abolished the activity. These observations pointed to the benzenesulfonamide residue as the active structural unit, and led to considering *p*-aminobenzenesulfonamide (sulfanilamide, **48**) as the putative metabolite responsible for the antibacterial activity. They suggested that prontosil was converted to sulfanilamide in animals and showed that sulfanilamide was as effective as the parent dyestuff in protecting mice infected with streptococci. They also showed that sulfanilamide exerted a bacteriostatic effect *in vitro* on susceptible organisms. Soon after, Colebrook and Kenny [104] observed that although prontosil was inactive *in vitro*, the blood of patients treated with it had bacteriostatic activity. They also reported the dramatic cure of 64 cases of puerperal sepsis by prontosil, whereas Buttle et al. [105] showed that sulfanilamide could cure streptococcal and meningococcal infections in mice.

Fuller's [106] demonstration of the presence of sulfanilamide in the blood and its isolation from urine of patients (and mice) under treatment with prontosil firmly established that prontosil is reduced in the body to form sulfanilamide **48**, a compound synthesized as early as 1909 by Gelmo [107]. Fuller concluded that the therapeutic action of prontosil was very likely due to its reduction *in vivo* to sulfanilamide. Among the early patients to be treated with sulfanilamide was Franklin D. Roosevelt Jr. (son of President Franklin D. Roosevelt of the United States). His recovery from a streptococcal throat infection helped to overcome early reservations on the medicinal value of antibacterial chemotherapy with sulfonamides. Although Ehrlich's concept of a relationship between the affinity of dyes for a parasite and their antimicrobial activity, which focused attention on sulfonamide azo dye, was found to be irrelevant to the activity of the latter, but sulfanilamide proved to be the "magic bullet" of Ehrlich and heralded the era of "chemotherapy," a term coined by Ehrlich to emphasize the concept of selective action of chemicals on microbes as opposed to the action on host cells. The era of modern chemotherapy had now begun. Domagk was awarded the Nobel Prize for Medicine in 1939 primarily for the discovery of the antibacterial activity of sulfonamides.

Earlier Sulfonamides. These discoveries had a tremendous impact not only on the development of sulfonamides as antimicrobials but also on the developments in chemotherapy in general. Sulfanilamide, being easy to prepare, cheap and not covered by patents, became available for widespread use and brought a new hope for the treatment of microbial infections. Recognizing the potential of sulfonamides, almost all major research organizations the world over initiated research programs for the synthesis and study of analogs and derivatives of sulfanilamide, particularly with a view to improve its antimicrobial spectrum, therapeutic ratio, and pharmacokinetic properties. New sulfonamides were introduced in quick succession sulfapyridine [M&B 693, (**49**)] [108], reported in 1938, was one of the earliest of the new sulfonamides to be used in clinical practice for the treatment of pneumonia and remained the drug of choice until it was replaced by sulfathiazole. Sulfapyridine was used on Winston Churchill to cure pneumonia in 1943 during a trip to Africa.

Sulfathiazole (50) [109] was the second sulfonamide to be introduced in clinical practice. It replaced sulfapyridine because of its wider antibacterial spectrum and higher therapeutic index. Substitution of the thiazole ring with alkyl groups did not improve the activity, while a 4-phenyl residue enhanced both the activity and the toxicity.

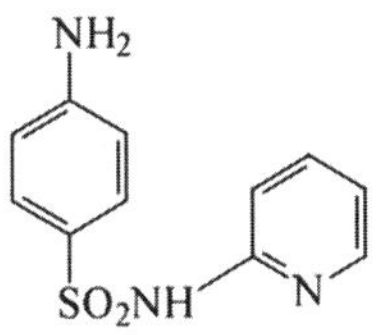

(49) 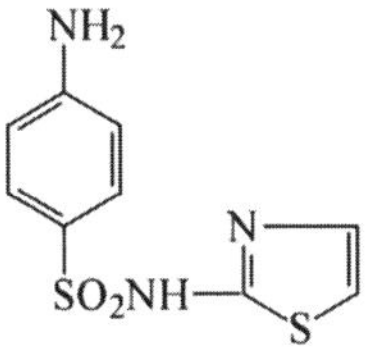   (50)

Some of the other important sulfonamides introduced in clinical practice during this period were sulfacetamide, the corresponding N^4-pthallyl and succinyl derivatives, sulfadiazine (51), sulfamerazine (52), sulfamethazine, sulfisomidine, sulfamethizole, and sulfisoxazole (Table 2). These compounds differed widely in their pharmacokinetic profile and helped in enlarging the scope of therapeutic use of sulfonamides. This work was described in 1948 in a very exhaustive monograph by Northey, which may be consulted for research work of this period [110].

Later Sulfonamides. This widespread interest in new sulfonamides continued till about 1945, when interest gradually shifted to antibiotics after the introduction of penicillin.

However, after about a decade of the use of penicillins problems encountered with antibiotics, such as emergence of resistant strains, superinfection, and allergic reactions, brought about a revival of interest in sulfonamides. The knowledge gained during this period about the selectivity of action of sulfonamides on the pathogens, the relationship between their solubility and toxicity, and their pharmacokinetics gave a new direction to further developments, and a second generation of sulfonamides began to appear with improved properties.

A major advance in sulfonamide therapy came with the proper appreciation of the role of pharmacokinetic studies in determining the dosage schedule of these drugs. It was realized that some of the "earlier" sulfonamides such as sulfadiazine (51) and sulfamerazine (52) had a long half-life (17 and 24 h, respectively) and required less frequent administration than was normally prescribed. The era of newer long-acting sulfonamides started in 1956 with the introduction of sulfamethoxypyridazine (53) [111] having a half-life of around 37 h, the longest known at that time, which needed to be administered only once a day [112]. In 1959, sulfadimethoxine was introduced with a half-life of approximately 40 h [113–115]. A related 4-sulfonamidopyrimidine, sulfadoxine (54) [116,117], having the two methoxyl radicals in 5,6-positions, was soon introduced. It has by far the longest half-life, about 150 h, and needs administration once a week.

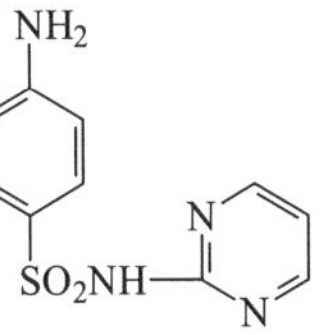

(51) 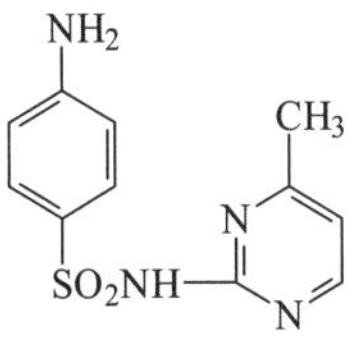   (52) 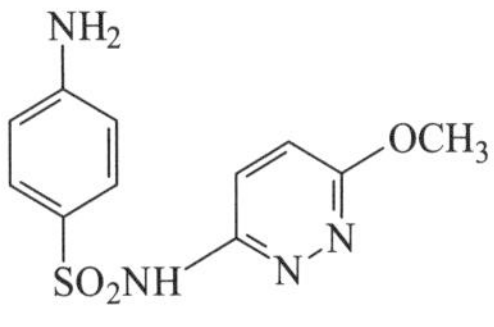   (53)

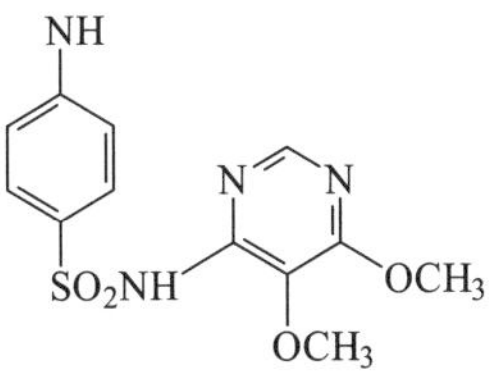

(54) 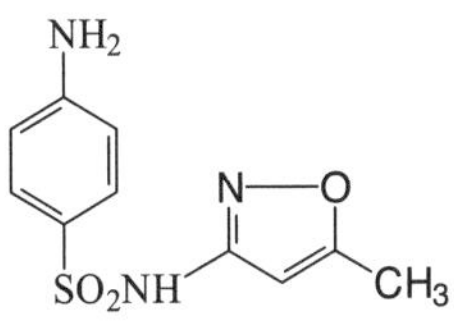   (55)

Table 2. Characteristics of Commonly Used Sulfonamides and Sulfones[a]

H_2N—(4) benzene ring (1)—SO_2NHR

Generic Name	R	Common Proprietary Names	In Vivo Activity[b] Against E. Coli (μmol/L)	Water Solubility[c] (mg/100 mL at 25°C)	pK_a	Lipo-solubility[c] (%)	Protein Binding at 1.0 μmol/mL, % Bound	Plasma "Half-life/h" (Human)	%N^4-Metabolite in Urine[d] (Human)
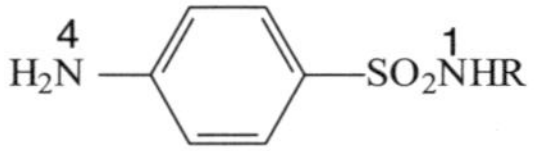 1	2	3	4	5	6	7	8	9	10
Poorly absorbed, locally acting									
Phthalylsulfathiazole[e]	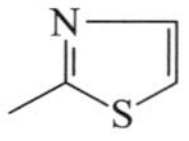 (2-substituted thiazole)	Thalazole Sulfthaladine		Insoluble	Acid				
Sulfaguanidine	$C(=NH)NH_2$	Guanicil Resulfon	4[h]	100	Base				
Well absorbed, rapidly excreted									
Sulfamethizole Sulfamethylthiadiazole	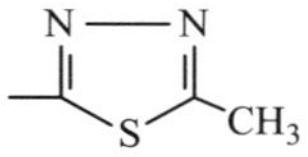 (5-methyl-1,3,4-thiadiazol-2-yl), CH_3	Methisul Lucosil Ultrasul		25 (pH 6.5)	5.5		22	2.5	6
Sulfathiazole	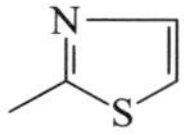 (thiazol-2-yl)	Cibazole Thiazamide	1.6	60 (pH 6)	7.25	15.3	68	4	30 (40)
Sulfisoxazole Sulfafurazola	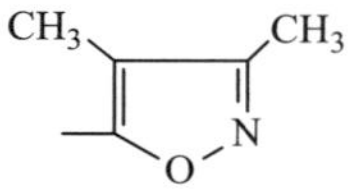 (3,4-dimethylisoxazol-5-yl), CH_3, CH_3	Gantrisin Urosulfin	2.15	350 (pH 6)	5.0	4.8	76.5	6.0	16 (30)

Name	R	Trade names						
Sulfisomidine	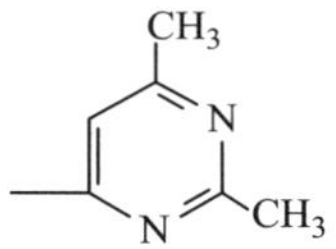 (2,6-dimethylpyrimidin-4-yl)	Elkosin Aristamid	1.5	300 (30°)	7.4	19.0	67	7.5	4
Sulfacetamide	–COCH₃	Albucid	2.3	670	5.4	2.0	9.5	7	5
Sulfapyridine	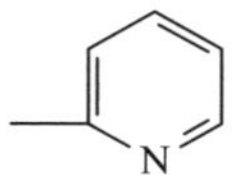 (2-pyridyl)	Eubasin Dagenan MB693	4.8	30	8.4	14	70	9	30
Sulfanilamide	H	Prontosil albrem Prontalbin	128	750	10.5	71	9	9	
Readily absorbed, medium rate of excretion									
Sulfaphenazole	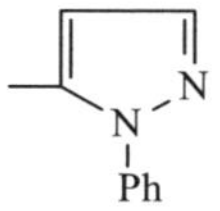 (1-phenylpyrazol-5-yl)	Orisul	1.0	150	6.09	69	87.5	10	20 (80)
Sulfamethoxazole	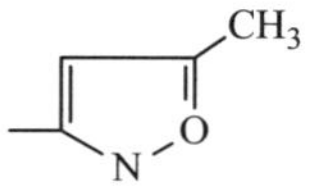 (5-methylisoxazol-3-yl)	Gantanol	0.8	Springly soluble	6.0	20.5	60	11	60 (14)
Sulfadiazine	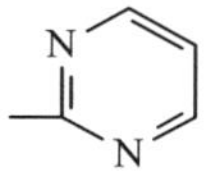 (2-pyrimidyl)	Debenal Pyrimal	0.9	8	6.52	26.4	37.8	17	25

(Continued)

511

Table 2 (*Continued*)

Generic Name 1	R 2	Common Proprietary Names 3	*In Vivo* Activity[b] Against *E. Coli* (µmol/L) 4	Water Solubility[c] (mg/100 mL at 25°) 5	pK_a 6	Lipo-solubility[c] (%) 7	Protein Binding at 1.0 µmol/mL, % Bound 8	Plasma "Half-life/h" (Human) 9	%N^4-Metabolite in Urine[d] (Human) 10
Readily absorbed slowly excreted									
Sulfaperine	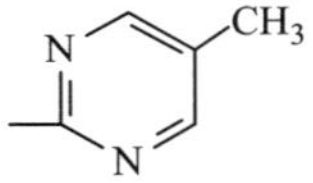	Pallidin	1.0	40 (pH 5.5)	6.7	69.6	74.0	35	
Sulfameter Sulfamethoxydiazine	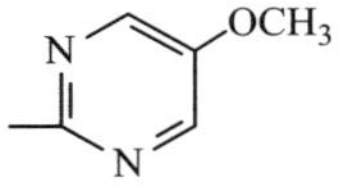	Durenat Sulfametorine	2.0	Very sparingly soluble	7.0	64.0	74.2	37	20 (30)
Sulfamethoxypyridazine	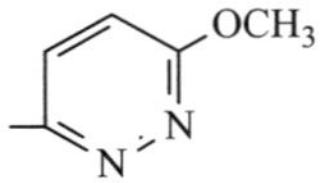	Lederkyn Kynex	1.0	147 (pH 6.5)	7.2	70.4	77	37	50 (15)
Sulfadimethoxine	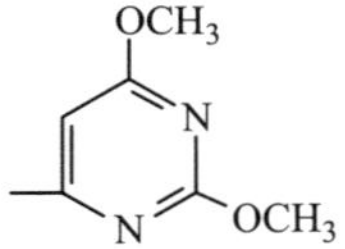	Madribon	0.7	29.5 (pH 6.7)	6.1	78.7	92.3	40	15 (70)
Sulfamethoxpyrazine Sulfametopyrazine	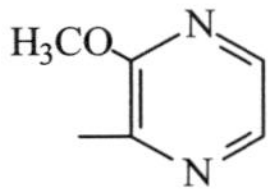	Sulfalene Kelfizina	1.85	Very sparingly soluble	6.1		65	65	65
Sulfadoxine Sulformethoxine	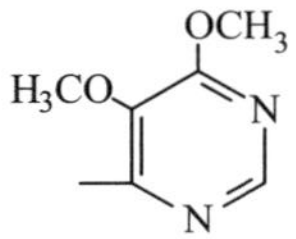	Fanasil	0.8	—	6.1	5	95	150	60 (10)

512

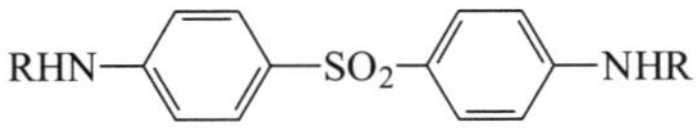

RHN—⟨C₆H₄⟩—SO$_2$—⟨C₆H₄⟩—NHR

		R						
Diaminodiphenylsulfone	Dapsone Avlosulphon	H	44	14	Base	13	50	20
Diacetamidodiphenyl-sulfone	Acedapsone	COCH$_3$		0.3				43 days

Arranged in order of increasing plasma half-life.

[a] Unless otherwise stated, the data is from Rieder (156).
[b] From Struller [327].
[c] Determined by partition between ethylene dichloride and sodium phosphate buffer [327].
[d] From William and Park [186].
[e] N^4-Phthalyl.

Some of the other sulfonamides introduced in clinical practice in this period were sulfamethyldiazine, sulfaphenazole, sulfamoxol, and sulfamethoxazole (**55**) [118] (Table 2). Sulfamethoxazole is a particularly important sulfonamide of this period in view of its well matched half-life (~11 h) with trimethoprim, and a fixed-dose combination of the two, cotrimoxazole is widely used in clinical practice. **Sulfones.** The demonstration that experimental tuberculosis could be controlled by 4,4′-diaminodiphenylsulfone (DDS, dapsone **56**) [119] and disodium 4,4′-diamino-diphenylsulfone -*N,N′*-didextrose sulfonate, (promin, **57**) [120], was a major advance in the chemotherapy of mycobacterial infections. Although dapsone and promin proved disappointing in the therapy of human tuberculosis, the interest aroused in the possibility of treatment of mycobacterial infections with sulfones led to the demonstration of the favorable effect of promin in rat leprosy [121]. This was soon followed by the successful treatment of leprosy patients, first with promin and later with dapsone itself. Since then dapsone has re-

mained the main stay for the treatment of all forms of human leprosy [122]. It has now been shown that *Mycobacterium leprae* is unusually sensitive to dapsone [123] and that its growth can be inhibited by very low concentration of the latter.

An important advance in the use of dapsone took place with the demonstration that *N,N′*-diacyl derivatives and certain Schiff bases of dapsone are prodrugs and have a repository effect and release dapsone slowly; *N,N′*-diacetamidodiphenylsulfone (acedapsone, DADS **58**) and the Schiff's base 4′,4-[p-phenylene-bis(methyledeneimino-*p*-phenylenesulfonyl)] bisacetanilide (PSBA, **59**) are particularly useful as repository forms [124]. After a single intramuscular injection of 225 mg of acedapsone, a therapeutic level of DDS (20–25 µg/mL) is maintained in the blood for as long as 60–68 days, and it is useful in the prophylaxis and treatment of leprosy.

With a view to improving upon the antimycobacterial and antiprotozoal (especially antimalarial) activities of dapsone, a variety of substituted sulfones have been prepared.

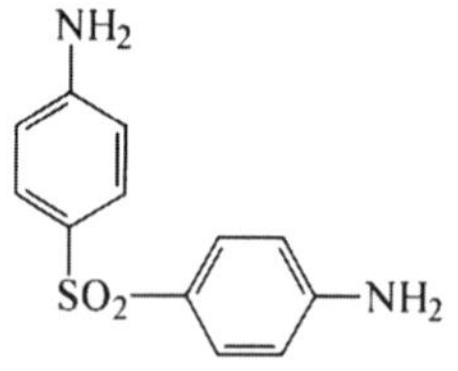

(**56**) 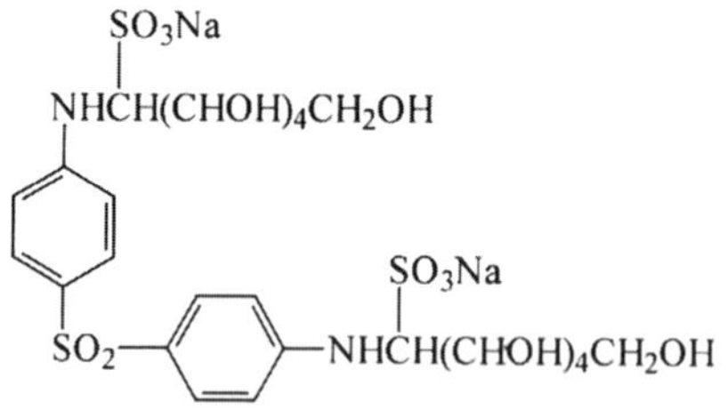 (**57**) 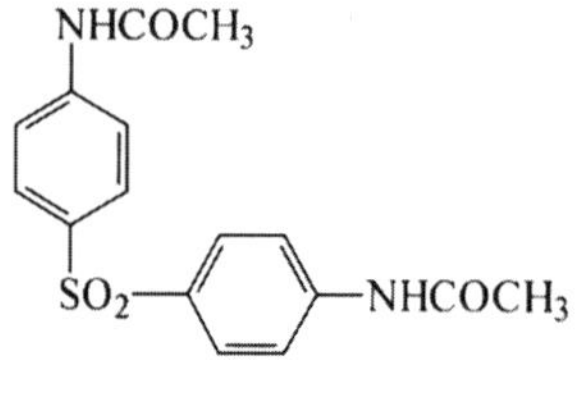 (**58**) 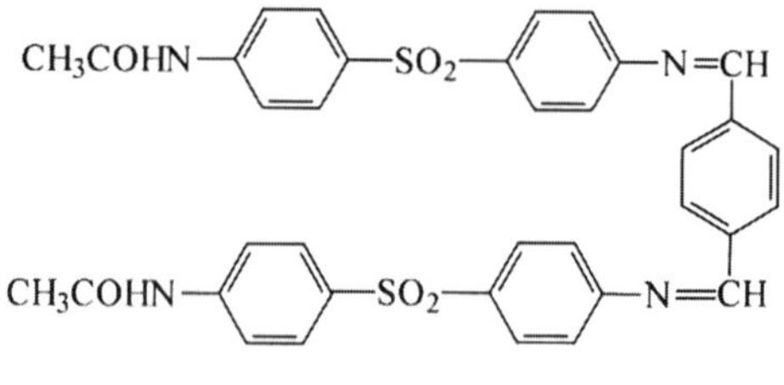 (**59**)

Overall, none of the substituted diaminodiphenylsulfones was significantly more active *in vivo* than DDS to offer much advantage [125]. Even after almost 50 years of use in

clinical practice, DDS alone or in combination with other drugs (as in multidrug therapy) continues to be the main stay of chemotherapy of leprosy.

3.3.1.2 Structure–Activity Relationship

Structure and Biological Activity. Although the story of sulfonamides started with the discovery of their antimicrobial action, subsequent follow up of their observed side effects established their usefulness also as carbonic anhydrase inhibitors, diuretics (saluretics), and antidiabetics (insulin releasers), and more recently as endothelin antagonists. Compounds with each type of action possess certain specific common structural features. The present discussion, however, is restricted only to the antimicrobial sulfonamides and sulfones, characterized by their ability to inhibit the *de novo* biosynthesis of folic acid by competing with PABA for 7,8-dihydro-6-hydroxymethylpterin pyrophosphate at the active site of dihydropteroate synthase [126–128].

Sulfonamides   Because sulfanilamide (**48**) is a rather small molecule and there are not too many variations that can be carried out without changing the basic nucleus, the following generalizations regarding structure–activity relationships were arrived at quite early in the development of sulfonamides, which guided the subsequent work on molecular modification, and these generalizations still hold:

(1) The amino and sulfonyl radicals on the benzene ring should be in 1,4-disposition for activity; the amino group should be unsubstituted or have a substituent that is removed readily *in vivo*.

(2) Replacement of the benzene ring by other ring systems, or the introduction of additional substituents on it, decreases or abolishes the activity.

(3) Exchange of the SO_2NH_2 by $SO_2C_6H_4$-p-NH_2 retains the activity, while exchange by $CONH_2$, or by COC_6H_4-pNH_2 markedly reduces the activity.

(4) N^1-Monosubstitution results in more active compounds with greatly modified pharmacokinetic properties.
N^1-Disubstitution in general leads to inactive compounds.

(5) The N^1-substitution should be such whose pK_a would approximate the physiological pH.

The presence of a *p*-aminobenzensulfonyl radical thus seems inviolate for maintaining good activity and practically all the attention was focused on N^1-substituents. These substituents seem to affect mainly the physicochemical and the pharmacokinetic characteristics of the drugs.

Sulfones   The following broad generalization hold for the SAR of sulfones:

(1) One *p*-aminophenylsulfonyl residue is essential for activity; the amino group in this moiety should be unsubstituted or have a substituent that is removed readily *in vivo*.

(2) The second benzene ring should preferably have small substituents that will make this ring electron rich (such as CH_3, OCH_3, OH, NH_2, NHC_2H_5); *p*-substitution is most favorable for activity.

(3) Replacement of the second phenyl ring by heterocycles does not improve the activity.

Diaminodiphenyl sulfone (DDS) has retained its preeminent therapeutic position even after 50 years of its use.

3.3.1.3 Quantitative SAR

Studies to find a correlation between physicochemical properties and bacteriostatic activity of sulfonamides have been pursued almost since their discovery. The substituents that attracted the attention of investigators quite early were the amino and the sulfonamido groups in the molecule, and several groups of investigators almost simultaneously noted a correlation between the bacteriostatic activity and the degree of ionization of sulfonamides. The primary amino group in sulfonamides apparently plays a vital part in producing bacteriostasis, since any substituent on it causes complete loss of activity. Seydel et al. [129,130], from a study of infrared (IR) spectra and activity of a number of sulfonamides, concluded that the amount of negative charge on the aromatic amino group is important for the activity. However, variation in activity within a series of compounds could not be related to a change in base strength, since all the active sulfonamides (and sulfones) have a basic dissociation constant of about 2, which is close to that of PABA. Foernzler and Martin [131] computed the electronic characteristics of a series of 50 sulfonamides by the combination of linear atomic and molecular orbital methods (LCAO-MO methods) and found that the electronic charge on the p-amino group did not vary significantly with a change in the N^1-substituent.

Thus, attention was focused mainly on the N^1-acidic dissociation values, which vary widely about from 3 to 11. Fox and Rose [132] noted that sulfathiazole and sulfadiazine were about 600 times as active as sulfanilamide against a variety of microorganisms, and that approximately 600 times more PABA was required to antagonize their action as to antagonize the action of sulfanilamide; however, the same amount of PABA was required to antagonize the MIC of each drug. This suggested that the active species in both cases were similar, and that the increase in bacteriostatic activity was due to the presence of a larger proportion of the drug in an active (ionized) form. They found that the concentration of the ionized form of each drug at the minimum effective concentration was of the same order. Thus, if only the ionized fraction at pH 7 was considered instead of the total concentration, the PABA/drug ratio was reduced to 1:1.6–6.4. They also observed that with a 10-fold increase in ionization of sulfanilamide on altering the pH from 6.8 to 7.8, there was an eightfold increase in bacteriostatic activity. On the basis of these observations, Fox and Rose suggested that only the ionized fraction of the MIC is responsible for the antibacterial action. Schmelkes et al. [133] also noted the effect of pH of the culture medium on the MIC of sulfonamides and suggested that the active species in a sulfonamide solution is the anionic species.

Bell and Roblin [134], in an extensive study of the relationship between the pK_a of a series of sulfonamides and their *in vitro* antibacterial activity against *E. coli*, found that the plot of log 1/MIC against pK_a was a parabolic curve, and that the highest point of the curve lay between pK_a of 6 and 7.4; the maximal activity was thus observed in compounds whose pK_a approximated the physiological pH. Since the pK_a values are related to the nature of the N^1-substituent, the

investigators emphasized the value of this relationship for predicting the MIC of new sulfonamides. The pK_a of most of the active sulfonamides discovered since then, and particularly of the long-acting ones, falls in this range (Table 2). Bell and Roblin correlated Woods and Fildes's hypothesis regarding the structural similarity of a metabolite and its antagonist with the observed facts of ionization. They emphasized the need of polarization of the sulfonyl group of active sulfonamides, so as to resemble as closely as possible the geometric and electronic characteristics of the p-aminobenzoate ion, and postulated: "the more negative the SO_2 group of N^1-substituted sulfonamides, the more bacteriostatic the compound will be." The acid dissociation constants were considered to be an indirect measure of the negative character of the SO_2 group. The hypothesis of Bell and Roblin stated that the unionized molecules had a bacteriostatic activity too, although weaker than that of the ionized form. Furthermore, it was supposed that increasing the acidity of a compound decreased the negativity of the SO_2 group, thus reducing the bacteriostatic activity of the charged and uncharged molecules.

Cowles [135] and Brueckner [136], in a study of the effect of pH of the medium on the antibacterial activity of sulfonamides, found that the activity increased with increase in pH of the medium only up to the point at which the ionization of the drug was about 50%, and then it decreased. Brueckner assumed different intra- and extracellular pH values to explain the observed effects. Cowles suggested that the sulfonamides penetrate the bacterial cell in the unionized form, but once inside the cell, the bacteriostatic action is due to the ionized form. Hence for maximum activity, the compounds should have a pK_a that gives the proper balance between the intrinsic activity and penetration; the half-dissociated state appeared to present the best compromise between transport and activity. This provided an alternative explanation for the parabolic relationship observed by Bell and Roblin between pK_a and MIC.

Seydel et al. [129,137,138] and Cammarata and Allen [139] have cited examples of active sulfonamides whose pK_a values lie outside the optimal limits given by Bell and Roblin, and showed that if a small homologous series is used, a linear relationship of the pKa to the MIC is obtained.

Seydel and associates in a study of sulfanilides and N^1-(3-pyridyl)-sulfanilamides extrapolated the electron density on the 1-NH group from the study of IR and NMR data and Hammett sigma values of the parent anilines and correlated the data with the MIC against *E. coli*. Anilines were used for studying the IR spectra because they could be dissolved in nonpolar solvents, thus giving more valid data; this was not possible with sulfanilamides because of low solubility in such solvents. Seydel [140] and Garrett et al. [141] found an approximately linear relationship between bacteriostatic activity, Hammett sigma value, and electron density of the N^1-nitrogen of a group of *m*- and *p*-substituted sulfanilides and emphasized the possibility of predicting the *in vitro* antibacterial activity of sulfanilamides by use of this relationship. Later, Seydel [142] included in this study 3-sulfapyridines, and carried out regression analyses of the data, and obtained a very acceptable correlation coefficient.

The functional relationship between the acid dissociation constant and the activity of sulfonamides has not been questioned since the investigations just cited were published. This, however, does not imply that the ions of different sulfonamides are equally active; other factors also have an influence and account for the observed differences in activity of different sulfonamides, such as affinity for the concerned enzyme. The pK_a is related to solubility, distribution, and partition coefficients, permeability across membranes, protein binding, tubular secretion, and reabsorption in the kidneys.

Fujita and Hansch [143], in a multiparameter linear free energy approach, correlated the, pK_a, hydrophobicity constant, and Hammett sigma values of a series of sulfanilides and N^1-benzoyl and N^1-heterocyclic sulfanilamides with their MIC data against Gram-positive and Gram-negative organisms and their protein binding capacity. They devised suitable equations by regression analyses for the *meta*- and *para*-substituted compounds; the correlation for the *para*-substituted

compounds was rather poor. The hydrophobicity of the compounds was found to play a definite role in the activity. It was shown that keeping the lipophilicity of the substituents unchanged, the logarithmic plot of activity against the dissociation constant gives two straight lines with opposite slopes, the point of intersection of which corresponds to the maximal activity for a series of sulfonamides. They suggested the optimal values of the dissociation constant and hydrophobicity for maximum activity against the organisms studied.

Yamazaki et al. [144], in their study of the relationship between antibacterial activity and pK_a of 14 N^1-heterocyclic sulfanilamides, considered separately the activities of the compounds in terms of the concentrations of their ionized and unionized forms and their total concentrations in the culture medium. They found that when the relationship between pK_a and ions is considered, it is linear for ionized and unionized states giving two lines having opposite slopes and intersecting each other. The point of intersection corresponds to the pH of the culture medium. They found the pK_a for optimal activity to be between 6.6 and 7.4.

In these studies, it was noticed that some of the sulfonamides had lower antibacterial activity than expected, possibly because of their poor permeation. To define the role of permeability in the antibacterial activity of sulfonamides, Miller et al. [145] extended these investigations to cell-free folate synthesizing systems and correlated the inhibitory activity of these compounds on this enzyme system and on the intact organisms to their pK_a, Hammett sigma, chemical shift, and π-values. The rate determining steps for sulfonamide action in the cell-free system and a whole cell system were found to have similar substituent dependencies. From a comparison of the linear free energy relationships obtained in the two systems, they suggested that the observed parabolic dependence of the antibacterial activity indicates that it is not the extracellular ionic concentration, which, in turn, is limited by the permeation of unionized compounds, thus supporting Cowles and Brueckner's postulates (*loc. cit.*). They concluded that the lipophilic factors are not important in the cell-free system or for *in vitro* antibacterial activity when permeability is not limited by ionization.

Intensive subsequent work in this field over the last four decades has fully supported the views expressed quite early in the development of sulfonamides of the predominant role of ionization for their antibacterial activity, and that degree of ionization determines the antibacterial activity, because the ionized form is more potent than the unionized form.

Sulfones Ever since the discovery of the antimycobacterial activity of sulfones in 1940s and that they share a common biological mode of action with sulfonamides (competitive antagonism of PABA), the question of their structural similarity with sulfonamides that enables them to inhibit dihydropteroate synthase has attracted much attention. It was realized quite early in these studies that as with sulfonamides, $4\text{-}NH_2\text{-}C_6H_4\text{-}SO_2$ was inviolate for their optimal activity and the substituents in the second phenyl could modulate the activity. A number of QSAR studies have been reported [146–154] on 4-aminodiphenylsulfones with a view to analyzing the contribution of these substituents to the biological activity using linear free energy, molecular modeling and conformational analysis methods. It has been shown that electronic and steric effects have the decisive role both on binding to the enzyme and on the overall biological activity. The electronic effects were rationalized in terms of electronic charge perturbations that are transmitted from the multisubstituted aryl ring to the essential structural moiety, $4\text{-}NH_2\text{-}C_6H_4\text{-}SO_2$, through the SO_2 group mainly via hyperconjugation [151]. In conformational analysis using the MINDO semiempirical molecular orbital method, it was found that 4-aminodiphenylsulfones show multiple conformational energy minima, mainly due to the torsional freedom of the sulfur–carbon bond of the substituted aryl ring with the $4\text{-}NH_2\text{-}C_6H_4\text{-}SO_2$. The highly active derivatives were in general shown to be less flexible and inhibition potency increased as entropy decreased [152,153]; a "butterfly" structure (Fig. 1) was considered to best represent the active conformations.

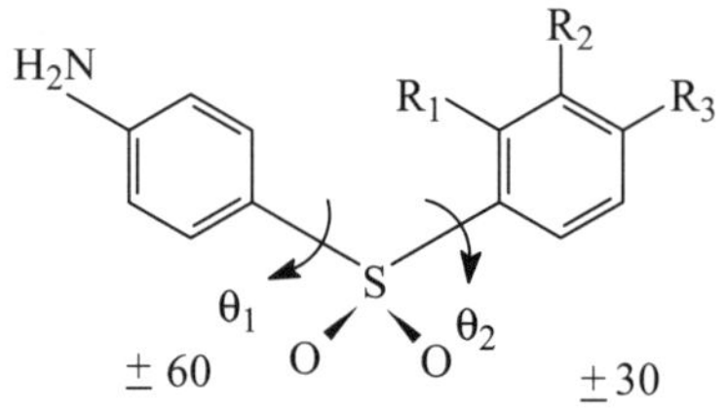

Water/Lipid Solubility. The clinically used sulfonamides being weak acids, are, in general,

Figure 1. Proposed active conformation of 4-aminodiphenylsulfones.

soluble in basic aqueous solutions. As the pH is lowered, the solubility of their N^1-substituted sulfonamides decreases, usually reaching a minimum in the pH range of 3–5. This minimum corresponds to the solubility of the molecular species in water (Table 2). With a further decrease in pH corresponding to that of a moderately strong acid, the sulfa drugs dissolve as cations.

The solubility of sulfonamides is of clinical and toxicological significance because damage to kidneys is caused by crystallization of sulfonamides or their N^4-acetyl derivatives. Their solubility in the pH range of urine (i.e., pH 5.5–6.5) is, therefore, of practical interest. One of the significant advances in the first phase of sulfonamide research was the development of compounds with greater water solubility, such as sulfisoxazole, which helped to overcome the problem of crystallization in the kidney of earlier sulfonamides. However, apart from the solubility of the parent compounds, the solubility of their N-acetyl derivatives, which are the main metabolic products, is of great importance because these are generally less soluble than the parent compounds. For example, sulfathiazole, which itself is unlikely to be precipitated, is metabolized to its N^1-acetyl derivative, which has a poor solubility that is likely to lead to its crystallization in the kidney. The solubility of sulfonamides and their principal metabolites in aqueous media, particularly in buffered solutions and body fluids, therefore, has been the subject of many studies aimed at enhancing our understanding of their behavior in clinical situations [156,157].

An important factor affecting the chemotherapeutic activity of sulfonamides and their *in vivo* transport is lipophilicity of the undissociated molecule. The partition coefficients measured in solvents of different dielectric constants have been used to determine the lipid solubility and hydrophobicity constant [141–156]. Chromatographic R_1 values in a number of thin-layer chromatography systems have also been used as an expression of the lipophilic character of sulfonamides and found to correspond well with the Hansch values in an isobutyl alcohol–water system [158].

Table 2 gives the percentage of various sulfonamides passing from aqueous phase into ethylene chloride as determined by Rieder [156]. Lipid solubility of different sulfonamides varies over a considerable range. These differences unquestionably influence their pharmacokinetics and antibacterial activity. It has been noted by Rieder [156] that long-acting sulfonamides with a high tubular reabsorption are generally distinguished by a high degree of lipid solubility. The antibacterial activity and the half-life are also related to lipid solubility. Although a precise relationship between these factors has not been established, it has been shown in general, that as the lipid solubility increases, so does the half-life and *in vitro* activity against *E. coli*.

Protein Binding. A particularly important role in the action of sulfonamides is played by their binding to proteins. Protein binding, in general, blocks the availability of sulfonamides as of many other drugs (the bound drug is chemotherapeutically inactive), and reduces their metabolism by the liver. The binding is reversible; thus, the active free form is liberated as its level in the blood is gradually lowered. The sulfonamide concentration in other body fluids too is dependent on its protein binding. Thus, the unbound fraction of the drug in the plasma seems to be significant for activity, toxicity, and metabolism, whereas protein binding appears to modulate the availability of the drug and its half-life. The manner and extent of binding of sulfonamides has been the subject of many studies [156,159–161], and the important characteristics of the binding are now reasonably clear. The binding affinity of different sulfonamides varies widely with their structure (Table 2) as also with the animal species and the physiological status of the animal [156,162]. In plasma the drug binds

predominantly to the albumin fraction. The binding is weak (4–5 kcal) and is easily reversed by dilution. It appears to be predominantly hydrophobic, with ionic binding being relatively less significant [143,161]. Thus, the structural features that favor binding are the same as those that increase lipophilicity, such as the presence of alkyl, alkoxy, or aryl groups [133,159,163,164]. N^4-Acetyl derivatives are more strongly bound than the parent drugs. Introduction of hydroxyl or amino groups decreases protein binding and glucuronidation almost abolishes it. Seydel [164], in a study of the effect of the nature and position of substituents on protein binding and lipid solubility, has shown that among isomers, *ortho*-substituted compounds have the lowest protein binding. This would indicate that steric factors have a role in protein binding and that N^1-nitrogen atom of the sulfonamide is involved. The binding seems to take place with the basic centers of arginine, lysine, and histidine in the proteins [156]. The locus of binding of several sulfonamides to serum albumin has been shown by high-resolution NMR spectral studies to involve the benzene ring more than the heterocycle [165].

There have been attempts to establish correlations between physicochemical properties of sulfonamides, their protein binding, and their biological activity. Martin [166] established a functional relationship between excretion and distribution and binding to albumin, and Kruger-Thiemer et al. [160] have derived a mathematical relationship. Moriguchi et al. [167] observed a parabolic relationship between protein binding and *in vitro* bacteriostatic activity in a series of sulfonamides, and suggested that too strong an affinity between sulfonamides and proteins would prevent them from reaching their site of action in bacteria; with too low an affinity, they would not be able to bind effectively with enzyme proteins to cause bacteriostasis, assuming that affinity for enzyme proteins is paralleled by affinity to bacterial proteins. In a multiparameter study of a series of N^1-heterocyclic sulfonamides, Fujita and Hansch [143] considered that in the free state sulfonamides exist as two different species, neutral and ionized, whereas in the bound state they exist only in one form. They developed suitable equations by regression analysis and showed that for the series of sulfonamides of closely related structure, whose pK_a does not vary appreciably the binding is governed mainly by the N^1-substituent, which supported the earlier results [159].

The implications of protein binding for chemotherapeutic activity are not fully understood. The factors favoring protein binding are also those that would favor transport across membranes, tubular reabsorption, and increased binding to enzyme protein. N^1-Acetyl derivatives are more strongly bound to proteins and yet are better excreted. No universally applicable relationship has been found between half-life of sulfonamides and protein binding, although it has been established in general that protein binding modulates bioavailability and prolongs the half-life of sulfonamides, as of other drugs.

3.3.1.4. Clinical Use of Sulfonamides and Sulfones

About 20 sulfonamides and sulfones have been commonly used in clinical practice (Table 2). These vary widely in their absorption, distribution, and excretion patterns. Some remain largely unabsorbed after oral administration and are, therefore, considered useful for gastrointestinal tract infections. Sulfonamides of another group characterized by high solubility, quick absorption and rapid excretion, mainly in the unaltered form, are widely used in urinary tract infections. Those belonging to yet another group are absorbed rapidly but excreted slowly, or reabsorbed, resulting in maintenance of high blood levels for long periods; these sulfonamides require less frequent administration and are particularly useful for chronic conditions and for prophylaxis. Because of this wide choice they provide agents with greatly differing pharmacokinetic characteristics, their wide antimicrobial spectrum, with the benefits of their synergistic action in combination with DHFRI with highly selective action on the microbes and minimal effects on the host, ease of administration and favorable pharmacoeconomics, sulfonamides can meet the requirements of varied clinical situations and are widely used in clinical practice, even six decades after their introduction. Furthermore, p,p'-diaminodiphenylsulfone (dapsone), remains the main stay for the treatment of all forms of leprosy.

Present Status in Therapeutics. The number of conditions for which sulfonamides are drugs of first choice has declined on account of gradual increase in bacterial resistance to them, and the addition of new classes of antimicrobials, but they still have a distinct and significant place in therapeutics [168–173].

Sulfonamides combined with trimethoprim are of special value in the treatment of urinary tract infections, bacillary dysentery (particularly that caused by *Shigella*), salmonellosis, and chronic bronchitis. In meningococcal infections, sulfonamides are of value when the strains of *Neisseria meningitides* or *Haemophilus influenzae* are sensitive to them. Sulfonamides are commonly used in preventing streptococcal infections and recurrence of rheumatic fever among susceptible subjects, especially in patients who are hypersensitive to penicillins. In methicillin-resistant staphylococcal and streptococcal infections and vancomycin-resistant enterococcal infections, co-trimaxazole—a fixed-dose combination of sulfamethoxazole and trimethoprim is often considered as one of the treatment options.

Sulfacetamide sodium eye drops are employed extensively for the management of ophthalmic infections; a combination of topical and systemic application is of value in some conditions. Topical sulfonamides such as silver sulfadiazine and mafenide inhibit enterobacteriacease, *P. aeruginosa,* staphylococci and streptococci, and they are extensively used to reduce the bacterial load in burn eschars.

Sulfonamides have been found useful for the treatment of infections due to *Listeria monocytogenes* especially in penicillin allergic patients. They are commonly used for the prophylaxis and treatment of otitis media in children.

Sulfonamides, alone or combined with trimethoprim, are the drugs of choice in the treatment of infections due to *Nocardia* sp., including cerebral nocardiosis; sulfisoxazole, sulfamethoxazole, and sulfadiazine are the more commonly used drugs [174]. Some clinicians prefer to use sulfonamides alone to avoid the greater risk of hemolytic toxicity observed more commonly with combination therapy. A pyrimethamine-sulfadiazine combination is commonly used for the treatment of all forms of toxoplasmosis, including materno-fetal toxoplasmosis. Co-trimoxazole and fan-sidar (fixed-dose combinations of sulfadoxine and pyrimethamine) are commonly used for the prophylaxis and treatment of *Pneumocystis carinii* infection, a common sequelae in patients with AIDS.

Dapsone remains the drug choice for all forms of leprosy and is an essential component of all multidrug therapy regimens. Dapsone has also been reported to cure some cases of Crohn's disease, which may have a mycobacterial origin. Although sulfonamides in general are not very effective against tuberculosis, some are active against nontuberculous mycobacterial infections, which have acquired importance in immunocompromised subjects such as in cases of AIDS; co-trimoxazole has been found effective in patients with *Mycobacterium marinum* infection while sulfisoxazole has been used successfully for *Mycobacterium fortuitum* infections [175].

Other therapeutic uses. Shortly after the introduction of sulfa drugs, sulfapyridine was found to have unique beneficial effects on some inflammatory conditions, especially dermatologic, unrelated to their antibacterial activity [176a]. Later dapsone was found to share the same properties at a much lower dose and with improved therapeutic index [176b]. The disorders that respond are dermatitis herpetiformis (DH), pyoderma gangrenosum, subcorneal pustular dermatosis, acrodermatitis continua, impetigo herpetiformis, ulcerative colitis, and cutaneous lesions of patients with lupus erythematosus. Dapsone today is the drug of choice for the treatment of DH and other similar inflammatory conditions that are characterized by neutrophil infiltration. These disorders are characterized by edema followed by granulocytic inflammation or by vesicle or bullae formation [177]. Coleman et al. have described useful *in vitro* test systems for the study of inhibition of neutrophil function that could help in picking up more leads and active compounds in this area [178]. The mechanism of action is not fully understood, but it has been proposed that these drugs enter or influence the protein moiety of glycosaminoglycans and decrease tissue viscosity, resulting in prevention of edema, dilution of tissue fluid and decrease in inflammation, vesicle, and bullae formation. It is likely that this additional action of DDS may in part account for the extraordinary sensitivity of lepra bacilli to it. Overall, the action of dapsone may be twofold; a direct antibacterial action, and modulation of the host-response [179]. Salicylazosulfapyridine is the treatment of choice for ulcerative colitis.

Adverse Reactions. The sulfonamides are generally safe drugs, even although the list of possible adverse reactions is long [172,173]. The most common side effects are related to allergic skin reactions, which vary from relatively minor skin rashes, maculopapular rashes, and urticarial reactions to severe, even life-threatening reactions such as erythema multiforme, Stevens-Johnson syndrome and toxic epidermal necrolysis (TEN). The severe hypersensitivity reactions occur most commonly after treatment with long-acting sulfonamides, whether used alone or in combination with pyrimethamine as for malaria prophylaxis or treatment. The skin eruption is also frequent in patients with AIDS being treated with pyrimethamine-sulfadoxine for *P. carinii* pneumonia and is associated with pancytopenia in some patients and may be severe enough to require discontinuation of drugs [176]. Individuals seropositive for HIV are more susceptible to developing adverse reactions to sulfonamides/sulfones: 40–80% in patients with AIDS as compared to 5% with other immune deficiencies [178,180]. Photosensitivity reactions are also relatively common with sulfonamides.

Hemolytic adverse reactions may occur occasionally, and when they occur, drug administration may need to be discontinued. These include hematologic reactions such as methemoglobinemia, agranulocytosis, thrombocytopenia, kernicterus in the newborn, and hemolytic anemia in patients with G6PD deficiency. Kernicterus can result from administration of sulfonamides to the mother or to the newborn, because sulfonamides displace bilirubin from albumin in the newborn. Therefore, pregnant women, near term, or newborns should not be given sulfonamides. Hemolytic anemia is relatively more common with sulfone therapy in leprosy patients, and most often is related to the undernourished status of these patients; discontinuation of treatment is often not necessary and only supplemental therapy is required.

The minor adverse reactions reported include GI reactions such as nausea, vomiting, and diarrhea; and neurologic effects, such as peripheral neuritis, insomnia, and headache. Crystalluria, one of the earliest serious toxic reactions reported with sulfonamides, has been more or less overcome with the discovery of agents that are highly soluble at the pH of urine, or are excreted mainly as water-soluble metabolites.

By binding to albumin sites, sulfonamides may displace drugs such as warfarin, methotrexate, and hypoglycemic sulfonylurea drugs, and may thus potentiate the action of these drugs. Similarly, sulfonamide concentrations are increased by indomethacin, salicylates, and probenecid.

It has been suggested that adverse reactions of sulfonamides may be due to the formation of reactive hydroxylamine metabolites, together with a deficient glutathione system needed for scavenging these reactive molecules [181]. It has been suggested that the covalent adducts formed by the N^4-hydroxylamine metabolites with human epidermal keratinocytes are very likely responsible for the initiation and propagation of the cutaneous hypersensitivity reaction occasionally observed with these drugs [182]. This is supported by *in vitro* experiments in which sulfamethoxazole hydroxylamine has been found to be cytotoxic for lymphocytes, whereas the parent compound was not [183,184]. With dapsone it has been shown that its hydroxylamine metabolite seems to be responsible for methemoglobinemia; when dapsone is combined with cimetidine, an inhibitor of N-oxidation, the increase of methemoglobinemia is reduced [185].

3.3.1.5. Pharmacokinetics and Metabolism

Sulfonamides The sulfonamide drugs vary widely in their pharmacokinetic properties (Table 2). Those that are highly ionized are not absorbed from the gastrointestinal tract after oral administration, leading to a high local concentration of the drug, and were, therefore, considered useful for enteric infections. A majority of the sulfonamides, however, are well absorbed, mainly from the small intestine, and insignificantly from the stomach. Absorption occurs of the unionized part, related to their lipid solubility. In rate and extent of absorption most sulfonamides behave similarly within the pK_a range 4.5–10.5. After absorption, they are fairly evenly distributed in all the body tissues. High levels are achieved in pleural, peritoneal, synovial, and ocular fluids that approximate 80% of serum levels; CSF levels are effective in meningeal infections. Those that are highly soluble do not, in general, attain a high tissue concentration, show no tendency to crystallize in the kidney, are more readily excreted, and are useful in treating genitourinary infections. The relatively less soluble ones build up high levels in blood, tissues, and extravascular fluids and are useful for treating systemic infections. This wide range of solubilities and pharmacokinetic characteristics of different sulfonamides permits the access of one or the other member of the group to almost any site in the body; thus, adding greatly to their usefulness as chemotherapeutic agents. The free, nonprotein bound drugs and their metabolic products are ultrafiltered in the glomeruli and then partly reabsorbed. Tubular secretion also plays an important role in the excretion of sulfonamides and their metabolites. The structural features of the compounds have a marked effect on these processes and determine the rate of excretion. The renal clearance rates of the metabolites are generally higher than those of the parent drugs.

Metabolism of sulfonamides takes place primarily in the liver and involves mainly N^4-acetylation, to a lesser extent glucuronidation and to a very small degree C-hydroxylation of phenyl and heterocyclic rings and of alkyl substituents, and O- and ring N-dealkylation. Variation of the substituents markedly influences the metabolic fate of the sulfonamides (Table 2); the metabolism also differs markedly in different animal species [186–191]. Some of the sulfonamides, such as sulfisomidine, are excreted almost unchanged, in most of them N^4-acetylation occurs to a substantial degree, but some of the newer sulfonamides, such as sulfadimethoxine and sulfaphenazole, are excreted mainly as the glucuronide. The metabolites in human urine of the commonly used sulfonamides reveal the wide variation in their metabolic disposition [192].

Fujita [193] has carried out regression analyses on the rates of metabolism and renal excretion of sulfonamides in terms of their substituent constants. Equations showing the best correlation indicate that the most important factor governing the rate-determining step of the hepatic acetylation is the hydrophobicity of the drug and that pK_a does not play a significant role. The excretion pattern seems to be more complex and would have to take into consideration additional parameters to give an acceptable correlation.

Sulfones   Dapsone is well absorbed after oral administration, and is evenly distributed in almost all the body tissues. It is excreted mainly through the kidneys; less than 5% is excreted unchanged, very little N-acetylation takes place, and most of it is present as the mono-N-glucuronide [194–196]. It has been shown that there are marked animal species differences in the metabolism of dapsone; humans are relatively slow acetylators as compared to rhesus monkey [197,198]. Dapsone has a half-life of about 20 h. Acedapsone following intramuscular injection is very slowly absorbed and deacetylated. It has a half-life of about 42.6 days. There are marked animal species differences in the metabolism of acedapsone also; mice deacetylate acedapsone efficiently, but rats do not [199].

Half-Life   The half-lives of sulfonamides are of importance because the dosage regimen is related to it; dose schedule is a function of the pharmacokinetic parameters. Kruger-Thiemer and his associates have reported a mathematical model for correlating these parameters with dose schedules [200].

The half-life of different sulfonamides in clinical use vary widely from 2.5 to 150 h (Table 2), and also show marked differences in different animal species. Reider [156] correlated the pK_a, liposolubility, surface activity, and protein binding of a group of 21 sulfonamides with their half-life in humans. It was reported that long-acting sulfonamides were, in general, more lipid soluble than were the short-acting compounds, but no clear-cut relationship could be established; factors such as tubular secretion and tubular reabsorption are also involved. In 2-sulfapyrimidines; a 4-CH_3 group increases the half-life, 4,6-$(CH_3)_2$ reduces it to less than one-half, the corresponding methoxy derivatives have a much longer half-life, and both 5-CH_3 and 5-OCH_3 prolong half-life to the same extent. Similarly, in a 4-sulfapyrimidines, the 2,6-$(OCH_3)_2$ analog is the most persistent sulfonamide known; sulfamethoxypyridazine has a half-life about twice as long as that of sulfapyrazine. Thus, although no clear-cut pattern of relationship between structure and half-life is discernible, the methoxy and methyl groups in general seem to prolong half-life.

Antimicrobial Spectrum   Following the initial dramatic results obtained with sulfonamides in the treatment of streptococcal infections, studies with these drugs were extended to other microorganisms including bacteria, viruses, protozoa, and fungi. It was found that many Gram-positive and Gram-negative bacteria, mycobacteria, some large viruses, protozoa and fungi are susceptible to the action of sulfonamides and sulfones (Table 3). In almost all cases, their action is related to PABA antagonism.

The sulfonamides and sulfones have a relatively broad antibacterial spectrum. Individual sulfonamides do differ in their antibacterial spectrum, but these differences are more quantitative than qualitative. The bacteria most susceptible to sulfonamides include pneumococci, streptococci, meningococci, staphylococci, some coliform bacteria, and shigellae. Lepra bacilli are susceptible to sulfones. One limitation of sulfonamides is their weak activity against bacteria responsible for typhoid fever, diphtheria, and subacute bacterial endocarditis. They have practically no activity against *P. aeruginosa*. Another limitation with sulfonamides is the rising incidence of resistant isolates in the community. Synergism of their action by dihydrofolate reductase inhibitors, and the introduction of combination therapy with them, has to some extent helped to remedy this situation [201]. Sulfamethoxazole has been shown to have impressive *in vitro* activity against *M. avium* and *M. intracellulare* [202].

Sulfonamides have been shown to be highly active against *Eimeria* [203–206], Toxoplasma [207,208], and *Nocardia* sp. [209,210], and in combination with pyrimethamine are

Table 3. Antimicrobial Spectrum of Sulfonamides and Sulfones

Gram-Positive/Acid Fast	Gram Negative	Others
Highly susceptible		
Bacillus anthracis (some strains)	*Calymmatobacterium granulomatis*	*Actinomyces bovis*
Corynebacterium diphtheria trachomatis (some strains)	*Hemophilus ducreyi*	*Chlamydiae*
	H. influenzae	*Coccidia*
M. leprae venereusm (to sulfones)	*L. monocytogenes*	*Lymphogranuloma virus*
	N. gonorrhoeae	
S. aureus falciparum	*N. Meningitiitis*	*Plasmodium*
Streptococcus pneumoniae	*Pasteurella pestis*	*P. malariae*
S. pyogenes (Group A)	*Proteus mirabilis*	*P. carinii*
	Shigella flexneri	*Nocardia* sp.
	S. sonnei	*Toxoplasma*
	Vibrio cholerae	*Trachoma* viruses
Weekly susceptible		
Clostridium welchii	*Aerobacter aerogenes*	*Plasmodium vivax*
M. tuberculosis	*Brucella abortus*	
Mycobacterium avium	*E. coli*	
Mycobacterium intracellulare	*Klebsiella pneumoniae*	
Streptococcus viridans	*P. aeruginosa*	
	Salmonella	

widely used for coccidiosis [211], toxoplasmosis [212] and nocardiosis [174,213,214].

McCallum and Findlay [215] showed that experimental *Lymphogranuloma venereum* virus infection in mice was cured by sulfonamides. Later, other *Chlamydiae* were also found to be inhibited by sulfonamides, which led to the successful clinical use of these drugs in the treatment of trachoma [216].

Sulfonamides have also high activity against *P. carinii* [217] and combined with trimethoprim are largely used for the treatment of *P. carinii* pneumonia in AIDS patients.

3.3.1.6. Mechanism of Action

Site of Folate Inhibition. The antimicrobial action of sulfonamides is characterized by a competitive antagonism with PABA, an essential metabolite vital to the metabolism of the microorganisms. Evidence for this antagonism started coming soon after the discovery of sulfonamides. It was found that substances antagonizing the action of sulfonamides were present in peptones [218], various body tissues and fluids, especially after autolysis or acid hydrolysis [219], pus [220], bacteria [221,222], and yeast extract. [223,224]. Woods [223] obtained evidence that PABA is the probable antagonistic agent in yeast extract, and showed that synthetic PABA could completely reverse the bacteriostatic activity of sulfanilamide against various bacteria *in vitro*. Selbie [225] and Findlay [226] soon after found that PABA could antagonize the action of sulfonamides *in vivo* as well. Blanchard [227], McIllwain [228], and Rubbo et al. [229] finally isolated PABA from these sources. This led Woods [223] to suggest that because of its similarity of structure with PABA, sulfanilamide interfered with the utilization of PABA by the enzyme system necessary for the growth of bacteria. Based on these observations, a more general and clear enunciation of the theory of metabolite antagonism to explain the action of chemotherapeutic agents was given by Fildes in 1940 [230] in his classic paper entitled "A rational approach in chemotherapy."

Further studies showed that the inhibition of growth by sulfonamides in simple media can be reversed not only competitively by PABA but also noncompetitively by a number of compounds not structurally related to PABA, such as L-methionine, L-serine, glycine, adenine, guanine, and thymine [231,232]. The relationship of sulfonamides to purine was uncovered by the finding that sulfonamides-inhibited cultures accumulated 4-amino-5-imidazolecarboxamide ribotide [233], a compound later shown by Shive et al. [234] and Gots [235] to be a precursor of purine biosynthesis.

With the concurrent knowledge gained in the field of bacterial physiology and metabolism, these isolated facts could be gradually fitted into a pattern. The determination of the structure of folic acid by Angier et al. [236] and Mowat et al. [237] revealed that PABA was an integral part of its structure. Following this, Tschesche [238] made the suggestion that folic acid is formed by the condensation of PABA or p-aminobenzoylglutamic acid (PABG) with a pteridine and that sulfonamides compete in this condensation. Soon the structure of the active coenzyme form of folic acid, leucovorin (folinic acid, citrovorum factor), was established and its involvement in biosynthetic steps where one-carbon units are added was elucidated [239,240]; the amino acids, purines, and pyrimidines that are able to replace or spare PABA are precisely those whose formation requires one-carbon addition catalyzed by folic acid.

Direct evidence of the inhibition of folic acid synthesis by sulfonamides was soon obtained by studies on bacterial cultures. It was already known that a number of organisms could use PABA and folic acid as alternative essential growth factors [241]. Lampen and Jones [242,243] found that the growth of some strains of Lactobacillus arabinosus, and Lactobacillus plantarum in media containing PABA was inhibited competitively by sulfonamides, whereas folic acid caused a noncompetitive type of reversal of this inhibition, suggestive of its being the product of the inhibited reaction. Nimmo-Smith et al. [244] reported a similar inhibition of folic acid synthesis by sulfonamides and its competitive reversal by PABA in nongrowing suspensions of L. plantarum. Inhibition of folic acid synthesis by sulfonamides was also demonstrated in a PABA-requiring mutant, in the parent wild strain of E. coli [245,246], and in cultures of S. aureus.

The demonstration of the enzymic synthesis of dihydropteroate (DHP) and dihydrofolate (DHF) (Fig. 2) in cell-free extracts of a number of organisms [247–251] set the stage for examining the action of sulfonamides at the enzyme level. It was soon demonstrated that the synthesis of DHP from PABA is sensitive to inhibition by sulfonamides, and that the relation between a sulfonamide and PABA remained strictly competitive as long as the two compounds were added simultaneously. If the enzyme and sulfonamide are preincubated with a low concentration of pteridine, subsequent addition of PABA failed to reverse the inhibition; if, however, a high pteridine concentration is used, preincubation results in a much lesser degree of inhibition. Brown [252] showed that the enzyme was not irreversibly inactivated. These results were suggestive of sulfonamide incorporation. It was soon realized that sulfonamides could act as alternate substrates for the enzymes [251–254] resulting in the formation of sulfa-pteroates. Roland et al. [255], however, showed that dihydropterinsulfonamide thus formed did not inhibit DHPS or other folate enzymes. Consequently, this incorporation was not considered of physiological significance.

Brown [252] observed that the enzymic synthesis was much more sensitive to inhibition by sulfonamides than bacterial growth, suggestive of impeded permeability of the intact organisms to sulfonamides as compared to PABA. The more potent inhibitors of folate biosynthesis were, in general better growth inhibitors also. Hotchkiss and Evans [256] have suggested that differences in the response of various organisms to sulfonamides may be due to quantitative differences in the ability of individual isoenzymes to produce folic acid from PABA in the presence of sulfonamides.

In a more recent study of the enzymic mechanism and sulfonamide inhibition of DHPS from S. pneumoniae [252], it has been shown that the sulfonamides were capable of displacing PABA in a competitive manner, with equilibrium binding constants that were significantly higher than the equivalent K_i values deduced from steady-state kinetic measurements, indicating that the target for sulfonamide inhibition of S. pneumoniae DHPS is the enzyme–DHPP binary complex, rather than the apoprotein form of the enzyme.

Richey and Brown [257] purified dihydropteroate synthetase/synthase (H_2-pteroate synthase; DHPS) from E. coli, and showed

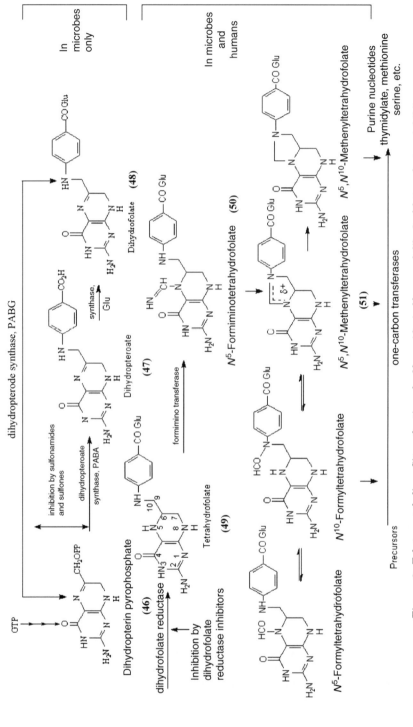

Figure 2. Folate metabolism: Sites of action of sulfonamides/sulfones and dihydrofolate reductase inhibitors.

that it could use *p*-aminobenzoylglutamate (PABG) also as the substrate to form dihydrofolate directly (Fig. 2). PABA is, however, not the natural substrate for this enzyme except in a few bacteria such as *M. tuberculosis*, which forms directly dihydrofolate from dihydropterin pyrophosphate. Shiota et al. [258] and Ortiz and Hotchkiss [259] have shown that the utilization of both the substrates, PABA and PABG, is competitively inhibited by sulfonamides.

The cell-free H_2-pteroate synthesizing system isolated from *E. coli* has become a very useful tool for studying structure–activity correlations among agonists and antagonists of PABA and the inhibitory effect of sulfonamides [259–262].

The mechanism of action of dapsone (and other sulfones) is similar to that of sulfonamides, because the action is antagonized by PABA in mycobacteria [261–263], other bacteria [264], and protozoa [265]. The exceptionally high antibacterial activity of DDS against *M. leprae* has attracted special attention [266]. There is evidence that, as with sulfonamides [253], DDS is also incorporated to form an analog of dihydropteroate, although this also may not be of much physiological importance. In *M. kansasii*, Panitch and Levy [267] found a 14–15-fold accumulation of DDS within the bacterial cells after 8 days of treatment [271]; there may be similar accumulation within the *M. leprae bacilli* also. Additional sites of action outside the folate synthesizing enzyme system have also been proposed. DDS has unique beneficial effects on some dermal inflammatory conditions (*loc. cit.*), and it is likely that this action may contribute to its activity against *M. leprae*.

A similar mode of action of sulfonamides and sulfones has been demonstrated in most of the other classes of microbes tested that are susceptible to their action. In the case of chlamydia, it has been shown that the sulfonamide-sensitive members of this group, such as trachoma inclusion conjunctivitis viruses, have a folic acid metabolism similar to that of bacteria, and that the action of sulfonamides against them is competitively antagonized by PABA [268–270].

Selectivity of Action. The presence of the folate-synthesizing system has been demonstrated in a variety of bacteria [250,253,259,261,271], protozoa [272–274], yeasts [275], and plants [276–278], and this serves to explain the broad spectrum of action of sulfonamides. Higher organisms (e.g., mammals) do not possess this biosynthesis system and require preformed folic acid, and are, thus, unaffected by sulfonamides. This selective action on the parasite, based on the difference in the metabolic pathway between the microbes and humans, makes sulfonamides "ideal" chemotherapeutic agents.

Synergism with Dihydrofolate Reductase Inhibitors. The discovery by Hitchings et al. in 1948 [279] of certain diaminopyrimidines showing good antimicrobial activity through antifolate mechanism, and the reports that antifolates acted synergistically with sulfonamides [280–282], added a new dimension to the therapeutic use fulness of sulfonamides [283]. The elucidation of the folic acid pathway and the demonstration of its inhibition by both sulfonamides and dihydrofolate reductase inhibitors (Fig. 2) elucidated the mechanism of this synergism. It is a consequence of the sequential occurrence of the twin loci of inhibition in the *de novo* folic acid biosynthesis. Factors resulting from this combination that contribute to its usefulness include a several-fold increase in chemotherapeutic indices, better tolerance of the drugs, ability to delay development of resistance, and ability to produce cures where the curative effects of the individual drugs were minimal [284].

Recent crystallographic studies of DHPS and DHFR enzymes from different organisms have greatly helped to understand the structure of the ligand binding sites on these enzymes and the molecular basis of their action and synergism (*loc. cit.*). The choice of the individual drugs used in the combinations is based on the best pharmacokinetic fit [285]. For example, trimethoprim with sulfamethoxazole, both having a half-life of about 11 h, is a commonly used antibacterial combination. Dihydrofolate reductases from various sources differ markedly in their binding ability to various inhibitors; pyrimethamine is bound much more strongly to the enzyme from plasmodia than from bacteria, and the converse is true for trimethoprim (**64a**) [286,287]. This explains the choice of trimethoprim for bacterial infections and of pyrimethamine for antimalarial chemotherapy. Thus, while pronounced differences exist in the affinity of DHF inhibitors for dihydrofolate reductases of different origins the structural requirements for inhibitors of the dihydropteroate synthases for the various species studied are somewhat similar [284]. Co-trimoxazole, a fixed-dose combination of trimethoprim and sulfamethoxazole (TMP-SMX), is a very commonly used drug for a variety of bacterial infections [288].

(64a)

Dihydropteroate Synthase. The gene encoding the DHPS from a number of organisms has been cloned, sequenced, and expressed [289–297]. While DHPS is a monofunctional enzyme in prokaryotes including *Mycobacterial* sp, in plants [296] and protozoa [294] it is part of a bifunctional enzyme and in yeasts [295] of a trifunctional enzyme combining the preceding one and two more steps respectively of the folate biosynthetic pathway [289]. DHPS is reported to be a homodimer in most prokaryotes, including *E. coli* [291], *S. aureus* [293] and *M. tuberculosis/leprae* [289], whereas eukaryotic bifunctional DHPS is reported to be a dimer or a trimer. The DHPSs from *E. coli* [291], *S. aureus* [293], and *M. tuberculosis* [289] have now been crystallized and their high-resolution crystal structures determined. Based on the information available from the crystal structure studies and that of the distribution of known sulfonamide/sulfone resistance mutations, the binding sites for the substrates could be located, and the possible mechanism of action of PABA, sulfonamides/sulfones proposed [289]. The implications of this model for the catalytic mechanisms and the likely geometry of the transition state have also been proposed [289].

There are individual variations in the structure of the DHPSs from different organisms, but overall there are many common structural features and a unified picture of

the site and mode of binding of the substrates and the inhibitors has emerged. The DHPS consists of 282 amino acids in case of *E. coli* [291,292], of 267 amino acids in *S. aureus* and of 280 amino acids in *M. tuberculosis* [289]. The DHPSs belong to the TIM-barrel class of protein structures.

The polypeptide chain is folded into an eight-loop α/β-barrel with a distorted cylindrical shape. It has eight α-helices stacked around the outside of an inner cylinder of parallel β-strands. The residues comprising the outer eight helices, the inner parallel β-sheets and of the α,β-connections have been identified. The intermolecular contacts within the crystal structure suggest a dimeric structure for the enzyme, the interface deriving from the proximity of extensive shallow concave areas of each monomer.

The overall TIM-barrel fold and dimerization interface of DHPSs of *M. tuberculosis* (Mtb), *E. coli*, and *S. aureus* are similar, with 38% sequence identity [289]. The folded Mtb DHPS dimer structure as obtained from crystal structure studies is shown in Fig. 3.

It has been shown that the pterin binding pocket of DHPS of Mtb is formed by the side chains of 12 amino acid residues (Fig. 4), and that this binding pocket occurs in a deep cleft in the barrel [289]. Each hydrogen bond donor/acceptor group of the pterin moiety is engaged in interactions with hydrogen bond donors/acceptors provided by the DHPS amino acid side chains. The residues involved in forming polar bonds and hydrophobic interactions have also been identified. The residues that form the DHP binding site are highly conserved in a number of bacterial and even fungal species, and the residues involved in forming the binding site of the phosphate moiety are somewhat different between different organisms. This has been attributed to different conformations the enzyme assumes during catalysis. The loop 1 containing the C-terminal pole of the β-barrel has been suggested to play a crucial and dynamic function during the catalytic action of the enzyme, and it undergoes extensive conformational changes to place the functionally relevant residues, such as Asp 21, in the proper position for catalysis. It thus appears that high level of sequence conservation with relative confor-

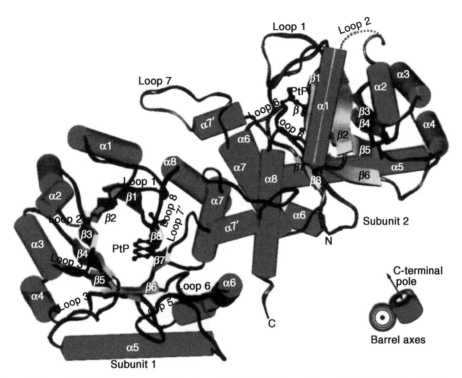

Figure 3. Overall folded structure of *M. tuberculosis* DHPS dimer. From Ref. [289]. (See color insert.)

mational flexibility of loop 1 seem to be important for the catalytic reaction mechanism of DHPS. It has been suggested that the loops of DHPS that serve an important functional role, are flexible and can assume different conformations [289].

Baca et al. [289] proposed a mechanism in which both loops 1 and 2 play important roles in catalysis by shielding the active site from bulk solvent and allowing PP transfer to occur. Based on this data, the transition-state geometry as shown in Fig. 5 has been proposed for the catalytic site in which the 4-amino group of the attacking nucleophile displaces the pyrophosphate from the opposite side of the 6-methyl carbon atom.

The main picture that emerges from these crystallographic studies is of a highly conserved pterin binding pocket spanning both prokaryotic and lower eukaryotic DHPS's from a wide range of species. Inhibitors designed to fit this site should have a broad spectrum of activity against a variety of microbial pathogens. The fact that this site is highly conserved would imply that drug-resistance mutations

are less likely to occur which would minimize the resistance development problems in inhibitors based on this target. Further, having no counterpart in the mammalian host specificity would not be a concern in the design of inhibitors of this class and selectivity is ensured. This target is not very well exploited and offers good scope for design of antimicrobial agents, including against mycobacteria. The only concern may be overlap with dihydrofolate reductase inhibitors, which have a mammalian counterpart. Sulfones/sulfonamides (and PABA) bind in a less conserved site, which offers greater scope for selectivity of action for different classes of microbes. Most of the sulfonamides so far designed belong to this class. The knowledge gained about the PABA/sulfones/sulfonamides binding sites of DHPS of different organisms would offer better scope for design of inhibitors selective to the microbes. These current developments in the understanding of molecular mechanism of action of sulfonamides/sulfones offers good scope for design of a second generation of dihydropteroate synthase inhibitors.

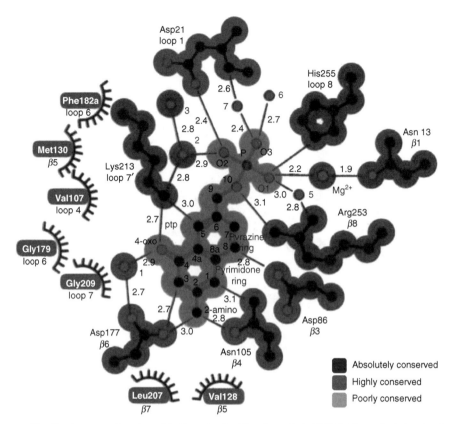

Figure 4. The Pterin monophosphate binding site in *M. tuberculosis* DHPS. From Ref. [289]. (See color insert.)

Drug Resistance. Emergence of drug-resistant strains is a serious problem with sulfonamides as with many other antimicrobials. Due to long use of this group of drugs, the incidence of drug-resistant isolates in the community has become quite alarming. The majority of isolates of *N. meningitides* of serogroups B and C in the United States and of group A isolated from other countries are now resistant. A similar situation prevails with respect to *Shigella* and strains of *E. coli* isolated from patients. Since the mode of action of all sulfonamides/sulfones antimicrobials involves the same basic mechanisms, different sulfonamides usually show cross-resistance, but not to antimicrobials of other classes acting by different mechanisms.

Resistance can arise by one or more of the following mechanisms: (a) increased production of PABA by the pathogen [298,299], (b) mutation in the DHPS gene resulting in altered sensitivity of the enzyme, making it

selectively more sensitive to the natural substrate [300–305], (c) gene amplification of the enzyme so that more enzyme is produced, thus rendering its saturation by antagonist difficult, (d) a bypass mechanism by which the microorganism develops an ability to utilize more effectively the folic acid present in the host [306], and (e) reduction in permeability of the cell to sulfonamides so that less drug is transported in [300].

In bacteria, the first two mechanisms, namely, overproduction of PABA and causing point mutations reduced sensitivity of the DHPS to sulfonamides seem to be the most common. Resistant mutants develop by random mutation and selection or by transfer of resistance factors (R-factors) by plasmids [303]. With the advent of molecular cloning techniques and sequence analysis of the DHPS gene/enzyme from resistant isolates the development of resistance and resistance-transfer have now been studied at the

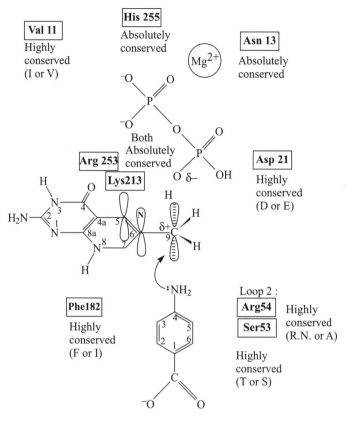

Figure 5. Possible geometry of catalytic transition state. From Ref. [289].

molecular level. It has been shown that a single point mutation can confer resistance to sulfonamides and sulfones. Most of the high-level sulfonamide resistance in Gram-negative bacteria appears to be accounted for by only two plasmid borne genes Sul-I and Sul-II [307]. It has been known for many years that multiple drug resistance involving streptomycin, chloramphenicol, tetracycline, and sulfonamides could be transferred between *Shigella* and *E. coli* in mixed cultivation in the host [308]. Drug resistance acquired in this manner is usually persistent and irreversible and can be transferred to other sensitive strains indefinitely. However, in meningococci the sulfonamide resistance has been reported to be chromosomally located. Similarly, with *S. aureus* it has been reported that of the nine resistant clinical isolates from different geographical locations analyzed, all had mutations in their chromosomal gene leading to an

altered DHPS [293]. These isolates differed in 15 amino acid residues from the wild-type sequence, and in this way DHPS appears to be different from DHFR [309]. In *M. leprae*, resistance to dapsone has been shown to be due to mutation at highly conserved amino acid residues 53 or 55 [310].

In the case of plasmodia a bypass mechanism (i.e., ability to use preformed folic acid) seems to be more commonly operative. Bishop has described strains resistant to both sulfonamides and pyrimethamine [306,311] that can presumably utilize the reduced forms of folic acid available in the host erythrocytes.

3.3.2. Dihydrofolate Reductase Inhibitors

Introduction Folate coenzymes are ubiquitous in distribution and are present in plants, animals, and microorganisms. The biosynthetic steps involved in their formation are described in Fig. 2. Tetrahydrofolate (THF) is unique in that it is required for its own biosynthesis. The role of DHFR is to supply tetrahydrofolate (THF), which functions as the carrier of one-carbon units required for the biosynthesis of purines, pyrimidines, and amino acids and part of THF is regenerated intact after transfer of the one-carbon unit, except in thymidylate biosynthesis where 5,10-methylene-tetrahydrofolate, the one-carbon carrier, is also oxidized to provide the two hydrogens needed for thymine synthesis, resulting in regeneration of DHF. Thus, under normal circumstances, DHFR is essential to the growth and survival of bacterial and mammalian cells, and provides a useful target for development of antibacterials [288,312]. The big challenge was to discover bacterial DHFR selective inhibitors, which has been successfully met and some very effective and useful antibacterials of this class were discovered, which are described below.

3.3.2.1 Structure–Activity Relationship The discovery that sulfonamides are inhibitors of folic acid metabolism focused attention on antibacterial screening of folic acid biosynthesis related analogs. In 1947, two laboratories independently reported the discovery that 2,4-diaminopteridines were

powerful inhibitors of folic acid (**60**). Seeger et al. [313,314] reported that 4-amino derivatives of folic acid such as aminopterin (**61a**) exhibited strong inhibitory effects against both bacterial species and mammalian systems, which led to the discovery and development of methotrexate (**61b**), one of the most widely used antitumor drugs available today. Later studies showed that the antitumor activity was due to the competitive inhibition of DHFR [315,316]. Almost concurrently Daniel et al. [317,318] and Malette et al. [219] reported antibacterial activity in a variety of 2,4-diaminopteridines, (**62**) lacking the *p*-aminobenzoylglutamic acid moiety. Daniel et al. [318] also reported the synergistic effect with sulfonamides and stated that as sufonamides and pterins competed with different parts of the FA molecule, this synergism could be expected. Although this work of Daniel et al. did not result in the development of a new drug, mainly because of lack of selectivity of action against bacteria, it provided a few landmarks; it established the broad contours of substructure features of the two classes of antifolates and paved the way to combination therapy with diamino-pyrimidines and sufonamides.

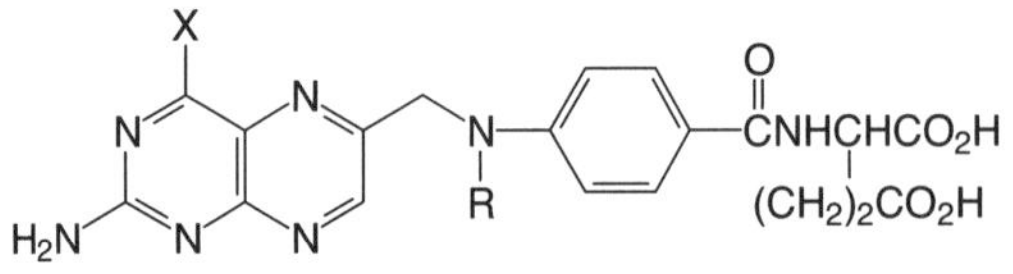

(**60**)   X = OH, R = H
(**61a**) X = NH$_2$, R = H
(**61b**) X = NH$_2$, R = CH$_3$

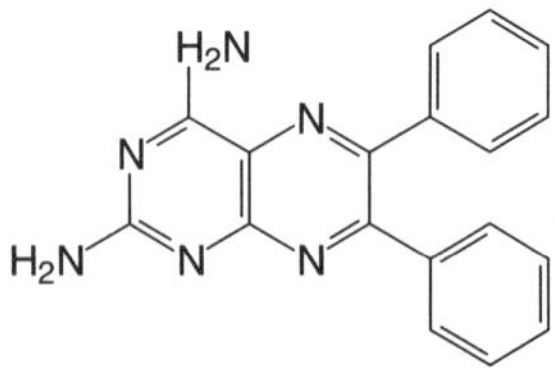

(**62**)

The major breakthrough in this field came with the discovery by Hitchings et al. from 1948 onwards of potent antibacterial activity in plain 2,4-diaminopyrimidines [319–325]. Based on a study of hundreds of these diaminopyrimidines Hitchings et al. [320–324] reported amazing and unprecedented selectivity of inhibition of the DHFRs of mammalian, protozoan or bacterial origin by differently substituted diaminopyrimidines. These results led to the development of

trimethoprim (**64a**) as an antibacterial with tremendous selectivity for bacterial DHFR, of pyrimethamine (**65**) for plasmodial DHFR, of a dihydrotriazine (**66**) for mammalian enzymes and equally interesting ubiquitous DHFR inhibitory activity of methotrexate. The comparative binding data of commonly used DHFRI to reductases from bacterial and mammalian sources shown in Table 4 illustrates the striking selectivity of inhibitors binding to the enzymes from different species [325].

Table 4. Comparative Binding of Inhibitors to Dihydrofolate Reductases from Various Species

Compound	IC_{50} ($\times 10^{-8}$ M)		
	E. coli	*S. aureus*	Rat Liver
Methotrexate	0.01	0.02	0.02
Pyrimethamine	250	300	180
Trimethoprim	0.7	1.5	35,000
Dihydrotriazine	65,000	50,000	24

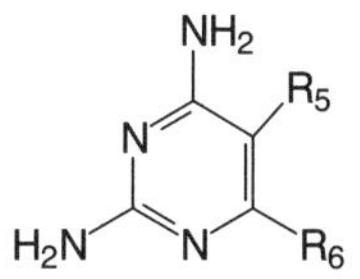

(63a): R_5,R_6 = CH_3
(63b): R_5 = CH_3; R_6 = H

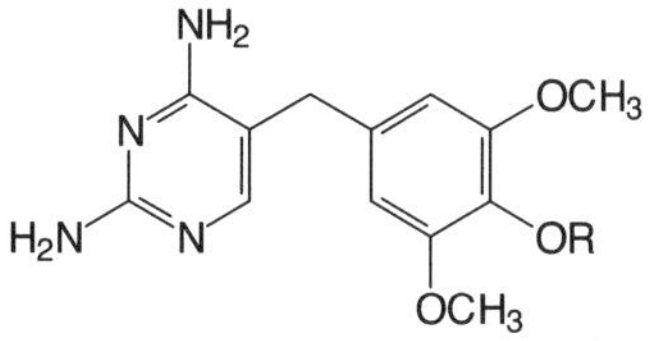

(64a): R = CH_3
(64b): R_5 = $CH_2CH_2OCH_3$

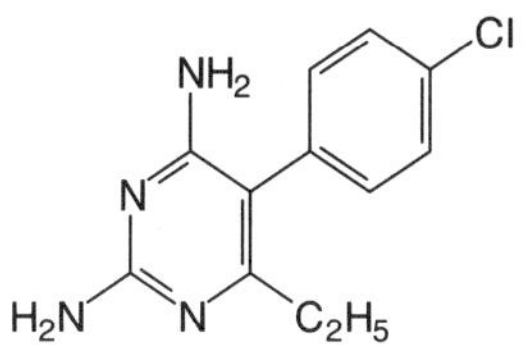

(65)

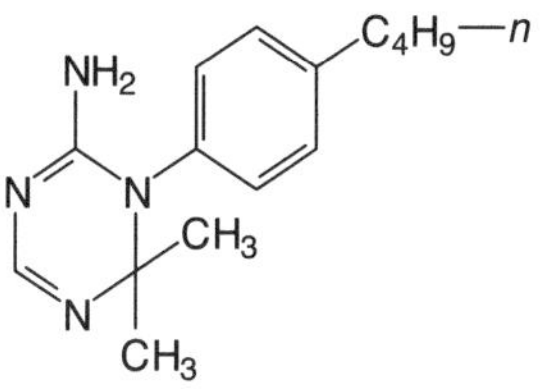

(66)

These compounds used alone or in combination with sulfonamides, emerged as promising antibacterial and antiplasmodial drugs respectively. A large variety of diamino pyrimidines and triazines have since then been synthesized, but none has surpassed the activity of these compounds based on consideration of selectivity of action, antimicrobial spectrum, and potency, and even after almost five decades trimetheprim and pyrimethamine continue to be the most commonly used DHFRI drugs. The only other antibacterial discovered more recently that seems to offer some significant advantages over TMP is Iclaprim (ICL, **67**) [326], which is now in phase III clinical trials. ICL is active against TMP resistant aerobic bacteria when tested *in vitro* against a variety of clinical isolates. ICL was generally reported 16-fold more potent than TMP and vancomycin (VAN), and comparable in potency to TMP-SMX. It was active against methicillin-resistant *S. aureus* (MRSA). In addition, ICL has shown activity against penicillin, er-

ythromycin, levofloxacin, TMP-SM-resistant *Spneumoniae*. In humans, it has been shown that oral ICL is rapidly absorbed with C_{max} attained between three-fourth to 3 h, and $t_{1/2}$ of oral and i.v. ICL was 3.9 and 4.1 h, respectively. With this good oral bioavailability and favorable pharmacokinetic profile, ICL seems a promising antibacterial agent. Early Phase II and Phase III clinical trials have shown special promise for its use for complicated skin and skin structure infections caused by MRSA. It is a bit too early to say whether it will be better to use it alone or in combination with a sulfonamide, and which sulfonamide, which will be settled in the future clinical trials.

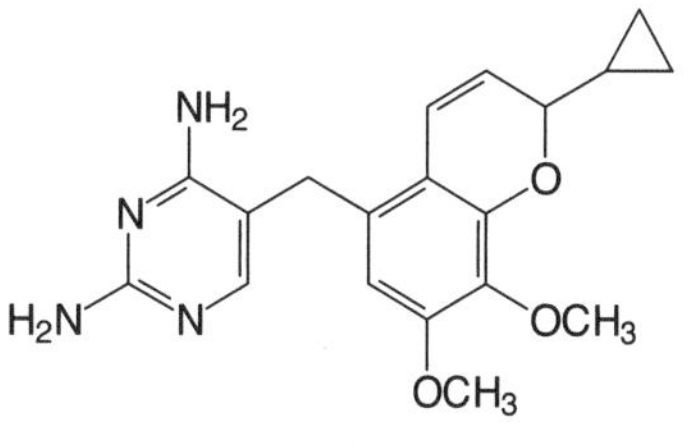

(67)

Structure–activity relationship studies of benzylpyrimidines for antibacterial activity showed that 3′,4′,5′-trisubstituted derivatives were in general more active and selective than disubstituted derivatives, which were in turn more active than monosubstituted analogs, and alkoxy group were the preferred substitutents for antibacterial activity.

Trimethoprim (TMP) and Trimethoprin-Sulfamethoxazole Combination (Co-Trimoxazole; TMP-SMX) Trimethoprim has a reasonably broad antibacterial spectrum, covering most of the Gram-negative and Gram- positive microorganisms; species that are relatively insensitive are *P. aeruginosa, Bacterioides* sp, and *M. tuberculosis* [327]. Bacteria readily develop resistance against trimethoprim, so it is mainly used in combination with sulfonamides. The combination most commonly used is with sulfamethoxazole, as the half-lives of trimethoprim and sulfamethoxazole are well matched, and this helps to maintain the optimal inhibitory concentrations of the combination drugs. The other combination that is occasionally used is with sulfadiazine, but the half-lives of the individual drugs range widely and for some period it would be like exposure to only one drug, which can easily lead to resistance development. The trimethoprim—sulfamethoxazole combination, widely known as co-trimoxazole, is the most commonly used DHFRI—sulfonamide antibacterial combination [312].

The pharmacokinetic profiles of sulfamethoxazole and trimethoprim are closely matched, and a ratio of around 20:1 in their concentrations is maintained in the blood and tissues.

3.3.2.2. Mechanism of Action

The antimicrobial activity of the combination of TMP and SMX results not only from its action on two sequential steps of the enzymatic pathway for the synthesis of THF but also from the whole cascade of events leading to THF. As shown in Fig. 2, sulfonamides inhibit the incorporation of PABA into folic acid, and TMP prevents the reduction of DHF to THF, the form of folate essential for one-carbon transfer reactions required for the synthesis of a variety of purines, pyrimidine, and amino acids, and the two thus supplement each other. The physiological action of this combination, however, goes beyond this. TMP will increase the concentration of DHFA, which by the law of mass action, will drive the reaction to the right and produce THFA, partially overcoming the TMP-induced metabolism block. This biologic effect can be minimized by inclusion of a sulfonamide, which blocks the synthesis of DHFA. This sequential blockade in the biosynthetic pathway of THFA thus results in potentiation of the action of the combination of TMP and sulfonamide over the action of each component alone (synergy) [288] This synergism in the antibacterial activity of this combination has been reported for many microorganisms, in both *in vitro* and *in vivo*.

Bacterial Resistance. Bacterial resistance to TM-SMX combination was much lower and slower to develop than with each drug alone, although ultimately even with this combination resistance is becoming an increasing problem. Resistance most often is due to the acquisition of a plasmid that codes for an altered DHFR. Emergence of TMP-SM-resistant *S. aureus* and Enterobacteriaceae is a special problem in AIDS patients receiving the drug for prophylaxis of *P. carinii* pneumonia.

Side Effects. In routine use, this combination produces little serious toxicity, even during long-term administration. This may be due, in part, to the relatively greater affinity of TMP for bacterial DHFR compared with the mammalian enzyme. About 75% of the untoward effects involve the skin, which are typical of those described for sufonamides, although a little more severe for this combination. However, side effects are more common when the patients are deficient in folate, and this combination may cause or precipitate megaloblastosis, leukopenia, or thrombocytopenia.

3.3.2.3. Therapeutic Uses

The combination appears to have special efficacy in chronic and recurrent infections of the urinary tract, bacterial prostatitis, childhood otitis media, shigellosis, pneumocystosis, is a second choice for acute exacerbations of chronic bronchitis, for gastro intestinal infections such as shigollesis, for typhoid fever, and for gonorrhea.

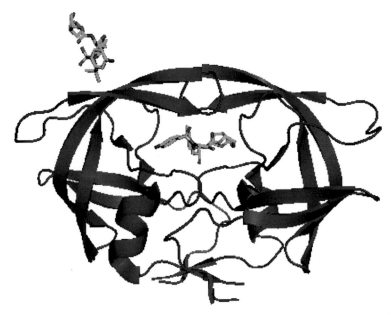

Figure 39 (Chapter 1). Two binding sites of DRV observed in the HIV PR complex [188].

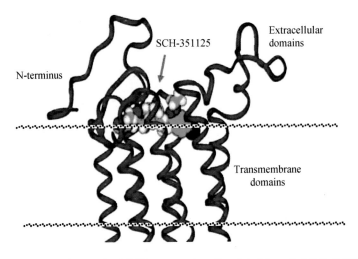

Figure 36 (Chapter 3). Binding mode of CCR5 antagonists. Reprinted from Ref. [11]. © 2008, Elsevier, Inc.

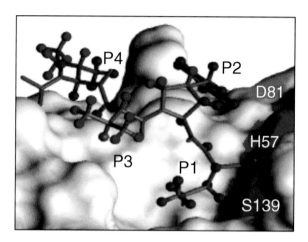

Figure 4 (Chapter 5). Model of NS3/4A protease with **6**. Hydrogens highlighted in blue indicate resonances for which no broadening perturbations were observed, while hydrogens in red showed significant resonance broadening upon addition of protease. Terminal Ac-Asp-Asp dipeptide is not shown [141]. Reproduced with permissions by Wiley-VCH Verlag GmbH & Co. KGaA and Prof. Youla S. Tsantrizos.

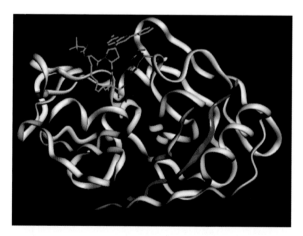

Figure 5 (Chapter 5). The crystal structure of inhibitor **13** (carbon atoms colored green) complexed to NS3 protease domain (gray ribbon) and NS4A (magenta ribbon) is shown [141]. Reproduced with permissions by Wiley-VCH Verlag GmbH & Co. KGaA and Prof. Youla S. Tsantrizos.

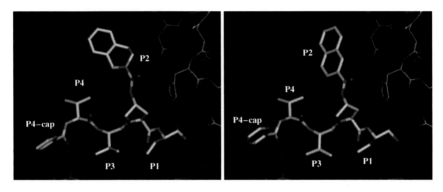

Figure 7 (Chapter 5). Binding of **19c** (left) and **19b** to NS3/4A [155]. Reproduced with permission by Elsevier.

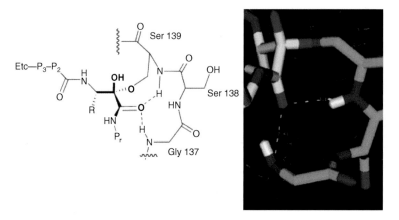

Figure 8 (Chapter 5). A representation of the covalent interaction between a bound ketoamide inhibitor and the serine active site (left). The X-ray crystal structure of **20c** bound to NS3/4A (right) [158]. Reproduced with permission by Elsevier.

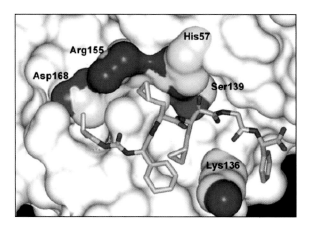

Figure 11 (Chapter 5). X-ray crystal structure of hexapeptide **28** bound to NS3/4A [173]. Reproduced with permission by Elsevier.

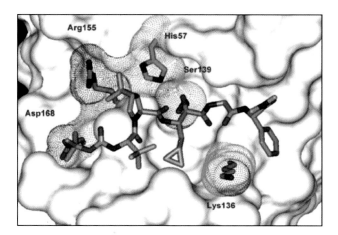

Figure 12 (Chapter 5). X-ray crystal structure of **30** bound to NS3/4A protease [176]. Reproduced with permission by the American Chemical Society.

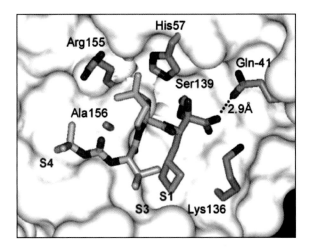

Figure 13 (Chapter 5). X-ray crystal structure of **25** bound to NS3/4A [170]. Reproduced with permission by the American Chemical Society.

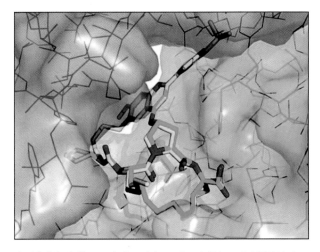

Figure 14 (Chapter 5). Model of ciluprevir (cyan) bound to full length NS3/4A (protease, green; helicase, purple) with key protein–inhibitor interactions shown overlaid with **43** [188]. Reproduced with permission by the American Chemical Society.

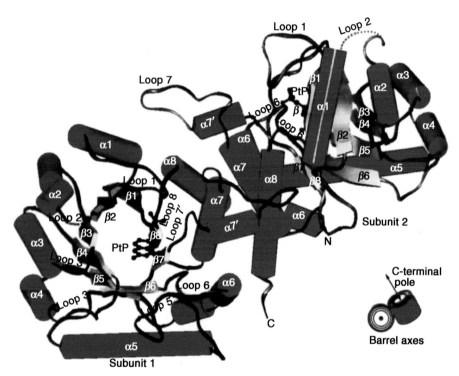

Figure 3 (Chapter 9). Overall folded structure of *M. tuberculosis* DHPS dimer. From Ref. [289].

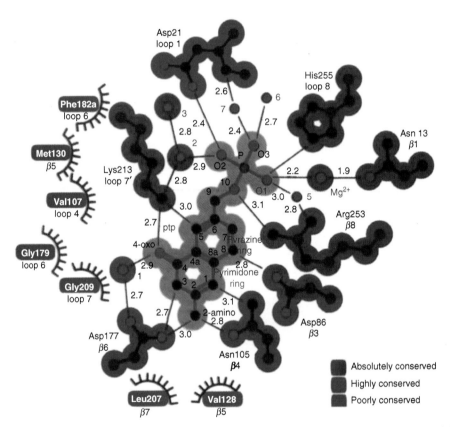

Figure 4 (Chapter 9). The Pterin monophosphate binding site in *M. tuberculosis* DHPS. From Ref. [289].

3.4. Quinolones and Fluoroquinolones[1]

3.4.1. Introduction After antifolates fluoroquinolones and related analogs have been the most important new class of antibacterials that emerged specially from around 1980 onward. Their history started with the discovery of antibacterial activity of 1-ethyl-1,4-dihydro-7-methyl-1,8-naphthyridene-3-carboxyllic acid (nalidixic acid, **68**) [329]. Though the activity was not very powerful and confined mainly to Gram-negative pathogens (**68**), found use for UTI. This lead led to the discovery of antibacterial activity in analogous quinolones and cinnolones resulting in the development of oxolinic acid (**69**) in 1968 and cinoxacin (**70**) in 1972 as antibacterials.

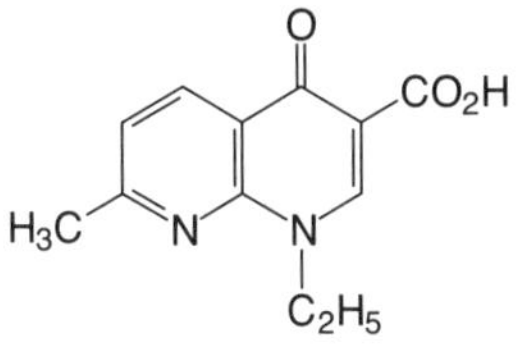

(68) 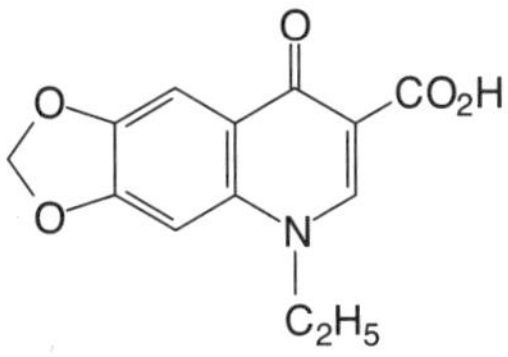   (69) 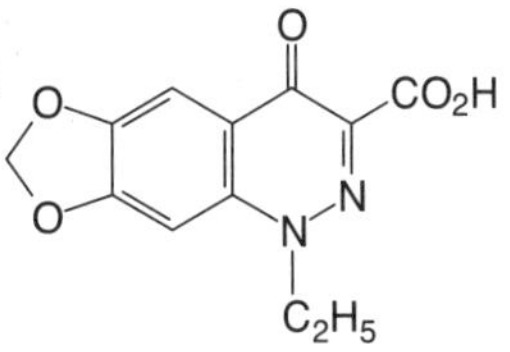   (70)

Although their antibacterial activity was not very powerful and broad, and they were used mainly for UTI, their activity established broadly the structural contours for antibacterial activity in this new class of antibacterials. Variants of this new class drew much attention for development of new antibacterials with the pressure from widespread development of resistance to known antimicrobial drugs from mid-1970s [330]. It was soon discovered that combination of a F atom at position 6 and a piperazinyl group at position 7 resulted in compounds with broad spectrum and highly potent antimicrobial activity against both Gram-positive and Gram-negative bacteria, including anaerobic species and mycobacteria, and got to be generically classed as fluoroquinolones [331]. Norfloxain (**71**) [332] was the first antibacterial of this second generation of broad-spectrum quinolone antibacterials introduced in 1978. And since then research on variants of this classic quinolone/naphthyridone structures has continued unabated, and introduction of new agents of this class continues [333]. However, many quinolones launched in more recent years were beset by unexpected toxicity issues of varying severity and were withdrawn from a number of markets, but many more are in clinical development. The main challenge in fluoroquinolones today is to find drugs that are safe, expand the pathogen spectrum of existing drugs, and show therapeutically effective potency against current quinolones-resistant strains [333]. The current more commonly clinically used fluoroquinolones include norfloxacin (**71**), ciprofloxacin (**72**), gatifloxacin (**73**), moxifloxacin (**74**), the tricyclic analog ofloxacin (**75**) and its (s)-enantiomer, levofloxacin, sitafloxacin (**76**), and some new 1,8-naphthyridene analogs of nalidixic acid (**68**), such as enoxacin (**77**).

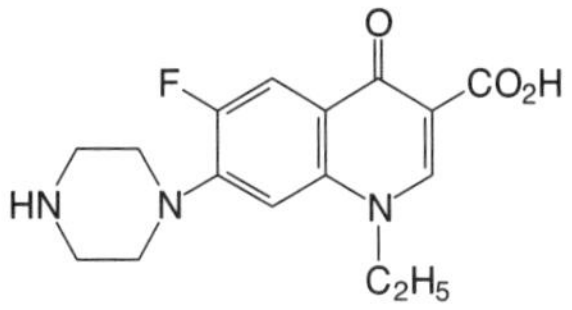

(71)

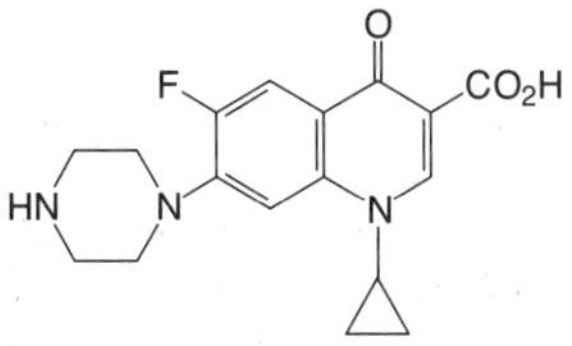

(72)

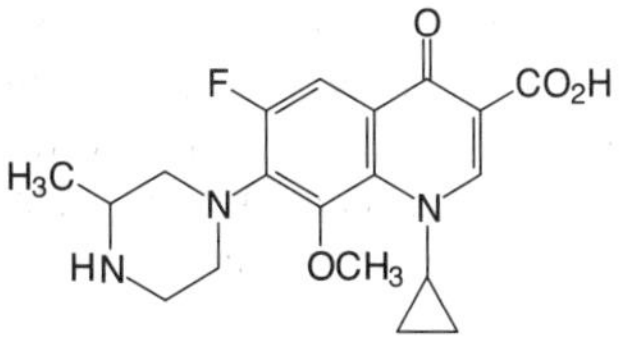

(73)

---

[1] Although the earliest and some of the more recent drugs covered in this group are not strictly quinolones, and some do not carry a fluorine atom in the aromatic ring, such as (**68**), (**78**), and (**79**), they share a common 3-carboxy-4-quinolone pharmacophore, and all are generically covered under fluoroquinolones.

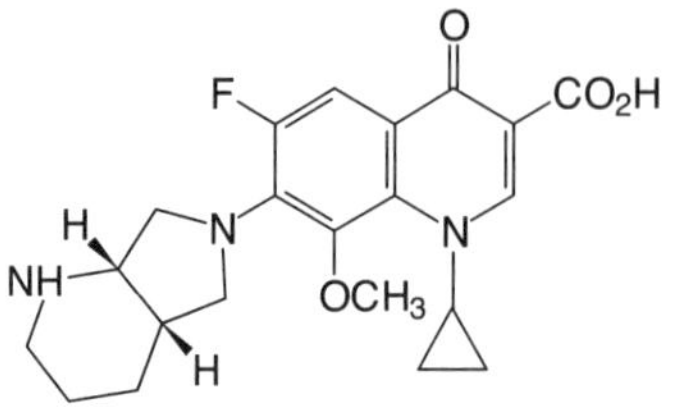

(74)

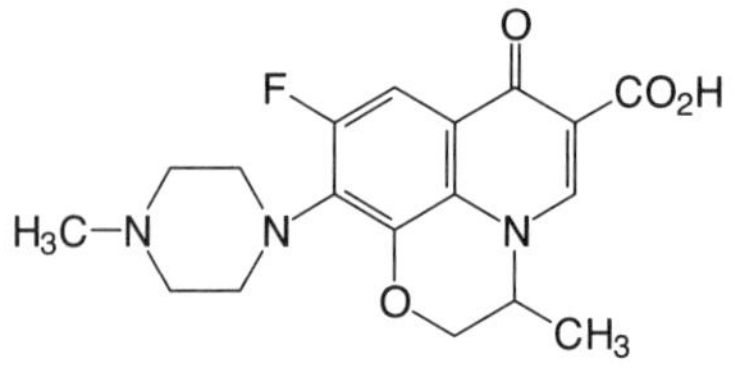

(75)

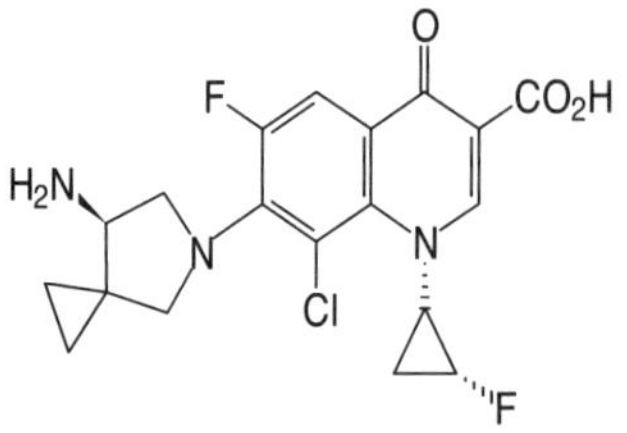

(76)

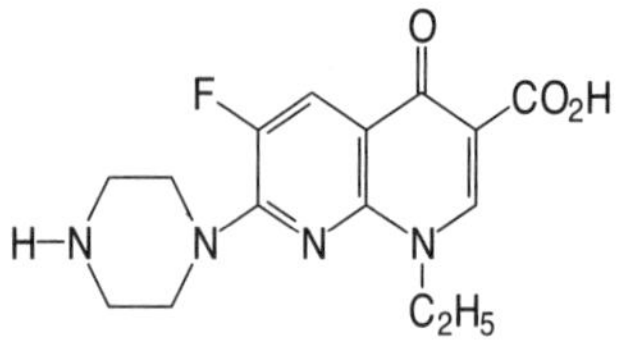

(77)

Interest in this class for new antibacterials continues and several new analogs are in clinical development. A few that show special promise are delafloxacin (**78**) and nemofloxacin (**79**). Both of these antibacterials are several fold more potent than comparators such as ciprofloxacin, levofloxacin, and moxifloxacin against quinolone-resistant Gram-positive pathogens, including against many MRSA, while maintaining good Gram-negative potency: both appear specially promising for community-acquired pneumonia [333].

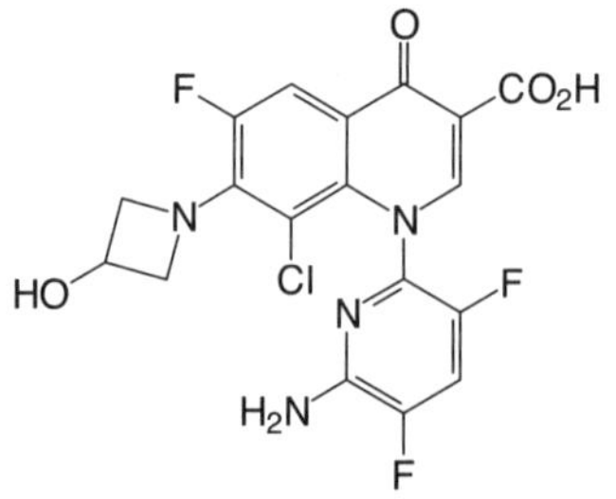

(78)

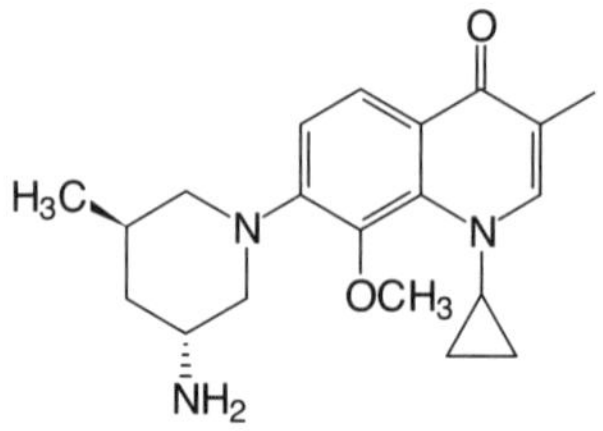

(79)

3.4.2. Antibacterial Activity Fluoroquinolones are broad-spectrum antibacterial agents. All of them are active against species such as *Enterobacter cloacea*, *P. mirabilis*, *M. morganii*, and *S. epidermis*. Furthermore, most of them are active against *H. influenzae*, *Providencia rettgeri*, *P. aeruginosa*, *Serratia marcesans*, *S. aureus*, *Enterococcus fecalis*, *Mycoplasma pneumonia*, *Chlamidia pneumonia*, and *N. gonorrhoeae*. When anthrax infections danger resulting from terrorist activity emerged in the United States in October 2001, ciprofloxacin was the principal drug for treating this infection. Although many other antibacterial agents such as penicillin and doxycycline are active against anthrax infections, ciprofloxacin is effective against most strains of anthrax. The preferred clinical indications for quinolones and fluoroquinolones are given in Table 5.

A number of different classification systems have been used in the literature to

Table 5. Preferred Therapeutic Indications for Different Quinolones

Compound	Indications
Nalidixic acid	Urinary tract infections
Cinoxacin[a]	Urinary tract infections
Ciprofloxacin	Acute sinusitis, lower respiratory tract infections, nosocomial pneumonia, skin infections, bone/joint infections, urinary tract infections, gonorrhoea, anthrax infections
Enoxacin[a]	Gonorrhoea, urinary tract infections
Gatifloxacin[a]	Chronic bronchitis, acute sinusitis, urinary tract infections, pyelonephritis
Levofloxacin	Chronic bronchitis, acute sinusitis, urinary tract infections, pneumonia, skin infections
Norfloxacin	Urinary tract infections, gonorrhoea, chronic bacterial prostatitis
Ofloxacin	Liver cirrhosis, epididmytis, gonorrhoea, chlmydia
Moxifloxacin	Respiratory infections

[a] Discontinued in some markets.

describe the evolution of naphthyridones → quinolones → fluoroquinolones. A system that designates the existing fluoroquinolones by the evolutionary stage, related with clinical utility, is more commonly accepted and is listed as follows:

I Generation	II Generation
Nalidixic Acid	Norfloxacin
Cinoxacin	Ciprofloxacin
	Enoxacin
	Ofloxacin
III Generation	**IV Generation**
Levofloxacin	Sitafloxacin
Gatifloxacin	Moxifloxacin

3.4.3. Structure–Activity Relationship The minimum pharmacophore required for significant antibacterial activity consists of the 4-pyridone ring with a 3-carboxylic acid group (443) (Fig. 6). Reduction of the 2,3-double bond eliminates activity. Most of the highly active quinolones have a fluorine atom at C6 (fluoroquinolones). It increases lipophilicity, which would facilitate penetration into cells. Many analogs have piperazino groups on C7; this appears to broaden the activity spectrum, especially to include Gram-negative organisms such as *P. aeruginosa*; however, they also seems to increase affinity for the GABA receptor, which contributes to CNS side effects. This receptor binding affinity can be reduced by adding a methyl or ethyl group to the piperazine ring or by placing a bulky substituent on N1 [334a]. Substituents on the piperazine ring appears to shift excretion of the compound from kidney to liver and they extend its half-life. Quinolones with greater amounts of liver metabolism and biliary excretion are useful in patients with impaired renal function [334b]. Replacement of C8 by nitrogen, to give a naphthyridine (e.g., enoxacin and trovafloxacin) increases bioavilability [335], whereas a methoxy group in place of hydrogen or fluorine on C8 provides greater stability to ultraviolet light and less phototoxicity in mice [336]. Compounds such as sparfloxacin, with an amino group at C5, also have reduced phototoxicity.

Isosteric replacement of nitrogen for C2 provides cinnolines such as cinoxacin that

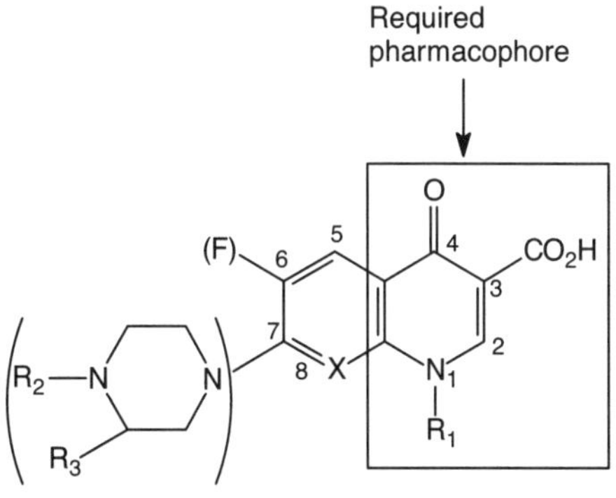

Figure 6. Quinolone pharmacophore and substituents.

have good antibacterial activity and pharma-cokinetic properties. Isomeric naphthyridines including the 1,5 and 1,6 isomers retain antibacterial activity. Compounds with ring fusions at 1,8 (Ofloxacin, **74**); 5,6; and 7,8 also are effective antibacterials.

Stereochemistry of the methyl group in the third ring of ofloxacin (**74**) is important for antibacterial activity; the (S)-enantiomer (marketed separately as levofloxacin) is 10-fold more potent than the (R)-enantiomer, but it is less selective for topoisomerase II [337,338]. Interestingly, the corresponding methylene analog (which flattens the ring to allow stronger intercalation between base pairs) has 20-fold greater topoisomerase activity than either of the methyl enantiomers [339].

Fluorine at C6 enhances inhibition of DNA gyrase and provides activity against *Staphylococci*, whereas a piperazine substituent at C7 affords the best activity against Gram-negative bacteria. Addition of a second fluorine at C8 increases absorption and half-life. Ring alkylation improves Gram-positive potency and half-life. A number of newer quinolones such as ciprofloxacin (**70**), gatifloxacin (**74**) [340], and moxifloxacin (**75**) [341] have cyclopropyl sunstituents at N1. This substituent, or the combination of an amine at C5 and fluorine at C8 (sparfloxacin), increases potency against mycoplasma and *Chlamydiae* sp.

Earlier antibacterial quinolones such as nalidixic acid and cinoxacin have only the 3-carboxylic acid as an ionizable group. Its relatively high pK_a in the range of 5.4 to 6.4 is thought to result from an acid-weakening hydrogen bond with the 4-carbonyl group [342]. More recent quinolones with a piperazine or other substituent with a basic nitrogen at C7 have a second pK_a in the range of 8.1–9.3. Consequently, significant fractions of these compounds exist as zwitterions at physiological pH values. Decreased solubility in urine of higher pH presents a potential problem for these compounds.

The 4-carbonyl group and 3-carboxylic acid functionalities of quinolones provide an excellent site for chelation with divalent or trivalent metals. Quinolones can form 1:1, 2:1, or 3:1 chelates, depending on the particular metal ion, relative concentration of the quinolone, and the pH. The relative insolubility of these chelates causes incompatibilities with antacids (Ca^{2+}, Mg^{2+}, and Bi^{3+}), hematinics (Fe^{2+}), and mineral supplements (Zn^{2+}).

It has been noted that if just 20 different substituents are taken two at a time for the seven available positions on quinolones, there would be 84,000 possible compounds to synthesize and test [343]. The use of computer assisted quantitative structure–activity relationships has helped to narrow down the search for new compounds of this type. Koga and coworkers developed an equation that related the potency of compounds against *E. coli* (MIC) to the length of the substituent on N^1, the size of substituents on C8, an enhancement factor for C7 substituents, and a factor for the detrimental effect of attachment of C7 substituents by an NCO function [344].

3.4.4. Mechanism of Action Fluoroquinolones act by inhibiting two bacterial enzymes, DNA gyrase and topoisomerase IV, that human cells lack, but are essential for bacterial DNA replication, thereby enabling these agents to be both specific and bactericidal [345,346]. DNA topoisomerases are responsible for separating the strands of duplex bacterial DNA, inserting another strand of DNA through the break, and then resealing the original separated strands. DNA gyrase introduces a negative superhelical twist in the DNA double helix ahead of the replication fork, thereby catalyzing the separation of "daughter chromosomes". This activity is essential for initiation of DNA replication and allows for binding of initiation proteins. Topoisomerase IV is responsible for decatenation, that is delinking of daughter chromosomes, thereby allowing segregation into two daughter cells at the end of a round of replication. The interaction of fluoroquinolones with enzyme bound DNA complex, produces conformational changes, which result in the inhibition of normal enzyme activity, and blockage of the progression of replication and bacterial cell death. It has been shown that DNA gyrase tends to be the primary target in gram-negative organisms wheras Topo-IV is typically the primary target in gram-positive bacteria and some degree of overlap in activity may exist. Data from trials with resistant mutant species suggest that newer fourth generation fluoroquinolones such as gatifloxain (**73**) and moxifloxacin (**74**) have a dual binding action, inhibiting both DNA-gyrase and Topo IV in gram-positive species, and therefore lesser propensity to resistance development.

The antibacterial activity of quinolones is antagonized by chloramphenicol and rifampicin, which suggests that protein synthesis is required for their action [347]. This mechanism is consistent with apoptosis accruing rather than necrosis.

3.4.5. Microbial Resistance

Drug resistance was observed even in the early clinical trials with nalidixic acid [348] and since fluoroquinolones have come into clinical use there have been increasing reports of resistant cases [348]. One mechanism of resistance is by mutations at various locations on the gyrase gene. These mutations confer cross-resistance to quinolone antibacterials in general. Another mechanism is by mutations in the genes that code for porins, which are membrane proteins by which quinolones enter Gram-negative cells. They raise tolerance fourfold. Other mutations of serious concern are those that reduce membrane lipopolysaccharides to afford cross-resistance with antibacterial agents of some other chemical classes also [349]. In view of the importance of fluoroquinolones for combating bacterial diseases, especially for deep tissue infections, consensus is emergence that quinolones

should be used more judiciously, and reserved for more serious conditions. Moellering in his review of the problem of resistance development concludes "The future viability of the quinolones will in large part depend on the ability of the medical community to use them wisely" [348]. In particular, with increasing use of quinolones for infection, consensus is emerging that quinolones should be used more judiciously: not so serious conditions such as for oral periodontal treatments could bring about an expansion of resistance to quinolones that would limit their value in treating deep tissue infections.

3.4.6. Pharmacokinetic Properties

Phamacokinetic properties of quinolones are listed in Table 6. Bioavalibility after oral administration is generally good, but it is substantially reduced by magnesium or aluminum antacids. Distribution to tissues is superior to that of most other drugs because there is little binding to plasma proteins. Quinolones achieve tissue to serum ratios of over two to one, in contrast to less than one-half for β-lactams and aminoglycosides. Clearance is by kidneys (ofloxacin), or by liver (pefloxacin and difloxacin), or by both (norfloxacin, ciprofloxacin, and enoxacin). Renal clearance correlates with creatinine clearance; consequently, reduced drug dosage is appropriate for patients having creatinine clearance under 30 mL/min. The renal clearance rates of ciprofloxacin and norfloxacin exceed the glomerular filtration rates, indicating net renal tub-

Table 6. Pharmacokinetics of Quinolones

Compound	Single Oral Dose (mg)	Peak Serum Concentration (g/mL)	Half-Life (h)	Protein Binding (%)	Urinary Recovery, % unchanged
Nalidixic acid	1000	20–40	6	93–97	3
Cipro-floxacin	200	0.8	4–6	40–50	20–40
Enoxacin	200	1.0	5	40	20–40
Lome-floxacin	200	0.7	3–4	10	65
Norfloxacin	100	1.0	5	10–15	26–32
Gatifloxacin	200	2.0	7.8	20	74
Ofloxacin	200	1.5	9	32	65–80
Sparfloxacin	400	1.3	20	46	10
Moxifloxacin	400	3.4	12		
Trova-floxacin	100	1.0	9.1	76	6

Abstracted from Drug Facts and Comparisons.

ular secretion. Lomefloxacin has the advantage of a relatively long half-life and so can be administered once daily.

Metabolism of quinolones is primarily by glucuronide conjugation at the 3-carboxyl group and is inactivating. The piperazine ring is readily metabolized in the compounds that have this functionality, and this metabolism reduces antimicrobial activity [350]. Approximately one-eighth of enoxacin is cleared as the oxo-metabolite. Six metabolites with modifications in the piperazine ring were found for norfloxacin [334].

3.4.7. Adverse Reactions A variety of adverse reactions of quinolones are described in Section 3.4.1. They also have shown CNS toxicity. Quinolones can affect the central nervous system by two mechanisms: accumulation of ingested xanthines including caffeine and theophylline [351] and blockade of GABA receptors, which can cause convulsions [352]. A study on proconvulsant effects of quinolones in a strain of DBA/2 mice susceptible to sound-induced seizures showed an increase in incidence in the order enoxacin > norfloxacin > cinoxacin > ciprofloxacin > nalidixic acid [353]. Another study based on the induction of fatal convulsions by a combination of nonsteriodal anti-inflammatory drugs and quinolones gave the following order of potency when fenbrufen was the anti-inflammatory agent enoxacin > lomefloxacin > norfloxacin, with ofloxacin, and ciprofloxacin causing no deaths [354].

Some of the other serious toxicological effects of varying severity noted with some flouroquinolones include hepatoxicity for trovafloxacin hemolytic reactions and cardiotoxicity for grepafloxacin and, glucose homeostasis for gatifloxacin. Other side effects associated with fluoroquinolone have been phototoxicity and tendonitis which resulted in the withdrawal of some of these drugs from the market [333]. The therapeutical use of the newer fluoroquinolones thus has to be monitored carefully.

3.4.8. Present status in Therapeutics Quinolones have some special features, which make them an attractive class of therapeutic agents. These feature include (a) wide antimicrobial spectrum covering most of the Gram-positive and Gram-negative pathogen, both anaerobes

and acrobes, including mycobacteria; (b) good oral absorption with good tissue distribution, and relatively long serum half-lives with good intestinal fluid and urinary tract concentrations after oral administration; and (c) different mechanism of action than of other commonly used antibacterials, and thus posing no problem of cross-resistance. These special pharmacokinetic and pharmacodynamic features have made fluoroquinolones important in treating diarrheal diseases, urinary tract infections, prostatitis, sexually transmitted diseases, respiratory infections and infections of the skin and bones. Fluoroquinolones are especially suitable for home treatment in infections such as osteomyelitis that earlier required hospitalization. After more than two decades, there is growing use and new indications for some known fluoroquinolones and new analogs continue to be developed. On the other hand, some fluoroquinolines have produced serious adverse events that have caused their discontinuation or limitation to topical use. It is therefore, advised that fluoroquinolones should be preserved for serious clinically condition where other drugs may not be therapeutically effective. The preferred therapeutical indications for the different commonly used quinolones are described in Table 5.

3.5. Oxazolidinones

3.5.1. Introduction The oxazolidinones are a new class of synthetic antibacterial agents with activity against a broad spectrum of Gram-positive pathogens, including those resistant to currently used antibacterials [355]. Following the activity discovered in a series of 5-(halomethyl)-3-aryl-2-oxazolidinones against plant pathogens in 1978, scientists at E.I. Du Pont de Nemours (Wilmington, DE) observed antibacterial activity in (R)-5-hydroxymethyl-3-aryl-2-oxazolidinone (S-6123) against human pathogens [356]. Further optimization led to the emergence of two highly active antibacterial drug candidates [356]: (S)-[(3-(4-methylsulfinylphenyl)-2-oxo-5-oxazolidinyl)methyl] acetamide (DUP-105, **80**) and (S)-[(3-(4-acetylphenyl)-2-oxo-5-oxazolidinyl)methyl] acetamide (DUP-721, **81**) [357,358], with a number of special features that included

- activity against a number of therapeutically important multidrug-resistant Gram-positive organisms [356–361],
- equally active when administered by oral or parenteral routes, showing excellent oral absorption [357,361], and
- a novel mechanism of action, and consequently not likely to have cross-resistance

with existing antimicrobials [356,358, 362,363].

Further, the prototype structure consisting of distinct structural units offered much scope for molecular modification.

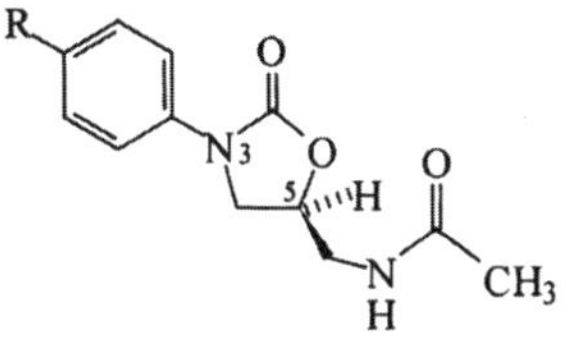

(80): DUP 105, R = CH₃SO
(81): DUP 721, R = CH₃CO

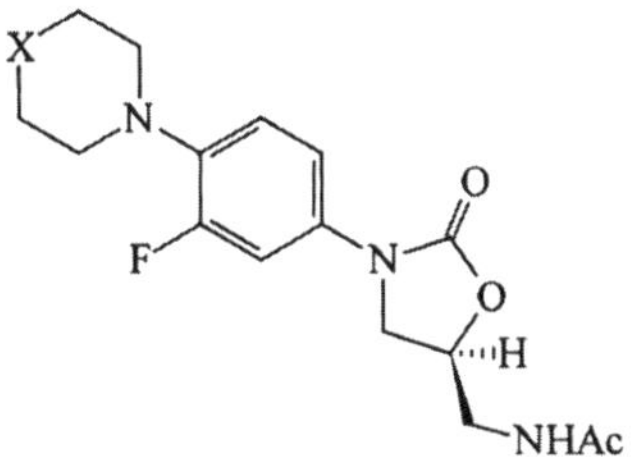

(82): PNU 100596, X = NCOCH₂OH
(83): PNU 1007, X = O

The development of these two agents was subsequently discontinued consequent upon DUP-721 (81) exhibiting toxicity in rodents [364], but the special features of their antibacterial activity attracted much attention and prompted studies on oxazolidinones in a number of laboratories. Pharmacia-Upjohn (USA) scientists from their studies were able to identify two drug candidates for human studies, eperezolid (PNU-100592) (82) and linezolid (PNU-100766) (83) [364–366]. Both compounds were equally active *in vitro* and *in vivo* (experimental mouse models) against MRSA and *S. epiderdmidis* (MRSE), against penicillin and cephalosporin-resistant *S. pneumoniae*, comparing favorably with vancomycin activity, and against vancomycin-sensitive and resistant *Enterococcus* sp (VSE and VRE). Both eperezolid and linezolid went successfully through Phase I human trials without any significant safety concerns. Linezolid has undergone more extensive Phase II and Phase III clinical evaluation [367].

3.5.2. Linezolid (83) Linezolid (Zyvox, Zyvoxam) is the first of this new class of oxazolidinone antibacterials to be approved in the United States, United Kingdom, and Canada for the treatment of Gram-positive infections. Specific indications include complicated and

uncomplicated skin and soft-tissue infections (SSTIs), community and clinically acquired pneumonia, and vancomycin-resistant enterococcal infections [368–371].

Synthesis Linezolid and related oxazolidinones have been prepared via a novel asymmetric synthesis involving the reactions of *N*-lithiocarbamates of the appropriate aniline with (*R*)-glycidylbutyrate as the key step, and the resultant (*R*)-5-(hydroxymethyl)oxazolidinone converted to linezolid in a few steps in excellent yield and high enantiomeric purity [364,368,400].

Antibacterial Activity Linezolid has inhibitory activity against a broad range of Gram-positive bacteria, including MRSA, glycopeptide-intermediate *S. aureus* (GISA), vancomycin-resistant enterococci (VRE), and penicillin/cephalosporin-sensitive, -intermediate, and -resistant streptococci and pneumococci [366]. Linezolid is in general bacteriostatic and displays bactericidal activity only against some strains, which include some pneumococci, *B. fragilis*, and *C. perfringens* [366,367]. Initial breakpoint criteria established for MICs of linezolid are ≤ μg/mL for susceptibility and ≥16 μg/mL for resistance [360,369,372].

Gram-Negative Bacteria Linezolid is significantly less active against most Gram-negative organisms. It has only moderate activity against *Moraxella catarrhalis*. *H. influenzae*, *Legionella* sp and *Bordatella pertussis* and practically no activity against eneterobacteriaceae, Klebsiella, Proteus, and *P. aeruginosa*. The few Gram-negative organisms against which linezolid has good activity are *Flavobacterium meningosepticum* and *Pasteurella multicida* with MIC values of 2 µg and 4 µg/mL, respectively [366,370,371].

Activity Against Anaerobes   Linezolid demonstrated comparable activity to vancomycin (MIC: 1–2 µg/mL) against *Clostridium difficile* and *C. perfringens*. It also showed good activity against Gram-negative anaerobes including *Bacteroids* sp (MIC: 4 µg/mL), *Fusobacterium nucleatum* (MIC: 0.5 µg/mL), *F. meningosepticum* (MIC: 2–4 µg/mL) and *Prevotella* sp (MIC: 1–2 µg/mL) [370,372,373].

In vivo Antibacterial Activity   In murine bacteremia models, linezolid was more active than vancomycin against methicillin-sensitive *Staphylococcus aureus* (MSSA), and displayed comparable activity against MRSA, although less active for MRSE. In addition, linezolid displayed consistent *in vivo* activity against pneumococci, including against multidrug-resistant strains and vancomycin-resistant *E. faecium*, but was less active than vancomycin against aminoglycoside-resistant *E. faecalis* [374].

Of particular interest is the report by Cynamon et al. [375] that oral linezolid (25,

50, and 100 mg/kg) demonstrated efficacy against *M. tuberculosis* in a murine model, although it was somewhat less active than isoniazid. Subsequently, PNU-100480, the thiomorpholine analog of linezolid, has been reported to be as active as INH against *M. tuberculosis*. This provides a new lead for the design of antimycobacterial agents. Linezolid also showed promising activity in a rat experimental endocarditis model [376], and in an experimental model of acute otitis media [377] produced by a multidrug-resistant pneumococcal isolate.

Mechanism of Action   It has been established that linezolid (and related oxazolidinones) act via inhibition of the initiation phase of bacterial protein synthesis. Although the exact mode of action at the molecular level is not fully elucidated, linezolid has been reported to bind directly to a site on 23S ribosomal RNA of the bacterial 50S ribosomal subunit, thereby preventing the formation of the functional 70S- initiation complex [378,379], formed with 30S ribosomal subunit, mRNA, initiation factors, fMet-tRNA and 50S ribosome, which is an essential step of the bacterial translation process (Fig. 7). In a subsequent study it has been reported that mutations in the central loop of domain V of 23S rRNA, a component of the ribosomal peptidyl transferase center, conferred resistance to linezolid [380]. It would thus appear that

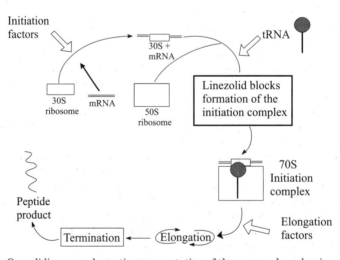

Figure 7. Oxazolidinones: schematic representation of the proposed mechanism of action.

linezolid and other oxazolidinones disrupt the interaction of fMet-tRNA with the 50S subunit during formation of the preinitiation complex, and affect the translocation step.

The mechanism for the poor activity against Gram-negative bacteria is not clear. One possible reason is the operation of selective efflux mechanism of Gram-negative bacteria.

This inhibition of the protein synthesis at an early stage is a new site/mechanism of action, and therefore there is little chance of development of cross-resistance between linezolid and other existing antibacterial agents; in fact, none has been reported so far [381].

Effect on Virulence Factors   Linezolid inhibited the expression of virulence factors from *S. aureus* and *Streptococcus pyogenes in vitro* at concentration 12.5–50% of the MIC for the organism; production of α-hemolysin and coagulase by *S. aureus* and of streptolysin O and DNAase by *S. pyogenes* was markedly inhibited at these concentrations [382].

Pharmacokinetics and Metabolism   Linezolid follows similar pharmacokinetic (PK) profile by both oral and intravenous routes of administration. It is rapidly and completely absorbed in humans after oral administration with a mean absolute availability of almost 100%; peak plasma concentration is reached in 1–2 h, with elimination half-life of 5.5 h and volume of distribution of 45 L [383,384]. The circulating drug is moderately (31%) bound to plasma proteins [385]. At steady state after 15 days of twice daily administration of 375 and 625 mg of linezolid in 24 volunteers C_{max} values were 12 and 18 µg/mL, respectively, while the MIC_{90} for susceptible pathogens are ≥ 4 µg/mL [349]. With intravenous linezolid (500 or 625 mg bid for 16 doses) the minimum plasma concentrations were 3.5 and 3.8 µg/mL with plasma concentration exceeding 4 µg/mL for $\geq 75\%$ of the dosage interval, above the MIC of the most pathogens targeted [384].

The pharmacokinetic properties of linezolid do not seem to be influenced by age. The clearance was somewhat lower in females, both young and old, but this was not of much significance and dose adjustments are not warranted on the grounds of age or gender [385].

Metabolism   Linezolid appears to be metabolized by oxidation of the morpholine ring to form two inactive carboxylic acid metabolites [386]. In volunteers, unchanged linezolid accounted for 90% of the circulating dose with the major metabolite accounting for <6%. After a single 500 mg oral dose 80–85% of linezolid was recovered in urine and 7–12% in feces over a 7-day period. In elimination, 35% of the drug appeared unchanged in the urine, and 50% appeared as one of the two major inactive metabolites [386,387].

Therapeutic Uses   The impressive antimicrobial activity against organisms resistant to other antimicrobial agents, high bioavailability after oral administration, favorable metabolic stability, low or no incidence of cross-resistance with other antimicrobials, low propensity to developing microbial resistance and favorable safety profile make linezolid an attractive antimicrobial agent for the treatment of problem Gram-positive infections. Oral and intravenous linezolid have been reported to be equally effective in the treatment of plain or complicated SSTIs [388,389], UTIs caused by methicillin-sensitive or -resistant *Stephylococcus* sp, and pneumonia, including nosocomial and community-acquired pneumonia, which normally require hospitalization [390]. The clinical response had a parallel favorable microbiological response. In these studies, linezolid was as effective as established treatments including third-generation cephalosporins, oxacillin, flucloxacillin and clarithromycin.

Other serious Gram-positive bacterial infections: Linezolid has also been evaluated in a variety of other infections (e.g., bacteremia, intra-abdominal abscesses, osteomyelitis, and lower and upper respiratory tract infections) caused by vancomycin-resistant *E. faecium / faecalis*, MRSA, or MRSE, with clinical and microbiological cures ranging from 70% to 90% [391,392]. Linezolid thus appears an effective treatment option for a variety of serious multidrug-resistant Gram-positive bacterial infections.

Microbial Resistance   There are as yet very few definitive reports of the development of resistance to linezolid, but these are bound to appear as the use increases. Development of resistance to linezolid was reported first in two patients who had *E. faecium* bacteremia with long-standing indwelling devices that could not be removed and had more than 4 weeks of i.v. linezolid; the MIC, which was initially 2 μg/mL dose, rose to 16 and 32 μg/mL [381], respectively, after treatment. Five more cases of linezolid resistance have been reported more recently; out of 45 patients under treatment, one of them developed resistance during treatment [393].

Toxicity and Adverse Effects

Preclinical Toxicology. In dogs, the "no observed adverse effect level (NOAEL)" of linezolid was 20 mg/kg for both sexes when administered orally for 28 days. Doses of 40 and 50 mg/kg/day were well tolerated with only mild effects. At toxic levels, hypocellularity of the bone marrow (reversible decrease in white blood cells and platelets) and atrophy of the lymphoid tissue were observed.

Human Safety. Linezolid was well tolerated in human volunteers after oral or intravenous administration of daily doses up to 625 mg bid [383,384,394,395]. The most common adverse effects were nausea (5.4%), diarrhea (5.2%), or oral cavity symptoms (tongue discoloration, 2.5%, oral monilia 2.2%). Serious drug-related adverse events (e.g., elevated liver enzymes, atrial fibrillation or worsening renal failure) occurred in <1% of cases. In the linezolid compassionate-use trial of patients with significant, resistant Gram-positive infections, the overall adverse event rate was about 33% of which approximately 6% were considered serious events [394]. The most frequent adverse events reported were thrombocytopenia (2.6%) and dermatological reaction (2.5%) [395]. Overall linezolid, at the end of therapy was well tolerated by about 78% of patients [395].

Myelosuppression (including anemia, leukopenia, pancytopenia, and thrombocytopenia) has been reported in three patients receiving linezolid for 2 and 6 weeks, and 4 months, respectively. With discontinuation of linezolid treatment the affected hematological parameters rose toward pretreatment levels [396]. The U.S. FDA has recommended that complete blood counts should be monitored weekly, particularly in patients who receive linezolid for longer than 2 weeks.

3.5.3. Structure–Activity Relationship The special features of the antibacterial activity of oxazolidinones highlighted earlier made oxazolidinones a hot lead for development of new antibacterials. A number of research publication and reports have appeared describing new oxazolodinones with improved antibacterial activities. On the basis of the early structure–activity studies [355–364], some structural features that appeared important for good antibacterial activity in oxazolidinones could be identified and are presented in Fig. 8 [397].

This picture acted as a useful guide for subsequent studies and broadly still holds. The structure–activity relationship of the reported oxazolidinones [398] is presented in the context of this picture of the pharmacophore.

A Ring Modification The oxazolidinone ring structure seems essential for good antibacterial activity and relatively few successful modification of the A ring have been reported [398]. The tricyclic analogs having a methylene bridge between rings A and B have been reported, with the transfused *trans* homolog **84**

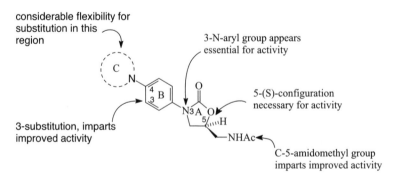

Figure 8. Oxazolidinones as antibacterials: important structural features.

having good activity [365,366], although the exact linezolid analog (85) was only weakly active. The 3-pyridyl analog (86) is the most active compound in this series [399].

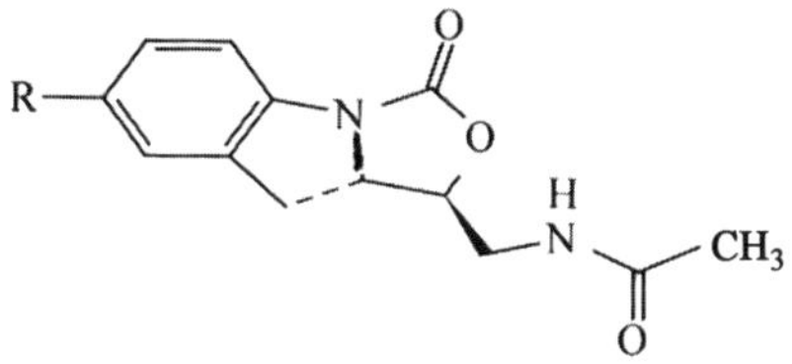

(84): R = COCH₃

(85): R =

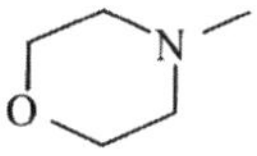

(86): R =

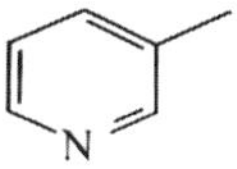

B Ring Modifications The replacement of the B aromatic residue by heteroaromatic rings as in (87–91) gave compounds that had modest to good activity by subcutaneous administration [400,401]; only the benzofuran analog (91) had good Gram-positive antibacterial activity [402]. Thus, the replacement of ring B did not seem to result in any significant improvement in the antibacterial profile.

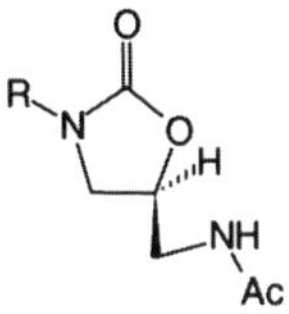

(87): R =

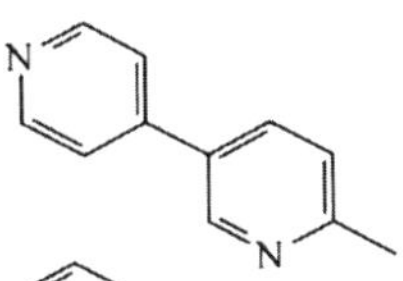

(88): R =

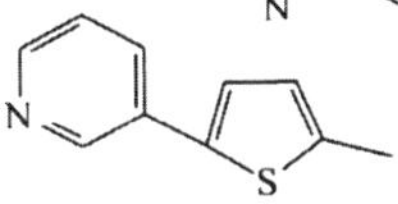

(89):

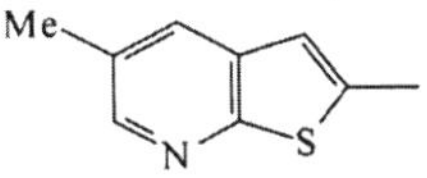

(90): R = Me

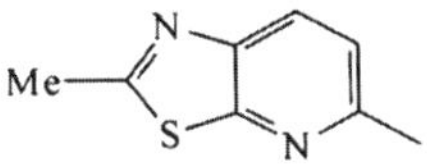

(91): R =

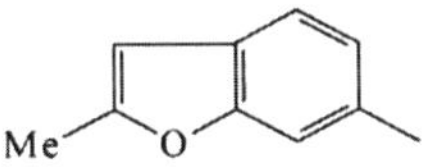

Analogs that incorporate a fused hetero ring on aromatic ring B with a lactam residue as in (92–96) have been reported to exhibit good antibacterial activity. The benzoxazinone (92) has *in vitro* activity comparable with linezolid, with better i.v. PK parameters [403,404]. The benzoxazolone (93) and benzothiazolone (95) exhibit greater potency than linezolid (MIC range 0.25–2 µg/mL) [405]. Other active compounds reported in this group include the oxazolopyridine analog (94) and the quinolone analog (96) [406,407].

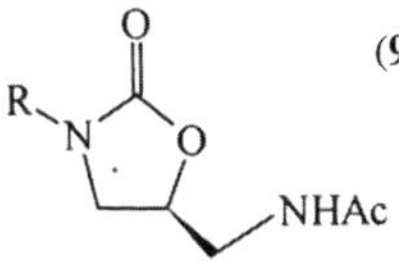

(92): R =

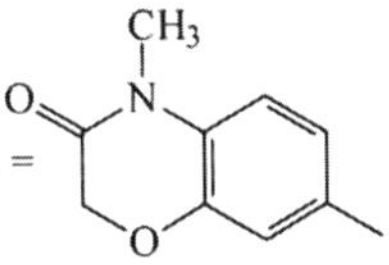

(95): R =

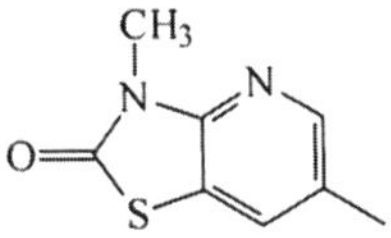

(93): : R =

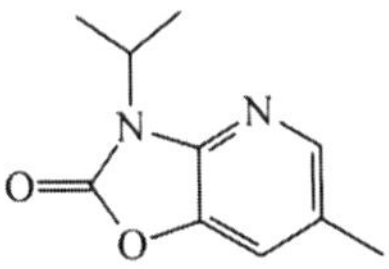

(96): : R =

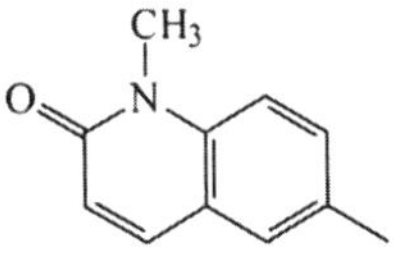

(94): : R =

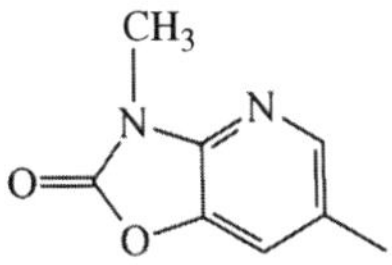

C Ring Modification   A great deal of flexibility exists around the site C. A series of oxazolidinones in which the distal nitrogen on the aromatic ring is replaced by a five-membered heteroaromatic residue were reported to have good activity. They included the pyrrole analog PNU-107922 (**97**), cyanopyrrole analog (**98**), and the cyanopyrazole analog PNU-172576 (**99**) [408]. These analogs, apart from being more active than linezolid against Gram-positive pathogens, are also active against fastidious Gram-negative organisms; (**98**) and (**99**) showed significant activity against *H. influenzae* and *M. catarrahalsis* and represent the first oxazolidinones with potentially useful activity against Gram-negative pathogens; MIC values of <0.125–0.5 g/mL against Gram-positive organisms and of 1–4 µg/mL against Gram-negative bacteria have been reported. These compounds are also orally active in mice. The cyanothiazole (**100**) and 5-cyanothiophene (**101**) analogs were even more potent against both Gram-positive and fastidious Gram-negative organisms (MIC > 0.125 µg/mL) and were orally active [409]. Similar activity is reported for cyanoethylthiadiazole (**102**) [410]. The pyrazoles (**103**) and (**104**) were also active but were less potent than other members of this group [409].

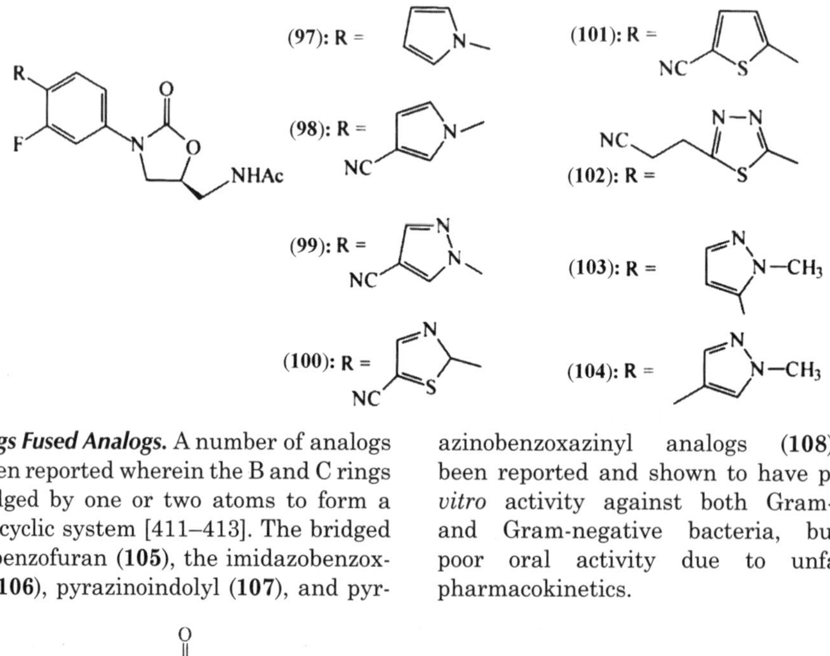

B–C Rings Fused Analogs. A number of analogs have been reported wherein the B and C rings are bridged by one or two atoms to form a rigid tricyclic system [411–413]. The bridged pyrido-benzofuran (**105**), the imidazobenzoxazinyl (**106**), pyrazinoindolyl (**107**), and pyr-azinobenzoxazinyl analogs (**108**) have been reported and shown to have potent *in vitro* activity against both Gram-positive and Gram-negative bacteria, but have poor oral activity due to unfavorable pharmacokinetics.

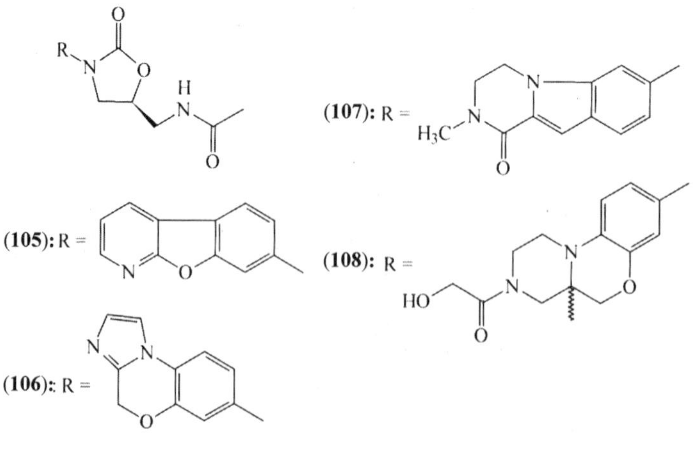

D Ring Analogs. These oxazolidinones are quite flexible for substitution around ring C and can tolerate a ring on the distal nitrogen of the piperazinyl ring. The analogs (**109–115**) have been reported to have good *in vitro* activity against Gram-positive organisms and are also orally active *in vivo* mouse model [414]. The isooxazolylpiperazines (**114**) have even better activity [415]. A QSAR analysis of these compounds has been carried out and suggests that steric factors are the most important determinants of activity in this class [416].

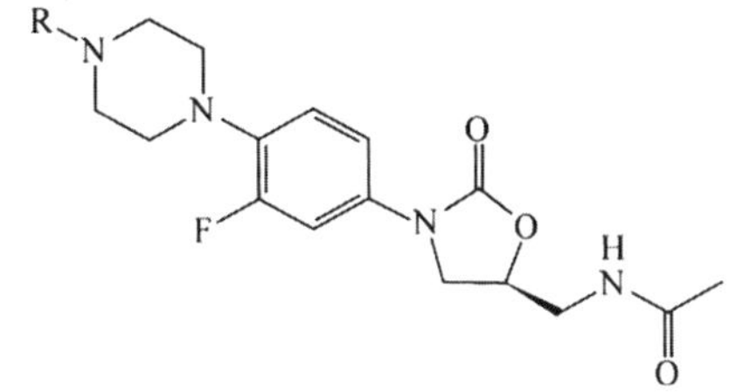

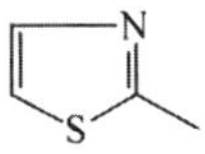

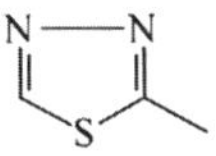

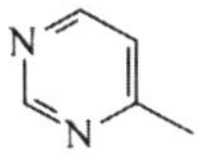

Acetamide Side-Chain Modification The tolerance limits for change around the acetamide side chain are rather limited. A study with the benzthiazolones (**116**) and the piperazinoindoles (**117**) showed that good antimicrobial activity was retained when R was small alkyl or alkoxy, or corresponding thioamide or thiourea derivatives; the thioamides in some cases resulted in improvement of activity. The thioamide (**117**) is fourfold more active than the corresponding carboxamide, with MIC values against staphylococci, streptococci, and enterococci ranging from 0.12 to 0.5 µg/mL and with good activity against *H. influenzae* with MIC of 0.5 to 1 µg/mL [404,417]. Tokuyama et al. in a recent SAR study, on 5-substituted oxazolidinones, have also shown that elongation of the methylene chain and conversion of the acetamido moiety into a guanidino group decreased the antibacterial activity [418]. However, replacement of carbonyl by thiocarbonyl or thiocarbamate groups greatly enhanced the *in vitro* antibacterial activity, and some of the compounds have stronger activity than linezolid [418].

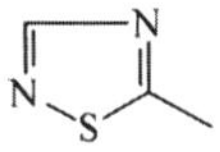

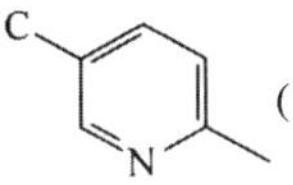

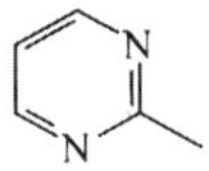

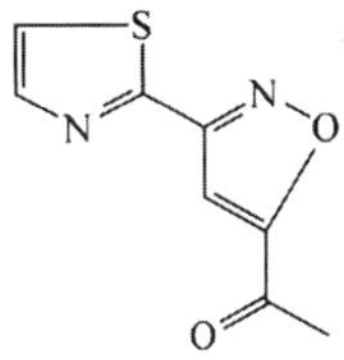

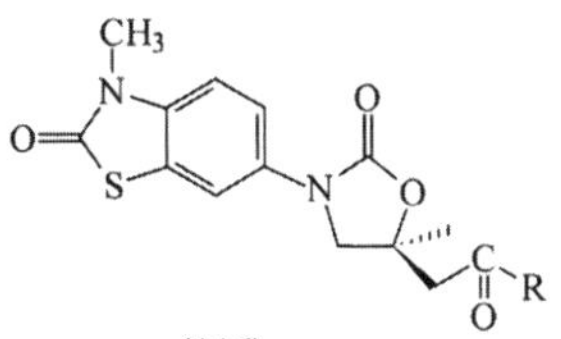

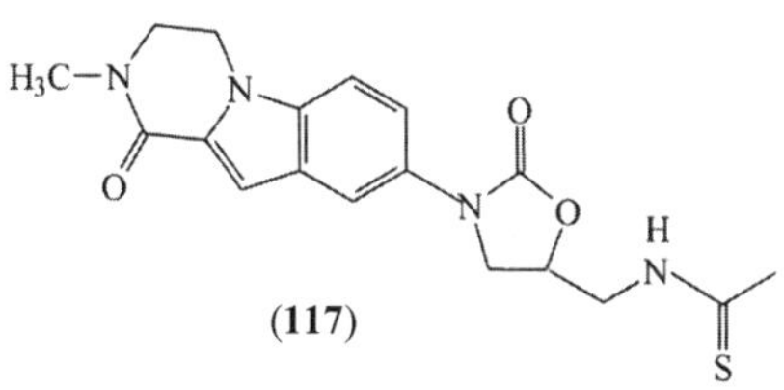

3.5.4. Perspective Oxazolidinones described above, offer some special features as antibacterial agents; their unique mode of action would provide agents with low likelihood of developing cross-resistance with existing antibacterials; their excellent oral bioavailability offers good flexibility in patient management from hospital to ambulatory setting; their chemical structure offers good scope for molecular modification to improve their therapeutic profile such as reduced toxicity and improved safety. The structure–activity studies carried out so far described in Section 3.5.3 indicate the promise that this class holds and provide a broad picture as it has emerged. A number of new analogs are in different stages of development [419–421].

In the sixth edition, in the section on "The Challenge of Antibacterial Chemotherapy" a few candidate oxazolidinone drugs were described that had some special features and were under clinical development at that time. Of these, RBx 7644 was in Phase I studies, which has since been shows to have short half-life in humans, and had to be dropped. The second oxazolidone mentioned under development was AZD 2563. Nothing more has been published on this compound, and it would appear to have also been dropped.

Linezolid, the first drug of this new class of antibacterials marketed has a broad spectrum of activity against many problem Gram-positive infections, and is a very valuable addition to therapeutics. It may also find use in combination therapy with other antibacterials, including in mycobacterial infections. Being a new class, there would be need for monitoring during treatment for sometime.

3.6. Other Systemic Synthetic Antibacterials

3.6.1. Nitrofurans   Following the discovery of sulfonamides in the early 1930s, several other classes of antibacterials were discovered, some of which filled some special problem gaps, and nitrofurans has been one such class.

The nitrofurans are unique among antibacterials for low (or even no) emergence of resistance to them even after several decades of clinical use and their activity against many organisms that have developed resistance to existing antibacterials. Another favorable feature is their pharmacokinetics characteristics that make one of them specially suitable for topical use and the other one for urinary tract infections.

The first nitrofuran to become available for clinical use was nitrofurazone (**118**, also named nitrofural), around 1940, which gained importance as a useful antibacterial agent in the care of battle wounds of soldiers in Europe during Word War II [422–424,427]. A large variety of nitrofuran compounds were synthesized subsequently but only three derivatives have become established in clinical practice: nitrofurazone (**118**), nitrofurantoin (**119**), and furazolidone (**120**). Of these, nitrofurazone and nitrofurantoin are more commonly used to meet special needs [425,426]. Nitrofurans are active against a wide spectrum of Gram-positive and Gram-negative bacteria, including most of the gastrointestinal and pathogens, except no activity against *P. aeruginosa*. Today, the primary use of nitrofurazone (**118**) is as a topical antibacterial agent, especially in patients with burns and skin grafts while nitrofurantoin is used as an oral antibacterial agent for the treatment of genitourinary infections. More recently, it is also being used for the prevention of catheter-associated urinary tract infections (CAUTI) by using nitorfurazone-impregnated catheters. This novel modality in the prevention of CAUTI reflects a continuing interest in the usefulness of nitrofurans [425].

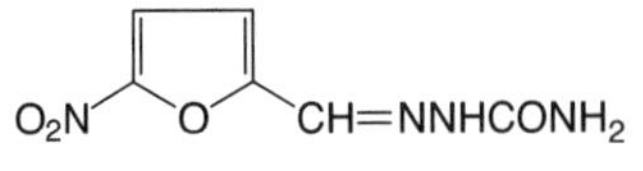

O_2N —furan— $CH=NNHCONH_2$

(118)

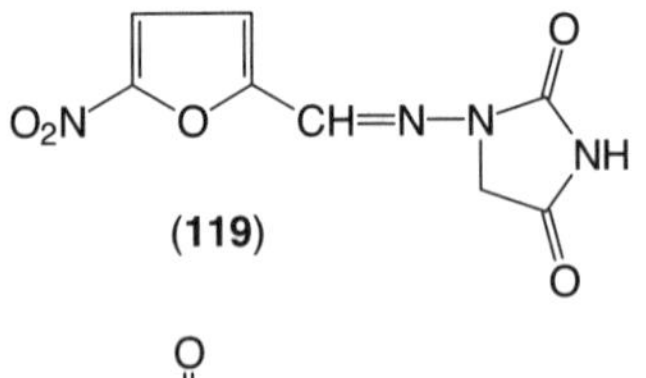

O_2N —furan— $CH=N-N$ (imidazolidine-2,4-dione)

(119)

O_2N —furan— $CH=N-N$ (oxazolidin-2-one)

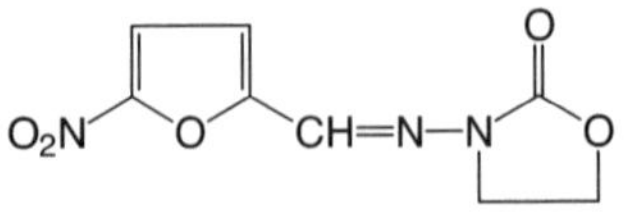

(120)

Structure–Activity Relationship A 5-nitro group and substituent at 2-position appear essential for the antibacterial activity of nitrofurans. Nitrofurans with 3- or 4-substituents have also been made and tested, but these variations did not add to the activity [428]. Some flexibility is allowable for 2-substituents, which can vary from azomethine (>C=N–), with or without an additional vinyl (>C=C<) to a heterocycle, but should have elements of extended conjugation. Thus, it appears that the essential structural requirements are a nitro group on an extended conjugated system across an electron rich heterocycle, which must be imparting specific redox potential to the nitro group on one end affecting its reduction, and some special binding characteristics to the substituents at 2-position. Rigol et al. [429] have carried out theoretical study of molecular conformations and electronic property calculations of eight 5-nitrofuryl thiosemicarbazones, and observed that the molecules seem to adopt mainly two conformations, folded and extended, both showing a specific pattern of spin density delocalization, usual for free radicals formed from aromatic nitro compounds, which must be reflecting the characteristic redox potential or the hyperfine coupling constants of the nitrofuran antibacterials.

N = 0,1

Mechanism of Action These studies indicated that enzymatic reduction of nitrofurans is an essential step for their activity. The activated molecular species thus formed have been shown to react with and inhibit a number of bacterial enzymes, which include those involved in DNA and RNA synthesis, carbohydrate metabolism and other metabolic processes [430–432]. Nitrofurans thus seem to act on multiple sites of and this may be one reason for low propensity to development of bacterial resistance to them.

Pharmacokinetic Properties Nitrofurantoin is rapidly absorbed after oral administration and excreted mainly by kidney, which gives it therapeutic value as a urinary antibacterial drug. It has a terminal disposition half-life of around 20 min with 40% of the drug is rapidly excreted into urine (via glomerular filtration and tubular secretion in the unchanged form, with very little systemic accumulation) [433,434]. When taken with food the bioavailability of nitrofurantoin is enhanced by about 40%.

Nitrofurazone is used mainly as a topical antibacterial in a water-soluble base of PEG, and is not absorbed systemically when used in this form from vagina, urethera or wounds. When impregnated into the external surface and inner lumen of a catheter, it elutes into the urethral catheter boundary producing local antibacterial activity, with very little systemic absorption [435,436].

Antibacterial Spectrum Nitrofurans were, and have remained, clinically useful against a wide spectrum of Gram-positive and Gram-negative bacteria, including most of the common strains of gastrointestinal and urinary tract pathogens [437], and a majority of the organisms responsible for skin and skin structure infections [438,439], except most of the strains of *P. aeruginosa* against which nitrofurans have very low or no activity [425]. This broad antibacterial spectrum and special pharmacokinetic profile described above reflects the special therapeutic potential of nitrofurans. For example, Shah and Wade reported that in the treatment of UTI caused by *E. coli*, *E. faecalis*, and *S. aureus*, the susceptibility of these three microorganisms to nitrofurantoin was 92%, 96%, and 100%, respectively [433].

Clinical Use Numerous studies extending over five decades have demonstrated the effectiveness of nitrofurantoin in eliminating Gram-negative and Gram-positive pathogens from the urinary tract in adults and children, and in catheterized patients. Today nitrofurantoin is still considered as the first-line therapy for urinary tract infections and cystitis.

Nitrofurazone, was historically used for wound infections, burns and skin grafts, but over the years it has found many more clinical applications as a locally acting antibacterial, which include vaginal surgery, external ocular infections, stasis ulcers, ear infections and in middle ear surgery. More recently, it has been used for impregnating catheters to prevent cather-associated UTI, where it has been reported to be more effective then even a silver hydrogel impregnated catheter [425].

Safety clinical studies have shown that nitrofuran drugs are reasonably well tolerated, and no adverse events of any serious nature have been reported. The common adverse events include nausea, headache and in less than 1% cases diarrhea, dizziness, and pruritis.

3.6.1.6. Perspective
Nitrofurantoin and nitrofurazone are active against many Gram-positive and Gram-negative bacteria, including common gastrointestinal and UTI bacterial pathogens. Because of nitrofurantoin's good oral bioavailability and high degree of renal excretion, coupled with its low intrinsic, therapeutically relevant antibacterial activity is achieved only within the urinary tract. Selection pressure for the development of resistance in other parts of the body is negligible, except to some extent in GI tract. Nitrofurantoin has thus an established role in the treatment of acute cystitis in women and for long-term prophylaxis of UTI. With a long history of well tolerated and effective special clinical uses of nitrofurans, and the continued lack of evolution of bacterial resistance to them, these agents continue to be useful drugs for these special disease conditions.

3.6.2. Methenamine
Methenamine (hexamethylenetetramine; 121) is prepared by evaporating a mixture of formaldehyde and strong ammonia water [437]. Methenamine can be considered as a special case of a prodrug. The free base has almost no antibacterial activity, but acidification results in the liberation of formaldehyde, which is strongly bactericidal. Acidification is provided by formulating methenamine as a mandelate or hippurate salt, or by administering ammonium chloride or sodium biphosphate to acidify the urine. Methenamine is sometimes used in long-term suppression of bacterial urinary tract infections, although it is not a treatment of choice for corresponding acute infections [438]. Certain bacteria are resistant to methenamine because they liberate urease, an enzyme that hydrolyzes urea to generate

ammonia that raises urinary pH. This problem can be overcome by giving acetohydroxamic acid (122), which inhibits urease, and acts as an antibacterial adjunct [439].

(121)   (122)

Methenamine is well absorbed from the GI tract, but is amenable to degradation by stomach acidity and has to have enteric coating. Nearly all the absorbed drug appears in the urine, where the conversion to formaldehyde takes place.

Methenamine is used only as an alternative agent in urinary tract infections, in common drug resistance cases or some factors resulting in chronic recurrence of infection.

The most frequent adverse effects associated with methenamine are GI distress and bladder irritation resulting in painful and fragmented urination.

3.6.3. "Hybrid" Antibacterial Agents
Widespread emergence of bacterial resistance to currently available therapeutic antibacterial agents has sharply focused attention to evolve strategies which would prevent or delay the development of resistance, and on the need to develop new classes of antibacterials to target these resistant (including multidrug-resistant) bacterial strains. A strategy that has been used with considerable clinical success has been to use a combination of two (or more) antibacterials, with a complimentary mode of action, which has been described in Section 3.2. In an alternative to this strategy, the two different prototype molecules, acting by different mechanisms, are covalently linked to form "hybrid" molecules, presenting unhindered the pharmacophore of each component drug, and presumably acting on two different essential targets. The likely advantages of a dual-action "hybrid antibacterial agent" are (a) extended spectrum of antibacterial activity, including against the resistant strains; (b) reduced potential to resistance development;

(c) synergistic activity from the two components pharmacophores; and (d) likely to have less potential for toxicity.

Although the concept of "dual acting" antibacterials carrying pharmacophores of two different drug types has been under consideration for a long time, this concept has been given a practical shape only recently [439]. Two examples of synthetic "hybrid" antibacterials that are in advanced stages of testing are described below. They illustrate effectively the potential value of this concept for antibacterial development, especially to get over the problem of drug resistance.

Fluoroquinolone–Oxazolidinone Hybrid

MCB3681 (123) [440,441], a hybrid of fluoroquinolone and oxazolidinone antibacterials, joined together by a metabolically stable linkage, is in an advanced stage of drug development. It exhibits broad-spectrum antibacterial activity, covering Gram-positive, most Gram-negative (excluding *P. aeruginosa*) and anaerobic organisms, reflecting dual targeting in its action of DNA gyrases, and ribosomal-mediated protein synthesis inhibition. The spectrum of MCB 3681, although similar to that of linezolid, proved superior in terms of bactericidal activity. The compound exhibits activity against both linezolid and fluoroquinolone—resistant strains of pathogenic Gram-positive bacteria, including MRSA, GISA, VRE, and MDR *S. pneumoniae*. Spontaneous emergence of resistance to MCB3681 appears to be rare, even in strains with multiple resistance mechanisms. Its phosphate ester prodrug (MCB 3837) has progressed into human clinical trials [442]. When administered to healthy human volunteers, a single ascending dose was without serious adverse events at doses upto 3 mg/kg [439].

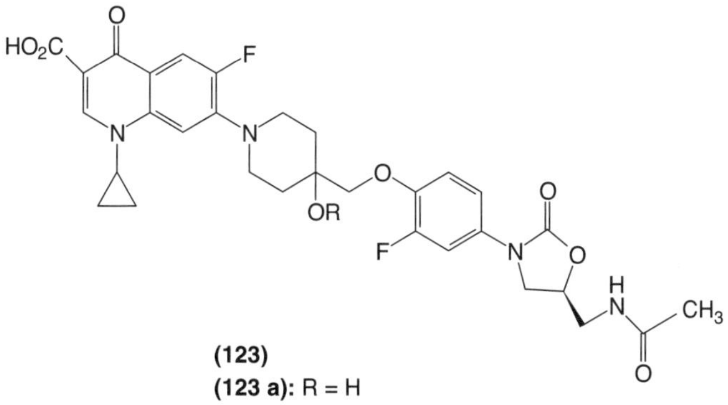

(123)
(123 a): R = H
(123 b): R = P(O)(OH)$_2$

DNA Polymerase IIIC–Fluoroquinolone hybrid: MBX-500 (124)

The hybrid MBX-500 (124) binds two DNA replication inhibitors, targeting bacterial DNA gyrase and topoisomerase IV, with a DNA polymerase IIIC inhibitory fragment, and a substituted anilinouracil [444].

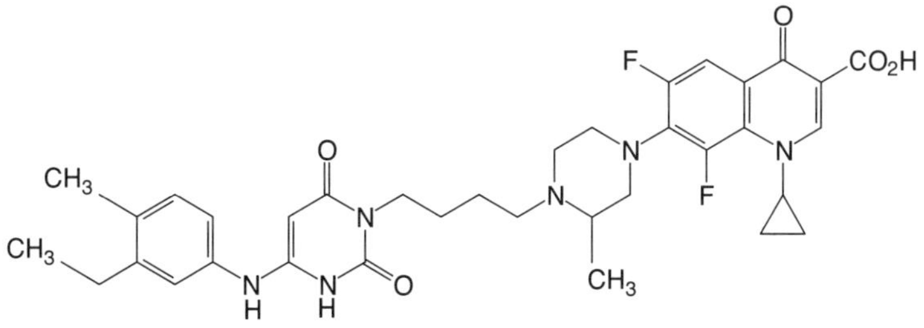

(124)

MBX 500 is a potent nanomolar-level inhibitor of bacterial poly-IIIC, with an outstanding selectivity profile [445], and high activity against *B. subtilis* topoisomerase IV and gyrase, although at a lower level than commonly used fluoroquinolones. Spontaneous mutation frequency studies have shown that the hybrid had a lower frequency of resistance development than did the individual drugs. Due to high molecular weight the compound is facing some formulation and bioavailability problems.

Perspective   Hybrid antibacterials, with dual action, is an area of marked contrasts, with promises and problems. With rising incidence of bacterial resistance to practically all the existing therapeutic antibacterial agents, hybrid molecules offer coverage of problematic MDR organisms, with resistance development minimized in many cases and with improved efficacy. But these benefits are also riddled with some formulation and bioavailability problems, due mainly to increase in molecular weight. The balance, however, seems to be in favor of hybrid molecules offering good opportunity to explore and exploit [439].

3.7. The Perspective of Antibacterial Chemotherapy

The story of antibacterial chemotherapy forms one of the most illustrious and instructive chapters in the annals of medicinal chemistry. The discovery of antibacterial activity of sulfonamides in the early 1930s, providing agents of unprecedented efficacy for that time, ushered in the modern era of chemotherapy. The research that followed not only provided many very effective drugs which made a major contribution to the control of common serious bacterial infections and improvement of human (and animal) health but also provided the first clear demonstration of metabolite antagonism as a mechanism of drug action. These studies put the concept of biochemical differences between the host and parasites as the basis for a rational approach to the design of chemotherapeutic agents on a very broad and sound footing. These biochemical differences could be either in the absence of the essential enzyme systems in the host as in the case of sulfonamides or in the selectivity of inhibition of an essential enzyme between the host and the microbe. These concepts, described more in detail in section "Site of Folate Inhibition" and "Introduction" section of Section 3.3.2 of this chapter continue to be the mainstay of drug design and discovery to this day, of course much refined by recent developments in structural biology and target identification. Following folate inhibitors, quinolines/fluoroquinolines and oxazolidinones were the major classes of additional systemic synthetic antibacterials. These compounds, along with natural and semisynthetic antibiotics discovered also from the 1940s onward enlarged greatly the scope of antibacterial chemotherapy. With these advances, not only the major infections have been controlled but also the practice of medicine in general has been greatly advanced [446]. Many specialized surgical procedures would not have been possible but for the availability of these antibacterials. These compounds have also helped in the rearing of food-and-domestic animals. These advances have undoubtedly made a major contribution to improvements in both human and animal welfare; however, major problems are now emerging that pose risks to public health. This happens with many big scientific advances and requires immediate attention and concerted action.

The biggest problem is the alarming rise in the prevalence and emergence of resistance to known antibacterials. This problem appears to be accelerating, accumulating, and spreading worldwide. A certain propensity to resistance development could be expected in bacteria exposed to antibiotics because of their rapid rate of multiplication, which promotes selection of less susceptible (resistant) mutants continuously from a population with mixed sensitivities. This effect, coupled with overprescription and indiscriminate use of antibacterial agents, is to a large measure responsible for the emergence of this alarming situation.

This situation was aggravated further by a false sense of complacency created by the discovery of sulfonamides and antibiotics by the early 1950s that created the impression that the battle against bacterial diseases had been won, and R&D efforts for new antibacterials waned. For many years little attention was paid to new agents for antibacterial chemotherapy, despite the inherent nature of infectious agents to develop resistance, and despite the fact that the developing world still has significant morbidity and morality from bacterial infections.

The problem of resistance development has to be faced squarely, and recent developments in biological science offer many approaches that would help to control this problem. It cannot be taken in a defeatist mode, which many scientists are trying to project. Gary Taube wrote [445] "In their ongoing war against antibiotics, the bacteria seem to be winning, and the drug pipeline is verging on empty" in *Science*. Scientists need to be responsible and innovative enough to find solutions to such serious problems so that this will never happen.

The pragmatic approach that is emerging to prevent or delay this happening requires a judicious mix of preventive measures to keep the environment cleaner to avoid infections taking place, and curative measures for control and eradication of infections. These preventive measures include the use of topical synthetic antibacterials, which are described in Section 86.2. Where infections have been established, treatment and curative measures will be necessary. They are discussed in Section 3. It is now realized that certain basic precepts and principles must be followed to obtain optimum benefits from antibacterial chemotherapy whether with topical or systemic antibacterial agents, which are discussed in Sections 2.2 and 3.3.

Necessary steps needed to control the situation include (a) judicious use of the available antibacterials at appropriate dosages and for the prescribed time; using combinations of drugs when warranted; (b) ensure a steady supply of new antibacterials, preferably acting by new mechanisms of action; and (c) improved infection control to limit the spread of resistant organisms as discussed in Section 3.2.2.

A continued concerted action is necessary to preserve the usefulness of this most important group of therapeutic agents.

ACKNOWLEDGMENT

Sincere thanks to Mr. V. Kanal for putting together this manuscript for publication.

REFERENCES

1. Chambers CW. J Milk Food Technol 1956;19:183.
2. Martin AR.In: Delgado JN, Remers, WA, editors. Wilson and Gisvold's Textbook of Organic Medicinal and Pharmaceutical Chemistry. 9th ed. Philadelphia: J.B. Lippincott; 1991. p 129.
3. Block SS, editor. Disinfection, Sterilization, and Preservation. 4th ed. Philadelphia: Lea & Febiger; 1991. p 3.
4. Costerton JW, Ingraham JM, Cheng K-J. Bacteriol Rev 1974;38:87.
5. Hammond SM, Lambert PA, Rycroft AN. The Bacterial Cell Surface. London: Croom Helm; 1984.
6. Jones IG, Midgley M. FEMS Microbiol Lett 1985;28:355.
7. Harvey SC.In: Gilman AG, Goodman LS, Gilman A, editors. The Pharmacological Basis of Therapeutics. 6th ed. New York: Macmillan; 1980. p 966.
8. Allawala NA, Riegelman S. J Am Pharm Assoc Sci Ed 1953;42:267.
9. Sutton SWV.In: Ascenzi JM, editors. Handbook of Disinfectants and Antiseptics. New York: Marcel Dekker; 1966. p 43–62.
10. Cunniff P, editor. Official Methods of Analysis of the Association of Official Analytical Chemists International. 16th ed. Vol. 1. Arlington, VA: AOAC International; 1995.
11. Bruch MK.In: Block SS, editor. Disinfection, Sterilization and Preservation. 4th ed. Philadelphia: Lea & Febiger; 1991. p 1028–1046.
12. Cade AR. J Soc Cosmet Chem 1951;2:281.
13. Bruch MK.In: Block SS, editor. Disinfection, Sterilization and Preservation. 4th ed. Philadelphia: Lea & Febiger; 1991. p 3.
14. Labarraque A-G. The Use of Sodium and Calcium Hypochlorites. Paris: Huzard; 1825.
15. Alcock T. Lancet 1827;11:643.
16. Holmes OW. N Engl Quart J Med Surg 1843;1:503.
17. Semmelweiss IP. The Etiology, Concept, and Prophylaxis of Childbed Fever. F.R. Murphy, translator, Medical classics 1941; 5:350.
18. Lister J. Lancet 1867;2:353.
19. Koch R. Mittheilungen aus dem Kaiserlichen Gesundheitsamte 1881;1:234.
20. Kronig B, Paul TL. A Hyg Infekt 1897;25:1.
21. Rideal S, Walker JTA. J R Sanit Inst 1903;24:424.

22. Bechold H, Ehrlich P. Z Physiol Chem 1906;47:173.

23. Domagk G. Dtsch. Med. Wochenschr. 1935;61:829.

24. Rose FL, Swain G. J Chem Soc 1956; 4422.

25. Cremieux, Fleurette J.In: Block SS, editor. Disinfection, Sterilization, and Preservation. 4th ed. Philadelphia: Lea & Febiger; 1991. p 1009–1027.

26. Race J. Chlorination of Water. New York: John Wiley & Sons; 1988. p 1–132.

27. Norman TS, Harms LL, Looyegna RW. J Am Water Works Assoc 1980;72:176.

28. Reddish GF, Pauley AW. Bull Nat Formul Commun 1945;13:11.

29. Thompson JS. Soap Chem Spec 1964;40:45.

30. Friberg L, Acta Pathol Microbiol Scand. 1957;40:67.

31. Knox WE, Stumpf PK, Green DE, Auerbach VH. J Bacteriol 1948;55:451.

32. Kosugi M, Kaminski JJ, Selk SH, Pitman IH, Bodor N, Higuchi N. J Pharm Sci 1976;65:1743.

33. Chang SL. J Sanit Eng Div Proc ASCE 1971;97:689.

34. Apostolov K. J Hyg 1980;84:381.

35. Shelanski HA, Shelanski MV. J Int Coll Surg 1956;25:727.

36. Tilley FW, Schaeffer JM. J Bacteriol 1926;12:303.

37. Lilly BD, Brewer JH. J Am Pharm Assoc 1953;52:6.

38. Nair CKK, Pradham DS, Sreenivasan A. J Bacteriol 1965;121:392.

39. FDA Advisory Panel on Nonprescription Contraceptive Products. Fed. Reg. 1980;Dec 12. 45:82014.

40. Judis J. J Pharm Sci 1963;52:126.

41. Richardson EM, Reid EE. J Am Chem Soc 1940;62:413.

42. Klarman EG, Shternov VA, Gates LW. J Am Chem Soc 1933;55:2576.

43. Klarman EG, Gates LW, Shternov VA, Cox PH. J Am Chem Soc 1933;55:4657.

44. Suter CM. Chem Rev 1941;28:209.

45. http://dailymed.nlm.nih.gov./dailymed/druginfo.cfm?id=2625.

46. O'Connor DO, Rubino JR.In: Block SS, editor. Disinfection, Sterilization, and Preservation. 4th ed. Philadelphia: Lea B. Febiger; 1991. p 205.

47. Gump WS.US patent 2,250,480. 1941.

48. Bambury RE.In: Wolff ME, editor. Burger's Medicinal Chemistry. Part II, 4th ed. New York: John Wiley & Sons; 1979. p 49.

49. Gilbert GL, Gambill VM, Spiner DR, Hoffmann RK, Phillips CR. Appl Microbiol 1964;12:496.

50. Hart, Brown MW. Appl Microbiol 1974;28:1069.

51. Margel S, Rembaum A. Macromolecules 1980;13:19.

52. Ayliffe GA, Babb JR, Bradley CR. J Hosp Infect 1986;7:295.

53. Hughes RC, Thurman PF. Biochem J 1970;119:925.

54. Hopwood D. Histochem J 1975;7:267.

55. Jawetz ER.In: Katzung BG, editor. Basic and Clinical Pharmacology. 6th ed. Norwalk, CT: Appleton and Lange; 1995. p 748.

56. Garrett ER, Woods OR. J Am Pharm Sci 1953;42:736.

57. http://www.nlm.nih.gov/medlineplus/druginfo/medmaster/a603020.html.

58. http://en.wikipedia.org/wiki/Boric_acid.

59. Fridovich Am Sci 1975;63:54.

60. Martin AR.In: Delgado JN, Remers, WA, editors. Wilson and Gisvold's Textbook of Organic Medicinal and Pharmaceutical Chemistry. 9th ed. Philadelphia: Lippincott; 1991. p 140.

61. Jawetz ER.In: Katzung BG, editor. Basic and Clinical Pharmacology. 6th ed. Norwalk, CT: Appleton and Lange; 1995. p 749.

62. Harvey SC.In: Gilman AG, Goodman LS, Gilman A, editors. The Pharmacological Basis of Therapeutics. 6th ed. New York: Macmillan; 1980. p 976.

63. Beaver DJ, Roman DP, Stoffel PJ. J Am Chem Soc 1957;79:1236.

64. Thrower WR, Valentine FC. Lancet 1943;1:133.

65. Berg SS, Newberry G. J Chem Soc 1949; 642.

66. Winrow MJ. J Periodont Res 1973;12:(Suppl):45.

67. Hnatko SI. Can Med Assoc J 1977;117:223.

68. Smylie HG, Logie JRC, Smith G. Br Med J 1973;4:586.

69. Peterson AF, Rosenberg A, Alatary SD. Surg Gynecol Obstet 1978;146:63.

70. Addy M. J Clin Periodontol 1986;13:957.

71. Woodcock PM.In: Payne KP, editor. Industrial Biocides. Chichester: John Wiley & Sons; 1988. p 19–36.

72. Enyaert CR.In: Schick MJ, editor. Nonionic Surfactants. New York: Marcel Dekker; 1967.

73. Miller MJ.In: Ascenzi JM, editor. Handbook of Disinfectants, Antiseptics. New York: Marcel Dekker; 1996. p 83–107.

74. Martin AR.In: Delgado JN, Remers WA, editors. Wilson and Gisvold's Textbook of Organic Medicinal and Pharmaceutical Chemistry. 9th ed. Philadelphia: J.B. Lippincott; 1987. p 137.

75. Blois DW, Swarbrick J. J Pharm Sci 1972;61:393.

76. Kourai H. J Antibact Antifung Agents 1985;13:245.

77. Hansch C, Leo A. Exploring QSAR: Fundamentals and Applications in Chemistry and Biology. Washington, DC: American Chemical Society; 1995. p 418–419.

78. Green DF, Petrocci AN. Soap Cosmet Chem Spec 1980;8:33.

79. Petrocci AN, Green HA, Merianos JJ, Like B. C.S.M.A. Proceedings of the 60th Mid-Year Meeting. May 1974. p 78–79.

80. Stark RL.US patent 4,525,346. 1985.

81. Prince HN, Prince RN. *Chemical Times and Trends* July 1987, p 8.

82. Swisher RD. Surfactant Biodegradation. New York: Marcel Dekker; 1987. p 181–209.

83. Schmitz.US patent 2,684,946.. 1954.

84. Sykes G. Disinfection and Sterilization. 2nd ed. Philadelphia: J.B. Lippincott; 1965. p 377–378.

85. Albert A, Anand N. Principles of Antimicrobial Chemotherapy in Principles of Pharmacology. Ed-in-Chief, P.L. Munson, New York, USA: Chapman & Hall; 1995. p 1273–1288.

86. Ritts RE. Antibiotics as biological response modifiers. J Antimicrob Chemother 1990;26 (Suppl C): 31–36.Labro MT. Cefodizime as a biological response modifier. A review of its *in vivo*, *ex vivo* and *in vitro* immunomodulatory properties. J Antimicrob Chemother 1990;6: (Suppl C): 37–47.

87. Gary Taubs Bacteria Fight Back in Special Section on Drug Resistance. Science 2008;321:356, and references cited therein.

88. Jacoby GA, Archer GL, New mechanisms of bacterial resistance to antimicrobial agents. N Engl J Med 1991;324(9): 601.

89. Lisa MJ. Chem Eng News 2008;86(23) 15.

90. Deo MG, Chaturvedi RM, Kartikeyan S, A candidate anti-leprosy vaccine from ICRC bacilli. Trop. Med Parasitol 1990;41:367.

91. Chatterjee RK, Fatma N, Jain RK, Gupta CM, Anand N, *Litomosoides carinii* in rodents: immunomodulation in potentiating action of diethylcarbamazine. Jpn J Exp Med 1988; 58:243.

92. Misra S, Singh DP, Gupta CM, Chatterjee RK, Anand N, Acanthocheilonema vitea in *Mast-*

omys natalensis: effect of immunomodulation on establishment and course of infection. Med Sci Res 1991;19:53.

93. Bryk R, et al. Cell Host Microbe 2008;3:137.

94. Liu CI, et al. Science 2008;319:1391.

95. Singh R, et al. Science 2008;322:1392.

96. Davis BD. The basis of chemotherapy. In: Davis BD, Dulbecco R, Eisen HN, Ginsberg HS, editors. Microbiology. 3rd ed. Harper International Edition; 1980. p 111–126.

97. Neu HC. Therapy and prophylaxis of bacterial infections. In: Wilson JD,et al. Harison's Principles of Internal Medicine. 12th ed. New York: McGraw Hill; 1991. Chapter 85. p 478–493.

98. Horlein H, Dressel O, Kethe R, Mietzsch F. Chem Ber 1939;71A:15.

99. Heidelberger M, Jacobs WA. J Am Chem Soc 1939;41:2131.

100. Mietzsch F, Klarer J. Ger Pat 1935;607:537. Mietzsch F, Klarer J. Chem Abstr 1935;29: 4135.

101. Domagk G. Deut Med Wochenscher 1935;61:250.

102. Foerster R. Zbt Haut-u Geschlechiskr 1933;45:549.

103. Trefouel J, Mm J, Trfouel F, Nitti, Bovet D. C R Soc Biol 1935;120:756.

104. Colebrook L, Kenny M. Lancet 1936;1:1279.

105. Buttle GAH, Grey WH, Stephenson D. Lancet 1936;1:1286.

106. Fuller AT. Lancet 1937;1:194.

107. Gelmo P. J Prakt Chem 1908;77:369.Gelmo P. Chem Abstr 1908;2:2551.

108. Whitby LEH. Lancet 1938;2:1210.

109. Fosbinder RJ, Walter LA. J Am Chem Soc 1939;61:2032.

110. Northey EH. The Sulfonamides and Allied Compounds. Reinhold, New York: American Chemical Society Monograph Services; 1948.

111. Nichols RL, Jones WF Jr, Finland M. Proc Soc Exp Biol Med 1956;92:637.

112. Weinstein L, Madoff MA, Samet CM. New Engl J Med 1960;263: 793, 842, 900, 952.

113. Neipp L, Meyer RL. Ann NY Acad Sci 1957;69:447.

114. Klotzer W, Bretschneider H. Monatsh Chem 1956;87:136.Klotzer W, Bretschneider H. Chem Abstr 1957;51:15610.

115. Fust B, Bohni E. Antibiot Med Clin Ther 1959;6:(Suppl 1): 3.

116. Hitzenberger G, Spitzky KH. Med Klin 1962;57:310.Hitzenberger G, Spitz KH. Chem Abstr 1962;57:5274.

117. Reber M, Rutshauser G, Tholen H.In: 3rd International Congress on Chemotherapy. Vol. 1.Stuttgart: Thieme Stutgart; 1963. p 648.

118. Fust B, Bohni E, Schweiz Z. Med Wochenschr 1962;92:1599.

119. Rist N. Nature 1940;146:838.

120. Feldman WH, Hinshaw HC, Moses HE. Am Rev Tuberc 1942;45:303.

121. Cowdry EV, Ruangsiri C. Arch Pathol 1941;32:632.

122. Browne SG. Adv Pharmacol Chemother 1969;7:211.

123. Shepard CC, McRae DH, Habas JA. Proc Soc Exp Biol Med 1966;122:893.

124. Elslager EF. Progr Drug Res 1974;18:99.

125. Anand N.In: Wolff ME, editor. Burger's Medicinal Chemistry and Drug Discovery. 5th ed. Vol. 2.New York: John Wiley & Sons; 1996. p 538.

126. Seydel JK. Physico Chemical Aspects of Drug Action.New York:Pergamon Press;1968.p 169.

127. De Beneditti PG. Adv Drug Res 1987;16:227.

128. Sammes PG. Comprehensive Medicinal Chemistry. 1st ed. Vol. II.Oxford: Pergamon Press; 1990. p 255.

129. Seydel JK, Wempe E. Arzneim-Forsch 1964;14:705.

130. Seydel JK, Kruger-Thiemer E, Wempe E. Z Naturforsch 1960;15b:620.

131. Foernzler EC, Martin AN. J Pharm Sci 1967;56:608.

132. Fox CL Jr, Rose HM. Proc Soc Exp Biol Med 1942;50:142.

133. Schmelkes FC, Wyss O, Marks HC, Ludwig BJ, Stranskov FB. Proc Soc Exp Biol Med 1942;50:145.

134. Bell PH, Roblin RO Jr. J Am Chem Soc 1942;64:2905.

135. Cowles PB. Yale J Biol Med 1942;14:599.

136. Brueckner AH. Yale J Biol Med 1943;15:813.

137. Seydel JK. Arzneim-Forsch 1966;16:1447.

138. Seydel JK, J Pharm Sci. 1967;57:1455.

139. Cammarata A, Allen RC. J Pharm Sci 1967;56:640.

140. Seydel JK. Mol Pharmacol 1966;2:259.

141. Garrett ER, Mielck JB, Seydel JK, Kessler HJ. J Med Chem 1971;14:724.

142. Seydel JK. J Med Chem 1971;14:724.

143. Fujita T, Hansch C. J Med Chem 1967;10:991.

144. Yamazaki M, Kakeya N, Morishita T, Kamada A, Aoki A. Chem Pharm Bull 1970;18:702.

145. Miller GH, Doukas PH, Seydel JK. J Med Chem 1972;15:700.

146. Koch, Seydel JK, Gasco A, Tirani C, Fruttero R. Quant Struct Act Relat 1993;12:373.

147. De Beneditti PG, Iarossi D, Folli U, Frassineti C, Menziani MC, Cennamo C, J Med Chem. 1989;32:396.

148. Deneditti PG, Iarossi D, Folli U, Frassineti C, Menziani MC, Cennamo C, J Med Chem. 1987;30:459.

149. Wiese M, Seydel JK, Pieper H, Kruger G, Noll KR, Keck J. Quant. Struct.-Act. Relat. 1987;6:164.

150. Koehler MG, Hopfinger AJ, Seydel JK. J Mol Struct 1988;179:319.

151. Hopfinder AJ, Lopez de Compadre RL, Koshler MG, Emery S, Seydel JK. Quant Struct Act Relat 1987;6:111.

152. Lopez de Compadre RL, Pearlstein RA, Hopfinder AJ, Seydel JK. J Med Chem 1987;30:900.

153. De Beneditti PG. Prog Drug Res 1991;36:361.

154. Cocchi M, Iarossi D, Menziani MC, De Beneditti PG, Frassineti C. Struct Chem 1992;3:129.

155. Sokolov YU, Menziani MC, Cocchi M, Beneditti PG. Theo Chem 1991;79:293.

156. Rieder J. Arzneim Forsch 1963;13: 81, 89, 95.

157. Lehr D. Ann NY Acad Sci 1957;69:417.

158. Biagi GL, Barbaro AM, Guerra MC, Forti GC, Fracasso ME. J Med Chem 1974;17:28.

159. Scholtan W. Arzneim Forsch 1968; 14: 348; 1964.18:505.

160. Kruger-Thiemer Diller W, Bunger P. Antimicrob Agents Chemother 1965; 183.

161. Irmscher K, Gabe D, Jahnke K, Scholtan W. Arzneim Forsch 1966;16:1019.

162. Scholtan W. Chemotherapia 1963;6:180.

163. Shannon JA. Ann NY Acad Sci 1943;44:455.

164. Seydel JK, editor. Drug Design. Vol. 1.New York: Academic Press; 1971. p 343.

165. Jardetzky O, Wade-Jardetzky NG. Mol Pharmacol 1965;1:214.

166. Martin BK. Nature 1965;207:274.

167. Moriguchi S, Wada T. Nishizawa. Chem Pharm Bull 1968;16:601.

168. Weinstein L, Madoff MA, Samet CM. New Eng. J Med 1960;263: 793, 842, 900, 952.

169. Fischl MI, Dickinson GM, La Voie L. J Am Med Assoc 1988;259:1185.

170. Garrod LP, James DG, Lewis AAG. Postgrad Med J 1969;45:(Suppl): 1.

171. US, Food, Drug Administration FDA Drug Efficacy Reports. J Am Pharm Assoc 1969; NS9:535.

172. Berkow R, editor. The Merck Manual. Parkway, NJ: Merck & Co. Inc; 1987. p 43–44.

173. Archer GL, Polk RE. Harison's Principles of Internal Medicine. 15th ed. New York: McGraw Hill, Ind; 2001. p 877.

174. Bach MC, Sabath LD, Finland M. Antimicrob Agents Chemotherap 1973;3:1.

175. Iseman MD.In: Gorbach SL, Bartlest JG, Blacklow NR, editors. Infectious Diseases. 2nd ed. W.B. Saunders; 1998. p 1513–1528.

176. (a) Costells MJ. Arch Dermatol Syph 1940;42:161. (b) Lorinez AL, Pearson RW. Arch Dermatol 1962;85:2. (c) Zone JJ. Curr Probl Derm 1991;3:4.

177. Sione OJ. Medical Hypothesis 1990;31:99.

178. (a) Coleman MD, Smith JK, Perris AD, Buck S, Seydel JK. J Pharm Pharmacol 1997;49:53. (b) Van Der Ven AJM, Koopmans PP, Vree TB, Van Der Mer JWM. J Antimicrob Chemother 1994;34:1.

179. Tsutsumi S, Gidoh M. Int J Leprosy 1985;53:713.

180. Kovacs JA, Hiemens JW, Macher AM. Ann Int Med 1984;100:663.

181. Sheer NH, Spelberg SP, Grant DM, Tang BK, Kalow W. Ann Int Med 1986;105:179.

182. Reilly TP, Lash LH, Doll MA, et al. J Invest Dermal 2000;114:1164.

183. Rieder MJ, Uetrecht J, Shear NH, Spielberg SP. J Pharmacol Expt Ther 1988;244:724.

184. Rieder MJ, Sisson E, Bird I, Almawi WY. Int J Immunopharmacol 1992;14:1175.

185. Coleman MD, Scott AK, Breckenridge AM, Park BK. Br J Clin Pharmacol 1990;30:761.

186. Williams RT, Parke DV. Ann Rev Pharmcol 1964;4:85.

187. Nogami H, Hasegawa A, Hanano M, Imaoka K. Yakugoku Zazzi 1968;88:893.

188. Yamazaki M, Aoki M, Kamada A. Chem Pharm Bull 1968;16:707.

189. Kakemi K, Arita T, Kakemi K. Arch Pract Pharm 1965;25:22.

190. Koizumi T, Arita T, Kakemi K. Chem Pharm Bull 1964;12:428.

191. Adamson RH, Bridges JW, Kibby MR, Walker SR, Williams RT. Biochem J 1970;118:41.

192. Zbinden G. Molecular modification in the development of newer anti-infective agents: the sulfa drugs. In: Gould RF, editor. Molecular Modification in Drug Design. Washington, DC: American Chemical Society; 1964. p 25.

193. Fujita T. Substituted-effect analyses of the rates of metabolism and excretion of sulfonamide drugs. In: Gould RF, editor. Biological Correlations The Hansch Approach. Washington, DC: American Chemical Society; 1972. p 80.

194. Ellard GA. Brit J Pharmacol 1966;26:212.

195. Bushby SRM, Woiwood AJ. Am Re. Tuberc Pulmo Dis 1955;72:123.

196. Bushby SRM, Woiwood AJ. Biochem J 1956;63:406.

197. Hucker HB. Ann Rev Pharmacol 1970;10:99.

198. Gordon GR, Peters JH, Gelber R, Levy L. Proc West Pharmacol Soc 1970;13:17.

199. Thompson PE. Int J Lepr 1967;35:605.

200. Kruger-Thiemer E, Bunger P. Arzneim Forsch 1961;16:1431.Kruger-Thiemer E, Bunger P. Arzneim Forsch 1961;11:867.

201. Bush by SRM. J Infect Dis [suppl] 1973, 128, 442.

202. Raszka WVJ, Skillman LP, McEvoy PL. Diagn Microbial Infect Dis 1994;18:201.

203. Peters W. Adv Parasitol 1974;12:69.

204. Levine PP. Cornell Vet 1939;29:309.

205. Levine PP. J Parasitol 1940;26:233.

206. Joyner LP, Davies SFM, Kendall SB. Chemotherapy of coccidiosis. In: Schnitzer RJ, Hawking F, editors. Experimental Chemotherapy. New York: Academic Press; 1963. p 445.

207. Sabin AB, Waren J. J Bacteriol 1941;41: M50, 80.

208. Biocca E. Arg Biol 1943;7:27.

209. Strauss RE, Kilgman AM, Pilsbury DM. Am Rev Tuberc 1951;63:441.

210. Connar RG, Ferguson TB, Sealy WC, Conant NF. J Thorac Surg 1951;22:424.

211. Kendall SB, Joyner LP. Vet Record 1958;70:632.

212. Werner H. Biol Chil Parasitol 1970;25:65.

213. Smego RA, Moeller MB, Gallis HA. Arch Intern Med 1983;143:711.

214. Herkes GK, Fryer J, Rushworth R, et al. Aust NZ J Med 1989;19(5): 475.

215. McCallum FO, Findlay GM. Lancet 1938;2:136.

216. Forster WG, McGibony JR. Am J Ophalmol 1944;27C:1107.

217. Fischl MA, Dickinson GM, Law Voie L. J Am Med Assoc 1988;259:1185.

218. Lockwood JS. J Am Med Assoc 1938;111:2259.

219. MacLod CM. J Exp Med 1940;72:217.

220. Boroff DA, Cooper A, Bullowa JGM. J Immunol 1942;43:341.

221. Stamp TC. Lancet 1939;2:10.

222. Green HN. Br J Exp Pathol 1940;21:38.

223. Woods DD. Br J Exp Pathol 1940;21:74.

224. Ratner S, Blanchard M, Coburn AF, Green DE. J Biol Chem 1944;155:689.

225. Selbie FR. Br J Exp Pathol 1940;21:90.

226. Findlay GM. Br J Exp Pathol 1940;21:356.

227. Blanchard KC. J Biol Chem 1941;140:919.

228. McIllwain H. Br J Exp Pathol 1942;23:265.

229. Rubbo SD, Maxwell M, Fairbridge RA, Gillespie JM. Aust J Exp Biol Med Sci 1941;19:185.

230. Fildes P. Lancet 1940;1:955.

231. Bliss EA, Long PH. Bull John Hopkins Hosp 1941;69:14.

232. Snell EE, Mitchell HK. Arch Biochem 1943;1:93.

233. Stetten MR, Fox CL Jr. J Biol Chem 1945;161:333.

234. Shive W, Ackermann WW, Gordon M, Getzendaner ME, Eakin RE. J Am Chem Soc 1947;69:725.

235. Gots JS. Nature 1953;172:256.

236. Angier RB, Boothe JH, Hutchings BL, Mowat JH, Semb J, Stokstad ELR, Subbarow Y, Waller CW, Cosulich DB, Fahrenbach MJ, Hultquist ME, Kuh E, Northey EH, Seeger DR, Sickless JP, Smith JM Jr. Science 1946;103:667.

237. Mowat JH, Boothe JH, Hutchings BL, Stokstad ELR, Waller CW, Angier R, Semb J, Consulich DB, Subbaow Y. Ann NY Acad Sci 1946;48:279.

238. Tschesche R. Z Naturforsch 1947;26b:10.

239. Welch AD, Nichol CA. Ann Rev Biochem 1952;21:633.

240. Friedkin M. Ann Rev Biochem 1963;32:185.

241. Woods DD. Relation of p-aminobenzoic acid in micro-organisms. In: Chemistry and Biology of Pteridines. (Ciba Foundation Symposium.) Boston: Little Brown; 1954. p 220.

242. Lampen JO, Jones MJ. J Biol Chem 1946;166:435.

243. Lampen JO, Jones MJ. J Biol Chem 1947;170:133.

244. Miller AK. Proc Soc Exp Biol Med 1944;57:151.

245. Miller AK, Bruno P, Berglund RM. J Bacteriol 1947;54,: G20, 9.

246. Lascelles J, Woods DD. Brit J Exp Pathol 1952;33:288.

247. Nimmo-Smith RH, Lasceles J, Woods DD. Br J Exp Pathol 1948;29:264.

248. Shiota T, Disraely MM. Biochim Biophys Acta 1961;52:467.

249. Shiota T, Disraely MN, McCan MP. J Biol Chem 1961;236:2534.

250. Brown GM, Weisman RA, Molnar DA. J Biol Chem 1961;236:2534.

251. Weisman R, Brown GM. J Biol Chem 1964;239:326.

252. Brown GM. J Biol Chem 1962;237:536.

253. Bock L, Miller GH, Schaper KJ, Seydel JK. J Med Chem 1974;17:23.

254. Swedberg G, Castensson S, Skold O. J Bacterial 1979;1: 137, 129.

255. Roland S, Ferone R, Harvey RJ, Styles YL, Morrison RW. J Biol Chem 1979;254:10337.

256. Hotchkiss RD, Evans AH. Fed Proc 1960;19:912.

257. Richey DP, Brown GM. J Biol Chem 1969;244:1582.

258. Shiota T, Baugh CM, Jackson R, Dillarde R. Biochemistry 1969;8:5022.

259. Ortiz PJ, Hotchkiss RD. Biochemistry 1969;31:174.

260. Ortiz PJ. Biochemistry 1970;9:355.

261. Toth-Martinez BL, Papp S, Dinya Z, Hernadi FJ. Biosystems 1975;7:172.

262. Thjssen HHW. J Med Chem 1977;20:233.

263. Brownice G, Green AF, Woodbine M. Br J Pharmacol 1948;3:15.

264. Levaditti C. C R Soc Biol 1941;135:1109.

265. Ramakrishnan SP, Basu PC, Singh H, Singh N. Bull World Health Organ 1962;27:213.

266. Seydel JK, Richter M, Wemple E. Int J Leprosy 1977;48:18.

267. Panitch ML, Levy L. Lep Rev 1978;49:131.

268. Cenedella RJ, Jarrell JJ. Am J Trop Med Hyg 1970;19:592.

269. Morgan HR. J Exp Med 1948;88:285.

270. Moulder JW. The Biochemistry of Intracellular Parasitism. Chicago: University of Chicago Press; 1962. p 105.

271. Jones LP, Williams FD. Can J Microbiol 1968;14:933.

272. Ferone R. J Protozool 1973;20:459.

273. Walter RD, Konigk E. Hoppe Seyler's Z Physiol Chem 1974;355:431.

274. McCullough JL, Maren TH. Mol Pharmacol 1974;10:140.

275. Jaenicke L, Chan PHC. Angew Chem 1960;72:752.

276. Okinaka O, Iwai K. Anal Biochem 1969;31:174.

277. Mitsuda H, Suzuki Y. J Vitaminol 1968;14:106.

278. Iwai K, Okinaka O. J Vitaminol 1968;14:170.

279. Roth B. Selective inhibitors of bacterial dihydrofolate reductase: structure–activity relationship. In: Hitchings GH, editor. Inhibition of Folate Metabolism in Chemotherapy. Germany: Springer-Verlag; 1983. p 107–127.

280. Greenberg J. J Pharmacol Exp Ther 1949;97:484.

281. Greenberg J, Richeson EM. J Pharmacol Exp Biol Med 1950;99:444.

282. Greenberg J, Richeson EM. Proc Soc Exp Biol Med 1951;77:174.

283. Garrod LP, James DG, Lewis AAG. Postgrad Med J 1969;Suppl 45: 1.

284. Hitchings GH. Med J Aust 1973;1:(Suppl): 5.

285. Seydel JK, Wempe E. Chemotherapy 1975;21:131.

286. Bushby SRM, Hitchings GH. Br J Pharmacol Chemother 1968;33:72.

287. Burchall JJ, Hitchings GH. Mol Pharmacol 1965;1:126.

288. Wormser GP, Kausch GT. Trimethoprim/sulfamethoxazole: an overview. In: Hitchings GH, editor. Inhibition of Folate Metabolism in Chemotherapy: the Origins and Uses of Co-Trimoxazole. Germany: Springer-Verlag; 1983. p 1.

289. Baca AM, Sivaraporn R, Turlly S, Sirawaraporne W, Hol WGJ. J Mol Biol 2000;302:1193.

290. Nopponpunth V, Sirawaraporn W, Greene PJ, Santi DV. J Bacteriol 1999;181:6814.

291. Achari A, Somers DO, Champness JN, Bryant PK, Rosemond J, Stammers DK. Nat Struct Biol 1997;4:490.

292. Dallas WS, Gowen JE, Ray PD, Cox MJ, Dev IK. J Bacteriol 1992;174:5961.

293. Hampele IC, D'Arcy A, Dale GE, Kostrewa D, Nielsen J, Oefner C, Page MGF, Schonfeld HJ, Stuber D, Then RL. J Mol Biol 1997;268:21.

294. Triglia T, Cowman AF. Proc Natl Acad Sci USA 1997;91:7149.

295. Volpe F, Dyer M, Scaife JG, Darby G, Stammers DK, Delves CJ. Gene 1992;112:213.

296. Rebeille F, Macherel D, Mouillon JM, Garin J, Douce R. EMBO J 1997;16:947.

297. Brooks DR, Wang P, Read M, Watkins WM, Sims PF, Hyde JE. Eur J Biochem 1994;224:397.

298. Landy M, Larkun NW, Oswald EJ, Strighoff F. Science 1943;97:265.

299. White PJ, Woods DD. J Gen Microbiol 1965;40:243.

300. Pato ML, Brown GM. Arch Biochem Biophys 1963;103:443.

301. Ho R, Cormen L. Antimicrob Agents Chemother 1974;5:388.

302. Wise EM Jr, Abou-Donia MM. Proc Natl Acad Sci USA 1975;72:2621.

303. Bishop A. Biol Rev 1959;34:445.

304. Huovinen P, Sundstrom L, Swedberg G, Skold O. Antimicrob Agetns Chemother 1995;39:279.

305. Vinnicombe HG, Derrick JP. Biochem Biophys Res Commun 1996;258:752.

306. Bishop A. Parasitology 1963;53:10.

307. Radstrom P, Swedberg G, Skold O. Antimicrob Agents Chemother 1991;35:1840.

308. Watanab T. Bacteriol Rev 1963;27:87.

309. Dale GE, Broger C, D'Arcy A, Hartman PG, et al. J Mol Biol 1997;266:23.

310. Kai M, Matsuoka M, Nakata N, Maeda S, Gidoh M, Maeda Y, Hashimoto K, Kobayashi K, Kashiwabara Y. FEMS Microbiol Lett 1999;177:231.

311. Bishop A.In: Goodwin LG, Nimmo-Smith RN, editors. Drug parasites and hosts. Boston: Litle Brown; 1962. p 98.

312. Hitchings GH. Functions of tetrahydrofolate and the role of dihydrofolate reductase in cellular metabolism. In: Hitchings GH, editor. Inhibition of Folate Metabolism in Chemotherapy. Germany; Springer-Verlag;1983. p 11–24.

313. Seeger DR, Smith JM Jr, Hultquist ME, Antagonist for pteroylglutamic acid. J Am Chem Soc 1947;69:2567.

314. Seeger DR, Cosulich DB, Smith JM Jr, Hultquist ME, Analogs of pteroylglutamic acid. III. 4-Amino derivatives. J Am Chem Soc 1949;71: 1753–1758.

315. Zakrzewski SF, Nichol CA, On the enzymatic reduction of foic acid by a purified hydrogenase. Biochim Biopys Acta 1958;27:425–426.

316. Werkheiser WC, Specific binding of 4-aminofoic acid analogues by folic acid reductase. J Biol Chem 1960;236:888–93.

317. Daniel LJ, Norris LC, Growth inhibition of bacteria by synthetic pterins. II. Studies with Escherichia coi, Staphyococcus aureus and Lactobacillus arabinosus showing synergism between pterin and sulfonamide. J Biol Chem 1947;170:747–756.

318. Daniel LJ, Norris LC, Scott ML, Heuser GF, Growth inhibition of bacteria by synthetic

pterins. I. Studies with Streptococcus faecais, Lactobacilus casei, and Lactobacillus arabinosus. J Biol Chem 1947;169:689–697.

319. Mallette MF, Cain CK, Taylor EC Jr, Pyrimido [4,5-*b*]pyrazines. II. 2,4-Diaminopyrimido[4,5-*b*]pyrazine and derivatives. J Am Chem Soc 1947;69:1814–1816.

320. Faco EA, Goodwin LG, Hitchings GH, Rollo IM, Russell PB, 2,4-Diaminopyrimidines: a new series of antimaarials. Br J Pharmacol 1951;6:185–200.

321. Hitchings GH, Bushby SRM. 5-Benzy-2,4-diaminopyrimidines, a new class of systemic antibacterial agents. In: Sissakian NM, editor. Vth International Congress of Biochemistry,. Moscow; 1961. p 165–171.

322. Hitchings GH, Burchall JJ, Ferone R, Comparative enzymology of dihydrofolate reductase as a basis for chemotherapy. Proc Int Pharmaco Meet 1966;3(5): 3–18.

323. Roth B, Falco EA, Hitchings GH, Bushby SRM, 5-Benzy-2, 4-diaminopyrimidines as antibacterial agents. I. Synthesis and antibacterial activity in vitro. J Med Pharm Chem 1962;5: 1103–1123.

324. Roth B, Aig E, Rauckman BS, et al. J Med Chem 1981;24:933–941.

325. Burchall JJ, Hitchings GH, Inhibitor binding analysis of dihydrofolate reductases from various species. Mol Pharmaco 1965;1:126–136.

326. Brendt R, Newenhoffer D, Thomsen T, et al. 47th Interscience Conference on Antimicrobial Agents and Chemotherapy, San Diego, CA September 27-30 2007; Schneider P. Hawser S, Islam K. Biorg. Chem Lett 2003, 13, 4217; Am Soc Microbiol Abstract 804, 806.

327. Struller T. Progress in sulfonamide research Prog Drug Res 1968;12:389–457.

328. Budavari S, editor. The Merck Index. 12th ed. Rahway, NJ: Merck & Co; 1996.

329. Lesher GY, Froelich ED, Grant MD, Bailey JH, Brundage RP. J Med Pharm Chem 1962;5:1063.

330. Normark BH, Normark S. J Int Med 2002;91:252.

331. Neu HC. Am J Med 1989;87:(Suppl 6C): 28–95. Med Clin North Am1988;72(3): 623.

332. Irikura T.US patent 4,146,719. 1978.

333. Bisacchi GS, Dumas J. Ann Rep Med Chem 2009;44:379–396.

334. (a) Bryskier Chantot JF. Drugs 1995;49(Suppl 2): 16–18.(b) Drusano GL, Wolfson JS, Hooper DC, editors. Quinolone Antimicrobial Agents. Washington, DC: American Society for Microbiology; 1989. p 71–105.

335. Gooding BB, Jones RN. Antimicrob Agents Chemother 1993;37:349.

336. Marutani K, Matsumoto M, Otabe Y, Nagamuta M, Tanaka K, Miyoshi A, Hasegawa T, Nagana H, Matsubara S, Kamide R, Yokata T, Matsumoto F, Ueda Y. Antimicrob Agents Chemother 1993;37:2217.Matsumoto M, Kojima K, Nagano N, Matsubara S, Yokota T. Antimicrob Agents Chemother 1992;36:1715.

337. Hayakawa I, et al. Antimicrob Agents Chemother 1986;29:163.

338. Mitscher LA, et al. J Med Chem 1987;30:2283.

339. Koshino K, Sato K, Ure T, Osada Y. Antimicrob Agents Chemother 1989;33:1816.

340. Sanchez JP, et al. J Med Chem 1995;38:4478.

341. Petersen U, et al. Curr Opin Investig Drugs 2000;1:45.

342. Shelanski HA, Shelanski MV. J Int Coll Surg 1956;25:727.

343. Hansch C, Leo A. Exploring QSAR: Fundamentals and Applications in Chemistry and Biology. Washington, DC: American Chemical Society; 1995. p 440.

344. Yamashita Y, Ashizawa T, Morimoto M, Hosomi J, Nakano H. Cancer Res 1992;52:2818.

345. Ronald AR, Turck M, Petersdorf RG. New Engl J Med 1966;275:1081.

346. Drlica K, Zhao X. Microbiol Mol Biol Rev 1997;61:377.

347. Hooper DC, Wolfson, editors. Quinolone Antimicrobial Agents. Washington, DC: American Society for Microbiology; 1989. p 249–271.

348. Moellering RC.In: Wolfson JS, Hooper DC, editors. Quinolone Antimicrobial Agents. Washington, DC: American Society for Microbiology; 1989. p 273–283.

349. Sanders CC.In: Sanders WE, Sanders CC, editors. Fluoroquinolines in the Treatment of Infectious Diseases. Glenview, IL: Physicians and Scientists Publications; 1990. p 1–27.

350. Schentag JJ, Nix DE.In: Sanders WE, Sanders CC, editors. Fluoroquinolines in the Treatment of Infectious Diseases. Glenview, IL: Physicians and Scientists Publications; 1990. p 5–34.

351. Wolfson JS, Hooper DC, Swartz MN.In: Wolfson JS, Hooper DC, editors. Quinolone Antimicrobial Agents. Washington, DC: American Society for Microbiology; 1989. p 5–34.

352. Leitman PS. Drugs 1995;49:(Suppl 2): 159.

353. DeSarro M, Zappala A, Chimirri S, Grasso S, DeSarro GB. Antimicrob Agents Chemother 1993;37:1497.

354. Murayama S, Hara Y, Ally A, Suzuki T, Tamagawa M. Nippon Yakurigaku Zasshi 1992;99:13.

355. Ford CW, Hamel JC, Stapert D, et al. Trends in Microb 1997;5:196.

356. Daly JS, Eliopoulos GM, Willey S, Moellering RC Jr. Antimicrob Agents Chemother 1988;32:1341.

357. Slee AM, Uonola MAW, Mcripley RJ, et al. Antimicrob Agents Chemother 1987;31:1791.

358. Daly JS, Eliopoulos GM, Reiszner E, Moellering RC Jr. J Antimicrob Chemother 1988;21:721.

359. Neu HC, Novelli A, Saha G, et al. Antimicrob Agents Chemother 1988;32:580.

360. Brumfitt W, Hamilton-Miller JMT. J Antimicrob Chemother 1988;21:711.

361. Zajac GM, Lam HE, Hoffman AM. 27th Interscience Conference on Antimicrobial Agents and Chemotherapy, New York, 1987. Abstract 247.

362. Eustice DC, Feldman PA, Slee AM. Biochem Biophys Res Commun 1988;150:965.

363. Eustice DC, Feldman PA, Zajac I, Slee AM. Antimicrob Agents Chemother 1988;32:1218.

364. Brickner SJ, Hutchinson DK, Barbachyn MR. J Med Chem 1996;39:673.

365. Brickner SJ. Curr Pharmacol Des 1996;2:175.

366. Zurenko GE, Yagi BH, Schaadt RD, et al. Antimicrob Agents Chemother 1996;40:839.

367. Biedenbach DJ, Jones RN. J Clin Microbiol 1997;35:3198.

368. Diekema DJ, Jones RN. Drugs 2000;59:7.

369. Xiong Y-Q, Yeaman MR, Bayer AS. Drug of Today 2000;36:631.

370. Perry CM, Jarvis B. Drugs 2001;61:525.

371. Di Pentima MC, Mason EO Jr, Kaplan SL. Clin Infect Dis 1998;26:1169.

372. Goldstein EJC, Citron DM, Merriam CV. Antimicrob Agents Chemother 1999;43:1469.

373. Edlund C, Oh H, Nord CE. Clin Microbiol Infect 1999;5:51.

374. Ford CW, Hamel JC, Wilson DM, et al. Antimicrob Agents Chemother 1996;40:1508.

375. Cynamon MH, Klemens SP, Sharpe CA, et al. Antimicrob Agents Chemother 1999;43: 1189.

376. Gehman MJ, Pitsakis PG, Mallela SV, et al. 37th Annual Meeting of American Society of Infectious Disease, Philadelphia, PA; November 18–21 1999. Abstract 192.

377. Pelton SI, Figueira M, Albut R, et al. Antimicrob Agents Chemother 2000;44:654.

378. Swaney SM, Aoki H, Ganoza MC. Antimicrob Agents Chemother 1998;42:3251.

379. Lin AH, Murray RW, Vidmar TJ, Marotti KR. Antimicrob Agents Chemother 1997; 41:2127.

380. Kloss P, Xiong L, Shinabarger DL, et al. J Mol Biol 1999;294:93.Xiong L, Kloss P, Douthwaite S, et al. J Bact 2000;182:5325.

381. Zurenko GE, Todd WM, Hafkin B, et al. 39th Interscience Conference on Antimicrobial Agents and Chemotherapy, San Francisco, CA, 1999. Abstract C848.

382. Gemell CG, Ford CW. 39th Interscience Conference on Antimicrobial Agents and Chemotherapy, San Francisco, CA, 1999. Abstract B-118.

383. Stalker DJ, Wajszczuk CP, Batts DH, et al. 37th Interscience Conference on Antimicrobial Agents and Chemotherapy, Toronto, Canada, 1997. Abstract A115.

384. Stalker DJ, Wajszczuk CP, Batts DH, et al. 37th Interscience Conference on Antimicrobial Agents and Chemotherapy, Toronto, Canada, 1997. Abstract A116.

385. Pharmacia and Upjohn Company, Zyvox (linezolid). General review (Data on file Kalamazoo, MI, 1999;).

386. Wienkers IC, Wynakla MA, Feenstra KL, et al. 39th Interscience Conference on Antimicrobial Agents and Chemotherapy, San Francisco, CA, 1999. Abstract A68.

387. Feenstra KI, Slatter JG, Stalker DJ, et al. 38th Interscience Conference on Antimicrobial Agents and Chemotherapy, San Diego, CA, 1998. Abstract 17.

388. Cammarata SK, Hafkin B, Demke DM, et al. Clin Microbiol Infect 1999;5:133.

389. Moellering RC Jr. Ann Intern Med 1999;130: 155.

390. Cammarata SK, Hafkin B, Todd WM, et al. Am J Respir Crit Care Med 1999;159: A844.

391. Birmingham MC, Zimmer GS, Hafkin B, et al. 38th Interscience Conference on Antimicrobial Agents and Chemotherapy, San Diego, CA, 1998. Abstract MN26. (1998).

392. Chien JW, Kucia ML, Salata RA. Clin Infect Dis 2000;30:146.

393. Gonzales RD, Schreckenberger PC, Mary BG, et al. Lancet 2001;357:1179.

394. Wilks NE, McConnell-Martin MA, Oliphant TH, et al. 39th Interscience Conference on Antimicrobial Agents and Chemotherapy, San Francisco, CA, 1999, Abstract 1763.

395. Birmingham MC, Zimmer GS, Hafkin B, et al. 39th Interscience Conference on Antimicrobial Agents and Chemotherapy, San Francisco, CA, 1999. Abstract 1098.

396. Green SL, Maddox JC, Huttenbach ED. J Am Med Assoc 2001;285:1291.

397. Zurenko GE, Ford CW, Hutchinson DK, Brickner SJ, Barbachyn MR. Exp Opin Invest Drugs 1997;6:151.

398. Robert G, Dean AS. Annu Rep Med Chem 2001;35:136.

399. Gleave DM, Brickner SJ, Manninen PR, et al. Bioorg Med Chem Lett 1998;8:1231.

400. Gleave MD, Brickner SJ. J Org Chem 1996;61:6470.

401. Bartel S, Endermann WR, Guamieri W, et al. 37th Interscience Conference on Atimicrobial Agents and Chemotherapy., Toronto, Ontario, Canada, 1997. Abstract F18.

402. Riedl B, Habich D, Stolle A, Wild H, et al. US patent 5,684,023. 1997.

403. Habich D, Bartel S, Endermann R, et al. 39th Interscience Conference on Antimicrobial Agents and Chemotherapy, San Francisco, CA, 1999. Abstract F-566.

404. Bartel S, Guamieri W, Habich D, et al. WO9937641. 1999.

405. Habich D, Bartel S, Endermann R, et al. 38th Interscience Conference on Antimicrobial Agents and Chemotherapy, San Diego, CA, 1998. Abstract F-129.

406. Bartel S, Endermann R, Uamieri W, et al. 38th Interscience Conference on Antimicrobial Agents and Chemotherapy, San Diego, CA, 1998. Abstract F-130.

407. Stolle A, Habich D, Riedl B, et al. US patent 5,869,659. 1999.

408. Gein MJ, Hutchinson DK, Alwine DA, et al. J Med Chem 1996;41:5144.

409. Gadwood RC, Thomasco LM, Weaver EA, et al. 39th Interscience Conference on Antimicrobial Agents and Chemotherapy, San Francisco, CA, 1999. Abstract 571.

410. Gadwood RC, Thomasco LM, Anderson DJ.US patent 5,977,373. 1999.

411. Bartel S, Endermann R, Guamieri W, et al. 37th IUPAC Congress, Berlin, Germany, 1999. Abstract SYN-2–140.

412. Raddetz S, Bartel S, Guamieri W, Rosentreter U, et al. WO9940094. 1998.

413. Bartel S, Guarnieri W, Habich D, et al. WO 9937652. 1999.

414. Tucker JA, Allwine DA, Grega KC, et al. J Med Chem 1998;41:3727.

415. Pae AN, Kim HY, Joo HJ, et al. Bioorg Med Chem Lett 1999;9:2679.

416. Pae AN, Kim SY, Kim HY, et al. Bioorg Med Chem Lett 1999;9:2685.

417. Bartel S, Endermann R, Guarnieri W, et al. 39th Interscience Conference on Antimicrobial Agents and chemotherapy, San Francisco, California, CA, 1999. Abstract F-565.

418. Tokuyama R, Takahashi Y, et al. Chem Pharm Bull 2001;49: 347 353 361.

419. Quesnelle GA, Gill P, Slepham R, Dodier M, et al. Biorg Mol Chem Lett 2005;5:728.

420. Renslow AR, Luchr GW, Gordeev MF. Biorg Med Chem 2006;14:4227.

421. Weidner-Wells MA, Boggs CM, Foleno BD, et al. Biorg Med Chem 2002;10:2345.

422. Stillman WB, Scott AB.US patent 2,416,234. 1947.

423. Dodd MC, Stillman WB, Roys N, Crosby C. J Pharmacol Exp Ther 1944;82:11.

424. Dann O, Moller EF. Chem Ber 1947;80:23.

425. Guay DR. Drugs 2001;61:353.

426. Andriole VT. Urinary tract agents: nitrofurantoin and methenamine. In: Mandell GL, Douglas RG, Bennett JE, editors. Principles and Practice of Infectious Disease. New York: Churchill Lioingstone; 1990. p 346–349.

427. Drake GD, Hayes KJ.US patent 2,759,931. 1956.

428. Bambury RE.In: Wolff ME, editor. Burger's Medicinal Chemistry. 4th ed. New York: John Wiley & Sons; 1979. p 65.

429. Rigol C, Olea-Azar C, et al. J Mol Struct 2006;770:125.

430. Chamberlain RE, J Antimicrob Ther. 1976;2:325–336.

431. McOsker CC, Fitzpatrick PM, Nitrofurantoin: mechanism of action and implications for resistance development in common uropathogens. J Antimicrob Chemother 1994;33:23–44.

432. McCalla DR. Nitrofurans. In: Hahn FE, editor. Mechanism of action of antibacterial agents. New York: Springer Verlag; 1979. p 176–213.

433. Shah RR, Wade G, Reappraisal of the risk/benefit of nitrofurantoIn: review of toxicity and efficacy. Adverse Drug React and Acute Poisoning Rev 1989;8:183–201.

434. Gleckman R, Alvarez S, Joubert DW, Drug therapy reviews: nitrofurantoin. Am J. Hosp Pharm 1979;36:342–351.

435. Marion-Landais G, Heotis JP, Herrett RJ, et al. Curr Ther Res Clin Exp 1975;18(3): 510.

436. Marion-Landais G, Heotis JP, Herrett RJ, et al. Curr Ther Res Clin Exp 1976;19(5): 550.

437. Johnson JR, Berggren T, Conway AJ. Antimicrob Agents Chemother 1993;37(9): 2033.

438. Snyder ML, Kiehn CL. Mil Sur 1945;97:380.

439. ReBarbachyn M. Ann Rep Med Chem 2005;40:281.

440. Gordeev MF, Hackbarth C, et al. Bioorg Med Chem Lett 2003;13:4213.

441. Gray CP, Cappi MW, Frimodt-Moller N. 45th Interscience Conference on Antimicrobial Agents and Chemotherapy, Washington, DC, 2005. Abstract F-513.

442. Dalhoff A. 47th Interscience Conference on Antimicrobial Agents and Chemotherapy, Washington, DC, 2007.

443. Zhi C, Long Z, et al. J Med Chem 2006;49:1455.

444. Butler MM, Foster KA, et al. Antimicrob Agents Chemother 2007;51:119.

445. (a) Taubes G. Science 2008;321:356. (b) Marshall E. Science 2008;321:362.

446. Wise R. Curr Sci 2008;95:181.

ANTIPROTOZOAL/ANTIPARASITIC AGENTS

Patrick M. Woster
Department of Pharmaceutical Sciences,
Eugene Applebaum College of Pharmacy
and Health Sciences, Wayne State
University, Detroit, MI

1. INTRODUCTION

Parasitic protozoan infections in humans such as amebiasis (caused by various species of *Entamoeba*), giardiasis (*Giardia lamblia*), and trichomoniasis (caused by species related to *Trichomonas vaginalis*) and infection caused by a variety of more obscure protozoans are considered minor health threats. These infections occur infrequently, and can be effectively managed with existing therapy. In addition, a subset of protozoan parasites cause important opportunistic infections in immunocompromized patients. Infections caused by *Microsporidia* (*Encephalitozoon cuniculi, Enterocytozoon bienusi*), *Cryptosporidium parvum, Toxoplasma gondii*, and the fungal-related *Pneumocystis carinii* are either self-limiting or can be effectively treated in patients with normal immune function. However, in immunocompromised patients, these infections can be difficult to treat, and currently available agents are often ineffective. For these patients, there is no effective therapy for infections caused by *Microsporidia* or *Cryptosporidia*, and the treatment of *T. gondii* and *P. carinii* produces variable and unsatisfactory results. Because they occur in developed nations, these parasitic diseases are being studied in a variety of laboratories, and new agents to treat these infections are being designed, synthesized, and tested.

The World Health Organization considers selected parasitic organisms to be serious threats to global health, and these major infectious diseases account for a significant percentage of total global morbidity. Malaria, which is caused by four strains of the *Plasmodium* family, is the most serious of these infections, and is a major cause of morbidity in a large portion of the world. Chemotherapeutic approaches to the treatment of malaria are outlined in Volume 7, Chapter 11. The focus of this chapter is the treatment of infectious diseases caused by protozoa in the kinetoplastid family *Trypanosomatidae*, including human African trypanosomiasis (HAT) and Chagas' Disease (also known as American trypanosomiasis), and the kinetoplastid family *Leishmania*. Like malaria, these diseases represent major threats to human health, particularly in the rural areas of underdeveloped countries. In 2004, these three diseases were responsible for 110,000 deaths and 4,077,000 disability adjusted life years (DALYs, the number of healthy years of life lost because of premature death and disability) in WHO member states where statistics have been kept [1]. The actual number of deaths and DALYs are much higher, as described below. Chemotherapy for parasitic infection by trypanosomatids has not changed appreciably over the past 50 years, an observation that is especially grim when one considers the recent emergence of multiple drug-resistant parasitic strains. Many of the drugs currently used require repeated dosing over long periods. In addition, many drugs are difficult to administer, particularly in the poor conditions found in areas where these diseases are endemic. Most of the drugs are also quite toxic or sporadically efficacious, and there are no effective treatments for some late-stage parasitic diseases. Drug discovery efforts against the diseases mentioned above are limited, either because impoverished patients in underdeveloped areas cannot afford newly developed therapy or because the infected population is too small to justify the required research expenditures. Efforts to fight parasitic diseases in Third World nations are also hampered by economic issues and political turmoil. These facts virtually assure that the world's most impoverished people will continue to bear the major burden of these parasitic diseases. Thus, there is an ongoing need for new antiparasitic agents that are potent, nontoxic and inexpensive to manufacture. Importantly, the recent publication of the complete genomes for *Trypanosoma brucei, Trypanosoma cruzi*, and *Leishmania major* [2–5], the so called "hat trick" of antiparasitic research [6], presents a unique opportunity for drug discovery. Molecular biology, genomic, and proteomic approaches to the study of these parasites will facilitate characterization and validation of new targets for chemotherapy aimed at the trypanosomatids.

2. KINETOPLASTID PROTOZOAN INFECTIONS

Two members of the kinetoplastid family *T. brucei, T. brucei gambiense* and *T. brucei rhodesiense*, are the causative organisms of HAT [7]. *T. b. rhodesiense* produces an acute form of the disease known as East African trypanosomiasis, while *T. b. gambiense* produces a chronic disease called West African trypanosomiasis. A third strain of the parasite, *T. b. brucei,* infects livestock rather than humans, and is thus a threat to the livelihood of the rural population in endemic areas. In addition, livestock and other animals can act as a reservoir for *T. b. gambiense* and *T. b. rhodesiense.* Sleeping sickness threatens over 60 million people in 36 countries of sub-Saharan Africa. However, only three to four million people in these areas are regularly monitored. Because detection of the disease calls for well-equipped health centers and qualified staff, which are absent in rural and impoverished areas, trypanosomiasis has reached epidemic proportions in many areas. The poor medical infrastructure in rural areas of the Third World means that most people who succumb to HAT die prior to diagnosis. Nearly 45,000 new cases are reported annually, although the actual number cannot be determined and may be as much as 10 times higher. The World Health Organization now estimates that more than 48,000 people died from HAT in 2004, and that 300,000–500,000 new cases occur each year [1]. Major epidemics of the disease occur periodically. The disease had nearly disappeared between 1960 and 1965, but relaxation of surveillance, combined with political unrest and destruction of the health care infrastructure, facilitated an epidemic that began in 1970 that persists today. Today, in some areas of Angola, the Democratic Republic of the Congo and southern

Sudan, the incidence of HAT is between 20% and 50%, and sleeping sickness has become the first or the second greatest cause of mortality, ahead of HIV/AIDS.

American trypanosomiasis was first characterized by Carlos Chagas in Brazil in 1909, and thus has come to be known as Chagas' disease. This parasitic infection is prevalent in tropical and subtropical Mexico, Central America, and South America and continues to be a serious threat to public health in these areas [8,9]. Chagas' disease is caused by the trypanosomatid species *T. cruzi,* which is similar but distinct from the species that cause HAT. According to the World Health Organization, 25% of the total population in Central and South America is at risk. Currently, there are between 16 and 18 million people infected, with 6 million cases advancing to clinically significant disease and more than 45,000 deaths annually.

Leishmaniasis is caused by one of the 20 strains of the trypanosomatid parasite *Leishmania*, and currently threatens 350 million men, women, and children in 88 countries around the world. Health statistics are only maintained in 32 of the 88 countries affected by leishmaniasis, and as such, a substantial number of cases are never reported. It is estimated by WHO that 2 million new cases (1.5 million cutaneous and 500,000 visceral, see below) occur annually, with an estimated 12 million people infected worldwide. It is transmitted through an insect vector following the bite of a female sandfly from one of the 30 species of the genus *Phlebotomus.* The disease can be divided into three categories (cutaneous, mucocutaneous, and visceral leishmaniasis), and is further categorized as Old World or New World leishmaniasis, depending on the geographic location of the various parasite species causing the disease. Cutaneous and mucocutaneous leishmaniasis are diseases that are generally not fatal, but cause disfigurement that can lead to social stigma and a significant impact on lifestyle. By contrast, visceral leishmaniasis, also called kala-azar, can produce life threatening systemic infection if left untreated [10]. Although leishmaniasis is endemic to rural South America and Africa, it is encroaching on urban areas with poor hygienic practices, and is also a risk for travelers in affected areas. In addition,

Leishmania as an opportunistic infection in HIV patients has become a significant health threat in some areas [11].

2.1. Kinetoplastid Biochemistry

The cellular biochemistry of kinetoplastids has not been fully elucidated, but a number of pathways that are parasite-specific have been identified as potential targets for chemotherapy. Trypanosomal metabolism has been most thoroughly studied, and is similar to metabolism in *Leishmania*, in that both organisms possess similar redox control mechanisms [12,13]. Trypanosomes are single-celled, flagellated protozoa that possess a number of organelles (including a nucleus, kinetoplast-mitochondrion, lysosome, endosome, flagellar pocket, Golgi, and glycosome) that each have specific cellular functions [14,15]. The trypanosomatid glycosome, a cellular microbody associated with trypanosomal peroxisomes, contains numerous metabolic enzymes, including the first seven steps of the glycolytic pathway and the pentose phosphate shunt [14,16]. The trypanosomatid glycolytic pathway is distinct from mammalian glycolysis, in that it does not occur in the cytoplasm, and has therefore been studied as a potential target for the design of inhibitors that exploit differences in the structure of individual glycolytic enzymes, or that interrupt metabolite transport into the glycosome [17]. Interestingly, the parasite develops a conventional cytochrome chain and TCA cycle when in the insect vector. However, in the vertebrate host, trypanosomes depend entirely upon glucose for energy and are highly aerobic, despite the fact that the kinetoplast-mitochondrion completely lacks cytochromes. Mitochondrial oxygen consumption in the vertebrate host is carried out using an alternative oxidase that does not produce ATP. Trypanosomal mitochondria can adapt to low oxygen levels in the host using unique anaerobic pathways that employ enzymes such as trypanosome alternative oxidase (TAO). The enzyme TAO is distinct from those of the host [18,19], and as such trypanosomatid respiration represents a viable target for chemotherapy.

Polyamine metabolism in trypanosomatids is analogous to mammalian polyamine metabolism, in that these organisms synthesize putrescine and spermidine from ornithine [20], and trypanosomatid ornithine decarboxylase and spermidine synthase have been identified. However, unlike mammalian cells, these organisms do not produce spermine. As shown in Fig. 1, the parasite converts host-derived glutathione (**1**) and two molecules of spermidine (**2**) via glutathionylspermidine (**3**) into reduced trypanothione (**4**), which is used to protect the organism against oxidative stress. The formation of reduced trypanothione (**4**, Fig. 1) is mediated by two ATP-dependent enzymes, glutathionylspermidine synthetase, which produces glutathionylspermidine (**3**), and trypanothione synthetase (TS), which converts **3** to **4** [21]. In the presence of oxidative stress, oxidized trypanothione (**5**) is formed, and must be recycled to the reduced form **4** by a third enzyme unique to the parasite, trypanothione reductase (TR). Importantly, the trypanothione pathway contains three enzymes that are unique to the parasite, and thus these enzymes may be viewed as targets for the rational design of antitrypanosomal agents.

2.2. HAT (African Sleeping Sickness)

Infections caused by *T. b. gambiense* and *T. b. rhodesiense* are transmitted by the bite of the three main species of tsetse flies *Glossina fuscipes, Glossina palpalis,* or *Glossina morsitans* [7]. During a blood meal from an infected host, the tsetse fly ingests the short, stumpy bloodstream trypomastigote form of the parasite, which is a growth-attenuated form possessing moderate mitochondrial activity, and which is adapted for transmission to the insect vector. Following ingestion by the vector, a complex life cycle begins (Fig. 1) with the formation of the trypanosomal procyclic trypomastigote (promastigote) form in the tsetse midgut, where they multiply through binary fission [7,15,22]. Procyclic trypomastigotes then move to the salivary gland, where they are converted into epimastigote form. Like the procyclic trypomastigote, the epimastigote morphological form proliferates by fission. Subsequently, the organism develops a variable surface glycoprotein (VSG) coat, and is converted into the nonproliferative metacyclic

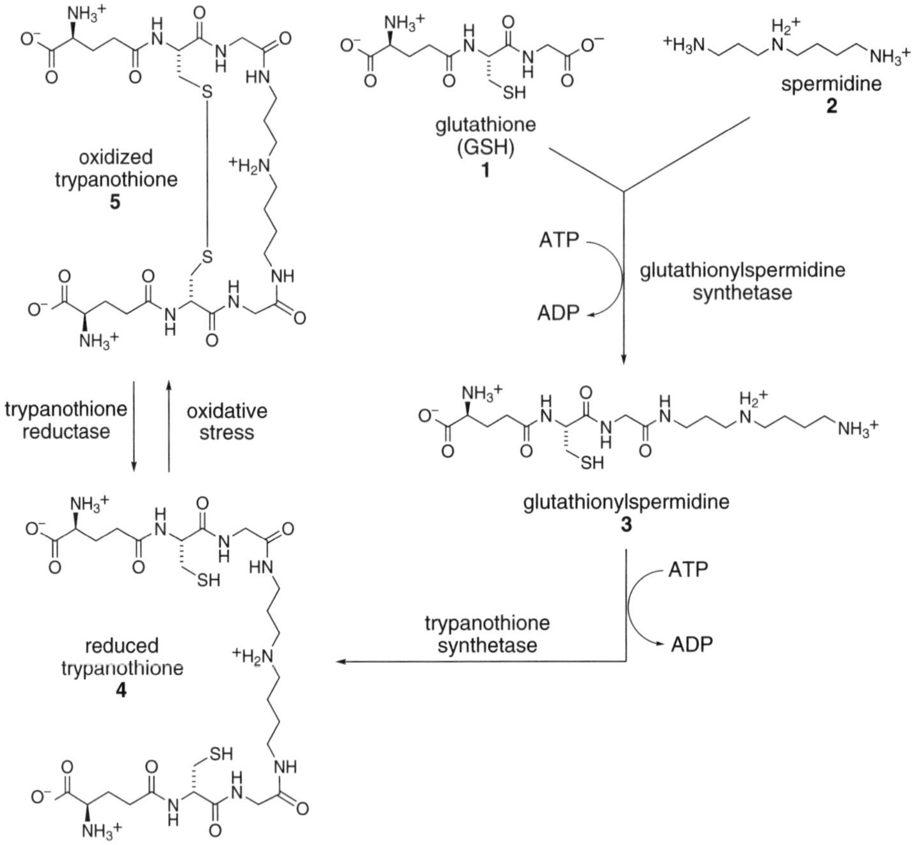

Figure 1. The synthesis and redox cycling of trypanothione.

trypomastigote form for transmission. The metacyclic form does not multiply, and the VSG helps the organism evade detection by the mammalian host immune system. Metacyclic trypomastigotes are injected into the mammalian host through the insect salivary gland during a second blood meal, and develop into the flagellated, morphologically slender bloodstream trypomastogites in the blood and lymphatic system of the host. The trypomastigote bloodstream form expresses the bloodstream-stage-specific VSG coat and is proliferative. In this form, the kinetoplast (the mitochondrial genome of the parasite) is located at the posterior end of the cell and mitochondrial activity is relatively repressed. As the parasite burden increases in the bloodstream, differentiation to morphologically stumpy bloodstream trypomastogites occurs, and the cycle begins anew. The bite of the tsetse fly produces a nodule or ulcer at the site of infection, and Stage 1 disease first appears in the lymph nodes (Fig. 2) [7]. Because early symptoms (malaise, headache, and undulating fever) are common to other infectious diseases, it is difficult to make an accurate differential diagnosis. More serious manifestations such as pericardial and pulmonary edema have been noted in the more acute *T. b. rhodesiense* form of Stage 1 infection. Stage 2 disease develops in a few weeks from *T. b. rhodesiense* infection, or in a few months or even years in the case of *T. b. gambiense*. This stage is initiated when the parasite invades internal organs and the CNS. The resulting variations in diurnal and nocturnal sleep patterns led to the coining of the phrase "sleeping sickness." Stage 2 disease can only be confirmed by lumbar puncture, however, once the parasite enters the cerebrospinal fluid they are diffi-

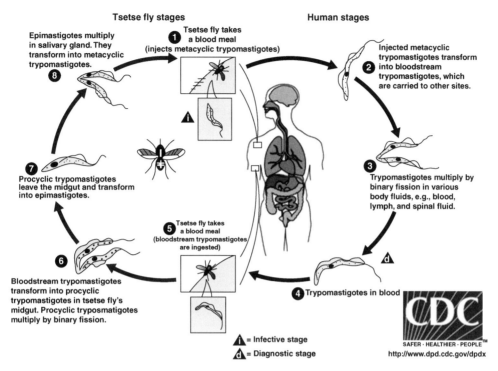

Figure 2. The life cycle of the African trypanosome. From http://www.dpd.cdc.gov/dpdx/HTML/Trypanoso-miasisAfrican.htm. (This figure is available in full color at http://mrw.interscience.wiley.com/emrw/9780471266945/home.)

cult to detect, and measurement of elevated levels of IgM and lymphocytes is often used for differential diagnosis.

2.2.1. Current Drug Treatments for HAT

Despite drug discovery efforts dating back to the work of Paul Ehrlich in the 1890s, there are only four drugs that are in common use for the treatment of early and late stage HAT (Fig. 3). Early stage trypanosomiasis can usually be successfully treated with available drugs. However, diagnosis of early stage disease is difficult, especially in rural areas, and many patients progress to late-stage disease before seeking treatment. Early stage disease is generally treated with either the polyanionic sulfonated naphthylamine suramin (**6**) or the aromatic diamidine pentamidine (**7**). Suramin enters the trypanosome by endocytosis, and is more than 75% bound to serum proteins following administration [23,24], a fact that may be related to its mechanism of action. In the presence of serum proteins, trypanosomes take up suramin by receptor-mediated endo-

cytosis 18-fold more efficiently than by fluid endocytosis alone [25,26]. The drug may hamper the required parasitic uptake of LDL by receptor-mediated endocytosis, it may associate with cytosolic enzymes inside the parasite, or it may associate with the highly positively charged glycolytic enzymes in the glycosome [23]. Suramin's mechanism of trypanocidal action remains uncertain. It has inhibitory activity against a number of trypanosomal enzymes and multiple mechanisms are probably involved in its therapeutic effect. Like suramin, the mechanism of action of pentamidine is not precisely known, but it is thought to act by inhibiting the P2 adenosine uptake system in the parasite (see below) [27–29]. Pentamidine reaches millimolar concentrations in cells and has been shown to bind to a number of negatively charged cellular components, including DNA, RNA, phospholipids, and a number of enzymes [30]. Trypanosomal strains that are resistant to suramin and pentamidine have been detected. Suramin resistance is most likely due to de-

Drugs for stage 1 trypanosomiasis:

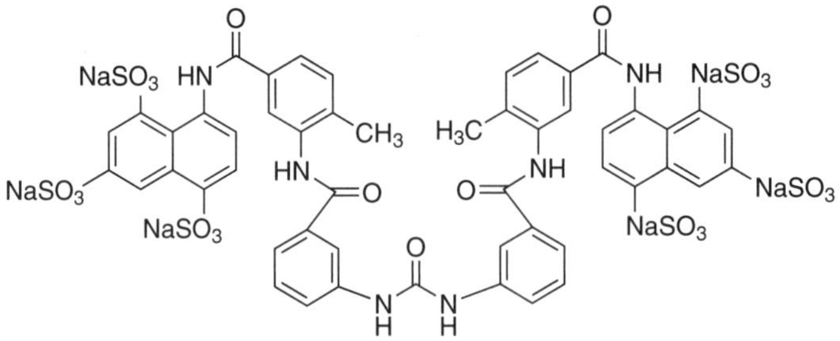

Drugs for stage 2 trypanosomiasis:

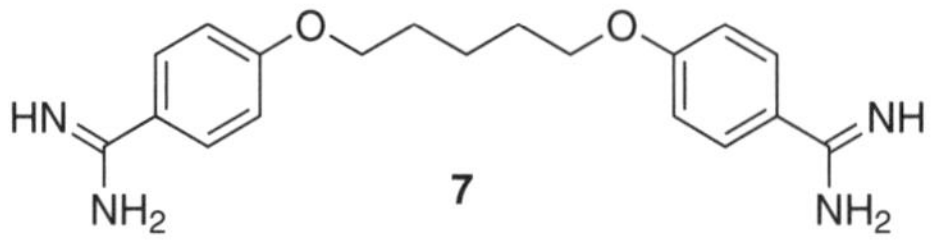

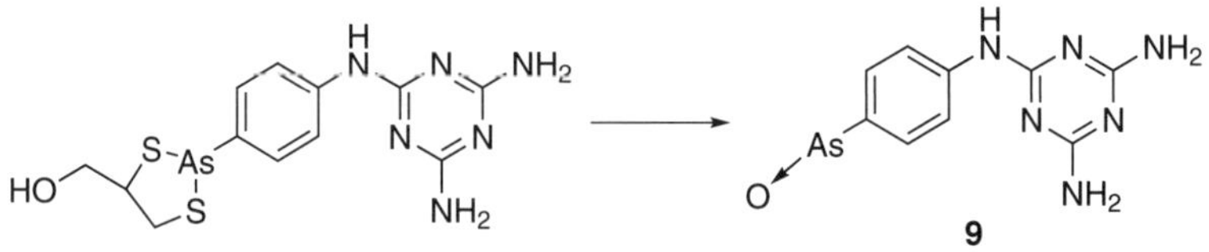

Figure 3. Drugs currently in use for the treatment of early- or late-stage African trypanosomiasis.

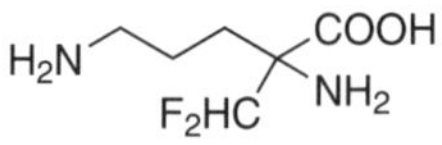

velopment of a drug extrusion complex [29], while pentamidine resistance is thought to be caused by mutations in trypanosomal transporter proteins, or to the ability of the parasite to use alternate adenosine transporters [29]. Only two trypanocidal agents are in current use as treatments for late-stage trypanosomiasis, and both must penetrate into the CNS in order to be effective. End stage trypanosomiasis is treated with melarsoprol (Mel B, **8**, Fig. 3), an organoarsenical that was first described in 1949. Following administration, melarsoprol is converted *in vivo* to its active metabolite, melarsen oxide (Mel Ox, **9**) [31], which has a plasma half-life of about 30 min. Mel Ox then produces a trypanocidal effect through formation of a covalent complex with

trypanothione known as Mel T. The inactivation of trypanothione exposes the organism to oxidative damage. Melarsoprol treatment of late-stage trypanosomiasis requires the use of an outdated and complicated regimen that requires patients to be hospitalized and monitored over a protracted course of therapy. Patients receive three series of four intravenous injections with a 10-day interval between each series [32]. This schedule may not be the most effective and accounts, in part, for frequently reported side effects [33,34], including a 10% incidence of reactive encephalopathy, which is fatal in 3–5% of patients [35]. Melarsoprol is only soluble in propylene glycol, and is marketed as a 3.6% solution. When a vial is opened, the drug must be used immediately, as it begins to deteriorate. In addition, administration is painful, and thrombophlebitis at the injection site is common [23]. Melarsoprol produces serious neurological sequellae in many cases, and additional adverse effects arise following the covalent binding of melarsoprol to native biomolecules that subsequently become antigenic. In addition, arsenic-resistant strains of *T. b. gambiense* and *T. b. rhodesiense* have emerged, and now comprise 30% of all trypanosomes [33]. It is likely that this resistance is mediated by mutations in the P2 transporter, which is necessary for the import of melarsoprol into the organism [27].

The ornithine decarboxylase (ODC) inhibitor eflornithine (**10**, Fig. 3) was initially synthesized as a potential antitumor agent, but was subsequently found to cure trypanosomal infections in mice [36,37]. Eflornithine has been shown to be curative in end stage infections caused by *T. b. gambiense*, but it much less ineffective against late stage *T. b. rhodesiense* infection [38–40], most likely because this parasite exhibits a much higher ornithine decarboxylase turnover. The reason for the parasite-selective toxicity of eflornithine is not fully understood. Since *T. b. gambiense* ODC is highly stable and does not turn over at a detectable rate, it has been proposed that differential toxicity is attributable to the differences in turnover between host and parasite ODCs [37]. Eflornithine, also known as difluoromethylornithine (DFMO), is the only new molecule approved for the treatment of HAT over the last 50 years, and is considered a second-line agent for the treatment of arsenic (and hence melarsoprol) resistant *T. b. gambiense*. The drug is most commonly dosed at 100 mg/kg of body weight as a short infusion at intervals of 6 h for 14 days (150 mg/kg in children). Adverse reactions to eflornithine are reversible at the end of treatment, and include convulsions (7%), gastrointestinal symptoms such as nausea, vomiting, and diarrhea (10–39%); bone marrow toxicity leading to anemia, leucopenia, and thrombocytopenia (25–50%); hearing impairment (5% in cancer patients); and alopecia (5–10%). Because it is trypanostatic rather than trypanocidal, it is a rather slow-acting drug. Eflornithine acts as an irreversible, enzyme-activated inactivator of ODC [41,42]. Like the substrate ornithine, eflornithine forms a Schiff base with the pyridoxal phosphate that is tightly bound to the enzyme through LYS-89 [42]. Decarboxylation results in elimination of a fluorine on the α-methyl group, and the resulting adduct then acts as a Michael acceptor, binding covalently to CYS 360 in the catalytic site, leading to irreversible inactivation. It has also been suggested that eflornithine rapidly reduces protein synthesis and formation of the VSG through polyamine deplation. Although the drug is an effective inactivator, new ODC is rapidly produced through compensatory protein synthesis, and thus eflornithine must be given in large doses over extended periods to be effective. Unfortunately, the synthesis of eflornithine on the industrial scale is difficult and expensive. Although it is marketed in the Unites States for a lifestyle disease, its availability in impoverished nations is limited. Comprehensive reviews of current agents used to treat trypanosomiasis have recently been published [43,44].

2.3. American Trypanosomiasis (Chagas' Disease)

Chagas' disease is transmitted through the bite of several species of triatomine bugs (also referred to as reduviid bugs or "kissing bugs"), including *Triatoma infestans*, *Triatoma dimidiata*, and *Rhodnius prolixa*. These insects, which are endemic to dry, forested areas, hide during the day in dark crevices or behind objects that are abundant in the type of housing used in endemic areas, or in animal nests and thatched roofs. At night, the insects emerge and feed on the blood of humans and a variety of mammals. As the insect feeds, it deposits feces containing the organism near the wound, and the parasite enters the host when the wound is scratched, or through the conjunctiva of the eye or the mucosa of the nose or mouth, and invades a variety of cell types including macrophages, smooth and striated muscle and fibroblasts. When the site of infection is near the eye, acute swelling of one eyelid is observed, a phenomenon known as Romaña's sign. After a 1–2-week incubation period, the disease progresses through three phases, termed acute, indeterminate, and chronic. In the acute phase, patients have a significant parasite burden in blood and tissues, and suffer from mild symptoms including high fever and edema. A more severe acute phase characterized by cardiac involvement and encephalomyelitis can develop in immunosuppressed patients and children. In the ensuing postacute phase, the parasite burden in blood and tissues decreases dramatically, although low levels of the parasite are still detectable in certain tissues. Patients then experience an asymptomatic period that is known as the indeterminate phase for anywhere from 10 to 30 years. A percentage of these patients advance to chronic Chagas' disease, and develop moderate to severe clinical symptoms including cardiomyopathy, heart failure and digestive tract abnormalities such as megacolon and megaloesophagus, and these manifestations of the disease are primary factors in morbidity. Extensive tissue damage can occur when parasite levels are low in the affected tissues, and thus it is possible that morbidity occurs as a result of an autoimmune response [45,46].

T. cruzi has a life cycle (Fig. 4) that is similar to that of *T. brucei* except that in the mammalian host, the parasite is mainly intracellular [8,9]. During a blood meal, the insect vector ingests both the trypomastigote and amastigote form of the organism, and these forms pass into the midgut of the insect. In the midgut, trypomastogotes exist in slender and broad (or short, stumpy) forms, and both forms are converted to amastigotes, which are able to replicate. Flagella develop and begin to function (sphaeromastigote form), followed by transition to the epimastigote stage, which is also replicative. The epimastigotes attach to the cuticle area of the hindgut through hydrophobic interactions, and undergo transformation to their metacyclic form, which detaches and is excreted in

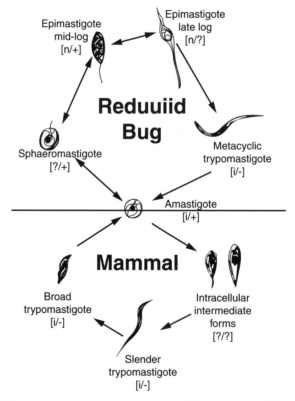

Figure 4. Life cycle of *Trypanosoma cruzi*. n: noninfective; i: infective; +: proliferative; -: nonproliferative. Used from Ref. [9] with permission.

feces. During a second blood meal, the organism enters the host through the wound, as described above, and penetrates the host cell using an energy-dependent mechanism [47] that appears to depend on various trypomastigote surface recognition glycoproteins. These mucin-like *O*-glycosylated proteins are rich in threonine, and function as sialic acid acceptors during the infective stage. Inside the host cell, trypomastigotes are contained in a parasitophorous vacuole, but subsequently escape, differentiate into amastigotes and replicate freely in the cytosol. After nine cycles of binary division, amastigotes differentiate back into highly motile trypomastigotes, which are released upon host-cell rupture, causing the acute form of Chagas' disease. Parasites invade muscle and other nonphagocytic cells by an unknown mechanism during the chronic stage of the disease as a means to evade the host immune system.

2.3.1. Current Drug Treatments for Chagas' Disease

The trypanosomatid *T. cruzi* is an intracellular parasite, and thus Chagas' disease is much more difficult to treat than HAT, since drugs used for the disease must pass through mammalian and parasite cell membranes to be effective. According to laboratory and clinical studies conducted 40 years ago, nifurtimox (**11**, Fig. 5) and benznidazole (**12**,

11

12

13

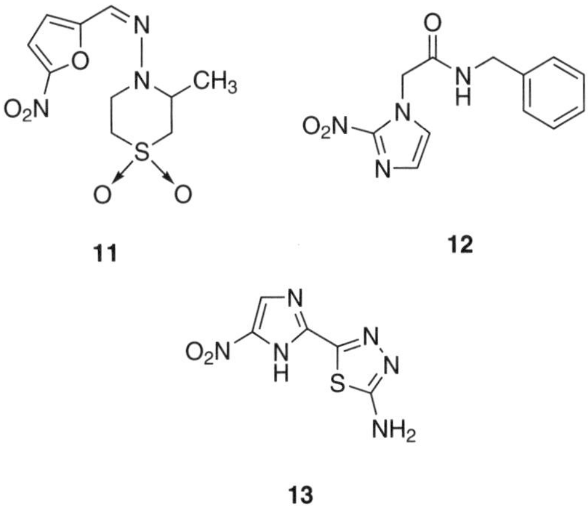

Figure 5. Structures of drugs currently used for *T. cruzi*: nifurtimox **11**, benznidazole **12**, and megazole **13**.

Fig. 5) are the most effective agents for treating human *T. cruzi* infection, with benznidazole being the drug of choice. However, these drugs are far from ideal because they can often exhibit low efficacy and produce significant side effects [48]. Nifurtimox and benznidazole are both indicated for acute *T. cruzi* infection, the congenital form of Chagas' disease, reactivation of disease associated with immunosuppression, and in transfusions and organ transplants involving infected individuals. The exact mechanism of action for nifurtimox has not been elucidated, but appears to require one electron reduction of the nitro group to form a nitro ion radical. The nitro ion radical is then thought to reduce molecular oxygen to form superoxide anion and regenerate the parent nitro compound as part of a complex redox cycle. Overproduction of superoxide anion swamps the cell's capacity to remove reactive oxygen species (superoxide, peroxide, and hydroxyl radical), resulting in lipid peroxidation and damage to membranes, proteins, and DNA. In addition, nifurtimox weakly inhibits trypanothione reductase [49]. The mechanism of trypanocidal activity of benznidazole is similar to that of nifurtimox. Nifurtimox and benznidazole-resistant strains of *T. cruzi* have been identified, although the mechanism of resistance is unknown, Nifurtimox is administered at 8–10 mg/kg/day in adults and <15 mg/kg/day in children for a period of 60–90 days, while benznidazole is given at 5 mg/kg/day in adults and <10 mg/kg/day in children for 60 days. Both drugs are orally active, but these must be given as two to three divided fractions after meals. These drugs are generally well tolerated by children, especially in the acute phase, but side effects including severe gastrointestinal or dermatological adverse reactions are relatively frequent. Recurrence of the disease is a significant problem, and as such these drugs are considered generally ineffective. The main limitations of both drugs are their long courses of administration and the occurrence of adverse side effects. A homolog of nifurtimox and benznidazole, megazol (**13**, Fig. 5) has historically been used for Chagas' disease, but an unacceptable incidence of severe mutagenic and cytotoxic side effects led to discontinuation of the drug [50].

2.4. Leishmaniasis

More than 20 species of *Leishmania*, distributed worldwide in tropical and subtropical regions, are known to be pathogenic to humans. Cutaneous leishmaniasis can be classified as one of the several forms based on the infecting species of parasite [11,44,51,52]. Old World cutaneous leishmaniasis is primarily caused by the species *L. major, L. aethiopica,* and *L. tropica*. It is usually transmitted by the phlebotomine sandflies *Phlebotomus papatasi* and *Phlebotomus sergentii* [11,51,52]. The recidivans (lupoid) form may appear as a complication of cutaneous infection with *L. tropica*, producing erythematous papules at sites near the scars of healed lesions [53]. Dogs and humans are the major reservoirs for Old World cutaneous leishmaniasis, although this form has also been detected in rats. Old World cutaneous leishmaniasis occurs in large part in Sudan, Afghanistan, Iran, Saudi Arabia, and Syria, producing skin ulcers on the exposed parts of the body such as the face, arms and legs. The disease can produce as many as 200 lesions, causing serious disability and permanent scarring. Old World cutaneous leishmaniasis regresses and cures occur spontaneously, but the healing process often takes a year or more. New World cutaneous leishmaniasis commonly occurs in a region that extends from Texas to central South America, and has also been found in the Caribbean. However, the majority of cases occur in Brazil and Peru [11,51,52]. The disease is transmitted by female sandflies of the genus *Lutzomyia*, and infections are caused by multiple *Leishmania* strains: *L. mexicana, L. garnhami, L. lainsoni, L. venezuelensis, L. peruviana, L. colombiensis, L. guyanensis, L. amazonensis, L. panamensis,* and *L. pifanoi*. Unlike Old World disease, New World cutaneous leishmaniasis infects various mammals (dogs, rodents, opossum, and anteaters), as well as humans, using them as both reservoirs and hosts. The symptoms of New World cutaneous leishmaniasis are similar to those of Old World disease, but there a wide strain-dependent variation in the degree of tissue destruction occurs. Ketoconazole or benznidazole are common treatments, especially if the infection involves the soft cartilage of the ear.

The leishmanial species *L. braziliensis* is the primary causative organism for mucocutaneous leishmaniasis. More than 90% of mucocutaneous leishmaniasis occurs in Bolivia, Brazil, and Peru [11,51,52]. Acute lesions are similar to those seen in both forms of cutaneous leishmaniasis, but develop into more severe lesions of the mucosa in about 80% of untreated cases. These secondary lesions can lead to partial or total destruction of the mucous membranes of the nose, mouth and throat, and in severe cases the resulting disfigurement can result in victims being humiliated and cast out from society.

Visceral leishmaniasis (kala-azar in India or dumdum fever in Africa) is caused by organisms of the *L. donovani* complex (*L. donovani, L. infantum,* and *L. chagasi*) [11,51,52,54]. More than 90% of visceral leishmaniasis cases occur in Bangladesh, Brazil, India, Nepal, and Sudan. *L. donovani* is the primary cause of visceral leishmaniasis in India and East Africa. The disease is also caused by *L. infantum* in Mediterranean countries and *L. chagasi* in Mexico and South America. Human beings are the only known reservoir of *L. donovani*, but both domestic and stray dogs provide a reservoir for *L. infantum* and *L. chagasi*. These differences have a major impact on the control of the disease and the emergence of drug resistance. Acute symptoms of visceral leishmaniasis include irregular, undulating fever, cough, abdominal pain, diarrhea, epistaxis, splenomegaly, hepatomegaly, substantial weight loss and moderate to severe anemia. For chronic, untreated infection, the fatality rate in developing countries can be as high as 100% within 2 years. As the organism develops in the skin cells, spleen, liver, or bone marrow of the host, patients experience anemia and cachexia, and ultimately succumb to the parasite. There were more than 41,000 recorded deaths due to visceral leishmaniasis in 2000 [54].

All *Leishmania* strains possess very similar life cycles, as summarized in Fig. 6. The *Leishmania* life cycle occurs in two distinct phases, one involving a mammalian host and one in an insect vector [51,55]. The insect phase begins when the sandfly vector ingests *Leishmania* amastigotes during a blood meal from a mammalian host carrier. The amasti-

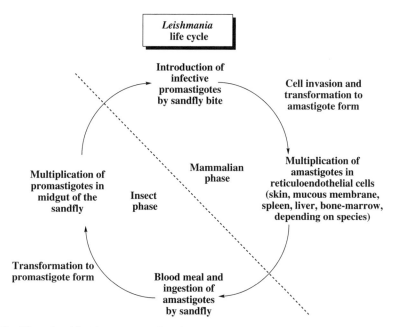

Figure 6. The life cycle of *Leishmania* sp. (This figure is available in full color at http://mrw.interscience. wiley.com/emrw/9780471266945/home.)

gote form is round or oval in shape, 3–5 mm in size, and contains a distinct nucleus, a kinetoplast and a short, intracytoplasmic flagellum. Amastigotes next transform into promastigotes, which are slender, motile organisms, 10–15 mm in length, with a single anterior flagellum. The promastigote form migrates to the midgut of the sandfly, multiplies by longitudinal fission, and then attaches to the wall of the insect hypostome through their flagella. When the insect takes a second blood meal, promastigotes are transferred into the mammalian host, initiating the mammalian phase. Promastigote *Leishmania* are engulfed by reticuloendothelial cells and transform back into amastigotes. Depending on the species, the affected reticuloendothelial cells can be subcutaneous (cutaneous leishmaniasis), mucosal (mucocutaneous leishmaniasis), or in other areas of the body such as bone, liver, and spleen (visceral leishmaniasis). The amastigote form reproduces by binary fission until the reticuloendothelial cell is destroyed, and the liberated parasites are then phagocytized by other reticuloendothelial cells of the same type.

2.4.1. Current Drug Treatments for Leishmaniasis Because *Leishmania* and trypanosomes are biochemically similar, many of the agents used against trypanosomal infection (see above) are also effective against infections caused by *Leishmania*. This is not universally true, however, since there are differences in tissue localization between the various species of the parasite. In all cases, the intracellular amastigote form is considered the optimal target for chemotherapy. The standard treatment for visceral leishmaniasis is sodium stibogluconate **14** or meglumine antimoniate **15** (Fig. 7), moderately toxic antimonials that are effective, but for which resistant strains are becoming more prominent [44,56,57]. Compounds **14** and **15** are essentially equivalent agents against *Leishmania*, and both are formulated as complex mixtures of carbohydrate/antimony complexes that are dosed based on their antimony(V) content. The mechanism of the antileishmanial activity of antimony is not precisely known, but it has been shown that **14** and **15** suppress glycolysis and fatty acid metabolism in the glycosome. These compounds may also interact with leishmanial

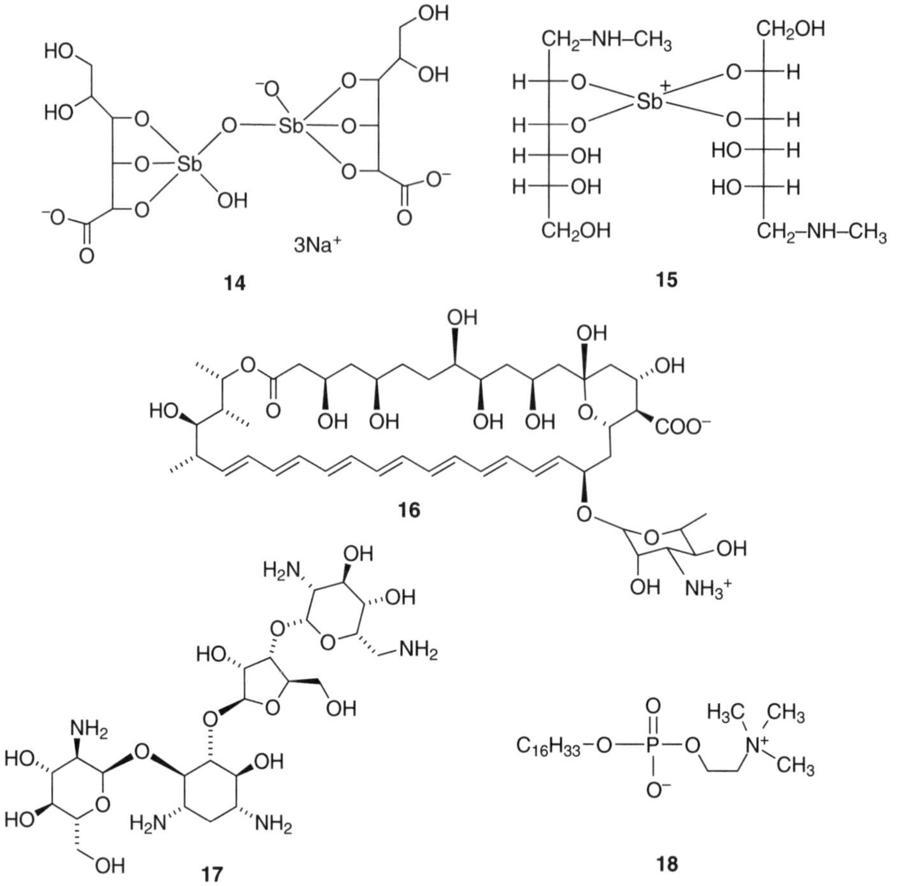

Figure 7. The structures of antileishmanial drugs: sodium stibogluconate **14**, meglumine antimoniate **15**, amphotericin B **16**, paramomycin **17**, and miltefosine **18**.

trypanothione in a fashion similar to the arsenical drugs mentioned above [58]. Antimonial courses of therapy are protracted, and they are administered intravenously at 20–40 mg/kg/day for 20–40 days. In addition to high cost and a lengthy course of administration, there are numerous resistant strains, and antimonial toxicity is frequent when HIV coinfection is present [54]. Quality control problems and batch-to-batch variability for both branded and generic antimonial preparations have been encountered, and the poor quality of some generic formulations of the drug in India has led to serious toxicity [59]. The antitrypanosomal drug pentamidine (**7**, Fig. 3) is marginally effective in the visceral form of leishmaniasis when given at 2–4 mg/kg by intramuscular injection, either daily or

every other day, for a course of 12–15 injections. Due to toxicity and resistance, especially in India, pentamidine is being abandoned as a second line treatment for leishmaniasis [54]. The macrocyclic antibiotic amphotericin B (**16**, Fig. 7) is currently used as a second line treatment for leishmaniasis. It is administered at 7–20 mg/kg total dose intravenously for up to 20 days. Cure rates as high as 97% have been reported, and to date there have been no reports of resistance. However, amphotericin B is not an ideal agent for the treatment of leishmaniasis due to frequent dose-limiting toxicity [54]. Lipid-associated formulations of amphotericin B are highly effective against visceral leishmaniasis and better tolerated than the conventional preparation. Liposomal amphotericin B was studied in India, Kenya, and Brazil [60], and minimum doses of 6, 14, and 21 mg/kg, respectively, were necessary to provide 95% cure rates [61]. However, such products are prohibitively expensive, and as such their utility in the Third World is severely restricted. Amphotericin B works by forming complexes with ergosterol in the cell membrane of the parasite. As a result, pores are formed in the membrane and ions are allowed to pass into the cell that promote cell death [62]. Paromomycin sulfate **17** is an effective alternative treatment for the antimonials sodium stibogluconate or meglumine antimoniate, and has been used for the treatment of all forms of leishmaniasis [63]. Paromomycin is an aminoglycoside antibiotic that is structurally related to neomycin. The agent is also effective in combination with the antimonials [64,65]. Paramomycin, like all aminoglycosides, exertsits antiparasitic activity through binding to polysomes, which inhibits protein synthesis, and causes misreading of DNA and premature termination of translation of mRNA [66,67]. Miltefosine **18** has more recently been found to be an effective treatment for leishmaniasis. Miltefosine has recently produced impressive results in both Phase I [66] and Phase II [67,68] clinical trials against Indian leishmaniasis, and as a result the drug was licensed in India in June 2002. A significant advantage of miltefosine is that it is orally active, unlike the other antileishmanial drugs. The effective dose range of oral miltefosine is 50–200 mg/day, but the optimal dose is 100–125 mg/day. The exact mechanism of action of miltefosine is not known, but it has been shown to have effects on signal transduction [69,70], lipid metabolism [71,72], and calcium homeostasis [73] in cell culture experiments.

3. PROGRESS IN DRUG RESEARCH FOR HAT, CHAGAS' DISEASE AND LEISHMANIASIS

As was mentioned above, drug development for parasitic diseases has been slow over the past 50 years, in part due to political and socioeconomic factors, but also because of a lack of suitable "druggable" targets. However, advances in the understanding of the genetics and biochemistry of protozoan parasites have facilitated the identification of a number of targets for the design of chemotherapies for trypanosomatid infections. As outlined in the sections below, considerable progress has been made in designing active compounds for a number of these new targets in an effort to develop agents that are safe, effective and inexpensive to produce. Significant challenges remain, however, before suitable agents can be made available for patients in the Third World.

3.1. Potential New Therapies for *T. brucei* and *T. cruzi*

3.1.1. Trypanocides That Utilize Unique Parasitic Nucleotide Transporters
Trypanosomes do not synthesize purines, but rather import them using a pair of unique adenosine transporters termed P1 and P2 [27,74,75]. The P1 transporter is responsible for importing adenosine and inosine, while the P2 receptor accepts a number of substrates, including adenine, adenosine, suramin **6**, pentamidine **7** and arsenical drugs such as melarsoprol, **8** (see Fig. 3). Arsenic-resistant trypanosome strains lack the P2 transporter [74,75]. A number of nucleoside analogs are substrates for the P1 or P2 transporter, and following import, produce trypanocidal activity by as yet unknown mechanisms. The *trans*-1S,4S isomer of **19** (Fig. 8) is an irreversible inactivator of mammalian and bacterial S-adenosylmethionine decarboxylase (AdoMet-DC), and also acts as a trypanocide with an IC_{50} of 0.9 μM [76]. Another inhibitor of AdoMet-DC, AbeAdo **20**, was a substrate for the P2 transporter in *T. b. rhodesiense*, exhibited a nanomolar IC_{50} value [77] and was curative for *T. b. rhodesiense* infections in mice [36,78,79]. AbeAdo acts as an irreversible inactivator of S-adenosylmethionine decarboxylase following activation by the enzyme catalytic cycle, and effectively disrupts polyamine biosynthesis in the parasite, causing accumulation of S-adenosylmethionine. Despite this impressive activity, this drug has never been developed for therapeutic use. Nucleoside analogs related to the methylthioadenosine analog HETA, **21**, enter trypanosomes via the P2 and S-adenosylmethionine transport systems [78]. HETA is concentrated

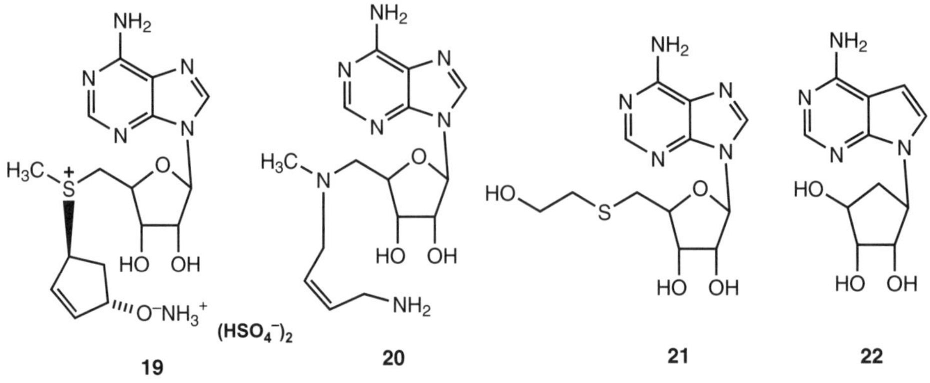

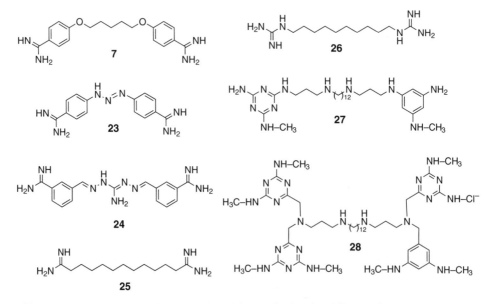

Figure 8. Antitrypanosomal nucleosides that are imported by the P1 or P2 transport system.

10–80-fold in trypanosomes, and kills the parasite through reduction of protein methylation. Compound **21** has been shown to produce *in vivo* cures against a number of strains [80]. The (+)-isomer of 7-deaza-noraristeromycin, **22**, also utilizes the trypanosomal P1 system, and shows potent activity against *T. b. brucei* (IC$_{50}$ = 0.2 μM) and the arsenic resistant K 243 As-10-3 strain (IC$_{50}$ = 5.3 μM) [81].

A number of amidines and guanidines have been synthesized and evaluated as antitrypanosomal agents, and many of these compounds (Fig. 9) are structurally related to

pentamidine (**7**). Compounds in this class were synthesized in order to eliminate the significant toxicity associated with the administration of pentamidine. In addition to pentamidine **7** and the closely related amidine berenil **23**, conformationally restricted methylglyoxal (bis)guanylhydrazone (MGBG) analogs such as CGP 40215 (**24**) possess significant antitrypanosomal activity [82]. Most of the compounds in this series are aromatic amidines that are structurally related to pentamidine **7**. Linear amidines and guanidines such as the undecanediamidine (**25**) and

Figure 9. Antitrypanosomal agents pentamidine and related amidines and guanidines **23**–**28**.

synthalin (**26**), respectively, have also shown promising antitrypanosomal activity [82]. Substituted (bis)guanidino homologs of synthalin were then identified by virtual screening, and found to inhibit TR from *T. cruzi* with K_i values between 2 and 47 µM [83], but the *in vivo* activity of these analogs has not been evaluated. Using the structure/activity data for analogs utilizing the P2 transport system, a series of triazine-substituted polyamines related to **27** and **28** were synthesized and evaluated. Compound **28** was an excellent substrate for the P2 transport system, and exhibited a 0.2 µM IC_{50} value against *T. b. rhodesiense* [84]. Unfortunately, none of the analogs in this series was effective *in vivo*.

Attempts to design conformationally restricted analogs of pentamidine have resulted in the discovery of agents with moderately improved activity (Fig. 10) for potential use in the treatment of early stage trypanosomiasis. Dicationic amidines with unsaturated internal carbon chains, such as **29** and **30** (Fig. 10), exhibited IC_{50} values between 2.0 and 9.0 µM against *T. b. brucei* and three strains of *T. b. rhodesiense* (KETRI 243, 269, and 243-As-10-3) [85]. Compound **30** was more potent *in vitro* against all strains of *T. b. rhodesiense* tested. Compounds **29** and **30** produced cures in murine models of trypanosomal infection involving *T. b. brucei* Lab 110, and the clinical isolates *T.b. rhodesiense* KETRI

269, 2002, and 2538, although with IC_{50} values two- to threefold higher than pentamidine. Also of interest are the conformationally restricted pentamidine analogs DB75 (**31**) and DB289 (**32**), which are currently in human clinical trials [86]. DB75 (**31**), also known as furamidine, is a potent trypanocide *in vitro* and *in vivo*, but does not exhibit significant oral bioavailability. In addition, it does not readily penetrate into the CNS following oral or intravenous administration, and thus is of little value in the treatment of late stage trypanosomiasis. To improve the bioavailability of **31**, the (bis)-*N*-methoxy analog DB289, **32** was synthesized as a prodrug form of **31** [86]. DB289 was found to have good oral bioavailability, leading to current clinical trials for early stage trypanosomiasis in Central Africa. However, **32** is not effective in late stage disease, regardless of route of administration [86]. Brain levels of DB75 and DB289 were low in treated animals, and the drug was either sequestered in brain parenchema (DB75) or poorly transported into the CNS (DB289). Furthermore, it has been demonstrated that DB289 is metabolized to DB75 in freshly isolated rat hepatocytes [87], and thus the activity of DB289 likely depends on conversion to the active constituent, DB75. This conversion appears to occur exclusively in the periphery, and thus little active drug crosses the blood–brain barrier. The

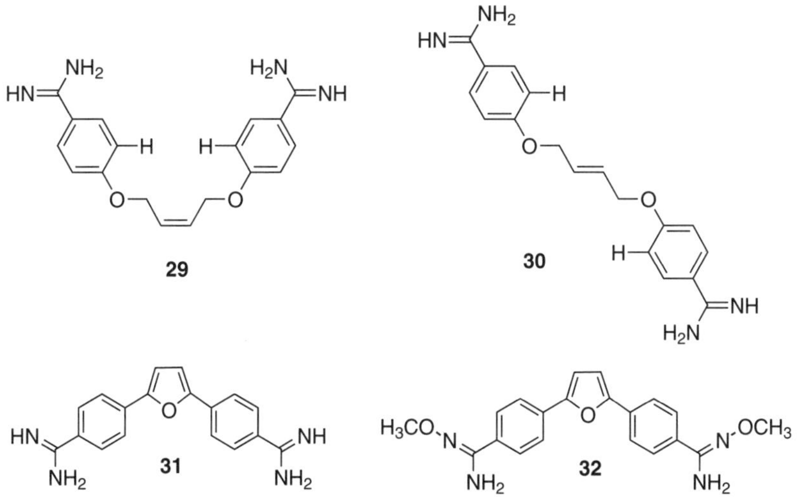

Figure 10. Conformationally restricted analogs of pentamidine with antitrypanosomal activity.

disappointing activity of DB289 in late stage trypanosomiasis underscores the continuing need to discover new, more effective agents for the treatment of late stage trypanosomiasis.

3.1.2. Inhibitors of Parasitic Lipid Metabolism

Inhibitors of glycosyl phosphatidylinositol biosynthesis have been evaluated as trypanocides. The rationale for this approach is that they interfere with the remodeling of surface recognition and anchoring glycoproteins [88]. Trypanosomatids require large amounts of myristate to support remodeling of glycosyl phosphatidylinositol glycoprotein anchors. Until recently, the parasite appeared to be unable to synthesize fatty acids, and myristate does not occur in sufficient amounts in the host bloodstream to support this requirement. However, it has now been demonstrated that trypanosomes can synthesize fatty acids using a synthetic pathway whereby myristate is incorporated into glycosyl phosphatidylinositols, but not into other lipids. The antibiotic thiolactomycin,

33, inhibits parasitic myristate synthesis, and has significant antitrypanosomal activity, suggesting that the myristate pathway is a valid chemotherapeutic target [89]. Homologs of thiolactomycin have been synthesized, and these are now being evaluated as antiparasitic agents [90]. The trypanosomal sterol biosynthetic pathway has also become a target of interest in the design of antiparasitic agents. Tipifarnib, an effective human protein farnesyl transferase inhibitor (**34**, Fig. 11) is also a potent inhibitor of protein farnesyl transferase from *T. cruzi*, exhibiting an IC_{50} of 75 nM. However, the IC_{50} against *T. cruzi* amastigotes in culture was considerably lower (4 nM), suggesting that **34** produces a trypanocidal effect through an alternate mechanism of action. These observations led to the discovery that tipifarnib also inhibits trypanosomal cytochrome P450 sterol 14-demethylase [91]. Sterols related to **35** were found to be excellent growth inhibitors in *L. donovanii*, *L. major*, and *T. cruzi* with relatively low toxicity to host

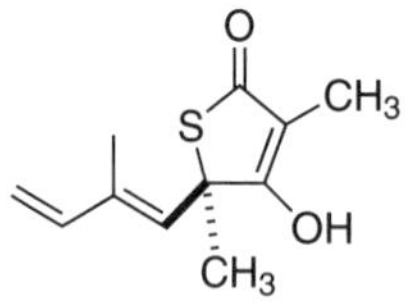

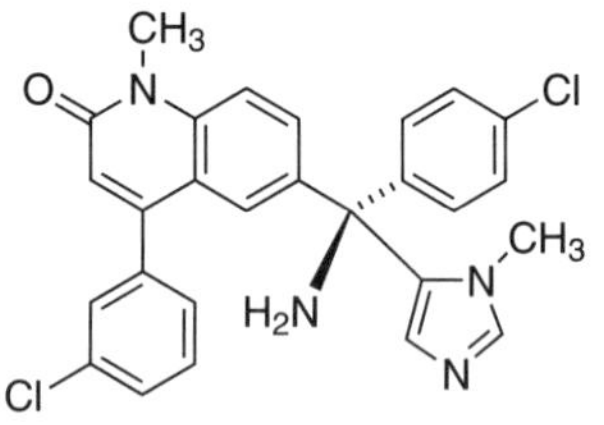

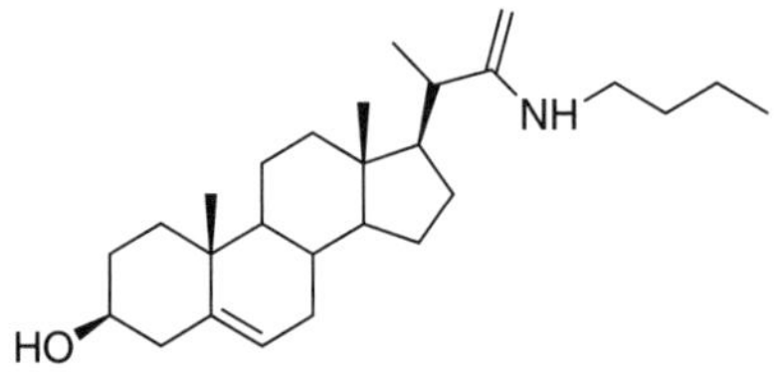

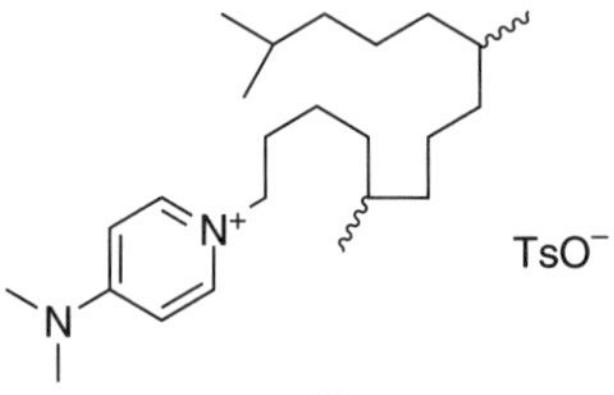

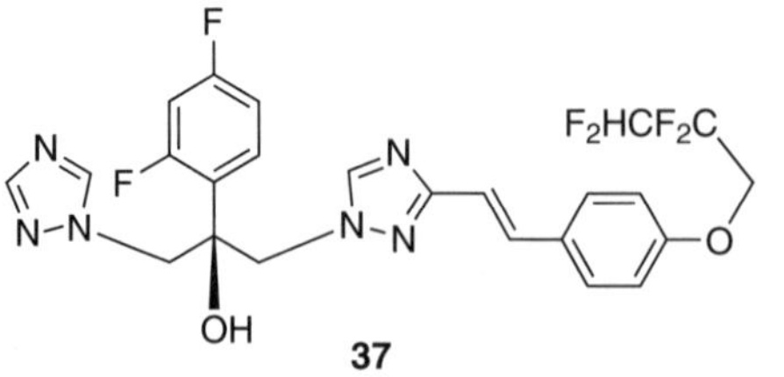

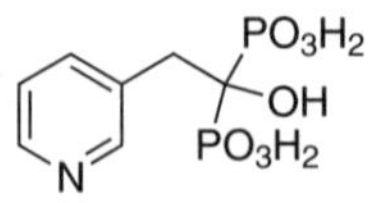

Figure 11. Inhibitors of trypanosomal lipid metabolism.

cells [92,93]. It was later determined that compound **35** and its homologs are potent transition state analog inhibitors of 24-sterol methyltransferase from *L. major* [93]. Some analogs in the series were also effective against *T. b. rhodesiense*, although this effect was mediated at a site other than trypanosomal 24-sterol methyltransferase. Inhibitors of oxidosqualene cyclase have been shown to possess antitrypanosomal activity when evaluated against four strains of *T. cruzi in vitro* [94]. The most effective of these agents, analog **36**, inhibited trypanosomal growth at concentrations between 2 and 6 nM, but produced significantly greater toxicity than ketoconazole or benznidazole [94]. The *bis*-triazole D0870, **37**, inhibits the growth of *T. cruzi* epimastigotes in culture ($IC_{50} = 0.1\,\mu M$), and also produces radical cures in murine models of *T. cruzi* infection [95]. Related triazoles, most notably the antifungal agents posaconazole and ravuconazole, are currently being evaluated as antitrypanosomal agents in preclinical trials [44]. Risedronate, **38**, and homogous(bis)phosphonatesalso have demonstrated activity against *T. brucei* and *T. cruzi*, and possess low micromolar antiparasitic activity against *L. donovani, Plasmodium falciparum*, and *T. gondii* [96]. Both **37** and **38** appear to act by disrupting parasitic sterol biosynthesis.

3.1.3. Inhibitors of Parasitic Proteases   Trypanosomatid proteases were first identified as validated drug targets in 1983 [97]. The protozoan parasites *T. cruzi, T. brucei*, and *Leishmania* sp. all produce significant quantities of papain-like proteases localized in the parasitic lysosome. In plants and mammals, analogous proteases are regulated by endogenous inhibitors of the cystatin family [98]. A search for proteinaceous regulators of parasite cysteine proteases led to the discovery of chagasin, a *T. cruzi* inhibitor of the endogenous cysteine protease cruzipain [99]. Subsequently, homologs were identified in the genomes of multiple parasites, as well as in bacteria [100]. A subset of these proteins were recombinantly expressed, and proved to be inhibitory against mammalian papain-like cysteine proteases [101]. In African trypanosomes, three major cysteine proteases have been identified and extensively studied: rho-

desain from *T. b. rhodesiense*, its equivalent form in cattle, congopain from *T. congolense,* and brucipain from *T. b. brucei* (also known as trypanopain-Tb). In addition, an important *T. cruzi* cysteine protease known as cruzain or cruzipain has also been identified, and has been a target for structure-based inhibitor design [102]. These cysteine proteases exhibit significant amino acid sequence homology to mammalian cathepsin L. They promote lysosomal activity and have been identified in all life cycle stages of the protozoa, but most notably during the infective stage of parasite development [103]. Inhibition of cysteine proteases *in vivo* by the diazomethyl ketone inhibitor Z-Phe-Ala-CHN_2 (**39**, Fig. 12) was lethal to *T. brucei* in culture and in a murine model [104], thus validating trypanosomal cysteine proteases as therapeutic drug targets. Treated mice survived for longer periods of time compared to untreated control mice, but parasitemia returned following discontinuation of **39**. More recently, additional inhibitors of trypanosomal cysteine protease activity have been developed as potential chemotherapeutic agents. Epoxysuccinate analogs including the protease inhibitor E-64 [105] have been shown to be effective irreversible inhibitors of the cysteine protease cruzain, isolated from *T. cruzi*. One such analog, compound **40**, inhibits the enzyme with an IC_{50} of <10 nM, and has little effect on non-targeted cysteine proteases such as cathepsin B or papain [106]. Compound **41**, also known as K777, is also a potent inhibitor of cruzain, and is currently being evaluated in preclinical trials [44]. Second-generation vinyl sulfonamides such as **42** are effective inactivators of isolated cruzain, and are effective against *T. cruzi* in cultured J744 macrophages [107]. Semicarbazones such as **43** are effective inhibitors of cruzain ($IC_{50} = 60$ nM) and the homologous cystein protease rhodesain ($IC_{50} = 50$ nM) [108,109]. Longer peptides, such as the 50 mer congopain inhibitor Pcp27, act as inhibitors of this protease, but are also rapidly hydrolyzed by the enzyme [110]. A number of sub-micromolar inhibitors for cruzain have been identified from libraries of ketone-based cysteine protease inhibitors generated using solid phase parallel synthesis [111]. By way of example, compound **44** inhibited cruzain with a

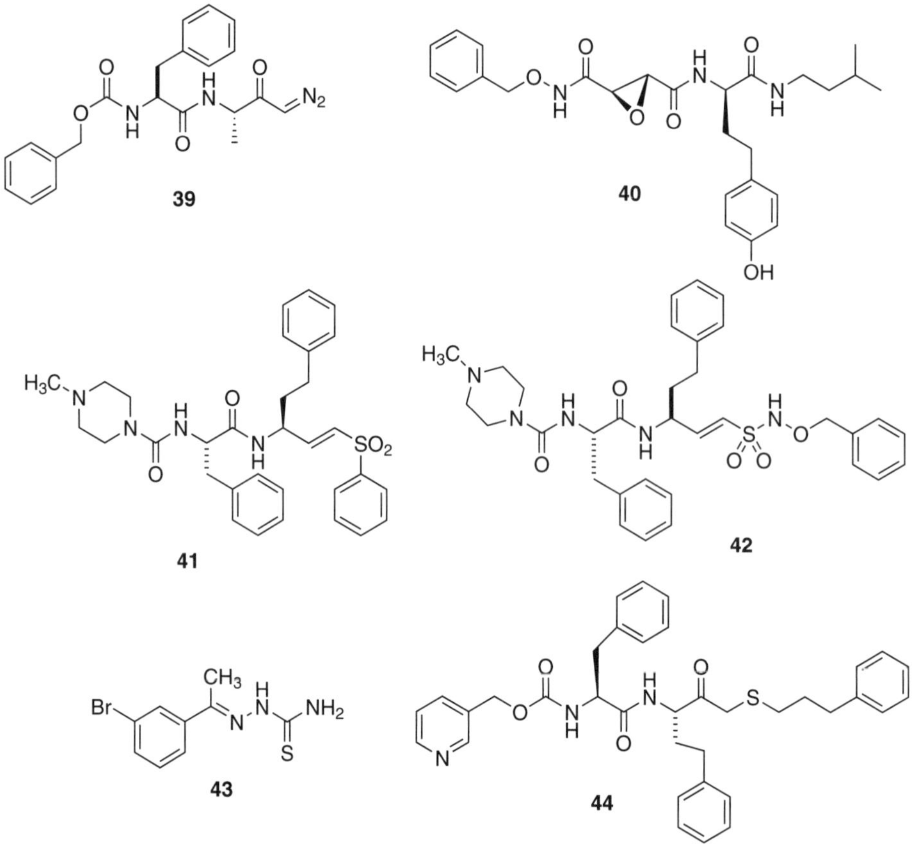

Figure 12. Inhibitors of trypanosomal cysteine proteases.

K_i of 0.9 nM, and had negligible activity against the nontargeted cysteine proteases cathepsin B and L. A complete description of cysteine protease inhibitors and their use as potential therapeutic agents is beyond the scope of this chapter, but this topic has been recently reviewed [112,113]. Despite intensive efforts to identify inhibitors of parasitic cysteine proteases as antiparasitic agents, to date, none of these analogs has been advanced to human clinical trials due to limited *in vivo* efficacy. However, recent advances in target validation and identification of new inhibitors are promising [114].

3.1.4. Inhibitors of Parasitic Glucose Metabolism and Glycosomal Transport Glycolysis occupies a central role for energy metabolism in bloodstream form trypanosomes [115]. In the bloodstream form, oxidative metabolism re-

quiring mitochondrial Krebs cycle enzymes, and oxidative phosphorylation are largely repressed, and the organism depends on the glycolytic conversion of glucose to pyruvate for its ATP supply (see Fig. 13) [116,117]. Not surprisingly, glycolysis is regarded as an important target for antitrypanosomal drug discovery. All of the enzymes involved in glycolosis in *T. brucei* have been purified or expressed from a bacterial vector, and their kinetic properties have been studied [118]. As described above, the majority of trypanosomal glycolytic enzymes are localized in the glycosome. Compartmentalization of the enzymes involved in glucose metabolism also plays an important role in trypanosomal glucose oxidation and energy production [119,120]. siRNA knockdown of trypanosomal hexokinase, phosphofructokinase (PFK), phosphoglycerate mutase, enolase,

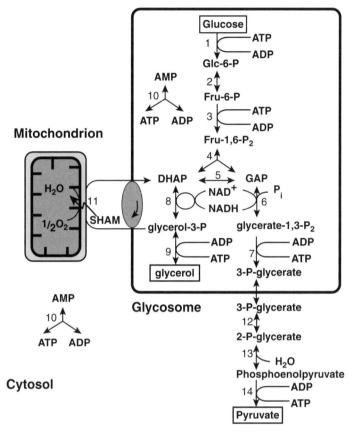

Figure 13. Glycolysis in the bloodstream form trypanosome. Boxed metabolites are nutrients or end products of metabolism. Enzymes: 1, hexokinase; 2, phosphoglucose isomerase; 3, phosphofructokinase; 4, aldolase; 5, triose-phosphate isomerase; 6, glyceraldehyde-3-phosphate dehydrogenase; 7, phosphoglyceratekinase; 8, glycerol-3-phosphate dehydrogenase; 9, glycerol kinase; 10, adenylate kinase; 11, glycerol-3-phosphate oxidase; 12, phosphoglycerate mutase; 13, enolase; 14, pyruvate kinase. From Ref. [118]. Used with permission.

and pyruvate kinase (PK) have revealed novel control mechanisms for glycolysis in trypanosomes, and demonstrate that hexokinase, PFK and PK are present in the glycosome in excess [121]. Depletion of PFK and enolase had an effect on the activity, but not the expression, of the first seven enzymes of the glycolytic pathway, which are sequestered in the glycosome, and also affected the activity of cytosolic enzymes associated with trypanosomal glucose metabolism.

A pentose phosphate pathway has been described in *T. cruzi* that can be detected in all morphological forms [122]. The procyclic stage of *T. brucei* expresses a soluble glycoso-

mal NADH-dependent fumarate reductase that produces about 70% of the excreted succinate, the major end product of glucose metabolism in the procyclic form of the parasite [123]. Procyclic *T. brucei* also uses the Krebs cycle for purposes other than degradation of mitochondrial substrates. Citrate synthase, pyruvate dehydrogenase, and malate dehydrogenase are used to transport acetyl-CoA used for fatty acid synthesis from the mitochondrion to the cytosol, while α-ketoglutarate dehydrogenase and succinyl-CoA synthetase are used to convert proline and glutamate to succinate. Succinate dehydrogenase and fumarase are also used for conversion of succinate into malate, which is used in gluconeogenesis [124].

Like glucose oxidation, glycosomal transport is a critical facet of energy production that is absolutely required for growth [125]. *T. brucei* bloodstream forms replicate extracellularly in an environment where plasma glucose concentrations are maintained between 3.5 and 5 mM. The high rate of glucose flux (170 nmol/min/mg of cellular protein) makes the parasite absolutely dependent on a continuous supply of exogenous glucose to maintain ATP levels. *T. brucei* long slender bloodstream forms take up glucose by facilitated transport with a K_m of approximately 1 mM [126,127]. Glucose transport in the bloodstream form of *T. brucei* is a concentration-dependent, saturable process typical of a carrier-mediated transport system, with an apparent K_m of 0.49 mM [128]. Multiple kinetoplastid genes encoding proteins involved in glucose transport have now been identified and cloned, and all belong to the same glucose transporter superfamily as the mammalian erythrocyte transporter GLUT1. Although these proteins are members of the GLUT1 superfamily, there are structural and kinetic differences between the mammalian and trypanosomal forms of the glucose transporter [129]. Some species (e.g., *T. b. brucei*) are exposed to drastically different glucose concentrations when in the mammalian bloodstream compared to the insect midgut, and possess two distinct transporters to accommodate this fluctuation. By comparison, *T. cruzi* completes its life cycle predominantly under glucose-deficient conditions, both inside mammalian host cells and within the reduviid bug midgut. As a result, *T. cruzi* have a single high-affinity glucose transporter [130]. As is the case with other glucose metabolic pathways, the glucose transport system is an important validated target for the design of chemotherapeutics with a novel mechanism of action. It is also possible that the trypanosomal glucose transporter can be used to selectively import substances that are toxic to the parasite [131].

Although parasitic glucose metabolism has been identified as a viable drug target [132], few efforts to design and synthesize specific inhibitors have been initiated. The adenosine analog tubercidin (**45**, Fig. 14) is known to

disrupt glucose metabolism in procyclic *T. brucei* [133]. Knockdown experiments with an RNAi library demonstrated that **45** is an inhibitor of trypanosomal hexokinase, as well as the parasitic hexose transporter. Adenosine also inhibits trypanosomal glycolysis, but has a very poor IC$_{50}$ value (50 mM). None the less, screening of a series of adenosine analogs [134] as inhibitors of glyceraldehyde-3-phosphate dehydrogenase resulted in the identification of compounds that are submicromolar inhibitors of trypanosomal glyceraldehyde-3-phosphate dehydrogenase, but that have little affinity for the analogous human enzyme. Adenosine derivatives such as **46** (Fig. 14) were effective inhibitors of the purified enzyme, and also inhibited the growth of *T. brucei* and *T. cruzi* with IC$_{50}$ values between 3.0 and 50 µM [135]. Selected members of a series of glucosamine analogs, most notabl **47** (Fig. 14), acted as competitive inhibitors of trypanosomal hexokinase, with a K_i of 2.8 µM [136] while having no effect on the corresponding yeast enzyme *in vitro*. Compound **47** also inhibited trypanosomal growth in culture, but with a relatively high LD$_{50}$ (3.5 mM). This high LD$_{50}$ value was likely observed because the inhibitor had to compete for the enzyme binding site with endogenous glucose in high concentration (5 mM). A series of 1-arylamino-2,5-anhydro-D-mannitols have been studied as inhibitors of trypanosomal PFK [137]. These compounds most likely bind to the ATP-binding site rather than the fructose 6-phosphate site, with affinity constants of approximately 100 mM. A derivative in this series bearing an electrophilic isothiocyanate group, **48**, was an irreversible inactivator of trypanosomal PFK, with K_i and k_{inact} values of 130 mM and 0.26 min^{-1}, respectively. The residue involved in this specific inactivation of the parasite enzyme was identified by site-directed mutagenesis as Lys 227. Hydroxynaphthaldehyde phosphates related to **49** have recently been shown to irreversibly inactivate fructose-1,6-bisphosphate aldolase from rabbit muscle [138]. It has been proposed that these analogs may be effective inhibitors of the trypanosomal form of the enzyme, and these studies are underway. These compounds also appear to bind to the ATP-binding site, instead of the fructose 6-phosphate site,

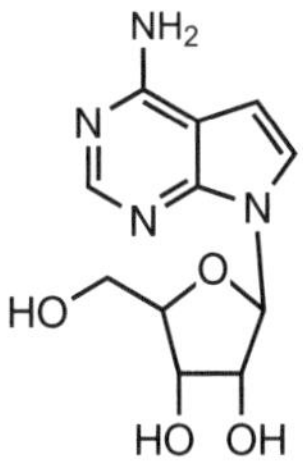

Figure 14. Inhibitors of trypanosomal glucose metabolism.

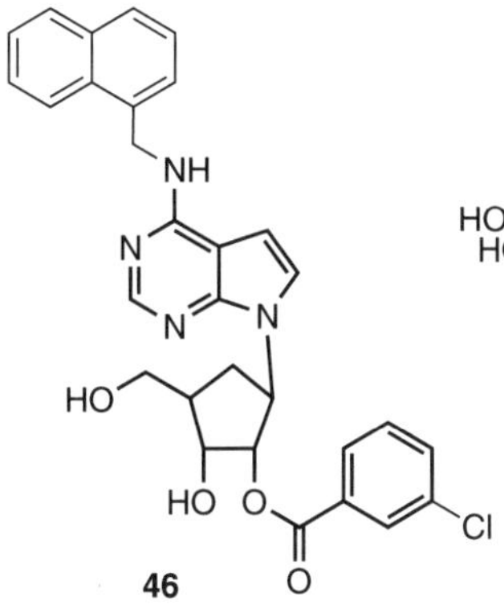

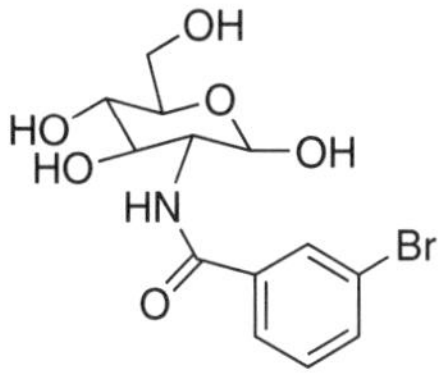

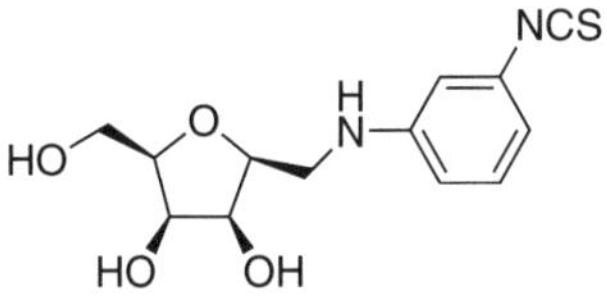

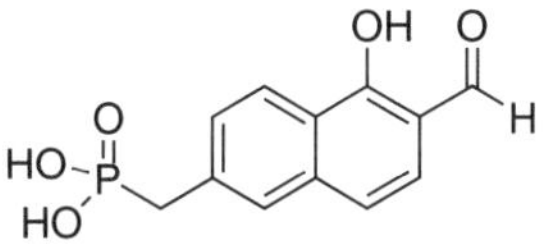

and also exhibit affinity constants of approximately 100 mM.

The glucose transport system is an important point for control of glycolytic flux in trypanosomatids [139]. Inhibitor studies of trypanosomal glucose uptake indicate that the process is sodium independent and unaffected by the H^+-ATPase inhibitor N,N'-dicyclohexylcarbodiimide or the uncoupler carbonyl-cyanide-4-(trifluoromethoxy)phenylhydrazone [128]. Significant inhibition of trypanosomal glucose import was observed with both phloretin (**50**, $K_i = 64\,\mu M$) and cytochalasin B (**51**, $K_i = 0.44\,\mu M$). These analogs are shown in Fig. 15. In each case, inhibition was noncompetitive, and the observed inhibition was partially reversible for phloretin and completely reversible for cytochalasin B. Interestingly, glucosamine derivatives related to compound **47** (Fig. 14) [136] were effective inhibitors of trypanosomal glucose transport, and K_i values as low as $200\,\mu M$ were reported [140]. Various triazine dyes also inhibit glucose transport in mammalian cell lines, and these were subsequently found to inhibitor trypanosomal glucose transport as well [129]. Among these analogs, cibacron blue

(**52**, Fig. 15) produced an 89% inhibition of glucose transport activity in *T. brucei* at a $100\,\mu M$ concentration. Although these triazine dyes proved to be reasonable inhibitors of trypanosomal glucose import, their effect of on trypanosomal growth was not determined. Other triazines have been recently described that exhibit antitrypanosomal activity, such as the nitroheterocycle **53** [141]. To date, all analogs containing a melamine core are substrates for the P2 transport system, most likely because they are structurally similar to known P2 substrates. Melamine-based analogs with a nitrofuran moiety were most active against *T. b. rhodesiense in vitro*, with IC_{50} values as low as 18 nM. Alterations to the nitro heterocycle, such as isosteric replacement of the ring nitrogen or removal of the nitro group resulted in dramatic decreases in activity. Compound **53** is also curative of *T. b. brucei* infections in a murine model when administered at 20 mg/kg for 4 days [142].

3.1.5. Agents Targeted to the Polyamine Pathway

As described above, the polyamine metabolic pathway in parasites presents a number of

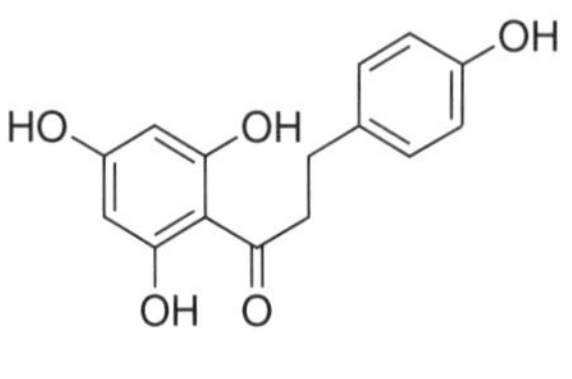

Figure 15. Inhibitors of the trypanosomal glucose transporter.

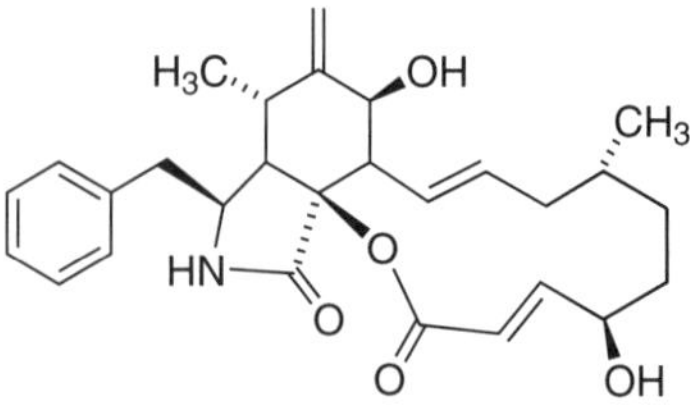

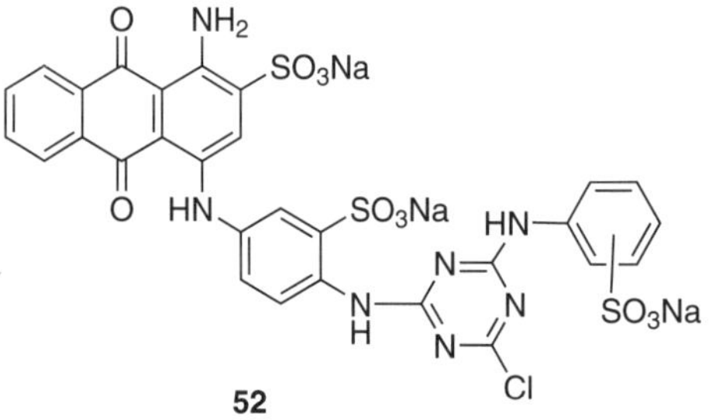

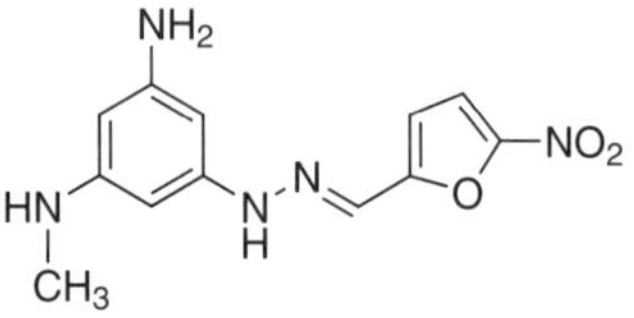

drug targets that are parasite specific. Novel agents have been developed which target the unique aspects of the trypanosomal polyamine biosynthetic pathway, and the associated trypanothione redox system. The phosphate-based transition state analogs **54** and **55** were designed to mimic the tetrahedral transition state of the first step in the synthesis of trypanothione from spermidine, glutathionylspermidine synthetase (GSpS) [143–145] (Fig. 16). These analogs inhibited the related enzyme glutathionylspermidine synthetase/amidase from *Escherichia coli* with K_i values of 6.0 and 3.2 µM, respectively. Compound **55** was later shown to be a slow binding inhibitor of the enzyme, and formed an E-I* complex with a 410-fold higher affinity than the collisional E-I complex. Despite these promising early results, compounds **54** and **55** have not been developed further as antiparasitic agents, most likely due to their poor uptake by the parasite. A number of *N*-(3-phenylpropyl) substituted spermine analogs have been reported that act as potent inhibitors of TR [146]. Compounds **56** and **57** were the most potent inhibitors in the series, with K_i values of 0.61 and 0.15 µM against TR from *T cruzi*. Compound **56** showed significant activity against African trypanosomes *in vitro*, with IC$_{50}$ values between 0.1 and 0.2 µM against four strains of trypanosomal clinical

isolates, including the arsenic-resistant K 243-As-10-3 variant of *T.b. rhodesiense*.

It has been suggested that alkyl- and aralkyl-substituted polyamine analogs disrupt polyamine metabolism because the nitrogen pK_a values have been altered, leading to reductions in their degree of protonation at physiological pH [21,147,148]. A key advantage to these compounds as antiparasitic agents is that they selectively enter proliferating cells using the trypanosomal polyamine transport system, where they down regulate the biosynthetic enzymes ODC and AdoMet-DC. However, these agents do not substitute for the natural polyamines in terms of their cell growth and survival functions [21], and ultimately produce polyamine depletion and cell death [149,150]. Compound **58**, also known as MDL 27695, was shown to possess significant antimalarial and antileishmanial activity *in vitro* and *in vivo*, and produced cures in murine models of malaria and *Leishmania* [151–154]. Subsequently, **58** was found to possess antitrypanosomal activity as well [155], prompting the synthesis of a series of alkyl- and aralkylpolyamine analogs with a 3-7-3 carbon architecture. Compounds **59** and **60** were both effective *in vitro* against *T.b. brucei* LAB 110, as well as the *T.b.* rhodesiense isolates K 243, K 269, and K 243 As-10-3

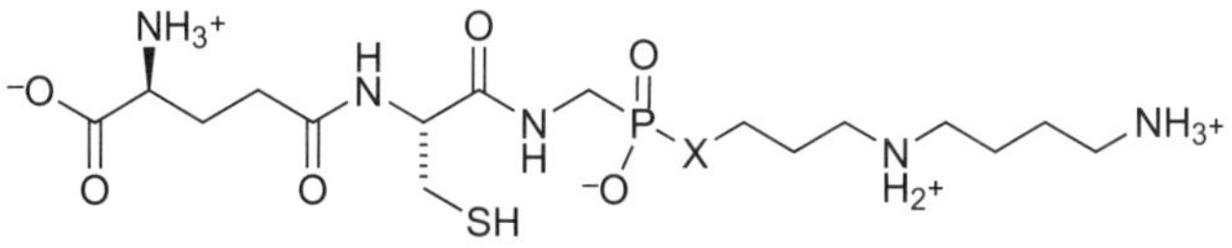

54 (X = O)
55 (X = CH₂)

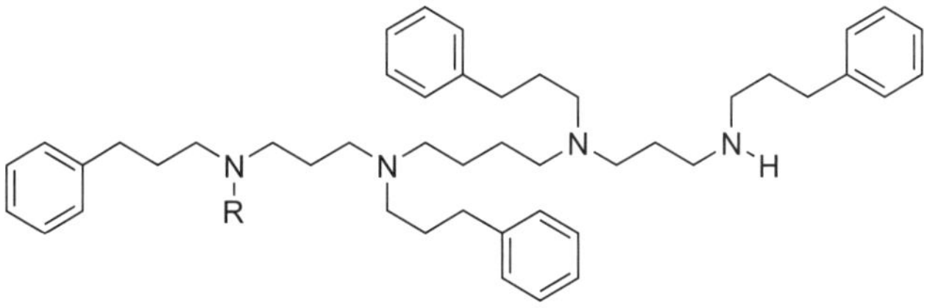

56 (R = H)
57 (R = CH₂CH₂CH₂-Ph)

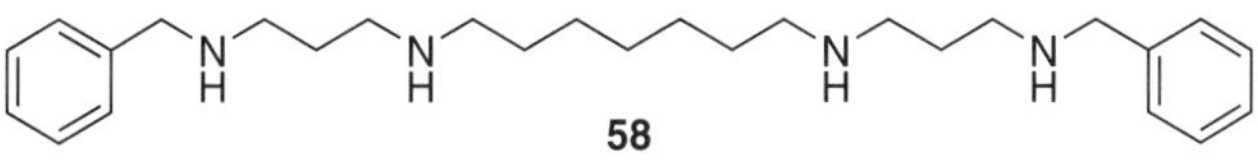

58

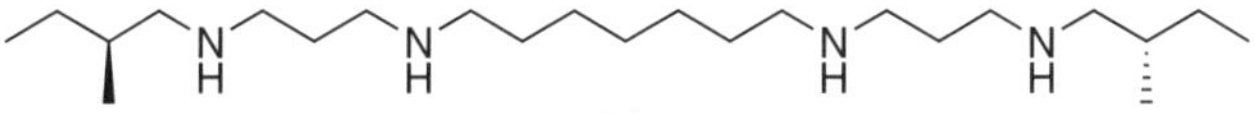

59

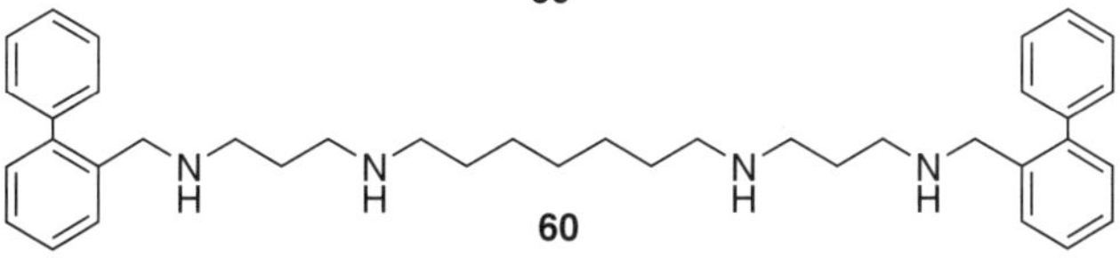

60

Figure 16. Polyamine-based antitrypanosomal agents **54–60**.

[21,156]. The most impressive activity was found in the case of **60**, which inhibited the growth of K 243 with an IC_{50} of 40 nM, a value that is comparable to the IC_{50} value for melarsen oxide. Importantly, compound **60** inhibited growth in the K 243 As-10-3 arsenic resistant strain ($IC_{50} = 165$ nM), against which melarsoprol is inactive. Recent studies indicate that **60** has a broad spectrum of antiparasitic activity, and was shown to produce cures in mice infected with *Microsporidia* [157]. In these initial studies, analogs with a 3-3-3 carbon backbone had poor activity as antiparasitic agents, but were effective antitumor compounds. By contrast, analogs with a 3-7-3 backbone architecture generally had poor antitumor activity, but were effective antiparasitic agents [21,155,156]. However, in structure/activity studies involving a library of more than 200 alkyl- and aralkylpolyamine analogs, it was demonstrated that both symmetrically and unsymmetrically substituted polyamine analogs can possess potent antitrypanosomal activity, and that the central chain length of these derivatives can vary between three and seven carbons, as shown in Fig. 17. Thus, the unsymmetrically substituted compound **61**, which has a 3-7-3 carbon backbone architecture, inhibits the growth of *T.b. brucei* Lab 110 and *T.b. rhodesiense* K 243, with IC_{50} values of 0.06 and 0.07 µM, respectively. When the terminal substituents are aralkyl, the effect of the length of the central carbon chain has a diminished effect on activity. Thus, compound **65**, which differs from **60** (Fig. 16) only in the length of the intermediate carbon

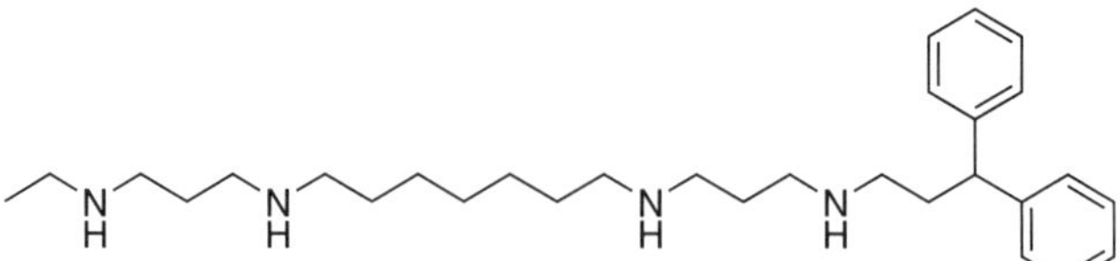

Figure 17. Antitrypanosomal polyamine analogs **61–65**.

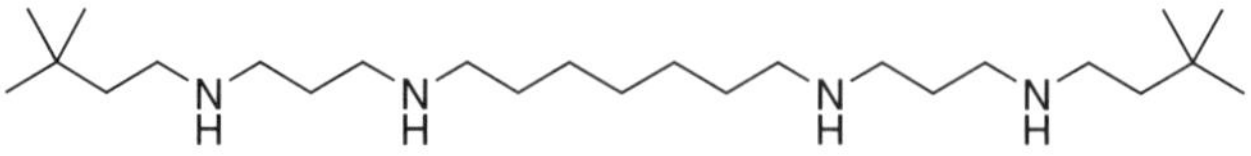

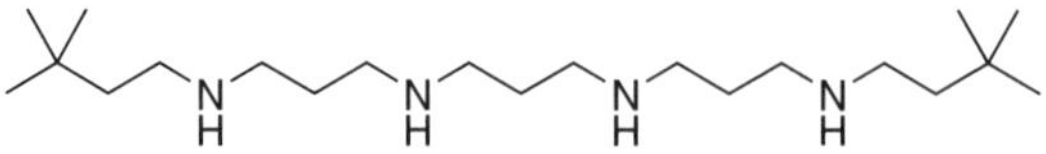

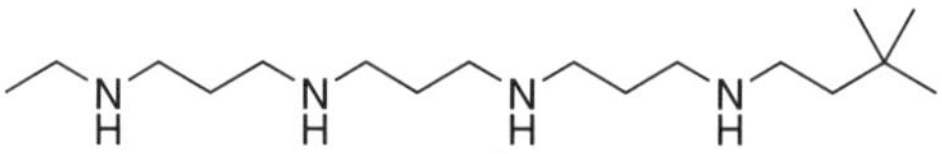

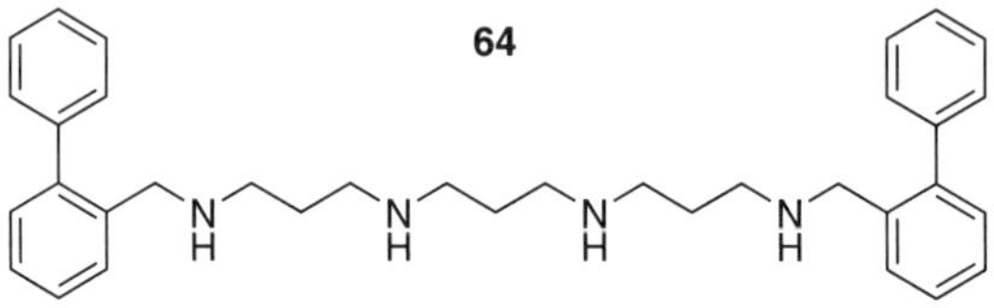

chain, inhibits the growth of *T.b. brucei* Lab 110 and *T.b. rhodesiense* K 243 with IC_{50} values of 1.6 and 0.9 µM, respectively. It is significant to note that like **60**, both **61** and **65** were effective against the K 243 As 10-3 arsenic resistant strain of *T. b. rhodesiense* with IC_{50} values of 0.19 and 6.3 µM, respectively. Analogs **61–65** have been shown to be effective inhibitors of TR, while having no activity against human glutathione reductase (GR). Compounds **59–65** are currently being evaluated for antitrypanosomal activity in a murine model of trypanosomiasis.

As outlined above, alkylpolyamines are able to disrupt cellular metabolism because the pK_a values for their internal and terminal nitrogen moieties have been altered, leading to changes in the percent ionization of each nitrogen. The natural polyamines exert their effects at various cellular sites, many of which have not been identified, and as such, the charge recognition of specific polyamines at these sites is critical to normal cellular function [147]. This strategy has been used to

develop a number of successful antitumor agents related to bis(ethyl)norspermine, some of which have entered human clinical trials. All of these analogs appear to take advantage of the specific polyamine transport system to enter cells. It was reasoned that 3-7-3 polyamine analogs containing substituted terminal guanidines would have similar effects on polyamine metabolism, since guanidine moieties would produce even greater charge perturbations when compared to the natural polyamines. A series of alkyl- and aralkyl-substituted polyaminoguanidines and polyamino(bis)guanidines represented by compounds **66–70** (Fig. 18) were thus synthesized and evaluated as inhibitors of TR, and as antitrypanosomal agents *in vitro*. These analogs are potent inhibitors of isolated TR, (IC_{50} values: **66**, 2.2 µM; **67**, 4.7 µM; **68**, 69.5 µM; **69**, 4.2 µM; **70**, 3.0 µM) while possessing no inhibitory activity against GR *in vitro* ($IC_{50} \gg 100$ µM) [158]. These analogs were found to have IC_{50} values as low as 90 nM against cultured blood forms of *T.b. brucei*, and *T. b. rhodesiense*

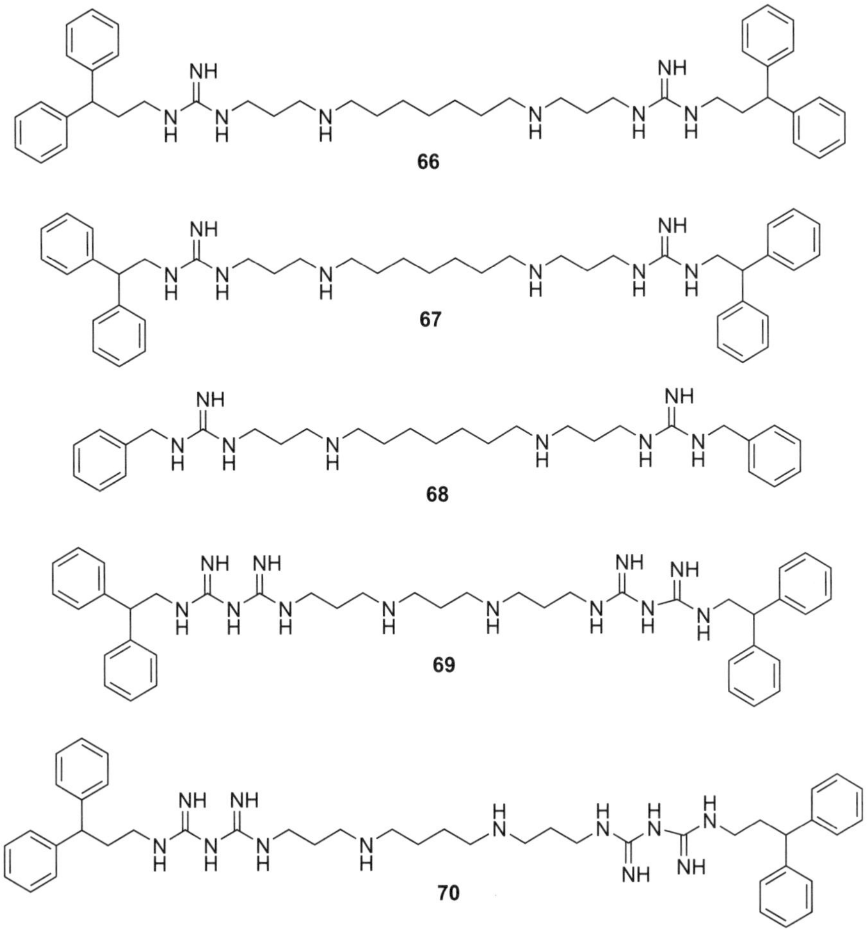

Figure 18. Terminally alkylated guanidines and biguanides with antitrypanosomal activity.

KETRI 243 at generally comparable levels (e.g., against *T. b. brucei*: compound **66**, IC_{50} 0.6 µM; compound **67**, $IC_{50} = 0.5$ µM; compound **68**, $IC_{50} = 0.1$ µM; compound **69**, $IC_{50} = 0.2$ µM; compound **70**, $IC_{50} = 0.2$ µM) [158]. In response to these promising results, **66–70** and their homologs are currently being examined in animal models of trypanosomiasis. It is of interest to note that the least effective inhibitor of TR in this series, **68**, was the most effective trypanocide *in vitro*, indicating that the observed antiparasitic effects were at least in part due to a secondary mechanism. Recent studies have revealed that **66**, **68** and their homologs are noncompetitive inhibitors of the chromatin remodeling enzyme lysine-specific demethylase 1, and promote the reexpression

of aberrantly silenced genes in tumor cells [159]. It remains to be determined whether trypanosomes possess a form of lysine-specific demethylase, and if so, whether it could be considered a valid target for antiparasitic drug design.

In silico screening studies suggest that various tricyclic antidepressant compounds theoretically have affinity for TR [160], and these observations have now been confirmed by screening selected analogs against purified TR from *T. cruzi* [161]. The most active of these analogs was the antidepressant clomipramine, **71** (Fig. 19), with a K_i of 6.5 µM against TR from *T. cruzi*. Subsequent studies indicated that phenothiazines such as chlorpromazine **72** were also effective TR

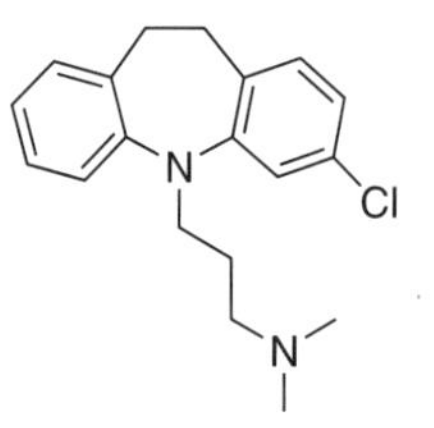

Figure 19. Structures of tricyclic amines and guanidines with antitrypanosomal activity.

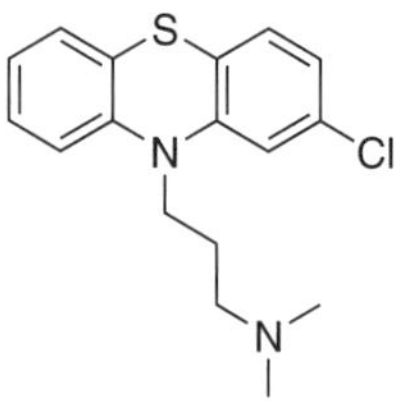

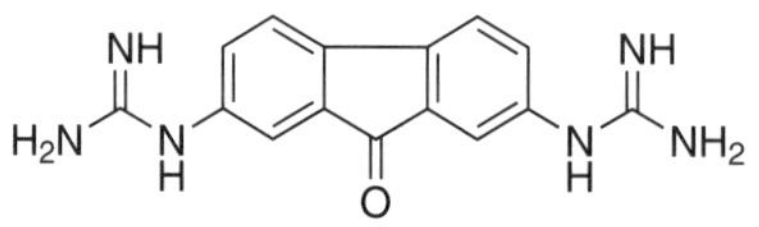

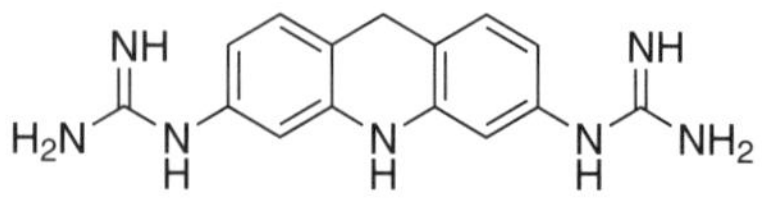

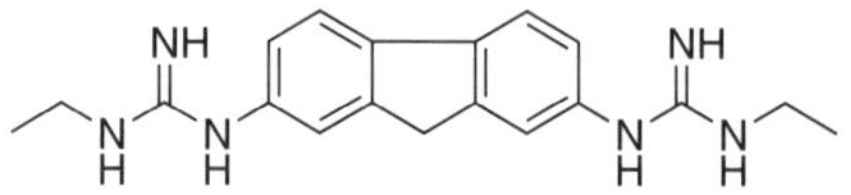

inhibitors [162]. Attempts to reduce the neuroleptic side effects of these analogs by forming diphenylsulfide derivatives related to **71** and **72**, either alone or as dimers linked by spermidine moieties, failed produce any analogs that were more inhibitory than **71** [163,164]. Fluorenone **73** and acridine **74**, which also feature guanidine moieties in their structure, were also effective inhibitors of trypanosomal growth, with IC_{50} values of 7.3 and 66.9 μM, respectively, against *T. b. rhodesiense* in culture [165]. *N*-Alkylated fluorine analogs such as **75** ($IC_{50} = 16.9\,\mu$M) were also effective against *T. b. rhodesiense in vitro*. Although they were not particularly potent against the organism *in vitro*, analogs **71–75** produced cures in murine models of *T. b. rhodesiense* infections in 60–75% of treated animals. The ability of compounds **71–75** and their homologs to inhibit TR was never determined.

3.2. Potential New Therapies for Leishmaniasis

As might be expected, the similarity between *Leishmania* and the organisms that cause

trypanosomiasis allow many of the approaches to therapy of trypanosomiasis to be used for the treatment of *Leishmania*. Emerging treatment modalities for leishmaniasis have recently been reviewed [54,56,57,68]. As outlined above, much recent attention has been paid to the agents paramomycin **17** and miltefosine **18** (Fig. 20), which are currently undergoing extended clinical trials [166]. Paramomycin **17** was found to possess activity against both the visceral and cutaneous forms of leishmaniasis in the 1960s. However, it has poor oral bioavailability, and must be administered parenterally. Development of a parenteral formulation for visceral leishmaniasis has been slow, but Phase II clinical trials in India and Kenya have been promising, with 90% of patients cured of visceral leishmaniasis following treatment with 15 mg/kg daily for 20 days [64]. The drug is also effective against antimony-resistant strains, and can be used topically in the treatment of cutaneous leishmaniasis. The utility of miltefosine **18** for leishmaniasis was initially discovered in the mid-1980s, when the drug was shown to be efficacious in multiple experimental

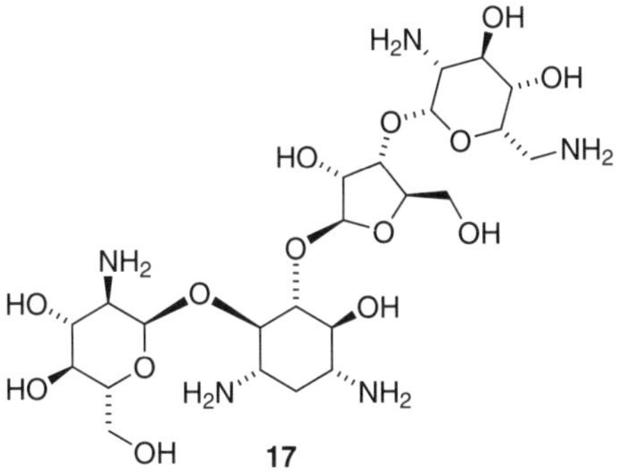

Figure 20. Agents in clinical trials for the treatment of visceral or cutaneous *Leishmania.*

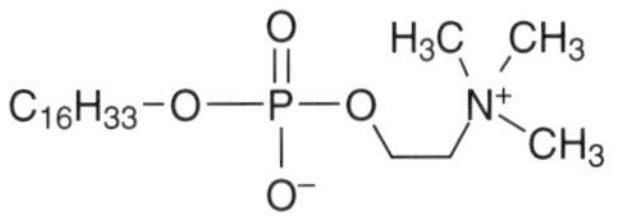

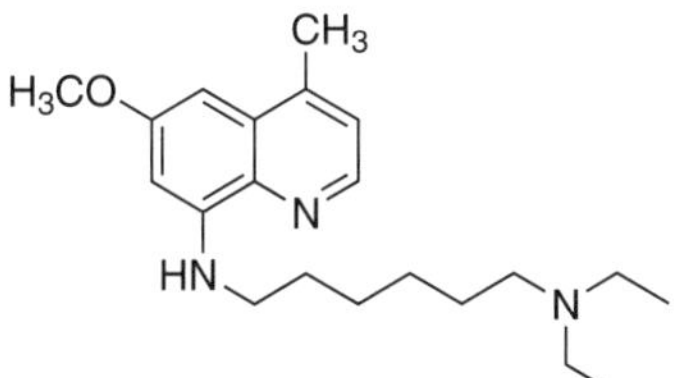

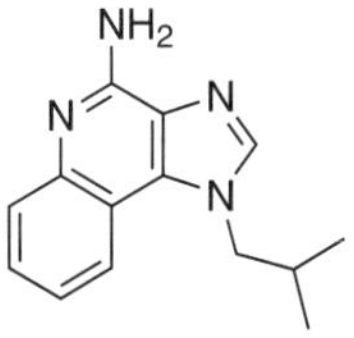

models [167]. In the mid-1990s, clinical trials and co-development of **18** was accomplished through a partnership between Zentaris and the World Health Organization. In a Phase III clinical trial, 94% of visceral leishmaniasis patients were cured after receiving an oral dose of 2.5/mg/kg of miltefosine daily for 28 days [168]. The orally acting 8-aminoquinoline sitamaquine **76** has demonstrated activity against visceral leishmaniasis. The antileishmanial activity of this compound was first identified in the 1970s [169]. Phase I and II clinical trials have been completed with varying levels of success. In one study, 67% of patients were cured of visceral *L. chagasi* infections in Brazil using a dosing regimen of 2 mg/kg daily for 28 days, while in Kenya, 92% were cured of visceral leishmaniasis when treated with 1.7 mg/kg daily for 28 days. Sitamaquine is rapidly metabolized, forming the corresponding desethyl and 4-hydroxymethyl derivatives. These species constitute active metabolites that are responsible for the activity of **76**. Toxicity appears to be relatively mild, and limited to methemglobinaemia. Recent studies indicate that cures produced by **76** are dependent upon the development of an effec-

tive immune response. In this response, host macrophages produce toxic nitrogen and oxygen metabolites that kill intracellular amastigotes [6,33,34,170,171]. Along these lines, immunopotentiating drugs have shown potential for the treatment of leishmaniasis. The imidazoquinoline imiquimod **77** induces nitric oxide (NO) production in macrophages, and was shown to have antileishmanial activity via macrophage activation in an experimental model [172], and in clinical studies where it was used in combination with antimonials against cutaneous leishmaniasis [173]. Oral treatment with 5 mg/kg of **77** over 5 days produced in a 60% reduction in the number of *L. donovani* liver amastigotes in mice [174].

As was mentioned above, the (bis)benzylpolyamine **58** (Fig. 16) has been shown to be an effective antileishmanial agent both *in vitro* and *in vivo* [151–154]. Despite these findings, the development of **58** for use in leishmaniasis was discontinued in the early 1990s. However, this compound as well as the associated polyamine analogs **59–65** are now being evaluated *in vitro* and *in vivo* against *Leishmania.* A number of antitrypanosomal (bis)phosphonates related to **38** (Fig. 11) are also effective

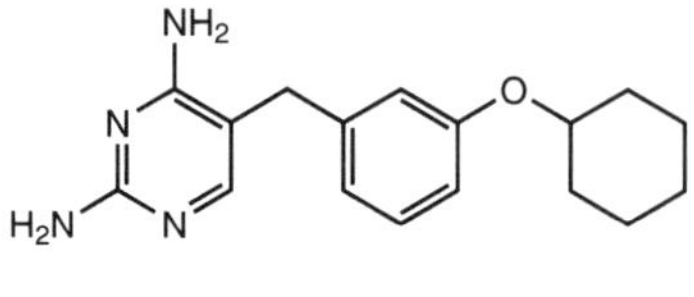

Figure 21. Antileishmanial drugs designed for novel biological targets.

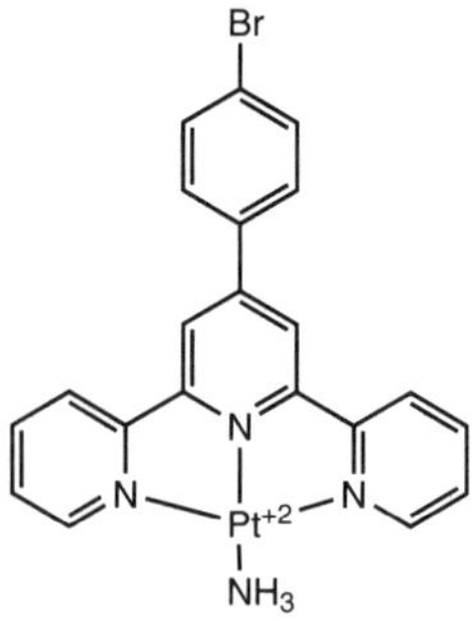

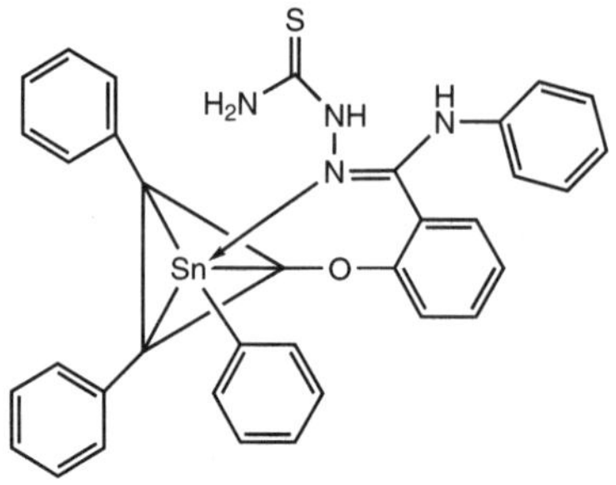

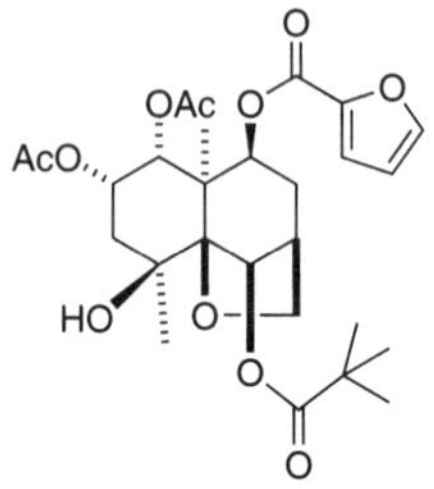

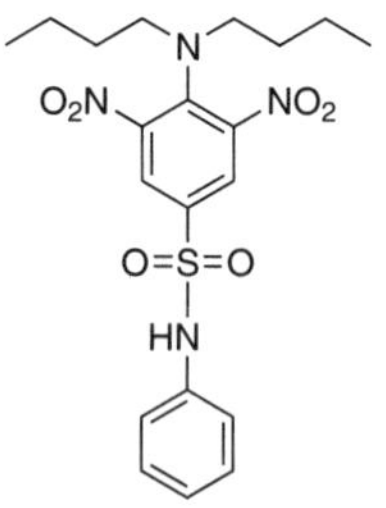

against *L. donovani in vitro* [96]. Novel approaches at the design of antileishmanial agents include the specific dihydrofolate reductase inhibitor **78** (IC$_{50}$ = 6.0 µM) (Fig. 21) [175] and (terpyridine)-platinum(II) complexes such as **79**, which are effective against *L. donovani* (100% inhibition at 1 µM), *T. cruzi* (65% inhibition at 1 µM), and *T. b. brucei* (100% inhibition at 30 nM) [176]. The triphenyltin complex **80** also has antileishmanial activity, and depletes amastigotes in cultured hamster macrophages to undetectable levels at a concentration of 10 mg/L [177]. A wide variety of natural products have been isolated

that exhibit antileishmanial activity, but few have been subjected to systematic SAR studies [178]. A series of dihydro-β-agarofuran sesquiterpenes were isolated, and from those leads a series of semisynthetic analogs were synthesized for evaluation as antileishmanial agents. Compound **81** was particularly effective, producing a 96.7% growth inhibition of multidrug resistant *L. tropica* at 15 µM [179]. Finally, antimitotic agents have been identified that disrupt tubulin assembly in both *L. donovani* and *T. brucei in vitro* [180]. The substituted 3,5-dinitrosulfanilamide **82** exhibited IC$_{50}$ values of 2.6 and 0.2 µM, respectively, against *L. donovani* amastigotes and *T. b. brucei* in culture, with little effect on the mammalian J774 macrophage and PC3 prostate host cells. Compound **82** produced a 100% inhibition of tubulin assembly in *L. donovani* at a concentration of 10 μM, but was much less effective *in vivo*.

An analysis of the genetics of *Leishmania*, coupled with recent genomic [2] and proteomic [181] studies, is being employed to identify new therapeutic targets for the treatment of *Leishmania*. For example, characterization of parasitic membrane transporters [182] should result in identification of new targets for selective drug design. The *Leishmania* surface coat is exquisitely regulated during the life cycle of the organism, and elucidation of its composition should provide new drug targeting strategies [183]. Cell trafficking in *Leishmania* involves unique methods of protein targeting that could present new sites for rational drug design [184]. *L. donovani* has a nucleotide importer analogous to the trypanosomal P1 protein, but to date, no analogs has been targeted to this transporter. The parasite also contains a trypanothione pathway that may be involved in the mechanism of activity of antimonials [58], but this pathway has not been specifically targeted for drug design. Finally, efforts are underway to identify an effective vaccine against *Leishmania*, but these studies have not yielded a marketable vaccine to date [185].

major cause of morbidity in some of the world's most impoverished nations. Drug discovery efforts for parasitic diseases in developed nations is limited for a variety of reasons, not the least of which is that the affected population is not regarded as a viable market for the development of new drug entities. In addition, these diseases are not common in the northern hemisphere, where the bulk of drug discovery efforts take place. However, many of the efforts to introduce new agents into the clinic are fueled by partnerships between the World Health Organization and the pharmaceutical industry.

Drug discovery efforts for parasitic disease have now been facilitated by the recent publication of complete genomes for the trypanosomatids mentioned above. Resulting genomic and proteomic studies will almost certainly result in the identification of new, parasite-specific targets, and a better understanding of the biochemistry of the various organisms. The drug discovery efforts outlined above have produced promising leads, and several compounds have been identified with activities that rival currently used agents, but with less toxicity and enhanced activity against resistant strains. These efforts, combined with new methods for vector control and higher levels of awareness in the affected population, could feasibly result in the eradication of these diseases in the foreseeable future.

4. CONCLUSIONS

Currently available agents for the treatment of trypanosomatid infection caused by the *T. brucei*, *T. cruzi*, and *Leishmania* are inadequate, and there is a clear need to develop new agents that are safe, effective and inexpensive to produce. Despite recent research, the standard of therapy for parasitic diseases is essentially the same as it was 25 years ago. Resistant strains of these organisms and the prevalence of coinfection with HIV are serious health threats in the Third World, and political and socioeconomic factors complicate the eradication of trypanosomatid diseases. Thus, parasitic diseases remain a

REFERENCES

1. World Health Organization. The World Health Organization Report 2004—Changing History, 2004.

2. Ivens AC, Peacock CS, Worthey EA, Murphy L, Aggarwal G, Berriman M, Sisk E, Rajandream MA, Adlem E, Aert R, Anupama A, Apostolou Z, Attipoe P, Bason N, Bauser C, Beck A, Beverley SM, Bianchettin G, Borzym K, Bothe G, Bruschi CV, Collins M, Cadag E, Ciarloni L, Clayton C, Coulson RM, Cronin A, Cruz AK, Davies RM, De Gaudenzi J, Dobson DE, Duesterhoeft A, Fazelina G, Fosker N, Frasch AC, Fraser A, Fuchs M, Gabel C, Goble A, Goffeau A, Harris D, Hertz-Fowler C, Hilbert H, Horn

D, Huang Y, Klages S, Knights A, Kube M, Larke N, Litvin L, Lord A, Louie T, Marra M, Masuy D, Matthews K, Michaeli S, Mottram JC, Muller-Auer S, Munden H, Nelson S, Norbertczak H, Oliver K, O'Neil S, Pentony M, Pohl TM, Price C, Purnelle B, Quail MA, Rabbinowitsch E, Reinhardt R, Rieger M, Rinta J, Robben J, Robertson L, Ruiz JC, Rutter S, Saunders D, Schafer M, Schein J, Schwartz DC, Seeger K, Seyler A, Sharp S, Shin H, Sivam D, Squares R, Squares S, Tosato V, Vogt C, Volckaert G, Wambutt R, Warren T, Wedler H, Woodward J, Zhou S, Zimmermann W, Smith DF, Blackwell JM, Stuart KD, Barrell B, Myler PJ. The genome of the kinetoplastid parasite, *Leishmania major*. Science 2005;309:436–442.

3. El-Sayed NM, Myler PJ, Blandin G, Berriman M, Crabtree J, Aggarwal G, Caler E, Renauld H, Worthey EA, Hertz-Fowler C, Ghedin E, Peacock C, Bartholomeu DC, Haas BJ, Tran A-N, Wortman JR, Alsmark UCM, Angiuoli S, Anupama A, Badger J, Bringaud F, Cadag E, Carlton JM, Cerqueira GC, Creasy T, Delcher AL, Djikeng A, Embley TM, Hauser C, Ivens AC, Kummerfeld SK, Pereira-Leal JB, Nilsson D, Peterson J, Salzberg SL, Shallom J, Silva JC, Sundaram J, Westenberger S, White O, Melville SE, Donelson JE, Andersson B, Stuart KD, Hall N. Comparative genomics of trypanosomatid parasitic protozoa. Science 2005;309:404–409.

4. El-Sayed NM, Myler PJ, Bartholomeu DC, Nilsson D, Aggarwal G, Tran A-N, Ghedin E, Worthey EA, Delcher AL, Blandin G, Westenberger SJ, Caler E, Cerqueira GC, Branche C, Haas B, Anupama A, Arner E, Aslund L, Attipoe P, Bontempi E, Bringaud F, Burton P, Cadag E, Campbell DA, Carrington M, Crabtree J, Darban H, da Silveira JF, de Jong P, Edwards K, Englund PT, Fazelina G, Feldblyum T, Ferella M, Frasch AC, Gull K, Horn D, Hou L, Huang Y, Kindlund E, Klingbeil M, Kluge S, Koo H, Lacerda D, Levin MJ, Lorenzi H, Louie T, Machado CR, McCulloch R, McKenna A, Mizuno Y, Mottram JC, Nelson S, Ochaya S, Osoegawa K, Pai G, Parsons M, Pentony M, Pettersson U, Pop M, Ramirez JL, Rinta J, Robertson L, Salzberg SL, Sanchez DO, Seyler A, Sharma R, Shetty J, Simpson AJ, Sisk E, Tammi MT, Tarleton R, Teixeira S, Van Aken S, Vogt C, Ward PN, Wickstead B, Wortman J, White O, Fraser CM, Stuart KD, Andersson B. The genome sequence of Trypanosoma cruzi, etiologic agent of Chagas' disease. Science 2005;309:409–415.

5. Berriman M, Ghedin E, Hertz-Fowler C, Blandin G, Renauld H, Bartholomeu DC, Lennard NJ, Caler E, Hamlin NE, Haas B, Bohme U, Hannick L, Aslett MA, Shallom J, Marcello L, Hou L, Wickstead B, Alsmark UC, Arrowsmith C, Atkin RJ, Barron AJ, Bringaud F, Brooks K, Carrington M, Cherevach I, Chillingworth TJ, Churcher C, Clark LN, Corton CH, Cronin A, Davies RM, Doggett J, Djikeng A, Feldblyum T, Field MC, Fraser A, Goodhead I, Hance Z, Harper D, Harris BR, Hauser H, Hostetler J, Ivens A, Jagels K, Johnson D, Johnson J, Jones K, Kerhornou AX, Koo H, Larke N, Landfear S, Larkin C, Leech V, Line A, Lord A, Macleod A, Mooney PJ, Moule S, Martin DM, Morgan GW, Mungall K, Norbertczak H, Ormond D, Pai G, Peacock CS, Peterson J, Quail MA, Rabbinowitsch E, Rajandream MA, Reitter C, Salzberg SL, Sanders M, Schobel S, Sharp S, Simmonds M, Simpson AJ, Tallon L, Turner CM, Tait A, Tivey AR, Van Aken S, Walker D, Wanless D, Wang S, White B, White O, Whitehead S, Woodward J, Wortman J, Adams MD, Embley TM, Gull K, Ullu E, Barry JD, Fairlamb AH, Opperdoes F, Barrell BG, Donelson JE, Hall N, Fraser CM, Melville SE, El-Sayed NM. The genome of the African trypanosome Trypanosoma brucei. Science 2005;309:416–422.

6. Butler D. Parasitology: triple genome triumph. Nature 2005;436:337.

7. Barrett MP, Burchmore RJS, Stich A, Lazzari JO, Frasch AC, Cazzulo JJ, Krishna S. The trypanosomiases. Lancet 2003;362: 1469–1480.

8. Andrade LO, Andrews NW. The Trypanosoma cruzi–host-cell interplay: location, invasion, retention. Nat Rev Microbiol 2005;3:819.

9. Tyler KM, Engman DM. The life cycle of *Trypanosoma cruzi* revisited. Int J Parasitol 2001;31:472.

10. Herwaldt BL. Leishmaniasis. Lancet 1999;354: 1191–1199.

11. Pasquau F, Ena J, Sanchez R, Cuadrado JM, Amador C, Flores J, Benito C, Redondo C, Lacruz J, Abril V, Onofre J. Leishmaniasis as an opportunistic infection in HIV-infected patients: determinants of relapse and mortality in a collaborative study of 228 episodes in a Mediterranean region. Eur J Clin Microbiol Infect Dis 2005;24:411–418.

12. Irigoin F, Cibils L, Comini MA, Wilkinson SR, Flohe L, Radi R. Insights into the redox biology of Trypanosoma cruzi: trypanothione metabolism and oxidant detoxification. Free Radic Biol Med 2008;45:733–742.

13. Krauth-Siegel RL, Comini MA. Redox control in trypanosomatids, parasitic protozoa with trypanothione-based thiol metabolism. Biochim Biophys Acta 2008;1780:1236–1248.

14. Guerra-Giraldez C, Quijada L, Clayton CE. Compartmentation of enzymes in a microbody, the glycosome, is essential in Trypanosoma brucei. J Cell Sci 2002;115:2651–2658.

15. McKean PG. Coordination of cell cycle and cytokinesis in Trypanosoma brucei. Curr Opin Microbiol 2003;6:600–607.

16. Clayton CE, Michels P. Metabolic compartmentation in African trypanosomes. Parasitol Today 1996;12:465.

17. Verlinde CLMJ, Hannaert V, Blonski C, Willson M, Perie JJ, Fothergill-Gilmore LA, Opperdoes FR, Gelb MH, Hol WGJ, Michels PAM. Glycolysis as a target for the design of new anti-trypanosome drugs. Drug Resist Updat 2001;4:50.

18. Kita K, Nihei C, Tomitsuka E. Parasite mitochondria as drug target: diversity and dynamic changes during the life cycle. Curr Med Chem 2003;10:2535–2548.

19. Nihei C, Fukai Y, Kita K. Trypanosome alternative oxidase as a target of chemotherapy. Biochim Biophys Acta 2002;1587:234.

20. Bacchi CJ, Yarlett N, Goldberg B, Bitonti AJ McCann PP. Biochemical Protozoology. Washington, DC: Taylor & Francis; 1991. p 469–481.

21. Casero RA Jr, Woster PM. Terminally alkylated polyamine analogues as chemotherapeutic agents. J Med Chem 2001;44:1–26.

22. Matthews KR. The developmental cell biology of Trypanosoma brucei. J Cell Sci 2005;118:283–290.

23. Nok AJ. Arsenicals (melarsoprol), pentamidine and suramin in the treatment of human African trypanosomiasis. Parasitol Res 2003;90:71.

24. Vansterkenburg EL, Coppens I, Wilting J, Bos OJ, Fischer MJ, Janssen LH, Opperdoes FR. The uptake of the trypanocidal drug suramin in combination with low-density lipoproteins by Trypanosoma brucei and its possible mode of action. Acta Trop 1993;54:237–250.

25. Fairlamb AH, Bowman IB. Trypanosoma brucei: maintenance of concentrated suspensions of bloodstream trypomastigotes in vitro using continuous dialysis for measurement of endocytosis. Exp Parasitol 1980;49:366–380.

26. Fairlamb AH, Bowman IB. Uptake of the trypanocidal drug suramin by bloodstream forms of Trypanosoma brucei and its effect on respiration and growth rate in vivo. Mol Biochem Parasitol 1980;1:315–333.

27. Carter NS, Berger BJ, Fairlamb AH. Uptake of diamidine drugs by the p2 nucleoside transporter in melarsen-sensitive and -resistant Trypanosoma brucei brucei. J Biol Chem 1995;270:28153–28157.

28. Berger BJ, Carter NS, Fairlamb AH. Characterisation of pentamidine-resistant Trypanosoma brucei brucei. Mol Biochem Parasitol 1995;69:289.

29. de Koning HP. Transporters in African trypanosomes: role in drug action and resistance. Int J Parasitol 2001;31:511.

30. Bailly C, Donkor IO, Gentle D, Thornalley M, Waring MJ. Sequence-selective binding to DNA of cis- and trans-butamidine analogues of the anti-Pneumocystis carinii pneumonia drug pentamidine. Mol Pharmacol 1994;46:313–322.

31. World Health Organization TDR News. World Health Organization TDR News 1992; 39: 1–2.

32. Friedham EAH. Mel B in the treatment of human trypanosomiasis. Am J Trop Med Hyg 1949;29:173–180.

33. Barrett MP, Fairlamb AH. The biochemical basis of arsenical-diamidine crossresistance in African trypanosomes. Parasitol Today 1999; 15:136–140.

34. Kuzoe FA. Current situation of African trypanosomiasis. Acta Trop 1993;54:153–162.

35. Pepin J, Milord F. The treatment of human African trypanosomiasis. Adv Parasitol 1994; 33:1–47.

36. Bitonti AJ, Byers TL, Bush TL, Casara PJ, Bacchi CJ, Clarkson AB Jr, McCann PP, Sjoerdsma A. Cure of Trypanosoma brucei brucei and Trypanosoma brucei rhodesiense infections in mice with an irreversible inhibitor of S-adenosylmethionine decarboxylase. Antimicrob Agents Chemother 1990;34:1485–1490.

37. Bitonti AJ, Cross-Doersen DE, McCann PP. Effects of alpha-difluoromethylornithine on protein synthesis and synthesis of the variant-specific glycoprotein (VSG) in Trypanosoma brucei brucei. Biochem J 1988;250:295–298.

38. Bacchi CJ, Nathan HC, Hutner SH, McCann PP, Sjoerdsma A. Polyamine metabolism: a potential therapeutic target in trypanosomes. Science 1980;210:332–334.

39. Schechter PJ, Sjoerdsma A. Parisitol Today 1984;2:223–224.

40. Burri C, Brun R. Eflornithine for the treatment of human African trypanosomiasis. Parasitol Res 2003;90(Supp 1): S49–S52.

41. Bey P, Gerhart F, Van Dorsselaer V, Danzin C. Alpha-(fluoromethyl)dehydroornithine and alpha-(fluoromethyl)dehydroputrescine analogues as irreversible inhibitors of ornithine decarboxylase. J Med Chem 1983;26: 1551–1556.

42. Poulin R, Lu L, Ackermann B, Bey P, Pegg AE. Mechanism of the irreversible inactivation of mouse ornithine decarboxylase by alpha-difluoromethylornithine. Characterization of sequences at the inhibitor and coenzyme binding sites. J Biol Chem 1992;267:150–158.

43. Werbovetz KA. Target-based drug discovery for malaria, leishmaniasis, and trypanosomiasis. Curr Med Chem 2000;7:835–860.

44. Croft SL, Barrett MP, Urbina JA. Chemotherapy of trypanosomiases and leishmaniasis. Trends Parasitol 2005;21:508.

45. Engman DM, Leon JS. Pathogenesis of Chagas' heart disease: role of autoimmunity. Acta Tropica 2002;81:123.

46. Kalil J, Cunha-Neto E. Autoimmunity in Chagas' disease cardiomyopathy: fulfilling the criteria at last? Parasitol Today 1996;12:396.

47. Burleigh BA, Andrews NW. The mechanisms of Trypanosoma cruzi invasion of mammalian cells. Annu Rev Microbiol 1995;49:175–200.

48. Paulinoa M, Iribarnea F, Dubinb M, Aguilera-Moralesc S, Tapiad O, Stoppani AO. The chemotherapy of Chagas' disease: an overview. Mini Rev Med Chem 2005;5:499–519.

49. Henderson GB, Ulrich P, Fairlamb AH, Rosenberg I, Pereira M, Sela M, Cerami A. "Subversive" substrates for the enzyme trypanothione disulfide reductase: alternative approach to chemotherapy of Chagas disease. Proc Natl Acad Sci USA 1988;85:5374–5378.

50. Poli P, Aline de Mello M, Buschini A, Mortara RA, Northfleet de Albuquerque C, da Silva S, Rossi C, Zucchi TMAD. Cytotoxic and genotoxic effects of megazol, an anti-Chagas' disease drug, assessed by different short-term tests. Biochem Pharmacol 2002;64:1617.

51. Garcia LS, Bruckner DA. Diagnostic Medical Parisitology. Washington, DC: American Society of Microbiology; 1993. p 139–158.

52. Davies CR, Kaye P, Croft SL, Sundar S. Leishmaniasis: new approaches to disease control. BMJ 2003;326:377–382.

53. Puig L, Pradinaud R. Leishmania and HIV co-infection: dermatological manifestations. Ann Trop Med Parasitol 2003;97(Suppl 1): 107–114.

54. Guerin PJ, Olliaro P, Sundar S, Boelaert M, Croft SL, Desjeux P, Wasunna MK, Bryceson ADM. Visceral leishmaniasis: current status of control, diagnosis, and treatment, and a proposed research and development agenda. Lancet Infect Dis 2002;2:494.

55. Hepburn NC. Cutaneous leishmaniasis. Clin Exp Dermatol 2000;25:363–370.

56. Croft SL, Coombs GH. Leishmaniasis: current chemotherapy and recent advances in the search for novel drugs. Trends Parasitol 2003;19:502.

57. Werbovetz KA. Promising therapeutic targets for antileishmanial drugs. Expert Opin Ther Targets 2002;6:407–422.

58. Ouellette M, Drummelsmith J, Papadopoulou B. Leishmaniasis: drugs in the clinic, resistance and new developments. Drug Resist Updat 2004;7:257.

59. Sundar S, Sinha PR, Agrawal NK, Srivastava R, Rainey PM, Berman JD, Murray HW, Singh VP. A cluster of cases of severe cardiotoxicity among kala-azar patients treated with a high-osmolarity lot of sodium antimony gluconate. Am J Trop Med Hyg 1998;59:139–143.

60. Sundar S, Goyal AK, More DK, Singh MK, Murray HW. Treatment of antimony-unresponsive Indian visceral leishmaniasis with ultra-short courses of amphotericin-B-lipid complex. Ann Trop Med Parasitol 1998;92:755–764.

61. Berman JD, Badaro R, Thakur CP, Wasunna KM, Behbehani K, Davidson R, Kuzoe F, Pang L, Weerasuriya K, Bryceson AD. Efficacy and safety of liposomal amphotericin B (ambisome) for visceral leishmaniasis in endemic developing countries. Bull World Health Organ 1998;76:25–32.

62. Saha AK, Mukherjee T, Bhaduri A. Mechanism of action of amphotericin B on Leishmania donovani promastigotes. Mol Biochem Parasitol 1986;19:195–200.

63. Olliaro PL, Bryceson AD. Practical progress and new drugs for changing patterns of leishmaniasis. Parasitol Today 1993;9:323–328.

64. Thakur CP, Kanyok TP, Pandey AK, Sinha GP, Messick C, Olliaro P. Treatment of visceral leishmaniasis with injectable paromomycin (aminosidine). An open-label randomized phase-II clinical study Trans R Soc Trop Med Hyg 2000;94:432–433.

65. Thakur CP, Kanyok TP, Pandey AK, Sinha GP, Zaniewski AE, Houlihan HH, Olliaro P. A prospective randomized, comparative, open-label trial of the safety and efficacy of paromomycin (aminosidine) plus sodium stibogluco-

nate versus sodium stibogluconate alone for the treatment of visceral leishmaniasis. Trans R Soc Trop Med Hyg 2000;94:429–431.

66. Sundar S, Rosenkaimer F, Makharia MK, Goyal AK, Mandal AK, Voss A, Hilgard P, Murray HW. Trial of oral miltefosine for visceral leishmaniasis. Lancet 1998;352: 1821–1823.

67. Sundar S, Gupta LB, Makharia MK, Singh MK, Voss A, Rosenkaimer F, Engel J, Murray HW. Oral treatment of visceral leishmaniasis with miltefosine. Ann Trop Med Parasitol 1999;93:589–597.

68. Sundar S, Rai M. Treatment of visceral leishmaniasis. Expert Opin Pharmacother 2005;6: 2821–2829.

69. Brachwitz H, Vollgraf C. Analogs of alkyllysophospholipids: chemistry, effects on the molecular level and their consequences for normal and malignant cells. Pharmacol Ther 1995;66: 39–82.

70. Arthur G, Bittman R. The inhibition of cell signaling pathways by antitumor ether lipids. Biochim Biophys Acta 1998;1390:85–102.

71. Vogler WR, Shoji M, Hayzer DJ, Xie YP, Renshaw M. The effect of edelfosine on CTP: cholinephosphate cytidylyltransferase activity in leukemic cell lines. Leuk Res 1996;20: 947–951.

72. Wieder T, Haase A, Geilen CC, Orfanos CE. The effect of two synthetic phospholipids on cell proliferation and phosphatidylcholine biosynthesis in madin-darby canine kidney cells. Lipids 1995;30:389–393.

73. Bergmann J, Junghahn I, Brachwitz H, Langen P. Multiple effects of antitumor alkyl-lysophospholipid analogs on the cytosolic free Ca^{2+} concentration in a normal and a breast cancer cell line. Anticancer Res 1994;14:1549–1556.

74. Carter NS, Fairlamb AH. Arsenical-resistant trypanosomes lack an unusual adenosine transporter. Nature 1993;361:173–176.

75. de Koning HP, Bridges DJ, Burchmore RJS. Purine and pyrimidine transport in pathogenic protozoa: from biology to therapy. FEMS Microbiol Rev 2005;29:987.

76. Guo J, Wu YQ, Rattendi D, Bacchi CJ, Woster PM. S-(5′-Deoxy-5′-adenosyl)-1-aminoxy-4-(methylsulfonio)-2-cyclopentene (AdoMao): an irreversible inhibitor of S-adenosylmethionine decarboxylase with potent in vitro antitrypanosomal activity. J Med Chem 1995;38: 1770–1777.

77. Goldberg B, Yarlett N, Sufrin J, Lloyd D, Bacchi CJ. A unique transporter of S-adenosyl-

methionine in African trypanosomes. FASEB J 1997;11:256–260.

78. Byers TL, Casara P, Bitonti AJ. Uptake of the antitrypanosomal drug 5′-([(z)-4-amino-2-butenyl]methylamino)-5′-deoxyadenosine (MDL 73811) by the purine transport system of Trypanosoma brucei brucei. Biochem J 1992;283 (Pt 3): 755–758.

79. Bacchi CJ, Nathan HC, Yarlett N, Goldberg B, McCann PP, Bitonti AJ, Sjoerdsma A. Cure of murine Trypanosoma brucei rhodesiense infections with an S-adenosylmethionine decarboxylase inhibitor. Antimicrob Agents Chemother 1992;36:2736–2740.

80. Bacchi CJ, Goldberg B, Rattendi D, Gorrell TE, Spiess AJ, Sufrin JR. Metabolic effects of a methylthioadenosine phosphorylase substrate analog on African trypanosomes. Biochem Pharmacol 1999;57:89.

81. Seley KL, Schneller SW, Rattendi D, Lane S, Bacchi CJ. Synthesis and antitrypanosomal activities of a series of 7-deaza-5′-noraristeromycin derivatives with variations in the cyclopentyl ring substituents. Antimicrob Agents Chemother 1997;41:1658–1661.

82. Dardonville C, Brun R. Bisguanidine, bis(2-aminoimidazoline), and polyamine derivatives as potent and selective chemotherapeutic agents against Trypanosoma brucei rhodesiense Synthesis and in vitro evaluation. J Med Chem 2004;47:2296–2307.

83. Meiering S, Inhoff O, Mies J, Vincek A, Garcia G, Kramer B, Dormeyer M, Krauth-Siegel RL. Inhibitors of Trypanosoma cruzi trypanothione reductase revealed by virtual screening and parallel synthesis. J Med Chem 2005;48:4793–4802.

84. Klenke B, Stewart M, Barrett MP, Brun R, Gilbert IH. Synthesis and biological evaluation of S-triazine substituted polyamines as potential new anti-trypanosomal drugs. J Med Chem 2001;44:3440–3452.

85. Donkor IO, Assefa H, Rattendi D, Lane S, Vargas M, Goldberg B, Bacchi C. Trypanocidal activity of dicationic compounds related to pentamidine. Eur J Med Chem 2001;36:531.

86. Sturk LM, Brock JL, Bagnell CR, Hall JE, Tidwell RR. Distribution and quantitation of the anti-trypanosomal diamidine 2,5-bis(4-amidinophenyl)furan (DB75) and its N-methoxy prodrug DB289 in murine brain tissue. Acta Trop 2004;91:131–143.

87. Zhou L, Thakker DR, Voyksner RD, Anbazhagan M, Boykin DW, Hall JE, Tidwell RR. Metabolites of an orally active antimicrobial

prodrug, 2,5-bis(4-amidinophenyl)furan-bis-O-methylamidoxime, identified by liquid chromatography/tandem mass spectrometry. J Mass Spectrom 2004;39:351–360.

88. Smith TK, Sharma DK, Crossman A, Brimacombe JS, Ferguson MA. Selective inhibitors of the glycosylphosphatidylinositol biosynthetic pathway of Trypanosoma brucei. Embo J 1999;18:5922–5930.

89. Morita YS, Paul KS, Englund PT. Specialized fatty acid synthesis in African trypanosomes: myristate for GPI anchors. Science 2000;288: 140–143.

90. McFadden JM, Medghalchi SM, Thupari JN, Pinn ML, Vadlamudi A, Miller KI, Kuhajda FP, Townsend CA. Application of a flexible synthesis of (5r)-thiolactomycin to develop new inhibitors of type I fatty acid synthase. J Med Chem 2005;48:946–961.

91. Hucke O, Gelb MH, Verlinde CLMJ, Buckner FS. The protein farnesyltransferase inhibitor tipifarnib as a new lead for the development of drugs against Chagas disease. J Med Chem 2005;48:5415–5418.

92. Orenes Lorente S, Rodrigues JCF, Jimenez Jimenez C, Joyce-Menekse M, Rodrigues C, Croft SL, Yardley V, de Luca-Fradley K, Ruiz-Perez LM, Urbina J, de Souza W, Gonzalez Pacanowska D, Gilbert IH. Novel azasterols as potential agents for treatment of leishmaniasis and trypanosomiasis. Antimicrob Agents Chemother 2004;48:2937–2950.

93. Lorente SO, Jimenez CJ, Gros L, Yardley V, de Luca-Fradley K, Croft SL, A. Urbina J, Ruiz-Perez LM, Pacanowska DG, Gilbert IH. Preparation of transition-state analogues of sterol 24-methyl transferase as potential anti-parasitics. Bioorg Med Chem 2005;13:5435.

94. Buckner FS, Griffin JH, Wilson AJ, Van Voorhis WC. Potent anti-Trypanosoma cruzi activities of oxidosqualene cyclase inhibitors. Antimicrob Agents Chemother 2001;45: 1210–1215.

95. Liendo A, Lazardi K, Urbina JA. In-vitro antiproliferative effects and mechanism of action of the bis-triazole d0870 and its s(-) enantiomer against Trypanosoma cruzi. J Antimicrob Chemother 1998;41:197–205.

96. Martin MB, Grimley JS, Lewis JC, Heath HT, Bailey BN, Kendrick H, Yardley V, Caldera A, Lira R, Urbina JA, Moreno SNJ, Docampo R, Croft SL, Oldfield E. Bisphosphonates inhibit the growth of Trypanosoma brucei, Trypanosoma cruzi, Leishmania donovani, Toxoplasma gondii, and Plasmodium falciparum: a potential route to chemotherapy. J Med Chem 2001;44:909–916.

97. North MJ, Coombs GH, Barry JD. A comparative study of the proteolytic enzymes of Trypanosoma brucei, T. equiperdum, T. evansi, T. vivax, Leishmania tarentolae and Crithidia fasciculata. Mol Biochem Parasitol 1983;9: 161–180.

98. McKerrow JH, Engel JC, Caffrey CR. Cysteine protease inhibitors as chemotherapy for parasitic infections. Bioorg Med Chem 1999;7:639.

99. Monteiro ACS, Abrahamson M, Lima APCA, Vannier-Santos MA, Scharfstein J. Identification, characterization and localization of chagasin, a tight-binding cysteine protease inhibitor in Trypanosoma cruzi. J Cell Sci 2001;114:3933–3942.

100. Rigden DJ, Mosolov VV, Galperin MY. Sequence conservation in the chagasin family suggests a common trend in cysteine proteinase binding by unrelated protein inhibitors. Protein Sci 2002;11:1971–1977.

101. Sanderson SJ, Westrop GD, Scharfstein J, Mottram JC, Coombs GH. Functional conservation of a natural cysteine peptidase inhibitor in protozoan and bacterial pathogens. FEBS Lett 2003;542:12.

102. McKerrow JH, McGrath ME, Engel JC. The cysteine protease of Trypanosoma cruzi as a model for antiparasite drug design. Parasitol Today 1995;11:279.

103. Lecaille F, Kaleta J, Bromme D. Human and parasitic papain-like cysteine proteases: their role in physiology and pathology and recent developments in inhibitor design. Chem Rev 2002;102:4459–4488.

104. Scory S, Caffrey CR, Stierhof Y-D, Ruppel A, Steverding D. Trypanosoma brucei: killing of bloodstream forms in vitro and in vivo by the cysteine proteinase inhibitor Z-Phe-Ala-CHN2. Exp Parasitol 1999;91:327.

105. Barrett AJ, Kembhavi AA, Brown MA, Kirschke H, Knight CG, Tamai M, Hanada K. L-trans-Epoxysuccinyl-leucylamido(4-guanidino)butane (E-64) and its analogues as inhibitors of cysteine proteinases including cathepsins B, H and L. Biochem J 1982;201:189–198.

106. Roush WR, Hernandez AA, McKerrow JH, Selzer PM, Hansell E, Engel JC. Design, synthesis and evaluation of D-homophenylalanyl epoxysuccinate inhibitors of the trypanosomal cysteine protease cruzain. Tetrahedron 2000;56:9747.

107. Roush WR, Cheng J, Knapp-Reed B, Alvarez-Hernandez A, McKerrow JH, Hansell E, Engel

JC. Potent second generation vinyl sulfonamide inhibitors of the trypanosomal cysteine protease cruzain. Bioorg Med Chem Lett 2001;11:2759.

108. Du X, Guo C, Hansell E, Doyle PS, Caffrey CR, Holler TP, McKerrow JH, Cohen FE. Synthesis and structure–activity relationship study of potent trypanocidal thio semicarbazone inhibitors of the trypanosomal cysteine protease cruzain. J Med Chem 2002;45:2695–2707.

109. Greenbaum DC, Mackey Z, Hansell E, Doyle P, Gut J, Caffrey CR, Lehrman J, Rosenthal PJ, McKerrow JH, Chibale K. Synthesis and structure–activity relationships of parasiticidal thiosemicarbazone cysteine protease inhibitors against Plasmodium falciparum, Trypanosoma brucei, and Trypanosoma cruzi. J Med Chem 2004;47:3212–3219.

110. Godat E, Chowdhury S, Lecaille F, Belghazi M, Purisima EO, Lalmanach G. Inhibition of a cathepsin l-like cysteine protease by a chimeric propeptide-derived inhibitor. Biochemistry 2005;44:10486–10493.

111. Huang L, Lee A, Ellman JA. Identification of potent and selective mechanism-based inhibitors of the cysteine protease cruzain using solid-phase parallel synthesis. J Med Chem 2002;45:676–684.

112. Dubin G. Proteinaceous cysteine protease inhibitors. Cell Mol Life Sci 2005;62:653–669.

113. Powers JC, Asgian JL, Ekici OD, James KE. Irreversible inhibitors of serine, cysteine, and threonine proteases. Chem Rev 2002;102:4639–4750.

114. McKerrow JH, Rosenthal PJ, Swenerton R, Doyle P. Development of protease inhibitors for protozoan infections. Curr Opin Infect Dis 2008;21:668–672.

115. Besteiro S, Barrett MP, Riviere L, Bringaud F. Energy generation in insect stages of Trypanosoma brucei: metabolism in flux. Trends Parasitol 2005;21:185.

116. Coustou V, Besteiro S, Biran M, Diolez P, Bouchaud V, Voisin P, Michels PAM, Canioni P, Baltz T, Bringaud F. Atp generation in the Trypanosoma brucei procyclic form: cytosolic substrate level phosphorylation is essential, but not oxidative phosphorylation. J Biol Chem 2003;278:49625–49635.

117. van Weelden SWH, Fast B, Vogt A, van der Meer P, Saas J, van Hellemond JJ, Tielens AGM, Boshart M. Procyclic Trypanosoma brucei do not use Krebs cycle activity for energy generation. J Biol Chem 2003;278:12854–12863.

118. Opperdoes FR, Michels PAM. Enzymes of carbohydrate metabolism as potential drug targets. Int J Parasitol 2001;31:481.

119. Kessler PS, Parsons M. Probing the role of compartmentation of glycolysis in procyclic form Trypanosoma brucei: RNA interference studies of pex14, hexokinase, and phosphofructokinase. J Biol Chem 2005;280:9030–9036.

120. Bakker BM, Mensonides FIC, Teusink B, van Hoek P, Michels PAM, Westerhoff HV. From the cover: compartmentation protects trypanosomes from the dangerous design of glycolysis. PNAS 2000;97:2087–2092.

121. Albert M-A, Haanstra JR, Hannaert V, Van Roy J, Opperdoes FR, Bakker BM, Michels PAM. Experimental and in silico analyses of glycolytic flux control in bloodstream form Trypanosoma brucei. J Biol Chem 2005;280:28306–28315.

122. Cazzulo JJ. Intermediate metabolism in Trypanosoma cruzi. J Bioenerg Biomembr 1994;26:157.

123. Coustou V, Besteiro S, Riviere L, Biran M, Biteau N, Franconi J-M, Boshart M, Baltz T, Bringaud F. A mitochondrial NADH-dependent fumarate reductase involved in the production of succinate excreted by procyclic Trypanosoma brucei. J Biol Chem 2005;280:16559–16570.

124. van Weelden SWH, van Hellemond JJ, Opperdoes FR, Tielens AGM. New functions for parts of the Krebs cycle in procyclic Trypanosoma brucei, a cycle not operating as a cycle. J Biol Chem 2005;280:12451–12460.

125. Furuya T, Kessler P, Jardim A, Schnaufer A, Crudder C, Parsons M. Glucose is toxic to glycosome-deficient trypanosomes. PNAS 2002;99:14177–14182.

126. Bakker BM, Walsh MC, ter Kuile BH, Mensonides FI, Michels PA, Opperdoes FR, Westerhoff HV. Contribution of glucose transport to the control of the glycolytic flux in Trypanosoma brucei. Proc Natl Acad Sci USA 1999;96:10098.

127. Wille U, Seyfang A, Duszenko M. Glucose uptake occurs by facilitated diffusion in procyclic forms of Trypanosoma brucei. Eur J Biochem 1996;236:228–233.

128. Seyfang A, Duszenko M. Specificity of glucose transport in Trypanosoma brucei. Effective inhibition by phloretin and cytochalasin B. Eur J Biochem 1991;202:191–196.

129. Bayele H. Triazinyl derivatives that are potent inhibitors of glucose transport in Trypanosoma brucei. Parasitology Research 2001;87:911.

130. Tetaud E, Barrett MP, Bringaud F, Baltz T. Kinetoplastid glucose transporters. Biochem J 1997;325(Pt 3): 569–580.

131. Barnard JP, Reynafarje B, Pedersen PL. Glucose catabolism in African trypanosomes. Evidence that the terminal step is catalyzed by a pyruvate transporter capable of facilitating uptake of toxic analogs. J Biol Chem 1993;268:3654–3661.

132. Perie J, Riviere-Alric I, Blonski C, Gefflaut T, de Viguerie NL, Trinquier M, Willson M, Opperdoes FR, Callens M. Inhibition of the glycolytic enzymes in the trypanosome: an approach in the development of new leads in the therapy of parasitic diseases. Pharmacol Ther 1993;60:347.

133. Drew ME, Morris JC, Wang Z, Wells L, Sanchez M, Landfear SM, Englund PT. The adenosine analog tubercidin inhibits glycolysis in Trypanosoma brucei as revealed by an RNA interference library. J Biol Chem 2003;278: 46596–46600.

134. Bressi JC, Verlinde CLMJ, Aronov AM, Shaw ML, Shin SS, Nguyen LN, Suresh S, Buckner FS, Van Voorhis WC, Kuntz ID, Hol WGJ, Gelb MH. Adenosine analogues as selective inhibitors of glyceraldehyde-3-phosphate dehydrogenase of Trypanosomatidae via structure-based drug design. J Med Chem 2001;44: 2080–2093.

135. Aronov AM, Suresh S, Buckner FS, Van Voorhis WC, Verlinde CLMJ, Opperdoes FR, Hol WGJ, Gelb MH. Structure-based design of submicromolar, biologically active inhibitors of trypanosomatid glyceraldehyde-3-phosphate dehydrogenase. PNAS 1999;96:4273–4278.

136. Willson M, Sanejouand Y-H, Perie J, Hannaert V, Opperdoes F. Sequencing, modeling, and selective inhibition of Trypanosoma brucei hexokinase. Chem Biol 2002;9:839.

137. Claustre S, Denier C, Lakhdar-Ghazal F, Lougare A, Lopez C, Chevalier N, Michels PAM, Perie J, Willson M. Exploring the active site of Trypanosoma brucei phosphofructokinase by inhibition studies: specific irreversible inhibition. Biochemistry 2002;41: 10183–10193.

138. Dax C, Coincon M, Sygusch J, Blonski C. Hydroxynaphthaldehyde phosphate derivatives as potent covalent Schiff base inhibitors of fructose-1,6-bisphosphate aldolase Biochem 2005;44:5430–5443.

139. Bakker BM, Walsh MC, ter Kuile BH, Mensonides FIC, Michels PAM, Opperdoes FR, Westerhoff HV. Contribution of glucose transport to the control of the glycolytic flux in Trypanosoma brucei. PNAS 1999;96:10098–10103.

140. Claustre S, Bringaud F, Azema L, Baron R, Perie J, Willson M. An easy stereospecific synthesis of 1-amino-2,5-anhydro-1-deoxy-D-mannitol and arylamino derivatives Carbohydr Res 1999;315:339–344.

141. Baliani A, Bueno GJ, Stewart ML, Yardley V, Brun R, Barrett MP, Gilbert IH. Design and synthesis of a series of melamine-based nitroheterocycles with activity against trypanosomatid parasites. J Med Chem 2005;48: 5570–5579.

142. Stewart ML, Bueno GJ, Baliani A, Klenke B, Brun R, Brock JM, Gilbert IH, Barrett MP. Trypanocidal activity of melamine-based nitroheterocycles. Antimicrob Agents Chemother 2004;48:1733–1738.

143. Lin CH, Chen S, Kwon DS, Coward JK, Walsh CT. Aldehyde and phosphinate analogs of glutathione and glutathionylspermidine: potent, selective binding inhibitors of the E coli bifunctional glutathionylspermidine synthetase/amidase. Chem Biol 1997;4:859–866.

144. Chen S, Lin CH, Kwon DS, Walsh CT, Coward JK. Design, synthesis, and biochemical evaluation of phosphonate and phosphonamidate analogs of glutathionylspermidine as inhibitors of glutathionylspermidine synthetase/amidase from Escherichia coli. J Med Chem 1997;40:3842–3850.

145. Kwon DS, Lin CH, Chen S, Coward JK, Walsh CT, Bollinger JM Jr. Dissection of glutathionylspermidine synthetase/amidase from E coli into autonomously folding and functional synthetase and amidase domains. J Biol Chem 1997;272:2429–2436.

146. Li Z, Fennie MW, Ganem B, Hancock MT, Kobaslija M, Rattendi D, Bacchi CJ, O'Sullivan MC. Polyamines with N-(3-phenylpropyl) substituents are effective competitive inhibitors of trypanothione reductase and trypanocidal agents. Bioorg Med Chem Lett 2001;11:251.

147. Bergeron RJ, McManis JS, Weimar WR, Schreier KM, Gao F, Wu Q, Ortiz-Ocasio J, Luchetta GR, Porter C, Vinson JR. The role of charge in polyamine analogue recognition. J Med Chem 1995;38:2278–2285.

148. Casero RA Jr, Woster PM. Recent advances in the development of polyamine analogues as antitumor agents. J Med Chem 2009;52: 4551–4573.

149. Porter CW, Pegg AE, Ganis B, Madhabala R, Bergeron RJ. Combined regulation of or-

nithine and S-adenosylmethionine decarboxy-lases by spermine and the spermine analogue N^{1}N^{12}-bis(ethyl)spermine. Biochem J 1990;268: 207–212.

150. Porter CW, Sufrin JR. Interference with poly-amine biosynthesis and/or function by analogs of polyamines or methionine as a potential anticancer chemotherapeutic strategy. Antic-ancer Res 1986;6:525–542.

151. Baumann RJ, Hanson WL, McCann PP, Sjoerdsma A, Bitonti AJ. Suppression of both antimony-susceptible and antimony-resistant Leishmania donovani by a bis(benzyl)polya-mine analog. Antimicrob Agents Chemother 1990;34:722–727.

152. Baumann RJ, McCann PP, Bitonti AJ. Sup-pression of Leishmania donovani by oral ad-ministration of a bis(benzyl)polyamine analog. Antimicrob Agents Chemother 1991;35: 1403–1407.

153. Bitonti AJ, Bush TL, McCann PP. Regulation of polyamine biosynthesis in rat hepatoma (HTC) cells by a bisbenzyl polyamine analo-gue. Biochem J 1989;257:769–774.

154. Bitonti AJ, Dumont JA, Bush TL, Edwards ML, Stemerick DM, McCann PP, Sjoerdsma A. Bis(benzyl)polyamine analogs inhibit the growth of chloroquine-resistant human malar-ia parasites (Plasmodium falciparum) in vitro and in combination with alpha-difluoromethy-lornithine cure murine malaria. PNAS 1989;86:651–655.

155. Bellevue FH III Boahbedason M, Wu R, Wos-ter PM, Casero JRA, Rattendi D, Lane S, Bacchi CJ. Structural comparison of alkylpo-lyamine analogues with potent in vitro anti-tumor or antiparasitic activity. Bioorg Med Chem Lett 1996;6:2765.

156. Zou Y, Wu Z, Sirisoma N, Woster PM, Casero RA Jr, Weiss LM, Rattendi D, Lane S, Bacchi CJ. Novel alkylpolyamine analogues that pos-sess both antitrypanosomal and antimicros-poridial activity. Bioorg Med Chem Lett 2001;11:1613–1617.

157. Bacchi CJ, Yarlett N, Faciane E, Bi X, Rattendi D, Weiss LM, Woster PM. Metabolism of an alkyl polyamine analog by a polyamine oxidase from the microsporidian Encephalitozoon cuniculi. Antimicrob Agents Chemother 2009;53:2599–2604.

158. Bi X, Lopez C, Bacchi CJ, Rattendi D, Woster PM. Novel alkylpolyaminoguanidines and al-kylpolyaminobiguanides with potent antitry-panosomal activity. Bioorg Med Chem Lett 2006;16:3229–3232.

159. Huang Y, Greene E, Murray Stewart T, Good-win AC, Baylin SB, Woster PM, Casero RA Jr. Inhibition of lysine-specific demethylase 1 by polyamine analogues results in reexpression of aberrantly silenced genes. Proc Natl Acad Sci USA 2007;104:8023–8028.

160. Benson TJ, McKie JH, Garforth J, Borges A, Fairlamb AH, Douglas KT. Rationally de-signed selective inhibitors of trypanothione reductase. Phenothiazines and related tricyc-lics as lead structures. Biochem J 1992;286(Pt 1): 9–11.

161. Garforth J, Yin H, McKie JH, Douglas KT, Fairlamb AH. Rational design of selective ligands for trypanothione reductase from Trypanosoma cruzi. Structural effects on the inhibition by dibenzazepines based on imipra-mine. J Enzyme Inhib 1997;12:161–173.

162. Chan C, Yin H, Garforth J, McKie JH, Jaou-hari R, Speers P, Douglas KT, Rock PJ, Yard-ley V, Croft SL, Fairlamb AH. Phenothiazine inhibitors of trypanothione reductase as po-tential antitrypanosomal and antileishmanial drugs. J Med Chem 1998;41:148–156.

163. Bonnet B, Soullez D, Davioud-Charvet E, Landry V, Horvath D, Sergheraert C. New spermine and spermidine derivatives as po-tent inhibitors of Trypanosoma cruzi trypa-nothione reductase. Bioorg Med Chem 1997;5:1249.

164. Girault S, Davioud-Charvet E, Salmon L, Be-recibar A, Debreu MA, Sergheraert C. Struc-ture–activity relationships in 2-aminodiphe-nylsulfides against trypanothione reductase from Trypanosoma cruzi. Bioorg Med Chem Lett 1998;8:1175–1180.

165. Arafa RK, Brun R, Wenzler T, Tanious FA, Wilson WD, Stephens CE, Boykin DW, Synth-esis, DNA affinity, and antiprotozoal activity of fused ring dicationic compounds and their prodrugs. J Med Chem 2005;48:5480–5488.

166. Berman J. Clinical status of agents being de-veloped for leishmaniasis. Expert Opin Inves-tig Drugs 2005;14:1337–1346.

167. Croft SL, Seifert K, Duchene M. Antiprotozoal activities of phospholipid analogues. Mol Bio-chem Parasitol 2003;126:165.

168. Sundar S, Jha TK, Thakur CP, Engel J, Sin-dermann H, Fischer C, Junge K, Bryceson A, Berman J. Oral miltefosine for Indian visceral leishmaniasis. N Engl J Med 2002;347:1739–1746.

169. Yeates C. Sitamaquine (glaxosmithkline/wal-ter reed army institute). Curr Opin Investig Drugs 2002;3:1446–1452.

170. Berhe N, Wolday D, Hailu A, Abraham Y, Ali A, Gebre-Michael T, Desjeux P, Sonnerborg A, Akuffo H, Britton S. Hiv viral load and response to antileishmanial chemotherapy in co-infected patients. Aids 1999;13:1921–1925.

171. Alvar J, Canavate C, Gutierrez-Solar B, Jimenez M, Laguna F, Lopez-Velez R, Molina R, Moreno J. Leishmania and human immunodeficiency virus coinfection: the first 10 years. Clin Microbiol Rev 1997;10:298–319.

172. Buates S, Matlashewski G. Treatment of experimental leishmaniasis with the immunomodulators imiquimod and S-28463: efficacy and mode of action. J Infect Dis 1999;179: 1485–1494.

173. Arevalo I, Ward B, Miller R, Meng TC, Najar E, Alvarez E, Matlashewski G, Llanos-Cuentas A. Successful treatment of drug-resistant cutaneous leishmaniasis in humans by use of imiquimod, an immunomodulator. Clin Infect Dis 2001;33:1847–1851.

174. Smith AC, Yardley V, Rhodes J, Croft SL. Activity of the novel immunomodulatory compound tucaresol against experimental visceral leishmaniasis. Antimicrob Agents Chemother 2000;44:1494–1498.

175. Chowdhury SF, Villamor VB, Guerrero RH, Leal I, Brun R, Croft SL, Goodman JM, Maes L, Ruiz-Perez LM, Pacanowska DG, Gilbert IH. Design, synthesis, and evaluation of inhibitors of trypanosomal and leishmanial dihydrofolate reductase. J Med Chem 1999;42: 4300–4312.

176. Lowe G, Droz AS, Vilaivan T, Weaver GW, Tweedale L, Pratt JM, Rock P, Yardley V, Croft SL. Cytotoxicity of (2,2′:6′,2″-terpyridine)platinum(II) complexes to Leishmania donovani, Trypanosoma cruzi, and Trypanosoma brucei. J Med Chem 1999;42:999–1006.

177. Raychaudhury B, Banerjee S, Gupta S, Singh RV, Datta SC. Antiparasitic activity of a triphenyl tin complex against Leishmania donovani. Acta Tropica 2005;95:1.

178. Rocha LG, Almeida JR, Macedo RO, Barbosa-Filho JM. A review of natural products with antileishmanial activity. Phytomedicine 2005;12:514–535.

179. Cortes-Selva F, Campillo M, Reyes CP, Jimenez IA, Castanys S, Bazzocchi IL, Pardo L, Gamarro F, Ravelo AG. SAR studies of dihydro-β-agarofuran sesquiterpenes as inhibitors of the multidrug-resistance phenotype in a Leishmania tropica line overexpressing a P-glycoprotein-like transporter. J Med Chem 2004;47:576–587.

180. Bhattacharya G, Herman J, Delfin D, Salem MM, Barszcz T, Mollet M, Riccio G, Brun R, Werbovetz KA. Synthesis and antitubulin activity of N^1- and N^4-substituted 3,5-dinitro sulfanilamides against African trypanosomes and Leishmania. J Med Chem 2004;47: 1823–1832.

181. Drummelsmith J, Brochu V, Girard I, Messier N, Ouellette M. Proteome mapping of the protozoan parasite Leishmania and application to the study of drug targets and resistance mechanisms. Mol Cell Proteomics 2003;2:146.

182. Landfear SM. Genetics and biochemistry of Leishmania membrane transporters. Curr Opin Microbiol 2000;3:417.

183. Ilgoutz SC, McConville MJ. Function and assembly of the Leishmania surface coat. Int J Parasitol 2001;31:899.

184. Costa-Pinto D, Trindade LS, McMahon-Pratt D, Traub-Cseko YM. Cellular trafficking in trypanosomatids: a new target for therapies? Int J Parasitol 2001;31:536.

185. Ghosh M, Bandyopadhyay S. Present status of antileishmanial vaccines. Mol Cell Biochem 2003;253:199–205.

ANTIMALARIALS

DAVID C. SMITHSON
W. ARMAND GUIGUEMDE
R. KIPLIN GUY
Chemical Biology and Therapeutics,
St Jude Children's Research
Hospital, Memphis, TN

1. INTRODUCTION

Malaria, has the highest morbidity among tropical diseases, with 300 to 500 million people infected annually worldwide, and the highest mortality, with 1.5 to 2 million deaths annually. Nearly 40% of the world population is at risk, with 90% of the infections affecting children in Africa [1]. The disease also affects Western travelers, and is responsible for significant economic burdens in endemic regions. [2, 3] The disease is currently largely controlled via treatment with small molecule drugs. This is likely to remain the dominant paradigm in the foreseeable future, as vaccine development has thus far proven elusive. However, the emergence of parasite strains resistant to currently used drugs has necessitated an expanded discovery effort.

Towards that end, this chapter will initially focus on the basic biology of the causative agent, including the parasitic life cycle as well as the clinical features and pathogenicity of the disease. This will familiarize the medicinal chemist with the overall context in which potential novel agents will be employed. Following this, the history, chemistry and pharmacology of existing anti-malarial agents will be discussed. The major focus of this section is the quinolines, which represent the oldest anti-malarials still in use. Other agents currently used clinically will be discussed here as well, including the artemisinins and antifolates. This section is a good overview of chemotypes which have been proven in the clinic, and which may continue to yield useful compounds in the future. Finally, the remained of the chapter will be devoted to potential biochemical targets within the parasite which have been successfully inhibited by small molecules. These include targets involved with cell cycle regulation, heme metabolism, amino

acid salvage, DNA synthesis, repair and regulation, cellular respiration, the electron transport chain, cellular oxidative stress management, fatty acid biosynthesis, isoprenoid biosynthesis. A short section has also been devoted to targets which have not been successfully inhibited by small molecules, and are generally less rigorously validated than those listed previously. Both groups of targets represent the current cutting edge in the effort to expand the chemotypes available for development as anti-malarial agents. However, the chemotypes presented here have typically not been proven in the clinic, and as such, should be regarded as hypothetical.

1.1. The *Plasmodium* Life Cycle

Plasmodium has a complex life cycle (Fig. 1) that has profound implications for the pathology of the disease, its treatment, and its eradication. *Plasmodium* is an obligate intracellular parasite with a life cycle that encompasses two major stages: an asexual stage called schizogony that takes place in humans, and a sexual stage, called sporogony, that takes place in the *Anopheles* mosquito.

The asexual stage begins when an infected female *Anopheles* mosquito transmits the parasites to a human during feeding. The mosquitoes are most active between dusk and dawn. The parasites injected during the mosquito's feeding are at a life cycle state stage called sporozoites. During the mosquito blood meal, the sporozoites move from the mosquito salivary glands and are injected with the mosquito's saliva. Only female mosquitoes take blood meals and are able to transmit the disease because they rely on human blood proteins to allow fertilization of their eggs. Male mosquitoes survive on nectar feeding. The sporozoites reach the liver within 30 min where they invade hepatocytes. After hepatocyte invasion, the parasites multiply and differentiate to produce thousands of merozoites in each infected hepatocyte. This liver, exoerythrocytic, phase of the parasite life cycle is symptom free and lasts for between 1 and 2.5 weeks. The *Plasmodium falciparum* and *malariae* species exit the liver phase completely to enter the intraerythrocytic phase of the life cycle. The

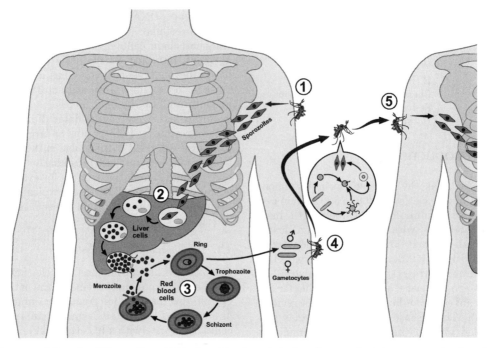

Figure 1. Life cycle of *Plasmodium*. (1) During a blood meal, the female mosquito injects sporozoites into the human host. They migrate through the blood to the liver. (2) Sporozoites invade hepatocytes where they replicate and mature then release merozoites that penetrate the blood stream (*P. ovale* and *P. vivax* at this stage can persist in a dormant state for months). (3) In the blood merozoites infect erythrocytes and undergo an asexual replication through different states: ring then throphozoite, which matures in a schizont. The ruptured schizont releases merozoites and the cycle resumes. (4) Some merozoites will differentiate into gametocytes that are ingested by another mosquito during its blood meal. (5) The gametocytes undergo a sexual replication and the mosquito injects the matured parasite to another human host. (This figure is available in full color at http://mrw.interscience.wiley.com/emrw/9780471266945/home.)

Plasmodium vivax and *ovale* species can form hypnozoites that can remain quiescent in hepatocytes for several months, eventually leading to recrudescent infections. Of existing drugs, only the 8-aminoquinolines have activity during liver stages of disease and only primaquine is currently approved for use.

After the hepatocytic incubation and proliferation period, the merozoites rupture the hepatocytes and migrate to the blood stream where within minutes they infect red blood cells to initiate the erythrocytic phase of the life cycle. This portion of the life cycle accounts for most of the symptoms of the disease. During the erythrocytic phase, the parasites follow a repetitive subcycle of asexual reproduction. The parasite differentiates through different forms within the infected erythrocyte: ring, trophozoite, and schizont, which then to reinitiate the subcycle by bursting the erythrocyte

to release 8–32 merozoites per infected erythrocyte. This cyclic phase of the asexual stage lasts 42–72 h, depending largely on the parasite species and strain. After several intraerythrocytic cycles, a small proportion of merozoites differentiate into gametocytes, the sexual forms that are differentiated for reuptake by mosquitoes during a blood feeding. Essentially, all antimalarial drugs in use or in trials, with the exception of primaquine and tafenoquine, act on the erythrocytic stages of the disease.

The sexual stage of the parasite life cycle, known as the sporogonic cycle, takes place in the mosquito. While in the mosquito's stomach, the male gametocyte matures into a microgamete that fertilizes the macrogamete (the matured female gametocyte) thus producing a zygote. The zygote then goes through several morphological changes to become an ookinete that penetrates the mosquito's midgut wall to mature into an oocyst. The oocyst grows and bursts, with the immediate release of infective sporozoites. The sporozoites migrate into the salivary gland cells, where they remain for up to 2 months, waiting to be inoculated in another human host. The duration of the sexual stage in *P. falciparum* is 10–12 days. No agents either in use or in development specifically target the parasite during the sexual phase. However, vector control, both through the use of insecticides and through the use of screens to block access to humans, remains a critical component of all control and eradication campaigns.

1.2. Clinical Features and Pathogenicity

After an incubation period of 7–14 days following a mosquito bite, disease symptoms begin to manifest with the entry into the erythrocytic subcycle of the life cycle. Depending on the severity of those symptoms, the disease is classified as uncomplicated malaria or severe malaria. Symptoms of uncomplicated malaria include fever, headaches, nausea, vomiting, chills, and sweats. Fever, induced by a physiological response to the rupture of infected erythrocytes, is the most common symptom. In classic malaria, the symptoms occur in a special order, and in repeated cycles. In the first stage, the patient exhibits by chills and shivering. In the second stage, the patient experiences a high fever, headaches, and vomiting. Finally, the last stage is characterized by sweating and general fatigue. For disease caused by *P. falciparum*, *P. vivax*, and *P. ovale*, this cycle reoccurs every 48 h, which corresponds to the time needed for synchronized parasites to mature into schizonts. Because of its periodicity, it is called tertian malaria. Disease caused by *P. malariae* cycles over 72 h and is called quartan malaria. *P. malariae* infections account for roughly 15–30% of disease in malaria-endemic regions, usually as mixed infections with *P. falciparum*. Infections tend to occur mostly in children and clinical symptoms are similar those of mild malaria, with fever threshold lower than in *P. falciparum* [4].

Untreated, the complicated form of malaria can rapidly turn into its severe form, which includes cerebral malaria. In cerebral malaria, parasites are sequestered in the brain by adhesion of infected erythrocytes to the capillary bed. This obstructs cerebral blood flow and leads to symptoms including neurological abnormalities, impaired consciousness, and coma. Other manifestations of complicated disease include severe anemia, hemoglobinuria, thrombocytopenia, respiratory distress, and cardiovascular shock. Those severe symptoms are the downstream effects of the destruction of the erythrocytes and release of cellular debris. Other physiological manifestations are hyperparasitemia with more than 5% of infected erythrocytes, low glucose levels, metabolic acidosis, enlarged spleen and liver, and nephropathies. Nephropathies are the result of immune complexes, clumps and activated endothelial cells that are ultimately deposited in the kidneys. Chronic malarial nephropathy is common among children of age group 4–8 years and can eventually to renal failure [5,6].

Children are particularly vulnerable to malaria, although children younger than 5 months seem to have an innate immune response [7]. Over time, adults living in endemic area become gradually less susceptible to severe malaria. This protective immunity to severe pathology in adults is achieved by multiple infections [8]. However, this model is oversimplified since children in endemic area with exposure to the parasite still develop severe malaria [9].

2. ANTIMALARIAL DRUGS

2.1. Quinolines

2.1.1. Quinine   Peruvian Indians have used cinchona trees for centuries to treat fever and shivering. Quinine, an alkaloid derived from the bark of the cinchona tree was brought to Europe from Peru in the early 1600s and used to treat malaria. The isolation of quinine was achieved by French researchers Pelletier and Caventou in the nineteenth century [10]. The complete chemical synthesis of quinine was realized in 1944 by Woodward and Doering but natural sourcing is still utilized to produce quinine.

Quinine (Fig. 2a) and its analogs act on the intraerythrocytic asexual stage of the parasite and target the normal function of the parasite's food vacuole where hemoglobin is digested. There is general agreement that the mechanism of action of quinine and its derivatives is the inhibition of heme crystallization. Heme is the catabolic product of hemoglobin degrada-

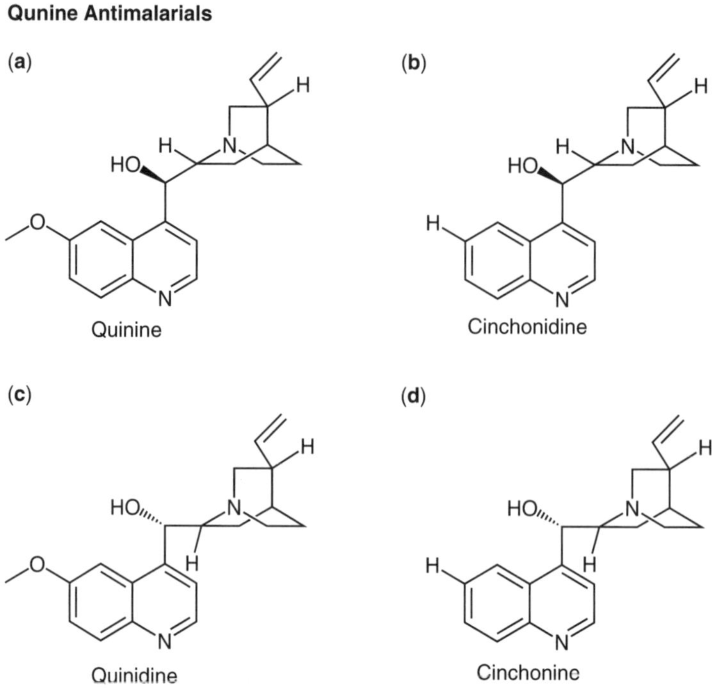

Qunine Antimalarials

(a)

Quinine

(b)

Cinchonidine

(c)

Quinidine

(d)

Cinchonine

Figure 2. (a) Quinine, first isolated molecule with antimalarial properties, is an alkaloid derived from the bark of the cinchona tree brought to Europe from Peru in the early 1600s [10]. (b)–(d) Cinchona analogs of quinine. (c) Quinidine is more potent but more toxic than quinine.

tion by the parasite, which utilizes hemoglobin to source amino acids for protein synthesis. Heme is quite toxic and thus its accumulation must be controlled. Under normal conditions, heme is crystallized within the parasite into hemozoin, which sequesters the heme and mitigates its toxic effects. Heme crystallization is a chemical process that is induced and dependent on the presence of heme derived material associated with hemozoin [11]. It can also be induced by a vacuole protein, the histidine-rich protein [12]. Lipids play a major role in heme crystallization [13]. The molecules of heme are linked into dimers through reciprocal iron–carboxylate bonds to one of the propionic side chains of each porphyrin, and the dimers form chains linked by hydrogen bonds in the crystal [14]. However, quinine binds weakly to heme ($K_d = 2.6 \times 10^{-6}$ M) and thus a secondary mechanism can not be excluded [15]. Recent investigations on quinine pharmacodynamics pointed out that passive diffusion and pH were only minor determinants of quinine accumulation in the food vacuole, and

that a carrier-mediated import system was predominant [16].

There have been limited studies of the structure–activity relationships of quinine and other cinchona alkaloids. Stereochemical evaluation of the relative activities of cinchona alkaloids showed that quinine and quinidine (Fig. 2c) were more than 100 times active than 9-epiquinine and 9-epiquinidine against chloroquine-sensitive *P. falciparum* and more than 10 times active against chloroquine-resistant *P. falciparum*. Differential hydrogen-bonding patterns play a role [17]. Similar relationships exist in the synthetic quinolines. Moreover, cinchonine (Fig. 2d) is more potent than cinchonidine (Fig. 2b) and quinidine is not only more potent but also more toxic than quinine [18].

As will be discussed below, quinine served as the model for the development of a number of synthetic aminoquinoline drugs that are currently in use and in further development. Currently, quinine is mainly used in complicated malaria. The standard treatment of severe malaria with quinine involves intravenous administration of 8 mg/kg, three times per day, for 7 days. Both intramuscular and intrarectal routes are available as alternatives. Uncomplicated malaria may be cleared by quinine formate following a 5-day course of treatment with 25 mg/kg/day given orally to children as syrup [19].

Quinine pharmacokinetics is comparable in severe and nonsevere malaria. Patients with cerebral malaria receiving the standard dose of 10 mg/kg every 8 h have plasma quinine levels that consistently exceed 10 mg/L, reaching a peak 60 h after treatment is begun. Quinine total clearance (Cl) and total apparent volume of distribution (V_d) were significantly lower in severe malaria (Cl, 0.92 mL/min/kg versus 1.3 mL/min; V_d, 1.18 L/kg versus 1.67 L/kg). Elimination half-times ($t_{1/2}$) were 18 h versus 16 h and renal clearances were equal (0.21 mL/min/kg) [20]. The main metabolite of quinine is 3-hydroxyquinine.

Although quinine has good efficacy by intravenous administration, its usage in rural areas in Africa is often limited due to lack of equipment and trained staff. To circumvent this problem, intrarectal quinine formulations were developed. Intrarectal quinine is a safe and efficacious alternative for the treatment of childhood cerebral malaria [21,22], with comparable bioavailability [23]. However, the stability of the intrarectal formulation remains a concern.

Quinine is quite toxic and has a low therapeutic index. This is especially problematic in children where dosage is more critical. Quinine induced arrhythmia has been reported [24]. Otoxicity has been also documented in healthy subjects, as well as in patients with malaria. The otoxicity is reversible [25].

Chemoresistance to quinine monotherapy is increasing and consequently the drug is increasingly used in combination with other antimalarials agents. Early efforts focused on the combination of quinine with clindamycin [26]. A number of other combinations have been evaluated [27]. A recent *in vivo* study indicated that the quinine doxycycline combination was more potent than those with sulfadoxin or pyrimethamine [28]. The quinine doxycycline combination may also be better in preventing relapses [29]. Quinine combinations with artesunate or azithromycin were safe and efficacious combination treatments for uncomplicated falciparum malaria [30], although parenteral artesunate quinine combination did not prove synergistic for treatment of severe malaria [31].

The mechanism of quinine resistance at the genetic level is still poorly understood. *Pfmdr1* (*Plasmodium falciparum* multi drug resistance), a P-glycoprotein homolog, has been linked to quinine resistance [32]. The N1042D mutation appears to play a significant role. Furthermore, a triple mutation S1034C/N1042D/D1246Y, highly prevalent in South America, was also found to enhance parasite susceptibility to mefloquine, halofantrine, and artemisinin [33]. Recent data suggest that PfMDR1 transports quinine and chloroquine, but not halofantrine, whereas polymorphic PfMDR1 variants associated with altered drug responsiveness, transport halofantrine but not quinine and chloroquine [34]. Elevated PfNHE activity is found in strains with high levels of quinine resistance, regardless of their chloroquine-resistant status [35]. Increased resistance to quinine has been noted in recent years and combination therapies are currently being explored with quinine.

2.1.2. Chloroquine The history of chloroquine (Fig. 3a) development goes back to the early 1900s. During the World War I, malaria was increasingly a problem across Europe. Given the toxicological limitations associated with quinine antimalarial therapy (cinchonism at high dosages), its cost, and the risk of shortage, there were incentives toward the end of the war to reduce the reliance on quinine. In the 1920s, the laboratory of the IG Farbenindustrie from Bayer led the discovery of synthetic alternatives to quinine by conducting systematic screening of chemicals they produced on a malaria *in vivo* model (canaries infected with *P. reticulum*) [36].

Additional contributions were made by Andersag and colleagues who successfully evaluated the antimalarial activity of 12,000 compounds they synthesized. Mepacrine (Fig. 3b) was discovered as potent antimalarial compound, with undesirable side effects (the substance dyed the skin yellow-orange). Chloroquine was discovered and used under the

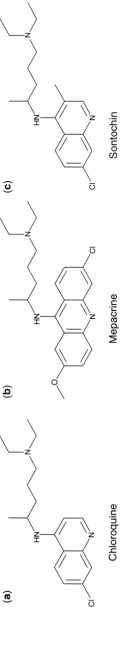

(a) Chloroquine

(b) Mepacrine

(c) Sontochin

Figure 3. The discovery of 4-aminoquinolines: It was partly the work of Andersag and colleagues who successfully evaluated the antimalarial activity of 12,000 compounds they synthesized. Mepacrine (b) was discovered as potent antimalarial compound. But its undesirable effect (the substance dyed the skin) brought reconsiderations. Derivatives of mepacrine ((a) chloroquine and (b) sontochin) would subsequently be discovered. Chloroquine was later established as superior to sontochin and became the first line antimalarial treatment for decades.

brand name Resochin. It was then abandoned because of toxicity issues and replaced with an analog sontochin (Fig. 3c). During World War II, quinine became unavailable due to the Japanese capture of Java and mepacrine became the favored quinine replacement in treating malaria infected Allied soldiers in the Pacific. However, in the same period chloroquine was reevaluated by the Allies, based on information captured on sontochin during the liberation of Tunis.

Chloroquine was later established as superior to sontochin and became the first line antimalarial treatment for decades. Resistance to chloroquine started to emerge in the 1960s and became a worldwide problem in the late 1980s. This sparked an interest in reexploring this scaffold to develop analogs active against chloroquine-resistant strains.

A comprehensive review of structure–activity relationship studies of chloroquine analogs up until the late 1990s has been published. [37]. Early studies focused on the side-chain length, which was modifiable without losing the antimalarial activity. Aminoquinolines with widely variant alkyl substitutents on the terminal amine (ethyl to dodecyl) side chains were equally active against chloroquine-susceptible *P. falciparum* (IC_{50} values = 5–15 nM) and many were also active against chloroquine, mefloquine, and multiresistant *P. falciparum* (IC_{50} values = 5–20 nM) [38]. Moreover, some of those compounds with shorter side chains were active in monkey models of human *P. vivax* infection (the rhesus monkey, *Plasmodium cynomolgi* model of human *P. vivax* infection) and *P. falciparum* infection (the squirrel monkey, *P. falciparum* model of human *P. falciparum* infection) [39]. The development of AQ-13 as a replacement for chloroquine was based on a propyl side-chain modification of chloroquine that gave compounds potent against parasites in *in vivo* and *in vitro* models. Development was slowed because of cross-resistance with chloroquine in clinical isolates and enhanced liver toxicity in animal models [40]. Some modifications on the external tertiary amine keep the compounds' activity against chloroquine-sensitive and chloroquine-resistant strains [41,42]. Radically changing the side amino alkyl chain to generate 7-chloroquino-

lylhydrazones, methoxyquinolylhydrazones, tricyclic derivatives, hydrazides, and sulfonylhydrazides generated compounds with comparable hematin formation inhibition to chloroquine. Their activities against chloroquine-resistant strains were not substantially improved [43]. Analogs in which the side chain of chloroquine was modified by introducing a hydrophobic ferrocenyl group with the 1–4 relative position of the two exocyclic N atoms maintained in such derivatives. Of those compounds, one was particularly active against a chloroquine-resistant strain of *P. falciparum in vitro*, as well as against *Plasmodium berghei* and *Plasmodium yoelii* NS *in vivo* [44]. Ferroquine, the successful compound from the series was further developed and entered clinical trials in 2007 [45]. A number of other modifications have been studied [46–48].

While there has been ample evidence for generating active compounds against chloroquine-resistant strains by side-chain modification, modifications on the quinoline nucleus itself was assumed to lessen the activity. However, recently, unsubstituted quinoline rings other than the 7-chloroquinoline ring in chloroquine were found to have significant activity against the drug-resistant strain of *P. falciparum* W2 [49]. High-throughput chemistry and combinatorial chemistry have been used as new tools to explore chloroquine chemical space by generating chemical libraries of chloroquine. This approach has proved successful with the generation of new chloroquine analogs with antimalarial activity against both chloroquine-sensitive and chloroquine-resistant strains [42,50].

The mechanism of action of chloroquine is generally agreed to mirror that of quinine, the inhibition of hemozoin formation. Chloroquine is accumulated from nanomolar concentrations in the plasma to millimolar concentrations in the parasite's acidic food vacuole where it becomes diprotonated and trapped. Chloroquine interacts with heme, thus preventing its crystallization into hemozoin. Incorporation of chloroquine in the chain heme polymer prevents its elongation by capping [51]. The chloroquine-heme complex is believed to be responsible for the toxicity by peroxidizing the parasite's membrane lipids, which ultimately permeabilizes the membrane [52]. Other models exist [53].

Chloroquine is extensively distributed within the body with a large apparent V_d ($> 100 \, L/kg$), and a terminal elimination half-life of 1–2 months. As a consequence, distribution processes, rather than elimination, dominate the blood concentration profile of chloroquine in patients with acute malaria. Oral bioavailability exceeds 75% [54]. The major metabolite of chloroquine is desethylchloroquine, which is produced by cytochrome P450 N-de-ethylation and is detectable in plasma within 30 min of chloroquine oral administration [55]. After two N-dealkylations, the final degradation product is 4-aminoquinoline. Desethylchloroquine remains the major metabolite and has an equal antimalarial potency to chloroquine on sensitive strains.

Like quinine, chloroquine has a narrow therapeutic window. Nevertheless, it is generally safe when used at recommended antimalarial dosages in mild malaria. Chloroquine related cardiotoxicity is mainly a class 1c effect with a prolongation of the QRS complex. Hypotensive effects are induced upon parenteral administration of chloroquine [56] by a transiently high plasma concentration of the drug in the early phases its distribution. Retinopathies and cardiopathies are among the toxic effects [57] and ocular toxicity has been reported [58].

Widespread chemoresistance to chloroquine has led to its removal as a first line treatment against malaria. Chloroquine resistance first emerged at the Thai–Cambodian border in the late 1950s [59]. Since then, the mechanism of chloroquine resistance has been intensively studied. Early studies pointed to vacuolar acidic pH as mechanism of chloroquine trapping. Food vacuole accumulation is lower in chloroquine-resistant strains and this led to the conclusion that a vacuolar pH differences between chloroquine-sensitive and chloroquine-resistant strains could explain the mechanism of resistance. However, direct measurements found no significant difference in vacuolar pH between chloroquine-sensitive and chloroquine-resistant strains [60]. Instead, it was found that resistant strains of the parasite release chloroquine 40–50 times more rapidly than the susceptible strains, although their initial rates of chloroquine ac-

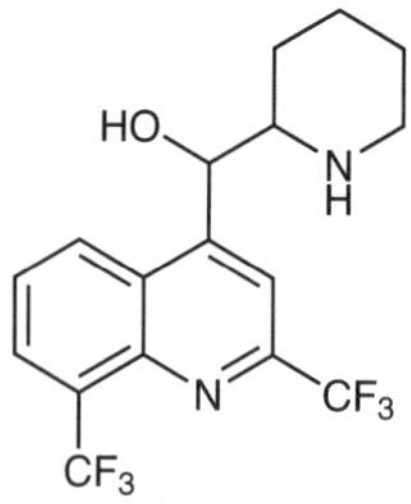

Figure 4. Mefloquine, a synthetic analog of quinine, was developed in the 1970s as replacement for chloroquine for use against resistant strains by the Walter Reed Army Institute [65].

cumulation are the same, thus implying an efflux mechanism [61]. The genetic marker linked to chloroquine resistance is the gene *pfcrt* [62]. Evidence suggests that mutations such as the K76T mutation of *pfcrt* lead to strong increases in the efflux of chloroquine from the parasite digestive vacuole [63]. Although the efflux model is generally accepted, normal PfCRT function is unknown [64].

2.1.3. Mefloquine Mefloquine (Fig. 4) was developed in the 1970s as replacement for chloroquine for use versus resistant strains by the Walter Reed Army Institute [65]. Mefloquine is a synthetic analog of quinine.

Mefloquine's mode of action is believed to be similar to that of the other quinolines [66]. It has been shown to have weak DNA intercalating properties that do not account for the antimalarial activity. Moreover, mefloquine does not inhibit RNA polymerase transcription [67].

Mefloquine has a V_d of roughly $20 \, L/kg$, with a systemic Cl of approximately 0.026 $L/h/kg$ and a terminal elimination half-life of about 20 days. All of the pharmacokinetic parameters of mefloquine are subject to extreme variation within patient populations. Furthermore, systemic clearance appears to be increased in late pregnancy. In nonsevere falciparum malaria, peak blood levels are two to three times higher than those in healthy subjects. Systemic clearance is usually reduced but elimination rates are increased (possibly because of reduced enterohepatic recycling). Mefloquine absorption appears to be reduced in severe malaria. No important drug interactions have been identified as yet, but the potential for serious interactions with quinine has not been adequately investigated. More studies are needed on the disposition of mefloquine in children [68].

Mefloquine is generally well tolerated in both adults and children. Adverse effects include nausea, vomiting, diarrhea, headache, dizziness, rash, pruritus, and abdominal pain. Cardiovascular changes, such as bradycardia, occasionally occur. Most notably neuropsychiatric disturbances have been associated with mefloquine [69]. Studies indicate that serious central nervous system (CNS) related toxicities to mefloquine occur in prophylaxis in 1:10,000 patients. In therapy, this number varies from 1:1200 in Asians to 1:200 in Caucasians and Africans. This incidence in therapy is correlated with high dosing, previous history of CNS events, and disease severity. Mild CNS events occur in 25% of patients [70]. The mechanism of the CNS related toxicity has been investigated. *In vitro* data suggest disruption of the neuronal calcium homeostasis by mefloquine induced calcium release of the endoplasmic reticulum [71]. It is also possible that interaction with biogenic amine receptors is involved.

Chemoresistance to mefloquine is linked to a multidrug-resistant protein PfMDR1 [32,72].

2.1.4. Amodiaquine Based on early discoveries from the 4-aminoquinoline series, modifications on the quinoline side chain were explored by synthesizing a group of 122 heterocyclic dialkyl amino-*o*-cresols and benzylamines derivatives. Amodiaquine (Fig. 5a) emerged out of this program with an excellent potency/toxicity profile [73,74]. It has been marketed since the 1950s and was added to the WHO Essential Drug List in 1977. It was used for prophylaxis until 1990 but was removed from the same list when cases of agranulocytosis and hepatitis were associated with its use [75].

Although more potent than chloroquine against chloroquine-resistant strains, amodiaquine has some liabilities in terms of liver toxicity and agranulocytosis. Animal and *in vitro* studies demonstrated that amodiaquine is metabolized in amodiaquine quinoneimine, which covalently binds to thiol groups of endogenous proteins and triggers immunogenic responses [76].

SAR work on the series showed that certain variations on the side chain are compatible with antimalarial activity. Hybridized molecules of amodiaquine and diethylcarbamazines at the tertiary amine were found active against *P. berghei* in mice and moderately potent than amodiaquine [77]. Oxidation of the nitrogen N-1 of amodiaquine increases the potency in mice infection by three- to fourfold [78]. O'Neill et al. investigated the effect of fluorine substitution on the metabolism and antimalarial activity of amodiaquine and presented evidence that specific fluorine substitutions produce potent antimalarial analogs. Those analogs are more resistant to oxidation hence less likely to form toxic quinone imine metabolite *in vivo* [79].

Manipulating the *N*-alkyl substituent in amodiaquine by pyrrolidine (amopyroquine) (Fig. 5f) or *N*-tertbutyl substitutions generates compounds with comparable antimalarial activity to amodiaquine and with a significant decrease in cross-resistance [80]. Compounds with alkyl substitutions in the 5'-position of the 4'- hydroxyanilino side chain were found to be threefold more active than amodiaquine *in vitro and in vivo* [81]. Removing the 4' OH, responsible for toxicity led to a new series of 4-aminoquinolines whose structures contains the aromatic ring of amodiaquine. A morpholino derivative was potent *in vitro and in vivo* and displayed a lower toxicity than amodiaquine on mouse macrophages [82]. To avoid toxic quinoneimine formation, O'Neill proposed that interchanging the 3'-hydroxyl and the 4' Mannich side-chain function of amodiaquine would provide a new series of analogs incapable of forming quinoneimine metabolites. Among the analogs synthesized, isoquine (Fig. 5b) emerged as a new second-generation lead molecule [83]. Further studies revealed that isoquine does not undergo *in vivo* biodegradation and has a low oral bioavailability. A backup, a 4'-fluoro-*N*-*tert*-butylamodiaquine, was subsequently identified. The Phase I clinical trial with Glaxo SmithKline (GSK) started in April 2008 [84]. The isotebuquine (Fig. 5e) analogs and their *N*-oxides have also been evaluated. The drugs were highly active against both chloroquine-sensitive and chloroquine-resistant strains [85]. Replacing the phenolic ring of amodiaquine with a set of pyrrole analogs produced drugs with antimalarial activity comparable to chloroquine and isoquine [86].

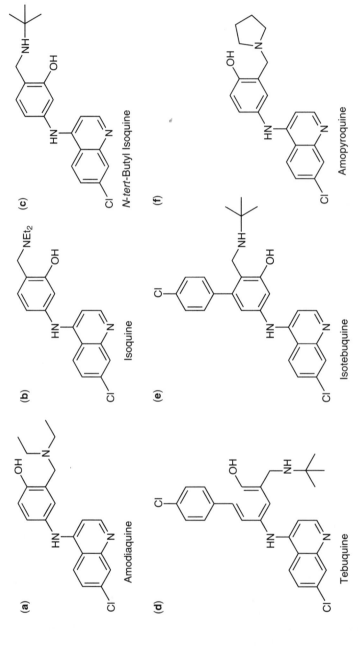

Figure 5. (a) Amodiaquine emerged out of an antimalarial screening of 122 heterocyclic dialkyl amino-*o*-cresols and benzylamines derivatives, synthesized based on early discoveries from the 4-aminoquinoline series by modifications on the quinoline side chain [73,74]. (b) Isoquine. O'Neill proposed that interchanging the 3′-hydroxyl and the 4′-Mannich side-chain function of amodiaquine would provide a new series of analogs incapable of forming quinoneimine metabolites. Among the analogs synthesized, isoquine emerged as a new second-generation lead molecule [83]. (c)–(f) Amodiaquine analogs with antimalarials activities against chloroquine-resistant strains.

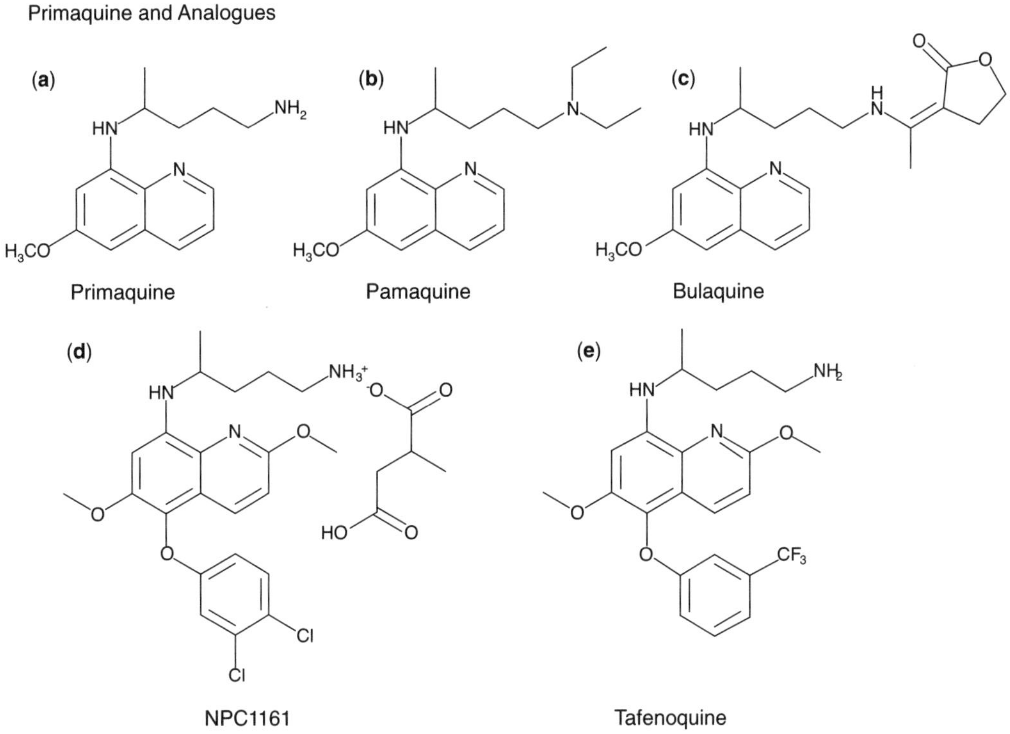

Primaquine and Analogues

Figure 6. (a) Primaquine emerged as best candidate out of a screening in 1946 over 12,000 aminoquinolines compounds of which 21 went to clinical trials. (b) Pamaquine, an earlier 8-aminoquinoline, was potent against the exoerythrocytic stages of the parasites and was given in combination with quinine. Its greatest disadvantage was its high toxicity [89]. (c) Bulaquine was developed by the CDRI in the late 1980s. It showed potent *in vivo* antimalarial radical cure activity [105] and was carried through clinical trial [106]. (d) NPC 1161 was developed in the 1980s [104]. The succinate salt is currently in preclinical development. (e) Tafenoquine is an 8-aminoquinoline antimalarial that is currently under development. It is contraindicated in G6PD deficient individuals and pregnant women. In clinical studies, tafenoquine was highly potent in both radical cure of relapsing malaria and causal prophylaxis of *P. vivax* and *P. falciparum* infections [107].

Amodiaquine is metabolized to desethylamodiaquine and a minor metabolite 2-hydroxydesethylamodiaquine [87]. CYP2C8 in the blood mediates the metabolism to desethylamodiaquine that in turn is metabolized by extrahepatic CYP1A1 [75]. Amodiaquine has a short terminal half-life of 4–12 h among patients as compared to 3–12 days for desethylamodiaquine [88].

2.1.5. Primaquine World War II prompted a strategic need in the United States for drugs to prevent malaria relapses. Pamaquine (Fig. 6b) or plasmochin were the only available drug for cure. Pamaquine was mainly potent against the exoerythrocytic stages of the

parasites and was given in combination with quinine. Its greatest disadvantage was its high toxicity. In 1946, over 12,000 aminoquinolines compounds were tested and 21 went to clinical trials. Isopentaquine and primaquine (Fig. 6a) were the best candidates [89] emerging from these studies.

Primaquine, despite its low therapeutic index, is the drug of choice for the radical cure of vivax and ovale malaria. Primaquine and related 8-aminoquinolines (i.e., pamaquine and pentaquine) are active against all parasite stages in humans. Their mechanism of action is still unclear. Primaquine has an elimination half-life of 7 h and is rapidly metabolized in the plasma to carboxyprimaquine [90].

In the mid-1950s, just after its introduction for clinical use, biological evidence of toxicity began to accumulate. Early observations included direct oxidation of glucose in red blood cells of primaquine-sensitive subjects that in turn was affected by the glucose-6-phosphate dehydrogenase activity [91]. Erythrocytes are sensitive to toxic oxidative species that normally are reduced by glutathione, which itself is reduced by NADPH. Peroxide toxicity plays an important role in the drug induced toxicity through the glucose-6-phosphate dehydrogenase pathway in red blood cells [92]. Persons who are deficient in this enzyme could become victim of hemolysis following primaquine treatment.

Limited analog studies have been carried out on the 8-aminoquinolines. Substitutions at C-2 have been evaluated. A series of 2-benzyloxy and 2-benzylthio analogs of primaquine showed significant tissue schizonticidal activity in monkey models with a decreased toxicity [93,94]. Several 5-phenoxy derivatives have been tested in murine and monkey models and show more activity and less toxicity [95]. 4-Substituted primaquine analogs [96,97], 5-substituted primaquine analogs [98], and 4,5-disubstituted analogs [99,100] displayed radical curative antimalarial activity with decreased activity. Peptides substitutions at the terminal primary amine of primaquine increased the radical cure activity against the monkey parasite *P. cynomolgi* nevertheless their activities were comparable to primaquine in mice [101]. Compounds with dipeptides substitutions [102] or with imidazolidin-4-one derivatives were potent against *P. berghei* gametocytes in Balb C mice [103].

Several primaquine analogs are currently in preclinical development or clinical trials. NPC 1161 (Fig. 6d) was developed in the 1980s [104]. The succinate salt is currently in preclinical development. Bulaquine (Fig. 6c) was developed by the Central Drug Research Institute (CDRI) in the late 1980s. It showed potent *in vivo* antimalarial radical cure activity [105] and was carried through clinical trial [106]. It is currently under limited clinical use in India. Tafenoquine (Fig. 6e) is an 8-aminoquinoline antimalarial that is currently under development. Its half-life is approximately 14 days and is generally safe and well tolerated, although contraindicated in G6PD

deficient individuals and pregnant women. In clinical studies, tafenoquine was highly potent in both radical cure of relapsing malaria and causal prophylaxis of *P. vivax* and *P. falciparum* infections [107].

2.2. Other Agents

2.2.1. Artemisinins Artemisinin (Fig. 7a) and its derivatives are currently essential components in malaria chemotherapy. Artemisinin was discovered during a systematic screening of indigenous plants with antimalarial properties in the late 1960s in China. The screening of plants used in traditional medicine was prompted by the Chinese government in the context of the Vietnam War in which malaria casualties were a serious problem for both the American and the Vietnamese armed forces, at the time a Chinese ally [108]. Scientists from China identified the plant qinghao, a sweet wormwood (*Artemisia annua L*) as a candidate. Its use to reduce fevers was recommended by Ge Hong in 340 AD and its specific use for malaria was by the famous herbalist Li Shizhen [109]. Early attempts to confirm the antimalarial and antipyretic activities from aqueous extracts of *A. annua* failed. It was later discovered that low temperature ethyl ether extractions contained the antimalarial principle. Further refinements of the active fractions and purifications led to a crystalline compound named artemisinin, determined by X-ray crystallography to possess an unusual structure with a sesquiterpene lactone bearing an endoperoxide [110].

The first full chemical synthesis establishing the absolute stereochemistry of artemisinin was reported in 1983 by Schmidt with isopulegol as starting material [111]. Since then, several routes for the total synthesis of artemisinin have been explored [112], although as for quinine, those strategies remain overly expensive for pharmaceutical production. Partial synthesis approaches have been explored as well. Artemisinic acid, which is relatively abundant in *A. annua* was converted into artemisinin in two steps via reduction of the exocyclic methylene group and photooxidation of the resulting dihydroartemisinic acid [113]. Another route uses oxygenation of artemisinic acid allowed the

First Generation Artemisinins

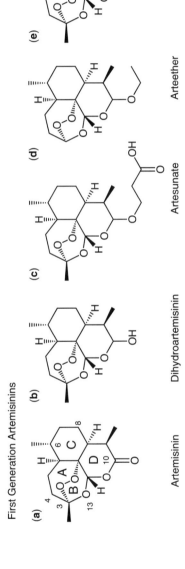

(a)	(b)	(c)	(d)	(e)
Artemisinin	Dihydroartemisinin	Artesunate	Arteether	Artemether

Figure 7. Artemisinin (a) and its derivatives are currently essential components in malaria chemotherapy. Artemisinin was discovered during a systematic screening of indigenous plants with antimalarial properties in the late 1960s in China. The first-generation of artemisinin derivatives including dihydroartemisinin (b), artesunate (c), arteether (**7D**) and artemether (e) are more active than artemisinin and came from modifications at the O-11 position.

conversion into artemisinin [114]. Recently, synthetic biology approaches using plant biosynthesis or microbial engineering techniques have been investigated in the production of artemisinin or its derivatives [115]. Keasling et al. engineered the expression of a synthetic amorpha-4,1,1-diene synthase gene, whose product amorphadiene is the sesquiterpene precursor of artemisinin; and the mevalonate isoprenoid pathway from yeast in *Escherichia coli* [116]. The engineering of *Saccharomyces cerevisiae* to produce high titers of artemisinic acid has been reported by generating transgenic yeast containing the mevalonate pathway, amorphadiene synthase, and the cytochrome P450 monooxygenase [117].

Extensive work on artemisinin derivatives has led to some insights in the general SARs. From a chemical point of view, artemisinin tolerates a large variety of reactions despite the peroxide bridge. The challenge is designing derivatives with improved oral bioavailability and long half-life while maintaining the intrinsic antimalarial activity [118]. The endoperoxide is critical for activity, its reduction to mono-oxy results in complete loss of activity [109,119]. However, 1-deoxyartemisins with increased antimalarial potency in comparison to artemisinin have been synthesized [120]. O-11 is not indispensable since 10-deoxoartemisin retains activity and is even more active than artemisinin *in vivo* [120–123]. Also, various substitutions at this position O-11 resulting in an increase antimalarial potency [124]. The first-generation of artemisinin derivatives including dihydroartemisinin (Fig. 7b), artemether (Fig. 7e), arteether (Fig. 7d), and artesunate (Fig. 7c) came from modifications at this position. Substitutions at carbon C-9 have been explored. Either the D or the A rings can be removed with retention or improvement of the pharmacological activity [120,125]. However, an apparently slight modification, epimerization of the methyl at C-9 of artemisinin, brings a drastic decrease in antimalarial activity [126]. Tricyclic analogs (by opening the D ring) result in improved potency [127]. Potency is also improved when groups that stabilize radicals are placed at C-4α but not C-4β [128]. The C-3 position allows modifications for generating more potent compounds than artemisinin [129]. Several fluorine substitutions have been explored with the rationale of decreasing *in vivo* oxidative degradation. Fluoroartemisinins have showed potent antimalarial activities with better ADME properties than artemisinin [118]. Recently, artemisinin dimers have showed potent antimalarial activity [130]. However, pharmacological advantage over the monomer still needs to be proven.

Mindful of the critical role of the peroxide functional group in the antimalarial activity, several groups searched for simplified analogs of artemisinin. In the late 1980s, synthetic peroxides were evaluated for their antimalarial properties [119,131,132], which led to the second generation of artemisinins. Since then, synthetic cyclic peroxides have been synthesized in great profusion and showed significant promise as antimalarial agents [133]. The 1,2,4-trioxolane, known as OZ277, became the first from this group to transition to drug development [134].

Artemisinins are lethal to all phases of the asexual stage and also have gametocidal properties. The gametocytocidal activity is particularly important because it decreases disease transmission. Killing of young rings results in rapid reduction of parasitemia and killing of more mature stages prevents sequestration in capillaries and venules [110]. This class of drugs does not affect parasites in the liver stage or latent stage (hypnozoites). Several mechanisms of action of artemisinins have been proposed. One proposed mechanism is that its activity seems to be mediated by free radicals. Once formed, those free radicals appear to damage specific intracellular targets. This model is supported by the finding that compounds lacking the peroxide bridge, a known source of oxygen free radicals, lack activity. Moreover, the antimalarial activity of the class is enhanced by free radical generating compounds such as doxorubicin. Similarly, their potencies are weakened in presence of antioxidants such as catalase and reduced glutathione [135]. Another proposed mechanism of action is through heme. There is both biological and chemical evidence for the role of heme in the catalytic activation of artemisinin [136]. The interference of artemisinins with the plasmodial hemoglobin catabolic pathway and inhibition of heme crystallization has been reported [137]. Artemisinin mediated heme alkylation has been observed *in vivo* in infected mice [138]. A third potential mechanism of action for artemisinins is the inhibition of the sarco endoplasmic reticulum Ca^{2+}-ATPase ortholog PfATP6 in *P. falciparum* [139].

The metabolism of artemisinins involves an oxidation reaction by cytochrome P450 (CYP3A4 and CYP2B6 primarily) producing four metabolites (deoxyartemisinin, deoxydihydroartemisinin, crystal-7, and 9,10-dihydrodeoxyartemisinin). All of these metabolites are inactive, most likely due to the loss of the peroxide. Dihydroartemisinin is the main metabolite for artemether (Fig. 7e), arteether, and sodium artesunate [140]. Its antimalarial activity is retained but it is rapidly cleared through Phase II glucuronidation. Fluorine incorporation to slow the rate of oxidative dealkylation has been explored [118]. The first-generation artemisinins have similar pharmacokinetic parameters in human volunteers. After oral administration, blood concentrations of artemisinin and artemether peak between 30–300 min and the compounds have half-lives from 1.8–3 h. Artesunate is almost immediately converted in dihydroartemisinin and eliminated with a half-life of 45 min [141]. Artemisinins are highly bound to plasma proteins especially α1-acid glycoprotein (88% binding) in healthy volunteers [75].

Although no human clinical evidence of neurotoxicity has been reported, there is a body of experimental data *in vitro* as well as *in vivo* supporting neurological symptoms at high doses of artemisinin derivatives [135,142–144].

Overall artemisinin and its derivatives represent a class of highly potent antimalarial molecules and artemisinin combination therapies (ACTs) are now the frontline treatment against malaria in many regions of the world. Combined efforts of synthetic chemistry and biosynthetic chemistry should allow in the near future the production of cheaper artemisinin analogs. Those are urgently needed because the current repertoire of ACTs is very limited and recent evidence points toward an emergence of artemisinin-resistant clones [145,146].

2.2.2. Antifolates

Biguanides and Pyrimethamine Antimalarial antifolates were initially described by British scientists at ICI who evaluated the antimalarial activity of biguanides. Proguanil (Fig. 8a) had an excellent prophylactic activity in *P. falciparum* and satisfactory suppressive activity for vivax malaria. Because it is a slow-acting compound, proguanil is administered in combination, currently with Atovaquone under the brand name Malarone®. Proguanil is metabolized into cycloguanil (Fig. 8b) by CYP2C19. Cycloguanil is a competitive inhibitor of dihydrofolate reductase (DHFR).

Pyrimethamine (Fig. 8c) is a molecule developed by Burroughs Wellcome in 1950. Antimalarial testing was initiated based on the similarity between proguanil and pyrimethamine. Pyrimethamine acts through inhibition of the parasite DHFR. Mutations in this enzyme are responsible for chemoresistance to cycloguanil. Mutation at position 108 is the most common, but mutations at other locations have been found. To prevent chemoresistance, pyrimethamine is used in combination with sulfadoxine (Fig. 8e).

2.2.3. Sulfonamides and Sulfones   The history of sulfonamides goes back to the discovery of prontosil, a sulfonamide-azo-dye, in 1932 in the laboratories of Bayer AG. Prontosil was the first molecule with a broad antimicrobial spectrum and until the emergence of penicillins, was the frontline drug for bacterial infections. As part of the general search for new antimalarials during World War II, this class was pushed forward in development.

The mechanism of action of sulfonamides is a competitive antagonism with p-aminobenzoic acid for the dihydroopterate synthase DHPS. Antimalarials from this class are slow-acting agents sulfadoxine and sulfalene. Other examples from this group include sulfamethoxazole (Fig. 8f), sulfisoxazole and dapsone (Fig. 8g) from the sulfone class.

The majority of sulfonamides is well absorbed from the small intestine. After absorption they are distributed throughout most of the tissues in the entire body. Metabolism of sulfonamides takes place mainly in the liver where they undergo acetylation and to a lesser extent glucuronidation. Sulfones are also distributed throughout the entire body, are excreted mostly as glucuronides, 5% is not metabolized.

Antifolates

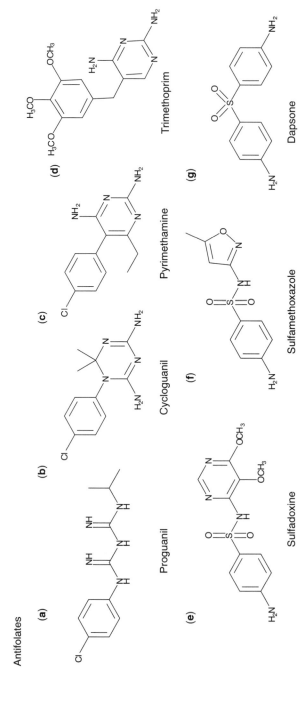

Figure 8. Antifolates. (a) Proguanil has an excellent prophylactic activity in *P. falciparum* and satisfactory suppressive activity for vivax malaria. It is administered in combination, currently with atovaquone. (b) Cycloguanil is the metabolite of proguanil. (c) Pyrimethamine is a molecule developed by Burroughs Wellcome in 1950. It acts through inhibition of the parasite DHFR. (d) Trimethoprim is a structurally and pharmacologically related agent to pyrimethamine, is less used as antimalarial treatment. (e) Sulfadoxine, (f) sulfamethoxazole, and (g) dapsone are examples of sulfonamides and sulfones used in the treatment of malaria. Those are slow acting agent and act through competitive antagonism with *p*-aminobenzoic acid for the dihydropteroate synthase with *p*-amino acid benzoic.

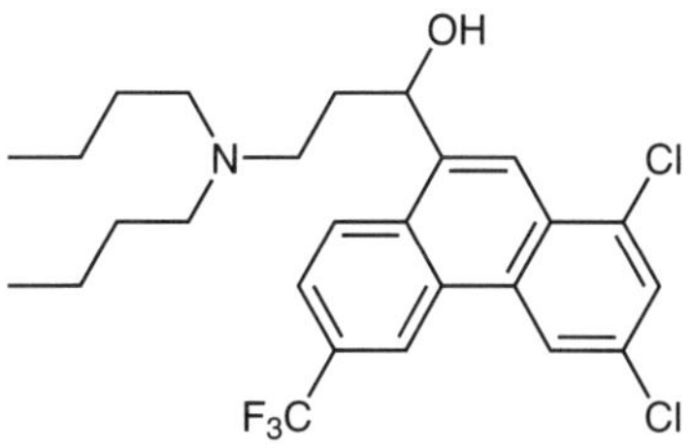

Halofantrine

Figure 9. Halofantrine, a 9-phenantrenemethanol, was first discovered to possess antimalarial activity during the World War II by Wiselogle. The drug was not developed until the 1960s when the Walter Reed Army Institute engaged in identifying new antimalarials. Halofantrine was as potent as chloroquine when tested against *P. falciparum* in monkeys, and equally effective against quinine, chloroquine, and pyrimethamine-resistant strains [147]. Halofantrine entered the market in 1984. It is a blood schizonticide without gametocytocidal activity [148].

2.2.4. Halofantrine Halofantrine (Fig. 9), a 9-phenantrenemethanol, was first discovered to possess antimalarial activity during the World War II by Wiselogle. But with the success of other antimalarials at that time, the drug was not developed until the 1960s when the Walter Reed Army Institute engaged in identifying new antimalarials. Halofantrine was as potent as chloroquine when tested against *P. falciparum* in monkeys, and equally effective against quinine, chloroquine and pyrimethamine-resistant strains. Its mechanism of action seems to involve binding to ferriprotoporphyrin and possibly affects the mitochondria [147].

After a lengthy development process, halofantrine entered the market in 1984. It is a blood schizonticide without gametocytocidal activity [148]. Halofantrine is metabolized primarily by CYP3A4, the main metabolite is *N*-desbutylhalofantrine [149]. Its protein binding in human blood is 83%, mainly to the low density and high-density lipoproteins. Halofantrine has low binding affinities to the serum major proteins, alpha 1-acid glycoprotein and albumin. It has some clear disadvantages: it is poorly soluble in water and has variable intrasubject bioavailability. Its elimination half-life in healthy volunteers is 1–2 days and 3–5 days for the major metabolite. However, halofan-

trine can also induce long QT syndrome (LQTS) and torsades de pointes, a potentially life-threatening ventricular arrhythmia [150].

2.2.5. Hydroxynaphtoquinones Another series of compoudns that emerged from screening during World War II were the hydroxynapthoquinones. From an initial screening of thousands of chemicals, several hundred hydroxynaphtoquinones were synthesized and tested in ducklings infected with *P. lophorue*. Some of those compounds had a greater potency than quinine. In the 1960s, the hydroxynaphtoquinone lapinone (Fig. 10a) showed a clinical activity against *P. vivax* but had a poor absorption. Interest in naphtoquinones as antimalarials faded until decades later when scientists at the Wellcome Research Laboratories in the United Kingdom, with the knowledge of the antiprotozoal activity of menoctone (Fig. 10b) and its electron transport inhibitory activity, decided to reinvestigate naphtoquinones. Based on parvaquone (Fig. 10c) analogs were synthesized and atovaquone (Fig. 10d) was later identified as the best candidate [151].

Atovaquone's mechanism of action is based on the inhibition of the parasite cytochrome bc$_1$ complex of the mitochondrial electron transport system. It specifically binds the ubiquinol oxidation pocket of the bc$_1$ complex [152]. During Phase I clinical trials, the measured elimination half-life was 70 h and plasma levels were found to be significantly higher when food was ingested prior to drug administration [153]. The pharmacokinetics of atovaquone in combination with proguanil is not significantly different from the pharmacokinetics as a monotherapy [154].

Clinical treatment failures to atovaquone in combination with proguanil have been documented. The molecular basis for the resistance has been linked to specific mutations in the cytochrome b gene [155–157].

2.2.6. Pyronaridine Pyronaridine (Fig. 11) is the end result of a long research process carried out mainly in China. Inspired by the activity of quinacrine and its derivatives against chloroquine-resistant strains of *Plasmodium*, Chinese scientists optimized the scaffold series in an effort to improve the potency and deal with toxicity issues. The compound has been regis-

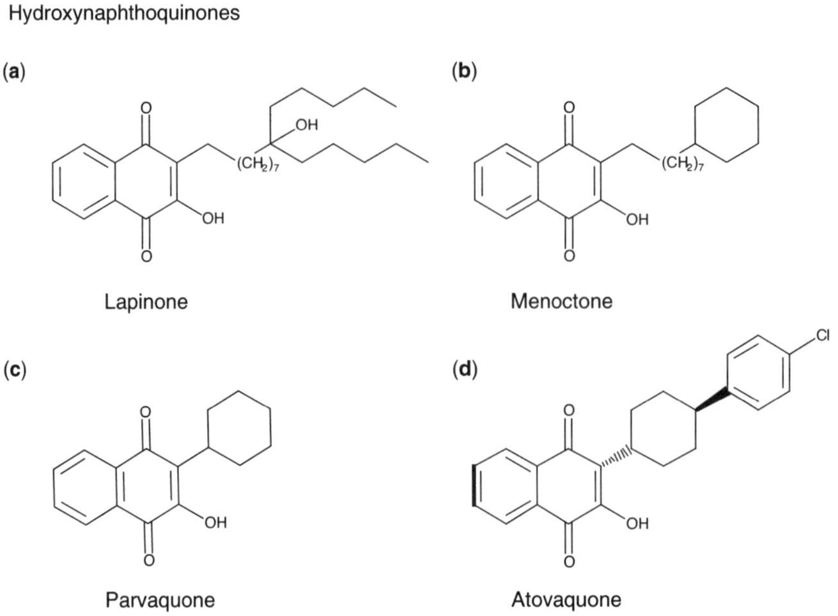

Hydroxynaphthoquinones

(a)

Lapinone

(b)

Menoctone

(c)

Parvaquone

(d)

Atovaquone

Figure 10. (a) Lapinone. In the 1960s, this hydroxynaphtoquinone showed a clinical activity against *P. vivax* but had a poor absorption. Scientists at the Wellcome Research Laboratories in the United Kingdom, with the knowledge of the antiprotozoal activity of menoctone (b) and its electron transport inhibitory activity, decided to reinvestigate naphtoquinones. Based on parvaquone (c) analogs were synthesized and atovaquone (d) was later identified as the best candidate [151].

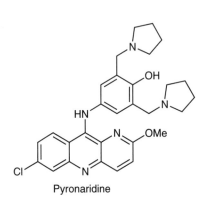

Pyronaridine

Figure 11. Pyronaridine is the end result of a long research process carried out mainly in China. Based on the activity of quinacrine and its derivatives against chloroquine-resistant strains of *Plasmodium*, Chinese scientists optimized the scaffold series to improve the potency and decrease the toxicity. The compound has been registered in China only since the 1980s [158]. The drug is active versus the asexual stage of malaria and its mode of action is poorly understood.

tered in China since the 1980s though no other countries have approved it for use due to issues with international regulatory standards [158]. Its development, optimization and clinical studies have been reviewed [159–161]. The drug is active versus the erythrocytic stage of malaria and its mode of action is poorly understood. Some groups have suggested that it may act throughout topoisomerase II [162,163]. Others have hypothesized that it works through inhibition of heme crystallization in a manner similar to 4-amino quinolines [164–166].

Clinically, it has proven efficacious as a monotherapy in Cameroon and Thailand. A 3-day regimen was reported to produce a 100% cure rate in Cameroon in both children and adults, which contrasted starkly with chloroquine that was reported to be 44% effective in adults and 40% effective in children in the same studies [167,168]. Studies in Thailand have reported somewhat lower cure rates of 63% and 88% for 3- and 5-day treatment regimens, respectively [169]. The discrepancies between the studies is likely due to the fact that the studies in Cameroon had a 14-day follow-up whereas the Thai trials followed patients for 28 days following treatment. *In vitro* studies have shown that resistance to pyronaridine is relatively easily acquired in laboratory settings, suggesting that the drug should be used in combination therapies rather than as a monotherapy [170,171]. A combination of pyronaridine, sulfadoxine, and pyrimethamine has shown promising early results, with 100% cure rates for *P. falciparum* infections in China [172,173]. Combinations with artesunate have also proven efficacious, with a 100% cure rate after 28 days in African children [174]. Pyronaridine is synergistic with primaquine as well as with artemisinin [171,175,176]. However, it has shown antagonism in combination with mefloquine and dihydroartemisinin [177].

It is estimated that the cost of treating a patient with pyronaridine is roughly half that of treating with oral quinine, halofantrine, or sulfadoxine/pyrimethamine/mefloquine and approximately three times as much as treating with chloroquine. Given the rising resistance to chloroquine, pyronaridine has been suggested as a relatively inexpensive alternative treatment option [167]. Given the efficacy of this drug versus a wide range of multidrug-resistant parasite strains, it seems that its use will likely rise in the future [178–184].

2.2.7. Antibiotics Several antibiotics also have potent antimalarial activities. Most act via targets located in the apicoplast (also referred to as the plastid), an organelle unique to *Plasmodium* sp. and other members of the phylum *Apicomplexa*. This chloroplast-like organelle was first observed in the early 1970s when it was presumed to be a mitochondria and largely ignored until the 1990s when DNA sequencing techniques made the characterization of this unique structure possible [185,186]. The apicoplast is thought to have been acquired by the parasite through secondary endosymbiosis of either a red or a green algal ancestor after which the photosynthetic role of the organelle was lost [187,188]. It possesses four membranes and a small circular genome, with many genes that are homologous to plant and algal sequences [189,190]. There is one apicoplast per cell, with organelle

replication occurring prior to schizogony. The apicoplasts are segregated into the resulting daughter cells faithfully [191,192]. The activity of the apicoplast in the insect and liver stages of the *Plasmodium* lifecycle is uncharacterized, though it is assumed to be present, since it has been demonstrated that the apicoplast cannot be generated *de novo* [193]. The exact biological role of the apicoplast is not fully understood, although it has been shown to be involved with isoprene biosynthesis, fatty acid synthesis, and heme synthesis [194].

The apicoplast has been chemically and genetically validated as a drug target in *Plasmodium* sp. and in *Toxoplasma gondii,* a related *Apicomplexan* [195–204]. A characteristic delayed-death phenotype in which the parasite dies one generation following inactivation of the apicoplast is observed in all of these cases. It seems that although the parasite is able to survive without apicoplast function while remaining in the same host cell, it is unable to establish new infection. The mechanistic reason for this is still unknown. However, the delayed-death phenotype is a convenient biomarker for identifying compounds acting via apicoplast pathways. It should be noted that this has been disputed recently, and though the delayed-death phenotype is characteristic of some of the antibiotic classes below, it is by no means universal [205–207]. Many of the antibiotics also have other known targets besides the apicoplast, and activity at those targets makes deconvolution of the observed phenotypes problematic [205–207].

Due to the slow-acting nature of many antibiotics, it is recommended to use most in combination with a faster-acting antimalarial, such as quinine or quinidine [208]. The tetracycline antibiotics, both tetracycline (Fig. 12a) and the closely related doxycycline (Fig. 12b), are thought to act by preventing peptidyl tRNA molecules from binding to the 70S ribosomes in the apicoplasts of the parasite. Both display the delayed-death phenotype typical of apicoplast action [207,209–213]. A 7-day course of tetracycline–quinine combination has proven efficacious in treating drug-resistant infections in Southeast Asia [214,215]. Doxycycline has been used prophylactically in both travelers and military per-

Clinically used antibiotics

Tetracyclines

(a)

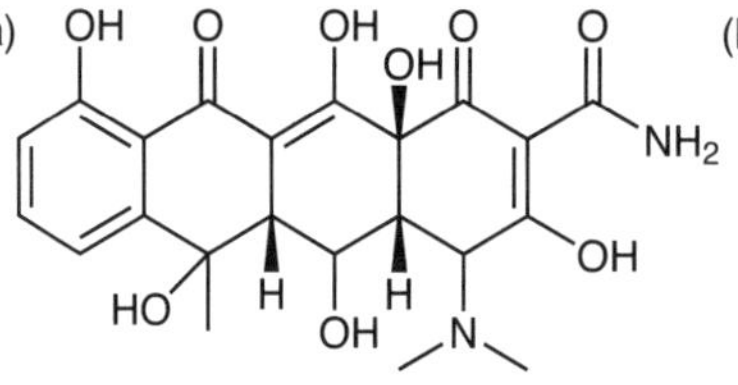

Tetracycline
P. falciparum IC_{50} = 3.1 µM
Apicoplast targeted

(b)

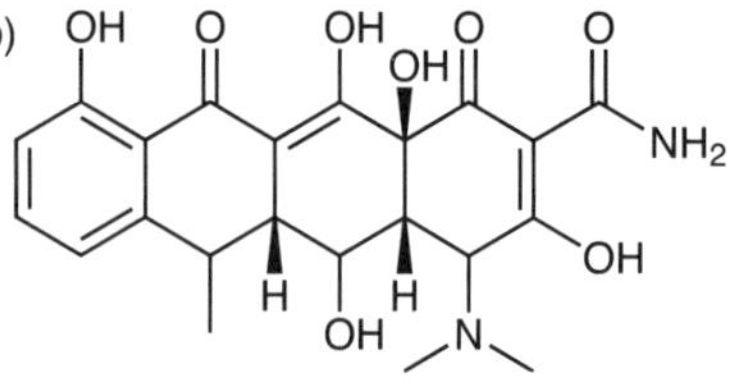

Doxycycline
P. falciparum IC_{50} = 5.6 µM
Apicoplast targeted

(c)

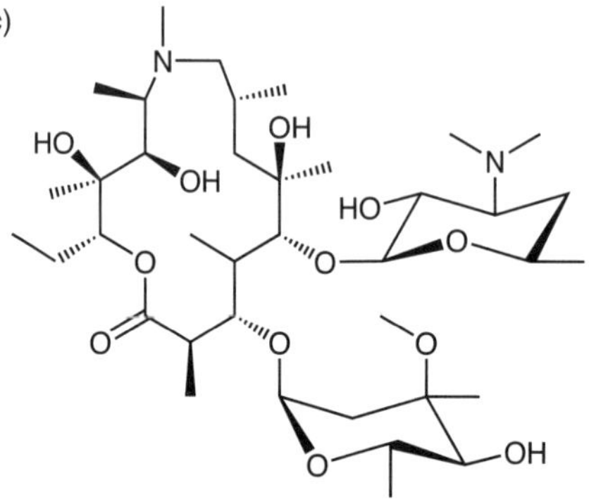

Azithromycin
P. falciparum IC_{50} = 3.0 µM
Apicoplast targeted

(d)

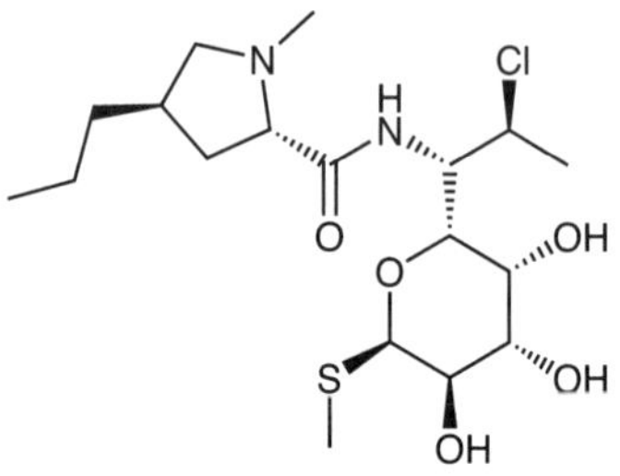

Clindamycin
P. falciparum IC_{50} = 12.5 µM
Apicoplast targeted

(e)

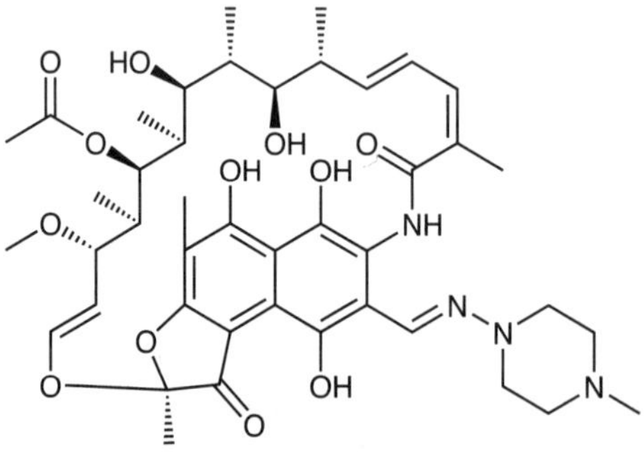

Rifampicin
P. falciparum IC_{50} = 0.27 µM
RNA Polymerase Inhibitor

Figure 12. (a) Tetracycline, a modestly potent antimalarial that displays the "delayed-death" phenotype typical of apicoplast targeted compounds [207,209–213]. This compound has been used in combination with quinine in Southeast Asia [214,215]. (b) Doxycycline, a related tetracycline antibiotic also targeted at the apicoplast.

Fluoroquinolone Antibiotics

Inhibitors of DNA Gyrase

(f)

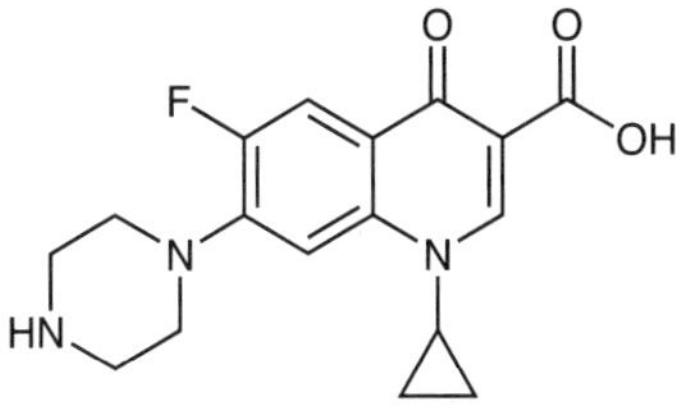

Ciprofloxacin
P. falciparum IC_{50} = 27 µM

(g)

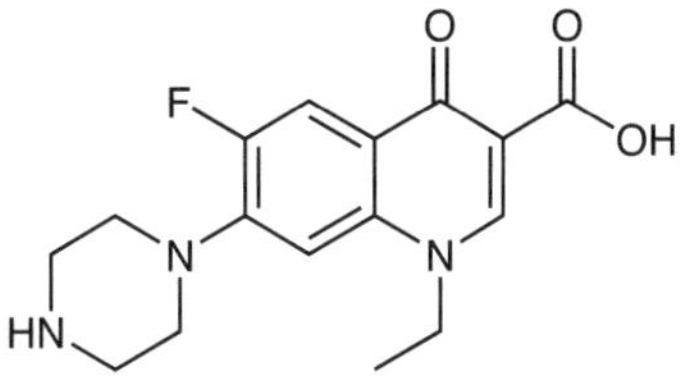

Norfloxacin
P. falciparum IC_{50} = 54 µM

(h)

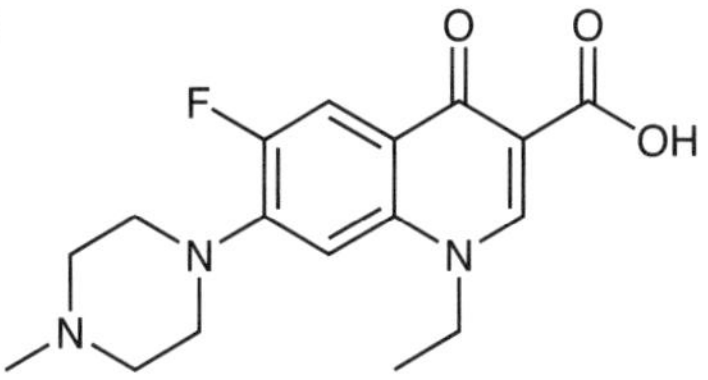

Pefloxacin
P. falciparum IC_{50} = 251 µM

Figure 12. (*Continued*) This drug is typically used in combination with quinine or primaquine and has been used prophylactically as well as a primary treatment [216–220]. (c) Azithromycin, a modestly potent antimalarial often used in combination therapies [223,224]. This compound targets the 70 S ribosome in malarial apicoplasts by blocking the peptide exit tunnel [205,213,225]. It is safe for use by pregnant women [30,226–228]. (d) Clindamycin a potent apicoplast-targeted antimalarial [205,207,209,211]. This compound is efficacious in combination with quinine, artesunate, and fosmidomycin, but not with chloroquine [26,27,230,231,234,237–243]. It is also safe for use by pregnant women [244–248]. (e) Rifampicin, a modestly potent antimalarial causing rapid arrest of parasitic growth in the trophozoite stage. The mechanism of action of this compound in malaria has not yet been fully characterized, but it is thought to act by inhibition of RNA polymerase [205,207,212,254]. Though it has been used in various combination therapies, none are efficacious when compared to other treatment options, and combinations with chloroquine or quinine are antagonistic [255–257]. (f) Ciprofloxacin, a fluoroquinolone DNA gyrase inhibitor displaying poor *in vitro* potency, and modest activities *in vivo* [205,207,258–260]. Although initially promising in mouse models, this compound has not proven clinically useful as of yet [261–265]. (g) Norfloxacin, a fluoroquinolone DNA gyrase inhibitor displaying poor *in vitro* potency, and modest activities *in vivo* [205,207,258–260]. Although initially promising in mouse models, this compound has not proven clinically useful as of yet [261–265]. (h) Pefloxacin, a fluoroquinolone DNA gyrase inhibitor displaying poor *in vitro* potency, and modest activities *in vivo* [205,207,258–260]. Although initially promising in mouse models, this compound has not proven clinically useful as of yet [261–265].

sonnel, though it proved ineffective for causal prophylaxis in hyperendemic areas, even when used in combination with primaquine [216–220]. It should be noted that none of the tetracyclines are recommended for use by pregnant women or by children less than 8-year old [221]. Both tetracycline and doxycycline have modest potencies *in vitro* against whole-cell parasites (IC_{50} = 3.1 and 5.6 µM, respectively) [209,222].

Azithromycin (Fig. 12c) is also a modestly potent antimalarial (IC_{50} = 3.0 µM *in vitro*) and is able to reach low micromolar concentrations in human plasma and tissue [223,224]. Like the tetracyclines, it targets the 70 S ribosome in the apicoplast of the parasite, but by blocking the peptide exit tunnel rather than preventing tRNA binding. This results in the delayed-death phenotype characteristic of apicoplast targeted compounds [205,213,225]. Because of this, azithromycin is typically used in combination with other chemotherapeutic agents. It has been used in clinical trials in combination with artesunate, quinine, chloroquine, and sulfadoxine-pyrimethamine as a treatment for uncomplicated malaria, in pregnancy, and as a prophylactic in both Africa and Southeast Asia [30,226–229]. In all cases, results were extremely promising, with the combinations proving efficacious and no counterindications for use even in pregnant women.

Clindamycin (Fig. 12d) is much more potent ($IC_{50} = 12.5$ mM) than the other antibiotics previously discussed [207]. It too exhibits the delayed-death phenotype and is thought to act in a manner similar to the tetracyclines (preventing the binding of peptidyl tRNA to the 70 S ribosome) [205,207,209,211]. Although clindamycin has been used as a monotherapy (98% efficacy reported), the mean parasite clearance time was 4–6 days, which is much slower than most other antimalarial drugs (typically 2–3 days or 1 day for artesunate) [230–233]. As such, it is recommended that it be used in combination with one of the other faster acting antimalarials. Quinine–clindamycin have been used effectively since the 1970s with good efficacy using a 3-day treatment course [26,230,231,234]. However, for children a 4-day treatment regimen is recommended [235,236]. Chloroquine–clindamycin combinations have also been evaluated, though in general these were less efficacious than quinine–clindamycin combinations, particularly in nonimmune individuals [237–239]. A single study on the use of atresunate–clindamycin has been reported in African school children, showing a more rapid parasite clearance with this combination than with quinine–clindamycin, suggesting that this combination will prove efficacious in the treatment of malaria [27]. No serious adverse effects were reported from this combination. Clindamycin has also been used in combination with fosmidomycin in both adult and pediatric patients in Thailand and Gabon. This synergistic combination showed 100% removal of asexual parasites after only 2 days of treatment [240–242].

However, it was only effective against asexual parasites, suggesting that longer treatment regimens would be needed to prevent recurrence [243]. In addition to its efficacy in combination therapies, a small number of clinical trials suggest that clindamycin is safe for use by pregnant women [244–248]. It should be noted that clindamycin is not effective versus *P. vivax* malaria [230,249–251].

Rifampicin (Fig. 12e) is a modestly potent antimalarial (IC_{50} values from 0.27–2.8 μM) thought to act via inhibition of RNA polymerase [252,253]. This compound does not reliably display the delayed-death phenotype, and its mechanism of action in malaria is debated. It has been shown to arrest parasite growth at the end of the trophozoite stage, suggesting that targets independent of the apicoplast may be the primary site of action [205,207,212,254]. This antibiotic has been used in combination therapies, particularly together with cotrimoxazole and isoniazid, though it has not proved particularly efficacious when compared with other possible treatment regimens [255]. Furthermore, this compound is antagonistic with quinine in the clinic and has shown antagonistic behavior in mouse models of *P. berghei*, making unsuitable for use in combination therapies with more commonly used antimalarials [256,257].

The fluoroquinolone antibiotics ciprofloxacin (Fig. 12f), norfloxacin (Fig. 12g), and pefloxacin (Fig. 12h) display a wide range of potencies versus *P. falciparum*. (IC_{50} values from 27 to 251 μM *in vitro*) These compounds are thought to act via inhibition of DNA gyrase, either in the apicoplast or at the genomic level [258]. They also display a range of delayed-death phenotypes, depending on the *P. falciparum* strain tested, though this phenotype is less pronounced than with the tetracyclines or azithromycin [205,207,259,260]. Ciprofloxacin has shown promise in mouse models of *P. berghei* and *P. yoelii*, displaying synergy with both mefloquine and artesunic acid [261,262]. Early clinical studies suggested that this class of antimicrobials possessed antimalarial efficacy, but later studies did not support this [263–265]. Due to their relatively poor *in vitro* potencies, and the lack of clear clinical efficacy thus far, it is likely that this class of antibiotic will not be useful as an antimalarial.

2.3. Experimental Agents

There are currently twelve translational research projects in preclinical through Phase III trials being pursued by the Medicines for Malaria Venture (MMV), currently the major organizing body for the development of novel antimalarials. Four of these are in either Phase III or registration currently, and all four are new combinations of existing drugs. The most advanced is Coartem®, a combination of artemether, an artemisinin analog, and lumefantrine (Fig. 13a), a quinoline alcohol related to quinine and mefloquine. This combination has shown high efficacy and tolerability in African adults and children with uncomplicated *P. falciparum* malaria [266–269]. Furthermore, this combination is cost effective in comparison to other antimalarial treatment options in areas in which it will be heavily used [270,271]. As a result, this combination is now a first-line therapy in more than 20 African countries including Kenya, Malawi, Uganda, Tanzania, Mozambique, Nigeria, South Africa, and Ethiopia [272]. Another combination under investigation is Pyramax®, a fixed ratio of pyroaridine with artesunate that has proved highly efficacious in the treatment of children in Africa [174]. Also in Phase III trials is the combination of azithromycin and chloroquine, which has proved efficacious in treating malaria in pregnant women without adverse affects to their children [174]. The final combination therapy in late-stage clinical trials is Euratesim™, a combination of dihydroartemisinin and piperaquine (Fig. 13b). Although resistance to piperaquine is already present in China where it was used as first-line monotherapy following its development in the 1970s, the combination has proved highly effective in both Southeast Asia and Africa. Clinical trials have shown that a 3-day course with once-a-day dosing is effective and well tolerated [273–279].

The remaining projects in the MMV pipeline are focused on single agents rather than combinations. Two of these are in Phase II trials. The first is the development of an IV artesunate formulation in an attempt to decrease the recrudescence rate. Prior studies have not shown a large improvement with i.v. formulation of artesunate, but large-scale trials have yet to be published [280–282]. The second project in Phase II trials is the development of a novel artemisinin analog known as artemisone(Fig. 13c) [283]. This compound is an extremely potent antimalarial, with IC_{50} values in the subnanomolar range for most *P. falciparum* strains tested (IC_{50} values from 0.7 to 1.5 nM). Additionally, it does not display any neurotoxicity in rodent models, a failing of many of the artemisinin analogs previously characterized. It is orally efficacious in both *P. berghei* and *P. yoelii* mouse models and *P. falciparum* infections in primates. Preliminary experiments in humans to establish safety, tolerability and pharmacokinetic properties have also been conducted, showing that the compound has a profile comparable to other artemisinin derivatives [284]. Efficacy studies in humans are underway.

There are two projects in Phase I trials as well. The first of these is tafenoquine (Fig. 13d), an improved derivative of the 8-amino quinolines. This compound is active versus both erythrocytic and liver stages of the parasite and has shown promise as a prophylactic agent [158,285–288]. It has also shown efficacy versus *P. vivax* in a primate model [289]. The second Phase I project is isoquine (Fig. 13e) an improved quinoline with potent activities (IC_{50} values from 11.2 to 31.2 nM) versus a wide range *P. falciparum* isolates [83,84]. The compound has been through full preclinical evaluations and has shown both efficacy and acceptable pharmacokinetic properties. A number of close analogs have also been prepared in an effort to address any potential surprises that may occur upon testing in humans, such as metabolic degradation [290]. No human data has been reported for this compound, as yet.

The remaining six translational projects in the MMV pipeline are in preclinical development. The first of these is mirincamycin (Fig. 13f), an antibiotic which has shown synergy with primaquine versus *P. cynomolgi* in primate models [291]. The next is the synthetic peroxide OZ439, a compound which has shown efficacy in mouse models of *P. berghei* [134]. The +enantiomer of mefloquine is also under investigation, as it seems to possess better pharmacokinetic parameters than the -enantiomer [292]. Finally, two inhibitors of the electron transport chain are also being studied. Both of these compounds

Compounds in clinical development

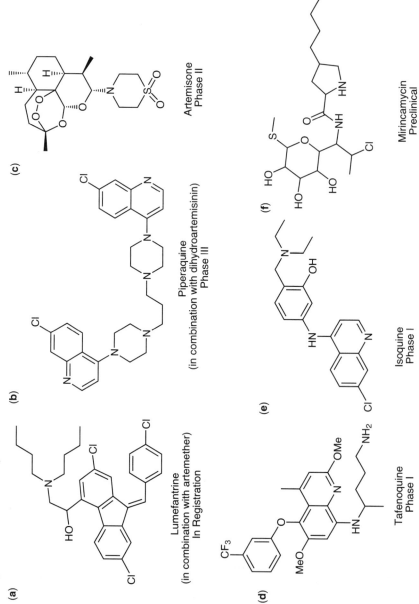

Figure 13. (a) Lumefantrine, a quinoline alcohol related to quinine and mefloquine used in combination with artemether. This combination has shown high efficacy and tolerability in African adults and children with uncomplicated *P. falciparum* malaria [266–269]. (b) Piperaquine, a drug developed in China in the 1970s now being used in combination with dihydroartemisinin. The combination has proved highly effective in both Southeast Asia and Africa. Clinical trials have shown that a 3-day course with once-a-day dosing is effective and well tolerated [273–279]. (c) Artemisone an extremely potent antimalarial, with IC$_{50}$ values in the subnanomolar range for most *P. falciparum* strains tested [283]. (d) Tafenoquine, an improved derivative of the 8-amino quinolines. This compound is active versus both erythrocytic and liver stages of the parasite and has shown promise as a prophylactic agent [158,285–288]. (e) Isoquine, an improved quinoline with potent activities (IC$_{50}$ values from 11.2 to 31.2 nM) versus a wide range *P. falciparum* isolates [83,84]. (f) Mirincamycin, an antibiotic that has shown synergy with primaquine versus *P. cynomolgi* in primate models [291].

626

(MK 4815 and GSK932121) are being perused in collaboration with industrial partners and, as such, there is very little publicly available data about them at this point. In summary, there is a wide range of both novel and reformulated or revisited antimalarial compounds at various stages in the drug development pipeline. It is likely that at least some of these will prove highly efficacious in the field.

The Drugs for Neglected Disease Initiatives (DNDi) is also pursuing efforts in the development of new drugs against malaria. Currently in their pipeline, at the development or clinical stage, are two fixed dose combinations of antimalarials used in patients. Those two combinations are artesunate-amodiaquine and artesunate-mefloquine, which are particularly effective against chloroquine-resistant strains of *P. falciparum* for the treatment of uncomplicated malaria [293]. Resistance to artesunate-mefloquine in the Cambodia–Thailand border has been reported with the mechanism of resistance linked to an increased *pfmdr* copy number [294–296]. Artesunate-mefloquine is safe and well tolerated [297,298] Artesunate-amodiaquine is also safe and well tolerated, efficacious in children younger than 5 years [299] with gametocyticidal activity [300]; nevertheless, the total drug exposure to both drugs is reduced when used in combination in healthy volunteers [301]. DNDi with Sanofi Aventis registered artesunate-amodiaquine in Morocco while the prequalification dossier has been submitted to WHO [302].

3. POTENTIAL TARGETS FOR ANTIMALARIAL DRUG DEVELOPMENT

3.1. Cell Cycle Regulation

3.1.1. Kinases Protein kinases (PKs) are the enzymes responsible for phosphorylating serine, theronine, or tyrosine residues on a wide range of cellular proteins. This covalent modification is one of the most ubiquitous regulatory mechanisms for eukaryotic cells. The human genome encodes more than 500 PKs, accounting for $\sim$2% of the total encoded genes [303,304]. The kinases also play a major role in many human diseases and have attracted much interest as chemotherapeutic targets. The prototypical example is the oncology drug Gleevic®, which inhibits BCR-ABL, a cytoplasmic tyrosine kinase which has been shown to be constitutively active in most patients with chronic myelogenous leukemia [305]. Most kinase inhibitors block more than one kinase; indeed, Gleevic is useful in treating other cancers due to its ability to inhibit other tyrosine kinases [306,307]. Kinases have been targeted for the treatment of neurodegenerative diseases, chronic inflammation, metabolic disorders, and a host of cancers and other conditions. There are more than 60 kinase-targeted drugs in clinical development. It has been estimated that 30% of all drug discovery efforts have been focused on this target class [308,309].

Eukaryotic PKs (ePKs) fall into seven major phylogenetic classes, each sharing conserved amino acid sequences and common structural folds [310]: CK1 (casein kinase 1), CMGC (cyclin-dependent kinases (CDKs), mitogen-activated protein kinases (MAPKs), glycogen synthase kinase 3 (GSK3), and CDK-like kinases (CLKs)), TKL (tyrosine-kinase-like), AGC (cyclic-adenosine-monophosphate-dependent protein kinase (PKA), cyclic-guanosine-monophosphate-dependent protein kinase (PKG), and protein kinase C (PKC)), CamK (calcium/calmodulin-dependent kinases), STE (regulators of MAPKs), and TyrK (tyrosine kinases). Kinases that do not fit into one of these groups are typically referred to as other or orphan kinases (OPKs).

P. falciparum expresses a much more limited set of PKs than do mammalian cells. The genome encodes between 86 and 99 PK homologs; it lacks two of the seven major mammalian kinase families (the TyrK and STE groups) [311,312]. There is also a new family not present in mammalian cells, the calcium-dependent kinases (CDPKs) in which a kinase domain is fused to a calmodulin domain. This family is also found in plants and alveolates, but not metazoans [313]. There is also group of 21 kinases that appear to be unique to Apicomplexan parasites [314,315]. Additionally, the genome contains a number of orphan kinases with no clear homologs or orthologs in the human genome. Even malarial enzymes that do fit into one of the canonical mammalian families often lack clear mammalian homologs. The divergence of the malarial kinome from the mammalian counterpart suggests that it should be possible to develop novel inhibitors that are specific for *Plasmodium* enzymes.

Generally speaking, the function of the malarial kinases is poorly understood. This is largely due to the difficulty of performing classical genetics experiments such as knockouts in the parasite. However, reverse genetics techniques are becoming more feasible, and it is likely that more malaria targets will be validated in the coming years [316]. Currently kinase targets have been chosen largely though sequence-based homology approaches, in which it is assumed that a malaria kinase bearing a high degree of sequence homology to a characterized kinase in another system will share a similar function. Despite the pharmacological attractiveness of this target family, comparatively little work has been done to develop inhibitors for specific malarial kinases, or even specific kinase families in malaria.

One initial focus has been Pfmrk, a homolog of CDK7, a cyclin-dependent kinase known to play critical roles in mammalian transcription and cell cycle control. Early work identified the 3-phenyl-quinolinone scaffold as a potential lead compound (Fig. 14a). This series displayed only modest potencies against the enzymatic target (EC_{50} values of 18–387 µM); none were reported to be active intact parasites [317]. Continuing work on this target led to discovery of the oxindole and isoquinoline sulfonamide-based scaffolds. Both series display reasonable potencies (EC_{50} values 0.7–500 µM) against Pfmrk, but lack efficacy against cultured malaria (Fig. 14b,c) [318,319]. The most promising series of Pfmrk inhibitors emerged from a pharmacophore-based approach in which a model derived from diverse promiscuous kinase inhibitors displaying a wide range of potencies against Pfmrk was used to select a set of 16 Pfmrk inhibitors from an existing compound library. The most potent compounds identified in this effort were the trypanthrins (Fig. 14d), which displayed moderate potencies (EC_{50} values 40 nM to 1.1 mM) against the enzyme and better potency (EC_{50} values 1.5 nM to 211 µM) against cultured *P. falciparum* [320,321]. The structure–activity relationships of this series were not discussed with only two members of the family reported as active.

A second targeted kinase is Pfnek-1, which is homologous to the NIMA kinases that regulate cytokinesis in mammalian cells [322]. Screening of crude natural product extracts led to the isolation and characterization of xestoquinone from a marine sponge (Fig. 14e) [323]. This compound is moderately potent (EC_{50} 1.1 µM) and highly selective for Pfnek-1 in preference over other malarial and mammalian kinases including PfPK5, PfPK7, PfGSK-3, GSK-3α/β, CDK1/cyclin B, CDK5/p25, Erk2, PKA, pp60, and EGFR. Furthermore, it possesses reasonable growth inhibitory potency against cultured *P. falciparum* (EC_{50} 3 µM) and shows some efficacy in *in vivo* in murine models of *P. berghei* infection. However, the therapeutic

Figure 14. (a) 3-phenyl-quinolinone, an early inhibitor developed for Pfmrk, a homolog of CDK7. This inhibitor was not tested in whole-cell assays and displays only moderate potency against the enzymatic target [317]. (b) Oxindole Pfmrk inhibitors. These compounds are more potent against the enzymatic target but lack appreciable whole-cell efficacy [318]. (c) An isoquinoline sulfonamide inhibitor displaying potent inhibition of Pfmrk, but lacking appreciable efficacy versus whole-cell *P. falciparum* [319]. (d) Tryptanthrin inhibitors of Pfmrk identified using a pharmacophore approach. These compounds are moderately potent versus the enzymatic target, and show promising growth inhibitory potencies against culutured parasites [321]. (e) Xestoquinone, a natural product inhibitor of Pfnek-1isolated from a marine sponge. This compound reduces parasitemia in a murine model of infection by 47% following 4 daily IP injections at a dosage of 5 mg/kg [323]. (f) A pyridazine PfPK7 inhibitor from a series of similar compounds possessing modest potencies in both enzymatic and growth inhibitory assays. A structure of the enzyme bound to an exemplar inhibitor has been determined [324]. (g) Purvalanol B, an inhibitor of various CDKs shown to inhibit PfPK5 with an IC_{50} of 130 nM. This compound was also effective in blocking growth of parasites with an IC_{50} of 7.7 µM. Affinity chromatography approaches have identified a casein kinase rather than PfPK5 as being the major intracellular target of this compound [334]. (14) A pyridine kinase inhibitor used to identify a new kinase target in the apicomplexan *E. tenella*. This compound is also quite potent versus other parasite species and is orally bioavailable in chickens. The efficacy in malaria models is unreported [335,336].

Inhibitors of *Plasmodium* Protein Kinases

(a)

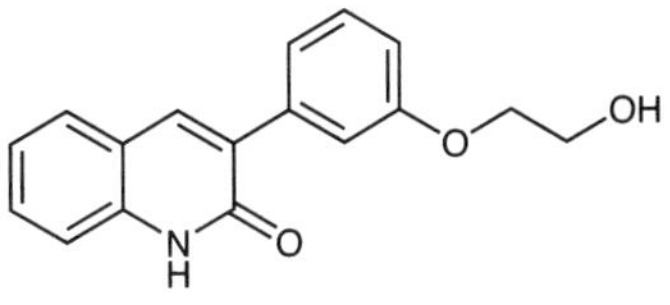

Pfmrk IC$_{50}$ = 18 μM

(b)

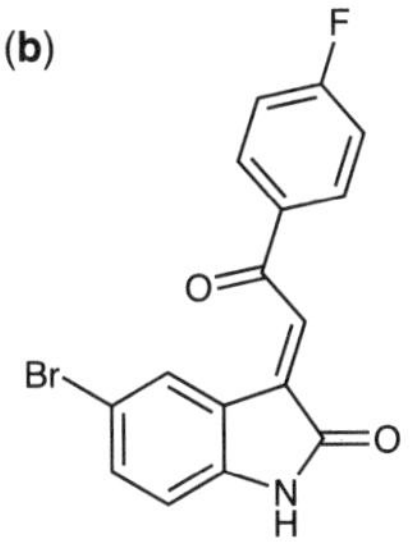

Pfmrk IC$_{50}$ = 1.4 μM
P. falciparum IC$_{50}$ = >14.4 μM
PfPK5 IC$_{50}$ = 190 μM

(c)

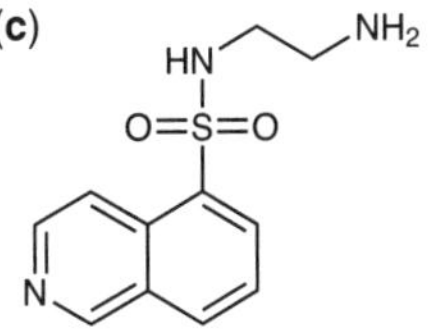

Pfmrk IC$_{50}$ = 0.7 μM
P. falciparum IC$_{50}$ = >72 μM

(d)

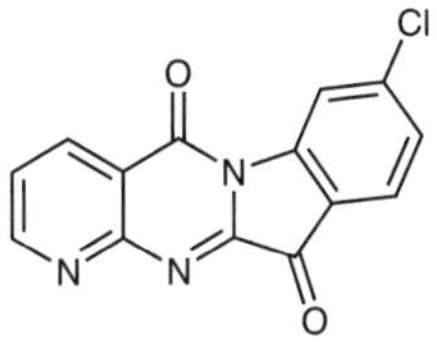

Pfmrk IC$_{50}$ = 3.5 μM
P. falciparum IC$_{50}$ = 0.9 μM

(e)

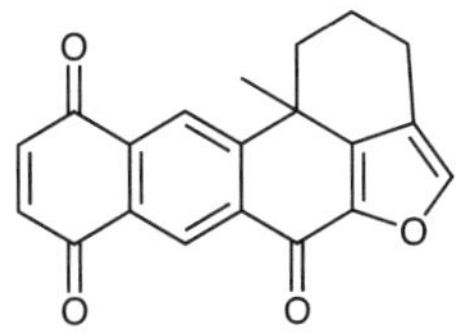

Pfnek-1 IC$_{50}$ = 1.1 μM   *P. falciparum* IC$_{50}$ = 3 μM
PfPK5 IC$_{50}$ = 17 μM   5 mg/kg IP/4 days results in
PfPK7 IC$_{50}$ = >100 μM   47% reduction in parasitemia
PfGSK-3 IC$_{50}$ = >100 μM

(f)

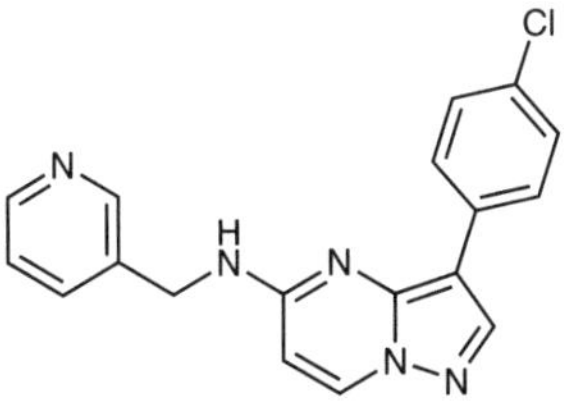

PfPK7 IC$_{50}$ = 4.6 μM
P. falciparum IC$_{50}$ = 1.0 μM

(g)

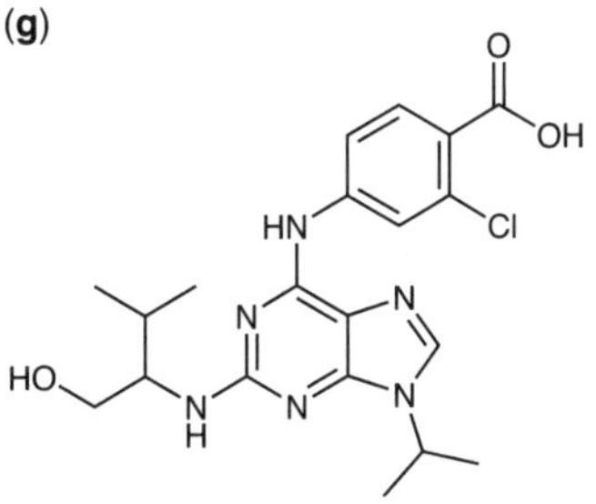

PfPK5 IC$_{50}$ = 130 nM
CDK2 IC$_{50}$ = 5 nM
P. falciparum IC$_{50}$ = 7.07 μM

(h)

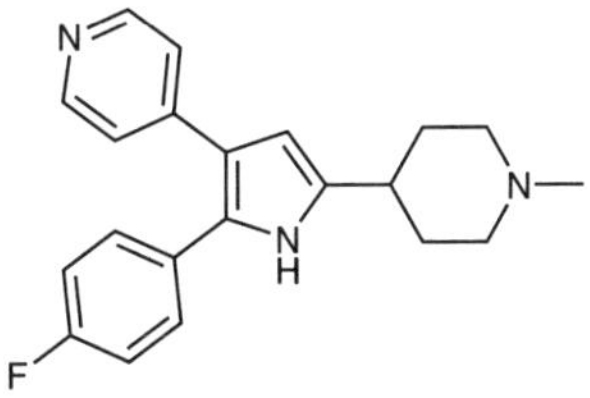

Inhibits *Eimeria sp.* oocyst output at 50 ppm in chicken feed
PKG k$_i$ = 0.21 nM
E. tenella IC$_{50}$ = > 5 μM
T. gondii IC$_{50}$ = 210 nM
B. jellisoni IC$_{50}$ = 20 nM
N. caniunum IC$_{50}$ = 20 nM

Figure 14. (*Continued*)

index for this compound is fairly low: sevenfold for *in vitro* assays and only fourfold over efficacious dose of 5 mg/kg *in vivo*.

Only two malarial kinases have been crystallized, PfPK5, a homolog of both CDK1 and CDK5, and PfPK7, an orphan kinase that has been shown to be involved with parasite proliferation and development [324–326]. Both of these enzymes were crystallized with and without various small molecule inhibitors. The availability of this data makes structure-based drug design approaches realistic possibilities for both of these enzymes. However, no compound series have been designed as of yet using these structures as a starting point.

Although *P. falciparum* possesses two MAPK encoding genes (Pf*map*-1 and Pf*map*-2), it lacks an ortholog to the MAPK kinase (MEK) typically responsible for activating these genes [311,312,327–330]. This pathway is known to play critical roles in mammalian cellular proliferation [331]. The malarial kinase bearing the greatest homology to MEK is PfPK7, which has sparked interest in it as a potential drug target [332]. The PfPK7 structure includes a pyridazine-based inhibitor from a series with moderate potencies against both the enzyme (EC$_{50}$ values 4.3–100 µM) and growth inhibition of *P. falciparum* (EC$_{50}$ values 1.0–75 µM) (Fig. 14f) [324]. These inhibitors were discovered using a thermal shift assay and have been shown to be ATP competitive. They were also screened against a 78 kinase panel of *P. falciparum* kinases and shown to inhibit a number of these with similar potencies suggesting that their whole-cell activities may be a result of inhibition of multiple malarial kinases.

The other malaria kinase for which structural data exists is PfPK5. The structure of this homolog of CDK1 and CDK5 was solved both without inhibitor bound and with a set of 3 known CDK inhibitors. While most of the inhibitors had modest potencies (EC$_{50}$ values of 130 nM to 5.5 µM), none showed selectivity for PfPK5 when compared to CDK2. There was, however, some reverse selectivity seen, suggesting that structural differences between the enzymes might be exploited in the effort to develop inhibitors selective for the parasitic enzyme. The most potent of the compounds tested was purvalanol B, which had an IC$_{50}$ of 130 nM against PfPK5 and a growth inhibitory EC$_{50}$ of 7.07 µM [325,333].

Interestingly, purvalanol B was also immobilized on an agarose matrix and used to identify other potential kinase targets in malaria. This approach led to the identification of CK1 as being the major pyruvalanol B binding protein in *P. falciparum*, *Leishmania mexicana*, *T. gondii* and *Trypanosoma cruzi* [334]. This suggests that the relevant target of these inhibitors may be CK1 and that this target may be relevant in a wide range of parasitic diseases. However, despite this promising observation, no additional work has been done to identify potent inhibitors of this kinase. This general approach to kinase target identification has been used in other apicomplexan parasites as well. A substituted pyridine (Fig. 14h) shown to posses potent growth inhibitory activity against *Eimeria tenella*, *T. gondii*, *Neospora caninum*, and *Besnoitia jellisoni* was used as a probe to purify and characterize a cGMP-dependent protein kinase (PKG) from *E. tenella* extract [335]. This kinase was later shown to be the relevant target using knockin experiments with a resistant form of the enzyme [336].

The main shortcoming in the field of antimalarial kinase inhibitors has not been a lack of potential targets or assay technologies. Many different PK values have been inactivated via genetic techniques, and more are added to the list every year [326,337–343]. Assays for kinases are readily available and amenable to high-throughput techniques [344]. Additionally, there are a wide range of known kinase inhibitors for mammalian kinases available for use as controls [308,309]. It seems that the major barrier has been access to high-quality kinase inhibitor libraries for screening, which is largely held within the pharmaceutical industry. Therefore, the time seems ripe for further exploitation of this target family.

3.1.2. Farnesylation Protein farnesyl transferase (PFT) is an enzyme in eukaryotes that modifies proteins posttranslationally by addition of a farnesyl group, a C15 isoprenoid lipid [345]. The action of PFT is directed by the presence of a consensus sequence—CaaX, where C is cysteine, a is aliphatic side-chain amino acid, and X is any amino acid—at the carboxy termini of target proteins. Farnesyl is transferred to the cysteine residue in the CaaX motif thus conferring membrane association to the protein. Protein farnesylation is a key component in many signal transduction cascades where protein association to membrane is essential for successful transduction. This property has made farnesylation a potential target for drug development, particularly in the Ras signaling pathway. Mutations in Ras, which occur in 20–30% of all cancers, enhance the growth signal by allowing cells to evade cell progression control, thereby rendering them highly proliferative [346].

The potential for the use of PFT inhibitors in cancer therapy has been proven although such agents have been difficult to develop [347]. PFT inhibitors have also as found use as antiparasitic agents [348]. PFT has been identified in trypanosomes, schistosomes, and malaria [348–350]. Since its identification in the late 90s, PfPFT has been evaluated as a potential drug target. Peptidomimetics L-745,631 and L-744,832, which are potent mammalian PFT inhibitors, are good inhibitors of *P. falciparum* growth in culture [349]. 2-Oxotetrahydroquinoline-PFT inhibitors are highly potent antimalarials *in vitro* [351]. Also, the emergence of PfPFT inhibitor-resistant clones in culture reinforces the need for a combination therapy-based approach [352].

Efforts to design inhibitors of *Plasmodium* protein farnesyltransferase (*Pf*PFT) and coworkers identified a series of peptidomimetic inhibitors based on the CaaX (C = Cys, aa = aliphatic dipeptide, and X = Met, Glu, or Ser) recognition sequence of the mammalian enzyme [353] (Fig. 15a). While relatively little biological testing was performed with this series, it provided a valuable proof of concept by demonstrating that these inhibitors were capable of slowing parasite growth. Testing of these compounds revealed no correlation between inhibitory potency against the mammalian enzyme and antiparasitic potency, suggesting either a difference in active sites between the mammalian and the *Plasmodium* enzymes or off-target effects. Despite these early shortcomings, other efforts were able to

generate compounds based on this series that exhibited modest potencies (IC$_{50}$ 0.9–6.3 μM) against *Pf*PFT and were capable of preventing farnesylation of proteins in whole parasites at a concentration of 5 μM [354]. Due to relatively poor whole-cell potencies, the initial series was not suitable for *in vivo* work. However, further work was able overcome problems with poor membrane permeability using an ester-based prodrug approach. This resulted in a compound that decreased parasitemia by 50% in a standard Peter's 4-day suppressive test (daily, i.p., 50 mg/kg) [355]. This represented the first *in vivo* proof-of-concept study for the validity of this target in treatment of malaria.

During this same time-frame, a newly discovered antimalarial scaffold was hypothesized to be an inhibitor of malarial protein farnesyltransferase [356–358].(Fig. 15b) An intensive period of optimization followed, in which structure–activity relationships were determined using a parasite growth inhibition assay with the drug-resistant *P. falciparum* strain Dd2 [359–363]. These efforts resulted in optimized compounds with potency in the low nanomolar range (IC$_{50}$ values 47 nM to 24 μM). However, none of these compounds had in murine malaria models. Hypothesizing that this was due to low compound solubility the authors produced compounds with increased solubility by introducing a methylpiperazinyl group [364]. This optimized compound was active *in vivo* in the *Plasmodium vinckei* mouse model (ED$_{90}$ 25 mg/kg, i.p., 3 days). The same study also showed activity against *P. falciparum* protein farnesyltransferase in whole-cell assays, strongly suggesting that the antiparasitic activities displayed by the compounds were due to inhibition of PFT. Following this study, the authors attempted to replace the methylpiperazinyl group with other solubulizing groups in order to increase potencies versus both cultured parasites and *Pf*PFT. These efforts were largely unsuccessful, offering only slight increases in selectivity for the parasitic enzyme versus the human homolog with no major increases in potency [365–368]. Later, using molecular docking studies with a PfPFT homology model, the group replaced the methylpiperazine with an ethylenediamine

Protein farnesyltransferase inhibitors

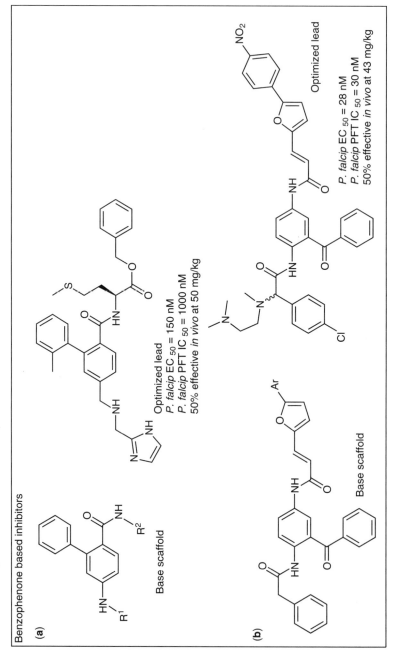

Figure 15. The benzophenone scaffold developed by Hamilton and coworkers [353]. The optimized lead compound in this series was shown to reduce parasitemia by 50% in mouse models of infection [355]. (b) A second series of benzophenone inhibitors reported by Wiesner and coworkers. This series was highly optimized over several years, resulting in compounds showing activity in mouse models [356–369]. No orally bioavailable compound has been reported from this series. (c) An inhibitor series developed by Glenn and coworkers. The compounds have *in vitro* IC$_{50}$ values in the low nanomolar range and are orally bioavailable in rats [370,371]. The compounds have not yet been reported to be active in animal models of infection. (d) An early stage scaffold reported by Millet and coworkers in 2004 [377,378]. This series does not show a high degree of correlation between enzymatic inhibition and whole-cell antimalarial activity. (e) A compound from Bristol-Myers Squibb reported in 2005 by Nallan et al. as a potent inhibitor of *Pf*PFT and as a potent antimalarial [372]. (f) A second scaffold was also reported by Nallan et al. in 2005 that was subsequently modified to improve pharmacokinetic properties. This scaffold is orally bioavailable in rats [375].

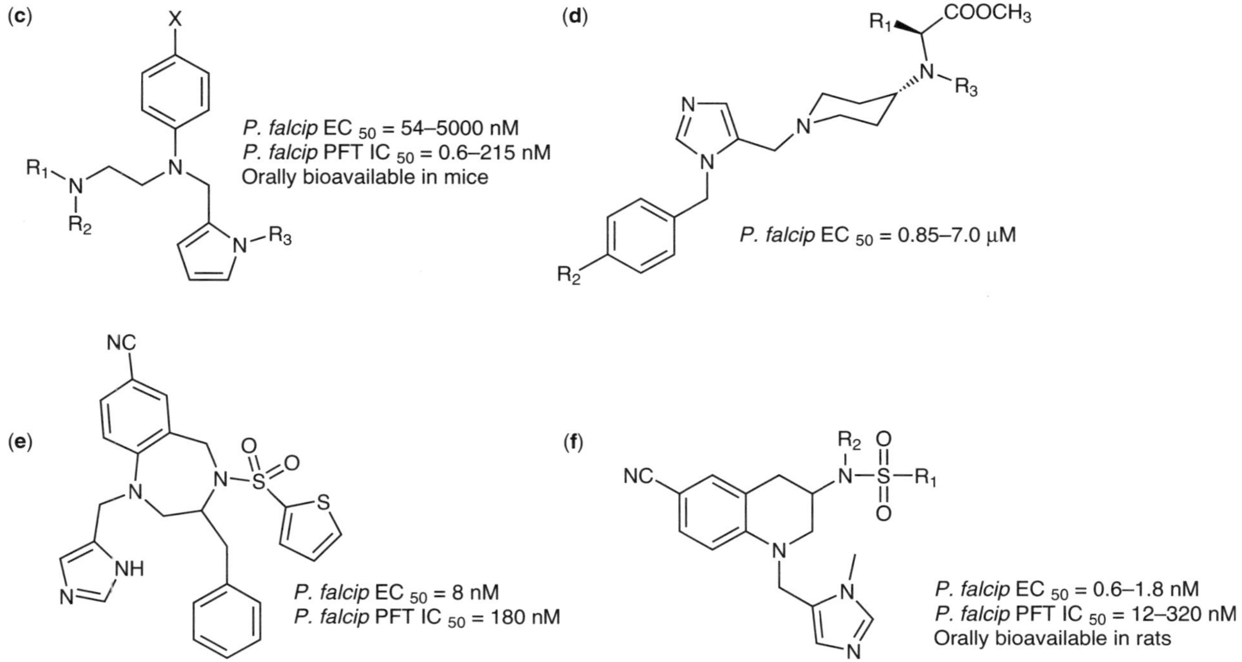
(c)
X
R1
N
R2
N
N
R3
P. falcip EC 50 = 54–5000 nM
P. falcip PFT IC 50 = 0.6–215 nM
Orally bioavailable in mice
(d)
R1
COOCH3
N
R3
N
N
N
R2
P. falcip EC 50 = 0.85–7.0 μM
(e)
NC
N
N
S
O
O
S
NH
N
P. falcip EC 50 = 8 nM
P. falcip PFT IC 50 = 180 nM
(f)
NC
R2
N
S
O
O
R1
N
N
N
P. falcip EC 50 = 0.6–1.8 nM
P. falcip PFT IC 50 = 12–320 nM
Orally bioavailable in rats

Figure 15. *(Continued).*

[369] yielding compounds with improved *in vitro* and *in vivo* activities, as well as improved selectivity for malaria parasites in comparison to human cells. While this was a promising approach, the group has not yet reported an orally active analog, an important step in the development of any antimalarial.

Simple tetra-substituted ethylenediamines (Fig. 15c), designed using flexible ligand-docking to a homology model of *Pf*PFT, are competent enzyme inhibitors [370]. Of the nine compounds synthesized to test this model, eight inhibited *Pf*PFT with IC_{50} values better than 50 nM and inhibited growth of both 3D7 and K1 *P. falciparum* strains *in vitro* with submicromolar EC_{50} values. In this series, enzyme inhibition generally correlated with whole-cell activities. The compounds were shown to be orally bioavailable and reasonably metabolically stable in rats. Expansion of the initial series provided compounds with better than 100-fold selectivity for the malarial enzyme versus the rat while maintaining potency in the nanomolar range (EC_{50} 0.5 nM to 1 μM) [371]. Despite this promising profile, no compounds in the series have been reported to be active in rodent malaria models.

In another study, a wide selection of PFT inhibitors developed by industry as cancer chemotherapeutic agents were tested for inhibition of *Pf*PFT *in vitro* and growth inhibitory activity against *P. falciparum* (strain 3D7) [372]. Among the scaffolds identified as potential leads were both benzodiazepine and tetrahydroquinoline (THQ)-based scaffolds (Fig. 15e) possessing potent activity against both malaria parasites (IC_{50} 5 nM to 20 μM) and the enzymatic target (IC_{50} 0.6 nM to 1 μM). The authors chose to pursue the THQ series for further development due to the fact that the initial lead compounds tested were slightly more potent in both assays than the benzodiazepines. Compounds within this series were shown to be highly effective in the *P. berghei* mouse model, with 60% of the mice treated at 200 mg/kg/day via implanted osmotic pumps surviving for 60 days with no recrudescence. Further evidence that the compounds were acting at *Pf*PFT was garnered by selecting for resistant parasites, which displayed a single amino acid mutation in the *Pf*PFT sequence [373]. After these initial stu-

dies, the scaffold was further developed to improve activity versus the enzymatic target and the parasite as well as to increase oral bioavailability and improve other PK parameters [374,375]. This work resulted in an orally available compound that was curative in rats at 50 mg/kg (gavage, tid 3 days) (Fig. 15f). Despite this success, the compounds did not meet the profile for further development due to rapid clearance [351,376].

Another series of *Pf*PFT inhibitors was developed, initially as an inhibitor of the mammalian enzyme [377,378] (Fig. 15d). These compounds were shown to be potent inhibitors of mammalian PFT while maintaining selectivity against the closely related geranylgeranyltransferase-I. This profile was pursued because simultaneous inhibition of both enzymes has been linked to heightened *in vivo* toxicity [379]. The series was tested for antimalarial activity and found several compounds with micromolar potencies (IC_{50} 0.13–7.0 μM). The compounds were not assayed directly for their ability to inhibit malarial PFT, and their antimalarial potencies did not correlate with inhibition of mammalian PFT. This is expected since the active site of *Pf*PFT differs from that of the mammalian enzyme. This scaffold is less developed than others presented, but represents a possible starting point for selective antimalarial compounds.

3.2. Heme Metabolism and Amino Acid Salvage

During the erythrocytic stages of its life cycle *Plasmodium* mainly relies on hemoglobin as nutrient source for homeostasis. Hemoglobin is transported to the parasite in cytosomes and degraded in the parasite food vacuole to peptides and amino acids by the two classes of proteases: falcipains and plasmepsins. The falcipains are cysteine proteases, while the plasmepsins are aspartyl proteases. Due to preexisting work in other therapeutic indications providing a large body of precedent for target druggability, both classes of proteases have been popular targets for malaria.

3.2.1. Falcipains   It has been known for approximately 20 years that inhibitors of cysteine protease inhibitors effectively kill cultured *Plasmodium in vitro*. It has long been speculated that a likely protease responsible for these effects was the calpain-like protease falcipain (FP2) [380–382]. The development of potential antimalarials targeting FP2 has led to the discovery of a number of scaffolds (Fig 16) with activity against the protease. Early efforts were focused on peptidyl compounds capped with electrophilic warheads such as the vinyl sulfone scaffold (Fig. 16e). Other warheads used for this purpose include halomethylketones, epoxides, azidines, aldehydes, nitriles, epoxysuccinates, and acyloxymethyl ketones [383,384]. While most of these afford compounds with potent activity against the protease *in vitro*, these peptidyl compounds often have poor pharmacokinetic behavior especially low oral bioavailability. This structure property relationship prompted investigators to begin looking for nonpeptidyl inhibitors of the enzyme.

Several new effective inhibitor scaffolds have been identified. The first of these the isoquinoline series (Fig 16a) [385]. These compounds were designed by docking a virtual library of potential candidates for synthesis against a homology model of FP2. The docking approach was validated in earlier studies by using vinyl-sulfone inhibitors with known affinity [386]. These compounds had modest potency (IC$_{50}$ 3–10 µM) and no evident activity against whole parasites. These findings imply that these compounds are poorly suited as potential antimalarial leads.

The second class of inhibitors is a series of isatin-chloroquine conjugates (Fig. 16b) [387,388]. These compounds also have relatively low potencies against falcipain (IC$_{50}$ values from 4 to 42 µM). While they exhibit relatively high potencies against *Plasmodium in vitro* (IC$_{50}$ values from 51 nM to 1.45 µM), this is likely due to the presence of the chloroquine moiety rather than inhibition of falcipain. There was poor correlation between inhibition of the enzymatic target and antimalarial activity.

The third class of inhibitors is an aziridine-based scaffold (Fig. 16c) [389]. This study evaluated inhibition of both FP-2 and FP-3, as well as growth inhibition of *P. falciparum in vitro* for both W2 and FCBR strains. This compound series has a wide range of potencies in both enzymatic and *in vitro* assays (IC$_{50}$ values from 0.43 to 243 µM). No simple direct correlations were observed between enzymatic inhibitory potency and *in vitro* antimalarial potency. Of 16 compounds with growth inhibitory potency below 10 µM; only 4 inhibit both FP-2 and FP-3, while 7 only moderately inhibit (EC$_{50}$ <10 µM) one of the enzymes with the remainder apparently being completely inactive. This suggests that other targets may be responsible for the *in vitro* activity of these compounds. Despite this issue, there is clear SAR for enzyme inhibition for both FP-2 and FP-3 in this series.

The fourth class of inhibitors is aminoquinoline γ- and δ-lactams (Fig. 16d) [390]. This series has very weak potency against FP-2 with only 1 active compound (IC$_{50}$ = 18 µM) and relatively strong to relatively weak *in vitro* growth inhibitory activities (IC$_{50}$ values from 96 nM to 1 sµM). Although no SAR can be established, the most potent compound *in vitro* is the compound reported to have enzymatic activity.

The fifth class of inhibitors is peptidyl vinyl sulfones (Fig. 16e) [391,392]. This series is highly potent against both the enzymatic target and the whole-cell parasites (IC$_{50}$ values from 0.7 nM to 10 µM). However, is still poor correlation between the potencies observed in the enzymatic and *in vitro* assays, suggesting off-target effects. Additionally, given the well-known promiscuity of bioavailable derivatives of this scaffold, specificity must be addressed in order to minimize off-target activities.

The sixth falcipain inhibitor series is phenylurenyl calchones (Fig. 16f). When assayed for inhibition of the enzyme, this series showed moderate potency (IC$_{50}$ values 2–10 µM) with very similar potencies against cultured *Plasmodium*. The series exhibited a loose correlation between enzymatic potencies and whole-cell potencies, suggesting that the compounds are acting through inhibition of falcipain. This series was the only set of falcipain inhibitors to show efficacy in an animal model of infection with some compounds significantly reduce parasitemia and increasing postinfection survival time.

The seventh class of inhibitors is 1,4-benzodiazepine (Fig. 16g) [393]. Like the com-

Inhibitors of Falcipain

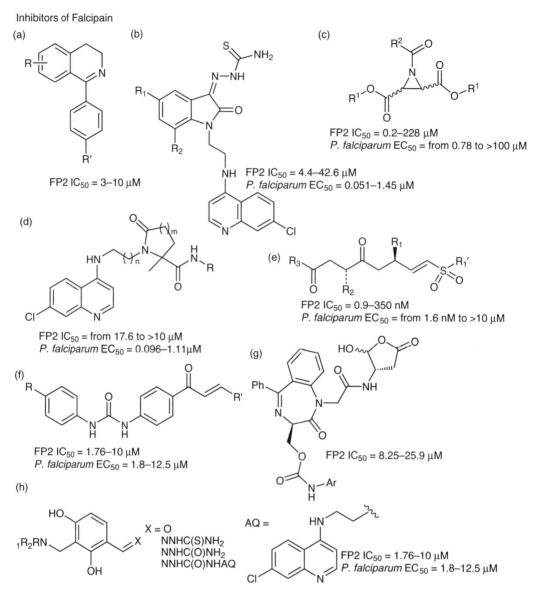

(a)

R—

R'

FP2 IC$_{50}$ = 3–10 μM

(b)

R$_1$—

R$_2$

NH

FP2 IC$_{50}$ = 4.4–42.6 μM
P. falciparum EC$_{50}$ = 0.051–1.45 μM

Cl

(c)

R^2

R^1—O

O—R^1

FP2 IC$_{50}$ = 0.2–228 μM
P. falciparum EC$_{50}$ = from 0.78 to >100 μM

(d)

HN

m

N

H

N—R

O

Cl

FP2 IC$_{50}$ = from 17.6 to >10 μM
P. falciparum EC$_{50}$ = 0.096–1.11μM

(e)

R$_3$—

R$_2$

R$_1$

R$_1$'

FP2 IC$_{50}$ = 0.9–350 nM
P. falciparum EC$_{50}$ = from 1.6 nM to >10 μM

(f)

R—

O

R'

H   H

FP2 IC$_{50}$ = 1.76–10 μM
P. falciparum EC$_{50}$ = 1.8–12.5 μM

(g)

Ph

N

N

O

HO

O

O

NH

O

O

N—Ar

H

FP2 IC$_{50}$ = 8.25–25.9 μM

(h)

HO

$_1$R$_2$RN

OH

X

X = O
NNHC(S)NH$_2$
NNHC(O)NH$_2$
NNHC(O)NHAQ

AQ =

HN

Cl

FP2 IC$_{50}$ = 1.76–10 μM
P. falciparum EC$_{50}$ = 1.8–12.5 μM

Figure 16. (a) An isoquinoline-based scaffold series [385]. Inhibitors were designed using molecular docking and had IC$_{50}$ values ranging from 3 to 10 μM against FP-2. They were not tested versus whole-cell *Plasmodium* species. (b) An isatin-based scaffold series incorporating a thiosemicarbazone warhead and a chloroquinoline moiety [387,388]. IC$_{50}$ values against FP-2 ranged from 4 to 44 μM while activity against whole-parasite strains ranged from 51 nM to 1.23 μM. There was poor correlation between whole-cell and enzymatic potencies. (c) An aziridine-based scaffold series [389] with enzymatic IC$_{50}$ values against FP-2 ranging from 0.2 to 228 μM and IC$_{50}$ values against whole parasite (W2) ranging from 0.78 to >100 μM. (d) An aminoquinoline γ- and δ-lactam series [390] IC$_{50}$ values against whole W2 parasites ranged from 0.096 to 1.11 μM while IC$_{50}$ values against isolated FP-2 ranged from 17.62 to >10 μM. (e) A peptidyl vinyl sulfone scaffold series [392] IC$_{50}$ values versus FP-2 range from 0.7 to 350 nM while IC$_{50}$ values versus W2 parasites ranged from 1.6 to >10,000 nM. There was poor correlation between whole-cell and enzymatic potencies. (f) Phenylurenyl calchone derivatives [819]. This compound series is the only falcipain inhibitor that has been used successfully in the mouse model of malaria. While none of the compounds were curative, many

pounds in the first series, these inhibitors have low potency against falcipain-2, (IC$_{50}$ values from 8.25 to 25.9 μM). These compounds were not tested against whole parasites. Given the wide promiscuity of this scaffold for many target classes, substantial selectivity would be required for successful development.

The eighth and final class of inhibitors is phenolic Mannich bases of benzaldehydes and thiosemicarbazones (Fig. 16h) [394]. This series also displays a wide range of potency against both FP-2 enzyme (IC$_{50}$ values from 77 nM to 20 μM) and *Plasmodium* (W2 strain) *in vitro* (EC$_{50}$ values from 77 nM to 10 μM). The most potent compounds against cultured malaria are those that are conjugates of 4-aminoquinoline and, while two of these show significant improvements in efficacy against the enzyme in comparison to chloroquine, only one inhibits FP-2 with a potency below 20 μM. For enzymatic inhibitors that do not have the aminoquinoline moiety, only one also shows *in vitro* activity. Further work to demonstrate that the cellular mechanism of action involves targeting the enzyme is needed.

Taken together, the generally poor correlations seen between enzymatic and whole-cell potencies seen with these inhibitors seem to suggest that the development of compounds targeting and acting solely through FP2 will be difficult. A series of studies reporting the knockouts of various proteases within the hemoglobin degradation pathway in *Plasmodium* suggest that it is highly robust, and that inhibitors targeting a single protease are unlikely to be efficacious [395–399]. However, knockouts of FP2 are highly susceptible to nonspecific aspartyl protease inhibitors, raising the possibility that combination therapies based on inhibitors of both cysteine and aspartyl proteases may prove effective. For this reason, further development of novel FP2 inhibitors may be warranted. However, these compounds should be assayed in combination with nonspecific or pluripotent aspartyl protease inhibitors when tested in whole-cell models.

3.2.2. Plasmepsins The plasmepsins (PLM) are a family of aspartyl proteases with four known homologs (Plm I, II, HAP, and IV) and six putative homologs predicted from the plasmodium genome [400]. Cathepsin-D is the closest human homolog to the plasmepsins (35% sequence identity, and a highly conserved active site) [401]. Other important human aspartyl proteases such as renin, cathepsin-E, and pepsin A exhibit lower sequence homologies [402]. For this reason, inhibition of cathepsin-D is often used as a test for selectivity when developing novel plasmepsin inhibitors.

The plasmepsins are involved in the early steps of hemoglobin degradation. They are able to recognize intact hemoglobin and make an initial cleavage in the hemoglobin α-chain between Phe-33 and Leu-34. This cleavage is believed to unravel the protein secondary structure, facilitating subsequent proteolytic cleavages [395]. The plasmepsins are synthesized as integral membrane proenzymes that are activated by cleavage from the membrane. Plasmepsin processing is carried out primarily by the falcipains. However, if falcipain activity is blocked by exogenous inhibitors, autoprocessing can serve as an alternate activation system [403].

Although hemoglobin digestion is a vital function for the parasite, the current understanding of plasmepsin function indicates that the proteases involved should be approached cautiously as drug targets. Knockouts of individual plasmepsins have shown that parasites lacking any one of the homologs are still viable in standard culture media. The only noticeable phenotypes are slightly prolonged life cycle times for knockouts of Plm IV and Plm II and small population of cells with swollen food vacuoles for knockouts of Plm II [396,397]. Even in amino acid depleted

Figure 16. (*Continued*) significantly reduced parasitimia and at least one significantly increased postinfection survival time. (g) A 1,4-benzodiazepine-based scaffold series [393]. IC$_{50}$ values vs FP-2 ranged from 8.25 to 25.90 μM. Compounds were not tested against whole-cell parasites. (h) A scaffold series based on pheonlic Mannich bases of benzaldehydes and thiosemicarbazones [394]. IC$_{50}$ values against FP-2 ranged from 0.63 to >20 μM and from 0.077 to >10 μM against W2 parasites.

Plasmepsin inhibitors

Peptidyl transition state mimetics

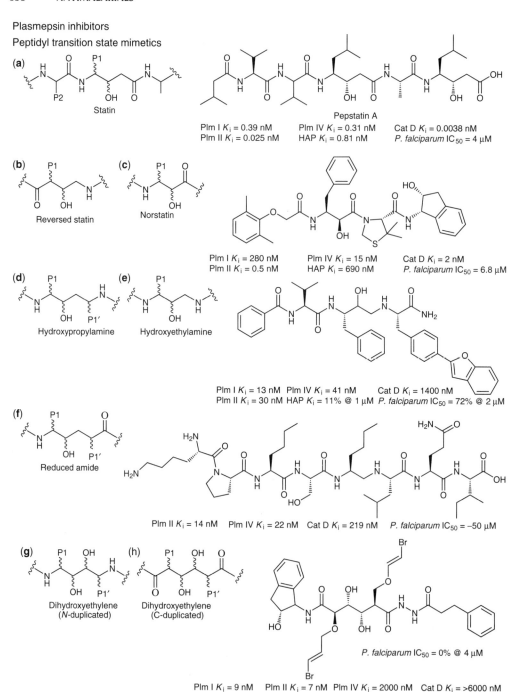

(a)

Statin

Pepstatin A

Plm I K_i = 0.39 nM   Plm IV K_i = 0.31 nM   Cat D K_i = 0.0038 nM
Plm II K_i = 0.025 nM   HAP K_i = 0.81 nM   *P. falciparum* IC$_{50}$ = 4 μM

(b) Reversed statin   **(c)** Norstatin

Plm I K_i = 280 nM   Plm IV K_i = 15 nM   Cat D K_i = 2 nM
Plm II K_i = 0.5 nM   HAP K_i = 690 nM   *P. falciparum* IC$_{50}$ = 6.8 μM

(d) Hydroxypropylamine   **(e)** Hydroxyethylamine

Plm I K_i = 13 nM   Plm IV K_i = 41 nM   Cat D K_i = 1400 nM
Plm II K_i = 30 nM   HAP K_i = 11% @ 1 μM   *P. falciparum* IC$_{50}$ = 72% @ 2 μM

(f) Reduced amide

Plm II K_i = 14 nM   Plm IV K_i = 22 nM   Cat D K_i = 219 nM   *P. falciparum* IC$_{50}$ = −50 μM

(g) Dihydroxyethylene (*N*-duplicated)   **(h)** Dihydroxyethylene (*C*-duplicated)

P. falciparum IC$_{50}$ = 0% @ 4 μM

Plm I K_i = 9 nM   Plm II K_i = 7 nM   Plm IV K_i = 2000 nM   Cat D K_i = >6000 nM

Figure 17. (a) The statin aspartyl protease inhibitors. The gold standard for inhibitors of plasmepsins is the statin-based pepstatin A, a general aspartic protease inhibitor active against all four plamepsins [416]. It has been shown that large hydrophobic groups at the P1- and P2′-positions are necessary for activity, while β-branched P2- and basic P3-positions are important for defining selectivity versus Cat D [424–426]. (b) The reversed statin aspartyl protease inhibitors. These compounds have been shown to possess modest

growth media, none of the individual plasmepsins appear to be essential [396]. However, the knockouts are slightly more sensitive to cysteine protease inhibitors. Simultaneous knockout of multiple plasmepsins, in combination with knockouts of falcipain-2, show that the parasitic hemoglobin pathway is highly redundant [395,404]. Furthermore, in nutrient-rich environments, the parasite does not depend on hemoglobin degradation for its amino acid supply. This body of work implies that effective inhibitors of the pathway will have to target all four vacuolar plasmepsins and be used in conjunction with inhibitors of the falcipain cysteine proteases. Even in such cases, it is likely that such inhibitors would not work in treating individuals with normal levels of amino acids in their bloodstreams. Despite these issues, it should be noted that some clinically utilized HIV-1 (aspartyl) protease inhibitors show antimalarial properties both *in vitro* and *in vivo* [405,406]. This activity is not synergistic with cysteine protease inhibitors, suggesting that there may be other important aspartic proteases in malarial parasites [407].

Despite emerging biological data concerning shortcomings as potential drug targets, there has been extensive work done in the recent years to develop potent inhibitors of plasmepsins. Much of this work took place in the context of rapidly changing models of the essentiality of these proteases. Indeed, the failure of some inhibitors to provide efficacy in whole-parasite models has contributed to our understanding of the protease function. There are currently 19 plasmepsin structures available in the PDB, including *P. falciparum* ProPlm II, Plm II, Plm IV, *P. vivax* ProPlm IV and Plm IV along with *P. malariae* Plm IV [401,408–412]. This wealth of data has been used by many groups around the world to inform synthetic efforts, producing increasingly potent compounds.

Most pepstatin inhibitors utilize transition-state isosteres to mimic the tetrahedral intermediate stabilized by the enzyme during cleavage of the scissile peptide bond. Many of these isosteres were initially developed during extensive work on HIV protease as a target for AIDS. Mimetics that have been used for pepstatins include: statins, norstatins, reversed statins, hydroxypropylamines, hydroxyethylamines, reduced amides, phosphinates, and difluoroketones (Fig. 1a–h) [413–415]. Of these, the best characterized both structurally and chemically are the statins (Fig. 17a).

The first statin shown to be an inhibitor of the plasmepsins was pepstatin A (Fig. 17a), a general aspartic protease inhibitor. This compound is potently active against all four food vacuole plasmepsins (K_i values from 25 to 393 pM [416]). It also possesses modest whole-cell activity (EC$_{50}$ of 4 µM). Based on these observations, several groups attempted to modify pepstatin to achieve selectivity versus Cat D, while maintaining potency against the plasmepsins. Early analogs displaying some

◄ ───

Figure 17. (*Continued*) biochemical activities, but have not been reported to have whole-cell activities [427,428]. (c) The norstatin aspartyl protease inhibitors. The best characterized is the allophenylnorstatine, which is known to have low toxicity and good bioavailability [429]. Inhibitors showing submicromolar potencies in inhibiting growth of *P. falciparum* and subnanomolar potencies versus Plm II have been developed. However, correlation between these two activities is lacking [434,435]. (d) The hydroxypropylamine aspartyl protease inhibitors. While low nanomolar potencies have been reported for this series and several crystal structures of Plm II bound to the inhibitors have been determined, no growth inhibitory activities have been reported [436]. (e) The hydroxyethylamine aspartyl protease inhibitors. Several potent inhibitors of Plm II based on this scaffold have been reported [437]. Further optimization of the scaffold led to compounds displaying up to 100-fold selectivity against Cat D as well as modest growth potency [408,438–440]. (f) The reduced amide aspartyl protease inhibitors. This series has moderate potencies against Plm II, but very strong potencies against Plm IV. Selectivity versus Cat D was problematic in the higher potency compounds [420,441]. (g) The N-duplicated 1,2-dihydroxyethylene aspartyl protease inhibitors. This scaffold displays similar activities to the C-duplicated version depicted [443–448]. (h) The C-duplicated 1,2-dihydroxyethylene aspartyl protease inhibitors. While these compounds do have a high level of selectivity versus Cat D, they lack growth inhibitory efficacy. The compounds have also been shown to be active versus Plm I, II, and IV with varying degrees of potency [443–447,820].

degree of selectivity possessed a trifluoro-methyl substituent at the P1- and P3′-positions. Adding a methyl ester in place of the usual carboxylate terminus increased selectivity, but decreased potency versus the plasmepsin family [417,418]. Examination of a panel of Cat D inhibitors showed that cyclization between the P1- and the P3-positions, but not between the P2- and the P3-positions, were tolerated by Plm II. Attempts to decrease the size of the inhibitors in order to improve pharmacokinetic properties resulted in a decrease in potency against the pepstatins, but increased selectivity against Cat D [401,419–421]. Another approach involved elongating the side chain of the P1-position, which led to potent (K_i values from 0.5 to 819 nM) inhibitors [422]. A crystal structure of one such compound showed that these elongated chains filled the continuous S1 to S3 pocket in Plm II [423]. The same studies showed that incorporating a 2,4,6-trifluorophenyl at the P2 site granted upward of 100-fold selectivity for Plm II and Plm I over Cat D. Large combinatorial libraries of statin-based inhibitors have also been constructed. [424–426]. Testing of these libraries has shown that large hydrophobic groups at the P1- and P2′-positions are required in potent inhibitors, while β-branched P2- and basic P3-positions were important in creating selectivity between the plasmepsins and the Cat D. While many studies found successful strategies to improve activity against isolated plasmepsins *in vitro*, significant improvement of whole-cell potency has been problematic.

A reversed statin-based inhibitor can be produced by placing retroamides on the prime and nonprime side of the central core (Fig. 17b). These compounds possess modest potency (1.3–4.7 μM) against the plasmepsins, but have not been reported to have whole-cell activities. The preferred stereochemistry is with an (R)-configuration of the hydroxyl group and an (S)-configuration of the P1 side chain [427,428].

Shortening the statin core by one methylene group produces the norstatin peptidyl scaffold. (Fig. 17c) This moiety is found in inhibitors of HIV-I protease, and is often used in the context of an allophenylnorstatin-dimethylthioproline core, which has been shown to have low toxicity and good bioavailability [429]. The scaffold also bears a high degree of structural and chemical similarity to the hemoglobin primary cleavage site, with the dimethylthioproline core serving as an isostere for a conformationally constrained leucine in that peptide motif. Early studies using this isostere as the basis for plasmepsin inhibitors showed that the substitution patterns at the P2′-substituent were key for producing highly potent (K_i values from 0.02–96.9 μM) inhibitor [429,430]. Docking studies using this core predicted interactions primarily at sites conserved across the plasmepsin family, making this scaffold a good starting point for the development of pan-active inhibitors [431,432]. These compounds also showed good potencies versus HAP, Plm IV, and Plm I. Unfortunately, selectivity against Cat D was never achieved with these compounds. More recently, variations at the P1-substituent were shown to grant a modest (9-fold) selectivity for Plm II over Cat D, but with a significant drop in overall potency (IC_{50} from 20 nM to 11 μM) [433]. The effects of varying the P1′- and P2′-substituents have also been evaluated, leading to the discovery of potent (0.2–15 nM) inhibitors of Plm II. Some of this series of inhibitors had good potencies (1.2–8 μM) in whole-cell *P. falciparum* growth inhibition assays [434,435]. Despite promising potencies, correlation between whole-cell and biochemical activities was poor. This may imply that the mechanism of action in the intact parasite involves other targets than the plasmepsins.

Hydroxypropylamines are another isostere used as in aspartyl protease inhibitors (Fig. 17d). This scaffold is found in HIV-I protease inhibitors, and a large library of these inhibitors have been screened versus Plm II [436]. Optimization of the P1- and P1′-positions of these compounds using benzyl and isobutyl groups, respectively, produced highly potent inhibitors (K_i values from 18 to 30 nM) of the enzyme. Several crystal structures of these inhibitors bound to Plm II have been determined [436]. No whole-cell activities have been reported.

Shortening of the hydroxypropylamine moiety by one methylene group leads to the hydroxyethylamine transition-state mimetic

(Fig. 17e). A library of peptidyl compounds based on this scaffold has been screened against Plm II, revealing both potent (K_i values from 2 to 300 nM) and selective ($\sim$10-fold versus Cat D) inhibitors. Members of this library were also reasonably potent (IC$_{50}$ values from 1 to 2 μM) in *P. falciparum* growth inhibition assays [437]. Basic piperidine groups in the P2'-position were found to be important for the selectivity. Based on these promising early results, a crystal structure of the most potent compound bound to Plm II was determined [408]. Further optimization of the *C*-substituted version of the scaffold at the P3- and P1'-substituents resulted in quite potent (K_i values from 4.7 to 340 nM) inhibitors of Plm II with up to 100-fold selectivity against Cat D [438]. Large *meta*- or *para*-substituted benzyl groups or bicyclic oxygen containing ring systems in the P1'-position were necessary for high potency, with *meta*-substituted compounds showing higher potencies for Plm II and *para*-compounds showing higher potencies for Plm I. Indole-based side chains were preferred in the P3-position by Plm II [439]. If the amino terminus nitrogen was substituted, the P1' SAR patterns changed, with small large groups producing inactive compounds and relatively small groups yielding increased potencies. Molecular docking and 3D QSAR studies suggest that the *C*-substituted scaffolds and the *N*-substituted scaffold bind to different subsites in the enzyme [440]. Compounds from this series have not been extensively evaluated against Plm IV or HAP.

Another transition-state mimetic that has been used successfully in plasmepsin inhibitors is the reduced amide (Fig. 17f). This isostere has only been tested as the core of octapeptide inhibitors, in which hydrophobic amino acids were preferred at the P2 and P3 sites, while a wide range of amino acids were tolerated at the P2'- and P3'-sites [420,441]. Plm II showed preference for Nle at the P1 site, whereas other members of the family preferred Phe. In general, branched groups at the P1'-position were optimal for Plm II, whereas the other plasmepsins preferred large aromatic groups. None of the enzymes tolerated alanine in the P1'-position. Most of the compounds were inactive in *P. falciparum* growth

inhibition assays with a with a few displaying weak potency (IC$_{50}$ values $\sim$50 μM) [420,441]. Highly potent (K_i values from 26 pM to 117 nM) inhibitors of Plm IV based on this scaffold have also been described [420]. However, increased potency for Plm IV typically tracked with a decrease in potency versus Plm II, as well as a decrease in selectivity versus Cat D. The activities of these compounds in growth inhibition assays have not been reported.

The final isostere used in plasmepsin inhibitors is the 1,2-dihydroxyethylene group. This scaffold can be either the N-duplicated (Fig. 17g) or the C-duplicated (Fig. 17h) variety. Like most other inhibitors for the plasmepsins, these were first developed as inhibitors of HIV-1 protease [442]. Reoptimization of the HIV protease inhibitors for Plm I and Plm II potencies yielded smaller compounds, lacking the P3- and P3'-groups that displayed over 100-fold selectivity for plasmepsins over Cat D. Early results suggested that electron-withdrawing *p*-cyanophenoxy groups in the P1 and P1'-positions were important for high potency [443]. Examinations of the stereochemical requirements for activity showed that only the *SRRRS* isomers (originating from L-mannitol and L-valine) were active against Plm II [444]. It was hypothesized that this arose from electrostatic interactions of the inhibitors with Plm II. For reasons that remain unclear, this series showed extraordinary selectivity for plasmepsins over Cat D, with no detectible activity versus the human enzyme [445]. Replacement of the amide bonds with either diacylhydrazine or 1,3,4-oxadiazole groups was also explored, with the diacylhydrazine performing more favorably against both Plm I and II. Elongation of the P1- and P1'-groups in nonsymmetric diacylhydrazines did not increase potency [446]. Almost all inhibitors in these series display lower potencies against Plm IV relative to those for Plm I and II [447]. Efforts to increase potency by cyclizing the inhibitors met with limited success, although some were seen for Plm IV, suggesting that the strategy may prove useful in the development of pan-specific inhibitor [448]. All compounds in these series had poor growth inhibitory potency.

In addition to the wide range of peptidyl plasmepsin inhibitors described above, a significant number of nonpeptidyl small molecule inhibitors have been discovered. The earliest of these were based upon Hoffman-LaRoche inhibitors of renin, another aspartyl protease with a high degree of homology to the plasmepsins [449]. These chiral-substituted piperidine analogs (Fig. 18a) were tested against isolated Plm II and in growth inhibitory assays against intact parasite. Although exact potencies were not reported for the original compounds, they were reported to have "good" activities against the enzyme and submicromolar potencies in whole-cell models [450]. Detailed examination of the Hoffman-LaRoche patent reveals that 3-substituted 4-phenyl piperidine was the preferred scaffold with electron-donating aryls attached via a linker to the *para*-position of the 4-phenyl and other aryl ring systems in the 3-position [450]. A later high-throughput screen of a commercial library at Actelion Pharmaceuticals resulted in the discovery of nonchiral 4-piperidine derivatives (Fig. 18b) that exhibited potent activity (IC$_{50}$ values from 7 nM to 3.5 μM) against both Plm II and cultured *P. falciparum* [451,452]. A crystal structure of Plm II bound to a member of this compound series is also available [410]. Highly potent compounds from this series typically had substituted benzyl groups, a benzoyl moiety on the exocyclic nitrogen, and a lipophilic group on the ring nitrogen. In general, compounds from this series showed selectivity for Plm II over other members of the family. Attempts to improve activity against other plasmepsins resulted in loss of overall potency.

A third nonpeptidyl inhibitor scaffold was discovered using molecular modeling techniques with homology models based upon multiple aspartyl protease crystal structures, to construct a modified structure of Plm II with a novel large lipophilic flap pocket [401,412,453]. This model was then used to computationally design a series of 7-azabicyclo[2.2.1]heptane-based inhibitors of the enzyme (Fig. 18c) [453–455]. The protonated nitrogen of the bicyclic scaffold was predicted to displace the catalytic water and form hydrogen bonds with the catalytic aspartic acid groups [453]. Despite the rigorous modeling

efforts, only modestly potent inhibitors (IC$_{50}$ values from 3 to 5 μM) were developed. Efforts to improve potencies by using a more rigid 11-azatricyclo[6.2.1.0] undecatriene scaffold met with limited success [454]. However, utilization of the 7-azabicyclo[2.2.1]heptane scaffold yielded more potent inhibitors with activity against all members of the plasmepsin family (IC$_{50}$ values from 10 to 2100 nM) and improved activities in *P. falciparum* growth inhibitory assays (IC$_{50}$ values from 2.2 to 7.1 μM) [456,457].

High-throughput screening efforts at Walter Reed identified a fourth nonpeptidyl inhibitor of Plm II: a sulfonic acid-substituted diphenylurea (Fig. 18d). In general, the series had good potency (K_i values from 60 to 680 nM) in inhibition of Plm II and a high degree of selectivity (>1000-fold) for Plm II over Cat D. Growth inhibitory potencies were more modest (IC$_{50}$ values from 11 to 40 μM) [458]. Docking studies using models of both *P. falciparum* Plm II and *P. vivax* Plm II suggest that only one of the urea nitrogens is able to form a hydrogen bond with the active site aspartic acid residues, leaving space for the catalytic water residue to remain in place.

Efforts to develop more nonpeptidyl inhibitors of the plasmepsin family have continued in recent years. One potential scaffold is a triamine core capped with sulfone moieties (Fig. 18e) [459]. These compounds are modestly potent (K_i values from 2.2 to 170 μM) inhibitors of both Plm II and Plm IV. A *para*-aniline is preferred in the P2- and P2'-positions with a benzyl group in the P1 and P1'-positions. Most inhibitors in this series show a small amount of selectivity for Plm II versus Plm IV. Shorter linkers, of 1–2 carbons, were also generally preferred. The compounds were also tested against HIV-1 protease, renin, BACE-1 and pepsin. The majority of the inhibitors was selective for the plasmepsin family and showed a small amount of selectivity for Plm II over Plm IV. No growth inhibitory activities were reported.

Another active scaffold, identified using molecular docking techniques, is the acridinyl hydrazide (Fig. 18f) [460]. Only two compounds in this group were tested; the more potent has an IC$_{50}$ of 0.55 nM, which is comparable with pepstatin-A in the same assay

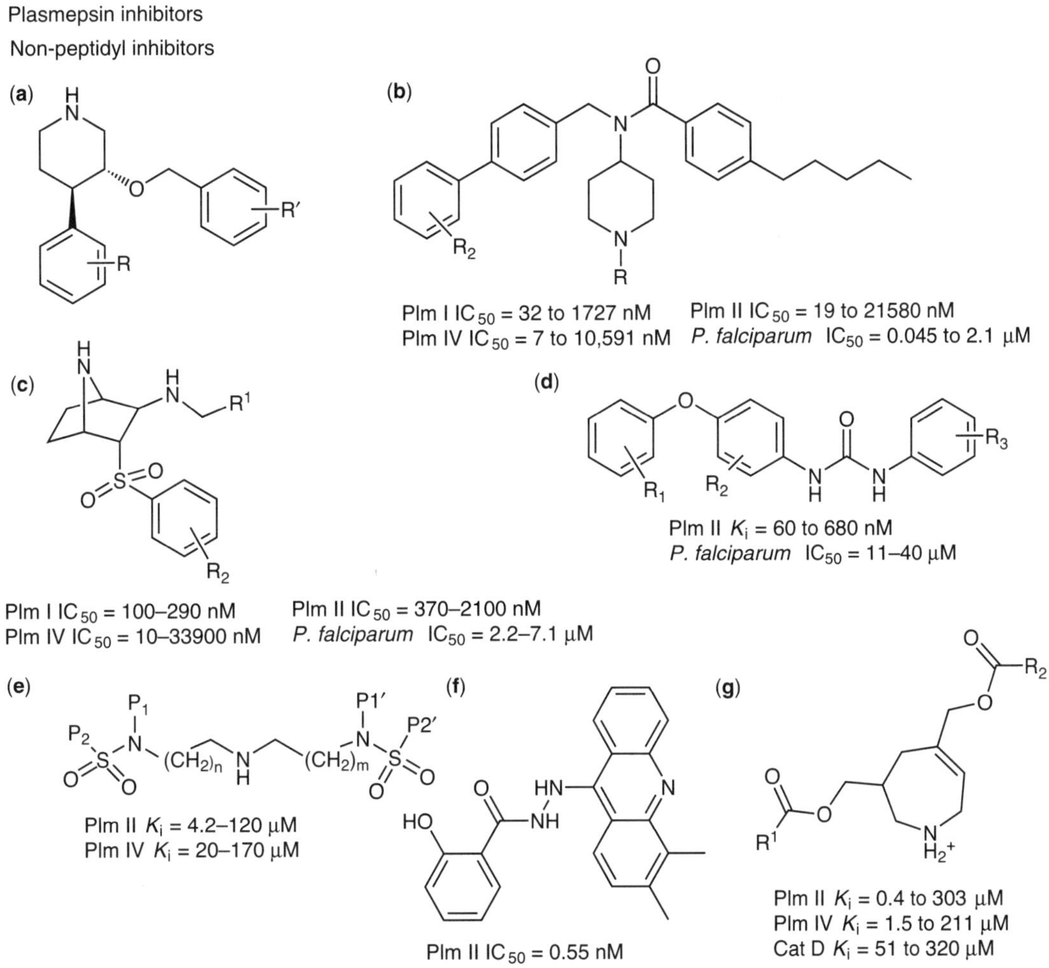

Plasmepsin inhibitors

Non-peptidyl inhibitors

(a)

(b)

Plm I IC_{50} = 32 to 1727 nM   Plm II IC_{50} = 19 to 21580 nM
Plm IV IC_{50} = 7 to 10,591 nM   *P. falciparum* IC_{50} = 0.045 to 2.1 μM

(c)

(d)

Plm II K_i = 60 to 680 nM
P. falciparum IC_{50} = 11–40 μM

Plm I IC_{50} = 100–290 nM   Plm II IC_{50} = 370–2100 nM
Plm IV IC_{50} = 10–33900 nM   *P. falciparum* IC_{50} = 2.2–7.1 μM

(e)

(f)

(g)

Plm II K_i = 4.2–120 μM
Plm IV K_i = 20–170 μM

Plm II IC_{50} = 0.55 nM

Plm II K_i = 0.4 to 303 μM
Plm IV K_i = 1.5 to 211 μM
Cat D K_i = 51 to 320 μM

Figure 18. (a) A chiral-substituted pyridine scaffold originally developed by Hoffmann-LaRoche as inhibitors of renin. These compounds were moderately potent in both growth inhibition and Plm II assays [450]. (b) A substituted pyridine scaffold with good inhibitory potencies (IC_{50} values from 7 nM to 3.5 μM) against both Plm II enzyme and growth inhibitory assays [451,452]. (c) The azabicyclo[2.2.1]heptane scaffold inhibitors of Plm II. Compounds from this series, as well as the related 11-azatricyclo[6.2.1.0]undecatriene series, possessed only modest enzymatic potencies and were not reported to have whole-cell activities [412,453–455]. This series was designed using molecular modeling approaches that took enzymatic flexibility into account [401,412,453,456,457]. (d) Diphenylurea inhibitors discovered through high-throughput screening efforts at Walter Reed. The compounds displayed a high degree of selectivity (>1000-fold) for Plm II against Cat D, as well as good inhibitory potencies (K_i values from 60 to 680 nM) for Plm II. Growth inhibitory potencies were more modest (IC_{50} values from 11 to 40 μM) [458]. (e) The triamine sulfone inhibitors [459]. These compounds are modestly potentn (K_i values from 2.2 to 170 μM) inhibitors of both Plm II and Plm IV. Most were selective for the plasmepsin family and showed a small amount of selectivity for Plm II over Plm IV. No whole-cell activities were reported. (f) Acridinyl hydrazide plasmepsin inhibitors [460]. This series was discovered using molecular docking techniques. The most potent of the compounds in this series has an IC_{50} of 0.55 nM. Neither of the compounds tested showed any selectivity versus Cat D. No whole-cell activities were reported for these compounds. (g) The azepine inhibitors. The original inhibitors bearing this core were modestly potent (IC_{50} of 40 μM) inhibitors of Plm II [461]. Further work on the scaffold series yielded more potent (K_i values from 0.4 to 303 μM) inhibitors Plm II with over 100-fold selectivity versus Cat D [462].

system. Neither of the compounds tested show any selectivity against Cat D and no whole-cell activities were reported for these compounds.

The final nonpeptidyl of plasmepsin inhibitors is the azepine group. The original inhibitors in this series were inspired by the substituted pyridine compounds discussed above, and were modestly potent (IC_{50} values from 40 to 1250 μM) inhibitors of Plm II [461]. Further work on the scaffold, with the aid of molecular modeling, yielded more potent (K_i values from 0.4 to 303 μM) inhibitors of Plm II with greater than 100-fold selectivity over Cat D (Fig. 18g) [462]. A *para*-aniline group was preferred in both the R_1- and R_2-positions, though *para*-nitro-substituted phenyl groups and naphthyl groups were tolerated. The potencies for the series were roughly equivalent for Plm IV, with the same general SAR, although Plm IV did not tolerate larger heterocyclic ring systems in the R_2-position. No growth inhibitory activities were reported for these compounds.

As described, extensive work has been put into the development of plasmepsin inhibitors. However, despite this effort, compound series displaying convincing growth inhibitory activities remain few and far between. Given the biological data available from the various plasmepsin knockouts, and the general lack of correlation between enzymatic and whole-cell activities, the feasibility of targeting plasmepsins for antimalarials must be regarded with caution. It now seems likely that any attempt to block the hemoglobin degradation pathway through the use of protease inhibitors must inhibit both the cysteine and aspartyl proteases in the food vacuole.

3.3. DNA Synthesis, Repair, and Regulation

As is the case with oncology and infectious diseases, the rapid expansion of the malaria parasite population in infected individuals makes them sensitive to inhibition of DNA synthesis and repair. A number of drugs and drug candidates target the pathways related to nucleotide synthesis, DNA synthesis and replication.

3.3.1. Antifolates DHFR and thymidylate synthase (TS) are enzymes that carry out the final steps of the folic acid metabolism pathway, the reduction of 5,6-dihydrofolate to 5,6,7,8-tetrahydrofolate. In protozoa, DHFR/TS activities are expressed as a single 110–140 kDa bifunctional enzyme made of these two subunits with DHFR positioned toward the N-terminus. In humans, the enzymes are separate [463]. DHFR enzyme fulfills the same role in the folate metabolic pathway in *Plasmodium* sp. as it does in mammalian cells. Folic acid (FA) is necessary for cell proliferation and maintenance and is especially important during cell division. FA is also indispensable for the synthesis of thymidine, a purine need for DNA replication. FA antagonists are effective drugs against rapid dividing cells in many settings including: human cancer, pathogenic bacteria, and parasites. FA inhibitors such as sulfonamides have been used as antimalarials since the mid-1940s and DHFR is one of the few clinically validated druggable malaria targets. The folic pathway has also been proven a suitable drug target in other related parasites such as trypanosoma and toxoplasma [464,465].

DHFR inhibitors were introduced in the 1970s, but resistance rapidly emerged (see above). Recent work on inhibitors of DHFR has focused mainly on overcoming resistance to existing drugs. Malaria acquires resistance to DHFR inhibitors by introducing steric clashes into the active site that negatively affect inhibitor binding. Resistance arises from a relatively small number of point mutations in the target enzyme, including S108N, S108T, I164T, A16V, C59R, and NI164L [466–472].

The major strategy for overcoming this resistance has been retreading the existing scaffolds. One major effort has been the development of a series of cycloguanil analogs using homology modeling and docking approaches (Fig. 19a) [473,474]. In this series, compounds with larger groups at one of the R-positions showed a 10-fold improved potency against the mutant enzymes while only decreasing potency against the wild-type enzyme by 2-fold. These compounds also showed improved potency in growth inhibitory assays with parasites expressing the mutant enzyme when compared with the parent compound. This finding supported earlier data showing that WR99210, a cycloguanil analog with a large

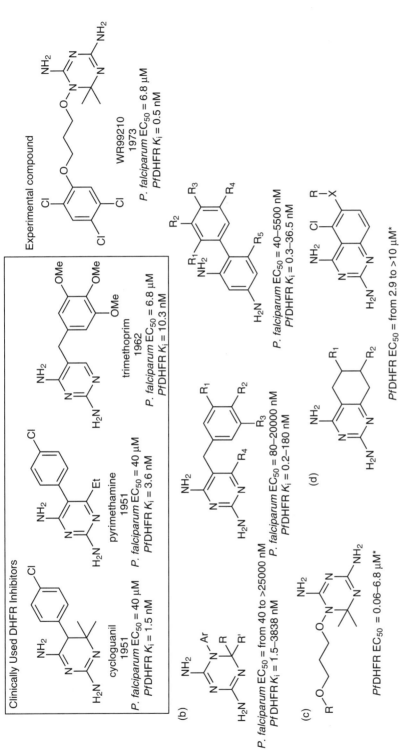

Figure 19. Early inhibitors of DHFR used clinically for the treatment of malaria and other microbial infections [821–823]. The experimental compound WR99210 was never used in the clinic but has maintained activity against fresh isolates despite point mutations in DHFR leading to resistance of the other compounds [475]. (b) Variations of existing drug scaffolds pursued by Yuthavong and coworkers [473,484–486]. This series of papers extensively explored the chemistry of the existing scaffolds, especially with respect to overcoming resistance. (c) Scaffold based on the experimental compound WR99210 [483]. The ether linker is thought to be responsible for the increased effectiveness of this scaffold against enzymes resistant to the other guanil-based drugs. (d) Compounds originally developed for inhibition of human DHFR that were identified in a yeast-based screen as potent and selective inhibitors of *Pf*DHFR [492]. (e) Scaffold identified by Brobey et al. as having antimalarial activity due to inhibition of *Pf*DHFR [495]. This scaffold was originally developed for use as an antineoplastic DHFR inhibitor, but was shown to possess potent antiparasitic activity, both *in vitro* and in the *P. berghei* mouse model. (f) Compounds modest inhibitory potency for *P. falciparum* DHFR identified using molecular docking studies against homology models of the enzyme [496].

645

(e)

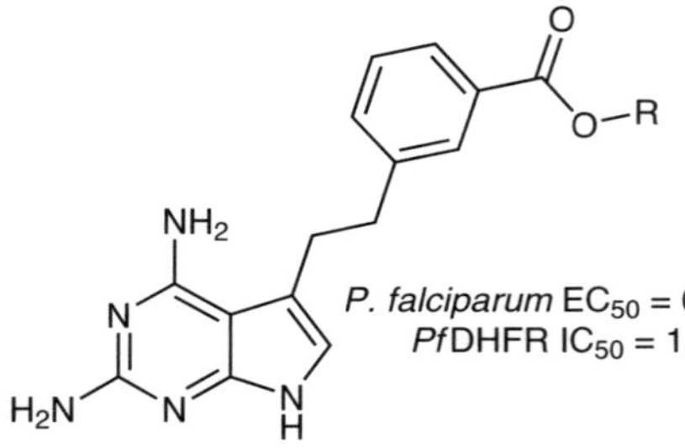

P. falciparum EC$_{50}$ = 0.17–30 nM
*Pf*DHFR IC$_{50}$ = 1.1–500 nM

(f)

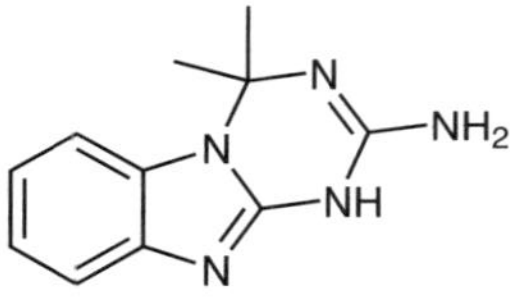

*Pf*DHFR K_i = 540 nM

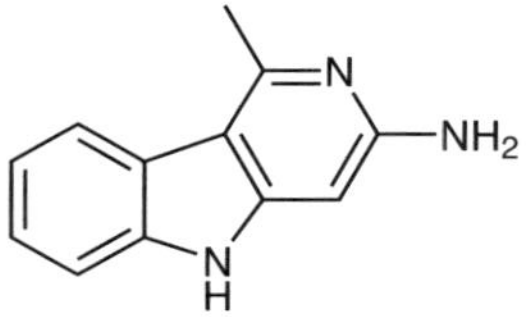

*Pf*DHFR K_i = 8700 nM

All data is for wild-type parasites and enzyme unless otherwise noted.
*Data is for quadruple mutant (51I/59R/108N/164L) in a yeast-based assay.

Figure 19. (*Continued*)

propylphenyl-ether substituent, maintained effectiveness against both wild-type and mutant enzymes [475–482]. It is thought that the increased flexibility of this large linker allows the compound to overcome the steric constraints imposed by the various enzyme mutations. More recently, it was found that using a 2-naphthyl or a 4-trifluoromethoxy-2-chloro-substituted benzene moiety in place of the trichloro benzene of WR99210 could increase the potency against the wild-type enzyme almost 10-fold (Fig. 19c) [483].

Based on these early successes, the development of novel pyrimethamine and trimethoprim analogs was pursued (Fig. 19b). Using homology modeling studies, it was hypothesized that the combination of addition of bulky substituents at the R_5-position and removal of the *para*-substituent at R_3 of pyrimethamine would improve potencies against a several mutant DHFR enzymes. This was the case when the compunds were tested against the S108N mutant (K_i values from 28.6 to 1.6 nM), and the C59R + S108N double mutant (K_i values from 53.9 to 1.4 nM) [484]. This general strategy was also successful in the trimethoprim analog series, where compounds having a 4-benzyloxy substituent at the R_2-position showed increased potency against wild-type (K_i values from 10.3 to 0.3 nM) and both mutant enzymes (K_i values from 132.3 to 1.6 nM for S108N and K_i values from 242.1 to 2.2 nM for C59R + S108N). Compounds in both series also showed increased potency against parasites expressing mutant enzymes.

Similar efforts have been focused on analogs of pyrimethamine, cycloguanil, and trimethoprim (Fig. 19b). Refinements in these series have led to increasingly potent compounds active against both wild-type and multiple-mutant enzymes [485–488]. The pyrimethamine analogs that had shown promise in earlier studies were screened versus triple (N51I + C59R + S108N and C59R + S108N + I164L) and quadruple (N51I + C59R + S108N + I164L) mutants and shown to follow similar SAR patterns and activities in these systems as well. (K_i values from 385 to 1.7 nM). A similar rationale was applied to the development of cycloguanil analogs with much improved activities versus the double A16V + S108T mutant. (K_i values from 1314 to 2.5 nM) Further optimization of the

trimethoprim analogs showed that substituted phenyl ethers were well tolerated in the R_2-position and that long hydrophobic substitutions on this phenyl group also increased the affinity of the molecule. A number of studies have contributed to these findings both by synthesizing further analog libraries and by conducting molecular modeling studies to further the understanding of binding modes [489–491].

In addition to the predominant focus on modification of existing scaffolds, several groups have also developed novel inhibitors. A large library of DHFR inhibitors developed for the human enzyme was screened against a panel of parasitic homologs in a yeast-based system [492]. This work resulted in the discovery of the quinazoline and tetra-hydroquinazoline series of inhibitors (Fig. 19d). Compounds from these series displayed potencies from low nanomolar to low micromolar levels (IC_{50} values 10 nM to 10 µM) against wild-type and a panel of mutant parasitic enzymes that included the S108N, the N41I + S108N, the C59R + S108N and the N51I + C59R + S108N + I164L mutants. It should be noted that, unlike WR99210, these compounds were not effective versus the quadruple mutant. Further work established that both series were potent inhibitors of growth (IC_{50} values 8.9 nM to 10 µM) of the multidrug-resistant *P. falciparum* strain V1S [493]. Compounds from these series were also shown to be effective against PvDHFR suggesting that these compounds will prove effective against multiple malarial subspecies [494].

In a similar approach, recombinant enzyme to test the efficacies of a series of antibacterial DHFR inhibitors against *pf*DHFR [495]. This study revealed that several compounds were potent inhibitors (IC_{50} values 0.8–500 nM) of wild-type as well as N16V + S108T and C59R S108N mutant *pf*DHFR. These compounds were also effective inhibitors of parasite growth (wild-type or DHFR-resistant mutant). Additionally, they were comparable to cycloguanil in efficacy and potency when tested in a *P. berghei* mouse model. However, the novel compounds had a smaller therapeutic index than the older compounds. In order for these compounds to be viable clinical development candidates improvements in both potency and therapeutic index would be necessary.

Other groups have used molecular docking studies to discover novel inhibitors of pfDHFR. A docking study based on a homology model of PfDHFR resulted in the discovery of two novel inhibitors (Fig. 19e) with K_i values of 0.54 and 8.7 μM, respectively [496]. Another similar study also proved successful when a larger virtual screening effort led to the discovery of 24 novel inhibitors including N-hydroxyamidines, pyrimidinines, triazines, urea, and thioureas with weak to strong potencies (K_i values 0.9–102 μM) [497,498]. In 2005, the crystal structure of $P. vivax$ DHFR was solved thus enabling the further development of novel inhibitors by molecular modeling techniques [499].

3.3.2. Dihydroorotate Dehydrogenase The dihydroorotate dehydrogenases (DHODs) catalyze the oxidation of dihydroorotate to orotate in the *de novo* pyrimidine biosynthesis. Pyrimidines are critical to all cells for the synthesis of DNA, RNA, phospholipids, and glycoproteins. In *P. falciparum*, DHOD is a 56 kDa protein localized in the mitochondrial membrane [500]. PfDHOD is substantially different from its human counterpart as DHOD inhibitors differentially inhibit both enzymes, suggesting a possibility for designing selective inhibitors [501]. However, unlike mammalian cells, *P. falciparum* is unable to salvage pyrimidines and relies completely upon synthesis [502].

DHODH was originally proposed as a target for malarial chemotherapy in 1969 [503]. Subsequent studies using known antimalarial compounds supported the idea and showed that atovaquone was likely acting at least

partially through inhibition of this enzyme [504,505]. A study surveying the inhibition of recombinant Pf DHODH and the human homolog revealed several potent inhibitors of human DHODH (Fig. 20a) (IC$_{50}$ values 13–350 nM) that were only weak inhibitors of malarial DHODH (IC$_{50}$ values 71 μM to 1 mM) [501]. This finding validated the concept that the active sites of the two enzymes were sufficiently dissimilar to allow for the development of selective inhibitors.

Subsequent studies furthered the search for potent and selective inhibitors of the malarial enzyme. The first selective *P. falciparum* DHODH inhibitor (Fig. 20b) was synthesized using brequinar, a potent human DHODH inhibitor, as a lead [506]. However, the inhibitors from this series exhibited relatively weak potency (IC$_{50}$ values 38–480 μM) for both human and malarial DHODH and weak growth inhibition (EC$_{50}$ values between 1 and 50 μM) as well. A second study found potent selective inhibitors of PfDHODH (IC$_{50}$ values 0.16–350 μM) that had weaker but reasonable antimalarial potencies (IC$_{50}$ values 1.8–4.0 μM) [507].

A high-throughput screen against recombinant PfDHODH [508] identified 13 potent inhibitors (Fig. 20d) of the malarial enzyme (IC$_{50}$ values 16–780 nM), most of which had better than 1000-fold selectivity for the malarial enzyme over the human homolog. However, despite the potency of these hits *in vitro*, none were efficacious at inhibition parasite growth at concentrations up to 100 μM. Subsequently, a compound series (Fig. 20e), based

Figure 20. Known inhibitors of DHODH enzymes. (a) A set of inhibitors of human DHODH tested against PfDHODH by Phillips and coworkers in 2002. All of these compounds show selective inhibition of the human enzyme [501] (b) Compounds reported in 2005 by McConkey and coworkers, based on brequinar a known inhibitor of human DHODH, displaying relatively weak inhibition of the parasitic enzyme as well as weak activity against whole parasities [506]. (c) Compounds reported in 2007 by McConkey and coworkers displaying potent and selective inhibition of PfDHODH. These compounds were not reported as having activity against intact parasite. (d) Primary high-throughput screening hit compounds reported by Phillips and coworkers in 2005. While these compounds are selective for the parasitic enzyme, none showed appreciable antiparasitic activity [508]. (e) The best compound from a series reported in 2008 by Phillips and coworkers based on a hit from their earlier high-throughput screen [509]. These compounds showed both potent and selective inhibition of PfDHODH and whole parasites. (f) Compounds discovered by Clardy and coworkers with selective enzymatic activity against PfDHODH as well as potent activities in whole-cell parasites. Positive selectivity (fold) values indicate selective inhibition of PfDHODH while negative values indicate selective inhibition of the human enzyme. These compounds represent potential starting points for further development of antimalarials.

Inhibitors of plasmodium dihydroorotate dehydrogenase

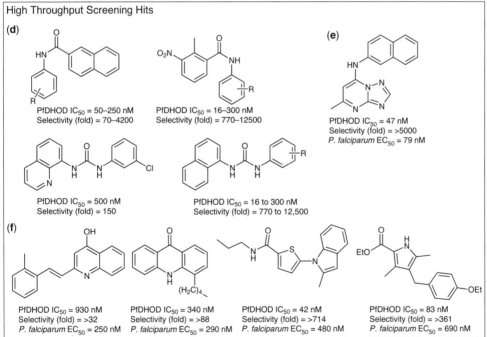

Figure 20. (*Continued*)

on a previously unreported hit from the HTS campaign [509], was revealed that exhibited both potent and selective *Pf*DHODH inhibition (IC$_{50}$ values 47 nM to 93 µM) as well as potent *in vitro* growth inhibitory activity (IC$_{50}$ values 79 nM to >100 µM). These studies also showed a strong positive correlation between the two activities; thus, suggesting the dominant effect came from enzyme inhibition. This study represented the first example of selective *Pf*DHODH inhibitors with good correlation of enzymatic and whole-parasite SARs. The *in vivo* efficacy of this compound series has not yet been reported.

However, despite these promising early results, it seems likely that the antimalarial activity of DHODH inhibitors will be susceptible to resistance acquired by point mutation of the enzyme. Studies have shown that mutations that do not affect the kinetic parameters of the enzyme are able to decrease effectiveness of some inhibitors by over 50-fold [510]. This suggests that a small number of point mutations that do not adversely affect parasite fitness may be able to grant either partial or total resistance to DHODH inhibitors.

A second HTS campaign, with an emphasis on whole-cell activity, has been reported [511]. This study discovered four novel scaffolds (Fig. 20f) with potent inhibition of *Pf*DHODH (IC_{50} values 60–930 nM) and upward of 700-fold selectivity for *Pf*DHODH over the human enzyme. Furthermore, all four compounds displayed potent growth inhibitory activity (IC_{50} values 320–890 nM) with negligible cytotoxicity in human cell lines. One scaffold from this study gave reasonable preliminary structure–activity relationships, suggesting that further development of these compounds as novel antimalarials may prove possible.

3.3.3. Topoisomerase Another target class that has been proposed for antimalarial therapy is the topoisomerases. Although there are many inhibitors of bacterial DNA gyrase and mammalian topoisomerases, relatively few compounds have been tested as antimalarials

and even fewer have been proven to act primarily at these targets. Several reviews have been published in recent years discussing many of the bacterial and mammalian enzyme inhibitors [512–515].

The topoisomerase enzymes change the topological state of double-stranded DNA during replication, transcription, recombination, and DNA repair processes. They are divided into three classes: IA, IB, and II [516–518]. Type I enzymes introduce single-stranded breaks in DNA followed by linking and rejoining, allowing single step changes in the linking number of circular DNA. Type IA enzymes bind covalently to the 5′-end and type IB enzymes from covalent bonds with the 3′-end of broken DNA strands [519]. Type II enzymes introduce transient double-stranded breaks, followed by passage and rejoining. They induce a wide range of structural changes in DNA including relaxation, catenation/decatenation, knotting/unknotting, and induction of supercoils [520,521]. *Plasmodium* sp. possess both type II and IB topoisomerases [522–524]. The type IB enzyme is 42% identical and 63% homologous to the human counterpart while the type II enzyme is 47% identical and 65% homologous to the human homolog. The IB enzyme is only expressed during the erythrocytic stages of the *Plasmodium* lifecycle [525]. Inhibition of the topoisomerases causes the generation of single or double-stranded breaks that cause point mutations, fragmentation of the genome, and cell death [526].

The *P. berghei* topoisomerases I and II were originally characterized in a study that included examining the inhibitory ability of analogs of the DNA intercalating agents ellipticine (Fig. 21a) and isoellipticinium (Fig. 21a)

Figure 21. (a) The earliest reported inhibitors of malarial topoisomerases [523]. These compounds were not tested versus whole parasites, and exact IC_{50} values for their enzymatic activities were not determined. (b) The fluoroquinolone antibiotics were shown to be effective against the enzymes and whole parasites in *in vitro* as well as in *in vivo* mouse models [260,262,531]. However, these compounds are less effective in treating human infections [261,534,535]. (c) The 9-Anilinoacridines. While effective *in vitro* versus both topoisomerase II and whole cell parasites, these compounds do not display *in vivo* activities [550]. (d) Camptothecin, a natural product known to inhibit topoisomerase in mammalian systems [513]. With IC_{50} values in the micromolar range for both malarial topoisomerase I and whole-cell parasites, this compound is not effective in and of itself, but represents a potential scaffold for further development as an antimalarial topoisomerase I inhibitor [554]. (e) Chalcones and bischalcones have been shown to be effective inhibitors of *P. berghei* topoisomerase II. Additionally, these compounds are effective in mouse models of infections and show synergy with chloroquine [555].

Inhibitors of malarial topoisomerases

(a)

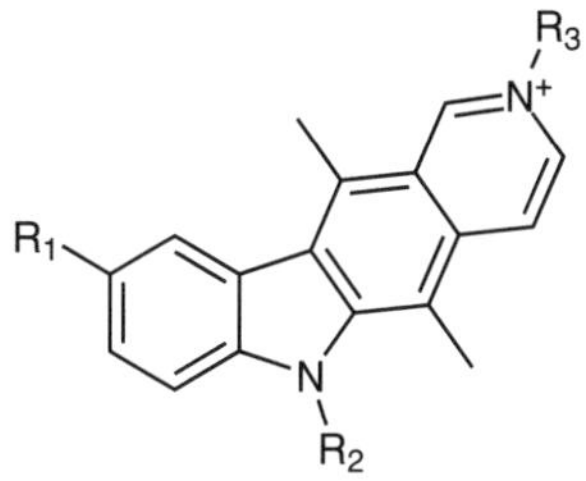

Ellipticine Derivatives
topoisomerase II $IC_{50} < 7$ μM
topoisomerase I $IC_{50} < 35$ μM
P. falciparum IC_{50} = N.T.

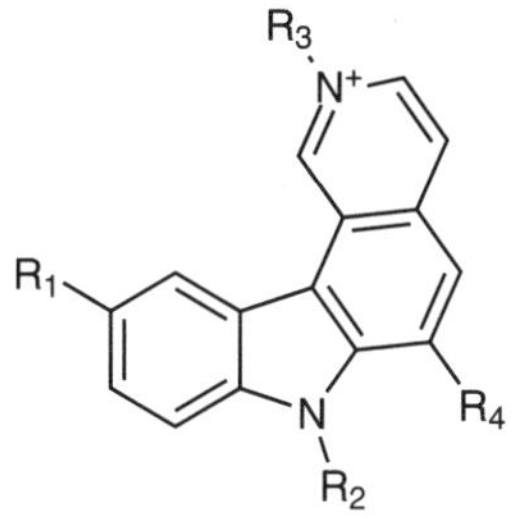

Isoellipicinium derivatives
topoisomerase II $IC_{50} < 3$ μM
topoisomerase I IC_{50} = N.D.
P. falciparum IC_{50} = N.T.

(b)

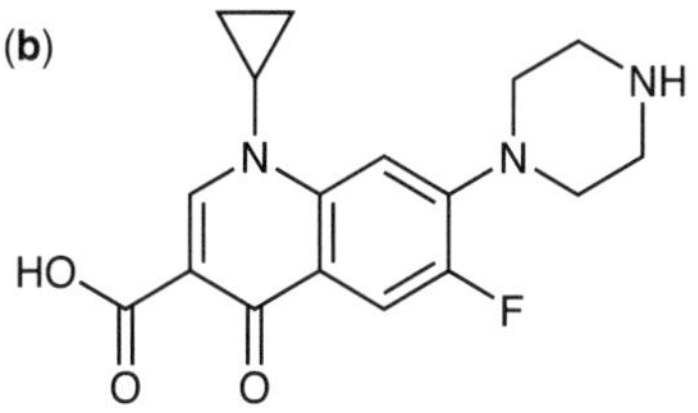

Ciprofloxacin
P. falciparum IC_{50} = 37 nM
topoisomerase II $IC_{50} > 18$ μM

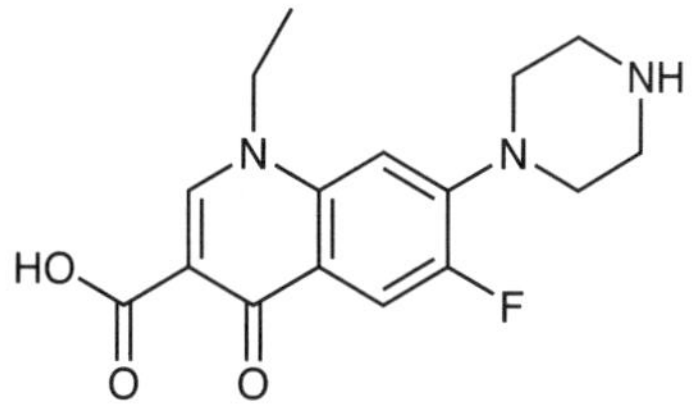

Norfloxacin
P. falciparum IC_{50} = 88 nM
topoisomerase II IC_{50} = N.T.

(c)

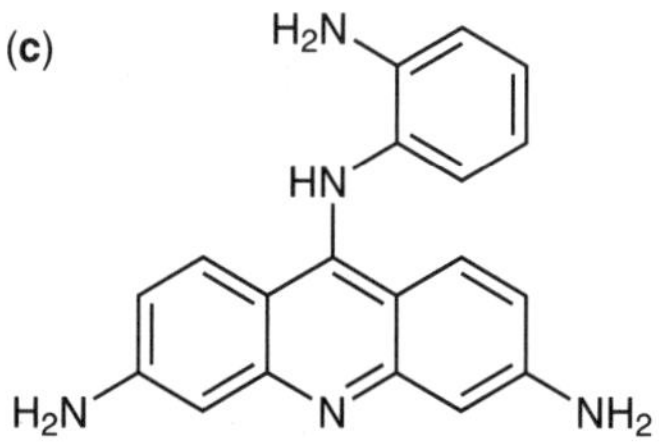

9-Anilinoacridines
P. falciparum IC_{50} = 14–2700 nM
topoisomerase II MIC = 6–50 μM

(d)

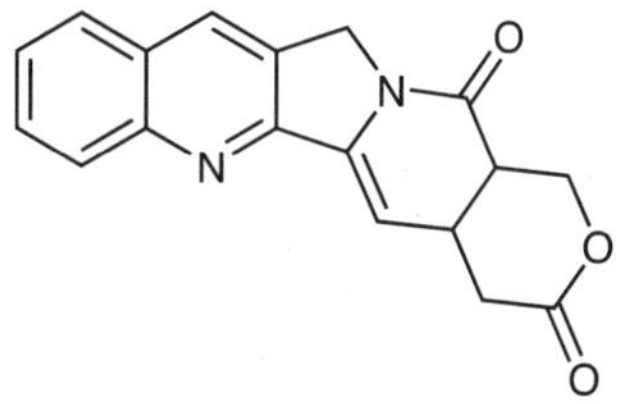

Camptothecin
P. falciparum IC_{50} = 36 nM
topoisomerase I $IC_{50} < 100$ μM

(e)

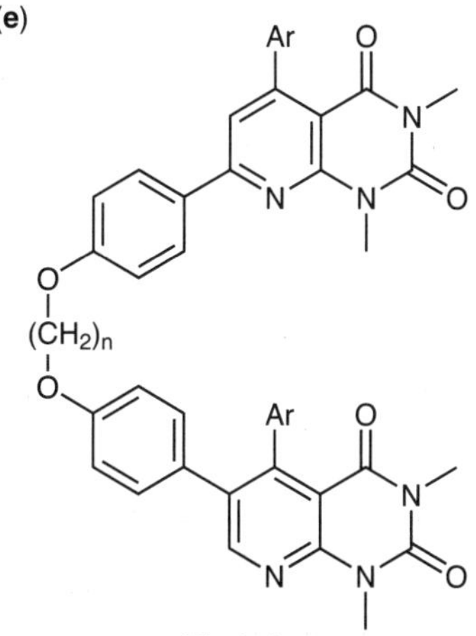

Bischalcones
topoisomerase II $IC_{50} < 0.2$ μg/μL

Figure 21. (*Continued*)

against the parasite enzyme [523]. Several analogs were identified with modest inhibitory potency (IC_{100} values from 3 to 77 μM). Several known antimalarial compounds were also tested although none inhibited either topoisomerase. Ellipticine was later shown to inhibit *P. falciparum* growth by 50–60% at 50 μM fixed concentration, suggesting that the compounds would likely not be potent in whole-cell models [527].

A later study examined fluoroquinolone antibiotics (Fig. 21b), which target this enzyme family, and found that they possessed modest antimalarial potency (IC_{50} values from 0.06 to 380 μM) [260]. Definitive mechanism of action studies proved that these compounds target the malarial topoisomerase II [528–531]. The fluoroquinolines were also efficacious in a *P. yoelii* mouse model against both blood and liver stages [258,262]. However, while the fluoroquinolone norfloxacin was shown to be clinically effective for treating human *P. falciparum* infections in India, its efficacy in Africa was much more questionable [265,532,533]. Furthermore, although ciprofloxacin (Fig. 21b) was shown to be synergistic with mefloquine and chloroquine *in vitro*, it was ineffective in treating human infections due to bioavailability issues [261,534,535]. Taken together, these studies suggest the fluoroquinolines have potential for treating malaria but will require substantial reoptimization for this use. A wide range of fluoroquinolines exist, but have not been tested for antimalarial properties [536–546], and may prove more effective than those tested to date. Two recent studies have produced fluoroquinolines with potent activities versus *T. gondii* but poor antimalarial activities [547,548].

A third series of topoisomerase inhibitors is 9-anilinoacridines (Fig. 21c), which have modest to moderate potencies (IC_{50} values from 0.1 to 40 μM) [549]. The series has been optimized for growth inhibitory potential leading to strongly potent compounds (IC_{50} values from 25 nM to 2.6 μM) active against multidrug-resistant malarial strains [162]. The compounds clearly inhibit *P. falciparum* topoisomerase II and this activity correlates with whole-parasite activities [163,550]. However, the most potent compounds were inactive in murine malaria models, most likely due

to poor exposure. Later studies established that these compounds were able to kill both gametocytes and asexual parasites, and that binding of hematin might also be part of their mechanism of action [551,552].

A fourth topoisomerase inhibitor series is analogs of camptothecin (Fig. 21d). This topoisomerase I targeted series has long been used clinically as anticancer agents [513,553]. Initial testing of camptothecin in *P. falciparum* growth inhibition assay revealed that the compound was cytocidal and clearly inhibited the malarial topoisomerase I [554]. However, potency against the enzyme was very poor (IC_{50} 100 μM) and the growth inhibitory potency was roughly equivalent (IC_{50} 30–40 μM). The activity was confirmed by a second group [525].

A final compound series that has been examined is the chalcones (Fig. 21e). These compounds were moderately potent inhibitors (IC_{50} values from 25 to 68 μM) of *P. berghei* topoisomerase II [555]. They were weakly potent (100 mg/kg, i.p.) in murine models. However, the compounds seemed to be synergistic with chloroquine *in vivo*, allowing doses to be reduced to 50 mg/kg bis-chalcone plus 15 mg/kg chloroquine. The ability of the compounds to inhibit topoisomerase II activity was also loosely correlated with their *in vivo* potency. These early results suggest that the bischalcones may be a promising lead for further development as antimalarials, although many issues affecting exposure clearly need to be taken in hand.

Taken together, these reports show that the topoisomerases of malaria represent a promising target for the development of new antimalarials. Early work in the area seems to indicate that selectivity between malarial, mammalian, and bacterial homologs is an achievable goal. *In vivo* proof of concept has been achieved, but better understanding of pharmacodynamics will be crucial to assessing the long-term utility of this target. Other methods for inhibiting topoisomerase activity have been reported, including the use of ruthenium or rhodium containing complexes and the use of antisense oligonucleotides [556–558]. While these methods show *in vitro* efficacy, further work is needed before they can be seriously considered as useful for development as antimalarial drugs.

3.3.4. Histone Deacetylase The histone deacetylase enzymes (HDACs) remove acetyl groups from lysines on histone proteins [559]. Histones the major proteins of chromatin and play a key role in DNA packaging, gene expression and DNA replication by providing ultrastructure to DNA. Histones are highly positively charged due to a high lysine content and interact electrostatically with negatively charged DNA. Acetylation by histone acetyl transferases (HATs) converts histone's lysines into amides, thus reducing the interaction with DNA [560]. The activities of both HATs and HDACs determine the degree of DNA packaging and thus gene regulation. Five HDACs have been found so far in *P. falciparum,* but only two are even partially characterized: PfHDAC and PfSir [561]. PfHDAC1 is a 50 kDa protein localized in the nucleus and predominantly expressed in the mature asexual stages of the parasite and the gametocyte [562]. PfHDAC1 has been suggested as antimalarial drug target since early studies found that apicidin, a nonselective HDAC inhibitor with broad antifungal and antiparasitic activities, was effective against malaria [563]. Nicotinamide, an inhibitor of PfSir, has also shown some antimalarial activity [564]. Pf*HDAC*-1 is highly homologous with human HDACs. Its overall role in malaria physiology is still relatively unknown [562]. PfSir has been shown to bind telomeres and cause gene silencing, especially of the genes encoding *P. falciparum* variant surface antigens [565–567]. The remaining three HDAC homologs encoded in the *P. falciparum* genome have not yet been characterized.

There are a wide range of histone deacetylase inhibitors that affect mammalian HDACs including trichostatin A (TSA) [568], trapoxin (TPX) [569], HC toxin [570], FK-228 [571], and sodium butyrate [572] as well as the synthetic compounds sodium phenylbutyrate [573], sodium valproate [574,575], suberoylanilide hydroxamic acid (SAHA) [576], straight chain TSA and SAHA analogs [577–579], 1,4-cyclohexylene and 1,4-phenylene-N-hydroxycarboxamides [580], scriptaid [581], oxamflatin [582,583], cyclic hydroxamic acid-containing peptides (CHAPs) [584,585], and benzamides [586,587]. However, relatively few of these compounds have been tested against either the malaria HDACs or the cultured malaria.

Researchers at Merck reported that apicidin, (Fig. 22a) a cyclic tetrapeptide natural product isolated from a Costa Rican fungus, was active against a wide range of apicomplexan parasites. The compound exhibits potent PfHDAC inhibition (IC_{50} values <1 nM) as well as potent growth inhibition (MIC = 200 nM) and is effective in mouse model infections at doses of 50 mg/kg [563,588]. However, toxicity, probably resulting from a lack of selectivity for the parasitic HDAC in preference to mammalian HDACs, prevented further development of apicidin as an antimalarial drug. For this reason, the group prepared several series of apicidin analogs, with an emphasis on modification of the tryptophan residue, leading to compounds displaying greater than 100-fold selectivity for malarial HDAC. [589–592]. In contrast with modifications of the indole ring system, any alterations of the ketone containing side chain were poorly tolerated [593].

Other studies have examined known inhibitors of mammalian HDACs for antimalarial activities (Fig. 22b), in both *in vitro* and *in vivo* mouse models [594]. This study focused mainly on the hydroxamic acid analogs, including suberohydroxamic acid (SBHA), which serve as mimetics of the natural acetylated lysine substrate of HDAC. The compounds displayed modest growth inhibitory potencies against both chloroquine-sensitive and chloroquine-resistant parasites (IC_{50} values 0.9 μM to 1.4 μM) as well as selective cytotoxicity for rapidly replicating tumor cells versus normal lines [595]. In mouse models, SBHA displayed modest efficacy, delaying the onset of high levels of parasitemia for up to 1 week at modest dosage levels (2×8 mg doses per day over 3 days). A second study expanded the series of HDAC inhibitors studied [561] by using a homology model of PfHDAC-1 to design analogs of 2-aminosuberic acid (Fig. 22c). The compounds showed potent growth inhibition (EC_{50} values 13–339 nM) and were generally at least 30-fold selective for parasites over human fibroblast cell lines. Furthermore, the inhibitors induced hyperacetylation of *P. falciparum* histones *in vitro*, suggesting that they are acting through inhibition of PfHDAC. The scaffold is known to be orally

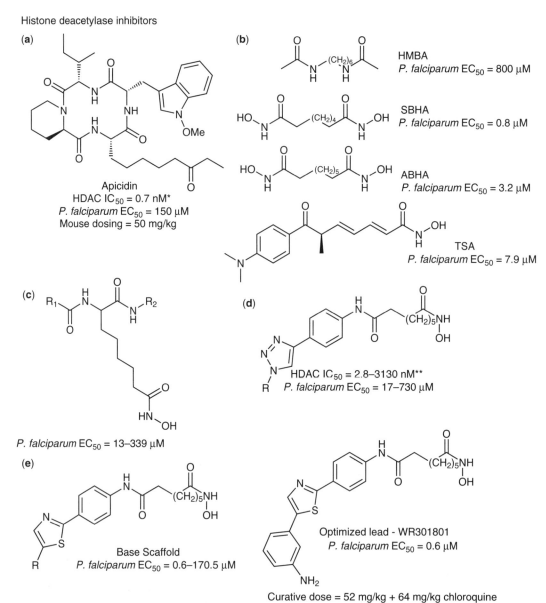

Histone deacetylase inhibitors

(a) Apicidin
HDAC IC_{50} = 0.7 nM*
P. falciparum EC_{50} = 150 μM
Mouse dosing = 50 mg/kg

(b) HMBA
P. falciparum EC_{50} = 800 μM

SBHA
P. falciparum EC_{50} = 0.8 μM

ABHA
P. falciparum EC_{50} = 3.2 μM

TSA
P. falciparum EC_{50} = 7.9 μM

(c) *P. falciparum* EC_{50} = 13–339 μM

(d) HDAC IC_{50} = 2.8–3130 nM**
P. falciparum EC_{50} = 17–730 μM

(e) Base Scaffold
P. falciparum EC_{50} = 0.6–170.5 μM

Optimized lead - WR301801
P. falciparum EC_{50} = 0.6 μM
Curative dose = 52 mg/kg + 64 mg/kg chloroquine

*Tested with *E. tenella* HDAC
**Tested with human HDAC

Figure 22. (a) Apicidin, a natural tetrapeptide with a wide range of potent antiparasitic activities including both *in vitro* and *in vivo* antimalarial properties [563,588]. Variations at the tryptophan residue are well tolerated and lead to selective antiparasitic activity while variations at the longer ketone moiety are not tolerated. This moiety is thought to serve as a mimetic for the acetylated lysine substrate [589–592]. (b) Known inhibitors of mammalian HDAC with antimalarial properties [594]. The hydroxamate moiety serves as a zinc binding group and a mimetic of acetylated lysine. (c) A series of hydroxamate containing inhibitors with potent *in vitro* antimalarial activities [561]. These compounds have not been shown to possess *in vivo* activity. (d) A series of hydroxamate-based inhibitors containing a triazole linker [597]. These compounds were tested against a panel of human HDAC isoforms and were shown to possess varying selectivities. (e) A second series of hydroxamate-based inhibitors containing a phenylthiazol linker. This series contains WR301801, which was taken as far as nonhuman primate efficacy models. Despite early indications *in vitro* and in rodent models, the compounds are not curative as monotherapies. However, when combined with subtherapeutic levels of chloroquine, researchers were able to cure infected mice. The lack of potent *in vivo* activities was linked to metabolic degradation of the hydroxamate moiety [599].

bioavailable in rats and is a promising lead [596].

Several other studies have produced even more potent hydroxamic acid inhibitors. The first of these, a series of triazolyl-phenyl compounds (Fig. 22d), established that compounds displaying selective inhibition of various human HDAC enzymes retained potent growth inhibitory activity (EC_{50} values from 17 to 560 nM) [597]. This is an important finding as a number of selective HDAC inhibitors are being developed as cancer chemotherapeutic agents. It may prove possible to "piggyback" much of the early clinical testing for new antimalarial compounds onto these more financially lucrative projects [598]. The second series was phenylthiazolyl-bearing hydroxamates (Fig. 22e) [599]. This compound series was extensively tested including both mouse and monkey models of infection. The best compound from this series, WR301801 (Fig. 22e), displayed potent growth inhibition (IC_{50} of 0.6 nM), and was orally bioavailable in both mice and monkeys. However, while it was able to reduce parasite load in a dose-dependent manner as a monotherapy, it was incapable of curing infections in either model. This was most likely due to rapid metabolic degradation ($t_{1/2}$ about 11 min in mouse microsomes) of the active hydroxamate to the inactive carboxylate. Despite this liability, the compound was curative when combined with chloroquine. Further optimization may require replacing the hydroxamate zinc-binding motif with another group, eliminating a source of metabolic instability seen in this study [600,601].

Despite these promising early results, the hydroxymates were generally either antagonistic or simply additive with current malaria therapies. If this is a trait shared by other HDAC inhibitors, the further development of these compounds could be in jeopardy. However, two recent studies are of interest. In the first, a high-throughput assay revealed compounds that bind to malarial HDAC [602]. This could lead to the discovery of new inhibitors with better pharmacokinetic properties. The second reports the development of a sophisticated homology model of *Pf*HDAC [603], that could allow for structure-based design approaches.

3.4. Cellular Respiration and the Electron Transport Chain

In 1946, some 2-hydroxy-3-alkyl-napthoquinones were found to inhibit respiration of *Plasmodium* species [604]. This observation prompted an in depth investigation of their mechanism of action, leading to the discovery that the compounds act just below cytochrome *c* in the respiratory chain [605]. An extensive synthetic effort led to the production of the first naphthoquinone shown to be effective in mice (160 mg/kg, oral, single dose), 3-(8-cyclohexyl)-octyl-2-hydroxy-1,4-naphthoquinone (menoctone) (Fig 23a) [606,607]. Unfortunately, this compound proved inactive in humans at the maximum tolerated dose (500 mg, oral, daily) [608]. Despite this failure, the early results obtained using naphthoquinones prompted the examination of coenzyme Q analogs as agents targeting the electron transport chain of the malarial parasite [609].

Extensive studies based on these early results yielded the clinically useful antimalarial atovaquone (Fig. 23b) [153,610]. Atovaquone's exact mechanism of action was initially unclear. Eventually, it was shown that atovaquone was capable of inhibiting isolated cytochrome bc_1 complexes (Complex III) and that the site of inhibition was likely to lie between cytochromes *b* and c_1 [611]. Labeling experiments performed in the same study suggested that the interaction was irreversible. Further studies suggested that structural differences between the putative quinone binding sites of *Plasmodium* cytochrome b (cyt b) and those of mammalian species might be responsible for the selectivity of the naphthoquinone drugs [612]. While many structures of mammalian bc_1 complexes exist, both with and without inhibitors bound, no structures of the malarial complex has been reported [613–616]. Binding to the complex was also shown to result in collapse of the mitochondrial membrane potential [617]. When malaria parasites were selected for atovaquone resistance both *in vitro* and *in vivo* mutations were found in the cyt b gene, predominantly at the cytosolic Q_o binding site [618–620]. A bacterial model system has also been used to establish that only a few residues in malarial cyt b are responsible for its sensitivity to atovaquone, specifically

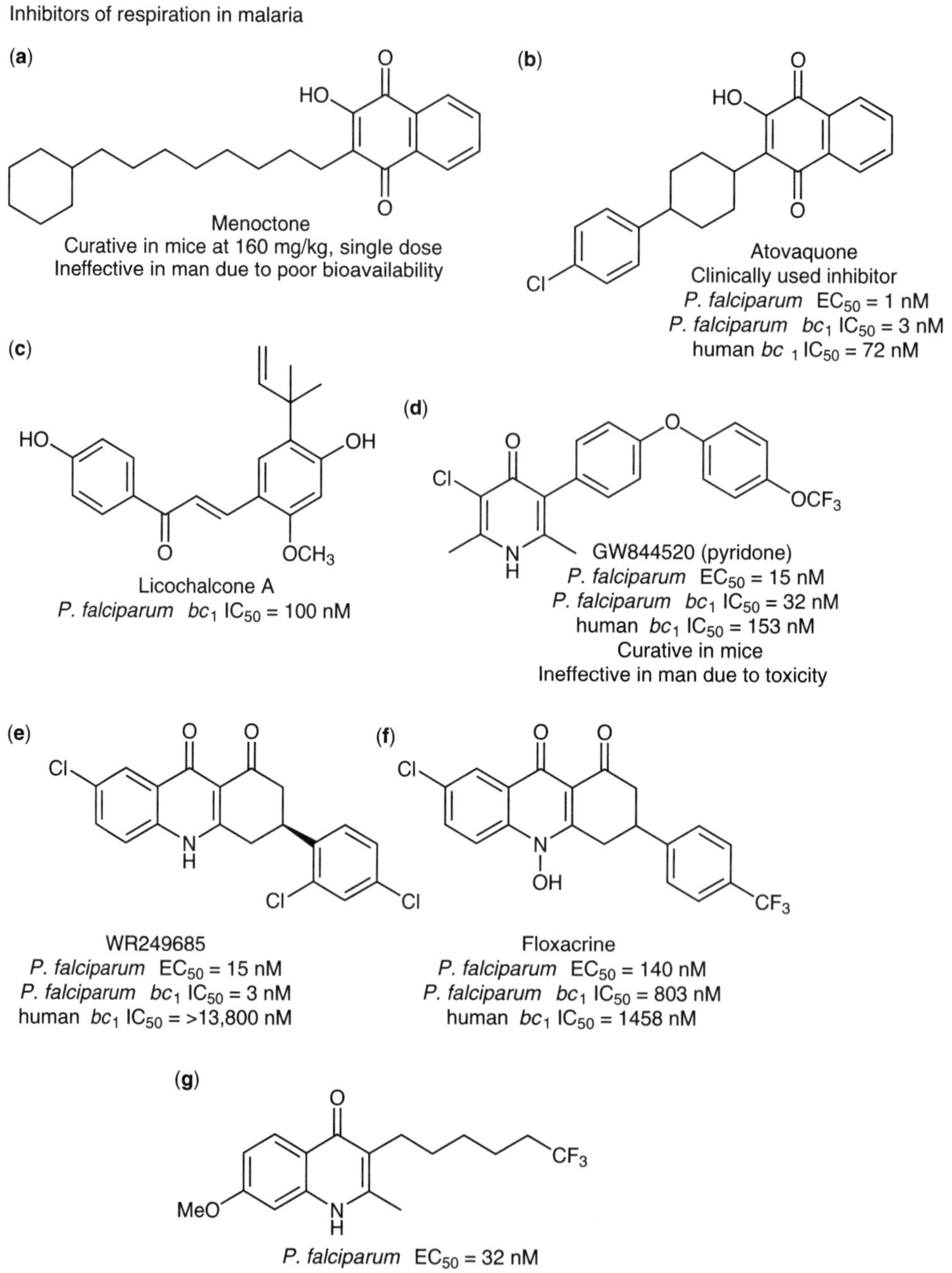

Inhibitors of respiration in malaria

Figure 23. (a) Menoctone, a compound synthesized in 1967 by Fieser et al. and shown to be effective in mouse models of malaria [606,607]. (b) Atovaquone, a clinically used inhibitor of the bc_1 complex [153,610]. This compound is part of the commonly used combination therapy malarone. (c) Licochalcone A, an inhibitor of both complex II and bc_1. While this compound is not currently selective, it may represent a reasonable starting point for the further development of novel inhibitors. [627]. (d) GW844520 (pyridone) an inhibitor of malarial bc_1, which advanced to human trials before being abandoned due to toxicity issues [628,629]. (e) WR249685—an acridinedione known to be both a potent antimalarial and selective inhibitor of malarial

met 304, lys 306, and cys 302 [621]. Despite the ease of raising resistant strains in the laboratory, a study of cyt b genes from clinical isolates not exposed to atovaquone revealed a low level of polymorphisms in drug-naïve populations suggesting that spontaneous resistance granting mutations are rare [622]. Atovaquone demonstrates strong synergy with proguanil, and is clinically used in a combination therapy consisting of a mixture of the two drugs known as malarone.

Malaria species seem to have a branched respiratory pathway involving both the cytochrome chain and an alternative oxidase. As such, inhibitors of alternative oxidases, such as propyl gallate act synergistically with atovaquone [623]. This pathway, also known as either complex I or complex II has been shown to be necessary for parasite survival, and its inhibition results in the collapse of the mitochondrial potential [624]. More recent evidence has shown that the main role of the malarial electron transport chain (ETC) is the regeneration of ubiquinone as an electron acceptor of DHODH, an essential enzyme in the pyrimidine biosynthetic pathway [625]. For this reason, it is possible to bypass the need for an intact ETC by introducing a DHODH that is independent of ubiquinone. Recently, an atovaquone-resistant parasite strain without a functional ETC has been discovered [626]. While the ETC is still a valid target for drug development, this discovery may have important implications for the development and monitoring of resistance in the field.

Based on the rigorous validation of this target, and the relatively limited chemotypes available for inhibition, development of novel inhibitors has been pursued by several groups in the recent years. Licochalcone A (Fig. 23c) has been shown to inhibit the both the malarial bc_1 complex with an IC_{50} of 0.1 μM and the malarial complex II with an IC_{50} of 1.3 μM. Additionally, the compound modestly potently inhibits growth of *P. falciparum* (EC_{50} of

7.7 μM). While it is not specific for the malaria bc_1 complex (inhibiting rat liver bc_1 with an IC_{50} of 0.077 μM) it does have some selectivity for malarial complex II (inhibiting rat liver complex II with an IC_{50} of 16.5 μM) [627]. It may represent a starting point for development of new, nonnaphthoquinone-based inhibitors of bc_1.

Another recently reported potent inhibitor of malarial bc_1 is GW844520 (Fig. 23d) (IC_{50} of 2 nM) [628]. This compound is effective in murine models of *P. falciparum* and *P. yoelli* following oral dosing (therapeutic dosing not reported, maximum tolerated dose 1400 mg/ kg) and shows no cross-resistance with known antimalarials *in vitro*. While it possesses an excellent pharmacokinetic profile, with a long half-life (89 h in cynomolgus monkeys), high oral bioavailability, and was inexpensive to synthesize, the compound was ultimately abandoned after toxicity issues in early human testing. A later study suggested that this might be due to a relatively low level of selectivity between human and malarial bc_1 [629]. This study also suggested that this property might also limit the use of murine models in the development of bc_1 complex inhibitors, given the lack of correlation between murine toxicity and human selectivity. Efforts are currently underway to develop a new analog of this compound with a better toxicity profile.

The most recently reported series of bc_1 complex inhibitors is the acridinediones. While these compounds have been known to possess antimalarial properties for quite some time, their mechanism of action was not clear [630–634]. Both WR249685 (Fig. 23e) and floxacrine (Fig. 23f) were thought to kill through binding to heme in a manner similar to chloroquine. However, studies have shown that WR249685 is a highly specific inhibitor of *P. falciparum* bc_1 complex, with an *in vitro* therapeutic index of >4600 when compared with human bc_1 [629]. The compound is a highly potent (IC_{50} of 3 nM) inhibitor of

Figure 23. (*Continued*) bc_1 [629,634]. (f) Floxamine—also an inhibitor of malarial bc_1, but kills parasites through binding to heme in a manner similar to chloroquine rather than by inhibition of the electron transport chain [629–633]. (g) A quinolone reported to inhibit malarial respiration in a manner similar to atovaquone, as well as acting synergistically with clopidol [636]. The exact mode of action for this compound is unknown but available evidence suggests that this is acting through inhibition of the electron transport chain.

malarial bc_1 and a potent inhibitor of parasite growth (EC_{50} of 15 nM). Furthermore, WR249685 had an IC_{50} of 130 μM. This suggests that WR249685 kills the parasite through inhibition of bc_1. Another similar compound, floxacrine was modestly potent against bc_1 (IC_{50} of 803 nM) but more potent in growth inhibitory assays (EC_{50} of 140 nM).

A study of related acridones discovered highly potent inhibitors of the growth of *P. falciparum* that the authors attributed to inhibition of bc_1. However, since only cell data is presented, it is difficult to attribute the SAR observed to a single molecular target [635]. The same group also reported a series of quinolones of which at least one member (Fig. 23g) inhibited respiration in *P. falciparum* [636]. This was a potent growth inhibitor (EC_{50} of 32 nM) and an *in vitro* therapeutic index of >20,800 over mammalian cells. Furthermore, it was synergistic with clopidol in a similar manner to atovaquone and did not display significant levels of cross-resistance with atovaquone [637]. These observations suggest that it may be acting through inhibition of the electron transport chain, and possibly at the bc_1 complex.

Taken together, these reports show that the bc_1 complex remains a valid chemotherapeutic target for malaria. However, these studies also illustrate the difficulty that is often present in determining structure–activity relationships for specific targets from whole-cell data, which is compounded in this series. It is suggested that any work to develop specific inhibitors of this pathway must use isolated complex as well as whole-cell assays in order to make decisions regarding SAR. Furthermore, it may be advisable to utilize a hemoglobin binding assay as well, since many of the features often found in inhibitors of the electron transport chain can also result in binding to heme, and a change in the cellular mechanism of action.

3.5. Cellular Stress and Oxidative Stress Management

3.5.1. PfATP6 PfATP6 is a member of the sarcoplasmic/endoplasmic reticulum Ca^{2+} ATPase (SERCA) family expressed by the *P. falciparum* parasite. Enzymes from this family maintain cytosolic Ca^{2+} levels by regulating release of Ca^{2+} from endoplasmic reticulum stores. The malaria enzyme shows low overall homology to the mammalian homologs (48% homology versus rabbit muscle SERCA) and possesses a large (200 amino acid) insertion at the C-terminus that is thought to regulate its activity [638]. Pharmacological studies have shown that the endoplasmic reticulum Ca^{2+} stores in the parasite have different susceptibility profiles than those in mammalian cells, with the parasite responding to cyclopiazonic acid, an inhibitor of plant SERCAs, but not compounds known to inhibit mammalian homologs [639]. This suggests that the development of selective PfATP6 inhibitors might be possible. However, hypothesis remains controversial as the initial inhibitor profile results were disputed in several later reports [139,640]. These reports also showed potent inhibition by thapsigargin (Fig. 24a), a known inhibitor of mammalian SERCAs [139,640].

The efforts to discover PfATP6 inhibitors were minimal until 2003, when a seminal study identified PfATP6 as a potential target of the artemisinin class of antimalarials (Fig. 24b). Initial reports demonstrated a strong correlation between potency against PfATP6 and growth inhibitory potency in *P. falciparum* with a series of analogous inhibitors suggested that PfATP6 plays an important role in the antimalarial properties of the artemisinins [139]. K_i values for the analogs studied ranged from 162 nM to 6 μM against PfATP6. This study also characterized the activity of several previously reported SERCA inhibitors against heterologously expressed enzyme. In contrast to previous reports, PfATP6 exhibited similar inhibition selectivity profiles to rabbit muscle SERCA.

Subsequently, many studies involving clinical isolates of *P. falciparum* were initiated, primarily focusing on the relationship between polymorphisms in PfATP6 and sensitivity to the growth inhibitor effects of artemisinin and its derivatives. One such study reported a S769N mutation in PfATP6 from isolates collected in French Guiana, which correlated with *in vitro* sensitivity to artemether [146]. Another *in vitro* study showed that *P. falciparum* strains could be made

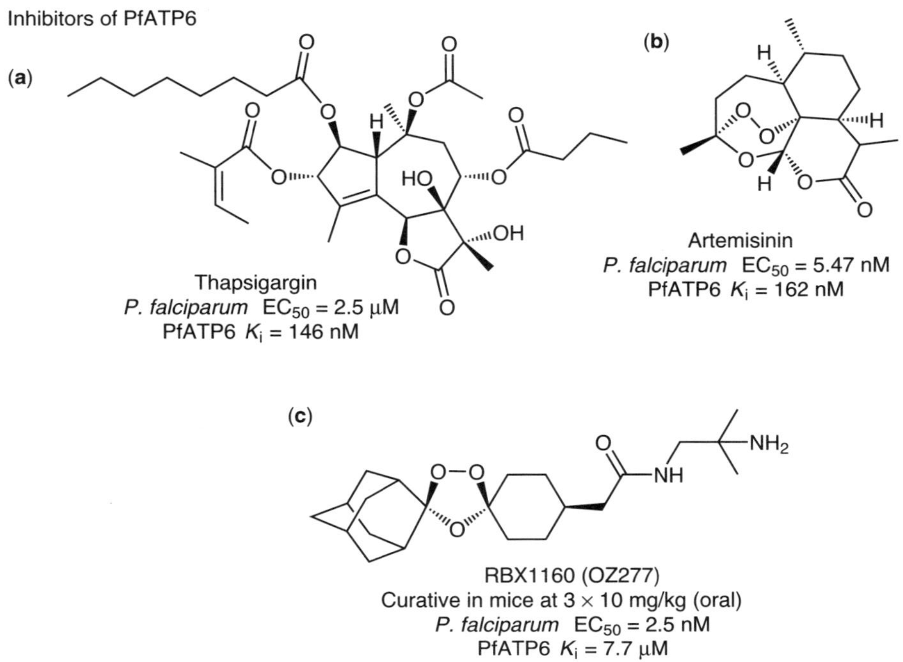

Inhibitors of PfATP6

(a)

Thapsigargin
P. falciparum EC$_{50}$ = 2.5 μM
PfATP6 K_i = 146 nM

(b)

Artemisinin
P. falciparum EC$_{50}$ = 5.47 nM
PfATP6 K_i = 162 nM

(c)

RBX1160 (OZ277)
Curative in mice at 3 × 10 mg/kg (oral)
P. falciparum EC$_{50}$ = 2.5 nM
PfATP6 K_i = 7.7 μM

Figure 24. (a) Thapsigargin, a known inhibitor of mammalian sarcoplasmic/endoplasmic reticulum Ca^{2+} ATPase (SERCA) enzymes that also shows efficacy versus the malarial homolog PfATP6 [139]. (b) Artemisinin, a clinically used antimalarial thought to act at least in part though inhibition of PfATP6 [139]. (c) OZ277 (RBX1160)—a synthetic superoxide analog of artemisinin also hypothesized to act via inhibition of PfATP6. This compound is curative in approximately 67% of mouse model malaria infections as a monotherapy [134,648].

659

resistant to artemisinin through a single L263E mutation [641]. However, most studies on clinical isolates showed no effect of polymorphisms in PfATP6 on *in vitro* sensitivity to artemisinins [72,642–646].

Despite strong clinical justification for development of inhibitors for PfATP6, very little medicinal chemistry has been reported. One docking study has been reported, using a homology model of PfATP6 to show that artemisinin analogs might be able to bind at the ATP binding site [647]. Most programs have driven the evolution of artemisinin analogs using whole-cell assays. Almost none of the analogs have been assayed against recombinant PfATP6, precluding the evaluation of correlations between biochemical and whole-cell potencies. One exception to this trend was the development of OZ277 (Fig. 24c), a novel artemisinin analog featuring a 1,2,4-trioxane in place of the parental bridged peroxide. This compound was shown to be a highly potent inhibitor of parasite growth (2.5 nM) and to cure *P. berghei* infections as a monotherapy in mouse models (2 of 3 cures, 10 mg/kg daily for 3 days) [134]. A later study of this compound showed that it inhibited recombinant PfATP6 (K_i of 7.7 μM) and that the compound localized to both the cytosol and the food vacuole in the parasite. Furthermore, the compound acted antagonistically with artemisinin, suggesting a similar mechanism of action. Taken together, these data suggest that PfATP6 plays a role in the activity of the ozonides, but that there may be other targets playing a significant role in the antimalarial properties of both artemisinins and OZ277 [648].

There is certainly convincing evidence implicating this target as playing a role in artemisinin activity. The fact that known mammalian SERCA inhibitors are effective antimalarials *in vitro* does supports the conclusion that the malarial enzyme may be a potentially useful target. However, the lack of correlation between artemisinin sensitivity of clinical isolates and polymorphisms in PfATP6 and the poor data correlating enzyme activity with whole-cell activity imply that the validity of this target must be regarded with some skepticism. Further efforts to synthesize PfATP6 inhibitors that are not dependent on radical mediated mechanisms may help to resolve this issue.

3.5.2. Glutathione Biosynthesis Compounds affecting proteins involved in maintaining intracellular reduction–oxidation potentials have also been investigated as potential sources of novel antimalarial compounds. The enzymes involved in the biosynthesis of glutathione and thioredoxin have been of particular interest. The maintenance of the intracellular oxidative environment is particularly important for malarial parasites, whose main source of nutrition is hemoglobin from host red blood cells. During proteolysis of this protein, superoxide radicals and hemin are released and must be detoxified, either by dismutation in the case of superoxide or by crystallization and reaction with free glutathione (GSH) in the case of hemin [649,650]. This oxidative potential is regulated in part by management of the glutathione pools through the activity of glutathione reductase (GR), a flavoenzyme that catalyzes the conversion of the disulphide form of glutathione (GSSG) to the free thiol form (GSH) in an NADPH dependant fashion. There is also a second, parallel, pathway responsible for redox management in the malaria parasite: the thioredoxin (Trx) system. However, although this system has been characterized in some detail, it has not yet been exploited for chemotherapeutic purposes [651,652].

The malarial GR enzyme (*Pf*GR) has been expressed recombinantly and characterized both biochemically and structurally [653,654]. The enzyme is 40–45% identical with GR enzymes from other species, and the structure revealed a number of differences in shape and chemical characteristics between the *Plasmodium* enzyme and the human homolog [655]. Predominantly, *Pf*GR has a largely neutral cavity, while the same cavity in hGR is more negatively charge. In addition, the phenylalanine residue that directly interacts with the aromatic group on most inhibitors of hGR is missing in *Pf*GR.

An initial effort to inhibit PfGR revealed that two known inhibitors of human glutathione reductase, BCNU and HeCNU (Fig. 25a), are potent inhibitors of *P. falciparum* growth [656]. Both of these compounds irreversibly inhibit *Pf*GR with modest potencies (IC$_{50}$ values 13 and 18 μM, respectively) and deplete intracellular glutathione levels. Previously, HeCNU had been shown to be

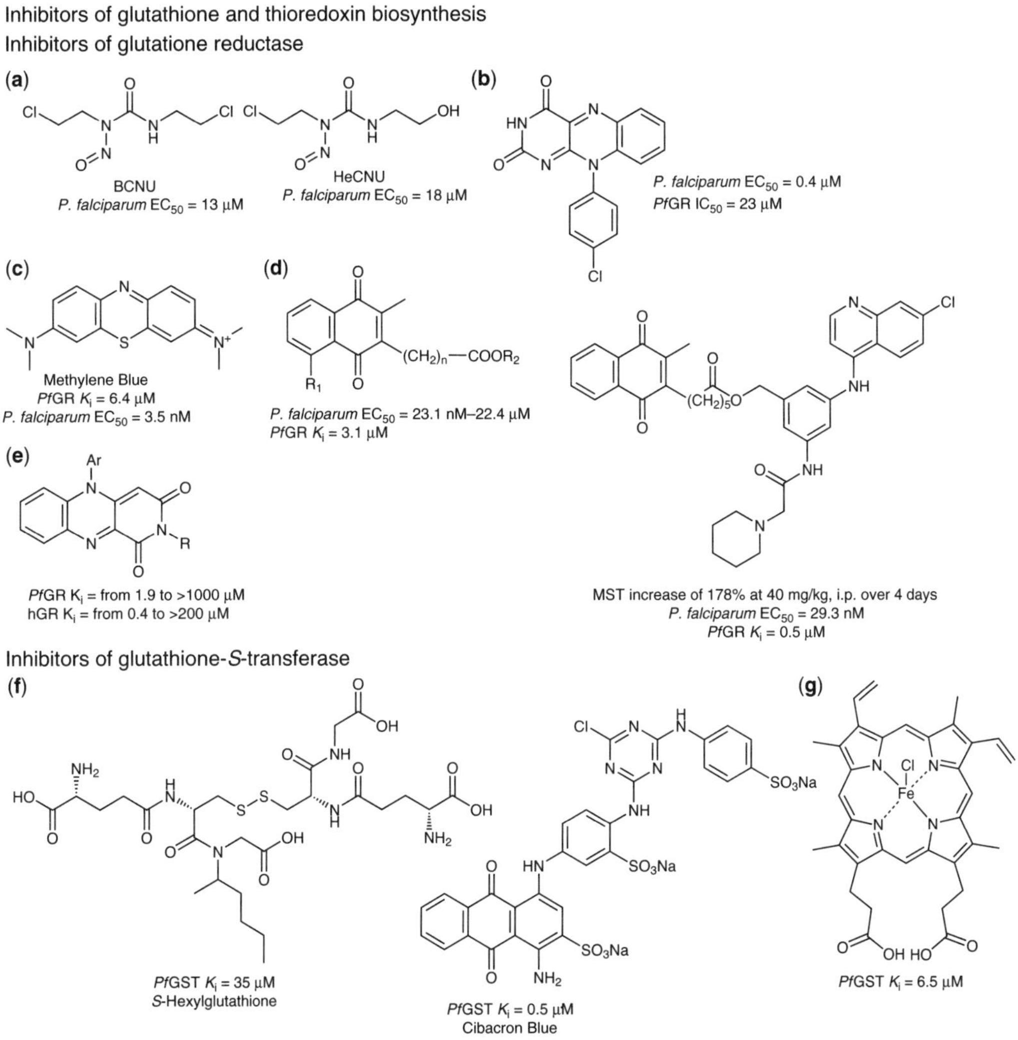

Inhibitors of glutathione and thioredoxin biosynthesis
Inhibitors of glutatione reductase

Figure 25. (a) Irreversible inhibitors of glutathione reductase. These compounds inhibit both human and malarial enzymes. HeCNU is curative in mouse models [657,658] (b) An exemplar from a flavin series of *P. falciparum* glutathione reductase inhibitors [658]. While these compounds were more efficacious in whole-cell models growth inhibition was not rescued by exogenous glutathione. (c) Methylene blue, the first synthetic antimalarial, is a reversible inhibitor of *Pf*GR that acts as a subversive substrate, reversing the enzymes normal function [653,659,660,663]. (d) A prodrug series produced by fusion of 1,4-napthoquione *Pf*GR inhibitors and 4-aminoquionlines [82,664]. This compound series showed *in vivo* activity in a mouse model of malaria by increasing mean survival time (MST) by 178% (i.p.,40 mg/kg, 4 days). (e) A series of arilloxazine inhibitors that are noncompetitive inhibitors that bind in a pocket at the dimer interface on the enzyme [655,667]. (f) Competitive inhibitors of *Pf*GS [675,676]. (g) Hemin, an uncompetitive inhibitor of *Pf*GST. Protoporphyrin IX, the nonmetallated version of this compound is a mixed mode inhibitor of the enzyme [675,676].

curative in *P. vinckei* mouse models of infection, though no mechanism of action was reported at the time [657]. A more potent series of flavin analogs (IC$_{50}$ values from 1.2 to

2.8 µM) (Fig. 25b) has been reported [658]. While quite potent growth inhibitors, parasites treated with these compounds are not rescued through the addition of exogenous glutathione to the culture media, suggesting that the inhibitors are either irreversible or their activities arise from inhibition of other targets.

Methylene blue, long known as an antimalarial, has been shown to be a modestly potent inhibitor of PfGR (K_i of $6\,\mu M$) [653,659,660] (Fig. 25c). Methylene blue is synergistic with the artemisinins *in vitro*, but antagonistic with 4-aminoquinolines [661,662]. A recent thorough examination of the mechanism of action under nominally physiological conditions showed that this compound is actually a subversive substrate for PfGR, meaning that it reverses the normal role of the enzyme, causing it to function as an H_2O_2 producing oxidant, rather than a reductase [663].

A series of prodrug inhibitors of PfGR in which 1,4-napthoquinone GR inhibitors were linked to 4-aminoquinolines through an ester has been reported [82,664] (Fig. 25d). The authors hypothesized that the two elements would separate in the parasites and that treating cells with glutathione reductase inhibitors would sensitize them to 4-aminoquinolines, a phenomena that had been observed before in studies using other GR inhibitors [53]. These compounds were capable of decreasing glutathione pools in whole-cell models and possessed *in vivo* activity. The best compound was able to decrease parasitemia by 99.5% after 4 days and increase mean survival time by 178%. The aminoquinoline containing subunit of the prodrug was also an effective growth inhibitor, but with an EC_{50} approximately sixfold weaker than that of the prodrug, suggesting that the presence of the PfGR inhibiting group does sensitize the parasites to aminoquinolines. It should also be noted that it has been suggested that the antimalarial activities of many quinones correlate better with their single-electron reduction potentials than with their K_i values for GR. This emphasizes the importance of establishing that any compounds thought to be acting through GR inhibition are capable of perturbing glutathione levels in whole-cell models [665].

Other work has utilized the 1,4-napthoquinone scaffold, with one study showing that the addition of a single fluorine to the 5-methyl group changed the inhibitors from subversive substrates into suicide substrates [666]. While this addition led to slightly more potent antimalarials, it also decreased the therapeutic index from 10-fold to less than 2-fold when compared to a human cell line. A 1.7 Å crystal structure of hGR shows this inhibitor covalently bound to the enzyme through the side chain of Cys78. This data suggests that irreversible inhibitors of GR may suffer from toxicity issues if they are not selective for parasitic enzyme.

Finally, a series of noncompetitive arilloxazine inhibitors have been reported to have modest potencies against PfGR (EC_{50} values 1.9 to $>1000\,\mu M$) and generally poor selectivity for the parasite enzyme (1/2 to $>1/80$th fold) [667] (Fig. 25e). These compounds bind to a pocket formed at the dimer interface of the enzyme, which is not well conserved between the host and the parasitic enzymes [655]. No growth inhibitory data has been reported for the scaffold series, thus it is impossible to evaluate any correlations between enzyme inhibition and growth inhibition SARs. These compounds are light sensitive, which is a major drawback for any further development.

Another enzyme in the glutathione pathway is glutathione-S-transferase, or GST. Although this enzyme is found in all *Plasmodium* species studied so far, believed to be essential for maintaining redox balance, and has high-resolution structures, there are relatively few known inhibitors [668–674]. Both Cibacron blue and S-hexylglutathione are competitive inhibitors of PfGST, with K_i values of 0.5 and $35\,\mu M$, respectively (Fig. 25f). Hemin (Fig. 25g) is an uncompetitive inhibitor with a K_i value of $6.5\,\mu M$ [675,676]. 5-Methylnaphthylquinone has been reported as an inhibitor of PfGST with an apparent K_i of $80\,\mu M$. More recently, a high-throughput screen for novel inhibitors of this enzyme reported 92 diverse compounds that inhibited *P. yoelii* and *P. falciparum* GSTs at a fixed inhibitory concentration of $100\,\mu M$ [677]. These compounds were also tested growth inhibitors at a single concentration of $100\,nM$. Unfortunately, potency in the enzymatic assays did not correlate strongly with activity in whole-cell models. However, given that none of the compounds reported had IC_{50} values lower than $50\,\mu M$, this is not surprising.

Taken together, these reports suggest that the redox pathways and in particular, the glutathione reductase pathway could represent promising targets for chemotherapeutic intervention. Full validation will require the development of more potent and less toxic inhibitors. Additionally, the thioredoxin system bears additional scrutiny and seems likely to offer additional targets for development of chemotherapeutic candidates.

3.6. Apicoplast Targets

3.6.1. Fatty Acid Biosynthesis Aliphatic fatty acids play critical roles in eukaryotes including energy storage, membrane synthesis, and hormone synthesis. Fatty acid biosynthesis in *Plasmodium* takes place in an organelle of cyanobacterial origin called the apicoplast. The apicoplast fatty acid biosynthesis is different from both human and multicellular eukaryotes in that human fatty acid biosynthesis involves a type I fatty acid synthase (FASI, a single protein with multiple catalytic domains) whereas the apicoplast route uses a type II fatty acid synthase system (FASII) in which each fatty acid biosynthetic step is carried out by discrete monofunctional enzymes, encoded by different genes, that are used iteratively to elongate and reduce the fatty acid chain. Of the enzymes of the FASII system, *Pf*ENR, an enoyl ACP reductase homologous to the bacterial FabI, has been intensively investigated as a potential drug target because inhibitors of bacterial FabI are potent inhibitors of bacterial growth. Recent work, however, has revealed that FABI is not expressed in blood-stage parasites, and is instead essential for the development of infectious liver-stage merozoites [678]. This indicates that work using blood-stage growth inhibitory potencies to guide medicinal chemistry is tracking off-target effects rather than the results of FABI inhibition. Despite this, FABI remains an important clinical target, especially given the difficulties in finding drugs that are effective against liver-stage infections [678].

Initial proof of concept for the efficacy of inhibition of the fatty acid synthesis pathway in malaria was obtained [679,680] using the antimicrobial compound triclosan (Fig. 26a), which is a modestly potent inhibitor of *P. falciparum* growth. Triclosan inhibits the *Plasmodium* enoyl-ACP reductase (*Pf*ENR in malaria or FABI in other systems) with modest potency (IC$_{50}$ of 2 μM) in whole parasites [680]. The compound was found to be curative in a *P. berghei* mouse models as a monotherapy at 40 mg/kg (subcutaneous, 1 injection per day over 4 days). At the same time, a homology model of *Pf*ENR [350] was used to predict the probable binding mode of triclosan to *Pf*ENR [681]. Later, triclosan was shown to inhibit recombinant *Pf*ENR with a K_i of 50 nM [682]. This study also reported the first crystal structure of the enzyme in the presence of triclosan and several triclosan analogs.

Following these reports, several studies expanded the structure–activity relationships for triclosan [683–686]. Despite extensive modifications at the 2-, 4-, and 5'-positions of triclosan that significantly increased potency against purified *Pf*ENR, correlation between growth inhibitory and enzymatic potencies was poor. This failure to correlate SARs suggested that this scaffold has other targets in malaria. This is particularly likely in light of recent findings indicating that the FABI pathway is unnecessary in blood-stage parasites and is instead a relevant liver-stage target [678]. However, these studies did provide several crystal structures of the enzyme bound to inhibitors that proved useful in the search for new scaffolds.

A virtual screening effort resulted in the discovery of several novel compounds [687]. While these represent potential starting points for the design of better *Pf*ENR inhibitor series, none of the primary hits had strong potency in growth inhibitory assays (all EC$_{50}$ values above 1 μM, most greater than 10 μM). Other groups have examined the flavanoids as a potential scaffold for inhibitors of PfENR [688,689]. While a number of compounds in this series have been reported to have modest potency (IC$_{50}$ values from 0.2 to 150 μM) against both enzyme and growth inhibition assays, both studies report quercetin (or close analogs), a known promiscuous inhibitor [690], as an example of a well-behaved member of this inhibitor series, which calls the work into question. Furthermore, one study reports an abnormal dependence on enzyme concentration in their studies of these compounds, another classical signature of aggregation-based inhibition [691,692]. Several other studies have reported diverse natural

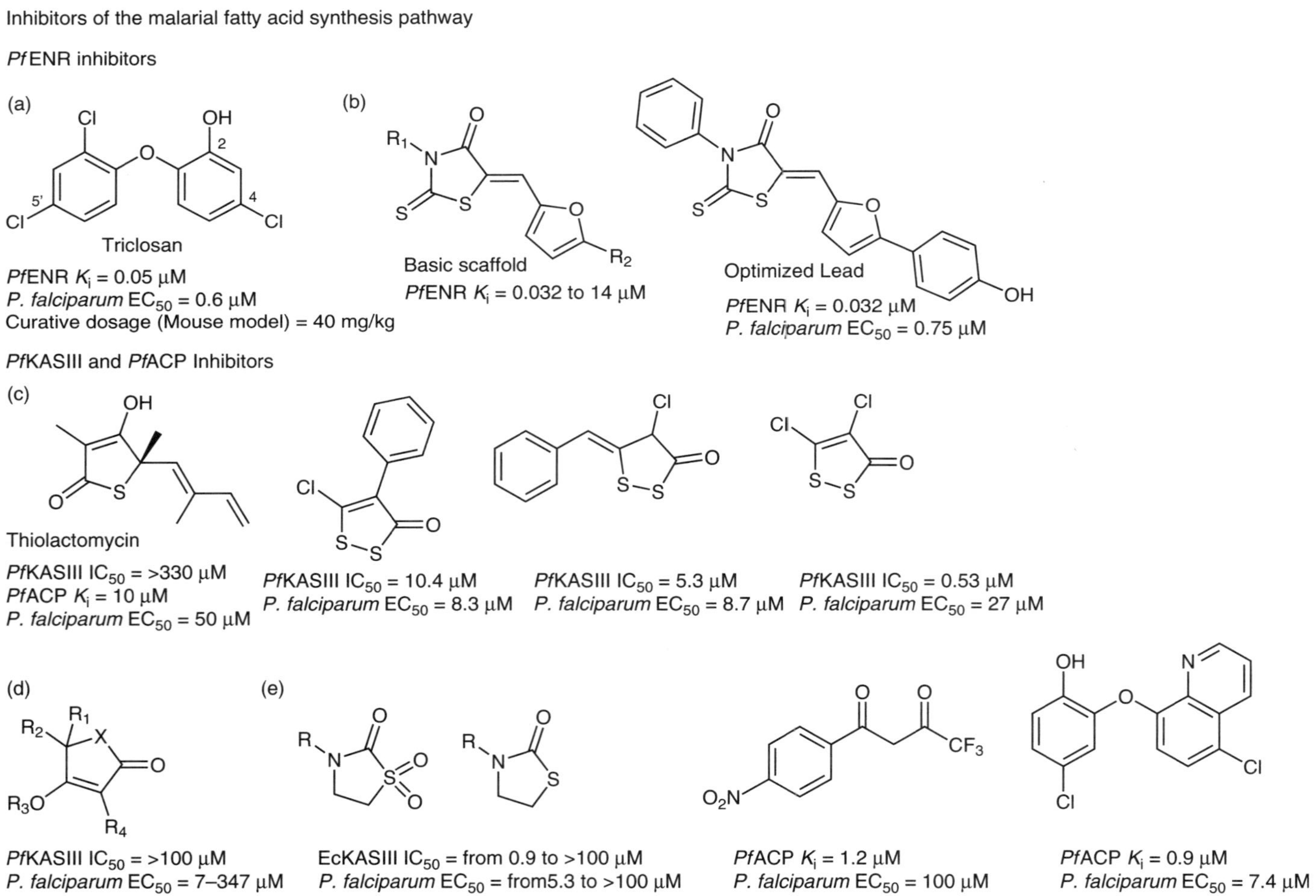

Figure 26. (a) Triclosan, the first reported inhibitor of malarial fatty acid synthesis. This compound targets the *Pf*ENR enzyme with high potency (K_i 50 nM) and has been shown to be curative as a monotherapy in mouse models of infection [679,680,682]. (b) Rhodanine-based inhibitors of *Pf*ENR. The most potent of these compounds has a K_i of 32 nM against the enzyme, and an EC$_{50}$ of 750 nM against whole-cell parasites. The majority of the compounds in this series is inactive in whole-cell models [697]. (c) Inhibitors of *Pf*KASIII [699]. Most *Pf*KASIII inhibitors reported are based on the natural product thioactomycin. Thioactomycin has also been shown to be active versus *Pf*ACP (d) A series of thioactomycin-based inhibitors, all with modest potency against the parasite. The correlation between enzymatic activity and whole-cell activity is poor [703,704]. (e) A series of *Pf*KASIII inhibitors with modest potency and poor correlation between enzymatic and whole-parasite potencies [705]. (f) Two inhibitors of *Pf*ACP [706]. These compounds are competitive inhibitors of the enzymatic target with modest antiparasitic activity. The compound series reported was too small to allow correlations between enzymatic activity and whole-cell activity.

664

product and synthetic scaffolds as inhibitors of *Pf*ENR enzyme with IC_{50} values ranging from 40 to 500 μM [693–696].

The most promising nontriclosan series reported so far is the rhodanine analog series [697] (Fig. 26b). While these compounds show a wide-ranging SAR, with K_i values from 32 nM to 14 μM, only one had activity in whole-cell assays. In order to be regarded as a true lead series for the development of novel antimalarials, these compounds will have to show activity in whole-parasite assays and good correlation between enzymatic and growth inhibition assays.

*Pf*ENR is not the only target in the fatty acid biosynthetic pathway. Several other enzymes have also been investigated as possible targets. One is that of the β-ketoacyl-ACP synthase III (*Pf*KASIII in malaria or FABH in other systems) [698]. Another potential target in the pathway is the β-hydroxyacyl-acyl carrier protein (*Pf*ACP or FABZ) [698]. A third enzymatic target, malonyl-coenzyme A: ACP transaceylase or *Pf*MCAT may also prove promising [699].

Inhibition of *Pf*KASIII by analogs of the natural product thiolactomycin, a known inhibitor of type II FAS pathways in bacteria, has been described (Fig. 26c). These compounds showed moderate potency against growth inhibitory assays (IC_{50} values from 50 to 500 μM) [700]. Further work led to optimized analogs of thiolactomycin with improved growth inhibitory potency (IC_{50} values from 8 to 471 μM) [701]. However, these compounds were not assayed for activity against isolated enzymes. A later study suggests that thiolactomycin may be acting against *Pf*ACP rather than *Pf*KASIII, since it has a K_i value of 10 μM for this enzyme and no detectible inhibition of *Pf*KASIII at concentrations up to 330 μM [702]. A later study reported more modestly potent growth inhibitory analogs (IC_{50} values from 7 to 351 μM) with equivalent activities against isolated *Pf*KASIII that had much better correlation between these two assays [703,704] (Fig. 26d). The only other reported *Pf*KASIII inhibitors (Fig. 26e) have modest potency (IC_{50} values from 0.9 to 100 μM) against the *E. coli* homolog of *Pf*KASIII and a similar absolute range of growth inhibitory potency [705]. However, correlation between the activities is not strong.

There is only one report of inhibitors specifically targeting the *Pf*ACP enzyme. This study used molecular docking against a homology model of the *Plasmodium* enzyme to design two novel inhibitors that killed parasites in a growth inhibition assay [706] (Fig. 26f). These compounds were both competitive inhibitors of the enzyme and displayed widely ranging antiparasitic activities. Since only two compounds were active against the enzyme, correlations between enzymatic and whole-cell data cannot be accurately assessed.

All inhibitor series reported for FASII targets have serious shortcomings. After an extremely promising start, with triclosan working as an *in vivo* monotherapy, all subsequent compounds represented decreases in efficacy. Generally, there is poor correlation between enzyme inhibition and whole-parasite killing. It seems likely that this disparity may relate to the relative importance of this metabolic pathway to blood and liver-stage parasites [678]. Therefore, the target remains theoretically valid, and a wealth of structural and chemical data is available to aid in the design of potential new inhibitors once liver-stage assays are more readily available.

3.6.2. Isoprenoid Biosynthesis Isoprenoids are a diverse group of fatty natural products including terpenes, steroids, and many other biologically important molecules. All of these are assembled from five-carbon building blocks derived from isopentyl pyrophosphate (IPP) and its isomer dimethylallyl pyrophosphate (DMAPP) [707,708]. The synthesis of isopentyl diphosphate had, until fairly recently, been assumed to progress via the cytosolic mevalonate pathway. However, in the late 1980s, a second, mevalonate independent, pathway known as the 1-deoxy-D-xylulose 5-phsophate (DOXP) pathway was discovered in bacteria, green algae, and chloroplasts of higher plants [709–713]. This seven-step pathway begins with the formation of DOXP from D-glyceraldehyde-3-phosphate and pyruvate via the action of DOXP synthase (DXS). Following this step, the enzyme DOXP reductoisomerase (DXR) transforms DOXP into 2-*C*-methyl- D-erythritol-4-phosphate (MEP) that is then acted on by 4-diphosphocytidyl-2-*C*-methyl-

D-erythritol synthase (YgbP or IspD) to produce 4-diphosphocytidyl-2-C-methylerythritol (CDP-ME). CDP-ME is transformed by 4-diphosphocytidyl-2-C-methyl- D-erythritol kinase (YchB or IspE) to produce 4-diphosphocyticyl-2-C-methyl- D-erythritol 2-phosphate (CDP-MEP), the substrate of 2-C-methyl- D-erythritol 2,4-cyclodiphosphate synthase (YgbB or IspF) that produces 2-C-methyl- D-erythritol 2,4-cyclopyrophosphate (MEcPP). MEcPP is acted upon by HMB-PP synthase (GcpE or IspG) to produce (E)-4-hydroxy-3-methyl-but-2-enyl pyrophosphate (HMB-PP), which is acted upon by HMB-PP reductase (LytB or IspH) producing the end product of the pathway, IPP, and DMAPP [714]. This pathway is not present in mammalian cells and is unique to plants, algae, bacteria, and apicomplexans [714,715]. Therefore, it represents a promising target for the development of novel antimalarials.

Homologs to the first two enzymes in this pathway, DXS and DXR, have been identified in the malarial genome [715]. The original study also showed that fosmidomycin (Fig. 27a) and its analog FR90098 (Fig. 27b), specific inhibitors of DXR, were able to potently inhibit the growth of P. falciparum (IC$_{50}$ values 290 and 90 nM, respectively) [715,716]. These compounds also proved efficacious in P. vinckei mouse models of infection, eliminating blood-stage parasites after a 4-day oral treatment at either 50 or 100 mg/kg [715]. Fosmidomycin has strong synergy with the lincosamide antibiotics, including the clinically used clindamycin [240]. Early clinical trials showed efficacy in humans comparable with other major antimalarial treatments [717,718]. When used in combination with either clindamycin or artesunate, fosmidomycin proved more efficacious than sulfadioxine-pyrimethamine in the treatment of both adult and pediatric patients infected with P. falciparum [241,242,719–721]. Recent, more complete, pharmacodynamic optimization studies have shown that utilization of the clindamycin/fosmidomycin combination gave a 100% cure rate whereas a fosmidomycin monotherapy produced a 22% cure rate (28-day follow-up, oral dosing every 12 h) [243]. Thus, DXR, and by inference the entire pathway, is a clinically validated target.

The crystal structure of E. coli DXR has been solved both with and without fosmidomycin by several groups [722–726]. The bacterial enzyme is generally regarded as a good model system for the malarial enzyme, which is much harder to work with [715,727]. The enzyme forms an elongated homodimer with a pronounced cleft-like structure in each monomer covered by a flexible active site loop. There are three prominent domains, an N-terminal NADH binding domain, an α-helical C-terminal domain thought to support the catalytic domain, and a central catalytic domain. The catalytic domain contains an Mn^{2+} ion, the phosphate-binding site, and the catalytic loop. The structure of the enzyme bound to formidomycin reveals that the oxygen of the aldehyde of the drug interacts directly with the catalytic Mn^{2+} and shows that the inhibitor binds in a substrate-like manner rather than as a transition-state mimetic. Kinetic analysis suggests that the initial binding is a relatively low affinity event followed by a structural shift that results in higher affinities [728]. There is also an apparent cavity behind the bound inhibitor, which harbors three water molecules. It is possible that designing an inhibitor that is able to take advantage of this cavity could yield improved potencies. A study of DXR genes in clinical isolates of P. falciparum revealed no polymorphisms within the active site residues, suggesting that this binding site is highly conserved [729]. A laboratory generated formidomycin-resistant strain of P. falciparum was shown to have gene duplication events leading to resistance rather than sequence changes [730]. This also lends support to the idea that resistance to compounds targeting this enzyme may be difficult to acquire in the field.

Efforts to improve the efficacy of fosmidomycin have met with some success. Masking the phosphonate moiety with a double ester improved bioavailability and in vivo activity (Fig. 27c) [731,732]. Introduction of α-substitutions (Fig. 27d) yielded compounds with 12-fold better growth inhibitory potencies (IC$_{50}$ values from 0.028 to 0.95 μM) most likely due to electron-withdrawing properties of the aryl substituents [733,734]. Restricting the flexibility of the linker by incorporation of a cyclopropyl group (Fig. 27e) was tolerated for the (1R,2S) isomer, but did not increase potencies

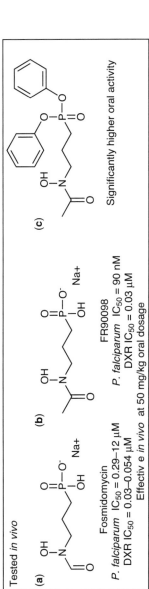

Inhibitors of DOXP Pathway

Tested *in vivo*

(a) Fosmidomycin
P. falciparum IC$_{50}$ = 0.29–12 μM
DXR IC$_{50}$ = 0.03–0.054 μM

(b) FR90098
P. falciparum IC$_{50}$ = 90 nM
DXR IC$_{50}$ = 0.03 μM
Effectiv e *in vivo* at 50 mg/kg oral dosage

(c) Significantly higher oral activity

(d) *P. falciparum* IC$_{50}$ = 28 nM
DXR IC$_{50}$ = 0.03 μM

(e) *P. falciparum* IC$_{50}$ = 320 nM
DXR IC$_{50}$ = 0.05 μM

(f) *P. falciparum* IC$_{50}$ = 980 nM
DXR IC$_{50}$ = 0.097 μM

(g) *P. falciparum* IC$_{50}$ = 360 nM
DXR IC$_{50}$ = 0.087 μM

DXR IC$_{50}$ values are for the *E. coli* enzyme

Figure 27. (a) Fosmidomycin, a specific inhibitor of 1-deoxy-D-xylulose 5-phsophate reductase (DXR), which has shown potent antimalarial properties [715,716]. This compound is effective in *P. vinckei* mouse models and in the clinic, both as a monotherapy and in combination with clindamycin or artesunate [241–243,719–721]. (b) An analog of fosmidomycin with improved *in vitro* and *in vivo* activities [715]. This compound is not clinically used. (c) A prodrug form of fosmidomycin with improved oral activities in *P. vinckei* mouse models of infection [731,732]. (d) An α-aryl-substituted fosmidomycin analog with much improved *in vitro* potency versus *P. falciparum*. Potencies versus the enzymatic target were largely unaffected. Electron-withdrawing groups are preferred on the aryl substituent [733,734]. (e) A conformationally constrained analog of fosmidomycin. While improvements in potencies were not seen with this series, a strong stereochemical preference was. Inclusion of α-aryl moieties into conformationally constrained analogs was not tolerated [735–737]. (f) A hydroxamic acid containing analog of formidomycin. This substitution was tolerated but did not lead to an increase in potency versus either the whole-cell parasites or the enzymatic target [738]. (g) A formidomycin analog containing an oxygen atom in β-position of the phosphonate moiety. This substitution was tolerated while the placement of an oxygen at the γ-position was not. Conversion of the β-oxy compound to the bis(pivaloyloxymethyl)ester prodrug increased its potency versus whole-cell parasites by approximately fivefold [738].

against either the enzymatic target (IC_{50} values from 0.05 to 30 µM) or the growth inhibition (IC_{50} values from 0.24 to 2.1 µM) [735]. Inclusion of an α-aryl moiety on compounds conformationally restrained by the cyclopropyl group or by an α-β unsaturated bond was not tolerated [736,737]. The effects of replacing the *N*-hydroxyformamido moiety of formidomycin with a hydroxamic acid moiety (Fig. 27f) as well as the effects of adding an oxygen atom in either the β- or the γ-position of the phosphonate moiety (Fig. 27g) were also explored [738]. Addition of the hydroxamic acid moiety was tolerated, but did not increase potencies versus either the enzymatic target ($IC_{50} = 97$ nM) or the organism ($IC_{50} = 980$ nM). An oxygen atom was tolerated in the β-position of the phosphonate moiety, but not in the γ-position. Conversion of the β-oxy containing analog to the bis(pivaloyloxymethyl) ester prodrug increased its growth inhibitory potency approximately fivefold. The negative charge on the phosphonate moiety was also shown to be necessary for inhibition of DXR and growth inhibitory potency through replacement of this moiety with neutral sulphones, sulphonamides or monoalkylesters [739]. Attempts to move away from the formidomycin scaffold have met with extremely limited success [740].

In addition to DXR, the final enzyme in the DOXP pathway in *Plasmodium* (LytB) has been expressed exogenously and characterized [741]. The crystal structure of the *A. aeolicus* homolog of this enzyme has also been solved [742]. Although no inhibitors for this enzyme have yet been described and no genetic knockouts have been reported, it seems reasonable that this enzyme may also represent a tenable target for the development of more novel antimalarials. Indeed, the remaining five enzymes from the DOXP pathway are all absent from mammalian systems and therefore represent prime targets for chemotherapeutic intervention, especially since this pathway has been quite rigorously clinically validated.

3.7. Other Potential Targets

In addition to the targets discussed in previous sections, there are others that may prove susceptible to chemotherapeutic intervention. However, directed inhibitor development toward most of these potential targets has been limited. The combination of emerging genetic manipulation techniques and inhibitor development may validate these in the future.

One interesting target in this category is the signal peptide peptidases (SPP), a family of proteases responsible for cleaving signal sequences from a variety of secreted proteins [743,744]. The *Plasmodium* homologs of this family were discovered using a data mining approach [745]. Malarial SP1 from *P. falciparum,* as well as other *Plasmodium* species, has been isolated and characterized, although no inhibitors have been reported [746]. Likewise, the type 2 SPP from *P. falciparum* (mSPP) has been isolated and characterized. mSPP was sensitive both to (Z-LL)$_2$-ketone (Fig. 28a), an inhibitor of mammalian SPP, and to L411,575 (Fig. 28b), a γ-secretase inhibitor that inhibits other SPPs [747]. Finally, *Pf*SP21 has been shown to be critical for parasite growth, suggesting that this family of proteases may contain viable drug targets. However, much more work must be done, both biologically and chemically, before this enzyme family can be regarded as validated targets.

Another possible target is the plasmodial surface anion channel (PSAC). While it has been known for over 50 years that red blood cells infected by the malaria parasite have strikingly different membrane permeability and transport properties than uninfected cells, the reasons for these properties were only recently understood [748–750]. A seminal study reported that these differences could be attributed to a single transport channel—the PSAC [751–753]. Several nonspecific channel inhibitors are weakly potent inhibitors of PSAC (EC_{50} values 1.0–100 µM) on this target (Fig. 28c–f) [749,751,754,755]. These compounds show a rough correlation between growth inhibitory and isolated channel potencies. However, strains selected to be resistant to phloridzin, one of these inhibitors, do not have polymorphisms in PSAC, suggesting the mechanism may be more complex [756]. In order to further validate this target, specific inhibitors based on dantrolene were developed and shown to be effective antimalarials. The

Inhibitors of malarial signal peptide peptidase (mSPP)

(a) ZLL(2-ketone)
Inhibits overexpressed mSPP 100% at 200 nM

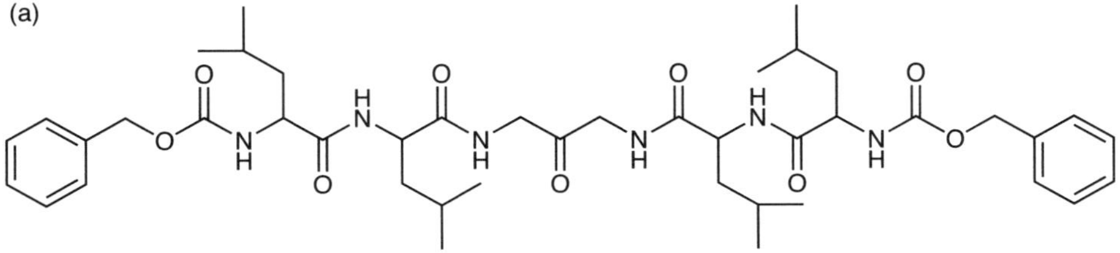

(b) L-411,575
Inhibits overexpressed mSPP 100% at 50 nM

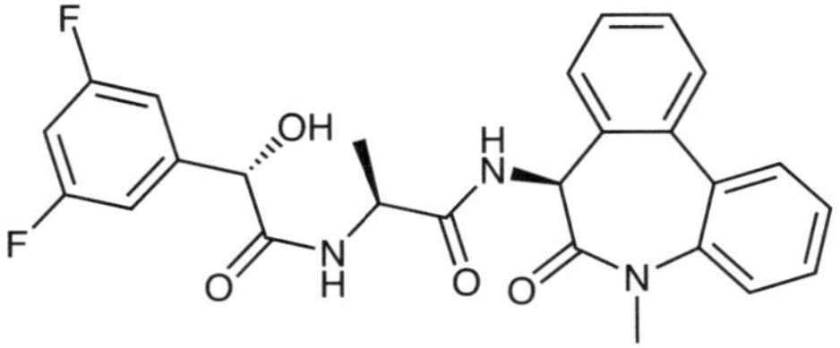

Inhibitors of *Plasmodium* surface anion channel (PSAC)

(c) Furosemide
PSAC IC$_{50}$ = ~15 μM
P. falciparum IC$_{50}$ = ~9 μM

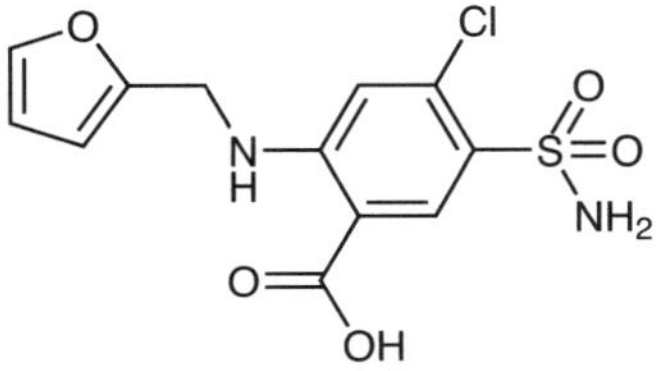

(d) Phloridzin
75% PSAC inhibition at 50 μM
P. falciparum IC$_{50}$ = 16 μM

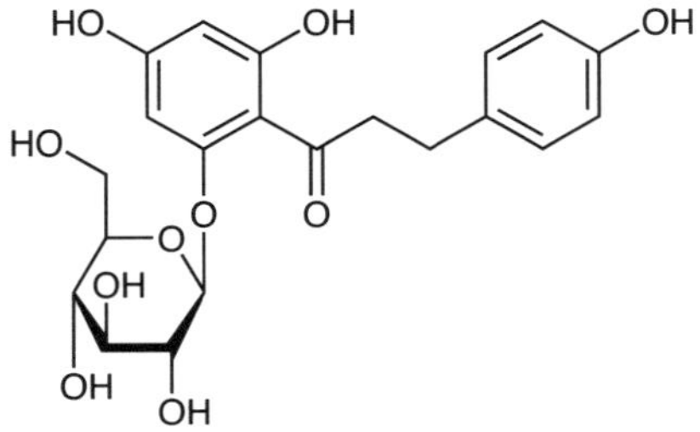

(e) NPPB
PSAC IC$_{50}$ = ~1 μM
P. falciparum IC$_{50}$ = ~0.9 μM

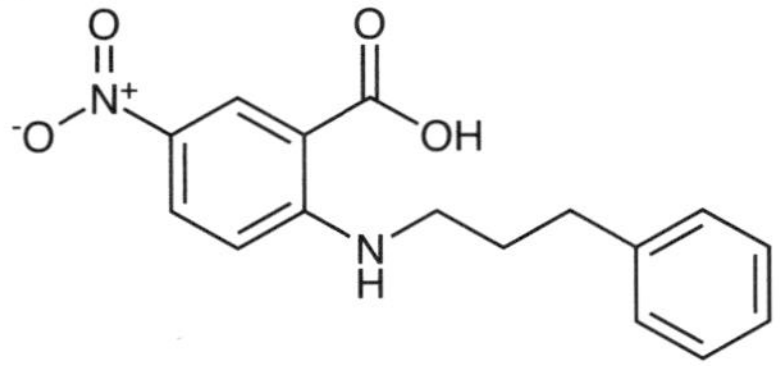

(f) Glybenclamide
85% PSAC inhibition at 100 μM
P. falciparum IC$_{50}$ = 39 μM

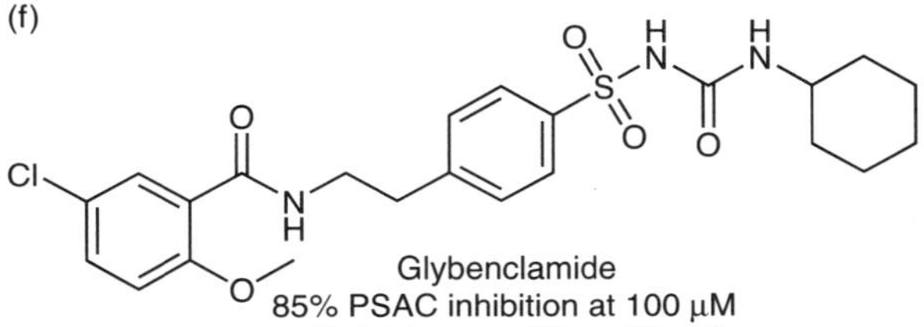

(g) Dantrolene
PSAC IC$_{50}$ = ~1.2 μM
P. falciparum growth ~95% inhibited at 15 μM

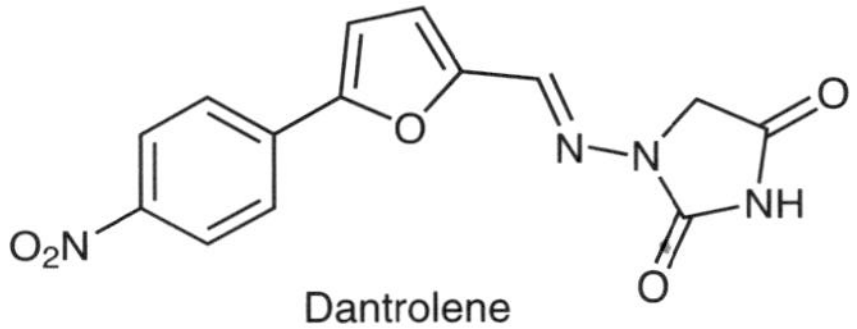

Figure 28. (*Continued*)

669

Inhibitors of malarial heat shock proteins (HSP)

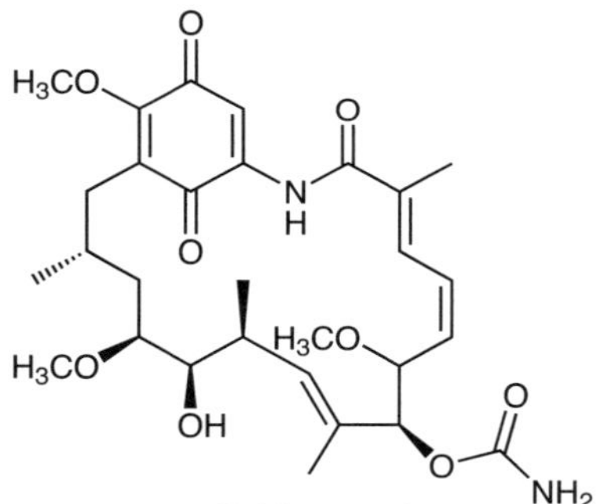

Geldanamycin
P. falciparum IC$_{50}$ = 20–200 nM
PfHSP90 binding to ATP abolished at ~17 μM

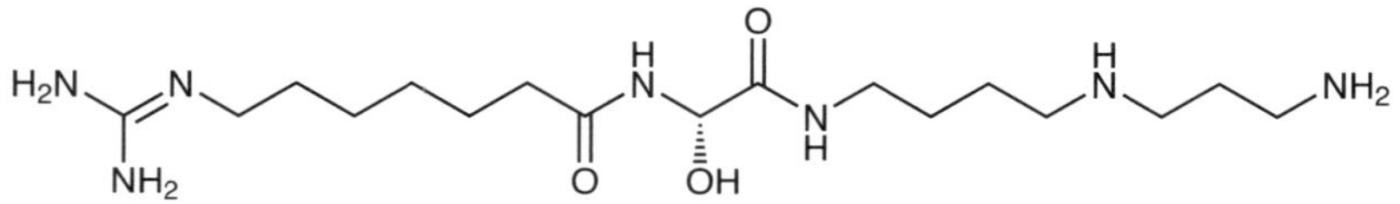

15-Deoxyspergualin
P. falciparum IC$_{50}$ = 148 nM
Does not directly inhibit chaperone activity of PfHSP70
Binds to "EEVD" motif blocking interaction with other binding partners

Figure 28. (a) (Z-LL)$_2$-Ketone, an inhibitor of mammalian SPP that inhibits the malarial enzyme at a single concentration of 200 nM in a reporter assay [748]. (b) L411,575, a inhibitor of mammalian SPP that completely inhibits the malarial homolog at a single concentration of 50 nM in a reporter assay [748]. (c) Furosemide, a anion channel inhibitor shown to be active against the PSAC with an IC$_{50}$ of approximately 15 μM [752]. The compound also inhibits growth of *P. falciparum* with an EC$_{50}$ of approximate 9 μM *in vitro* [750]. (d) Phloridzin, an anion channel inhibitor shown to be active against PSAC, inhibiting 75% of transport activity at 50 μM [752]. This compound inhibits *P. falciparum* growth with an IC$_{50}$ of 16 μM *in vitro* [755]. (e) NPPB, an anion channel inhibitor shown to be active versus PSAC with an IC$_{50}$ of approximately 1 μM [752]. This compound also inhibits *P. falciparum* growth *in vitro* with an IC$_{50}$ of approximately 0.9 μM [750] **28F**. Glybenclamide, an anion channel inhibitor inhibiting 85% of PSAC transport activity at 100 μM [752]. The compound also blocks growth of *P. falciparum* with an IC$_{50}$ of 39 μM *in vitro* [750]. (g) Dantrolene, an inhibitor of PSAC with an IC$_{50}$ value of approximately 1 μM. The compound inhibits proliferation of *P. falciparum*, inhibiting 95% of parasite growth at 15 μM [758,759]. (h) Geldanamycin, an inhibitor of mammalian HSP90 that interacts with malarial HSP90 with modest potency. The compound potently inhibits growth of *P. falciparum*, with IC$_{50}$ values between 20 and 200 nM [789,806]. (i) 15-deoxyspergualin, an immunosuppressant that interacts with both mammalian and malarial HSP70 [814–819]. The compound does not directly inhibit PfHSP70, but is thought to interfere with interactions between this protein and other binding partners [818]. This compound has also displayed *in vivo* efficacy [816].

compounds were also able to affect the membrane permeability *in vitro,* inhibited exogenously expressed PSAC, and remaining inactive against other tested anion channels [757,758]. In addition, PSAC was shown to be conserved across the *Plasmodium* species by using inhibitor panels to pharmacologically characterize the membrane permeability properties of multiple malarial species [759].

Further study of PSAC, using these and other channel inhibitors as chemical tools, revealed differences in affinities and effects on the transport of various substrates, suggesting multiple modes of ion transport. This was hypothesized to be due to PSAC acting in a multimeric channel complex with at least two major transport mechanisms and several possible sites of allosteric regulation [41]. In addition to being a target on its own, PSAC has been implicated in the transport of several other known antimalarial compounds including a DNA binding benzylthiazolium dye; leupeptin, a nonspecific protease inhibitor; and blasticidin, a translation inhibitor often used as a selection marker in other microbiological studies [760–762]. Taken together this data shows that while PSAC is clearly important for growth and health of the malarial parasite its exact biological role and mechanism of action are still somewhat unclear. The development of more specific inhibitors of this target and the exploration of its basic biology will be needed before it can be considered fully validated.

The final target family to be considered is the heat shock proteins (HSPs). The HSPs are found in almost all organisms; expressed at very high levels in most cell types; and are upregulated in response to a wide range of environmental stressors including temperature changes, presence of heavy metals, metabolic stress, and chemotherapeutic agents [763–765]. The HSPs regulate protein folding—both posttranscriptionally and refolding following denaturing events triggered by environmental forces [766]. Early work on *Plasmodium* HSPs focused on their potential as vaccine candidates. The malarial homolog of mammalian HSP70, PfHSP70, was found to be immunogenic in both infected humans and experimentally infected monkeys [767,768]. Homologs of the protein have been found expressed on the surface of infected cells in both hepatic and merozoite stages [769,770]. Furthermore, sera and T cells from malaria infected patients show increased reactivity to PfHSP70 [771]. Despite these promising data, no vaccine has been developed to a HSP epitope.

The *Plasmodium* HSP family accounts for as much as 2% of the coding regions of the genome, and members of the HSP90, HSP70, HSP60, HSP40, and many cochaperones have been identified [772–785]. Of these, PfHSP90 has raised particular interest as a possible target because there is a wide body of literature on the human homolog that is a validated target for oncology. The parasitic enzyme has approximately 50% homology to the vertebrate homolog, being more closely related to plant HSP90 than to human [773,786]. However, the ATP binding N-terminal domain is highly conserved, with 75% identity in comparison to the human protein [772]. PfHSP90 is known to be highly expressed at all stages of the parasite lifecycle, accounting for 1–2% of the total cellular protein in the parasite [787]. The enzyme is typically found in $\sim$450 kDa multichaperone complexes that include PfHSP70, another member of the heat shock protein family that has generated some interest as a potential drug target [788]. Although several potent inhibitors of human HSP90 exist [789–802], only geldanamycin (Fig. 28h) analogs has been tested in *Plasmodium.* Geldanamycin is a specific inhibitor of human HSP90 that has shown promise for oncology [803,804]. Geldanamycin is a potent (IC$_{50}$ between 20 and 200 nM) inhibitor of *P. falciparum* growth [788,805]. Additionally, geldanamycin is slightly synergistic with both chloroquine and cyclosporin A [805,806]. Although geldanamycin analogs have moved into Phase II clinical trials for oncology, all have so far failed due to toxicity concerns. The maximum tolerated dosages reported in these studies were approximately 320–450 mg/m^2, intravenously on a weekly basis, with dose limiting toxicities being gastrointestinal and hepatic [807–812]. Given the potency and synergy of geldanamycin and the fact that several series of orally available HSP90 inhibitors now exist, it would seem prudent to test panels of other known inhibitors of human HSP90 against the parasite. However, to our knowledge this has not yet been done.

In addition to PfHSP90, PfHSP70 has been suggested as a relevant target for malaria. 15-Deoxyspergualin (Fig. 28i), an immunosuppressant known to bind to human HSP70, has been shown to be a potent (IC_{50} 150 nM) suppressor of *P. falciparum* growth *in vitro* and is active *in vivo* [813–817]. Although initially thought to act through inhibition of polyamine biosynthesis, this compound was later shown to act via binding to the C-terminal EEVD motif of PfHSP70 and disrupting the trafficking of apicoplast proteins [817,818]. Interestingly, spergualin does not seem to function by inhibition of the chaperone properties of PfHSP70 directly, but rather by interference with the binding of the protein to a subset of its clients [818].

REFERENCES

1. Snow RW, Guerra CA, Noor AM, Myint HY, Hay SI. The global distribution of clinical episodes of *Plasmodium falciparum* malaria. Nature 2005;434(7030):214–217.

2. Schlagenhauf P. Malaria: from prehistory to present. Infect Dis Clin North Am 2004;18 (2):189–205, table of contents.

3. Sachs J, Malaney P. The economic and social burden of malaria. Nature 2002;415 (6872):680–685.

4. Mueller I, Zimmerman PA, Reeder JC. *Plasmodium malariae* and *Plasmodium ovale*: the "bashful" malaria parasites. Trends Parasitol 2007;23(6):278–283.

5. Barsoum RS. Malarial acute renal failure. J Am Soc Nephrol 2000;11(11):2147–2154.

6. Mehta SR, Lazar AI, Kasthuri AS. Experience on loading dose: quinine therapy in cerebral malaria. J Assoc Physicians India 1994;42 (5):376–378.

7. Franks S, Koram KA, Wagner GE, Tetteh K, McGuinness D, Wheeler JG, Nkrumah F, Ranford-Cartwright L, Riley EM. Frequent and persistent, asymptomatic *Plasmodium falciparum* infections in African infants, characterized by multilocus genotyping. J Infect Dis 2001;183(5):796–804.

8. Struik SS, Riley EM. Does malaria suffer from lack of memory? Immunol Rev 2004;201:268–290.

9. Artavanis-Tsakonas K, Tongren JE, Riley EM. The war between the malaria parasite and the immune system: immunity, immunoregulation and immunopathology. Clin Exp Immunol 2003;133(2):145–152.

10. Greenwood D. The quinine connection. J Antimicrob Chemother 1992;30(4):417–427.

11. Dorn A, Stoffel R, Matile H, Bubendorf A, Ridley RG. Malarial haemozoin/beta-haematin supports haem polymerization in the absence of protein. Nature 1995;374(6519):269–271.

12. Sullivan DJ Jr, Gluzman IY, Goldberg DE. *Plasmodium* hemozoin formation mediated by histidine-rich proteins. Science 1996;271 (5246):219–222.

13. Fitch CD. Ferriprotoporphyrin IX, phospholipids, and the antimalarial actions of quinoline drugs. Life Sci 2004;74(16):1957–1972.

14. Pagola S, Stephens PW, Bohle DS, Kosar AD, Madsen SK. The structure of malaria pigment beta-haematin. Nature 2000;404 (6775):307–310.

15. Foley M, Tilley L. Quinoline antimalarials: mechanisms of action and resistance and prospects for new agents. Pharmacol Ther 1998; 79(1):55–87.

16. Sanchez CP, Stein WD, Lanzer M. Dissecting the components of quinine accumulation in *Plasmodium falciparum*. Mol Microbiol 2008;67(5):1081–1093.

17. Karle JM, Karle IL, Gerena L, Milhous WK. Stereochemical evaluation of the relative activities of the cinchona alkaloids against *Plasmodium falciparum*. Antimicrob Agents Chemother 1992;36(7):1538–1544.

18. Wesche DL, Black J. A comparison of the antimalarial activity of the cinchona alkaloids against *Plasmodium falciparum in vitro*. J Trop Med Hyg 1990;93(3):153–159.

19. Le Jouan M, Jullien V, Tetanye E, Tran A, Rey E, Treluyer JM, Tod M, Pons G. Quinine pharmacokinetics and pharmacodynamics in children with malaria caused by *Plasmodium falciparum*. Antimicrob Agents Chemother 2005;49(9):3658–3662.

20. White NJ, Looareesuwan S, Warrell DA, Warrell MJ, Bunnag D, Harinasuta T. Quinine pharmacokinetics and toxicity in cerebral and uncomplicated falciparum malaria. Am J Med 1982;73(4):564–572.

21. Barennes H, Balima-Koussoube T, Nagot N, Charpentier JC, Pussard E. Safety and efficacy of rectal compared with intramuscular quinine for the early treatment of moderately severe malaria in children: randomised clinical trial. BMJ 2006;332(7549):1055–1059.

22. Achan J, Byarugaba J, Barennes H, Tumwine JK. Rectal versus intravenous quinine for the treatment of childhood cerebral malaria in Kampala, Uganda: a randomized, double-blind clinical trial. Clin Infect Dis 2007;45(11):1446–1452.

23. Barennes H, Sterlingot H, Nagot N, Meda H, Kabore M, Sanou M, Nacro B, Bouree P, Pussard E. Intrarectal pharmacokinetics of two formulations of quinine in children with falciparum malaria. Eur J Clin Pharmacol. 2003; 58(10):649–652.

24. Gunawan CA, Harijanto PN, Nugroho A. Quinine-induced arrhythmia in a patient with severe malaria. Acta Med Indones 2007; 39(1):27–32.

25. Tange RA, Dreschler WA, Claessen FA, Perenboom RM. Ototoxic reactions of quinine in healthy persons and patients with *Plasmodium falciparum* infection. Auris Nasus Larynx 1997;24(2):131–136.

26. Hall AP, Doberstyn EB, Nanokorn A, Sonkom P. *Falciparum* malaria semi-resistant to clindamycin. Br Med J. 1975;2(5961):12–14.

27. Ramharter M, Oyakhirome S, Klein Klouwenberg P, Adegnika AA, Agnandji ST, Missinou MA, Matsiegui PB, Mordmuller B, Borrmann S, Kun JF, Lell B, Krishna S, Graninger W, Issifou S, Kremsner PG. Artesunate–clindamycin versus quinine–clindamycin in the treatment of *Plasmodium falciparum* malaria: a randomized controlled trial. Clin Infect Dis 2005;40(12):1777–1784.

28. Best Plummer W, Pinto Pereira L. Diminished *Plasmodium falciparum* sensitivity to quinine exposure *in vitro* and in a sequential multidrug regimen A preliminary investigation in Guyana. South America. Int J Infect Dis 2008;12(6):e27–e31.

29. Ejaz A, Haqnawaz K, Hussain Z, Butt R, Awan ZI, Bux H. Treatment of uncomplicated *Plasmodium falciparum* malaria with quinine–doxycycline combination therapy. J Pak Med Assoc 2007;57(10):502–505.

30. Noedl H, Krudsood S, Chalermratana K, Silachamroon U, Leowattana W, Tangpukdee N, Looareesuwan S, Miller RS, Fukuda M, Jongsakul K, Sriwichai S, Rowan J, Bhattacharyya H, Ohrt C, Knirsch C. Azithromycin combination therapy with artesunate or quinine for the treatment of uncomplicated *Plasmodium falciparum* malaria in adults: a randomized, phase 2 clinical trial in Thailand. Clin Infect Dis 2006;43 (10):1264–1271.

31. Newton PN, Chierakul W, Ruangveerayuth R, Silamut K, Teerapong P, Krudsood S, Looareesuwan S, White NJ. A comparison of artesunate alone with combined artesunate and quinine in the parenteral treatment of acute falciparum malaria. Trans R Soc Trop Med Hyg 2001;95(5):519–523.

32. Sidhu AB, Uhlemann AC, Valderramos SG, Valderramos JC, Krishna S, Fidock DA. Decreasing pfmdr1 copy number in *Plasmodium falciparum* malaria heightens susceptibility to mefloquine, lumefantrine, halofantrine, quinine, and artemisinin. J Infect Dis 2006; 194(4):528–535.

33. Sidhu AB, Valderramos SG, Fidock DA. pfmdr1 mutations contribute to quinine resistance and enhance mefloquine and artemisinin sensitivity in *Plasmodium falciparum*. Mol Microbiol 2005;57(4):913–926.

34. Sanchez CP, Rotmann A, Stein WD, Lanzer M. Polymorphisms within PfMDR1 alter the substrate specificity for anti-malarial drugs in *Plasmodium falciparum*. Mol Microbiol 2008;70(4):786–798.

35. Bennett TN, Patel J, Ferdig MT, Roepe PD. *Plasmodium falciparum* Na^+/H^+ exchanger activity and quinine resistance. Mol Biochem Parasitol 2007;153(1):48–58.

36. Dascombe MJ, Drew MGB, Evans PG, Ismail FMD. Rational design strategies for the development of synthetic quinoline and acridine based antimalarials. Front Drug Des Discov 2007;3:559–609.

37. O'Neill PM, Bray PG, Hawley SR, Ward SA, Park BK. 4-Aminoquinolines: past, present, and future: a chemical perspective. Pharmacol Ther 1998;77(1):29–58.

38. De D, Krogstad FM, Cogswell FB, Krogstad DJ. Aminoquinolines that circumvent resistance in *Plasmodium falciparum in vitro*. Am J Trop Med Hyg 1996;55(6):579–583.

39. De D, Krogstad FM, Byers LD, Krogstad DJ. Structure–activity relationships for antiplasmodial activity among 7-substituted 4-aminoquinolines. J Med Chem 1998;41(25):4918–4926.

40. Ridley RG, Hofheinz W, Matile H, Jaquet C, Dorn A, Masciadri R, Jolidon S, Richter WF, Guenzi A, Girometta MA, Urwyler H, Huber W, Thaithong S, Peters W. 4-aminoquinoline analogs of chloroquine with shortened side chains retain activity against chloroquine-resistant *Plasmodium falciparum*. Antimicrob Agents Chemother 1996;40(8):1846–1854.

41. Lisk G, Scott S, Solomon T, Pillai AD, Desai SA. Solute-inhibitor interactions in the plas-

modial surface anion channel reveal complexities in the transport process. Mol Pharmacol 2007;71(5):1241–1250.

42. Madrid PB, Wilson NT, DeRisi JL, Guy RK. Parallel synthesis and antimalarial screening of a 4-aminoquinoline library. J Comb Chem 2004;6(3):437–442.

43. Fattorusso C, Campiani G, Kukreja G, Persico M, Butini S, Romano MP, Altarelli M, Ros S, Brindisi M, Savini L, Novellino E, Nacci V, Fattorusso E, Parapini S, Basilico N, Taramelli D, Yardley V, Croft S, Borriello M, Gemma S. Design, synthesis, and structure–activity relationship studies of 4-quinolinyl- and 9-acrydinylhydrazones as potent antimalarial agents. J Med Chem 2008;51(5):1333–1343.

44. Biot C, Glorian G, Maciejewski LA, Brocard JS. Synthesis and antimalarial activity *in vitro* and *in vivo* of a new ferrocene-chloroquine analogue. J Med Chem 1997;40(23):3715–3718.

45. Chavain N, Vezin H, Dive D, Touati N, Paul JF, Buisine E, Biot C. Investigation of the redox behavior of ferroquine, a new antimalarial. Mol Pharm 2008;5(5):710–716.

46. Natarajan JK, Alumasa JN, Yearick K, Ekoue-Kovi KA, Casabianca LB, de Dios AC, Wolf C, Roepe PD. 4-*N*-, 4-*S*-, and 4-*O*-Chloroquine analogues: influence of side chain length and quinolyl nitrogen pK_a on activity vs chloroquine resistant malaria. J Med Chem 2008;51(12):3466–3479.

47. Solaja BA, Opsenica D, Smith KS, Milhous WK, Terzic N, Opsenica I, Burnett JC, Nuss J, Gussio R, Bavari S. Novel 4-aminoquinolines active against chloroquine-resistant and sensitive *P. falciparum* strains that also inhibit botulinum serotype A. J Med Chem 2008;51(15):4388–4391.

48. Burgess SJ, Selzer A, Kelly JX, Smilkstein MJ, Riscoe MK, Peyton DH. A chloroquine-like molecule designed to reverse resistance in *Plasmodium falciparum*. J Med Chem 2006;49(18):5623–5625.

49. Madrid PB, Sherrill J, Liou AP, Weisman JL, Derisi JL, Guy RK. Synthesis of ring-substituted 4-aminoquinolines and evaluation of their antimalarial activities. Bioorg Med Chem Lett 2005;15(4):1015–1018.

50. Madrid PB, Liou AP, DeRisi JL, Guy RK. Incorporation of an intramolecular hydrogen-bonding motif in the side chain of 4-aminoquinolines enhances activity against drug-resistant *P. falciparum*. J Med Chem 2006;49(15):4535–4543.

51. Sullivan DJ Jr, Gluzman IY, Russell DG, Goldberg DE. On the molecular mechanism of chloroquine's antimalarial action. Proc Natl Acad Sci USA 1996;93(21):11865–11870.

52. Ginsburg H, Krugliak M. Chloroquine: some open questions on its antimalarial mode of action and resistance. Drug Resist Updat 1999;2(3):180–187.

53. Ginsburg H, Famin O, Zhang J, Krugliak M. Inhibition of glutathione-dependent degradation of heme by chloroquine and amodiaquine as a possible basis for their antimalarial mode of action. Biochem Pharmacol 1998;56(10):1305–1313.

54. Krishna S, White NJ. Pharmacokinetics of quinine, chloroquine and amodiaquine. Clinical implications. Clin Pharmacokinet 1996;30(4):263–299.

55. Walker O, Dawodu AH, Adeyokunnu AA, Salako LA, Alvan G. Plasma chloroquine and desethylchloroquine concentrations in children during and after chloroquine treatment for malaria. Br J Clin Pharmacol 1983;16(6):701–705.

56. White NJ. Cardiotoxicity of antimalarial drugs. Lancet Infect Dis 2007;7(8):549–558.

57. AlKadi HO. Antimalarial drug toxicity: a review. Chemotherapy 2007;53(6):385–391.

58. Puavilai S, Kunavisarut S, Vatanasuk M, Timpatanapong P, Sriwong ST, Janwitayanujit S, Nantiruj K, Totemchokchyakarn K, Ruangkanchanasetr S. Ocular toxicity of chloroquine among Thai patients. Int J Dermatol 1999;38(12):934–937.

59. Farooq U, Mahajan RC. Drug resistance in malaria. J Vector Borne Dis 2004;41(3–4):45–53.

60. Kuhn Y, Rohrbach P, Lanzer M. Quantitative pH measurements in *Plasmodium falciparum*-infected erythrocytes using pHluorin. Cell Microbiol 2007;9(4):1004–1013.

61. Krogstad DJ, Gluzman IY, Kyle DE, Oduola AM, Martin SK, Milhous WK, Schlesinger PH. Efflux of chloroquine from *Plasmodium falciparum*: mechanism of chloroquine resistance. Science 1987;238(4831):1283–1285.

62. Djimde A, Doumbo OK, Cortese JF, Kayentao K, Doumbo S, Diourte Y, Dicko A, Su XZ, Nomura T, Fidock DA, Wellems TE, Plowe CV, Coulibaly D. A molecular marker for chloroquine-resistant falciparum malaria. N Engl J Med 2001;344(4):257–263.

63. Naude B, Brzostowski JA, Kimmel AR, Wellems TE. *Dictyostelium discoideum* expresses a malaria chloroquine resistance mechanism upon

transfection with mutant, but not wild-type. Plasmodium falciparum transporter PfCRT. J Biol Chem 2005;280(27):25596–25603.

64. Sanchez CP, Stein WD, Lanzer M. Is PfCRT a channel or a carrier? Two competing models explaining chloroquine resistance in *Plasmodium falciparum*. Trends Parasitol 2007;23 (7):332–339.

65. Ohnmacht CJ, Patel AR, Lutz RE. Antimalarials 7. Bis(trifluoromethyl)-α-(2-piperidyl)-4-quinolinemethanols. J Med Chem 1971;14 (10):926–928.

66. Mungthin M, Bray PG, Ridley RG, Ward SA. Central role of hemoglobin degradation in mechanisms of action of 4-aminoquinolines, quinoline methanols, and phenanthrene methanols. Antimicrob Agents Chemother 1998; 42(11):2973–2977.

67. Davidson MW, Griggs BG, Boykin DW, Wilson WD. Molecular structural effects involved in the interaction of quinolinemethanolamines with DNA Implications for antimalarial action. J Med Chem 1977;20(9):1117–1122.

68. Karbwang J, White NJ. Clinical pharmacokinetics of mefloquine. Clin Pharmacokinet 1990;19(4):264–279.

69. Palmer KJ, Holliday SM, Brogden RN. Mefloquine A review of its antimalarial activity, pharmacokinetic properties and therapeutic efficacy. Drugs 1993;45(3):430–475.

70. Phillips-Howard PA, ter Kuile FO. CNS adverse events associated with antimalarial agents Fact or fiction? Drug Saf 1995;12 (6):370–383.

71. Dow GS, Hudson TH, Vahey M, Koenig ML. The acute neurotoxicity of mefloquine may be mediated through a disruption of calcium homeostasis and ER function in vitro. Malar J 2003;2:14.

72. Price RN, Uhlemann AC, Brockman A, McGready R, Ashley E, Phaipun L, Patel R, Laing K, Looareesuwan S, White NJ, Nosten F, Krishna S. Mefloquine resistance in *Plasmodium falciparum* and increased pfmdr1 gene copy number. Lancet 2004;364(9432):438–447.

73. Burckhalter JH, Tendick FH, Jones EM, Holcomb WF, Rawlins AL. Aminoalkylphenols as antimalarials II. (Heterocyclic-amino)-α-amino-o-cresols. The synthesis of camoquin. J Am Chem Soc 1948;70(4):1363–1373.

74. Burckhalter JH, Tendick FH, Jones EM, Holcomb WF, Rawlins AL. Aminoalkylphenols as antimalarials I. Simply substituted α-aminocresols. J Am Chem Soc 1946;68 (10):1894–1901.

75. German PI, Aweeka FT. Clinical pharmacology of artemisinin-based combination therapies. Clin Pharmacokinet 2008;47(2):91–102.

76. Christie G, Breckenridge AM, Park BK. Drug–protein conjugates XVIII. Detection of antibodies towards the antimalarial amodiaquine and its quinone imine metabolite in man and the rat. Biochem Pharmacol 1989;38 (9):1451–1458.

77. Go ML, Ngiam TL, Wan AS. Synthesis of some novel amodiaquine analogues as potential antimalarial and antifilarial compounds. J Med Chem 1981;24(12):1471–1475.

78. Werbel LM, Cook PD, Elslager EF, Hung JH, Johnson JL, Kesten SJ, McNamara DJ, Ortwine DF, Worth DF. Synthesis, antimalarial activity, and quantitative structure–activity relationships of tebuquine and a series of related 5-[(7-chloro-4-quinolinyl)amino]-3-[(alkylamino) methyl] [1 1′-biphenyl]-2-ols and N omega-oxides. J Med Chem 1986;29(6):924–939.

79. O'Neill PM, Harrison AC, Storr RC, Hawley SR, Ward SA, Park BK. The effect of fluorine substitution on the metabolism and antimalarial activity of amodiaquine. J Med Chem 1994;37(9):1362–1370.

80. Hawley SR, Bray PG, O'Neill PM, Naisbitt DJ, Park BK, Ward SA. Manipulation of the *N*-alkyl substituent in amodiaquine to overcome the verapamil-sensitive chloroquine resistance component. Antimicrob Agents Chemother 1996;40(10):2345–2349.

81. Raynes KJ, Stocks PA, O'Neill PM, Park BK, Ward SA. New 4-aminoquinoline Mannich base antimalarials 1. Effect of an alkyl substituent in the 5′-position of the 4′-hydroxyanilino side chain. J Med Chem 1999;42(15):2747–2751.

82. Delarue S, Girault S, Maes L, Debreu-Fontaine MA, Labaeid M, Grellier P, Sergheraert C. Synthesis and *in vitro* and *in vivo* antimalarial activity of new 4-anilinoquinolines. J Med Chem 2001;44(17):2827–2833.

83. O'Neill PM, Mukhtar A, Stocks PA, Randle LE, Hindley S, Ward SA, Storr RC, Bickley JF, O'Neil IA, Maggs JL, Hughes RH, Winstanley PA, Bray PG, Park BK. Isoquine and related amodiaquine analogues: a new generation of improved 4-aminoquinoline antimalarials. J Med Chem 2003;46(23):4933–4945.

84. O'Neill PM, Park BK, Shone AE, Maggs JL, Roberts P, Stocks PA, Biagini GA, Bray PG, Gibbons P, Berry N, Winstanley PA, Mukhtar A, Bonar-Law R, Hindley S, Bambal RB, Davis CB, Bates M, Hart TK, Gresham SL, Lawrence RM, Brigandi RA, Gomez-Delas-Heras FM,

Gargallo DV, Ward SA. Candidate selection and preclinical evaluation of *N-tert*-butyl isoquine (GSK369796), an affordable and effective 4-aminoquinoline antimalarial for the 21st century. J Med Chem 2009;52:1408–1415.

85. Miroshnikova OV, Hudson TH, Gerena L, Kyle DE, Lin AJ. Synthesis and antimalarial activity of new isotebuquine analogues. J Med Chem 2007;50(4):889–896.

86. Casagrande M, Basilico N, Parapini S, Romeo S, Taramelli D, Sparatore A. Novel amodiaquine congeners as potent antimalarial agents. Bioorg Med Chem 2008;16(14):6813–6823.

87. Churchill FC, Patchen LC, Campbell CC, Schwartz IK, Nguyen-Dinh P, Dickinson CM. Amodiaquine as a prodrug: importance of metabolite(s) in the antimalarial effect of amodiaquine in humans. Life Sci 1985; 36(1):53–62.

88. Gil JP. Amodiaquine pharmacogenetics. Pharmacogenomics 2008;9(10):1385–1390.

89. Vale N, Moreira R, Gomes P. Primaquine revisited six decades after its discovery. Eur J Med Chem 2009;44(3):937–953.

90. Kim YR, Kuh HJ, Kim MY, Kim YS, Chung WC, Kim SI, Kang MW. Pharmacokinetics of primaquine and carboxyprimaquine in Korean patients with vivax malaria. Arch Pharm Res 2004;27(5):576–580.

91. Alving AS, Carson PE, Flanagan CL, Ickes CE. Enzymatic deficiency in primaquine-sensitive erythrocytes. Science 1956;124(3220):484–485.

92. Cohen G, Hochstein P. Generation of hydrogen peroxide in erythrocytes by hemolytic agents. Biochemistry (3): 1964; 895–900.

93. Shetty RV, Wetter WP, Blanton CD Jr. Synthesis of 2-benzyloxy and 2-benzylthio analogues of primaquine as potential antimalarials. J Med Chem 1977;20(10):1349–1351.

94. Shetty RV, Blanton CD Jr. Synthesis of 2-substituted primaquine analogues as potential antimalarials. J Med Chem 1978;21(9):995–998.

95. Chen EH, Saggiomo AJ, Tanabe K, Verma BL, Nodiff EA. Modifications of primaquine as antimalarials 1. 5-Phenoxy derivatives of primaquine. J Med Chem 1977;20(8):1107–1109.

96. LaMontagne MP, Markovac A, Menke JR. Antimalarials 10. Synthesis of 4-substituted primaquine analogues as candidate antimalarials. J Med Chem 1977;20(9):1123–1127.

97. Carroll FI, Berrang BD, Linn CP. Synthesis of 4-alkyl and 4-(beta-alkylvinyl) derivatives of primaquine as potential antimalarials. J Med Chem 1979;22(11):1363–1367.

98. Tanabe K, Chen EH, Verma BL, Saggiomo AJ, Nodiff EA. Modifications of primiaquine as antimalarials 2. 5-Phenylthio and 5-anilino derivatives of primaquine. J Med Chem 1978;21(1):133–136.

99. Carroll FI, Berrang B, Linn CP. Sulfur-interrupted 8-amino side chain analogues of 4-methyl-5-[m-(trifluoromethyl)phenoxy]primaquine as potential antimalarial agents. J Med Chem 1985;28(12):1959–1962.

100. Carroll FI, Berrang B, Linn CP. 4-substituted 5-[*m*-(trifluoromethyl)phenoxy]primaquine analogues as potential antimalarial agents. J Med Chem 1985;28(11):1564–1567.

101. Philip A, Kepler JA, Johnson BH, Carroll FI. Peptide derivatives of primaquine as potential antimalarial agents. J Med Chem 1988;31(4):870–874.

102. Portela MJ, Moreira R, Valente E, Constantino L, Iley J, Pinto J, Rosa R, Cravo P, do Rosario VE. Dipeptide derivatives of primaquine as transmission-blocking antimalarials: effect of aliphatic side-chain acylation on the gametocytocidal activity and on the formation of carboxyprimaquine in rat liver homogenates. Pharm Res 1999;16(6):949–955.

103. Araujo MJ, Bom J, Capela R, Casimiro C, Chambel P, Gomes P, Iley J, Lopes F, Morais J, Moreira R, de Oliveira E, do Rosario V, Vale N. Imidazolidin-4-one derivatives of primaquine as novel transmission-blocking antimalarials. J Med Chem 2005;48(3):888–892.

104. LaMontagne MP, Blumbergs P, Strube RE. Antimalarials 14. 5-(aryloxy)-4-methylprimaquine analogues. A highly effective series of blood and tissue schizonticidal agents. J Med Chem 1982;25(9):1094–1097.

105. Saxena N, Pandey VC, Puri SK, Dutta GP. Effect of a new 8-aminoquinoline antimalarial compound on hepatic microsomal mixed function oxidase system of mice. Indian J Med Res 1989;89:330–333.

106. Adak T, Valecha N, Sharma VP. *Plasmodium vivax* polymorphism in a clinical drug trial. Clin Diagn Lab Immunol 2001;8(5):891–894.

107. Crockett M, Kain KC. Tafenoquine: a promising new antimalarial agent. Expert Opin Investig Drugs 2007;16(5):705–715.

108. Hsu E. Reflections on the 'discovery' of the antimalarial qinghao. Br J Clin Pharmacol 2006;61(6):666–670.

109. Klayman DL. Qinghaosu (artemisinin): an antimalarial drug from China. Science 1985; 228(4703):1049–1055.

110. White NJ. Qinghaosu (artemisinin): the price of success. Science 2008;320(5874):330–334.

111. Schmid G, Hofheinz W. Total synthesis of qinghaosu. J Am Chem Soc 1983;105(3):624–625.

112. Zhou WS, Xu XX. Total synthesis of the antimalarial sesquiterpene peroxide qinghaosu and yingzhaosu-A. Acc Chem Res 1994;27(7):211–216.

113. Roth RJ, Acton N. A simple conversion of artemisinic acid into artemisinin. J Nat Prod 1989;52(5):1183–1185.

114. Haynes RK, Vonwiller SC. Catalyzed Oxygenation of allylic hydroperoxides derived from qinghao (artemisinic) acid: conversion of qinghao acid into dehydroqinghaosu (artemisitene) and qinghaosu (artemisinin). J Chem Soc Chem Commun 1990;6:451–453.

115. Covello PS, Teoh KH, Polichuk DR, Reed DW, Nowak G. Functional genomics and the biosynthesis of artemisinin. Phytochemistry 2007;68(14):1864–1871.

116. Martin VJ, Pitera DJ, Withers ST, Newman JD, Keasling JD. Engineering a mevalonate pathway in *Escherichia coli* for production of terpenoids. Nat Biotechnol 2003;21(7):796–802.

117. Ro DK, Paradise EM, Ouellet M, Fisher KJ, Newman KL, Ndungu JM, Ho KA, Eachus RA, Ham TS, Kirby J, Chang MC, Withers ST, Shiba Y, Sarpong R, Keasling JD. Production of the antimalarial drug precursor artemisinic acid in engineered yeast. Nature 2006;440(7086):940–943.

118. Begue JP, Bonnet-Delpon D. Fluoroartemisinins: metabolically more stable antimalarial artemisinin derivatives. ChemMedChem 2007;2(5):608–624.

119. Kepler JA, Philip A, Lee YW, Morey MC, Carroll FI. 1 2 4-Trioxanes as potential antimalarial agents. J Med Chem 1988;31(4):713–716.

120. Avery MA, Gao F, Chong WK, Mehrotra S, Milhous WK. Structure–activity relationships of the antimalarial agent artemisinin 1. Synthesis and comparative molecular field analysis of C-9 analogs of artemisinin and 10-deoxoartemisinin. J Med Chem 1993;36(26):4264–4275.

121. Jung M, Li X, Bustos DA, elSohly HN, McChesney JD, Milhous WK. Synthesis and antimalarial activity of (+)-deoxoartemisinin. J Med Chem 1990;33(5):1516–1518.

122. Avery MA, Alvim-Gaston M, Vroman JA, Wu B, Ager A, Peters W, Robinson BL, Charman W. Structure–activity relationships of the antimalarial agent artemisinin. 7. Direct modification of (+)-artemisinin and *in vivo* antimalarial screening of new, potential preclinical antimalarial candidates. J Med Chem 2002;45(19):4321–4335.

123. Avery MA, Muraleedharan KM, Desai PV, Bandyopadhyaya AK, Furtado MM, Tekwani BL. Structure–activity relationships of the antimalarial agent artemisinin. 8. Design, synthesis, and CoMFA studies toward the development of artemisinin-based drugs against leishmaniasis and malaria. J Med Chem 2003;46(20):4244–4258.

124. Lin AJ, Miller RE. Antimalarial activity of new dihydroartemisinin derivatives. 6. alpha-Alkylbenzylic ethers. J Med Chem 1995;38(5):764–770.

125. Posner GH, McGarvey DJ, Oh CH, Kumar N, Meshnick SR, Asawamahasadka W. Structure–activity relationships of lactone ring-opened analogs of the antimalarial 1,2 4-trioxane artemisinin. J Med Chem 1995;38(4):607–612.

126. Jefford CW, Burger U, Millasson-Schmidt P, Bernardinelli G, Robinson BL, Peters W. Epiartemisinin, a remarkably poor antimalarial: implications for the mode of action. Helv Chim Acta 2000;83(6):1239–1246.

127. Avery MA, Fan P, Karle JM, Bonk JD, Miller R, Goins DK. Structure–activity relationships of the antimalarial agent artemisinin 3. Total synthesis of (+)-13-carbaartemisinin and related tetra- and tricyclic structures. J Med Chem 1996;39(9):1885–1897.

128. Posner GH, Oh CH, Wang D, Gerena L, Milhous WK, Meshnick SR, Asawamahasadka W. Mechanism-based design, synthesis, and *in vitro* antimalarial testing of new 4-methylated trioxanes structurally related to artemisinin: the importance of a carbon-centered radical for antimalarial activity. J Med Chem 1994;37(9):1256–1258.

129. Avery MA, Mehrotra S, Bonk JD, Vroman JA, Goins DK, Miller R. Structure–activity relationships of the antimalarial agent artemisinin 4. Effect of substitution at C-3. J Med Chem 1996;39(15):2900–2906.

130. Posner GH, Paik IH, Sur S, McRiner AJ, Borstnik K, Xie S, Shapiro TA. Orally active, antimalarial, anticancer, artemisinin-derived trioxane dimers with high stability and efficacy. J Med Chem 2003;46(6):1060–1065.

131. Kepler JA, Philip A, Lee YW, Musallam HA, Carroll FI. Endoperoxides as potential antimalarial agents. J Med Chem 1987;30(8):1505–1509.

132. Jefford CW, McGoran EC, Boukouvalas J, Richardson G, Robinson BL, Peters W. Medicinal

and biological chemistry synthesis of new 1,2 4-trioxanes and their antimalarial activity. Helv Chim Acta 1988;71(7):1805–1812.

133. Jefford CW. New developments in synthetic peroxidic drugs as artemisinin mimics. Drug Discov Today 2007;12(11–12):487–495.

134. Vennerstrom JL, Arbe-Barnes S, Brun R, Charman SA, Chiu FC, Chollet J, Dong Y, Dorn A, Hunziker D, Matile H, McIntosh K, Padmanilayam M, Santo Tomas J, Scheurer C, Scorneaux B, Tang Y, Urwyler H, Wittlin S, Charman WN. Identification of an antimalarial synthetic trioxolane drug development candidate. Nature 2004;430(7002):900–904.

135. Meshnick SR, Taylor TE, Kamchonwongpaisan S. Artemisinin and the antimalarial endoperoxides: from herbal remedy to targeted chemotherapy. Microbiol Rev 1996;60(2):301–315.

136. Meshnick SR. Artemisinin: mechanisms of action, resistance and toxicity. Int J Parasitol 2002;32(13):1655–1660.

137. Pandey AV, Tekwani BL, Singh RL, Chauhan VS. Artemisinin, an endoperoxide antimalarial, disrupts the hemoglobin catabolism and heme detoxification systems in malarial parasite. J Biol Chem. 1999;274(27):19383–19388.

138. Robert A, Benoit-Vical F, Claparols C, Meunier B. The antimalarial drug artemisinin alkylates heme in infected mice. Proc Natl Acad Sci USA 2005;102(38):13676–13680.

139. Eckstein-Ludwig U, Webb RJ, Van Goethem ID, East JM, Lee AG, Kimura M, O'Neill PM, Bray PG, Ward SA, Krishna S. Artemisinins target the SERCA of Plasmodium falciparum. Nature 2003;424(6951):957–961.

140. Lee IS, Hufford CD. Metabolism of antimalarial sesquiterpene lactones. Pharmacol Ther 1990;48(3):345–355.

141. Meshnick SR, Jefford CW, Posner GH, Avery MA, Peters W. Second-generation antimalarial endoperoxides. Parasitol Today 1996;12(2):79–82.

142. Fishwick J, McLean WG, Edwards G, Ward SA. The toxicity of artemisinin and related compounds on neuronal and glial cells in culture. Chem Biol Interact 1995;96(3):263–271.

143. Wesche DL, DeCoster MA, Tortella FC, Brewer TG. Neurotoxicity of artemisinin analogs in vitro. Antimicrob Agents Chemother 1994;38(8):1813–1819.

144. Brewer TG, Peggins JO, Grate SJ, Petras JM, Levine BS, Weina PJ, Swearengen J, Heiffer MH, Schuster BG. Neurotoxicity in animals due to arteether and artemether. Trans R Soc Trop Med Hyg 1994;88(Suppl1): S33–S36.

145. Noedl H, Se Y, Schaecher K, Smith BL, Socheat D, Fukuda MM. Evidence of artemisinin-resistant malaria in western Cambodia. N Engl J Med 2008;359(24):2619–2620.

146. Jambou R, Legrand E, Niang M, Khim N, Lim P, Volney B, Ekala MT, Bouchier C, Esterre P, Fandeur T, Mercereau-Puijalon O. Resistance of Plasmodium falciparum field isolates to in vitro artemether and point mutations of the SERCA-type PfATPase6. Lancet 2005;366 (9501):1960–1963.

147. de Villiers KA, Marques HM, Egan TJ. The crystal structure of halofantrine-ferriprotoporphyrin IX and the mechanism of action of arylmethanol antimalarials. J Inorg Biochem 2008;102(8):1660–1667.

148. Coleman RE, Clavin AM, Milhous WK. Gametocytocidal and sporontocidal activity of antimalarials against Plasmodium berghei ANKA in ICR Mice and Anopheles stephensi mosquitoes. Am J Trop Med Hyg 1992;46(2):169–182.

149. Baune B, Furlan V, Taburet AM, Farinotti R. Effect of selected antimalarial drugs and inhibitors of cytochrome P-450 3A4 on halofantrine metabolism by human liver microsomes. Drug Metab Dispos 1999;27(5):565–568.

150. Sanchez-Chapula JA, Navarro-Polanco RA, Sanguinetti MC. Block of wild-type and inactivation-deficient human ether-a-go-go-related gene K^+ channels by halofantrine. Naunyn Schmiedebergs Arch Pharmacol 2004;370 (6):484–491.

151. Sherman IW. The road to atovaquone. Adv Parasitol 2009;67:101–104.

152. Kessl JJ, Lange BB, Merbitz-Zahradnik T, Zwicker K, Hill P, Meunier B, Palsdottir H, Hunte C, Meshnick S, Trumpower BL. Molecular basis for atovaquone binding to the cytochrome bc$_1$ complex. J Biol Chem 2003;278 (33):31312–31318.

153. Hudson AT, Dickins M, Ginger CD, Gutteridge WE, Holdich T, Hutchinson DB, Pudney M, Randall AW, Latter VS. 566C80: a potent broad spectrum anti-infective agent with activity against malaria and opportunistic infections in AIDS patients. Drugs Exp Clin Res 1991;17(9):427–435.

154. Gillotin C, Mamet JP. Veronese, L. Lack of a pharmacokinetic interaction between atovaquone and proguanil. Eur J Clin Pharmacol 1999;55(4):311–315.

155. Gil JP, Nogueira F, Stromberg-Norklit J, Lindberg J, Carrolo M, Casimiro C, Lopes D, Arez AP, Cravo PV, Rosario VE. Detection of atovaquone and Malarone resistance conferring mutations

in *Plasmodium falciparum* cytochrome b gene (cytb). Mol Cell Probes 2003;17(2–3):85–89.

156. Schwartz E, Bujanover S, Kain KC. Genetic confirmation of atovaquone-proguanil-resistant *Plasmodium falciparum* malaria acquired by a nonimmune traveler to East Africa. Clin Infect Dis 2003;37(3):450–451.

157. Schwobel B, Alifrangis M, Salanti A, Jelinek T. Different mutation patterns of atovaquone resistance to *Plasmodium falciparum in vitro and in vivo*: rapid detection of codon 268 polymorphisms in the cytochrome b as potential *in vivo* resistance marker. Malar J 2003;2:5.

158. Olliaro PL, Milhous WK. The antimalarial drug portfolio and research pipeline. In: Rosenthal PJ, Antimalarial Chemotherapy: Mechanisms of Action, Resistance and New Directions in Drug Discovery. Totwa NJ: Humana Press; 2001. 219–232.

159. Chen C, Zheng X. Development of the new antimalarial drug pyronaridine: a review. Biomed Environ Sci 1992;5(2):149–160.

160. Shao BR. A review of antimalarial drug pyronaridine. Chin Med J 1990;103(5):428–434.

161. Fu S, Xiao SH. Pyronaridine: a new antimalarial drug. Parasitol Today 1991;7(11):310–313.

162. Chavalitshewinkoon P, Wilairat P, Gamage S, Denny W, Figgitt D, Ralph R. Structure–activity relationships and modes of action of 9-anilinoacridines against chloroquine-resistant *Plasmodium falciparum in vitro*. Antimicrob Agents Chemother 1993;37(3):403–406.

163. Auparakkitanon S, Wilairat P. Cleavage of DNA induced by 9-anilinoacridine inhibitors of topoisomerase II in the malaria parasite *Plasmodium falciparum*. Biochem Biophys Res Commun 2000;269(2):406–409.

164. Wu LJ, Rabbege JR, Nagasawa H, Jacobs G, Aikawa M. Morphological effects of pyronaridine on malarial parasites. Am J Trop Med Hyg 1988;38(1):30–36.

165. Naisbitt DJ, Williams DP, O'Neill PM, Maggs JL, Willock DJ, Pirmohamed M, Park BK. Metabolism-dependent neutrophil cytotoxicity of amodiaquine: a comparison with pyronaridine and related antimalarial drugs. Chem Res Toxicol 1998;11(12):1586–1595.

166. Kawai S, Kano S, Chang C, Suzuki M. The effects of pyronaridine on the morphology of *Plasmodium falciparum* in *Aotus trivirgatus*. Am J Trop Med Hyg 1996;55(2):223–229.

167. Ringwald P, Bickii J, Basco L. Randomised trial of pyronaridine versus chloroquine for acute uncomplicated falciparum malaria in Africa. Lancet 1996;347(8993):24–28.

168. Ringwald P, Bickii J, Basco LK. Efficacy of oral pyronaridine for the treatment of acute uncomplicated falciparum malaria in African children. Clin Infect Dis 1998;26(4):946–953.

169. Looareesuwan S, Kyle DE, Viravan C, Vanijanonta S, Wilairatana P, Wernsdorfer WH. Clinical study of pyronaridine for the treatment of acute uncomplicated falciparum malaria in Thailand. Am J Trop Med Hyg 1996;54(2):205–209.

170. Peters W. Pyronaridine against multiresistant falciparum malaria. Lancet 1996;347(9001):625.

171. Peters W, Robinson BL. The chemotherapy of rodent malaria LV. Interactions between pyronaridine and artemisinin. Ann Trop Med Parasitol 1997;91(2):141–145.

172. Shao BR, Huang ZS, Shi XH, Zhan CQ, Meng F, Ye XY, Huang J, Ha SH. Antimalarial and toxic effect of triple combination of pyronaridine, sulfadoxine and pyrimethamine. Southeast Asian J Trop Med Public Health 1989;20(2):257–263.

173. Shao BR, Huang ZS, Shi XH, Meng F. A 5-year surveillance of sensitivity *in vivo* of *Plasmodium falciparum* to pyronaridine/sulfadoxine/pyrimethamine in Diaoluo area Hainan Province. Southeast Asian J Trop Med Public Health 1991;22(1):65–67.

174. Ramharter M, Kurth F, Schreier AC, Nemeth J, Glasenapp I, Belard S, Schlie M, Kammer J, Koumba PK, Cisse B, Mordmuller B, Lell B, Issifou S, Oeuvray C, Fleckenstein L, Kremsner PG. Fixed-dose pyronaridine-artesunate combination for treatment of uncomplicated falciparum malaria in pediatric patients in Gabon. J Infect Dis 2008;198(6):911–919.

175. Ringwald P, Eboumbou EC, Bickii J, Basco LK. *In vitro* activities of pyronaridine, alone and in combination with other antimalarial drugs, against *Plasmodium falciparum*. Antimicrob Agents Chemother 1999;43(6):1525–1527.

176. Gupta S, Thapar MM, Mariga ST, Wernsdorfer WH, Bjorkman A. *Plasmodium falciparum*: *in vitro* interactions of artemisinin with amodiaquine, pyronaridine, and chloroquine. Exp Parasitol 2002;100(1):28–35.

177. Davis TM, Hamzah J, Ilett KF, Karunajeewa HA, Reeder JC, Batty KT, Hackett S, Barrett PH. *In vitro* interactions between piperaquine, dihydroartemisinin, and other conventional and novel antimalarial drugs. Antimicrob Agents Chemother 2006;50(8):2883–2885.

178. Dutta GP, Puri SK, Awasthi A, Mishra M, Tripathi R. Pyronaridine: an effective antimalarial against multidrug-resistant malaria. Life Sci 2000;67(7):759–763.

179. Tripathi R, Umesh A, Mishra M, Puri SK, Dutta GP. *Plasmodium yoelii* nigeriensis (MDR)-efficacy of oral pyronaridine against multidrug-resistant malaria in Swiss mice. Exp Parasitol 2000;94(3):190–193.

180. Pradines B, Mabika Mamfoumbi M, Parzy D, Owono Medang M, Lebeau C, Mourou Mbina JR, Doury JC, Kombila M. *In vitro* susceptibility of African isolates of *Plasmodium falciparum* from Gabon to pyronaridine. Am J Trop Med Hyg 1999;60(1):105–108.

181. Shao BR, Ye XY, Chu YH. Comparison of effects of pyronaridine, amodiaquine, mefloquine and qinghaosu on rodent malaria. Southeast Asian J Trop Med Public Health 1992;23(1):59–63.

182. Alin MH, Bjorkman A, Ashton M. *In vitro* activity of artemisinin, its derivatives, and pyronaridine against different strains of *Plasmodium falciparum*. Trans R Soc Trop Med Hyg 1990;84(5):635–637.

183. Basco LK, Le Bras J. *In vitro* activity of pyronaridine against African strains of *Plasmodium falciparum*. Ann Trop Med Parasitol 1992;86(5):447–454.

184. Basco LK, Le Bras J. *In vitro* susceptibility of Cambodian isolates of *Plasmodium falciparum* to halofantrine, pyronaridine and artemisinin derivatives. Ann Trop Med Parasitol 1994;88(2):137–144.

185. McFadden GI, Waller RF. Plastids in parasites of humans. Bioessays 1997;19(11):1033–1040.

186. Kilejian A. Circular mitochondrial DNA from the avian malarial parasite *Plasmodium lophurae*. Biochim Biophys Acta 1975;390 (3):276–284.

187. Williamson DH, Gardner MJ, Preiser P, Moore DJ, Rangachari K, Wilson RJ. The evolutionary origin of the 35 kb circular DNA of *Plasmodium falciparum*: new evidence supports a possible rhodophyte ancestry. Mol Gen Genet 1994;243(2):249–252.

188. Fast NM, Kissinger JC, Roos DS, Keeling PJ. Nuclear-encoded, plastid-targeted genes suggest a single common origin for apicomplexan and dinoflagellate plastids. Mol Biol Evol 2001;18(3):418–426.

189. Wilson RJ, Denny PW, Preiser PR, Rangachari K, Roberts K, Roy A, Whyte A, Strath M, Moore DJ, Moore PW, Williamson DH. Complete gene map of the plastid-like DNA of the malaria parasite *Plasmodium falciparum*. J Mol Biol 1996;261(2):155–172.

190. Cai X, Fuller AL, McDougald LR, Zhu G. Apicoplast genome of the coccidian *Eimeria tenella*. Gene 2003;321:39–46.

191. Waller RF, Reed MB, Cowman AF, McFadden GI. Protein trafficking to the plastid of Plasmodium falciparum is via the secretory pathway. EMBO J 2000;19(8):1794–1802.

192. Striepen B, Crawford MJ, Shaw MK, Tilney LG, Seeber F, Roos DS. The plastid of *Toxoplasma gondii* is divided by association with the centrosomes. J Cell Biol 2000;151(7):1423–1434.

193. Cavalier-Smith T. Membrane heredity and early chloroplast evolution. Trends Plant Sci 2000;5(4):174–182.

194. Ralph SA, van Dooren GG, Waller RF, Crawford MJ, Fraunholz MJ, Foth BJ, Tonkin CJ, Roos DS, McFadden GI. Tropical infectious diseases: metabolic maps and functions of the *Plasmodium falciparum* apicoplast. Nat Rev Microbiol 2004;2(3):203–216.

195. Foth BJ, McFadden GI. The apicoplast: a plastid in *Plasmodium falciparum* and other Apicomplexan parasites. Int Rev Cytol 2003;224:57–110.

196. Wilson RJ. Progress with parasite plastids. J Mol Biol 2002;319(2):257–274.

197. Ralph SA, D'Ombrain MC, McFadden GI. The apicoplast as an antimalarial drug target. Drug Resist Updat 2001;4(3):145–151.

198. Wilson RJ, Rangachari K, Saldanha JW, Rickman L, Buxton RS, Eccleston JF. Parasite plastids: maintenance and functions. Philos Trans R Soc Lond B Biol Sci 2003;358 (1429):155–162; discussion 162-154.

199. Fichera ME, Roos DS. A plastid organelle as a drug target in apicomplexan parasites. Nature 1997;390(6658):407–409.

200. He CY, Shaw MK, Pletcher CH, Striepen B, Tilney LG, Roos DS. A plastid segregation defect in the protozoan parasite *Toxoplasma gondii*. EMBO J 2001;20(3):330–339.

201. Fichera ME, Bhopale MK, Roos DS. *In vitro* assays elucidate peculiar kinetics of clindamycin action against T*oxoplasma gondii*. Antimicrob Agents Chemother 1995;39(7):1530–1537.

202. He CY, Striepen B, Pletcher CH, Murray JM, Roos DS. Targeting and processing of nuclear-encoded apicoplast proteins in plastid segregation mutants of *Toxoplasma gondii*. J Biol Chem 2001;76(30):28436–28442.

203. Roos DS, Crawford MJ, Donald RG, Kissinger JC, Klimczak LJ, Striepen B. Ori-

gin, targeting, and function of the apicomplexan plastid. Curr Opin Microbiol 1999;2 (4):426–432.

204. Roos DS, Crawford MJ, Donald RG, Fohl LM, Hager KM, Kissinger JC, Reynolds MG, Striepen B, Sullivan WJ Jr. Transport and trafficking: *Toxoplasma* as a model for *Plasmodium*. Novartis Found Symp 1999;226:176–195; discussion 195-178.

205. Dahl EL, Rosenthal PJ. Multiple antibiotics exert delayed effects against the *Plasmodium falciparum* apicoplast. Antimicrob Agents Chemother 2007;51(10):3485–3490.

206. Dahl EL, Rosenthal PJ. Apicoplast translation, transcription and genome replication: targets for antimalarial antibiotics. Trends Parasitol 2008;24(6):279–284.

207. Goodman CD, Su V, McFadden GI. The effects of anti-bacterials on the malaria parasite *Plasmodium falciparum*. Mol Biochem Parasitol 2007;152(2):181–191.

208. Griffith KS, Leis LS, Mali S, Parse ME. Treatment of malaria in the United States: a systematic review. JAMA 2007;97(20):2264–2277.

209. Geary TG, Jensen JB. Effects of antibiotics on *Plasmodium falciparum in vitro*. Am J Trop Med Hyg 1983;32(2):221–225.

210. Dahl EL, Shock JL, Shenai BR, Gut J, DeRisi JL, Rosenthal PJ. Tetracyclines specifically target the apicoplast of the malaria parasite *Plasmodium falciparum*. Antimicrob Agents Chemother 2006;0(9):3124–3131.

211. Ramya TN, Mishra S, Karmodiya K, Surolia N, Surolia A. Inhibitors of nonhousekeeping functions of the apicoplast defy delayed death in *Plasmodium falciparum*. Antimicrob Agents Chemother 2007;51(1):307–316.

212. Pradines B, Rogier C, Fusai T, Mosnier J, Daries W, Barret E, Parzy D. *In vitro* activities of antibiotics against *Plasmodium falciparum* are inhibited by iron. Antimicrob Agents Chemother 2001;45(6):1746–1750.

213. Yeo AE, Rieckmann KH. Increased antimalarial activity of azithromycin during prolonged exposure of *Plasmodium falciparum in vitro*. Int J Parasitol 1995;25(4):531–532.

214. Giboda M, Denis MB. Response of Kampuchean strains of *Plasmodium falciparum* to antimalarials: *in-vivo* assessment of quinine and quinine plus tetracycline; multiple drug resistance *in vitro*. J Trop Med Hyg 1988;91 (4):205–211.

215. Watt G, Loesuttivibool L, Shanks GD, Boudreau EF, Brown AE, Pavanand K, Webster HK, Wechgritaya S. Quinine with tetracycline for the treatment of drug-resistant falciparum malaria in Thailand. Am J Trop Med Hyg 1992;47(1):108–111.

216. Shanks GD, Edstein MD, Suriyamongkol V, Timsaad S, Webster HK. Malaria chemoprophylaxis using proguanil/dapsone combinations on the Thai–Cambodian border. Am J Trop Med Hyg 1992;46(6):643–648.

217. Rieckmann KH. Tetracycline prophylaxis for malaria. Lancet 1987;2(8557):507–508.

218. Ohrt C, Richie TL, Widjaja H, Shanks GD, Fitriadi J, Fryauff DJ, Handschin J, Tang D, Sandjaja B, Tjitra E, Hadiarso L, Watt G, Wignall FS. Mefloquine compared with doxycycline for the prophylaxis of malaria in Indonesian soldiers. A randomized, double-blind, placebo-controlled trial. Ann Intern Med 1997;126(12):963–972.

219. Andersen SL, Oloo AJ, Gordon DM, Ragama OB, Aleman GM, Berman JD, Tang DB, Dunne MW, Shanks GD. Successful double-blinded, randomized, placebo-controlled field trial of azithromycin and doxycycline as prophylaxis for malaria in western Kenya. Clin Infect Dis 1998;26(1):146–150.

220. Shanks GD, Barnett A, Edstein MD, Rieckmann KH. Effectiveness of doxycycline combined with primaquine for malaria prophylaxis. Med J Aust 1995;162(6):306–307, 309–310.

221. Phillips-Howard PA, Wood D. The safety of antimalarial drugs in pregnancy. Drug Saf 1996;14(3):131–145.

222. Pradines B, Spiegel A, Rogier C, Tall A, Mosnier J, Fusai T, Trape JF, Parzy D. Antibiotics for prophylaxis of *Plasmodium falciparum* infections: *in vitro* activity of doxycycline against Senegalese isolates. Am J Trop Med Hyg 2000;62(1):82–85.

223. Gingras BA, Jensen JB. Activity of azithromycin (CP-62 993) and erythromycin against chloroquine-sensitive and chloroquine-resistant strains of *Plasmodium falciparum in vitro*. Am J Trop Med Hyg 1992;47(3):378–382.

224. Foulds G, Shepard RM, Johnson RB. The pharmacokinetics of azithromycin in human serum and tissues. J Antimicrob Chemother 1990;25 (SupplA): 73–82.

225. Sidhu AB, Sun Q, Nkrumah LJ, Dunne MW, Sacchettini JC, Fidock DA. *In vitro* efficacy, resistance selection, and structural modeling studies implicate the malarial parasite apicoplast as the target of azithromycin. J Biol Chem 2007;282(4):2494–2504.

226. Noedl H, Krudsood S, Leowattana W, Tang-pukdee N, Thanachartwet W, Looareesuwan S, Miller RS, Fukuda M, Jongsakul K, Yin-gyuen K, Sriwichai S, Ohrt C, Knirsch C. *In vitro* antimalarial activity of azithromycin, artesunate, and quinine in combination and correlation with clinical outcome. Antimicrob Agents Chemother 2007;51(2):651–656.

227. Kalilani L, Mofolo I, Chaponda M, Rogerson SJ, Alker AP, Kwiek JJ, Meshnick SR. A randomized controlled pilot trial of azithromycin or artesunate added to sulfadoxine-pyrimethamine as treatment for malaria in pregnant women. PLoS ONE 2007;2(11):e1166.

228. Chico RM, Pittrof R, Greenwood B, Chandramohan D. Azithromycin-chloroquine and the intermittent preventive treatment of malaria in pregnancy. Malar J 2008;7:255.

229. Miller RS, Wongsrichanalai C, Buathong N, McDaniel P, Walsh DS, Knirsch C, Ohrt C. Effective treatment of uncomplicated *Plasmodium falciparum* malaria with azithromycin-quinine combinations: a randomized, dose-ranging study. Am J Trop Med Hyg 2006; 74(3):401–406.

230. Clyde DF, Gilman RH, McCarthy VC. Antimalarial effects of clindamycin in man. Am J Trop Med Hyg 1975;24(2):369–370.

231. Kremsner PG, Zotter GM, Feldmeier H, Graninger W, Rocha RM, Wiedermann G. A comparative trial of three regimens for treating uncomplicated falciparum malaria in Acre Brazil. J Infect Dis 1988;158(6):1368–1371.

232. Giadom B, de Veer GE, van Hensbroek MB, Corrah PT, Jaffar S, Greenwood BM. A comparative study of parenteral chloroquine, quinine and pyrimethamine-sulfadoxine in the treatment of Gambian children with complicated, non-cerebral malaria. Ann Trop Paediatr 1996;16(2):85–91.

233. Hassan Alin M, Ashton M, Kihamia CM, Mtey GJ, Bjorkman A. Multiple dose pharmacokinetics of oral artemisinin and comparison of its efficacy with that of oral artesunate in falciparum malaria patients. Trans R Soc Trop Med Hyg 1996;90(1):61–65.

234. Miller LH, Glew RH, Wyler DJ, Howard WA, Collins WE, Contacos PG, Neva FA. Evaluation of clindamycin in combination with quinine against multidrug-resistant strains of *Plasmodium falciparum*. Am J Trop Med Hyg 1974;23(4):565–569.

235. Kremsner PG, Radloff P, Metzger W, Wildling E, Mordmuller B, Philipps J, Jenne L, Nkeyi M, Prada J, Bienzle U, et al. Quinine plus clindamycin improves chemotherapy of severe malaria in children. Antimicrob Agents Chemother 1995;39(7):1603–1605.

236. White NJ. Assessment of the pharmacodynamic properties of antimalarial drugs *in vivo*. Antimicrob Agents Chemother 1997;41 (7):1413–1422.

237. Kremsner PG, Winkler S, Brandts C, Graninger W, Bienzle U. Curing of chloroquine-resistant malaria with clindamycin. Am J Trop Med Hyg 1993;49(5):650–654.

238. Kremsner PG, Wildling E, Jenne L, Graninger W, Bienzle U. Comparison of micronized halofantrine with chloroquine-antibiotic combinations for treating *Plasmodium falciparum* malaria in adults from Gabon. Am J Trop Med Hyg 1994;50(6):790–795.

239. Metzger W, Mordmuller B, Graninger W, Bienzle U, Kremsner PG. Sulfadoxine/pyrimethamine or chloroquine/clindamycin treatment of Gabonese school children infected with chloroquine resistant malaria. J Antimicrob Chemother 1995;36(4):723–728.

240. Wiesner J, Henschker D, Hutchinson DB, Beck E, Jomaa H. *In vitro* and *in vivo* synergy of fosmidomycin, a novel antimalarial drug, with clindamycin. Antimicrob Agents Chemother 2002;46(9):2889–2894.

241. Borrmann S, Adegnika AA, Matsiegui PB, Issifou S, Schindler A, Mawili-Mboumba DP, Baranek T, Wiesner J, Jomaa H, Kremsner PG. Fosmidomycin-clindamycin for *Plasmodium falciparum* Infections in African children. J Infect Dis 2004;189(5):901–908.

242. Borrmann S, Issifou S, Esser G, Adegnika AA, Ramharter M, Matsiegui PB, Oyakhirome S, Mawili-Mboumba DP, Missinou MA, Kun JF, Jomaa H, Kremsner PG. Fosmidomycin-clindamycin for the treatment of *Plasmodium falciparum* malaria. J Infect Dis 2004;190(9):1534–1540.

243. Na-Bangchang K, Ruengweerayut R, Karbwang J, Chauemung A, Hutchinson D. Pharmacokinetics and pharmacodynamics of fosmidomycin monotherapy and combination therapy with clindamycin in the treatment of multidrug resistant falciparum malaria. Malar J 2007;6:70.

244. Chow AW, Jewesson PJ. Pharmacokinetics and safety of antimicrobial agents during pregnancy. Rev Infect Dis 1985;7(3):287–313.

245. Czeizel AE, Rockenbauer M, Sorensen HT, Olsen J. A teratological study of lincosamides. Scand J Infect Dis 2000;32(5):579–580.

246. McGready R, Cho T, Samuel Villegas L, Brockman A, van Vugt M, Looareesuwan S, White

NJ, Nosten F. Randomized comparison of quinine–clindamycin versus artesunate in the treatment of falciparum malaria in pregnancy. Trans R Soc Trop Med Hyg 2001;95 (6):651–656.

247. Rolfe M. Multiple drug resistant *Plasmodium falciparum* malaria in a pregnant indigenous Zambian woman. Trans R Soc Trop Med Hyg 1988;82(4):554–557.

248. Procop GW, Jessen R, Hyde SR, Scheck DN. Persistence of *Plasmodium falciparum* in the placenta after apparently effective quinidine/ clindamycin therapy. J Perinatol 2001;21 (2):128–130.

249. Alecrim MdG Dourado H, Alecrim W, Albuquerque BC, Wanssa E, Wanssa Mdo C. Treatment of malaria (*P. falciparum*) with clindamycin. Rev Inst Med Trop Sao Paulo 1981;23 (2):86–91.

250. Pukrittayakamee S, Chantra A, Vanijanonta S, Clemens R, Looareesuwan S, White NJ. Therapeutic responses to quinine and clindamycin in multidrug-resistant falciparum malaria. Antimicrob Agents Chemother 2000; 44(9):2395–2398.

251. Pukrittayakamee S, Clemens R, Chantra A, Nontprasert A, Luknam T, Looareesuwan S, White NJ. Therapeutic responses to antibacterial drugs in vivax malaria. Trans R Soc Trop Med Hyg 2001;95(5):524–528.

252. McConkey GA, Rogers MJ, McCutchan TF. Inhibition of *Plasmodium falciparum* protein synthesis Targeting the plastid-like organelle with thiostrepton. J Biol Chem 1997;272 (4):2046–2049.

253. Lin Q, Katakura K, Suzuki M. Inhibition of mitochondrial and plastid activity of *Plasmodium falciparum* by minocycline. FEBS Lett 2002;515(1–3):71–74.

254. Divo AA, Geary TG, Jensen JB. Oxygen- and time-dependent effects of antibiotics and selected mitochondrial inhibitors on *Plasmodium falciparum* in culture. Antimicrob Agents Chemother 1985;27(1):21–27.

255. Genton B, Mueller I, Betuela I, Casey G, Ginny M, Alpers MP, Reeder JC. Rifampicin/Cotrimoxazole/Isoniazid versus mefloquine or quinine + sulfadoxine- pyrimethamine for malaria: a randomized trial. PLoS Clin Trials 2006;1(8):e38.

256. Pukrittayakamee S, Prakongpan S, Wanwimolruk S, Clemens R, Looareesuwan S, White NJ. Adverse effect of rifampin on quinine efficacy in uncomplicated falciparum malaria.

Antimicrob Agents Chemother 2003;47 (5):1509–1513.

257. Hou LJ, Raju SS, Abdulah MS, Nor NM, Ravichandran M. Rifampicin antagonizes the effect of choloroquine on chloroquine-resistant *Plasmodium berghei* in mice. Jpn J Infect Dis 2004;57(5):198–202.

258. Mahmoudi N, Ciceron L, Franetich JF, Farhati K, Silvie O, Eling W, Sauerwein R, Danis M, Mazier D, Derouin F. *In vitro* activities of 25 quinolones and fluoroquinolones against liver and blood stage *Plasmodium* spp. Antimicrob Agents Chemother 2003;47(8):2636–2639.

259. Krishna S, Davis TM, Chan PC, Wells RA, Robson KJ. Ciprofloxacin and malaria. Lancet 1988;1(8596):1231–1232.

260. Divo AA, Sartorelli AC, Patton CL, Bia FJ. Activity of fluoroquinolone antibiotics against *Plasmodium falciparum in vitro*. Antimicrob Agents Chemother 1988;32(8):1182–1186.

261. Andrade AA, de Pilla Varotti F, de Freitas IO, de Souza MV, Vasconcelos TR, Boechat N, Krettli AU. Enhanced activity of mefloquine and artesunic acid against *Plasmodium falciparum in vitro* and *P. berghei* in mice by combination with ciprofloxacin. Eur J Pharmacol 2007;558(1–3):194–198.

262. Salmon D, Deloron P, Gaudin C, Malhotra K, Lebras J, Pocidalo JJ. Activities of pefloxacin and ciprofloxacin against experimental malaria in mice. Antimicrob Agents Chemother 1990;34(12):2327–2330.

263. Deloron P, Aubry P, Ndayirabije A, Clavier F, Verdier F. Short report: pefloxacin does not potentiate quinine efficacy against *Plasmodium falciparum* malaria. Am J Trop Med Hyg 1995;53(6):646–647.

264. Deloron P, Lepers JP, Raharimalala L, Dubois B, Coulanges P, Pocidalo JJ. Pefloxacin for falciparum malaria: only modest success. Ann Intern Med 1991;114(10):874–875.

265. McClean KL, Hitchman D, Shafran SD. Norfloxacin is inferior to chloroquine for falciparum malaria in northwestern Zambia: a comparative clinical trial. J Infect Dis 1992;165 (5):904–907.

266. Makanga M, Premji Z, Falade C, Karbwang J, Mueller EA, Andriano K, Hunt P, De Palacios PI. Efficacy and safety of the six-dose regimen of artemether-lumefantrine in pediatrics with uncomplicated *Plasmodium falciparum* malaria: a pooled analysis of individual patient data. Am J Trop Med Hyg 2006;74 (6):991–998.

267. Falade C, Makanga M, Premji Z, Ortmann CE, Stockmeyer M, de Palacios PI. Efficacy and safety of artemether-lumefantrine (Coartem) tablets (six-dose regimen) in African infants and children with acute, uncomplicated falciparum malaria. Trans R Soc Trop Med Hyg 2005;99(6):459–467.

268. Dorsey G, Staedke S, Clark TD, Njama-Meya D, Nzarubara B, Maiteki-Sebuguzi C, Dokomajilar C, Kamya MR, Rosenthal PJ, Combination therapy for uncomplicated falciparum malaria in Ugandan children: a randomized trial. JAMA 2007;297(20):2210–2219.

269. Abdulla S, Sagara I, Borrmann S, D'Alessandro U, Gonzalez R, Hamel M, Ogutu B, Martensson A, Lyimo J, Maiga H, Sasi P, Nahum A, Bassat Q, Juma E, Otieno L, Bjorkman A, Beck HP, Andriano K, Cousin M, Lefevre G, Ubben D, Premji Z. Efficacy and safety of artemether-lumefantrine dispersible tablets compared with crushed commercial tablets in African infants and children with uncomplicated malaria: a randomised, single-blind, multicentre trial. Lancet 2008;372(9652):1819–1827.

270. Wiseman V, Kim M, Mutabingwa TK, Whitty CJ. Cost-effectiveness study of three antimalarial drug combinations in Tanzania. PLoS Med 2006;3(10):e373.

271. Chanda P, Masiye F, Chitah BM, Sipilanyambe N, Hawela M, Banda P, Okorosobo T. A cost-effectiveness analysis of artemether lumefantrine for treatment of uncomplicated malaria in Zambia. Malar J 2007;6:21.

272. Premji ZG, Abdulla S, Ogutu B, Ndong A, Falade CO, Sagara I, Mulure N, Nwaiwu O, Kokwaro G. The content of African diets is adequate to achieve optimal efficacy with fixed-dose artemether-lumefantrine: a review of the evidence. Malar J 2008;7:244.

273. Davis TM, Hung TY, Sim IK, Karunajeewa HA, Ilett KF. Piperaquine: a resurgent antimalarial drug. Drugs 2005;65(1):75–87.

274. Denis MB, Davis TM, Hewitt S, Incardona S, Nimol K, Fandeur T, Poravuth Y, Lim C, Socheat D. Efficacy and safety of dihydroartemisinin-piperaquine (Artekin) in Cambodian children and adults with uncomplicated falciparum malaria. Clin Infect Dis 2002;35 (12):1469–1476.

275. Ashley EA, Krudsood S, Phaiphun L, Srivilairit S, McGready R, Leowattana W, Hutagalung R, Wilairatana P, Brockman A, Looareesuwan S, Nosten F, White NJ. Randomized, controlled dose-optimization studies of dihydroartemisinin-piperaquine for the treatment of un-

complicated multidrug-resistant falciparum malaria in Thailand. J Infect Dis 2004; 190(10):1773–1782.

276. Karunajeewa H, Lim C, Hung TY, Ilett KF, Denis MB, Socheat D, Davis TM. Safety evaluation of fixed combination piperaquine plus dihydroartemisinin (Artekin) in Cambodian children and adults with malaria. Br J Clin Pharmacol 2004;57(1):93–99.

277. Mayxay M, Thongpraseuth V, Khanthavong M, Lindegardh N, Barends M, Keola S, Pongvongsa T, Phompida S, Phetsouvanh R, Stepniewska K, White NJ, Newton PN. An open, randomized comparison of artesunate plus mefloquine vs. dihydroartemisinin-piperaquine for the treatment of uncomplicated *Plasmodium falciparum* malaria in the Lao People's Democratic Republic (Laos). Trop Med Int Health 2006;11(8):1157–1165.

278. Smithuis F, Kyaw MK, Phe O, Aye KZ, Htet L, Barends M, Lindegardh N, Singtoroj T, Ashley E, Lwin S, Stepniewska K, White NJ. Efficacy and effectiveness of dihydroartemisinin-piperaquine versus artesunate-mefloquine in falciparum malaria: an open-label randomised comparison. Lancet 2006;367(9528):2075–2085.

279. Karema C, Fanello CI, van Overmeir C, van Geertruyden JP, van Doren W, Ngamije D, D'Alessandro U. Safety and efficacy of dihydroartemisinin/piperaquine (Artekin) for the treatment of uncomplicated *Plasmodium falciparum* malaria in Rwandan children. Trans R Soc Trop Med Hyg 2006;100 (12):1105–1111.

280. Alin MH, Kihamia CM, Bjorkman A, Bwijo BA, Premji Z, Mtey GJ, Ashton M. Efficacy of oral and intravenous artesunate in male Tanzanian adults with *Plasmodium falciparum* malaria and *in vitro* susceptibility to artemisinin, chloroquine, and mefloquine. Am J Trop Med Hyg 1995;53(6):639–645.

281. White NJ, Waller D, Crawley J, Nosten F, Chapman D, Brewster D, Greenwood BM. Comparison of artemether and chloroquine for severe malaria in Gambian children. Lancet 1992;339(8789):317–321.

282. Elhassan IM, Satti GH, Ali AE, Fadul I, Elkhalifa AA, Abedelrahim AM, Ming C, Theander TG. The efficacy of artemether in the treatment of *Plasmodium falciparum* malaria in Sudan. Trans R Soc Trop Med Hyg 1993; 87(6):685–686.

283. Haynes RK, Fugmann B, Stetter J, Rieckmann K, Heilmann HD, Chan HW, Cheung MK, Lam WL, Wong HN, Croft SL, Vivas L, Rattray L,

Stewart L, Peters W, Robinson BL, Edstein MD, Kotecka B, Kyle DE, Beckermann B, Gerisch M, Radtke M, Schmuck G, Steinke W, Wollborn U, Schmeer K, Romer A. Artemisone: a highly active antimalarial drug of the artemisinin class. Angew Chem Int Ed Engl 2006;45(13):2082–2088.

284. Nagelschmitz J, Voith B, Wensing G, Roemer A, Fugmann B, Haynes RK, Kotecka BM, Rieckmann KH, Edstein MD. First assessment in humans of the safety, tolerability, pharmacokinetics, and *ex vivo* pharmacodynamic antimalarial activity of the new artemisinin derivative artemisone. Antimicrob Agents Chemother 2008;52(9):3085–3091.

285. Brueckner RP, Coster T, Wesche DL, Shmuklarsky M, Schuster BG, Prophylaxis of *Plasmodium falciparum* infection in a human challenge model with WR 238605, a new 8-aminoquinoline antimalarial Antimicrob Agents Chemother 1998;42(5):1293–1294.

286. Lell B, Faucher JF, Missinou MA, Borrmann S, Dangelmaier O, Horton J, Kremsner PG. Malaria chemoprophylaxis with tafenoquine: a randomised study. Lancet 2000;355(9220):2041–2045.

287. Shanks GD, Oloo AJ, Aleman GM, Ohrt C, Klotz FW, Braitman D, Horton J, Brueckner R. A new primaquine analogue, tafenoquine (WR 238605), for prophylaxis against *Plasmodium falciparum* malaria. Clin Infect Dis 2001;33(12):1968–1974.

288. Walsh DS, Looareesuwan S, Wilairatana P, Heppner DG Jr, Tang DB, Brewer TG, Chokejindachai W, Viriyavejakul P, Kyle DE, Milhous WK, Schuster BG, Horton J, Braitman DJ, Brueckner RP. Randomized dose-ranging study of the safety and efficacy of WR 238605 (Tafenoquine) in the prevention of relapse of *Plasmodium vivax* malaria in Thailand. J Infect Dis 1999;180(4):1282–1287.

289. Obaldia N, 3rd Rossan RN, Cooper RD, Kyle DE, Nuzum EO, Rieckmann KH, Shanks GD, WR 238605:chloroquine, and their combinations as blood schizonticides against a chloroquine-resistant strain of *Plasmodium vivax* in Aotus monkeys. Am J Trop Med Hyg 1997;56(5):508–510.

290. O'Neill PM, Shone AE, Stanford D, Nixon G, Asadollahy E, Park BK, Maggs JL, Roberts P, Stocks PA, Biagini G, Bray PG, Davies J, Berry N, Hall C, Rimmer K, Winstanley PA, Hindley S, Bambal RB, Davis CB, Bates M, Gresham SL, Brigandi RA, Gomez-de-Las-Heras FM, Gargallo DV, Parapini S, Vivas L, Lander H, Taramelli D, Ward SA. Synthesis, antimalarial activity, and preclinical pharmacology of a novel series of 4'-fluoro and 4'-chloro analogues of amodiaquine. Identification of a suitable "back-up" compound for *N*-tert-butyl isoquine. J Med Chem 2009;52 (7):1828–1844.

291. Schmidt LH. Enhancement of the curative activity of primaquine by concomitant administration of mirincamycin. Antimicrob Agents Chemother 1985;27(2):151–157.

292. Gimenez F, Pennie RA, Koren G, Crevoisier C, Wainer IW, Farinotti R. Stereoselective pharmacokinetics of mefloquine in healthy Caucasians after multiple doses. J Pharm Sci 1994;83(6):824–827.

293. Pecoul B. New drugs for neglected diseases: from pipeline to patients. PLoS Med 2004;1(1):e6.

294. Alker AP, Lim P, Sem R, Shah NK, Yi P, Bouth DM, Tsuyuoka R, Maguire JD, Fandeur T, Ariey F, Wongsrichanalai C, Meshnick SR. Pfmdr1 and *in vivo* resistance to artesunate-mefloquine in falciparum malaria on the Cambodian–Thai border. Am J Trop Med Hyg 2007;76(4):641–647.

295. Rogers WO, Sem R, Tero T, Chim P, Lim P, Muth S, Socheat D, Ariey F, Wongsrichanalai C. Failure of artesunate-mefloquine combination therapy for uncomplicated Plasmodium falciparum malaria in southern Cambodia. Malar J 2009;8:10.

296. Wongsrichanalai C, Meshnick SR. Declining artesunate-mefloquine efficacy against falciparum malaria on the Cambodia–Thailand border. Emerg Infect Dis 2008;14(5):716–719.

297. Sirima SB, Tiono AB, Gansane A, Diarra A, Ouedraogo A, Konate AT, Kiechel JR, Morgan CC, Olliaro PL, Taylor WR. The efficacy and safety of a new fixed-dose combination of amodiaquine and artesunate in young African children with acute uncomplicated *Plasmodium falciparum*. Malar J. 2009;8:48.

298. Sagara I, Diallo A, Kone M, Coulibaly M, Diawara SI, Guindo O, Maiga H, Niambele MB, Sissoko M, Dicko A, Djimde A, Doumbo OK. A randomized trial of artesunate-mefloquine versus artemether-lumefantrine for treatment of uncomplicated *Plasmodium falciparum* malaria in Mali. Am J Trop Med Hyg 2008;79(5):655–661.

299. Koram K, Quaye L, Abuaku B. Efficacy of amodiaquine/artesunate combination therapy for uncomplicated malaria in children under five years in Ghana. Ghana Med J 2008;42 (2):55–60.

300. Sowunmi A, Balogun T, Gbotosho GO, Happi CT, Adedeji AA, Fehintola FA. Activities of

amodiaquine, artesunate, and artesunate-amodiaquine against asexual- and sexual-stage parasites in falciparum malaria in children. Antimicrob Agents Chemother 2007; 51(5):1694–1699.

301. Orrell C, Little F, Smith P, Folb P, Taylor W, Olliaro P, Barnes KI. Pharmacokinetics and tolerability of artesunate and amodiaquine alone and in combination in healthy volunteers. Eur J Clin Pharmacol 2008;64(7):683–690.

302. Sirima SB, Gansane A. Artesunate-amodiaquine for the treatment of uncomplicated malaria. Expert Opin Investig Drugs 2007;16 (7):1079–1085.

303. Kostich M, English J, Madison V, Gheyas F, Wang L, Qiu P, Greene J, Laz TM. Human members of the eukaryotic protein kinase family. Genome Biol 2002;3(9):RESEARCH0043.

304. Manning G, Whyte DB, Martinez R, Hunter T, Sudarsanam S. The protein kinase complement of the human genome. Science 2002;298(5600):1912–1934.

305. Schindler T, Bornmann W, Pellicena P, Miller WT, Clarkson B, Kuriyan J. Structural mechanism for STI-571 inhibition of abelson tyrosine kinase. Science. 2000;289(5486):1938–1942.

306. Demetri GD, von Mehren M, Blanke CD, Van den Abbeele AD, Eisenberg B, Roberts PJ, Heinrich MC, Tuveson DA, Singer S, Janicek M, Fletcher JA, Silverman SG, Silberman SL, Capdeville R, Kiese B, Peng B, Dimitrijevic S, Druker BJ, Corless C, Fletcher CD, Joensuu H. Efficacy and safety of imatinib mesylate in advanced gastrointestinal stromal tumors. N Engl J Med 2002;347(7):472–480.

307. Buchdunger E, Cioffi CL, Law N, Stover D, Ohno-Jones S, Druker BJ, Lydon NB. Abl protein-tyrosine kinase inhibitor STI571 inhibits *in vitro* signal transduction mediated by c-kit and platelet-derived growth factor receptors. J Pharmacol Exp Ther 2000;295 (1):139–145.

308. Giamas G, Stebbing J, Vorgias CE, Knippschild U. Protein kinases as targets for cancer treatment. Pharmacogenomics 2007;8(8):1005–1016.

309. Cohen P. Protein kinases: the major drug targets of the twenty-first century?. Nat Rev Drug Discov 2002;1(4):309–315.

310. Hanks SK. Genomic analysis of the eukaryotic protein kinase superfamily: a perspective. Genome Biol 2003;4(5):111.

311. Anamika Srinivasan N, Krupa A. A genomic perspective of protein kinases in *Plasmodium falciparum*. Proteins 2005;58(1):180–189.

312. Ward P, Equinet L, Packer J, Doerig C. Protein kinases of the human malaria parasite *Plasmodium falciparum*: the kinome of a divergent eukaryote. BMC Genomics 2004;5(1):79.

313. Zhang XS, Choi JH. Molecular evolution of calmodulin-like domain protein kinases (CDPKs) in plants and protists. J Mol Evol 2001;53(3):214–224.

314. Schneider AG, Mercereau-Puijalon O. A new Apicomplexa-specific protein kinase family: multiple members in *Plasmodium falciparum*, all with an export signature. BMC Genomics 2005;6(1):30.

315. Nunes MC, Goldring JP, Doerig C, Scherf A. A novel protein kinase family in *Plasmodium falciparum* is differentially transcribed and secreted to various cellular compartments of the host cell. Mol Microbiol 2007;63(2):391–403.

316. Menard R, Janse C. Gene targeting in malaria parasites. Methods 1997;13(2):148–157.

317. Xiao Z, Waters NC, Woodard CL, Li Z, Li PK. Design and synthesis of Pfmrk inhibitors as potential antimalarial agents. Bioorg Med Chem Lett 2001;11(21):2875–2878.

318. Woodard CL, Li Z, Kathcart AK, Terrell J, Gerena L, Lopez-Sanchez M, Kyle DE, Bhattacharjee AK, Nichols DA, Ellis W, Prigge ST, Geyer JA, Waters NC. Oxindole-based compounds are selective inhibitors of *Plasmodium falciparum* cyclin dependent protein kinases. J Med Chem 2003;46(18):3877–3882.

319. Woodard CL, Keenan SM, Gerena L, Welsh WJ, Geyer JA, Waters NC. Evaluation of broad spectrum protein kinase inhibitors to probe the architecture of the malarial cyclin dependent protein kinase Pfmrk. Bioorg Med Chem Lett 2007;17(17):4961–4966.

320. Bhattacharjee AK, Geyer JA, Woodard CL, Kathcart AK, Nichols DA, Prigge ST, Li Z, Mott BT, Waters NC. A three-dimensional *in silico* pharmacophore model for inhibition of *Plasmodium falciparum* cyclin-dependent kinases and discovery of different classes of novel Pfmrk specific inhibitors. J Med Chem 2004;47 (22):5418–5426.

321. Bhattacharjee AK, Hartell MG, Nichols DA, Hicks RP, Stanton B, van Hamont JE, Milhous WK. Structure–activity relationship study of antimalarial indolo [2,1-*b*]quinazoline-6,12-diones (tryptanthrins). Three dimensional pharmacophore modeling and identification of new antimalarial candidates. Eur J Med Chem 2004;39(1):59–67.

322. Dorin D, Le Roch K, Sallicandro P, Alano P, Parzy D, Poullet P, Meijer L, Doerig C. Pfnek-

1, a NIMA-related kinase from the human malaria parasite *Plasmodium falciparum* Biochemical properties and possible involvement in MAPK regulation. Eur J Biochem 2001; 268(9):2600–2608.

323. Laurent D, Jullian V, Parenty A, Knibiehler M, Dorin D, Schmitt S, Lozach O, Lebouvier N, Frostin M, Alby F, Maurel S, Doerig C, Meijer L, Sauvain M. Antimalarial potential of xestoquinone, a protein kinase inhibitor isolated from a Vanuatu marine sponge *Xestospongia* sp. Bioorg Med Chem 2006;14(13):4477–4482.

324. Merckx A, Echalier A, Langford K, Sicard A, Langsley G, Joore J, Doerig C, Noble M, Endicott J. Structures of *P. falciparum* protein kinase 7 identify an activation motif and leads for inhibitor design. Structure 2008;16(2):228–238.

325. Holton S, Merckx A, Burgess D, Doerig C, Noble M, Endicott J. Structures of *P. falciparum* PfPK5 test the CDK regulation paradigm and suggest mechanisms of small molecule inhibition. Structure 2003;11(11):1329–1337.

326. Dorin-Semblat D, Sicard A, Doerig C, Ranford-Cartwright L, Doerig C. Disruption of the PfPK7 gene impairs schizogony and sporogony in the human malaria parasite *Plasmodium falciparum*. Eukaryot Cell 2008;7(2):279–285.

327. Doerig CM, Parzy D, Langsley G, Horrocks P, Carter R, Doerig CD. A MAP kinase homologue from the human malaria parasite. Plasmodium falciparum. Gene 1996;177(1–2):1–6.

328. Dorin D, Alano P, Boccaccio I, Ciceron L, Doerig C, Sulpice R, Parzy D, Doerig C. An atypical mitogen-activated protein kinase (MAPK) homologue expressed in gametocytes of the human malaria parasite *Plasmodium falciparum*. Identification of a MAPK signature. J Biol Chem 1999;274(42):29912–29920.

329. Graeser R, Kury P, Franklin RM, Kappes B. Characterization of a mitogen-activated protein (MAP) kinase from *Plasmodium falciparum*. Mol Microbiol 1997;23(1):151–159.

330. Lin DT, Goldman ND, Syin C. Stage-specific expression of a *Plasmodium falciparum* protein related to the eukaryotic mitogen-activated protein kinases. Mol Biochem Parasitol 1996;78(1–2):67–77.

331. Raman M, Cobb MH. MAP kinase modules: many roads home. Curr Biol 2003;13(22): R886–888.

332. Dorin D, Semblat JP, Poullet P, Alano P, Goldring JP, Whittle C, Patterson S, Chakrabarti D, Doerig C. PfPK7, an atypical MEK-related protein kinase, reflects the absence of classical three-component MAPK pathways in the human malaria parasite *Plasmodium falciparum*. Mol Microbiol 2005;55(1):184–196.

333. Harmse L, van Zyl R, Gray N, Schultz P, Leclerc S, Meijer L, Doerig C, Havlik I. Structure–activity relationships and inhibitory effects of various purine derivatives on the *in vitro* growth of *Plasmodium falciparum*. Biochem Pharmacol 2001;62(3):341–348.

334. Knockaert M, Gray N, Damiens E, Chang YT, Grellier P, Grant K, Fergusson D, Mottram J, Soete M, Dubremetz JF, Le Roch K, Doerig C, Schultz P, Meijer L. Intracellular targets of cyclin-dependent kinase inhibitors: identification by affinity chromatography using immobilised inhibitors. Chem Biol 2000;7 (6):411–422.

335. Gurnett AM, Liberator PA, Dulski PM, Salowe SP, Donald RG, Anderson JW, Wiltsie J, Diaz CA, Harris G, Chang B, Darkin-Rattray SJ, Nare B, Crumley T, Blum PS, Misura AS, Tamas T, Sardana MK, Yuan J, Biftu T, Schmatz DM. Purification and molecular characterization of cGMP-dependent protein kinase from apicomplexan parasites. A novel chemotherapeutic target. J Biol Chem 2002;277(18):15913–15922.

336. Donald RG, Allocco J, Singh SB, Nare B, Salowe SP, Wiltsie J, Liberator PA. *Toxoplasma gondii* cyclic GMP-dependent kinase: chemotherapeutic targeting of an essential parasite protein kinase. Eukaryot Cell 2002;1 (3):317–328.

337. Ishino T, Orito Y, Chinzei Y, Yuda M. A calcium-dependent protein kinase regulates *Plasmodium* ookinete access to the midgut epithelial cell. Mol Microbiol 2006;59 (4):1175–1184.

338. Rangarajan R, Bei A, Henry N, Madamet M, Parzy D, Nivez MP, Doerig C, Sultan A. Pbcrk-1, the *Plasmodium berghei* orthologue of *P. falciparum* cdc-2 related kinase-1 (Pfcrk-1), is essential for completion of the intraerythrocytic asexual cycle. Exp Parasitol 2006;112 (3):202–207.

339. Rangarajan R, Bei AK, Jethwaney D, Maldonado P, Dorin D, Sultan AA, Doerig C. A mitogen-activated protein kinase regulates male gametogenesis and transmission of the malaria parasite *Plasmodium berghei*. EMBO Rep 2005;6(5):464–469.

340. Reininger L, Billker O, Tewari R, Mukhopadhyay A, Fennell C, Dorin-Semblat D, Doerig C, Goldring D, Harmse L, Ranford-Cartwright L, Packer J, Doerig C. A NIMA-related protein kinase is essential for completion of the sexual

cycle of malaria parasites. J Biol Chem 2005;280(36):31957–31964.

341. Siden-Kiamos I, Ecker A, Nyback S, Louis C, Sinden RE, Billker O. *Plasmodium berghei* calcium-dependent protein kinase 3 is required for ookinete gliding motility and mosquito midgut invasion. Mol Microbiol 2006;60(6):1355–1363.

342. Tewari R, Dorin D, Moon R, Doerig C, Billker O. An atypical mitogen-activated protein kinase controls cytokinesis and flagellar motility during male gamete formation in a malaria parasite. Mol Microbiol 2005;58(5):1253–1263.

343. Dorin-Semblat D, Quashie N, Halbert J, Sicard A, Doerig C, Peat E, Ranford-Cartwright L, Doerig C. Functional characterization of both MAP kinases of the human malaria parasite Plasmodium falciparum by reverse genetics. Mol Microbiol 2007;65(5):1170–1180.

344. Zaman GJ, Garritsen A, de Boer T, van Boeckel CA. Fluorescence assays for high-throughput screening of protein kinases. Comb Chem High Throughput Screen 2003;6(4):313–320.

345. Long SB, Casey PJ, Beese LS. Reaction path of protein farnesyltransferase at atomic resolution. Nature 2002;419(6907):645–650.

346. Wesierska-Gadek J, Kramer MP, Schmid G. A combined treatment of HeLa cells with the farnesyl protein transferase inhibitor L-744,832 and cisplatin significantly increases the therapeutic effect as compared to cisplatin monotherapy. J Cell Biochem 2008;104 (1):189–201.

347. Appels NM, van Maanen MJ, Rosing H, Schellens JH, Beijnen JH. Quantitative analysis of the farnesyl transferase inhibitor lonafarnib (Sarasartrade mark, SCH66336) in human plasma using high-performance liquid chromatography coupled with tandem mass spectrometry. Rapid Commun Mass Spectrom 2005;19(15):2187–2192.

348. Chen GZ, Bennett JL. Characterization of mevalonate-labeled lipids isolated from parasite proteins in *Schistosoma mansoni*. Mol Biochem Parasitol 1993;59(2):287–292.

349. Chakrabarti D, Azam T, DelVecchio C, Qiu L, Park YI, Allen CM. Protein prenyl transferase activities of *Plasmodium falciparum*. Mol Biochem Parasitol 1998;94(2):175–184.

350. Yokoyama K, Lin Y, Stuart KD, Gelb MH. Prenylation of proteins in *Trypanosoma brucei*. Mol Biochem Parasitol 1997;87(1):61–69.

351. Bulbule VJ, Rivas K, Verlinde CL, Van Voorhis WC, Gelb MH. 2-Oxotetrahydroquinoline-based antimalarials with high potency and metabolic stability. J Med Chem 2008;51 (3):384–387.

352. Eastman RT, White J, Hucke O, Yokoyama K, Verlinde CL, Hast MA, Beese LS, Gelb MH, Rathod PK, Van Voorhis WC. Resistance mutations at the lipid substrate binding site of *Plasmodium falciparum* protein farnesyltransferase. Mol Biochem Parasitol 2007; 152(1):66–71.

353. Ohkanda J, Lockman JW, Yokoyama K, Gelb MH, Croft SL, Kendrick H, Harrell MI, Feagin JE, Blaskovich MA, Sebti SM, Hamilton AD. Peptidomimetic inhibitors of protein farnesyltransferase show potent antimalarial activity. Bioorg Med Chem Lett 2001;11(6):761–764.

354. Chakrabarti D, Da Silva T, Barger J, Paquette S, Patel H, Patterson S, Allen CM. Protein farnesyltransferase and protein prenylation in *Plasmodium falciparum*. J Biol Chem. 2002;277(44):42066–42073.

355. Carrico D, Ohkanda J, Kendrick H, Yokoyama K, Blaskovich MA, Bucher CJ, Buckner FS, Van Voorhis WC, Chakrabarti D, Croft SL, Gelb MH, Sebti SM, Hamilton AD. *In vitro* and *in vivo* antimalarial activity of peptidomimetic protein farnesyltransferase inhibitors with improved membrane permeability. Bioorg Med Chem 2004;12(24):6517–6526.

356. Wiesner J, Mitsch A, Wissner P, Jomaa H, Schlitzer M. Structure–activity relationships of novel anti-malarial agents. Part 2. Cinnamic acid derivatives. Bioorg Med Chem Lett 2001;11(3):423–424.

357. Wiesner J, Wissner P, Dahse HM, Jomaa H, Schlitzer M. Discovery of a novel lead structure for anti-malarials. Bioorg Med Chem 2001; 9(3):785–792.

358. Schlitzer M. Structure based design of benzophenone-based non-thiol farnesyltransferase inhibitors. Curr Pharm Des 2002;8(19):1713–1722.

359. Wiesner J, Fucik K, Kettler K, Sakowski J, Ortmann R, Jomaa H, Schlitzer M. Structure-activity relationships of novel anti-malarial agents. Part 6. N-(4-Arylpropionylamino-3-benzoylphenyl)-[5-(4-nitrophenyl)-2-furyl]acryli c acid amides. Bioorg Med Chem Lett 2003;13(9):1539–1541.

360. Wiesner J, Kettler K, Jomaa H, Schlitzer M. Structure–activity relationships of novel anti-malarial agents. Part 3. N-(4-Acylamino-3-benzoylphenyl)-4-propoxycinnamic acid amides. Bioorg Med Chem Lett 2002;12(4):543–545.

361. Wiesner J, Kettler K, Sakowski J, Ortmann R, Jomaa H, Schlitzer M. Structure–activity relationships of novel anti-malarial agents. Part

5.   N-(4-Acylamino-3-benzoylphenyl)-[5-(4-ni-
trophenyl)-2-furyl]acrylic acid amides. Bioorg
Med Chem Lett 2003;13(3):361–363.

362. Wiesner J, Mitsch A, Jomaa H, Schlitzer M.
Structure–activity relationships of novel antimalarial agents. Part 7. N-(3-Benzoyl-4-toly-
lacetylaminophenyl)-3-(5-aryl-2-furyl)acrylic
acid amides with polar moieties. Bioorg Med
Chem Lett 2003;13(13):2159–2161.

363. Wiesner J, Mitsch A, Wissner P, Kramer O,
Jomaa H, Schlitzer M. Structure–activity relationships of novel anti-malarial agents. Part
4. N-(3-benzoyl-4-tolylacetylaminophenyl)-3-
(5-aryl-2-furyl)acrylic acid amides. Bioorg Med
Chem Lett 2002;12(19):2681–2683.

364. Wiesner J, Kettler K, Sakowski J, Ortmann R,
Katzin AM, Kimura EA, Silber K, Klebe G,
Jomaa H, Schlitzer M. Farnesyltransferase
inhibitors inhibit the growth of malaria para-
sites *in vitro* and *in vivo*. Angew Chem Int Ed
Engl 2004;43(2):251–254.

365. Kettler K, Wiesner J, Silber K, Haebel P, Ortmann R, Sattler I, Dahse HM, Jomaa H, Klebe G,
Schlitzer M. Non-thiol farnesyltransferase inhibitors: N-(4-aminoacylamino-3-benzoylphe-
nyl)-3-[5-(4-nitrophenyl)-2 furyl]acrylic acid
amides and their antimalarial activity. Eur J
Med Chem 2005;40(1):93–101.

366. Kettler K, Sakowski J, Wiesner J, Ortmann R,
Jomaa H, Schlitzer M. Novel lead structures
for antimalarial farnesyltransferase inhibitors. Pharmazie 2005;60(5):323–327.

367. Kettler K, Wiesner J, Fucik K, Sakowski J,
Ortmann R, Dahse HM, Jomaa H, Schlitzer M.
2-(aminoacylamino)benzophenones: farnesyltransferase inhibition and antimalarial activity. Pharmazie 2005;60(9):677–682.

368. Kettler K, Wiesner J, Ortmann R, Dahse HM,
Jomaa H, Schlitzer M. Antimalarial activity of
methylpiperazinyl-substituted benzophenone-
based farnesyltransferase inhibitors. Pharmazie 2006;61(1):63–65.

369. Kohring K, Wiesner J, Altenkamper M, Sakowski J, Silber K, Hillebrecht A, Haebel P, Dahse
HM, Ortmann R, Jomaa H, Klebe G, Schlitzer
M. Development of benzophenone-based farnesyltransferase inhibitors as novel antimalarials. ChemMedChem 2008; 3(8):1217–1231.

370. Glenn MP, Chang SY, Hucke O, Verlinde CL,
Rivas K, Horney C, Yokoyama K, Buckner FS,
Pendyala PR, Chakrabarti D, Gelb M, Van
Voorhis WC, Sebti SM, Hamilton AD. Struc-
turally simple farnesyltransferase inhibitors
arrest the growth of malaria parasites. Angew
Chem Int Ed Engl 2005;44(31):4903–4906.

371. Glenn MP, Chang SY, Horney C, Rivas K,
Yokoyama K, Pusateri EE, Fletcher S, Cummings CG, Buckner FS, Pendyala PR, Chakrabarti D, Sebti SM, Gelb M, Van Voorhis WC,
Hamilton AD. Structurally simple, potent,
Plasmodium selective farnesyltransferase inhibitors that arrest the growth of malaria parasites. J Med Chem 2006;49(19):5710–5727.

372. Nallan L, Bauer KD, Bendale P, Rivas K,
Yokoyama K, Horney CP, Pendyala PR, Floyd
D, Lombardo LJ, Williams DK, Hamilton A,
Sebti S, Windsor WT, Weber PC, Buckner FS,
Chakrabarti D, Gelb MH, Van Voorhis WC.
Protein farnesyltransferase inhibitors exhibit
potent antimalarial activity. J Med Chem
2005;48(11):3704–3713.

373. Eastman RT, White J, Hucke O, Bauer K,
Yokoyama K, Nallan L, Chakrabarti D, Ver-
linde CL, Gelb MH, Rathod PK, Van Voorhis
WC. Resistance to a protein farnesyltransfer-
ase inhibitor in *Plasmodium falciparum*. J Biol
Chem 2005;280(14):13554–13559.

374. Bendale P, Olepu S, Suryadevara PK, Bulbule
V, Rivas K, Nallan L, Smart B, Yokoyama K,
Ankala S, Pendyala PR, Floyd D, Lombardo LJ,
Williams DK, Buckner FS, Chakrabarti D, Verlinde CL, Van Voorhis WC, Gelb MH. Second
generation tetrahydroquinoline-based protein
farnesyltransferase inhibitors as antimalarials. J Med Chem 2007;50(19):4585–4605.

375. Van Voorhis WC, Rivas KL, Bendale P, Nallan
L, Horney C, Barrett LK, Bauer KD, Smart BP,
Ankala S, Hucke O, Verlinde CL, Chakrabarti
D, Strickland C, Yokoyama K, Buckner FS,
Hamilton AD, Williams DK, Lombardo LJ,
Floyd D, Gelb MH. Efficacy, pharmacokinetics,
and metabolism of tetrahydroquinoline inhi-
bitors of *Plasmodium falciparum* protein far-
nesyltransferase. Antimicrob Agents Che-
mother 2007;51(10):3659–3671.

376. Olepu S, Suryadevara PK, Rivas K, Yokoyama
K, Verlinde CL, Chakrabarti D, Van Voorhis
WC, Gelb MH. 2-Oxo-tetrahydro-1,8-naphthyr-
idines as selective inhibitors of malarial protein
farnesyltransferase and as anti-malarials.
Bioorg Med Chem Lett 2008;18(2):494–497.

377. Millet R, Domarkas J, Houssin R, Gilleron P,
Goossens JF, Chavatte P, Loge C, Pommery N,
Pommery J, Henichart JP. Potent and selec-
tive farnesyl transferase inhibitors. J Med
Chem 2004;47(27):6812–6820.

378. Ryckebusch A, Gilleron P, Millet R, Houssin R,
Lemoine A, Pommery N, Grellier P, Sergheraert C, Henichart JP. Novel *N*-(4-Piperidinyl)
benzamide antimalarials with mammalian

protein farnesyltransferase inhibitory activity. Chem Pharm Bull 2005;53(10):1324–1326.

379. Cox AD, Der CJ. Farnesyltransferase inhibitors: promises and realities. Curr Opin Pharmacol 2002;2(4):388–393.

380. Rosenthal PJ, McKerrow JH, Aikawa M, Nagasawa H, Leech JH. A malarial cysteine proteinase is necessary for hemoglobin degradation by Plasmodium falciparum. J Clin Invest 1988;82(5):1560–1566.

381. Rosenthal PJ, Wollish WS, Palmer JT, Rasnick D. Antimalarial effects of peptide inhibitors of a Plasmodium falciparum cysteine proteinase. J Clin Invest 1991;88(5):1467–1472.

382. Rosenthal PJ. Plasmodium falciparum: effects of proteinase inhibitors on globin hydrolysis by cultured malaria parasites. Exp Parasitol 1995;80(2):272–281.

383. Thompson SA, Andrews PR, Hanzlik RP. Carboxyl-modified amino acids and peptides as protease inhibitors. J Med Chem 1986;29 (1):104–111.

384. Greenspan PD, Clark KL, Tommasi RA, Cowen SD, McQuire LW, Farley DL, van Duzer JH, Goldberg RL, Zhou H, Du Z, Fitt JJ, Coppa DE, Fang Z, Macchia W, Zhu L, Capparelli MP, Goldstein R, Wigg AM, Doughty JR, Bohacek RS, Knap AK. Identification of dipeptidyl nitriles as potent and selective inhibitors of cathepsin B through structure-based drug design. J Med Chem 2001;44(26):4524–4534.

385. Batra S, Sabnis YA, Rosenthal PJ, Avery MA. Structure-based approach to falcipain-2 inhibitors: synthesis and biological evaluation of 1,6,7-trisubstituted dihydroisoquinolines and isoquinolines. Bioorg Med Chem 2003;11 (10):2293–2299.

386. Sabnis Y, Rosenthal PJ, Desai P, Avery MA. Homology modeling of falcipain-2: validation, de novo ligand design and synthesis of novel inhibitors. J Biomol Struct Dyn 2002;19 (5):765–774.

387. Chiyanzu I, Hansell E, Gut J, Rosenthal PJ, McKerrow JH, Chibale K. Synthesis and evaluation of isatins and thiosemicarbazone derivatives against cruzain, falcipain-2 and rhodesain. Bioorg Med Chem Lett 2003;13 (20):3527–3530.

388. Chiyanzu I, Clarkson C, Smith PJ, Lehman J, Gut J, Rosenthal PJ, Chibale K. Design, synthesis and anti-plasmodial evaluation in vitro of new 4-aminoquinoline isatin derivatives. Bioorg Med Chem 2005;13(9):3249–3261.

389. Schulz F, Gelhaus C, Degel B, Vicik R, Heppner S, Breuning A, Leippe M, Gut J, Rosenthal

PJ, Schirmeister T. Screening of protease inhibitors as antiplasmodial agents. Part I. Aziridines and epoxides. ChemMedChem 2007;2 (8):1214–1224.

390. Musonda CC, Gut J, Rosenthal PJ, Yardley V, Carvalho de Souza RC, Chibale K. Application of multicomponent reactions to antimalarial drug discovery. Part 2. New antiplasmodial and antitrypanosomal 4-aminoquinoline gamma- and delta-lactams via a 'catch and release' protocol. Bioorg Med Chem. 2006;14(16):5605–5615.

391. Rosenthal PJ, Olson JE, Lee GK, Palmer JT, Klaus JL, Rasnick D. Antimalarial effects of vinyl sulfone cysteine proteinase inhibitors. Antimicrob Agents Chemother 1996;40 (7):1600–1603.

392. Shenai BR, Lee BJ, Alvarez-Hernandez A, Chong PY, Emal CD, Neitz RJ, Roush WR, Rosenthal PJ. Structure–activity relationships for inhibition of cysteine protease activity and development of Plasmodium falciparum by peptidyl vinyl sulfones. Antimicrob Agents Chemother 2003;47(1):154–160.

393. Micale N, Kozikowski AP, Ettari R, Grasso S, Zappala M, Jeong JJ, Kumar A, Hanspal M, Chishti AH. Novel peptidomimetic cysteine protease inhibitors as potential antimalarial agents. J Med Chem 2006;49(11):3064–3067.

394. Chipeleme A, Gut J, Rosenthal PJ, Chibale K. Synthesis and biological evaluation of phenolic Mannich bases of benzaldehyde and (thio)semicarbazone derivatives against the cysteine protease falcipain-2 and a chloroquine resistant strain of Plasmodium falciparum. Bioorg Med Chem 2007;15(1):273–282.

395. Liu J, Istvan ES, Gluzman IY, Gross J, Goldberg DE. Plasmodium falciparum ensures its amino acid supply with multiple acquisition pathways and redundant proteolytic enzyme systems. Proc Natl Acad Sci USA 2006;103 (23):8840–8845.

396. Liu J, Gluzman IY, Drew ME, Goldberg DE. The role of Plasmodium falciparum food vacuole plasmepsins. J Biol Chem 2005;280 (2):1432–1437.

397. Omara-Opyene AL, Moura PA, Sulsona CR, Bonilla JA, Yowell CA, Fujioka H, Fidock DA, Dame JB. Genetic disruption of the Plasmodium falciparum digestive vacuole plasmepsins demonstrates their functional redundancy. J Biol Chem 2004;279 (52):54088–54096.

398. Sijwali PS, Rosenthal PJ. Gene disruption confirms a critical role for the cysteine protease falcipain-2 in hemoglobin hydrolysis by Plas-

modium falciparum. Proc Natl Acad Sci USA 2004;101(13):4384–4389.

399. Sijwali PS, Kato K, Seydel KB, Gut J, Lehman J, Klemba M, Goldberg DE, Miller LH, Rosenthal PJ. Plasmodium falciparum cysteine protease falcipain-1 is not essential in erythrocytic stage malaria parasites. Proc Natl Acad Sci USA 2004;101(23):8721–8726.

400. Coombs GH, Goldberg DE, Klemba M, Berry C, Kay J, Mottram JC. Aspartic proteases of Plasmodium falciparum and other parasitic protozoa as drug targets. Trends Parasitol 2001;17(11):532–537.

401. Silva AM, Lee AY, Gulnik SV, Maier P, Collins J, Bhat TN, Collins PJ, Cachau RE, Luker KE, Gluzman IY, Francis SE, Oksman A, Goldberg DE, Erickson JW. Structure and inhibition of plasmepsin II, a hemoglobin-degrading enzyme from Plasmodium falciparum. Proc Natl Acad Sci USA 1996;93(19):10034–10039.

402. Silva AM, Lee AY, Erickson JW, Goldberg DE. Structural analysis of plasmepsin II. A comparison with human aspartic proteases. Adv Exp Med Biol 1998;436:363–373.

403. Drew ME, Banerjee R, Uffman EW, Gilbertson S, Rosenthal PJ, Goldberg DE. Plasmodium food vacuole plasmepsins are activated by falcipains. J Biol Chem 2008;283(19):12870–12876.

404. Bonilla JA, Moura PA, Bonilla TD, Yowell CA, Fidock DA, Dame JB. Effects on growth, hemoglobin metabolism and paralogous gene expression resulting from disruption of genes encoding the digestive vacuole plasmepsins of Plasmodium falciparum. Int J Parasitol 37:(3–4): 2007; 317–327.

405. Parikh S, Gut J, Istvan E, Goldberg DE, Havlir DV, Rosenthal PJ. Antimalarial activity of human immunodeficiency virus type 1 protease inhibitors. Antimicrob Agents Chemother 2005;49(7):2983–2985.

406. Andrews KT, Fairlie DP, Madala PK, Ray J, Wyatt DM, Hilton PM, Melville LA, Beattie L, Gardiner DL, Reid RC, Stoermer MJ, Skinner-Adams T, Berry C, McCarthy JS. Potencies of human immunodeficiency virus protease inhibitors in vitro against Plasmodium falciparum and in vivo against murine malaria. Antimicrob Agents Chemother 2006;50(2):639–648.

407. Parikh S, Liu J, Sijwali P, Gut J, Goldberg DE, Rosenthal PJ. Antimalarial effects of human immunodeficiency virus type 1 protease inhibitors differ from those of the aspartic protease inhibitor pepstatin. Antimicrob Agents Chemother 2006;50(6):2207–2209.

408. Asojo OA, Gulnik SV, Afonina E, Yu B, Ellman JA, Haque TS, Silva AM. Novel uncomplexed and complexed structures of plasmepsin II, an aspartic protease from Plasmodium falciparum. J Mol Biol 2003;327(1):173–181.

409. Bernstein NK, Cherney MM, Yowell CA, Dame JB, James MN. Structural insights into the activation of P. vivax plasmepsin. J Mol Biol 2003;329(3):505–524.

410. Prade L, Jones AF, Boss C, Richard-Bildstein S, Meyer S, Binkert C, Bur D. X-ray structure of plasmepsin II complexed with a potent achiral inhibitor. J Biol Chem 2005;280 (25):23837–23843.

411. Clemente JC, Govindasamy L, Madabushi A, Fisher SZ, Moose RE, Yowell CA, Hidaka K, Kimura T, Hayashi Y, Kiso Y, Agbandje-McKenna M, Dame JB, Dunn BM, McKenna R. Structure of the aspartic protease plasmepsin 4 from the malarial parasite Plasmodium malariae bound to an allophenylnorstatine-based inhibitor. Acta Crystallogr D Biol Crystallogr 62(Pt 3): 2006; 246–252.

412. Bernstein NK, Cherney MM, Loetscher H, Ridley RG, James MN. Crystal structure of the novel aspartic proteinase zymogen proplasmepsin II from Plasmodium falciparum. Nat Struct Biol 1999;6(1):32–37.

413. Brik A, Wong CH. HIV-1 protease: mechanism and drug discovery. Org Biomol Chem 2003;1 (1):5–14.

414. Babine RE, Bender SL. Molecular recognition of Proteinminus signLigand complexes: Applications to drug design. Chem Rev 1997;97 (5):1359–1472.

415. Cooper JB. Aspartic proteinases in disease: a structural perspective. Curr Drug Targets 2002;3(2):155–173.

416. Banerjee R, Liu J, Beatty W, Pelosof L, Klemba M, Goldberg DE. Four plasmepsins are active in the Plasmodium falciparum food vacuole, including a protease with an active-site histidine. Proc Natl Acad Sci USA 2002;99 (2):990–995.

417. Molteni M, Pesenti C, Sani M, Volonterio A, Zanda M. Fluorinated pepttidomimetics: synthesis, conformational and biological features. J Fluorine Chem 2004;125:1735–1743.

418. Zanda M. Trifluoromethyl group: An effective xenobiotic function for peptide backbone modification. New J Chem 2004;28:1401–1411.

419. Luker KE, Francis SE, Gluzman IY, Goldberg DE. Kinetic analysis of plasmepsins I and II aspartic proteases of the Plasmodium falcipar-

um digestive vacuole. Mol Biochem Parasitol 1996;79(1):71–78.

420. Li T, Yowell CA, Beyer BB, Hung SH, Westling J, Lam MT, Dunn BM, Dame JB. Recombinant expression and enzymatic subsite characterization of plasmepsin 4 from the four *Plasmodium* species infecting man. Mol Biochem Parasitol 2004;135(1):101–109.

421. Binkert C, Frigerio M, Jones A, Meyer S, Pesenti C, Prade L, Viani F, Zanda M. Replacement of isobutyl by trifluoromethyl in pepstatin A selectively affects inhibition of aspartic proteinases. Chembiochem 2006;7(1):181–186.

422. Johansson PO, Chen Y, Belfrage AK, Blackman MJ, Kvarnstrom I, Jansson K, Vrang L, Hamelink E, Hallberg A, Rosenquist A, Samuelsson B. Design and synthesis of potent inhibitors of the malaria aspartyl proteases plasmepsin I and II. Use of solid-phase synthesis to explore novel statine motifs. J Med Chem 2004;47(13):3353–3366.

423. Johansson PO, Lindberg J, Blackman MJ, Kvarnstrom I, Vrang L, Hamelink E, Hallberg A, Rosenquist A, Samuelsson B. Design and synthesis of potent inhibitors of plasmepsin I and II: X-ray crystal structure of inhibitor in complex with plasmepsin II. J Med Chem 2005;48(13):4400–4409.

424. Carroll CD, Patel H, Johnson TO, Guo T, Orlowski M, He ZM, Cavallaro CL, Guo J, Oksman A, Gluzman IY, Connelly J, Chelsky D, Goldberg DE, Dolle RE. Identification of potent inhibitors of *Plasmodium falciparum* plasmepsin II from an encoded statine combinatorial library. Bioorg Med Chem Lett 1998;8 (17):2315–2320.

425. Carroll CD, Johnson TO, Tao S, Lauri G, Orlowski M, Gluzman IY, Goldberg DE, Dolle RE. Evaluation of a structure-based statine cyclic diamino amide encoded combinatorial library against plasmepsin II and cathepsin D. Bioorg Med Chem Lett 1998;8(22):3203–3206.

426. Dolle RE, Guo J, O'Brien L, Jin Y, Piznik M, Bowman KJ, Li W, Egan WJ, Cavallaro CL, Roughton AL, Zhao Q, Reader JC, Orlowski M, Jacob-Samuel B, Carroll CD. A statistical-based approach to assessing the fidelity of combinatorial libraries encoded with electrophoric molecular tags. Development and application of tag decode-assisted single bead LC/MS analysis. J Comb Chem 2000;2(6):716–731.

427. Dahlgren A, Kvarnstrom I, Vrang L, Hamelink E, Hallberg A, Rosenquist A, Samuelsson B. Solid-phase library synthesis of reversed-statine type inhibitors of the malarial aspartyl

proteases plasmepsin I and II. Bioorg Med Chem 2003;11(6):827–841.

428. Dahlgren A, Kvarnstrom I, Vrang L, Hamelink E, Hallberg A, Rosenquist A, Samuelsson B. New inhibitors of the malaria aspartyl proteases plasmepsin I and II. Bioorg Med Chem 2003;11(16):3423–3437.

429. Nezami A, Luque I, Kimura T, Kiso Y, Freire E. Identification and characterization of allophenylnorstatine-based inhibitors of plasmepsin II, an antimalarial target. Biochemistry 2002;41(7):2273–2280.

430. Kiso A, Hidaka K, Kimura T, Hayashi Y, Nezami A, Freire E, Kiso Y. Search for substrate-based inhibitors fitting the S2' space of malarial aspartic protease plasmepsin II. J Pept Sci. 2004;10(11):641–647.

431. Nezami A, Freire E. The integration of genomic and structural information in the development of high affinity plasmepsin inhibitors. Int J Parasitol 2002;32(13):1669–1676.

432. Nezami A, Kimura T, Hidaka K, Kiso A, Liu J, Kiso Y, Goldberg DE, Freire E. High-affinity inhibition of a family of *Plasmodium falciparum* proteases by a designed adaptive inhibitor. Biochemistry 2003;42(28):8459–8464.

433. Weik S, Luksch T, Evers A, Bottcher J, Sotriffer CA, Hasilik A, Loffler HG, Klebe G, Rademann J. The potential of P1 site alterations in peptidomimetic protease inhibitors as suggested by virtual screening and explored by the use of CC-coupling reagents. ChemMedChem 2006;1(4):445–457.

434. Hidaka K, Kimura T, Tsuchiya Y, Kamiya M, Ruben AJ, Freire E, Hayashi Y, Kiso Y. Additional interaction of allophenylnorstatine-containing tripeptidomimetics with malarial aspartic protease plasmepsin II. Bioorg Med Chem Lett 2007;17(11):3048–3052.

435. Hidaka K, Kimura T, Ruben AJ, Uemura T, Kamiya M, Kiso A, Okamoto T, Tsuchiya Y, Hayashi Y, Freire E, Kiso Y. Antimalarial activity enhancement in hydroxymethylcarbonyl (HMC) isostere-based dipeptidomimetics targeting malarial aspartic protease plasmepsin. Bioorg Med Chem 2008;16(23):10049–10060.

436. Asojo OA, Afonina E, Gulnik SV, Yu B, Erickson JW, Randad R, Medjahed D, Silva AM. Structures of Ser205 mutant plasmepsin II from *Plasmodium falciparum* at 1.8 Å in complex with the inhibitors rs367 and rs370. Acta Crystallogr D Biol Crystallogr 2002;58(Pt12): 2001–2008.

437. Haque TS, Skillman AG, Lee CE, Habashita H, Gluzman IY, Ewing TJ, Goldberg DE, Kuntz

ID, Ellman JA. Potent, low-molecular-weight non-peptide inhibitors of malarial aspartyl protease plasmepsin II. J Med Chem 1999;42 (8):1428–1440.

438. Noteberg D, Hamelink E, Hulten J, Wahlgren M, Vrang L, Samuelsson B, Hallberg A. Design and synthesis of plasmepsin I and plasmepsin II inhibitors with activity in *Plasmodium falciparum*-infected cultured human erythrocytes. J Med Chem 2003;46(5):734–746.

439. Noteberg D, Schaal W, Hamelink E, Vrang L, Larhed M. High-speed optimization of inhibitors of the malarial proteases plasmepsin I and II. J Comb Chem 2003;5(4):456–464.

440. Muthas D, Noteberg D, Sabnis YA, Hamelink E, Vrang L, Samuelsson B, Karlen A, Hallberg A. Synthesis, biological evaluation, and modeling studies of inhibitors aimed at the malarial proteases plasmepsins I and II. Bioorg Med Chem 2005;13(18):5371–5390.

441. Beyer BB, Johnson JV, Chung AY, Li T, Madabushi A, Agbandje-McKenna M, McKenna R, Dame JB, Dunn BM. Active-site specificity of digestive aspartic peptidases from the four species of *Plasmodium* that infect humans using chromogenic combinatorial peptide libraries. Biochemistry 2005;44(6):1768–1779.

442. Alterman M, Andersson HO, Garg N, Ahlsen G, Lovgren S, Classon B, Danielson UH, Kvarnstrom I, Vrang L, Unge T, Samuelsson B, Hallberg A. Design and fast synthesis of C-terminal duplicated potent C(2)-symmetric P1/P1′-modified HIV-1 protease inhibitors. J Med Chem 1999;42(19):3835–3844.

443. Oscarsson K, Oscarson S, Vrang L, Hamelink E, Hallberg A, Samuelsson B. New potent C2-symmetric malaria plasmepsin I and II inhibitors. Bioorg Med Chem 2003;11(7):1235–1246.

444. Ersmark K, Feierberg I, Bjelic S, Hulten J, Samuelsson B, Aqvist J, Hallberg A. C2-symmetric inhibitors of *Plasmodium falciparum* plasmepsin II: synthesis and theoretical predictions. Bioorg Med Chem 2003;11 (17):3723–3733.

445. Ersmark K, Feierberg I, Bjelic S, Hamelink E, Hackett F, Blackman MJ, Hulten J, Samuelsson B, Aqvist J, Hallberg A. Potent inhibitors of the *Plasmodium falciparum* enzymes plasmepsin I and II devoid of cathepsin D inhibitory activity. J Med Chem 2004;47(1):110–122.

446. Ersmark K, Nervall M, Hamelink E, Janka LK, Clemente JC, Dunn BM, Blackman MJ, Samuelsson B, Aqvist J, Hallberg A. Synthesis of malarial plasmepsin inhibitors and prediction of binding modes by molecular dy-

namics simulations. J Med Chem 2005;48 (19):6090–6106.

447. Gutierrez-de-Teran H, Nervall M, Ersmark K, Liu P, Janka LK, Dunn B, Hallberg A, Aqvist J. Inhibitor binding to the plasmepsin IV aspartic protease from *Plasmodium falciparum*. Biochemistry 2006;45(35):10529–10541.

448. Ersmark K, Nervall M, Gutierrez-de-Teran H, Hamelink E, Janka LK, Clemente JC, Dunn BM, Gogoll A, Samuelsson B, Qvist J, Hallberg A. Macrocyclic inhibitors of the malarial aspartic proteases plasmepsin I, II, and IV. Bioorg Med Chem 2006;14(7):2197–2208.

449. Oefner C, Binggeli A, Breu V, Bur D, Clozel JP, D'Arcy A, Dorn A, Fischli W, Gruninger F, Guller R, Hirth G, Marki H, Mathews S, Ml M, Ridley RG, Stadler H, Vieira E, Wilhelm M, Winkler F, Wostl W. Renin inhibition by substituted piperidines: a novel paradigm for the inhibition of monomeric aspartic proteinases?. Chem Biol 1999;6(3):127–131.

450. Boss C, Richard-Bildstein S, Weller T, Fischli W, Meyer S, Binkert C. Inhibitors of the *Plasmodium falciparum* parasite aspartic protease plasmepsin II as potential antimalarial agents. Curr Med Chem 2003;10 (11):883–907.

451. Boss C, Corminboeuf O, Grisostomi C, Meyer S, Jones AF, Prade L, Binkert C, Fischli W, Weller T, Bur D. Achiral, cheap, and potent inhibitors of Plasmepsins I, II, and IV. ChemMedChem 2006;1(12):1341–1345.

452. Corminboeuf O, Dunet G, Hafsi M, Grimont J, Grisostomi C, Meyer S, Binkert C, Bur D, Jones A, Prade L, Brun R, Boss C. Inhibitors of plasmepsin II-potential antimalarial agents. Bioorg Med Chem Lett 2006;16(24):6194–6199.

453. Carcache D, Hoertner S, Seiler P, Diederich F, Dorn A, Maerki H, Binkert C, Bur D. Development of a new class of inhibitors for the malarial aspartic protease plasmepsin II based on a central 7-azabicyclo[2.2.1] heptane scaffold. Helv Chim Acta 2003;86:2173–2191.

454. Carcache D, Hoertner S, Seiler P, Diederich F, Dorn A, Maerki H, Binkert C, Bur D. Development of a new class of inhibitors for the malarial aspartic protease plasmepsin II based on a central 11-azatricyclo[6.2.1.02,7] undeca-2,4,6-triene scaffold. Helv Chim Acta 2003;86:2192–2209.

455. Carcache DA, Hortner SR, Bertogg A, Binkert C, Bur D, Marki HP, Dorn A, Diederich F. *De novo* design, synthesis, and *in vitro* evaluation of a new class of nonpeptidic inhibitors of the

malarial enzyme plasmepsin II. Chembiochem 2002;3(11):1137–1141.

456. Hof F, Schutz A, Fah C, Meyer S, Bur D, Liu J, Goldberg DE, Diederich F. Starving the malaria parasite: inhibitors active against the aspartic proteases plasmepsins I, II, and IV. Angew Chem Int Ed Engl 2006;45(13):2138–2141.

457. Zurcher M, Gottschalk T, Meyer S, Bur D, Diederich F. Exploring the flap pocket of the antimalarial target plasmepsin II: the "55 % rule" applied to enzymes. ChemMedChem 2008;3(2):237–240.

458. Jiang S, Prigge ST, Wei L, Gao Y, Hudson TH, Gerena L, Dame JB, Kyle DE. New class of small nonpeptidyl compounds blocks *Plasmodium falciparum* development *in vitro* by inhibiting plasmepsins. Antimicrob Agents Chemother 2001;45(9):2577–2584.

459. Blum A, Bottcher J, Sammet B, Luksch T, Heine A, Klebe G, Diederich WE. Achiral oligoamines as versatile tool for the development of aspartic protease inhibitors. Bioorg Med Chem 2008;16(18):8574–8586.

460. Azim MK, Ahmed W, Khan IA, Rao NA, Khan KM. Identification of acridinyl hydrazides as potent aspartic protease inhibitors. Bioorg Med Chem Lett 2008;18(9):3011–3015.

461. Brass S, Chan N, Gerlach C, Luksch T, Bottcher J, Diederich WE. Synthesis of 2,3,4,7-tetrahydro-1H-azepines as privileged ligand scaffolds for the design of aspartic protease inhibitors via a ring-closing metathesis approach. J Orgmetal Chem 2006;691:5406–5422.

462. Luksch T, Chan NS, Brass S, Sotriffer CA, Klebe G, Diederich WE. Computer-aided design and synthesis of nonpeptidic plasmepsin II and IV inhibitors. ChemMedChem 2008;3 (9):1323–1336.

463. Ivanetich KM, Santi DV. Bifunctional thymidylate synthase-dihydrofolate reductase in protozoa. FASEB J. 1990;4(6):1591–1597.

464. Sienkiewicz N, Jaroslawski S, Wyllie S, Fairlamb AH. Chemical and genetic validation of dihydrofolate reductase-thymidylate synthase as a drug target in African trypanosomes. Mol Microbiol 2008;69(2):520–533.

465. Mui EJ, Schiehser GA, Milhous WK, Hsu H, Roberts CW, Kirisits M, Muench S, Rice D, Dubey JP, Fowble JW, Rathod PK, Queener SF, Liu SR, Jacobus DP, McLeod R. Novel triazine JPC-2067-B inhibits *Toxoplasma gondii in vitro* and *in vivo*. PLoS Negl Trop Dis 2008;2(3):e190.

466. Cowman AF, Morry MJ, Biggs BA, Cross GA, Foote SJ. Amino acid changes linked to pyrimethamine resistance in the dihydrofolate reductase-thymidylate synthase gene of Plasmodium falciparum. Proc Natl Acad Sci USA 1988;85(23):9109–9113.

467. Snewin VA, England SM, Sims PF, Hyde JE. Characterisation of the dihydrofolate reductase-thymidylate synthetase gene from human malaria parasites highly resistant to pyrimethamine. Gene 1989;76(1):41–52.

468. Basco LK, de Pecoulas PE, Le Bras J, Wilson CM. *Plasmodium falciparum*: molecular characterization of multidrug-resistant Cambodian isolates. Exp Parasitol 1996;82(2):97–103.

469. Foote SJ, Galatis D, Cowman AF. Amino acids in the dihydrofolate reductase-thymidylate synthase gene of Plasmodium falciparum involved in cycloguanil resistance differ from those involved in pyrimethamine resistance. Proc Natl Acad Sci USA 1990;87(8):3014–3017.

470. Peterson DS, Walliker D, Wellems TE. Evidence that a point mutation in dihydrofolate reductase-thymidylate synthase confers resistance to pyrimethamine in falciparum malaria. Proc Natl Acad Sci USA 1988;85 (23):9114–9118.

471. Thaithong S, Chan SW, Songsomboon S, Wilairat P, Seesod N, Sueblinwong T, Goman M, Ridley R, Beale G. Pyrimethamine resistant mutations in *Plasmodium falciparum*. Mol Biochem Parasitol 1992;52(2):149–157.

472. Zolg JW, Plitt JR, Chen GX, Palmer S. Point mutations in the dihydrofolate reductase-thymidylate synthase gene as the molecular basis for pyrimethamine resistance in *Plasmodium falciparum*. Mol Biochem Parasitol 1989;36 (3):253–262.

473. Yuthavong Y, Vilaivan T, Chareonsethakul N, Kamchonwongpaisan S, Sirawaraporn W, Quarrell R, Lowe G. Development of a lead inhibitor for the A16V + S108T mutant of dihydrofolate reductase from the cycloguanil-resistant strain (T9/94) of *Plasmodium falciparum*. J Med Chem 2000;43(14):2738–2744.

474. Rastelli G, Sirawaraporn W, Sompornpisut P, Vilaivan T, Kamchonwongpaisan S, Quarrell R, Lowe G, Thebtaranonth Y, Yuthavong Y. Y. Interaction of pyrimethamine, cycloguanil, WR99210 and their analogues with *Plasmodium falciparum* dihydrofolate reductase: structural basis of antifolate resistance. Bioorg Med Chem 2000;8(5):1117–1128.

475. Rieckmann KH. The *in vitro* activity of experimental anti-malarial compounds against strains of *Plasmodium falciparum* with varying degrees of sensitivity to pyrimethamine

and chloroquine. In: World Health Organization Technical Report Series. Geneva, Switzerland: World Health Organization; 1973. p 58.

476. Hastings MD, Sibley CH. Pyrimethamine and WR99210 exert opposing selection on dihydrofolate reductase from Plasmodium vivax. Proc Natl Acad Sci USA 2002;99(20):13137–13141.

477. Knight DJ, Mamalis P, Peters W. The antimalarial activity of N-benzyl-oxydihydrotriazines. III. The activity of 4,6-diamino-1,2-dihydro-2,2-dimethyl-1-(2,4,5,-trichloropropyloxy)-1,3,5-t riazine hydrobromide (BRL 51084) and hydrochloride (BRL 6231). Ann Trop Med Parasitol 1982;76(1):1–7.

478. Knight DJ, Williamson P. The antimalarial activity of N-benzyl-oxydihydrotriazines. IV. The development of resistance to BRL 6231 (4,6-diamino-1,2-dihyydro-2-,2-dimethyl-1-(2,4,5-trichloropropyloxy)-1,3,5 triazine hydrochloride) by Plasmodium berghei. Ann Trop Med Parasitol 1982;76(1):9–14.

479. Kinyanjui SM, Mberu EK, Winstanley PA, Jacobus DP, Watkins WM. The antimalarial triazine WR99210 and the prodrug PS-15: folate reversal of in vitro activity against Plasmodium falciparum and a non-antifolate mode of action of the prodrug. Am J Trop Med Hyg 1999;60(6):943–947.

480. Rieckmann KH, Yeo AE, Edstein MD. Activity of PS-15 and its metabolite, WR99210, against Plasmodium falciparum in an in vivo–in vitro model. Trans R Soc Trop Med Hyg 1996;90 (5):568–571.

481. Yuvaniyama J, Chitnumsub P, Kamchonwongpaisan S, Vanichtanankul J, Sirawaraporn W, Taylor P, Walkinshaw MD, Yuthavong Y. Insights into antifolate resistance from malarial DHFR-TS structures. Nat Struct Biol 2003;10(5):357–365.

482. Shearer TW, Kozar MP, O'Neil MT, Smith PL, Schiehser GA, Jacobus DP, Diaz DS, Yang YS, Milhous WK, Skillman DR. In vitro metabolism of phenoxypropoxybiguanide analogues in human liver microsomes to potent antimalarial dihydrotriazines. J Med Chem 2005;48 (8):2805–2813.

483. Hunt SY, Detering C, Varani G, Jacobus DP, Schiehser GA, Shieh HM, Nevchas I, Terpinski J, Sibley CH. Identification of the optimal third generation antifolate against P. falciparum and P. vivax. Mol Biochem Parasitol 2005;144(2):198–205.

484. Tarnchompoo B, Sirichaiwat C, Phupong W, Intaraudom C, Sirawaraporn W, Kamchonwongpaisan S, Vanichtanankul J, Thebtara-

nonth Y, Yuthavong Y. Development of 2,4-diaminopyrimidines as antimalarials based on inhibition of the S108N and C59R + S108N mutants of dihydrofolate reductase from pyrimethamine-resistant Plasmodium falciparum. J Med Chem 2002;45(6):1244–1252.

485. Kamchonwongpaisan S, Quarrell R, Charoensetakul N, Ponsinet R, Vilaivan T, Vanichtanankul J, Tarnchompoo B, Sirawaraporn W, Lowe G, Yuthavong Y. Inhibitors of multiple mutants of Plasmodium falciparum dihydrofolate reductase and their antimalarial activities. J Med Chem 2004;47(3):673–680.

486. Sirichaiwat C, Intaraudom C, Kamchonwongpaisan S, Vanichtanankul J, Thebtaranonth Y, Yuthavong Y. Target guided synthesis of 5-benzyl-2,4-diamonopyrimidines: their antimalarial activities and binding affinities to wild type and mutant dihydrofolate reductases from Plasmodium falciparum. J Med Chem 2004;47(2):345–354.

487. Kamchonwongpaisan S, Vanichtanankul J, Tarnchompoo B, Yuvaniyama J, Taweechai S, Yuthavong Y. Stoichiometric selection of tight-binding inhibitors by wild-type and mutant forms of malarial (Plasmodium falciparum) dihydrofolate reductase. Anal Chem 2005;77(5):1222–1227.

488. Thongpanchang C, Taweechai S, Kamchonwongpaisan S, Yuthavong Y, Thebtaranonth Y. Immobilization of malarial (Plasmodium falciparum) dihydrofolate reductase for the selection of tight-binding inhibitors from combinatorial library. Anal Chem 2007;79 (13):5006–5012.

489. Sardarian A, Douglas KT, Read M, Sims PF, Hyde JE, Chitnumsub P, Sirawaraporn R, Sirawaraporn W. Pyrimethamine analogs as strong inhibitors of double and quadruple mutants of dihydrofolate reductase in human malaria parasites. Org Biomol Chem 2003;1 (6):960–964.

490. Parenti MD, Pacchioni S, Ferrari AM, Rastelli G. Three-dimensional quantitative structure–activity relationship analysis of a set of Plasmodium falciparum dihydrofolate reductase inhibitors using a pharmacophore generation approach. J Med Chem 2004;47(17):4258–4267.

491. Fogel GB, Cheung M, Pittman E, Hecht D. In silico screening against wild-type and mutant Plasmodium falciparum dihydrofolate reductase. J Mol Graph Model. 2008;26(7):1145–1152.

492. Lau H, Ferlan JT, Brophy VH, Rosowsky A, Sibley CH. Efficacies of lipophilic inhibitors of dihydrofolate reductase against parasitic pro-

tozoa. Antimicrob Agents Chemother 2001;45 (1):187–195.

493. Ommeh S, Nduati E, Mberu E, Kokwaro G, Marsh K, Rosowsky A, Nzila A. *In vitro* activities of 2,4-diaminoquinazoline and 2,4-diaminopteridine derivatives against *Plasmodium falciparum*. Antimicrob Agents Chemother 2004;48(10):3711–3714.

494. Djapa LY, Basco LK, Zelikson R, Rosowsky A, Djaman JA, Yonkeu JN, Bolotin-Fukuhara M, Mazabraud A. Antifolate screening using yeast expressing *Plasmodium vivax* dihydrofolate reductase and *in vitro* drug susceptibility assay for *Plasmodium falciparum*. Mol Biochem Parasitol 2007;156(1):89–92.

495. Brobey RK, Sano G, Itoh F, Aso K, Kimura M, Mitamura T, Horii T. Recombinant *Plasmodium falciparum* dihydrofolate reductase-based *in vitro* screen for antifolate antimalarials. Mol Biochem Parasitol 1996;81(2):225–237.

496. Toyoda T, Brobey RK, Sano G, Horii T, Tomioka N, Itai A. Lead discovery of inhibitors of the dihydrofolate reductase domain of *Plasmodium falciparum* dihydrofolate reductase-thymidylate synthase. Biochem Biophys Res Commun 1997;235(3):515–519.

497. Rastelli G, Pacchioni S, Sirawaraporn W, Sirawaraporn R, Parenti MD, Ferrari AM. Docking and database screening reveal new classes of *Plasmodium falciparum* dihydrofolate reductase inhibitors. J Med Chem 2003;46 (14):2834–2845.

498. Rastelli G, Pacchioni S, Parenti MD. Structure of *Plasmodium vivax* dihydrofolate reductase determined by homology modeling and molecular dynamics refinement. Bioorg Med Chem Lett 2003;13(19):3257–3260.

499. Kongsaeree P, Khongsuk P, Leartsakulpanich U, Chitnumsub P, Tarnchompoo B, Walkinshaw MD, Yuthavong Y. Crystal structure of dihydrofolate reductase from Plasmodium vivax: pyrimethamine displacement linked with mutation-induced resistance. Proc Natl Acad Sci USA 2005;102(37):13046–13051.

500. Krungkrai J. Purification, characterization and localization of mitochondrial dihydroorotate dehydrogenase in *Plasmodium falciparum*, human malaria parasite. Biochim Biophys Acta 1995;1243(3):351–360.

501. Baldwin J, Farajallah AM, Malmquist NA, Rathod PK, Phillips MA. Malarial dihydroorotate dehydrogenase. Substrate and inhibitor specificity. J Biol Chem 2002;277(44):41827–41834.

502. Reyes P, Rathod PK, Sanchez DJ, Mrema JE, Rieckmann KH, Heidrich HG. Enzymes of purine and pyrimidine metabolism from the human malaria parasite, *Plasmodium falciparum*. Mol Biochem Parasitol 1982;5 (5):275–290.

503. Krooth RS, Wuu KD, Ma R. Dihydroorotic acid dehydrogenase: introduction into erythrocyte by the malaria parasite. Science 1969;164 (883):1073–1075.

504. Prapunwattana P, O'Sullivan WJ, Yuthavong Y. Depression of *Plasmodium falciparum* dihydroorotate dehydrogenase activity in *in vitro* culture by tetracycline. Mol Biochem Parasitol 27:(2–3): 1988; 119–124.

505. Ittarat I, Asawamahasakda W, Meshnick SR. The effects of antimalarials on the *Plasmodium falciparum* dihydroorotate dehydrogenase. Exp Parasitol 1994;79(1):50–56.

506. Boa AN, Canavan SP, Hirst PR, Ramsey C, Stead AM, McConkey GA. Synthesis of brequinar analogue inhibitors of malaria parasite dihydroorotate dehydrogenase. Bioorg Med Chem 2005;13(6):1945–1967.

507. Heikkila T, Ramsey C, Davies M, Galtier C, Stead AM, Johnson AP, Fishwick CW, Boa AN, McConkey GA. Design and synthesis of potent inhibitors of the malaria parasite dihydroorotate dehydrogenase. J Med Chem 2007;50 (2):186–191.

508. Baldwin J, Michnoff CH, Malmquist NA, White J, Roth MG, Rathod PK, Phillips MA. High-throughput screening for potent and selective inhibitors of *Plasmodium falciparum* dihydroorotate dehydrogenase. J Biol Chem 2005;280(23):21847–21853.

509. Phillips MA, Gujjar R, Malmquist NA, White J, El Mazouni F, Baldwin J, Rathod PK. Triazolopyrimidine-based dihydroorotate dehydrogenase inhibitors with potent and selective activity against the malaria parasite *Plasmodium falciparum*. J Med Chem 2008;51 (12):3649–3653.

510. Malmquist NA, Gujjar R, Rathod PK, Phillips MA. Analysis of flavin oxidation and electron-transfer inhibition in *Plasmodium falciparum* dihydroorotate dehydrogenase. Biochemistry 2008;47(8):2466–2475.

511. Patel V, Booker M, Kramer M, Ross L, Kennedy LM, Dvorin JD, Duraisingh MT, Sliz P, Wirth DF, Clardy J. Identification and characterization of small molecule inhibitors of *Plasmodium falciparum* dihydroorotate dehydrogenase. J Biol Chem 2008;283 (50):35078–35085.

512. Mitscher LA. Bacterial topoisomerase inhibitors: quinolone and pyridone antibacterial agents. Chem Rev 2005;105(2):559–592.

513. Pommier Y. Topoisomerase I inhibitors: camptothecins and beyond. Nat Rev Cancer 2006;6 (10):789–802.

514. Larsen AK, Escargueil AE, Skladanowski A. Catalytic topoisomerase II inhibitors in cancer therapy. Pharmacol Ther 2003;99(2):167–181.

515. Teicher BA. Next generation topoisomerase I inhibitors: rationale and biomarker strategies. Biochem Pharmacol 2008;75(6):1262–1271.

516. Champoux JJ. DNA topoisomerases: structure, function, and mechanism. Annu Rev Biochem 2001;70:369–413.

517. Wang JC. Cellular roles of DNA topoisomerases: a molecular perspective. Nat Rev Mol Cell Biol 2002;3(6):430–440.

518. Corbett KD, Berger JM. Structure, molecular mechanisms, and evolutionary relationships in DNA topoisomerases. Annu Rev Biophys Biomol Struct 2004;33:95–118.

519. Stewart L, Redinbo MR, Qiu X, Hol WG, Champoux JJ. A model for the mechanism of human topoisomerase I. Science 1998;279 (5356):1534–1541.

520. Wang JC. DNA topoisomerases. Annu Rev Biochem 1996;65:635–692.

521. Berger JM. Structure of DNA topoisomerases. Biochim Biophys Acta 1400:(1–3): 1998; 3–18.

522. Cheesman S, McAleese S, Goman M, Johnson D, Horrocks P, Ridley RG, Kilbey BJ. The gene encoding topoisomerase II from *Plasmodium falciparum*. Nucleic Acids Res 1994;22 (13):2547–2551.

523. Riou JF, Gabillot M, Philippe M, Schrevel J, Riou G. Purification and characterization of *Plasmodium berghei* DNA topoisomerases I and II: drug action, inhibition of decatenation and relaxation, and stimulation of DNA cleavage. Biochemistry 1986;25(7):1471–1479.

524. Tosh K, Kilbey B. The gene encoding topoisomerase I from the human malaria parasite *Plasmodium falciparum*. Gene 1995;163(1):151–154.

525. Tosh K, Cheesman S, Horrocks P, Kilbey B. *Plasmodium falciparum*: stage-related expression of topoisomerase I. Exp Parasitol 1999;91(2):126–132.

526. Baguley BC, Ferguson LR. Mutagenic properties of topoisomerase-targeted drugs. Biochim Biophys Acta 1400:(1–3): 1998; 213–222.

527. Pradhan A. Tuteja R. Plasmodium falciparum DNA helicase 60. dsRNA- and antibody-mediated inhibition of malaria parasite growth and downregulation of its enzyme activities by DNA-interacting compounds. FEBS J 2006;273(15):3545–3556.

528. Crumplin GC, Kenwright M, Hirst T. Investigations into the mechanism of action of the antibacterial agent norfloxacin. J Antimicrob Chemother 13:(Suppl B): 1984; 9–23.

529. Gellert M, Mizuuchi K, O'Dea MH, Nash HA. DNA gyrase: an enzyme that introduces superhelical turns into DNA. Proc Natl Acad Sci USA 1976;73(11):3872–3876.

530. Weissig V, Vetro-Widenhouse TS, Rowe TC. Topoisomerase II inhibitors induce cleavage of nuclear and 35-kb plastid DNAs in the malarial parasite *Plasmodium falciparum*. DNA Cell Biol 1997;16(12):1483–1492.

531. Williamson DH, Preiser PR, Moore PW, McCready S, Strath M, Wilson RJ. The plastid DNA of the malaria parasite *Plasmodium falciparum* is replicated by two mechanisms. Mol Microbiol 2002;45(2):533–542.

532. Tripathi KD, Sharma AK, Valecha N, Kulpati DD. Curative efficacy of norfloxacin in falciparum malaria. Indian J Med Res 1993;97:176–178.

533. Havemann K, Bhibi P, Hellgren U, Rombo L. Norfloxacin is not effective for treatment of *Plasmodium falciparum* infection in Kenya. Trans R Soc Trop Med Hyg 1992;86(6):586.

534. Watt G, Shanks GD, Edstein MD, Pavanand K, Webster HK, Wechgritaya S. Ciprofloxacin treatment of drug-resistant falciparum malaria. J Infect Dis 1991;164(3):602–604.

535. Kazzim OJ, Adegbolagun OM, Osho O, Anumudu CI. Additive effects of ciprofloxacin on the *in-vitro* activity of chloroquine against a clinical isolate of *Plasmodium falciparum*. Ann Trop Med Parasitol 2006;100(7):579–584.

536. Gu K, Bi L, Zhao M, Wang C, Dolan C, Kao MC, Tok JB, Peng S. Stereoselective synthesis and anti-inflammatory activities of 6- and 7-membered dioxacycloalkanes. Bioorg Med Chem 2006;14(5):1339–1347.

537. Foroumadi A, Ghodsi S, Emami S, Najjari S, Samadi N, Faramarzi MA, Beikmohammadi L, Shirazi FH, Shafiee A. Synthesis and antibacterial activity of new fluoroquinolones containing a substituted N-(phenethyl)piperazine moiety. Bioorg Med Chem Lett 2006;16 (13):3499–3503.

538. Zhao YL, Chen YL, Sheu JY, Chen IL, Wang TC, Tzeng CC. Synthesis and antimycobacterial evaluation of certain fluoroquinolone derivatives. Bioorg Med Chem 2005;13(12):3921–3926.

539. Culbertson TP, Sanchez JP, Gambino L, Sesnie JA. Quinolone antibacterial agents substituted at the 7-position with spiroamines. Synthesis and structure–activity relationships. J Med Chem 1990;33(8):2270–2275.

540. Kerns RJ, Rybak MJ, Kaatz GW, Vaka F, Cha R, Grucz RG, Diwadkar VU, Ward TD. Piperazinyl-linked fluoroquinolone dimers possessing potent antibacterial activity against drug-resistant strains of *Staphylococcus aureus*. Bioorg Med Chem Lett 2003;13 (10):1745–1749.

541. Shindikar AV, Viswanathan CL. Novel fluoroquinolones: design, synthesis, and *in vivo* activity in mice against *Mycobacterium tuberculosis* H37Rv. Bioorg Med Chem Lett 2005;15 (7):1803–1806.

542. Nagawade RR, Khanna VV, Bhagwat SS, Shinde DB. Synthesis of new series of 1-Aryl-1,4-dihydro-4-oxo-6-methyl pyridazine-3-carboxylic acid as potential antibacterial agents. Eur J Med Chem 2005;40 (12):1325–1330.

543. Srivastava BK, Solanki M, Mishra B, Soni R, Jayadev S, Valani D, Jain M, Patel PR. Synthesis and antibacterial activity of 4,5,6,7-tetrahydro-thieno[3,2-*c*]pyridine quinolones. Bioorg Med Chem Lett 2007;17(7):1924–1929.

544. Murphy ST, Case HL, Ellsworth E, Hagen S, Huband M, Joannides T, Limberakis C, Marotti KR, Ottolini AM, Rauckhorst M, Starr J, Stier M, Taylor C, Zhu T, Blaser A, Denny WA, Lu GL, Smaill JB, Rivault F. The synthesis and biological evaluation of novel series of nitrile-containing fluoroquinolones as antibacterial agents. Bioorg Med Chem Lett 2007;17 (8):2150–2155.

545. Al-Hiari YM, Al-Mazari IS, Shakya AK, Darwish RM, Abu-Dahab R. Synthesis and antibacterial properties of new 8-nitrofluoroquinolone derivatives. Molecules 2007;12 (6):1240–1258.

546. Dang Z, Yang Y, Ji R, Zhang S. Synthesis and antibacterial activity of novel fluoroquinolones containing substituted piperidines. Bioorg Med Chem Lett 2007;17(16):4523–4526.

547. Anquetin G, Greiner J, Mahmoudi N, Santillana-Hayat M, Gozalbes R, Farhati K, Derouin F, Aubry A, Cambau E, Vierling P. Design, synthesis and activity against *Toxoplasma gondii, Plasmodium* spp., and *Mycobacterium tuberculosis* of new 6-fluoroquinolones. Eur J Med Chem 2006;41(12):1478–1493.

548. Anquetin G, Rouquayrol M, Mahmoudi N, Santillana-Hayat M, Gozalbes R, Greiner J, Farhati K, Derouin F, Guedj R, Vierling P. Synthesis of new fluoroquinolones and evaluation of their *in vitro* activity on *Toxoplasma gondii* and *Plasmodium* spp. Bioorg Med Chem Lett 2004;14(11):2773–2776.

549. Figgitt D, Denny W, Chavalitshewinkoon P, Wilairat P, Ralph R. *In vitro* study of anticancer acridines as potential antitrypanosomal and antimalarial agents. Antimicrob Agents Chemother 1992;36(8):1644–1647.

550. Gamage SA, Tepsiri N, Wilairat P, Wojcik SJ, Figgitt DP, Ralph RK, Denny WA. Synthesis and *in vitro* evaluation of 9-anilino-3,6-diaminoacridines active against a multidrug-resistant strain of the malaria parasite *Plasmodium falciparum*. J Med Chem 1994;37 (10):1486–1494.

551. Chavalitshewinkoon-Petmitr P, Pongvilairat G, Ralph RK, Denny WA, Wilairat P. Inhibitory effects of 9-anilinoacridines on *Plasmodium falciparum* gametocytes. Trop Med Int Health 2001;6(1):42–45.

552. Auparakkitanon S, Noonpakdee W, Ralph RK, Denny WA, Wilairat P. Antimalarial 9-anilinoacridine compounds directed at hematin. Antimicrob Agents Chemother 2003;47 (12):3708–3712.

553. Bodley AL, Wani MC, Wall ME, Shapiro TA. Antitrypanosomal activity of camptothecin analogs. Structure–activity correlations. Biochem Pharmacol 1995;50(7):937–942.

554. Bodley AL, Cumming JN, Shapiro TA. Effects of camptothecin, a topoisomerase I inhibitor, on *Plasmodium falciparum*. Biochem Pharmacol 1998;55(5):709–711.

555. Srivastava SJ, Singh S, Alok R, Yadav S, Saxena AS, Ram VJ, Subhash C, Saxena JK. Oxygenated chalcones and bischalcones as a new class of inhibitors of DNA topoisomerase II of malarial parasites. Med Chem Res 2008;17(2):234–244.

556. Singh SK, Joshi S, Singh AR, Saxena JK, Pandey DS. DNA binding and topoisomerase II inhibitory activity of water-soluble ruthenium(II) and rhodium(III) complexes. Inorg Chem 2007;46(25):10869–10876.

557. Noonpakdee W, Pothikasikorn J, Nimitsantiwong W, Wilairat P. Inhibition of *Plasmodium falciparum* proliferation *in vitro* by antisense oligodeoxynucleotides against malarial topoisomerase II. Biochem Biophys Res Commun 2003;302(4):659–664.

558. Foger F, Noonpakdee W, Loretz B, Joojuntr S, Salvenmoser W, Thaler M, Bernkop-Schnurch A. Inhibition of malarial topoisomerase II in *Plasmodium falciparum* by antisense nanoparticles. Int J Pharm 319:(1–2): 2006; 139–146.

559. Lehrmann H, Pritchard LL, Harel-Bellan A. Histone acetyltransferases and deacety-

lases in the control of cell proliferation and differentiation. Adv Cancer Res 2002;86:41–65.

560. Cairns BR. Emerging roles for chromatin remodeling in cancer biology. Trends Cell Biol 2001;11(11):S15–S21.

561. Andrews KT, Tran TN, Lucke AJ, Kahnberg P, Le GT, Boyle GM, Gardiner DL, Skinner-Adams TS, Fairlie DP. Potent antimalarial activity of histone deacetylase inhibitor analogues. Antimicrob Agents Chemother 2008;52 (4):1454–1461.

562. Joshi MB, Lin DT, Chiang PH, Goldman ND, Fujioka H, Aikawa M, Syin C. Molecular cloning and nuclear localization of a histone deacetylase homologue in *Plasmodium falciparum*. Mol Biochem Parasitol 1999;99(1):11–19.

563. Darkin-Rattray SJ, Gurnett AM, Myers RW, Dulski PM, Crumley TM, Allocco JJ, Cannova C, Meinke PT, Colletti SL, Bednarek MA, Singh SB, Goetz MA, Dombrowski AW, Polishook JD, Schmatz DM. Apicidin: a novel antiprotozoal agent that inhibits parasite histone deacetylase. Proc Natl Acad Sci USA 1996;93 (23):13143–13147.

564. Prusty D, Mehra P, Srivastava S, Shivange AV, Gupta A, Roy N, Dhar SK. Nicotinamide inhibits *Plasmodium falciparum* Sir2 activity *in vitro* and parasite growth. FEMS Microbiol Lett 2008;282(2):266–272.

565. Freitas-Junior LH, Hernandez-Rivas R, Ralph SA, Montiel-Condado D, Ruvalcaba-Salazar OK, Rojas-Meza AP, Mancio-Silva L, Leal-Silvestre RJ, Gontijo AM, Shorte S, Scherf A. Telomeric heterochromatin propagation and histone acetylation control mutually exclusive expression of antigenic variation genes in malaria parasites. Cell 2005;121(1):25–36.

566. Renauld H, Aparicio OM, Zierath PD, Billington BL, Chhablani SK, Gottschling DE. Silent domains are assembled continuously from the telomere and are defined by promoter distance and strength, and by SIR3 dosage. Genes Dev 1993;7:(7A): 1133–1145.

567. Scherf A, Figueiredo LM, Freitas-Junior LH. *Plasmodium telomeres*: a pathogen's perspective. Curr Opin Microbiol 2001;4(4):409–414.

568. Yoshida M, Kijima M, Akita M, Beppu T. Potent and specific inhibition of mammalian histone deacetylase both *in vivo* and *in vitro* by trichostatin A. J Biol Chem 1990;265 (28):17174–17179.

569. Kijima M, Yoshida M, Sugita K, Horinouchi S, Beppu T. Trapoxin, an antitumor cyclic tetrapeptide, is an irreversible inhibitor of mammalian histone deacetylase. J Biol Chem 1993;268(30):22429–22435.

570. Shute RE, Dunlap B, Rich DH. Analogues of the cytostatic and antimitogenic agents chlamydocin and HC-toxin: synthesis and biological activity of chloromethyl ketone and diazomethyl ketone functionalized cyclic tetrapeptides. J Med Chem 1987;30(1):71–78.

571. Ueda H, Nakajima H, Hori Y, Fujita T, Nishimura M, Goto T, Okuhara M. FR901228, a novel antitumor bicyclic depsipeptide produced by *Chromobacterium violaceum* No. 968. I. Taxonomy, fermentation, isolation, physico-chemical and biological properties, and antitumor activity. J Antibiot 1994;47(3):301–310.

572. Kruh J. Effects of sodium butyrate, a new pharmacological agent, on cells in culture. Mol Cell Biochem 1982;42(2):65–82.

573. Gore SD, Carducci MA. Modifying histones to tame cancer: clinical development of sodium phenylbutyrate and other histone deacetylase inhibitors. Expert Opin Investig Drugs 2000;9 (12):2923–2934.

574. Gottlicher M, Minucci S, Zhu P, Kramer OH, Schimpf A, Giavara S, Sleeman JP, Lo Coco F, Nervi C, Pelicci PG, Heinzel T. Valproic acid defines a novel class of HDAC inhibitors inducing differentiation of transformed cells. EMBO J 2001;20(24):6969–6978.

575. Phiel CJ, Zhang F, Huang EY, Guenther MG, Lazar MA, Klein PS. Histone deacetylase is a direct target of valproic acid, a potent anticonvulsant, mood stabilizer, and teratogen. J Biol Chem 2001;276(39):36734–36741.

576. Richon VM, Emiliani S, Verdin E, Webb Y, Breslow R, Rifkind RA, Marks PA. A class of hybrid polar inducers of transformed cell differentiation inhibits histone deacetylases. Proc Natl Acad Sci USA 1998;95(6):3003–3007.

577. Jung M, Brosch G, Kolle D, Scherf H, Gerhauser C, Loidl P. Amide analogues of trichostatin A as inhibitors of histone deacetylase and inducers of terminal cell differentiation. J Med Chem 1999;42(22):4669–4679.

578. Remiszewski SW, Sambucetti LC, Atadja P, Bair KW, Cornell WD, Green MA, Howell KL, Jung M, Kwon P, Trogani N, Walker H. Inhibitors of human histone deacetylase: synthesis and enzyme and cellular activity of straight chain hydroxamates. J Med Chem 2002;45(4):753–757.

579. Woo SH, Frechette S, Abou Khalil E, Bouchain G, Vaisburg A, Bernstein N, Moradei O, Leit S, Allan M, Fournel M, Trachy-Bourget MC, Li Z, Besterman JM, Delorme D. Structurally

simple trichostatin A-like straight chain hydroxamates as potent histone deacetylase inhibitors. J Med Chem 2002;45(13):2877–2885.

580. Uesato S, Kitagawa M, Nagaoka Y, Maeda T, Kuwajima H, Yamori T. Novel histone deacetylase inhibitors: *N*-hydroxycarboxamides possessing a terminal bicyclic aryl group. Bioorg Med Chem Lett. 2002;12(10):1347–1349.

581. Su GH, Sohn TA, Ryu B, Kern SE. A novel histone deacetylase inhibitor identified by high-throughput transcriptional screening of a compound library. Cancer Res 2000;60 (12):3137–3142.

582. Kim YB, Lee KH, Sugita K, Yoshida M, Horinouchi S. Oxamflatin is a novel antitumor compound that inhibits mammalian histone deacetylase. Oncogene 1999;18(15):2461–2470.

583. Lavoie R, Bouchain G, Frechette S, Woo SH, Abou-Khalil E, Leit S, Fournel M, Yan PT, Trachy-Bourget MC, Beaulieu C, Li Z, Besterman J, Delorme D. Design and synthesis of a novel class of histone deacetylase inhibitors. Bioorg Med Chem Lett 2001;11(21):2847–2850.

584. Furumai R, Komatsu Y, Nishino N, Khochbin S, Yoshida M, Horinouchi S, Potent histone deacetylase inhibitors built from trichostatin A and cyclic tetrapeptide antibiotics including trapoxin. Proc Natl Acad Sci USA 2001;98 (1):87–92.

585. Komatsu Y, Tomizaki KY, Tsukamoto M, Kato T, Nishino N, Sato S, Yamori T, Tsuruo T, Furumai R, Yoshida M, Horinouchi S, Hayashi H. Cyclic hydroxamic-acid-containing peptide 31, a potent synthetic histone deacetylase inhibitor with antitumor activity. Cancer Res 2001;61(11):4459–4466.

586. Saito A, Yamashita T, Mariko Y, Nosaka Y, Tsuchiya K, Ando T, Suzuki T, Tsuruo T, Nakanishi O. A synthetic inhibitor of histone deacetylase, MS-27-275, with marked *in vivo* antitumor activity against human tumors. Proc Natl Acad Sci USA 1999;96(8):4592–4597.

587. Suzuki T, Ando T, Tsuchiya K, Fukazawa N, Saito A, Mariko Y, Yamashita T, Nakanishi O. Synthesis and histone deacetylase inhibitory activity of new benzamide derivatives. J Med Chem 1999;42(15):3001–3003.

588. Singh SB, Zink DL, Polishook JD, Dombrowski AW, Darkin-Rattray SJ, Schmatz DM, Goetz MA. Apicidins: novel cyclic tetrapeptides as coccidiostats and antimalarial agents from *Fusarium pallidoroseum*. Tetrahedron Lett 1996;37(45):8077–8080.

589. Meinke PT, Colletti SL, Doss G, Myers RW, Gurnett AM, Dulski PM, Darkin-Rattray SJ, Allocco JJ, Galuska S, Schmatz DM, Wyvratt MJ, Fisher MH. Synthesis of apicidin-derived quinolone derivatives: parasite-selective histone deacetylase inhibitors and antiproliferative agents. J Med Chem 2000;43(25):4919–4922.

590. Colletti SL, Myers RW, Darkin-Rattray SJ, Gurnett AM, Dulski PM, Galuska S, Allocco JJ, Ayer MB, Li C, Lim J, Crumley TM, Cannova C, Schmatz DM, Wyvratt MJ, Fisher MH, Meinke PT. Broad spectrum antiprotozoal agents that inhibit histone deacetylase: structure–activity relationships of apicidin. Part 2. Bioorg Med Chem Lett 2001;11(2):113–117.

591. Singh SB, Zink DL, Liesch JM, Dombrowski AW, Darkin-Rattray SJ, Schmatz DM, Goetz MA. Structure, histone deacetylase, and antiprotozoal activities of apicidins B and C, congeners of apicidin with proline and valine substitutions. Org Lett 2001;3(18):2815–2818.

592. Singh SB, Zink DL, Liesch JM, Mosley RT, Dombrowski AW, Bills GF, Darkin-Rattray SJ, Schmatz DM, Goetz MA. Structure and chemistry of apicidins, a class of novel cyclic tetrapeptides without a terminal alpha-keto epoxide as inhibitors of histone deacetylase with potent antiprotozoal activities. J Org Chem 2002;67(3):815–825.

593. Colletti SL, Myers RW, Darkin-Rattray SJ, Gurnett AM, Dulski PM, Galuska S, Allocco JJ, Ayer MB, Li C, Lim J, Crumley TM, Cannova C, Schmatz DM, Wyvratt MJ, Fisher MH, Meinke PT. Broad spectrum antiprotozoal agents that inhibit histone deacetylase: structure–activity relationships of apicidin. Part 1. Bioorg Med Chem Lett 2001;11(2):107–111.

594. Andrews KT, Walduck A, Kelso MJ, Fairlie DP, Saul A, Parsons PG. Anti-malarial effect of histone deacetylation inhibitors and mammalian tumour cytodifferentiating agents. Int J Parasitol 2000;30(6):761–768.

595. Breslow R, Jursic B, Yan ZF, Friedman E, Leng L, Ngo L, Rifkind RA, Marks PA. Potent cytodifferentiating agents related to hexamethylenebisacetamide. Proc Natl Acad Sci USA 1991;88(13):5542–5546.

596. Glenn MP, Kahnberg P, Boyle GM, Hansford KA, Hans D, Martyn AC, Parsons PG, Fairlie DP. Antiproliferative and phenotype-transforming antitumor agents derived from cysteine. J Med Chem 2004;47(12):2984–2994.

597. Chen Y, Lopez-Sanchez M, Savoy DN, Billadeau DD, Dow GS, Kozikowski AP. A series of potent and selective, triazolylphenyl-based histone deacetylases inhibitors with activity against pancreatic cancer cells and *Plasmo-*

dium falciparum. J Med Chem 2008;51 (12):3437–3448.

598. Glaser KB. HDAC inhibitors: clinical update and mechanism-based potential. Biochem Pharmacol 2007;74(5):659–671.

599. Dow GS, Chen Y, Andrews KT, Caridha D, Gerena L, Gettayacamin M, Johnson J, Li Q, Melendez V, Obaldia N, 3rd Tran TN, Kozikowski AP. Antimalarial activity of phenylthiazolyl-bearing hydroxamate-based histone deacetylase inhibitors. Antimicrob Agents Chemother 2008;52(10):3467–3477.

600. Kozikowski AP, Chen Y, Gaysin A, Chen B, D'Annibale MA, Suto CM, Langley BC. Functional differences in epigenetic modulators-superiority of mercaptoacetamide-based histone deacetylase inhibitors relative to hydroxamates in cortical neuron neuroprotection studies. J Med Chem 2007;50(13):3054–3061.

601. Chen B, Petukhov PA, Jung M, Velena A, Eliseeva E, Dritschilo A, Kozikowski AP. Chemistry and biology of mercaptoacetamides as novel histone deacetylase inhibitors. Bioorg Med Chem Lett 2005;15(5):1389–1392.

602. Mazitschek R, Patel V, Wirth DF, Clardy J. Development of a fluorescence polarization based assay for histone deacetylase ligand discovery. Bioorg Med Chem Lett 2008;18 (9):2809–2812.

603. Mukherjee P, Pradhan A, Shah F, Tekwani BL, Avery MA. Structural insights into the *Plasmodium falciparum* histone deacetylase 1 (PfHDAC-1): a novel target for the development of antimalarial therapy. Bioorg Med Chem 2008;16(9):5254–5265.

604. Wendel W. The influence of naphthoquinones upon the respiratory and carbohydrate metabolism of malarial parasites. Fed Proc 1946;5:406–407.

605. Ball EG, Anfinsen CB, Cooper O. The inhibitory action of naphthoquinones on respiratory processes. J Biol Chem 1947;168:257–270.

606. Fieser LF, Schirmer JP, Archer S, Lorenz RR, Pfaffenbach PI. Naphthoquinone antimalarials. XXIX. 2-Hydroxy-3-(omega-cyclohexylalkyl)-1,4-naphthoquinones. J Med Chem 1967;10(4):513–517.

607. Berberian DA, Slighter RG, Freele HW. Causal prophylactic effect of Menoctone (a new hydroxynaphthoquinone) against sporozoite-induced *Plasmodium berghei* infection in mice. J Parasitol 1968;54(6):1181–1189.

608. Canfield CJ, Rozman RS. Clinical testing of new antimalarial compounds. Bull World Health Organ 1974;50:203–212.

609. Porter TH, Folkers K. Antimetabolites of coenzyme Q. Their potential application as antimalarials. Angew Chem Int Ed Engl 1974;13 (9):559–569.

610. Hudson AT, Randall AW, Fry M, Ginger CD, Hill B, Latter VS, McHardy N, Williams RB. Novel anti-malarial hydroxynaphthoquinones with potent broad spectrum anti-protozoal activity. Parasitology 1985;90(Pt1): 45–55.

611. Fry M, Pudney M. Site of action of the antimalarial hydroxynaphthoquinone, 2-[trans-4-(4′-chlorophenyl) cyclohexyl]-3-hydroxy-1,4-naphthoquinone (566C80). Biochem Pharmacol 1992;43(7):1545–1553.

612. Vaidya AB, Lashgari MS, Pologe LG, Morrisey J. Structural features of *Plasmodium* cytochrome b that may underlie susceptibility to 8-aminoquinolines and hydroxynaphthoquinones. Mol Biochem Parasitol 1993;58(1):33–42.

613. Zhang Z, Huang L, Shulmeister VM, Chi YI, Kim KK, Hung LW, Crofts AR, Berry EA, Kim SH. Electron transfer by domain movement in cytochrome bc_1. Nature 1998;392(6677):677–684.

614. Esser L, Quinn B, Li YF, Zhang M, Elberry M, Yu L, Yu CA, Xia D. Crystallographic studies of quinol oxidation site inhibitors: a modified classification of inhibitors for the cytochrome bc_1 complex. J Mol Biol 2004;341(1):281–302.

615. Xia D, Yu CA, Kim H, Xia JZ, Kachurin AM, Zhang L, Yu L, Deisenhofer J. Crystal structure of the cytochrome bc_1 complex from bovine heart mitochondria. Science 1997;277(5322):60–66.

616. Crofts AR, Barquera B, Gennis RB, Kuras R, Guergova-Kuras M, Berry EA. Mechanism of ubiquinol oxidation by the bc_1 complex: different domains of the quinol binding pocket and their role in the mechanism and binding of inhibitors. Biochemistry 1999;38(48):15807–15826.

617. Srivastava IK, Rottenberg H, Vaidya AB. Atovaquone, a broad spectrum antiparasitic drug, collapses mitochondrial membrane potential in a malarial parasite. J Biol Chem 1997;272(7):3961–3966.

618. Srivastava IK, Morrisey JM, Darrouzet E, Daldal F, Vaidya AB. Resistance mutations reveal the atovaquone-binding domain of cytochrome b in malaria parasites. Mol Microbiol 1999;33(4):704–711.

619. Syafruddin D, Siregar JE, Marzuki S. Mutations in the cytochrome b gene of *Plasmodium berghei* conferring resistance to atovaquone. Mol Biochem Parasitol 1999;104(2):185–194.

620. Korsinczky M, Chen N, Kotecka B, Saul A, Rieckmann K, Cheng Q. Mutations in *Plasmodium falciparum* cytochrome b that are asso-

ciated with atovaquone resistance are located at a putative drug-binding site. Antimicrob Agents Chemother 2000;44(8):2100–2108.

621. Mather MW, Darrouzet E, Valkova-Valchanova M, Cooley JW, McIntosh MT, Daldal F, Vaidya AB. Uncovering the molecular mode of action of the antimalarial drug atovaquone using a bacterial system. J Biol Chem 2005;280(29):27458–27465.

622. Gebru T, Hailu A, Kremsner PG, Kun JF, Grobusch MP. Molecular surveillance of mutations in the cytochrome b gene of Plasmodium falciparum in Gabon and Ethiopia. Malar J 2006;5:112.

623. Murphy AD, Lang-Unnasch N. Alternative oxidase inhibitors potentiate the activity of atovaquone against Plasmodium falciparum. Antimicrob Agents Chemother 1999;43 (3):651–654.

624. Biagini GA, Viriyavejakul P, O'Neill P, Bray M, Ward PG, SA Functional characterization and target validation of alternative complex I of Plasmodium falciparum mitochondria. Antimicrob Agents Chemother 2006;50 (5):1841–1851.

625. Painter HJ, Morrisey JM, Mather MW, Vaidya AB. Specific role of mitochondrial electron transport in blood-stage Plasmodium falciparum. Nature 2007;446(7131):88–91.

626. Smilkstein MJ, Forquer I, Kanazawa A, Kelly JX, Winter RW, Hinrichs DJ, Kramer DM, Riscoe MK. A drug-selected Plasmodium falciparum lacking the need for conventional electron transport. Mol Biochem Parasitol 2008;159(1):64–68.

627. Mi-Ichi F, Miyadera H, Kobayashi T, Takamiya S, Waki S, Iwata S, Shibata S, Kita K. Parasite mitochondria as a target of chemotherapy: inhibitory effect of licochalcone A on the Plasmodium falciparum respiratory chain. Ann NY Acad Sci 2005;1056:46–54.

628. Xiang H, McSurdy-Freed J, Moorthy GS, Hugger E, Bambal R, Han C, Ferrer S, Gargallo D, Davis CB. Preclinical drug metabolism and pharmacokinetic evaluation of GW844520, a novel anti-malarial mitochondrial electron transport inhibitor. J Pharm Sci 2006;95 (12):2657–2672.

629. Biagini GA, Fisher N, Berry N, Stocks PA, Meunier B, Williams DP, Bonar-Law R, Bray PG, Owen A, O'Neill PM, Ward SA. Acridinediones: selective and potent inhibitors of the malaria parasite mitochondrial bc₁ complex. Mol Pharmacol 2008;73(5):1347–1355.

630. Raether W, Fink E. Antimalarial activity of Floxacrine (HOE 991) I. Studies on blood schizontocidal action of floxacrine against Plasmodium berghei, P. vinckei and P. cynomolgi. Ann Trop Med Parasitol 1979;73(6):505–526.

631. Schmidt LH. Antimalarial properties of floxacrine, a dihydroacridinedione derivative. Antimicrob Agents Chemother 1979;16(4):475–485.

632. Raether W, Fink E. Antimalarial activity of floxacrine (HOE 991) II: studies on causal prophylactic and blood schizontocidal action of floxacrine and related dihydroacridinediones against Plasmodium yoelii and P. berghei. Ann Trop Med Parasitol 1982;76 (5):507–516.

633. Kesten SJ, Degnan MJ, Hung J, McNamara DJ, Ortwine DF, Uhlendorf SE, Werbel LM. Synthesis and antimalarial properties of 1-imino derivatives of 7-chloro-3-substituted-3,4-dihydro-1,9(2H,10H)-acridinediones and related structures. J Med Chem 1992;35 (19):3429–3447.

634. Dorn A, Scovill JP, Ellis WY, Matile H, Ridley RG, Vennerstrom JL. Short report: floxacrine analog WR 243251 inhibits hematin polymerization. Am J Trop Med Hyg 2001;65 (1):19–20.

635. Winter RW, Kelly JX, Smilkstein MJ, Dodean R, Bagby GC, Rathbun RK, Levin JI, Hinrichs D, Riscoe MK. Evaluation and lead optimization of anti-malarial acridones. Exp Parasitol 2006;114(1):47–56.

636. Winter RW, Kelly JX, Smilkstein MJ, Dodean R, Hinrichs D, Riscoe MK. Antimalarial quinolones: synthesis, potency, and mechanistic studies. Exp Parasitol 2008;118(4):487–497.

637. Canfield CJ, Pudney M, Gutteridge WE. Interactions of atovaquone with other antimalarial drugs against Plasmodium falciparum in vitro. Exp Parasitol 1995;80(3):373–381.

638. Kimura M, Yamaguchi Y, Takada S, Tanabe K. Cloning of a Ca^{2+}-ATPase gene of Plasmodium falciparum and comparison with vertebrate Ca^{2+}-ATPases. J Cell Sci 1993;104(Pt4): 1129–1136.

639. Alleva LM, Kirk K. Calcium regulation in the intraerythrocytic malaria parasite Plasmodium falciparum. Mol Biochem Parasitol 2001;117(2):121–128.

640. Varotti FP, Beraldo FH, Gazarini ML, Garcia CR. Plasmodium falciparum malaria parasites display a THG-sensitive Ca^{2+} pool. Cell Calcium 2003;33(2):137–144.

641. Uhlemann AC, Cameron A, Eckstein-Ludwig U, Fischbarg J, Iserovich P, Zuniga FA, East

M, Lee A, Brady L, Haynes RK, Krishna S. A single amino acid residue can determine the sensitivity of SERCAs to artemisinins. Nat Struct Mol Biol 2005;12(7):628–629.

642. Afonso A, Hunt P, Cheesman S, Alves AC, Cunha CV, do Rosario V, Cravo P. Malaria parasites can develop stable resistance to artemisinin but lack mutations in candidate genes atp6 (encoding the sarcoplasmic and endoplasmic reticulum Ca^{2+} ATPase), tctp, mdr1, and cg10. Antimicrob Agents Chemother 2006;50(2):480–489.

643. Ferreira ID, Martinelli A, Rodrigues LA, do Carmo EL, do Rosario VE, Povoa MM, Cravo P. *Plasmodium falciparum* from Para state (Brazil) shows satisfactory *in vitro* response to artemisinin derivatives and absence of the S769N mutation in the SERCA-type PfAT-Pase6. Trop Med Int Health 2008;13(2):199–207.

644. Dahlstrom S, Veiga MI, Ferreira P, Martensson A, Kaneko A, Andersson B, Bjorkman A, Gil JP. Diversity of the sarco/endoplasmic reticulum Ca^{2+}-ATPase orthologue of *Plasmodium falciparum* (PfATP6). Infect Genet Evol 2008;8(3):340–345.

645. Legrand E, Volney B, Meynard JB, Mercereau-Puijalon O, Esterre P. *In vitro* monitoring of *Plasmodium falciparum* drug resistance in French Guiana: a synopsis of continuous assessment from 1994 to 2005. Antimicrob Agents Chemother 2008;52(1):288–298.

646. Sisowath C, Ferreira PE, Bustamante LY, Dahlstrom S, Martensson A, Bjorkman A, Krishna S, Gil JP. The role of pfmdr1 in *Plasmodium falciparum* tolerance to artemether-lumefantrine in Africa. Trop Med Int Health 2007;12(6):736–742.

647. Jung M, Kim H, Nam KY, No KT. Three-dimensional structure of *Plasmodium falciparum* Ca^{2+}-ATPase(PfATP6) and docking of artemisinin derivatives to PfATP6. Bioorg Med Chem Lett 2005;15(12):2994–2997.

648. Uhlemann AC, Wittlin S, Matile H, Bustamante LY, Krishna S. Mechanism of antimalarial action of the synthetic trioxolane RBX11160 (OZ277). Antimicrob Agents Chemother 2007;51(2):667–672.

649. Francis SE, Sullivan DJ Jr, Goldberg DE. Hemoglobin metabolism in the malaria parasite *Plasmodium falciparum*. Annu Rev Microbiol 1997;51:97–123.

650. Famin O, Krugliak M, Ginsburg H. Kinetics of inhibition of glutathione-mediated degradation of ferriprotoporphyrin IX by antima-

larial drugs. Biochem Pharmacol 1999;58(1):59–68.

651. Kanzok SM, Schirmer RH, Turbachova I, Iozef R, Becker K. The thioredoxin system of the malaria parasite *Plasmodium falciparum*. Glutathione reduction revisited. J Biol Chem 2000;275(51):40180–40186.

652. Rahlfs S, Schirmer RH, Becker K. The thioredoxin system of *Plasmodium falciparum* and other parasites. Cell Mol Life Sci 2002;59(6):1024–1041.

653. Farber PM, Arscott LD, Williams CH Jr, Becker K, Schirmer RH. Recombinant *Plasmodium falciparum* glutathione reductase is inhibited by the antimalarial dye methylene blue. FEBS Lett 1998;422(3):311–314.

654. Farber PM, Becker K, Muller S, Schirmer RH, Franklin RM. Molecular cloning and characterization of a putative glutathione reductase gene, the PfGR2 gene, from *Plasmodium falciparum*. Eur J Biochem 1996;239(3):655–661.

655. Schonleben-Janas A, Kirsch P, Mittl PR, Schirmer RH, Krauth-Siegel RL. Inhibition of human glutathione reductase by 10-arylisoalloxazines: crystalline, kinetic, and electrochemical studies. J Med Chem 1996;39(7):1549–1554.

656. Zhang YA, Hempelmann E, Schirmer RH. Glutathione reductase inhibitors as potential antimalarial drugs. Effects of nitrosoureas on *Plasmodium falciparum in vitro*. Biochem Pharmacol 1988;37(5):855–860.

657. Schirmer RH, Lederbogen F, Krauth-Siegel RL, Eisenbrand G, Schulz GE, Jung A, In: Bray RC, Engel PC, Mayhew G, editors. Flavins and Flavoproteins. Berlin: Walter de Gruyter; 1984. p 847–859.

658. Becker K, Christopherson RI, Cowden WB, Hunt NH, Schirmer RH. Flavin analogs with antimalarial activity as glutathione reductase inhibitors. Biochem Pharmacol 1990;39(1):59–65.

659. Vennerstrom JL, Makler MT, Angerhofer CK, Williams JA. Antimalarial dyes revisited: xanthenes, azines, oxazines, and thiazines. Antimicrob Agents Chemother 1995;39(12):2671–2677.

660. Guttmann P, Ehrlich P. Ueber die Wirkung des Methylenblau bei Malaria. Berl Klin Wochensch 1891;28:953–956.

661. Akoachere M, Buchholz K, Fischer E, Burhenne J, Haefeli WE, Schirmer RH, Becker K. *In vitro* assessment of methylene blue on chloroquine-sensitive and -resistant *Plasmodium falciparum* strains reveals synergistic action

with artemisinins. Antimicrob Agents Che-mother 2005;49(11):4592–4597.

662. Meissner PE, Mandi G, Coulibaly B, Witte S, Tapsoba T, Mansmann U, Rengelshausen J, Schiek W, Jahn A, Walter-Sack I, Mikus G, Burhenne J, Riedel KD, Schirmer RH, Kouyate B, Muller O. Methylene blue for malaria in Africa: results from a dose-finding study in combination with chloroquine. Malar J 2006;5:84.

663. Buchholz K, Schirmer RH, Eubel JK, Akoachere MB, Dandekar T, Becker K, Gromer S. Interactions of methylene blue with human disulfide reductases and their orthologues from *Plasmodium falciparum*. Antimicrob Agents Chemother 2008;52(1):183–191.

664. Davioud-Charvet E, Delarue S, Biot C, Schwobel B, Boehme CC, Mussigbrodt A, Maes L, Sergheraert C, Grellier P, Schirmer RH, Becker K. A prodrug form of a *Plasmodium falciparum* glutathione reductase inhibitor conjugated with a 4-anilinoquinoline. J Med Chem 2001;44(24):4268–4276.

665. Grellier P, Sarlauskas J, Anusevicius Z, Maroziene A, Houee-Levin C, Schrevel J, Cenas N. Antiplasmodial activity of nitroaromatic and quinoidal compounds: redox potential vs. inhibition of erythrocyte glutathione reductase. Arch Biochem Biophys 2001;393(2):199–206.

666. Bauer H, Fritz-Wolf K, Winzer A, Kuhner S, Little S, Yardley V, Vezin H, Palfey B, Schirmer RH, Davioud-Charvet E. A fluoro analogue of the menadione derivative 6-[2′-(3′-methyl)-1′, 4′-naphthoquinolyl]hexanoic acid is a suicide substrate of glutathione reductase. Crystal structure of the alkylated human enzyme. J Am Chem Soc 2006;128(33):10784–10794.

667. Sarma GN, Savvides SN, Becker K, Schirmer M, Schirmer RH, Karplus PA. Glutathione reductase of the malarial parasite *Plasmodium falciparum*: crystal structure and inhibitor development. J Mol Biol 2003;328 (4):893–907.

668. Dubois VL, Platel DF, Pauly G, Tribouley-Duret J. *Plasmodium berghei*: implication of intracellular glutathione and its related enzyme in chloroquine resistance *in vivo*. Exp Parasitol 1995;81(1):117–124.

669. Srivastava P, Puri SK, Kamboj KK, Pandey VC. Glutathione-*S*-transferase activity in malarial parasites. Trop Med Int Health 1999;4 (4):251–254.

670. Liebau E, Bergmann B, Campbell AM, Teesdale-Spittle P, Brophy PM, Luersen K, Walter RD. The glutathione *S*-transferase from *Plas-modium falciparum*. Mol Biochem Parasitol 124:(1–2): 2002; 85–90.

671. Burmeister C, Perbandt M, Betzel C, Walter RD, Liebau E. Crystallization and preliminary X-ray diffraction studies of the glutathione *S*-transferase from *Plasmodium falciparum*. Acta Crystallogr D Biol Crystallogr 2003;59 (Pt8): 1469–1471.

672. Perbandt M, Burmeister C, Walter RD, Betzel C, Liebau E. Native and inhibited structure of a Mu class-related glutathione *S*-transferase from *Plasmodium falciparum*. J Biol Chem 2004;279(2):1336–1342.

673. Fritz-Wolf K, Becker A, Rahlfs S, Harwaldt P, Schirmer RH, Kabsch W, Becker K. X-ray structure of glutathione S-transferase from the malarial parasite Plasmodium falciparum. Proc Natl Acad Sci USA 2003;100(24):13821–13826.

674. Deponte M, Becker K. Glutathione *S*-transferase from malarial parasites: structural and functional aspects. Methods Enzymol 401 2005; 241–253.

675. Harwaldt P, Rahlfs S, Becker K. Glutathione *S*-transferase of the malarial parasite *Plasmodium falciparum*: characterization of a potential drug target. Biol Chem 2002;383 (5):821–830.

676. Ahmad R, Srivastava AK. Inhibition of glutathione-*S*-transferase from *Plasmodium yoelii* by protoporphyrin IX, cibacron blue and menadione: implications and therapeutic benefits. Parasitol Res 2008;102(4):805–807.

677. Ahmad R, Srivastava AK, Tripathi RP, Batra S, Walter RD. Synthesis and biological evaluation of potential modulators of malarial glutathione-*S*-transferase(s). J Enzyme Inhib Med Chem 2007;22(3):327–342.

678. Yu M, Kumar TR, Nkrumah LJ, Coppi A, Retzlaff S, Li CD, Kelly BJ, Moura PA, Lakshmanan V, Freundlich JS, Valderramos JC, Vilcheze C, Siedner M, Tsai JH, Falkard B, Sidhu AB, Purcell LA, Gratraud P, Kremer L, Waters AP, Schiehser G, Jacobus DP, Janse CJ, Ager A, Jacobs WR Jr, Sacchettini JC, Heussler V, Sinnis P, Fidock DA. The fatty acid biosynthesis enzyme FabI plays a key role in the development of liver-stage malarial parasites. Cell Host Microbe 2008;4(6):567–578.

679. McLeod R, Muench SP, Rafferty JB, Kyle DE, Mui EJ, Kirisits MJ, Mack DG, Roberts CW, Samuel BU, Lyons RE, Dorris M, Milhous WK, Rice DW. Triclosan inhibits the growth of *Plasmodium falciparum* and *Toxoplasma gondii* by inhibition of apicomplexan Fab I. Int J Parasitol 2001;31(2):109–113.

680. Surolia N, Surolia A. Triclosan offers protection against blood stages of malaria by inhibiting enoyl-ACP reductase of *Plasmodium falciparum*. Nat Med 2001;7(2):167–173.

681. Suguna K, Surolia A, Surolia N. Structural basis for triclosan and NAD binding to enoyl-ACP reductase of *Plasmodium falciparum*. Biochem Biophys Res Commun 2001;283(1):224–228.

682. Perozzo R, Kuo M, Sidhu AS, Valiyaveettil JT, Bittman R, Jacobs WR Jr, Fidock DA, Sacchettini JC. Structural elucidation of the specificity of the antibacterial agent triclosan for malarial enoyl acyl carrier protein reductase. J Biol Chem 2002;277(15):13106–13114.

683. Chhibber M, Kumar G, Parasuraman P, Ramya TN, Surolia N, Surolia A. Novel diphenyl ethers: design, docking studies, synthesis and inhibition of enoyl ACP reductase of *Plasmodium falciparum* and *Escherichia coli*. Bioorg Med Chem 2006;14(23):8086–8098.

684. Freundlich JS, Wang F, Tsai HC, Kuo M, Shieh HM, Anderson JW, Nkrumah LJ, Valderramos JC, Yu M, Kumar TR, Valderramos SG, Jacobs WR Jr, Schiehser GA, Jacobus DP, Fidock DA, Sacchettini JC. X-ray structural analysis of *Plasmodium falciparum* enoyl acyl carrier protein reductase as a pathway toward the optimization of triclosan antimalarial efficacy. J Biol Chem 2007;282(35):25436–25444.

685. Freundlich JS, Yu M, Lucumi E, Kuo M, Tsai HC, Valderramos JC, Karagyozov L, Jacobs WR Jr, Schiehser GA, Fidock DA, Jacobus DP, Sacchettini JC. Synthesis and biological activity of diaryl ether inhibitors of malarial enoyl acyl carrier protein reductase. Part 2. 2′-Substituted triclosan derivatives. Bioorg Med Chem Lett 2006;16(8):2163–2169.

686. Freundlich JS, Anderson JW, Sarantakis D, Shieh HM, Yu M, Valderramos JC, Lucumi E, Kuo M, Jacobs WR Jr, Fidock DA, Schiehser GA, Jacobus DP, Sacchettini JC. Synthesis, biological activity, and X-ray crystal structural analysis of diaryl ether inhibitors of malarial enoyl acyl carrier protein reductase. Part 1. 4′-Substituted triclosan derivatives. Bioorg Med Chem Lett 2005;15(23):5247–5252.

687. Nicola G, Smith CA, Lucumi E, Kuo MR, Karagyozov L, Fidock DA, Sacchettini JC, Abagyan R. Discovery of novel inhibitors targeting enoyl-acyl carrier protein reductase in *Plasmodium falciparum* by structure-based virtual screening. Biochem Biophys Res Commun 2007;358(3):686–691.

688. Tasdemir D, Lack G, Brun R, Ruedi P, Scapozza L, Perozzo R. Inhibition of *Plasmodium falci-*

689. Sharma SK, Parasuraman P, Kumar G, Surolia N, Surolia A. Green tea catechins potentiate triclosan binding to enoyl-ACP reductase from *Plasmodium falciparum* (PfENR). J Med Chem 2007;50(4):765–775.

690. Seidler J, McGovern SL, Doman TN, Shoichet BK. Identification and prediction of promiscuous aggregating inhibitors among known drugs. J Med Chem 2003;46(21):4477–4486.

691. McGovern SL, Helfand BT, Feng B, Shoichet BK. A specific mechanism of nonspecific inhibition. J Med Chem 2003;46(20):4265–4272.

692. McGovern SL, Shoichet BK. Kinase inhibitors: not just for kinases anymore. J Med Chem 2003;46(8):1478–1483.

693. Tasdemir D, Brun R, Perozzo R, Donmez AA. Evaluation of antiprotozoal and plasmodial enoyl-ACP reductase inhibition potential of Turkish medicinal plants. Phytother Res 2005;19(2):162–166.

694. Giddens A, Nielsen L, Boshoff H, Tasdemir D, Perozzo R, Kaiser M, Wang F, Sacchettini JC, Copp B. Natural product inhibitors of fatty acid biosynthesis: synthesis of the marine microbial metabolites pseudopyronines A and B and evaluation of their anti-infective activites. Tetrahedron. 2008;64:1242–1249.

695. Karioti A, Skaltsa H, Linden A, Perozzo R, Brun R, Tasdemir D. Anthecularin: a novel sesquiterpene lactone from *Anthemis auriculata* with antiprotozoal activity. J Org Chem 2007;72(21):8103–8106.

696. Kuo MR, Morbidoni HR, Alland D, Sneddon SF, Gourlie BB, Staveski MM, Leonard M, Gregory JS, Janjigian AD, Yee C, Musser JM, Kreiswirth B, Iwamoto H, Perozzo R, Jacobs WR Jr, Sacchettini JC, Fidock DA. Targeting tuberculosis and malaria through inhibition of enoyl reductase: compound activity and structural data. J Biol Chem 2003;278(23):20851–20859.

697. Kumar G, Parasuraman P, Sharma SK, Banerjee T, Karmodiya K, Surolia N, Surolia A. Discovery of a rhodanine class of compounds as inhibitors of *Plasmodium falciparum* enoyl-acyl carrier protein reductase. J Med Chem 2007;50(11):2665–2675.

698. Waters NC, Kopydlowski KM, Guszczynski T, Wei L, Sellers P, Ferlan JT, Lee PJ, Li Z, Woodard CL, Shallom S, Gardner MJ, Prigge ST. Functional characterization of the acyl carrier protein (PfACP) and beta-ketoacyl ACP synthase III (PfKASIII) from *Plasmodium fal-*

ciparum. Mol Biochem Parasitol 2002;123 (2):85–94.

699. Prigge ST, He X, Gerena L, Waters NC, Reynolds KA. The initiating steps of a type II fatty acid synthase in *Plasmodium falciparum* are catalyzed by pfACP, pfMCAT, and pfKASIII. Biochemistry 2003;42(4):1160–1169.

700. Waller RF, Keeling PJ, Donald RG, Striepen B, Handman E, Lang-Unnasch N, Cowman AF, Besra GS, Roos DS, McFadden GI. Nuclear-encoded proteins target to the plastid in *Toxoplasma gondii* and *Plasmodium falciparum.* Proc Natl Acad Sci USA 1998;95 (21):12352–12357.

701. Waller RF, Ralph SA, Reed MB, Su V, Douglas JD, Minnikin DE, Cowman AF, Besra GS, McFadden GI. A type II pathway for fatty acid biosynthesis presents drug targets in *Plasmodium falciparum.* Antimicrob Agents Chemother 2003;47(1):297–301.

702. Lack G, Homberger-Zizzari E, Folkers G, Scapozza L, Perozzo R. Recombinant expression and biochemical characterization of the unique elongating beta-ketoacyl-acyl carrier protein synthase involved in fatty acid biosynthesis of *Plasmodium falciparum* using natural and artificial substrates. J Biol Chem 2006;281 (14):9538–9546.

703. Jones SM, Urch JE, Brun R, Harwood JL, Berry C, Gilbert IH. Analogues of thiolactomycin as potential anti-malarial and anti-trypanosomal agents. Bioorg Med Chem 2004;12 (4):683–692.

704. Jones SM, Urch JE, Kaiser M, Brun R, Harwood JL, Berry C, Gilbert IH. Analogues of thiolactomycin as potential antimalarial agents. J Med Chem 2005;48(19):5932–5941.

705. Alhamadsheh MM, Waters NC, Huddler DP, Kreishman-Deitrick M, Florova G, Reynolds KA. Synthesis and biological evaluation of thiazolidine-2-one 1,1-dioxide as inhibitors of *Escherichia coli* beta-ketoacyl-ACP-synthase III (FabH). Bioorg Med Chem Lett 2007;17 (4):879–883.

706. Sharma SK, Kapoor M, Ramya TN, Kumar S, Kumar G, Modak R, Sharma S, Surolia N, Surolia A. Identification, characterization, and inhibition of *Plasmodium falciparum* beta-hydroxyacyl-acyl carrier protein dehydratase (FabZ). J Biol Chem 2003;278(46):45661–45671.

707. Beytia ED, Porter JW. Biochemistry of polyisoprenoid biosynthesis. Annu Rev Biochem 1976;45:113–142.

708. Muller S, Kappes B. Vitamin and cofactor biosynthesis pathways in *Plasmodium* and other apicomplexan parasites. Trends Parasitol 2007;23(3):112–121.

709. Flesch G, Rohmer M. Prokaryotic hopanoids: the biosynthesis of the bacteriohopane skeleton. Formation of isoprenic units from two distinct acetate pools and a novel type of carbon/carbon linkage between a triterpene and D-ribose. Eur J Biochem 1988;175(2):405–411.

710. Rohmer M, Knani M, Simonin P, Sutter B, Sahm H. Isoprenoid biosynthesis in bacteria: a novel pathway for the early steps leading to isopentenyl diphosphate. Biochem J 1993;295 (Pt2): 517–524.

711. Schwender J, Seemann M, Lichtenthaler HK, Rohmer M. Biosynthesis of isoprenoids (carotenoids, sterols, prenyl side-chains of chlorophylls and plastoquinone) via a novel pyruvate/glyceraldehyde 3-phosphate non-mevalonate pathway in the green alga *Scenedesmus obliquus.* Biochem J 1996;316(Pt1): 73–80.

712. Orihara N, Furihata K, Seto H. Studies on the biosynthesis of terpenoidal compounds produced by actinomycetes. 2. Biosynthesis of carquinostatin B via the non-mevalonate pathway in Streptomyces exfoliatus. J Antibiot 1997;50(11):979–981.

713. Orihara N, Kuzuyama T, Takahashi S, Furihata K, Seto H. Studies on the biosynthesis of terpenoid compounds produced by actinomycetes. 3. Biosynthesis of the isoprenoid side chain of novobiocin via the non-mevalonate pathway in Streptomyces niveus. J Antibiot 1998;51(7):676–678.

714. Eisenreich W, Bacher A, Arigoni D, Rohdich F. Biosynthesis of isoprenoids via the non-mevalonate pathway. Cell Mol Life Sci 2004;61 (12):1401–1426.

715. Jomaa H, Wiesner J, Sanderbrand S, Altincicek B, Weidemeyer C, Hintz M, Turbachova I, Eberl M, Zeidler J, Lichtenthaler HK, Soldati D, Beck E. Inhibitors of the nonmevalonate pathway of isoprenoid biosynthesis as antimalarial drugs. Science 1999;285 (5433):1573–1576.

716. Kuzuyama T, Shimizu T, Takahashi S, Seto H. Fosmidomycin, a specific inhibitor of 1-deoxy-D-xylulose 5-phosphate reductoisomerase in the nonmevalonate pathway for terpenoid biosynthesis. Tetrahedron Lett 1998;39:7913–7916.

717. Lell B, Ruangweerayut R, Wiesner J, Missinou MA, Schindler A, Baranek T, Hintz M, Hutchinson D, Jomaa H, Kremsner PG. Fosmidomycin, a novel chemotherapeutic agent for malaria. Antimicrob Agents Chemother 2003;47 (2):735–738.

718. Missinou MA, Borrmann S, Schindler A, Issifou S, Adegnika AA, Matsiegui PB, Binder R, Lell B, Wiesner J, Baranek T, Jomaa H, Kremsner PG. Fosmidomycin for malaria. Lancet 2002;360(9349):1941–1942.

719. Oyakhirome S, Issifou S, Pongratz P, Barondi F, Ramharter M, Kun JF, Missinou MA, Lell B, Kremsner PG. Randomized controlled trial of fosmidomycin-clindamycin versus sulfadoxine-pyrimethamine in the treatment of *Plasmodium falciparum* malaria. Antimicrob Agents Chemother 2007;51(5):1869–1871.

720. Borrmann S, Lundgren I, Oyakhirome S, Impouma B, Matsiegui PB, Adegnika AA, Issifou S, Kun JF, Hutchinson D, Wiesner J, Jomaa H, Kremsner PG. Fosmidomycin plus clindamycin for treatment of pediatric patients aged 1 to 14 years with *Plasmodium falciparum* malaria. Antimicrob Agents Chemother 2006;50 (8):2713–2718.

721. Borrmann S, Adegnika AA, Moussavou F, Oyakhirome S, Esser G, Matsiegui PB, Ramharter M, Lundgren I, Kombila M, Issifou S, Hutchinson D, Wiesner J, Jomaa H, Kremsner PG. Short-course regimens of artesunate-fosmidomycin in treatment of uncomplicated *Plasmodium falciparum* malaria. Antimicrob Agents Chemother 2005;49(9):3749–3754.

722. Steinbacher S, Kaiser J, Eisenreich W, Huber R, Bacher A, Rohdich F. Structural basis of fosmidomycin action revealed by the complex with 2-*C*-methyl-D-erythritol 4-phosphate synthase (IspC). Implications for the catalytic mechanism and anti-malaria drug development. J Biol Chem 2003;278(20):18401–18407.

723. Yajima S, Nonaka T, Kuzuyama T, Seto H, Ohsawa K. Crystal structure of 1-deoxy-D-xylulose 5-phosphate reductoisomerase complexed with cofactors: implications of a flexible loop movement upon substrate binding. J Biochem 2002;131(3):313–317.

724. Reuter K, Sanderbrand S, Jomaa H, Wiesner J, Steinbrecher I, Beck E, Hintz M, Klebe G, Stubbs MT. Crystal structure of 1-deoxy-D-xylulose-5-phosphate reductoisomerase, a crucial enzyme in the non-mevalonate pathway of isoprenoid biosynthesis. J Biol Chem 2002;277(7):5378–5384.

725. Yajima S, Hara K, Sanders JM, Yin F, Ohsawa K, Wiesner J, Jomaa H, Oldfield E. Crystallographic structures of two bisphosphonate:1-deoxyxylulose-5-phosphate reductoisomerase complexes. J Am Chem Soc 2004;126(35):10824–10825.

726. Mac Sweeney A, Lange R, Fernandes RP, Schulz H, Dale GE, Douangamath A, Proteau PJ, Oefner C. The crystal structure of *E.coli* 1-deoxy-D-xylulose-5-phosphate reductoisomerase in a ternary complex with the antimalarial compound fosmidomycin and NADPH reveals a tight-binding closed enzyme conformation. J Mol Biol 2005;345 (1):115–127.

727. Giessmann D, Heidler P, Haemers T, Van Calenbergh S, Reichenberg A, Jomaa H, Weidemeyer C, Sanderbrand S, Wiesner J, Link A. Towards new antimalarial drugs: synthesis of non-hydrolyzable phosphate mimics as feed for a predictive QSAR study on 1-deoxy-D-xylulose-5-phosphate reductoisomerase inhibitors. Chem Biodivers 2008;5(4):643–656.

728. Koppisch AT, Fox DT, Blagg BS, Poulter CD. *E. coli* MEP synthase: steady-state kinetic analysis and substrate binding. Biochemistry 2002;41(1):236–243.

729. Tahar R, Basco LK. Molecular epidemiology of malaria in Cameroon. XXVII. Clinical and parasitological response to sulfadoxine-pyrimethamine treatment and *Plasmodium falciparum* dihydrofolate reductase and dihydropteroate synthase alleles in Cameroonian children. Acta Trop 2007;103(2):81–89.

730. Dharia NV, Sidhu AB, Cassera MB, Westenberger SJ, Bopp SE, Eastman RT, Plouffe D, Batalov S, Park DJ, Volkman SK, Wirth DF, Zhou Y, Fidock DA, Winzeler, EA.. Use of high-density tiling microarrays to identify mutations globally and elucidate mechanisms of drug resistance in *Plasmodium falciparum*. Genome Biol 2009;10(2):R21.

731. Ortmann R, Wiesner J, Reichenberg A, Henschker D, Beck E, Jomaa H, Schlitzer M. Acyloxyalkyl ester prodrugs of FR900098 with improved *in vivo* anti-malarial activity. Bioorg Med Chem Lett 2003;13(13):2163–2166.

732. Reichenberg A, Wiesner J, Weidemeyer C, Dreiseidler E, Sanderbrand S, Altincicek B, Beck E, Schlitzer M, Jomaa H. Diaryl ester prodrugs of FR900098 with improved *in vivo* antimalarial activity. Bioorg Med Chem Lett 2001;11(6):833–835.

733. Haemers T, Wiesner J, Van Poecke S, Goeman J, Henschker D, Beck E, Jomaa H, Van Calenbergh S. Synthesis of alpha-substituted fosmidomycin analogues as highly potent *Plasmodium falciparum* growth inhibitors. Bioorg Med Chem Lett 2006;16(7):1888–1891.

734. Haemers T, Wiesner J, Busson R, Jomaa H, Van Calenbergh S. Synthesis of alpha-aryl-substituted and conformationally restricted fosmidomycin analogues as promising antima-

larials. Eur J Org Chem 2006;2006 (17):3856–3863.

735. Devreux V, Wiesner J, Goeman JL, Van der Eycken J, Jomaa H, Van Calenbergh S. Synthesis and biological evaluation of cyclopropyl analogues of fosmidomycin as potent *Plasmodium falciparum* growth inhibitors. J Med Chem 2006;49(8):2656–2660.

736. Devreux V, Wiesner J, Jomaa H, Rozenski J, Van der Eycken J, Van Calenbergh S. Divergent strategy for the synthesis of alpha-aryl-substituted fosmidomycin analogues. J Org Chem 2007;72(10):3783–3789.

737. Devreux V, Wiesner J, Jomaa H, Van der Eycken J, Van Calenbergh S. Synthesis, evaluation of alpha,beta-unsaturated alpha-aryl-substituted fosmidomycin analogues as DXR inhibitors. Bioorg Med Chem Lett 2007;17 (17):4920–4923.

738. Haemers T, Wiesner J, Giessmann D, Verbrugghen T, Hillaert U, Ortmann R, Jomaa H, Link A, Schlitzer M, Van Calenbergh S. Synthesis of beta- and gamma-oxa isosteres of fosmidomycin and FR900098 as antimalarial candidates. Bioorg Med Chem 2008;16 (6):3361–3371.

739. Perruchon J, Ortmann R, Altenkamper M, Silber K, Wiesner J, Jomaa H, Klebe G, Schlitzer M. Studies addressing the importance of charge in the binding of fosmidomycin-like molecules to deoxyxylulosephosphate reductoisomerase. ChemMedChem 2008;3 (8):1232–1241.

740. Herforth C, Wiesner J, Heidler P, Sanderbrand S, Van Calenbergh S, Jomaa H, Link A. Antimalarial activity of *N*(6)-substituted adenosine derivatives. Part 3. Bioorg Med Chem 2004;12(4):755–762.

741. Rohrich RC, Englert N, Troschke K, Reichenberg A, Hintz M, Seeber F, Balconi E, Aliverti A, Zanetti G, Kohler U, Pfeiffer M, Beck E, Jomaa H, Wiesner J. Reconstitution of an apicoplast-localised electron transfer pathway involved in the isoprenoid biosynthesis of *Plasmodium falciparum*. FEBS Lett 2005;579 (28):6433–6438.

742. Rekittke I, Wiesner J, Rohrich R, Demmer U, Warkentin E, Xu W, Troschke K, Hintz M, No JH, Duin EC, Oldfield E, Jomaa H, Ermler U. Structure of (*E*)-4-hydroxy-3-methyl-but-2-enyl diphosphate reductase, the terminal enzyme of the non-mevalonate pathway. J Am Chem Soc 2008;130(51):17206–17207.

743. Paetzel M, Dalbey RE, Strynadka NC. The structure and mechanism of bacterial type I signal peptidases. A novel antibiotic target. Pharmacol Ther 2000;87(1):27–49.

744. Paetzel M, Karla A, Strynadka NC, Dalbey RE. Signal peptidases. Chem Rev 2002;102 (12):4549–4580.

745. Wu Y, Wang X, Liu X, Wang Y. Data-mining approaches reveal hidden families of proteases in the genome of malaria parasite. Genome Res 2003;13(4):601–616.

746. Sharma S, Pradhan A, Chauhan VS, Tuteja R. Isolation and characterization of type I signal peptidase of different malaria parasites. J Biomed Biotechnol 2005;2005 (4):301–309.

747. Nyborg AC, Ladd TB, Jansen K, Kukar T, Golde TE. Intramembrane proteolytic cleavage by human signal peptide peptidase like 3 and malaria signal peptide peptidase. FASEB J 2006;20(10):1671–1679.

748. Overman RR. Reversible cellular permeability alterations in disease; *in vivo* studies on sodium, potassium and chloride concentrations in erythrocytes of the malarious monkey. Am J Physiol 1948;152(1):113–121.

749. Kirk K, Horner HA, Elford BC, Ellory JC, Newbold Cl. Transport of diverse substrates into malaria-infected erythrocytes via a pathway showing functional characteristics of a chloride channel. J Biol Chem 1994;269(5):3339–3347.

750. Ginsburg H, Kutner S, Krugliak M, Cabantchik ZI. Characterization of permeation pathways appearing in the host membrane of *Plasmodium falciparum* infected red blood cells. Mol Biochem Parasitol 1985;14(3):313–322.

751. Desai SA, Bezrukov SM, Zimmerberg J. A voltage-dependent channel involved in nutrient uptake by red blood cells infected with the malaria parasite. Nature 2000;406 (6799):1001–1005.

752. Cohn JV, Alkhalil A, Wagner MA, Rajapandi T, Desai SA. Extracellular lysines on the plasmodial surface anion channel involved in Na$^+$ exclusion. Mol Biochem Parasitol 2003;132 (1):27–34.

753. Alkhalil A, Cohn JV, Wagner MA, Cabrera JS, Rajapandi T, Desai SA. *Plasmodium falciparum* likely encodes the principal anion channel on infected human erythrocytes. Blood 2004;104(13):4279–4286.

754. Kutner S, Breuer WV, Ginsburg H, Cabantchik ZI. On the mode of action of phlorizin as an antimalarial agent in in *vitro* cultures of *Plasmodium falciparum*. Biochem Pharmacol 1987;36(1):123–129.

755. Kirk K, Horner HA, Spillett DJ, Elford BC. Glibenclamide and meglitinide block the transport of low molecular weight solutes into malaria-infected erythrocytes. FEBS Lett 323: (1–2): 1993; 123–128.

756. Desai SA, Alkhalil A, Kang M, Ashfaq U, Nguyen ML. Plasmodial surface anion channel-independent phloridzin resistance in *Plasmodium falciparum*. J Biol Chem 2005;280 (17):16861–16867.

757. Kang M, Lisk G, Hollingworth S, Baylor SM, Desai SA. Malaria parasites are rapidly killed by dantrolene derivatives specific for the plasmodial surface anion channel. Mol Pharmacol 2005;68(1):34–40.

758. Lisk G, Kang M, Cohn JV, Desai SA. Specific inhibition of the plasmodial surface anion channel by dantrolene. Eukaryot Cell 2006;5 (11):1882–1893.

759. Lisk G, Desai SA. The plasmodial surface anion channel is functionally conserved in divergent malaria parasites. Eukaryot Cell 2005;4 (12):2153–2159.

760. Kelly JX, Winter RW, Braun TP, Osei-Agyemang M, Hinrichs DJ, Riscoe MK. Selective killing of the human malaria parasite *Plasmodium falciparum* by a benzylthiazolium dye. Exp Parasitol 2007;116(2):103–110.

761. Hill DA, Pillai AD, Nawaz F, Hayton K, Doan L, Lisk G, Desai SA. A blasticidin S-resistant *Plasmodium falciparum* mutant with a defective plasmodial surface anion channel. Proc Natl Acad Sci USA 2007;104 (3):1063–1068.

762. Lisk G, Pain M, Gluzman IY, Kambhampati S, Furuya T, Su XZ, Fay MP, Goldberg DE, Desai SA. Changes in the plasmodial surface anion channel reduce leupeptin uptake and can confer drug resistance in *Plasmodium falciparum*-infected erythrocytes. Antimicrob Agents Chemother 2008;52(7):2346–2354.

763. Lindquist S, Craig EA. The heat-shock proteins. Annu Rev Genet 1988;22:631–677.

764. Ellis RJ, Hemmingsen SM. Molecular chaperones: proteins essential for the biogenesis of some macromolecular structures. Trends Biochem Sci 1989;14(8):339–342.

765. Nirmalan N, Sims PF, Hyde JE. Quantitative proteomics of the human malaria parasite *Plasmodium falciparum* and its application to studies of development and inhibition. Mol Microbiol 2004;52(4):1187–1199.

766. Gething MJ, Sambrook J. Protein folding in the cell. Nature 1992;355(6355):33–45.

767. Mattei D, Scherf A, Bensaude O, da Silva LP. A heat shock-like protein from the human malaria parasite *Plasmodium falciparum* induces autoantibodies. Eur J Immunol 1989;19 (10):1823–1828.

768. Gysin J, Dubois P, Pereira da Silva L. Protective antibodies against erythrocytic stages of *Plasmodium falciparum* in experimental infection of the squirrel monkey. Saimiri sciureus. Parasite Immunol 1982;4(6):421–430.

769. Renia L, Mattei D, Goma J, Pied S, Dubois P, Miltgen F, Nussler A, Matile H, Menegaux F, Gentilini M, et al. A malaria heat-shock-like determinant expressed on the infected hepatocyte surface is the target of antibody-dependent cell-mediated cytotoxic mechanisms by nonparenchymal liver cells. Eur J Immunol 1990;20(7):1445–1449.

770. Ardeshir F, Flint JE, Richman SJ, Reese RT. A 75 kD merozoite surface protein of *Plasmodium falciparum* which is related to the 70 kD heat-shock proteins. EMBO J 1987;6(2):493–499.

771. Dubois P, Druilhe P, Arriat D, Jendoubi M, Jouin H. Changes in recognition of *Plasmodium falciparum* antigens by human sera depending on previous malaria exposure. Ann Inst Pasteur Immunol 1987;138(3):383–396.

772. Acharya P, Kumar R, Tatu U. Chaperoning a cellular upheaval in malaria: heat shock proteins in *Plasmodium falciparum*. Mol Biochem Parasitol 2007;153(2):85–94.

773. Bonnefoy S, Attal G, Langsley G, Tekaia F, Mercereau-Puijalon O. Molecular characterization of the heat shock protein 90 gene of the human malaria parasite *Plasmodium falciparum*. Mol Biochem Parasitol 1994;67 (1):157–170.

774. Kumar N, Koski G, Harada M, Aikawa M, Zheng H. Induction and localization of *Plasmodium falciparum* stress proteins related to the heat shock protein 70 family. Mol Biochem Parasitol 1991;48(1):47–58.

775. Syin C, Goldman ND. Cloning of a *Plasmodium falciparum* gene related to the human 60-kDa heat shock protein. Mol Biochem Parasitol 1996;79(1):13–19.

776. Bork P, Sander C, Valencia A, Bukau B. A module of the DnaJ heat shock proteins found in malaria parasites. Trends Biochem Sci 1992;17(4):129.

777. Watanabe J. Cloning and characterization of heat shock protein DnaJ homologues from *Plasmodium falciparum* and comparison

with ring infected erythrocyte surface antigen. Mol Biochem Parasitol 88:(1–2): 1997; 253–258.

778. Dobson S, Kar B, Kumar R, Adams B, Barik S. A novel tetratricopeptide repeat (TPR) containing PP5 serine/threonine protein phosphatase in the malaria parasite, *Plasmodium falciparum*. BMC Microbiol 2001;1:31.

779. Dobson S, May T, Berriman M, Del Vecchio C, Fairlamb AH, Chakrabarti D, Barik S. Characterization of protein Ser/Thr phosphatases of the malaria parasite, *Plasmodium falciparum*: inhibition of the parasitic calcineurin by cyclophilin–cyclosporin complex. Mol Biochem Parasitol 1999;99(2):167–181.

780. Monaghan P, Bell A. A *Plasmodium falciparum* FK506-binding protein (FKBP) with peptidyl-prolyl *cis–trans* isomerase and chaperone activities. Mol Biochem Parasitol 2005;139(2):185–195.

781. Hirtzlin J, Farber PM, Franklin RM, Bell A. Molecular and biochemical characterization of a *Plasmodium falciparum* cyclophilin containing a cleavable signal sequence. Eur J Biochem 1995;232(3):765–772.

782. Berriman M, Fairlamb AH. Berriman M, Fairlamb AH. Detailed characterization of a cyclophilin from the human malaria parasite *Plasmodium falciparum*. Biochem J 1998;334 (Pt2): 437–445.

783. Matambo TS, Odunuga OO, Boshoff A, Blatch GL. Overproduction, purification, and characterization of the *Plasmodium falciparum* heat shock protein 70. Protein Expr Purif 2004;33 (2):214–222.

784. Pesce ER, Acharya P, Tatu U, Nicoll WS, Shonhai A, Hoppe HC, Blatch GL. The *Plasmodium falciparum* heat shock protein 40, Pfj4, associates with heat shock protein 70 and shows similar heat induction and localisation patterns. Int J Biochem Cell Biol 2008;40 (12):2914–2926.

785. Pavithra SR, Kumar R, Tatu U. Systems analysis of chaperone networks in the malarial parasite *Plasmodium falciparum*. PLoS Comput Biol 2007;3(9):1701–1715.

786. Jendoubi M, Bonnefoy S. Identification of a heat shock-like antigen in *P. falciparum*, related to the heat shock protein 90 family. Nucleic Acids Res 1988;16(22):10928.

787. Khachane A, Kumar R, Jain S, Jain S, Banumathy G, Singh V, Nagpal S, Tatu U. "Plasmo2D": an ancillary proteomic tool to aid identification of proteins from *Plasmodium*

falciparum. J Proteome Res 2005;4 (6):2369–2374.

788. Banumathy G, Singh V, Pavithra SR, Tatu U. Heat shock protein 90 function is essential for *Plasmodium falciparum* growth in human erythrocytes. J Biol Chem 2003;278 (20):18336–18345.

789. Solit DB, Chiosis G. Development and application of Hsp90 inhibitors. Drug Discov Today 13:(1–2): 2008; 38–43.

790. Chaudhury S, Welch TR, Blagg BS. Hsp90 as a target for drug development. ChemMedChem 2006;1(12):1331–1340.

791. Taldone T, Sun W, Chiosis G. Discovery and development of heat shock protein 90 inhibitors. Bioorg Med Chem 2009;17(6):2225–2235.

792. Taldone T, Gozman A, Maharaj R, Chiosis G. Targeting Hsp90: small-molecule inhibitors and their clinical development. Curr Opin Pharmacol 2008;8(4):370–374.

793. Ganesh T, Min J, Thepchatri P, Du Y, Li L, Lewis I, Wilson L, Fu H, Chiosis G, Dingledine R, Liotta D, Snyder JP, Sun A. Discovery of aminoquinolines as a new class of potent inhibitors of heat shock protein 90 (Hsp90): synthesis, biology, and molecular modeling. Bioorg Med Chem 2008;16(14):6903–6910.

794. Muranaka K, Sano A, Ichikawa S, Matsuda A. Synthesis of Hsp90 inhibitor dimers as potential antitumor agents. Bioorg Med Chem 2008;16(11):5862–5870.

795. Du Y, Moulick K, Rodina A, Aguirre J, Felts S, Dingledine R, Fu H, Chiosis G. High-throughput screening fluorescence polarization assay for tumor-specific Hsp90. J Biomol Screen 2007;12(7):915–924.

796. Rodina A, Vilenchik M, Moulick K, Aguirre J, Kim J, Chiang A, Litz J, Clement CC, Kang Y, She Y, Wu N, Felts S, Wipf P, Massague J, Jiang X, Brodsky JL, Krystal GW, Chiosis G. Selective compounds define Hsp90 as a major inhibitor of apoptosis in small-cell lung cancer. Nat Chem Biol 2007;3(8):498–507.

797. Ansar S, Burlison JA, Hadden MK, Yu XM, Desino KE, Bean J, Neckers L, Audus KL, Michaelis ML, Blagg BS. A non-toxic Hsp90 inhibitor protects neurons from Abeta-induced toxicity. Bioorg Med Chem Lett 2007;17(7):1984–1990.

798. Sharp SY, Prodromou C, Boxall K, Powers MV, Holmes JL, Box G, Matthews TP, Cheung KM, Kalusa A, James K, Hayes A, Hardcastle A, Dymock B, Brough PA, Barril X, Cansfield JE, Wright L, Surgenor A, Foloppe N, Hubbard RE, Aherne W, Pearl L, Jones K, McDonald E,

Raynaud F, Eccles S, Drysdale M, Workman P. Inhibition of the heat shock protein 90 molecular chaperone *in vitro* and *in vivo* by novel, synthetic, potent resorcinylic pyrazole/isoxazole amide analogues. Mol Cancer Ther 2007;6 (4):1198–1211.

799. Sharp SY, Boxall K, Rowlands M, Prodromou C, Roe SM, Maloney A, Powers M, Clarke PA, Box G, Sanderson S, Patterson L, Matthews TP, Cheung KM, Ball K, Hayes A, Raynaud F, Marais R, Pearl L, Eccles S, Aherne W, McDonald E, Workman P. *In vitro* biological characterization of a novel, synthetic diaryl pyrazole resorcinol class of heat shock protein 90 inhibitors. Cancer Res 2007;67 (5):2206–2216.

800. Kasibhatla SR, Hong K, Biamonte MA, Busch DJ, Karjian PL, Sensintaffar JL, Kamal A, Lough RE, Brekken J, Lundgren K, Grecko R, Timony GA, Ran Y, Mansfield R, Fritz LC, Ulm E, Burrows FJ, Boehm MF. Rationally designed high-affinity 2-amino-6-halopurine heat shock protein 90 inhibitors that exhibit potent antitumor activity. J Med Chem 2007;50(12):2767–2778.

801. Park H, Kim YJ, Hahn JS. A novel class of Hsp90 inhibitors isolated by structure-based virtual screening. Bioorg Med Chem Lett 2007;17(22):6345–6349.

802. Le Bras G, Radanyi C, Peyrat JF, Brion JD, Alami M, Marsaud V, Stella B, Renoir JM. New novobiocin analogues as antiproliferative agents in breast cancer cells and potential inhibitors of heat shock protein 90. J Med Chem 2007;50(24):6189–6200.

803. DeBoer C, Meulman PA, Wnuk RJ, Peterson DH. Geldanamycin, a new antibiotic. J Antibiot 1970;23(9):442–447.

804. Whitesell L, Mimnaugh EG, De Costa B, Myers CE, Neckers LM. Inhibition of heat shock protein HSP90-pp60v-src heteroprotein complex formation by benzoquinone ansamycins: essential role for stress proteins in oncogenic transformation. Proc Natl Acad Sci USA 1994;91(18):8324–8328.

805. Kumar R, Musiyenko A, Barik S. The heat shock protein 90 of *Plasmodium falciparum* and antimalarial activity of its inhibitor, geldanamycin. Malar J 2003;2:30.

806. Kumar R, Musiyenko A, Barik S. *Plasmodium falciparum* calcineurin and its association with heat shock protein 90: mechanisms for the antimalarial activity of cyclosporin A and synergism with geldanamycin. Mol Biochem Parasitol 2005;141(1):29–37.

807. Solit DB, Osman I, Polsky D, Panageas KS, Daud A, Goydos JS, Teitcher J, Wolchok JD, Germino FJ, Krown SE, Coit D, Rosen N, Chapman PB. Phase II trial of 17-allylamino-17-demethoxygeldanamycin in patients with metastatic melanoma. Clin Cancer Res 2008;14(24):8302–8307.

808. Grem JL, Morrison G, Guo XD, Agnew E, Takimoto CH, Thomas R, Szabo E, Grochow L, Grollman F, Hamilton JM, Neckers L, Wilson RH. Phase I and pharmacologic study of 17-(allylamino)-17-demethoxygeldanamycin in adult patients with solid tumors. J Clin Oncol 2005;23(9):1885–1893.

809. Ramanathan RK, Egorin MJ, Eiseman JL, Ramalingam S, Friedland D, Agarwala SS, Ivy SP, Potter DM, Chatta G, Zuhowski EG, Stoller RG, Naret C, Guo J, Belani CP. Phase I and pharmacodynamic study of 17-(allylamino)-17-demethoxygeldanamycin in adult patients with refractory advanced cancers. Clin Cancer Res 2007;13(6):1769–1774.

810. Solit DB, Ivy SP, Kopil C, Sikorski R, Morris MJ, Slovin SF, Kelly WK, DeLaCruz A, Curley T, Heller G, Larson S, Schwartz L, Egorin MJ, Rosen N, Scher HI. Phase I trial of 17-allylamino-17-demethoxygeldanamycin in patients with advanced cancer. Clin Cancer Res 2007;13(6):1775–1782.

811. Banerji U, O'Donnell A, Scurr M, Pacey S, Stapleton S, Asad Y, Simmons L, Maloney A, Raynaud F, Campbell M, Walton M, Lakhani S, Kaye S, Workman P, Judson I. Phase I pharmacokinetic and pharmacodynamic study of 17-allylamino, 17-demethoxygeldanamycin in patients with advanced malignancies. J Clin Oncol 2005;23(18):4152–4161.

812. Goetz MP, Toft D, Reid J, Ames M, Stensgard B, Safgren S, Adjei AA, Sloan J, Atherton P, Vasile V, Salazaar S, Adjei A, Croghan G, Erlichman C. Phase I trial of 17-allylamino-17-demethoxygeldanamycin in patients with advanced cancer. J Clin Oncol 2005;23(6):1078–1087.

813. Nadler SG, Tepper MA, Schacter B, Mazzucco CE. Interaction of the immunosuppressant deoxyspergualin with a member of the Hsp70 family of heat shock proteins. Science 1992;258 (5081):484–486.

814. Nadler SG, Dischino DD, Malacko AR, Cleaveland JS, Fujihara SM, Marquardt H. Identification of a binding site on Hsc70 for the immunosuppressant 15-deoxyspergualin. Biochem Biophys Res Commun 1998;253(1):176–180.

815. Midorikawa Y, Haque QM. 15-Deoxyspergualin, an immunosuppressive agent, used in or-

gan transplantation showed suppressive effects on malarial parasites. Chemotherapy 1997;43(1):31–35.

816. Midorikawa Y, Haque QM, Nakazawa S. Inhibition of malaria-infected erythrocytes by deoxyspergualin: effect on in *vitro* growth of malarial cultures. Chemotherapy 1998;44 (6):409–413.

817. Ramya TN, Karmodiya K, Surolia A, Surolia N. 15-deoxyspergualin primarily targets the trafficking of apicoplast proteins in *Plasmodium falciparum*. J Biol Chem 2007;282 (9):6388–6397.

818. Ramya TN, Surolia N, Surolia A. 15-Deoxyspergualin modulates *Plasmodium falciparum* heat shock protein function. Biochem Biophys Res Commun 2006;348(2):585–592.

819. Dominguez JN, Leon C, Rodrigues J, Gamboa de Dominguez N, Gut J, Rosenthal PJ. Synthesis and evaluation of new antimalarial phenylurenyl chalcone derivatives. J Med Chem 48:(10): 3654–3658. 2005;.

820. Ersmark K, Samuelsson B, Hallberg A. Plasmepsins as potential targets for new antimalarial therapy. Med Res Rev 2006;26 (5):626–666.

821. Roth B, Falco EA, Hitchings GH, Bushby SR. 5-Benzyl-2,4-diaminopyrimidines as antibacterial agents. I. Synthesis and antibacterial activity in *vitro*. J Med Pharm Chem 1962;91:1103–1123.

822. Falco EA, Goodwin LG, Hitchings GH, Rollo IM, Russell PB. 2:4-Diaminopyrimidines: a new series of antimalarials. Br J Pharmacol Chemother 1951;6(2):185–200.

823. Carrington HC, Crowther AF, Davey DG, Levi AA, Rose FL. A metabolite of paludrine with high antimalarial activity. Nature 1951;168 (4288):1080.

ANTITUBERCULAR AGENTS

Courtney C. Aldrich[1]
Helena I. Boshoff[2]
Rory P. Remmel[3]

[1] Center for Drug Design,
Academic Health Center,
University of Minnesota,
Minneapolis, MN
[2] Tuberculosis Research Section,
National Institute of Allergy and
Infectious Diseases, Bethesda, MD
[3] Department of Medicinal
Chemistry,
University of Minnesota,
Minneapolis, MN

1. TUBERCULOSIS: A GLOBAL PUBLIC HEALTH THREAT

Tuberculosis (TB) is the second major cause of death due to an infectious disease worldwide, superseded only by HIV/AIDS. Since the advent of chemotherapy, the incidence of TB in the developed world rapidly declined, although rates started increasing by the mid-1980s. In the early 1990s, outbreaks of multidrug-resistant tuberculosis (MDR-TB) occurred in a few large cities, such as in New York City, with associated high fatality rates, arousing international health concerns. The World Health Organization (WHO) declared TB a global emergency in 1993. It is estimated that about one-third of the world's population is latently infected with *Mycobacterium tuberculosis*, the causative agent of this disease. The lifetime risk for immunocompetent individuals for developing active disease from their latent infection is estimated to be 10%. However, in individuals coinfected with HIV, the annual risk of developing active TB is much higher. The WHO reported 1.7 million deaths due to TB and 9.2 million new cases of TB for 2006 of which approximately 45% were smear-positive [1]. Smear-positive cases refer to those patients in whom mycobacteria can be visualized in the sputum by an acid-fast stain. The highest prevalence of TB was reported for India followed by China, Indonesia, South Africa, and Nigeria [1]. High rates of MDR-TB have also been reported in the Baltic States and Russia. The spread of HIV infec-

tion has contributed to the increase in TB with the global HIV prevalence in reported TB cases being about 7.7%. This incidence varies dramatically between countries with some countries, in particular Kenya, South Africa, and Zimbabwe, showing HIV prevalence rates from 43% to 52% in TB cases [1]. More than 98% of deaths from TB occur in developing countries with African countries generally having the highest mortality rates [1]. In the United States, over one-half of the reported cases are in foreign-born individuals; 13,779 cases were reported to the CDC in 2006.

The incidence of TB in terms of new cases per capita has decreased globally since 2003 in many countries, which is largely ascribed to the success of DOTS (directly observed therapy, short-course), a major recommendation by the WHO. DOTS is a five-point strategy involving government commitment to TB control programs, diagnosis through staining for mycobacteria in sputum smears in symptomatic patients, standardized short-course chemotherapy provided under direct observation for at least the first 2 months, sufficient drug supply, and a system for recording and reporting cases and treatment results. The most common form of short-course chemotherapy consists of an intensive phase of 2 months with daily dosing of isoniazid, rifampin (RIF), pyrazinamide (PZA), and ethambutol (EMB) (or streptomycin) followed by a 4-month continuation phase of isoniazid and rifampin (±ethambutol). This grueling 6-month regimen is associated with many unpleasant side effects, which often results in poor compliance of patients. In addition, the ability of the intensive phase to kill the majority of mycobacteria in the active lesions that are contributing to sputum counts within the first 2 months is associated with relief from many of the clinical symptoms with the results that patients sometimes discontinue therapy [2]. Thus, the theoretical 95% success rate of DOTS is often not achieved. Such patients likely relapse with the disease and stand the risk of developing drug-resistant TB.

The development of drug-resistant TB is indirectly correlated with the quality of TB control programs [3]. Drug-resistant TB arises when patients default on chemotherapy, irregularly take medications or when improper treatments such as monotherapy or inappropriate drug combinations are prescribed. Multidrug-resistant TB occurs when *M. tuberculosis* has become resistant to at least rifampin as well as isoniazid. Extensively drugresistant TB (XDR-TB) is defined as MDR-TB with additional resistance to a fluoroquinolone (ofloxacin or moxifloxacin) as well as a second-line injectable (capreomycin, amikacin, or kanamycin). Both MDR-TB and XDR-TB are global public health threats that threaten to overturn any successes made in global TB control. There are about half a million cases of MDR-TB worldwide although the numbers are unreliable due to lack of diagnosis in many of the countries bearing the highest burden of TB drug resistance in the world [4]. The prognosis of XDR-TB is extremely poor with few resources left for treatment [4].

2. HISTORY OF TUBERCULOSIS

Tuberculosis has plagued mankind for millennia and the implication for the antiquity of human infection with this disease comes from skeletal evidence of extrapulmonary dissemination to the bones in a 500,000-old *Homo erectus* fossil from Turkey [5]. Molecular evidence for the presence of *M. tuberculosis* DNA has been discovered in bones from excavations of Neolithic remains dating back as far as 9000 BC [6]. Macromorphological evidence for tuberculosis has been reported in mummies recovered from a period dating from predynastic (3500–2700 BC) up to late period (1450–500 BC) recovered from Egypt as evidenced by characteristic skeletal changes, in particular Pott's disease and even pulmonary lesions, of which many cases were verified by more precise molecular methods [7,8]. The ancient global spread of this disease is evidenced by the finding of paleopathological evidence of this disease in Neolithic remains from Scandinavia [9], reports about the disease in ancient Chinese literature (around 4000 BC) [10] and molecular evidence for *M. tuberculosis* DNA in a 1000-year-old Peruvian mummy [11] as well as microbiologic evidence from an Inca child from ca. 700 BC, both predating European colonization of the Americas. The original hypotheses that humans acquired tuberculosis

from animals during their domestication was overturned when whole genome sequencing and analysis of genome deletions revealed that *M. tuberculosis* evolutionary predates *Mycobacterium bovis*, the etiological agent of bovine and other mammalian tuberculosis [12,13].

Our understanding of the disease tuberculosis is based on the cumulative findings and paradigm shifts in accepted hypotheses over more than 2000 years. The ancient Greek physician Hippocrates (460–370 BC) described the concept of pulmonary phthisis (Greek for consumption), which is likely attributed to tuberculosis. Phthisis was reported to be the most common disease of that period and usually proved to be fatal. Hippocrates also observed tubercles in the tissues of animals but the connection with the symptoms was not made. The disease was thought to be heritable but Greek philosopher Aristotle (384–322 BC) questioned the heritability of phthisis by commenting on the apparently contagious nature of the symptoms. Claudius Galenus (129–200 AD) also alleged the contagious nature of phthisis. The fifth century Roman, Caelius Aurelianus, accurately described the symptoms of consumption. History shows that phthisis was still considered by many to be a hereditary disease or disease acquired by supernatural means. The Italian physician, Girolamo Fracastoro (1478–1553), proposed that the transmission of epidemic diseases such as phthisis was due to particulates or "spores" that could cause disease by direct or indirect contact and that could even travel great distances and he remarked on the hereditary susceptibility of consumption by noting on how this disease afflicted different generations of the same family. He also mentions that the disease comes from pus-discharging lung lesions. His thinking dominated the Italian medical field over the next century with laws created that stipulated that belongings from consumptive patients be burned after death. The German-born Dutch physician, Franciscus Sylvius (1614–1672), described the lung lesions and other organ lesions as a characteristic of all patients that died from phthisis. The word "tubercle" was coined by English physician Richard Morton (1637–1698), who noted that all lungs of tuberculosis patients had tubercles (tuberculosis lesions) and claimed that the disease had three stages: inflammation, followed by tubercle formation, and concluded in consumption. He described the various forms of tuberculosis, which is still an important challenge in understanding human tuberculosis today. The word "tubercle" was used in 1839 by Johann Lukas Schönlein in introducing the term "tuberculosis" to describe the disease underlying the lung lesions that defined consumption. Sylvius and to some extent Morton believed that the disease was hereditary. However, the English physician Benjamin Marten (1704–1722) wrote that phthisis could also be transmitted by contact with diseased individuals and that breathing the air exhaled by a consumptive individual could lead to disease in healthy persons. Leopold von Auenbrugg (1722–1809) developed percussion as a diagnostic technique for pulmonary diseases and demonstrated how percussion might be used to detect the nature and size of lung cavities in phthisis patients. His ideas were further developed by the French physician René-Théophile-Hyacinthe Laennec (1781–1826), who developed the stethoscope for diagnosis of diseases by auscultation. Laennec, who died from tuberculosis at a relatively young age, questioned the contagious nature of the disease by considering the growth of lesions as a cancerous development.

There was still strong support for the noncontagious nature of phthisis although evidence to the contrary was growing. Clearly, infectiousness is not self-evident since we now know that only about 10% of those infected with tuberculosis go on to develop symptomatic disease. Philipp Klencke (1831–1881) provided the first proof of the infectiousness of tuberculosis by showing the rabbits that were injected with tubercle material all became diseased and died although he still considered the disease cancerous in nature. Jean Antoine Villemin (1827–1892) developed this idea further by showing that rabbits or guinea pigs injected with tuberculous material from consumptive humans or cattle developed disease and that this disease could further be propagated between laboratory animals. He concluded that consumption was caused by a microorganism. Theodor Klebs (1834–1913) was able to culture the causative agent of tuberculosis *in vitro* and demonstrated that the cultured organism caused disease in animals. The next great pioneer in tuberculosis research was Robert Koch (1843–1910) who in 1882 was able to microscopically visualize *M. tuberculosis* in infected tissues with special staining reagents (acid-fast stain). He was finally able to grow pure cultures of this organism and demonstrated that it led to disease in animals upon their inoculation. His discovery led to the formulation of Koch's postulates for identifying the causal relationship between disease and the responsible microbe. Koch also developed an extract of dead tuberculosis bacilli (tuberculin), which initially raised interest as a potential vaccine. However, the use of tuberculin as a vaccine was a dismal failure but later proved to be tremendously valuable in identifying infected individuals. Thus, Clemens Peter von Pirquet (1874–1929) demonstrated that infected individuals displayed a hypersensitivity reaction when exposed to extracts from the infectious organism. This idea was developed further by Charles Mantoux (1877–1947), who introduced the intradermal skin test reaction (PPD test) to tuberculin to identify infected individuals. The discovery of X-rays by Wilhelm Röentgen (1845–1923) later proved to be invaluable for diagnosis and monitoring of tuberculosis.

The treatment of tuberculosis began to develop with the establishment of sanatoria in the mid-nineteenth century. Hermann Brehmer (1826–1889) founded the first sanatorium in Germany in 1856 and after that more sanatoria were developed in the Western world. Although patients often recovered in sanatoria, the subsequent relapse and mortality rate was high. Albert Calmette (1863–1933) and Camille Guérin (1872–1961) produced a strain of *M. bovis* (bacille Calmette-Guérin) after more than 230 passages in culture that was no longer virulent in laboratory animals. Vaccination started in the 1920s but retrospectively results showed that vaccination was not particularly effective at reducing pulmonary tuberculosis; although it dramatically protected children born into families with tuberculosis patients. This protection was later ascribed to protection against miliary TB and meningitis. In the 1930s, various forms of partial lung collapse therapy were introduced that showed more promising results in halting disease progression. These treatments were often quite effective at reducing sputum counts since the collapse often led to blockage of the bronchus linked to the major cavity associated with active disease. The prevention of bovine tuberculosis by slaughtering of tuberculin-positive animals from farming herds and the pasteurization of milk also had a positive outcome on incidence of tuberculosis caused by *M. bovis*. The discovery of streptomycin by Selman Waksman (1888–1973) catapulted the era of chemotherapy of tuberculosis. The first tuberculosis patient was treated with streptomycin in 1943 with astounding success. The first randomized trial with streptomycin for tuberculosis treatment was done in 1947 by the British MRC Tuberculosis Research Unit, which showed promising results although this study also encountered the selection of resistant mutants by this single-drug regimen (Mitchison, 1950). A rapid succession of other drugs were introduced soon thereafter for tuberculosis chemotherapy including thiacetazone (1946), *para*-aminosalicylic acid (1949), isoniazid (1952), pyrazinamide (1954), D-cycloserine (1955), ethionamide (1956), ethambutol (1962), and rifampin (1968).

3. *M. TUBERCULOSIS*: THE ORGANISM

M. tuberculosis belongs to the family Mycobacteriaceae within the order Actinomycetales within the phylum Actinobacteria. The family Mycobacteriaceae contains some of the oldest scourges of mankind including tuberculosis and leprosy, the latter caused by *Mycobacterium leprae*. Although more than a 125 mycobacterial species are known, the majority of mycobacteria are environmental saprophytes with only a few species causing chronic infections in man. Mycobacteria are classified as slow-growers or fast-growers depending on their ability to form colonies in solid media in 7 days, the exception being *M. leprae*, which cannot be cultured *in vitro*. Mycobacteria are aerobic nonmotile, nonsporulating rod-shaped bacteria that are usually acid-alcohol fast. One of the defining characteristics of mycobacteria is

their high lipid content comprising roughly 60% of dry cell weight and the mycolyl-arabinogalactan macromolecule, which is covalently linked to the cell wall peptidoglycan forming the mycolyl-arabinogalactan-peptidoglycan (mAGP) complex (discussed further in Section 5) [14]. An outer lipid layer exterior to the mycolates is also found that gives the mycobacterial cell wall model some similarity to the Gram-negative cell wall structure although mycobacteria are typically considered as Gram positive due to their lack of the classical Gram-negative outer membrane.

M. tuberculosis is a member of the *M. tuberculosis* complex (MTC), which also comprises *Mycobacterium africanum*, *M. microti*, *M. bovis*, *M. caprae*, and *M. pinnipedii* although the latter two are often considered subspecies of *M. bovis*. The natural host for *M. tuberculosis* is man although experimental infection in other animal models can be achieved. In contrast, *M. bovis* has the widest host range infecting a wide variety of mammalian species [12,13]. The wider host range of *M. bovis* can only be ascribed to differences in gene expression since it shares more than 99.9% sequence identity with *M. tuberculosis* with no genes being unique to *M. bovis* [12,13].

Members of the MTC are not unique in their ability to result in pulmonary disease although these are the only species for which natural transmission is almost exclusively by man–man or animal–man contact. Most other mycobacterial diseases, whether lung or nonpulmonary sites, are thought to be predominantly acquired from environmental sources and not transmitted through man-to-man or animal-to-man contact. The waxy cell wall makes mycobacteria particularly difficult to eradicate with common disinfectants and municipal tap water. Due to acquisition from environmental sources, infections with nontuberculous mycobacteria (NTM) show geographical bias in their distribution, with infections due to certain mycobacterial species predominating in areas where they are commonly found. The most frequent NTM associated with pulmonary disease are members of the *Mycobacterium avium* complex (MAC) followed by *M. kansasii*, *M. abscessus*, *M. fortuitum*, and *M. chelonae* [15,16]. Other mycobacteria associated with rare cases of pulmonary disease include *M. immunogenem, M. mucogenicum, M. smegmatis, M. goodii, M. massiliense,* and *M. bolletii* [15]. Pulmonary disease caused by NTM is often associated with other underlying chronic lung diseases such as bronchiectasis and cystic fibrosis. Disseminated disease with NTM is uncommon and is usually associated with immunosuppression or immunodeficiencies.

Prophylaxis of infections with NTM is problematic with most NTM being resistant to standard front-line antitubercular drugs [15,16]. *M. kansasii* is sensitive to isoniazid, rifampin, ethambutol, clarithromycin and these are generally used for treatment with such infections although a lengthy treatment (18 months) is generally required for pulmonary disease. Pulmonary MAC infections are usually treated with clarithromycin or azithromycin, rifampin, ethambutol, and streptomycin for 1 year. For other pulmonary NTM, the mainstay of treatment is usually amikacin and clarithromycin with lengthy treatments required to eradicate the bacilli.

4. LIFESTYLE OF *M. TUBERCULOSIS*

In immunocompetent individuals infection with *M. tuberculosis* is associated with pulmonary involvement in more than 85% of cases [17]. Members of the MTC parasitize the front-line of defense against invading microbes, the macrophage. Upon inhalation of *M. tuberculosis*, the organism invades alveolar macrophages that subsequently cross the lung epithelium. Invasion results in formation of a membrane-bound vacuole, the phagosome, containing the mycobacterium. Entry of host cells is mediated by a variety of receptors on the macrophage. Complement receptors and the mannose receptor are believed to be most important, although type A scavenger receptor and for some cell types DC-SIGN and CD14 may also play a role [18,19]. Invasion through the complement receptor route triggers the least production of reactive oxygen intermediates and other toxic host cell responses and suppresses IL-12 production, although utilization of other receptors in the absence of complement receptors appears to have little

effect on the outcome of disease [18]. Cell invasion through ligation of the host mannose receptor through mycobacterial lipoarabinomannans (LAMs) in the bacterial cell wall is similarly associated with lack of activation of NADP oxidase and use of this pathway appears to limit fusion of the phagosome with degradative lysosomes.

Key to the success of *M. tuberculosis* as a pathogen is its ability to interfere with host signaling pathways thereby inhibiting phagosome maturation and activation of the macrophage. The *M. tuberculosis*-infected phagosome of resting macrophages has many characteristics of early endosomes and maintains access to nutrients through the rapid recycling pathway. Although many mycobacterial lipids have been shown to inhibit phagosome maturation and other aspects of macrophage activation, there is a crucial difference between phagosomes containing dead as opposed to live *M. tuberculosis* with the former reaching a later stage of phagosome maturation. Several studies have investigated the transcriptional events that occur during various stages of macrophage infection and several candidates have been identified that are critical for this process including a serine/threonine kinase (PknG), a phosphatase (SapM), as well as components of a novel highly specialized protein secretion apparatus encoded by a genetic region (RD 1) that is deleted in the attenuated *M. bovis* BCG strain [20].

Clearly the interplay between host and pathogen is an intricate process with 90% of individuals that become productively infected not developing active tuberculosis. Multiplication of the bacillus in the macrophage and secretion of a set of mycobacterial antigens through a specialized secretion apparatus attracts other macrophages that form the next wave of host target cells [21]. These macrophages phagocytose apoptotic infected macrophages. The cytokines released by infected macrophages recruit lymphocytes that start forming a cuff around the infected focus. This leads to the formation of a granuloma, driven by complex signaling pathways of chemokines and adhesion molecules. Infected macrophages are able to egress from early granulomas and migrate to new areas of the lung where secondary granulomas develop [21].

M. tuberculosis also affects the interaction between infected macrophages and immune cells by modulating antigen presentation to T cells as well as direct effects on surrounding immune cells. Major histocompatibility complex (MHC) class II-restricted CD4+ cells are central mediators of protective immunity to *M. tuberculosis* although MHC class I-restricted CD8+ T cells also play an important role. The non-MHC CD1-restricted T cells have also been shown to be important in recognizing mycobacterial lipids and glycolipids including mycolates, lipoarabinomannan, trehalose sulfolipids, dideoxymycobactin, and mannosyl-β-1-phosphoisoprenoids. CD1-restricted T cells also play a role in control of infection through their cytolytic activity, secretion of proinflammatory cytokines, release of antimicrobial effectors, and, for some classes of these cells, maturation of dendritic cells [22]. T-cell activation is often incapable of completely eradicating live bacilli that can to some extent be ascribed to suppression of *M. tuberculosis*-specific CD4+ T cells by regulatory T cells [23]. The balance between successful T-cell activation and failure to develop critical aspects of immunity are not fully understood but have been shown to depend on both genetics of the *M. tuberculosis* strain as well as host genetic factors [24–27]. Genes that have been shown to be critically important for the host response to tuberculosis are ligands and receptors in the IFN-γ and IL-12 pathways [26,28]. However, other genes have also been implicated including SP110 [28], the ATP binding P2X(7) receptors [29], DC-SIGN, pentraxin 3, and vitamin D receptors [30]. The SP110 gene is the human homolog of the mouse Ipr1 gene that has been shown to be required for switching infected macrophages from a necrotic to an apoptic state resulting in a more mycobactericidal pathway [24]. During acquisition of acquired immunity, *M. tuberculosis*-specific T cells activate infected macrophages altering the fate of the pathogen. The stimulation of immune cells by mycobacterial products in this process leads to release of bactericidal products such as reactive oxygen intermediates by activated host macrophages. Nitric oxide is cidal for *M. tuberculosis* but at low levels results in activation of

the dormancy response in this organism. Dormancy is regulated by a key transcriptional regulator, DosR. DosR-mediated transcriptional regulation leads to a regulated shutdown of key metabolic processes and an adaptation to nonreplicating persistence [20,31,32].

Other factors that contribute to adaptation to nonreplicating persistence include the hypoxia that arises due to the growing wall of immune cells around the focus of infection, nutrient starvation, and low pH associated with phagosomes of activated macrophages [20]. The factors that lead to a state of nonreplicating persistence as opposed to killing of the mycobacteria by activated host cells are not clearly understood. Activation of host defenses through IFN-γ-mediated signaling is critical, resulting in not only iNOS activation with subsequent nitric oxide release, but also increased maturation of phagosomes through an LRG-47-mediated pathway (GTPase) that may recruit the acidifying capabilities of the H+-ATPase [33]. Clearly reactive oxygen intermediates and NO play a role although *M. tuberculosis* has developed effective mechanisms of dealing with damage caused by these effectors. Other killing mechanisms have also been described including autophagy [34] and antimicrobial peptides such as proteolytic products of ubiquitin [35]. The development of the granuloma halts the development and spread of the disease. It is thought that granulomas harboring nonreplicating bacilli characterize latent disease although latent disease is clearly a complex phenomenon with a heterogeneity of clinical phenotypes associated with "latent" disease. The factors that contribute to reactivation of these bacilli are not understood although it is clear that there is a constant interplay between host and pathogen with constant release of mycobacterial antigens leading to continued immune surveillance and proliferative activity [36]. In immune-compromised individuals and individuals in whom levels of a key cytokine critical for maintaining granulomas (TNF-α) are decreased, suppression of *M. tuberculosis* replication is compromised and reactivation occurs by unknown mechanisms [27]. Liquefaction of the granuloma center and florid mycobacterial growth occurs. Microscopic observation of granulomas excised from TB patients has revealed growth of *M. tuberculosis* in macrophages at the cavity wall surface [37] as well as extracellular growth in the liquefied granuloma centers [38,39]. The granulomas can then erode into the airways releasing their contents into the bronchus. Irritation of the bronchi and severe coughing up of blood (hemoptysis) is associated with severe active disease and detection of acid-fast bacilli in the sputum. Thus, granulomas are essential for containing the disease but are also vital for its transmission and common symptoms.

The challenge of chemotherapy of tuberculosis is that drugs need to overcome several of the obstacles associated with the lifestyle of this pathogen. First, during the intracellular stage of the disease, drugs must be able to cross the macrophage and phagosome membranes without being modified or pumped out by the host cell. The poor efficacy of β-lactams in tuberculosis chemotherapy has been ascribed to their poor penetration of host cells, although polar antibiotic such as streptomycin and amikacin are used as second-line agents. In addition, the metabolic shutdown that occurs during immune activation and granuloma formation leads to altered bacterial metabolism. Nonreplicating cells are not susceptible to isoniazid and many other inhibitors of cell wall synthesis whereas other front-line drugs such as rifampin have severely reduced potency, presumably due to the fact that they inhibit key macromolecular processes (RNA polymerase (RNAP) for rifampin) associated with replicating cells. In addition, the granuloma wall that forms around foci of infection has been postulated to impair drug penetration although there is limited data to support this notion. Macroscopic observation of granulomas recovered from TB patients has revealed a heterogeneity of lesion types substantiating the notion that different drugs are active in different compartments or lesion types [40].

5. METABOLISM AND DRUG TARGETS

The first complete genome sequence of *M. tuberculosis* was published in 1998 that allowed the first glimpse at the potential metabolic capacity of the most widely used laboratory strain (H37Rv) of this pathogen [41]. The genomic information has been instrumental in the identification and validation of potential drug targets as discussed in the following sections. Currently more than 40 other strains of *M. tuberculosis* have been or are in the processed of being sequenced mainly through the BROAD institute's initiative of understanding the disease diversity caused by *M. tuberculosis* through whole genome sequencing of a wide variety of clinical isolates including some MDR and XDR strains. The genome information of *M. tuberculosis* sequences can be accessed from a variety of Web sites (http://www.pasteur.fr/recherche/unites/Lgmb, http://www.sanger.ac.uk, http://tigr.org and http://www.broad.mit.edu). The genome sequences range in size from 4,261,330 to 4,443,138 base pairs encoding approximately 4000 genes. The circular genome has an average guanine + cytosine (G + C) content of 65.6% and as in most other bacteria, the majority of DNA encodes proteins.

Table 1 gives an approximate distribution of the various genes into major functional classes in *M. tuberculosis*. The genes encoding stable RNAs include the three rRNAs, tRNAs, 10Sa RNA as well as the RNA moiety of RNAseP. The genome includes many genes typically associated with its intracellular lifestyle as a pathogen including genes required for defense against host protective responses such as peroxiredoxin systems, superoxide dismutases, and catalase-peroxidase as well as genes required for cell adhesion and invasion including the *mce* family, hemolysins, phopholipases C, and other lipases.

5.1. Targeting Cell Wall Biosynthesis

The cell wall is an excellent drug target and many of the currently used TB drugs target cell wall synthesis. The mycobacterial cell wall consists of an inner peptidoglycan layer, which is covalently linked to a second layer consisting of a complex arabinogalactan (AG) molecule to which mycolic acids are esterified. Exterior to the arabinogalactan is a third layer of mainly glucans, arabinans, and arabinomannans [42]. Several other unusual lipids including diacylated polyketide diols and a

Functional Class	Number of Genes
Stable RNAs	50
Virulence, detoxification and adaptation	99
Lipid metabolism	233
Information pathways	229
Cell wall and cell processes	708
Insertion sequences and phages	149
PE and PPE proteins	170
Intermediary metabolism and respiration	894
Proteins of unknown function	272
Regulatory proteins	189
Conserved hypothetical proteins	1051

variety of glycolipids are intercalated in the mycolates to form an outer lipid layer [43–45] (Fig. 1).

5.1.1. Peptidoglycan Biosynthesis
The mycobacterial peptidoglycan consists of β-1,4-linked *N*-acetylglucosamine and *N*-acetylmuramic acid residues with the muramic acid lactoyl groups amidated with L-alanyl-γ-D-glutaminyl-(L)-*meso*-diaminopimelate-D-alanine stem tetrapeptides and L-alanyl-γ-D-glutaminyl-L-*meso*-diaminopimelate stem tripeptides. The muramic acid residues are further glycolated. The stem peptides are linked either via 4 → 3 interpeptide bridges where the carboxy-terminal D-Ala residue of a tetrapeptide stem is linked to the amino group of a neighboring strand diaminopimelic acid (DAP) residue or via 3 → 3 interpeptide bridges where the carboxy-terminus of DAP of a tripeptide is linked to the amino group of a lateral DAP residue [46]. The acyltransferases that catalyze the formation of 4 → 3 interpeptide bridges generally are penicillin binding proteins belonging to the SxxK family of D,D-transpeptidases. In contrast, the enzyme that catalyze the formation of 3 → 3 L,D-transpeptide cross-links generally belong to a different class of enzymes with a cysteine (instead of serine) active site residue of which some have been shown to be insensitive to β-lactamases [47]. Mycobacterial peptidoglycan is highly cross-linked and at least under certain

conditions has been shown to predominantly contain 3 → 3 cross-links [46,47].

The Mtb genome encodes five putative L,D-transpeptidases and many more potential D,D-transpeptidases of which some have been shown to be essential for growth *in vitro* [41,48]. It has already been demonstrated that at least one of the L,D-transpeptidases is functional although its role in mycobacterial cell wall synthesis is unclear [49]. At least three penicillin binding proteins (transpeptidases) in *M. tuberculosis* have been cloned and expressed. The roles of the other peptidoglycan biosynthetic genes have been largely established or can at least be deduced by their homology to other bacterial peptidoglycan biosynthetic orthologs. The structure of the peptidoglycan *in vivo* is not understood and the roles of the various potential transpeptidases in determining peptidoglycan structure and their differential susceptibility to various β-lactams needs to be elucidated.

The antitubercular drug cycloserine targets D-Ala racemase and the D-Ala-D-Ala ligase involved in the synthesis of the peptidoglycan. The penicillins were evaluated as early as 1946 against *M. tuberculosis*, but their lack of activity has been ascribed to a putative β-lactamase and the low permeability of the mycobacterial cell wall [50]. Recently, Blanchard, Barry and coworkers demonstrated the combination of meropenem (an approved β-lactam of the carbapenem class) and clavulanate (an FDA-approved oral β-lactamase inhibitor) were highly effective against XDR-TB strains *in vitro* [51]. These results have led to a renewed interest in β-lactam inhibitors.

5.1.2. Arabinogalactan Biosynthesis
The enzymes that play a role in synthesis of the arabinogalactan component have been largely identified although the factors that control the sites of arabinogalactan attachment to the peptidoglycan component and the control of the higher level three-dimensional structure generated by interstrand cross-linking of the peptidoglycan are unknown [49]. The O-6 of certain muramic acid residues in the peptidoglycan are linked to a α-L-rhamnose-(1 → 3)-α-β-D-*N*-acetylglucosamine-1-phosphate linker to which the galactan component of mAGP is attached. The galactan is a linear polymer of

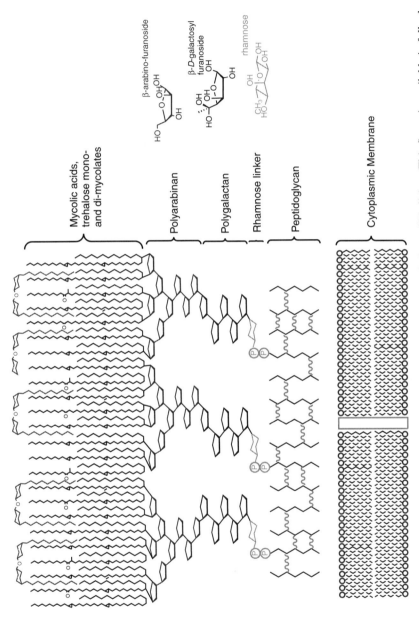

Figure 1. Mycobacterial cell wall. Figure from Prof. John Blanchard, Albert Einstein College of Medicine. (This figure is available in full color at http://mrw. interscience.wiley.com/emrw/9780471266945/home.)

β-arabino-furanoside

β-D-galactosyl furanoside

rhamnose

Mycolic acids, trehalose mono- and di-mycolates

Polyarabinan

Polygalactan

Rhamnose linker

Peptidoglycan

Cytoplasmic Membrane

about 30 alternating β-$(1 \rightarrow 5)$ and β-$(1 \rightarrow 6)$ galactofuranosyl units. The galactan chain is linked to two or three branched polymers of arabinosyl residues connected by $\alpha(1 \rightarrow 5)$, α $(1 \rightarrow 3)$, and $\beta(1 \rightarrow 2)$ linkages. The transferases contributing to the arabinosyl branching and linkages have been identified [42,52–54]. The nonreducing arabinan termini of arabinan contains t-arabinofuranose, 2-arabinofuranose, 5-arabinofuranose, and 3,5-arabinofuranose residues of which the first two can be esterified with mycolates at the 5-position.

The first-line anti-TB drug ethambutol targets the arabinosyl transferase EmbB, which together with EmbA and EmbC are responsible for synthesis of the terminal ararbinofuranose residues of the arabinogalactan. Cole and coworkers reported on a novel class of benzothiazinones with potent antimycobacterial activity that inhibit the enzymes DprE1 and DprE2, which are responsible for synthesis of decaprenylphosphoryl arabinose (DPA), the key monomeric building block of the arabinosc portion of the arabinogalactan [55]. Another promising target involved in arabinogalactan biosynthesis include the UDP-galactopyranose mutase (UGM) that is responsible for the synthesis of the UDP-galactofuranose (UDP-Galf), which is the monomeric building block of the galactan portion of arabinogalactan. The crystal structure of UGM is available and small molecule inhibitors have been described [56,57]. Other essential enzymes for arabinogalactan biosynthesis have been identified and include AftA a novel arabinofuranosyl transferase that catalyzes the addition of the first arabinofuranose residue to the galactan core and enzymes (RmlA–D) involved in synthesis of dTDP-

rhamnose [52,58]. Inhibitors of RmlC identified by high-throughput screening have been described [59].

5.1.3. Mycolic Acid Biosynthesis

The mycolic acids play a critical role in the structure and function of the mycobacterial cell wall. They constitute the inner leaflet of the lipid bilayer of cell wall and have extremely low fluidity [60]. It is this property of mycolic acids that accounts for the exceptionally low permeability of the mycobacterial cell wall [61]. The mycolic acid-based permeability barrier also shields mycobacteria from environmental stress and contributes to disease persistence during infection [62,63]. In addition, mycolic acid-containing glycolipids such as trehalose dimycolate (cord factor) have been implicated in the pathogenesis of *M. tuberculosis* [64,65].

The biosynthesis of the mycolic acids has been the focus of intense research for many years since the enzymes involved are attractive targets for the development of novel chemotherapeutic agents [66]. Mycolates are very long-chain (C_{60}–C_{90}) α-alkyl-β-hydroxy fatty acids and are present as complex mixtures with a long (C_{54}–C_{63}) hydrophobic main chain (R_1) derived from a meromycolic acid with a shorter (C_{22}–C_{24}) α-side chain (R_2) derived from a saturated fatty acid (Fig. 2) [67,68]. The meromycolates are further modified through cyclopropanation, desaturation, or oxygenation to ketomeromycolates or methoxymeromycolates [68]. Several genes encoding desaturases (*desA1*, *desA2*), cyclopropane synthases (*pcaA*, *mmaA2*) and hydroxymycolic acid synthases (*4*), *cis–trans* isomerases (mmA1), and *O*-methyltransferases (mmA3), have been implicated in meromycolate mod-

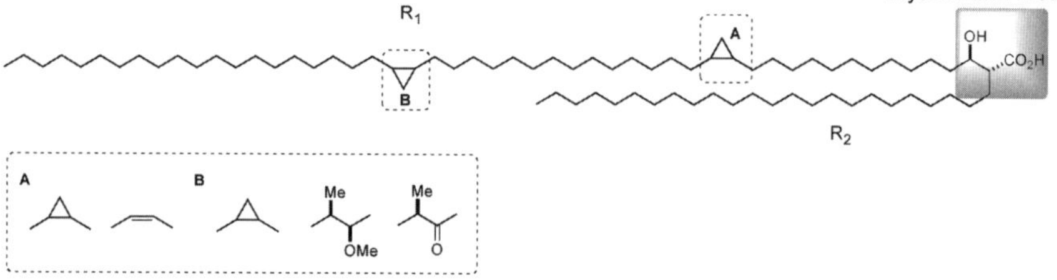

Figure 2. Mycolic acid structures.

ifications [68]. Mycolic acid cyclopropanation is essential for viability and second-line antitubercular drug thiacetazone was shown to inhibit the corresponding cyclopropane synthases [69]. Recently, two other small molecule cyclopropane synthases inhibitors have also been described that possess antimycobacterial activity [70,71]. The mycolates are esterified to the branched arabinofuranose motifs of the cell wall arabinogalactan with trehalose in the form of trehalose-monomycolate and trehalose dimycolate as carriers. The mycolyltransferase reactions are accomplished by three members of the Antigen 85 (Ag85) complex, Ag85A (FbpA), Ag85B (FbpB), and Ag85C2 (FbpC) [72]. Inhibitors of the antigen and Ag85C2 (FbpC) have been described [73].

Mycobacteria produce the meromycolic acids through the combined action of a type I fatty acid synthase (FAS-I) that produces medium chained fatty acids that are channeled to a type II fatty acid synthase (FAS-II) pathway where they are elongated to very long-chained C_{56}–C_{64} fatty acids [68]. The eukaryotic-like FAS-I is a large polypeptide with multiple enzymatic centers while the bacterial FAS-II complex is a multienzyme system where each catalytic activity is carried on a different polypeptide [74]. The organization of the FAS-II pathway is distinct from its mammalian FAS-I counterpart and has been considered an excellent target for antibacterial drug discovery, although a recent report by Brinster et al. has suggested the FAS-II pathway is dispensible for many Gram-positive pathogens since human serum is rich in fatty acids [75]. Mycobacteria are an exception since exogenous serum fatty acids cannot act as surrogates of the long-chained meromycolic acids. The β-ketoacyl-ACP synthetase encoded by *fabH* provides the link between the FAS-I and FAS-II fatty acid biosynthetic cycles. Each cycle through the FAS-II system elongates the fatty acid chain by two carbon units and requires the sequential activity of β-ketoacyl-ACP synthetase (with *kasA* encoding the synthetase required of chains up to 40 carbons in length and *kasB* encoding a synthetase for further chain elongation), β-ketoacyl-ACP reductase (FabG1, *mabA*), 3-hydroxyacyl-ACP dehydratase (Rv0635-Rv0637), and *trans*-2-enoyl-ACP reductase (InhA). Both

front-line antibiotics isoniazid and ethionamide act by inhibiting InhA. Triclosan derivatives have also been developed as potent InhA inhibitors [76,77]. The natural product thiolactomycin, which inhibits KasA and KasB, has been extensively analoged [78]. The recent determination of the cocrystal structure of thiolactomycin with KasA, which shows TLM preferentially binds the acyl-enzyme and the kinetic characterization, which shows TLM is a slow onset tight binding inhibitors provides detailed insight for future structure–activity relationship (SAR) studies [79,80]. Platensimycin a recently discovered antibiotic has also been shown to inhibit both KasA and KasB and possesses modest antitubercular activity [81]. Finally, a single report has provided small molecule inhibitors of the dehydratase encoded by Rv0636 [82].

The final condensation of the meromycolate chain with the shorter α-alkyl chain is accomplished by the action of the monomodular multifunctional polyketide synthase known as Pks13. Three other enzymes are required for this process and include (1) FadD32, which serves to activate the meromycolic acid by adenylation; (2) AccD4 that activates the C_{26} extender unit by carboxylation; and (3) Rv2509, which reduces the intermediate α-alkyl-β-oxo fatty acids to the α-alkyl-β-hydroxy fatty acids [44,83,84]. *Pks13*, *fadD32*, and *accD4* have been confirmed as essential through targeted knockouts of these genes while genetic inactivation of Rv2509 is not lethal, but results in an altered cell envelope. Flux-balance analysis of the entire mycolic acid biosynthetic pathway comprised of 28 proteins also identified Pks13 as an ideal target [85]. Bisubstrate inhibitors of FadD32 have been reported and a crystal structure of the homologous protein FadD28 was recently described [86,87]. The acyl CoA carboxylase AccD4 is also an attractive target and inhibitors of the homolog AccD5, which is not essential, have been described through structure-based drug design [88].

5.1.4. Polyketide-Derived Lipids

Polyketide synthases perform a similar chemistry to the fatty acid synthases except that they have a wider range of starter and extender substrates and can thus generate unusual fatty acids such as methyl-branched acyl chains [43,44]. The polyketide synthases require an acyl transferase domain that determines the choice and transfer of extender unit, an acyl carrier protein (ACP) domain with a phosphopantetheine arm and a β-ketoacyl synthase domain that condenses the starter and extender units. Polyketide synthases can utilize other domains such as a ketoreductase domain, a dehydratase domain, an enoyl reductase domain, and a thioesterase domain. These domains can be carried on a single or multiple polypeptides. The iterative polyketide synthases are responsible for synthesis of the methyl-branched fatty acids of the cell wall. Pks3/4 synthesizes mycolipenic, mycolipanolic, mycolipodienoic, and mycosanoic acids, Pks2 generates phthioceranic and hydroxy-phthioceranic acids and mycocerosic acid synthase generates mycocerosic acid. Pks8-Pks17 synthesizes monomethyl-branched unsaturated fatty acids. The methyl-branched mycocerosic acid chains of DIM and PDIM are synthesized by mycocerosic acid synthase whereas the phthiocerol moiety of PDIM, phenolphthiocerols, phthiodiolones, and phenolphthiodiolones are synthesized by polyketide synthases encoded by the neighboring *ppsABCDE* genes. Phthiodiolones and phenolphthiodiolones are variants of phthiocerols and phenolphthiocerols where the methoxy group has been converted to a keto group. The largest *pks* gene, *pks12*, synthesizes the mycoketide, mannosyl-β-1-phosphoisoprenoids [89]. The function of this mycoketide is unknown. The gene can be deleted without significant effects on *in vitro* growth of the organism but has immunological consequences since this is a potent CD1-restricted antigen [89]. It has been postulated that mycoketides play a role in intracellular growth possibly by regulating transmembrane transport of carbohydrates [89]. The phenolic glycolipids (PGLs) are produced by Pks15/1 and associated with a hypelethality phenotype in a mouse model of TB [25,90]. The polyketide-associated proteins (Paps) are encoded in the vicinity of their associated Pks genes and are the acyltransferases responsible for esterifying the methylated fatty acids to the acceptors such as trehalose. The products generated by all of the polyketide

synthase genes of *M. tuberculosis* (24 in total) have, however, not yet been identified. While none of the polyketide-derived lipids are absolutely essential for viability many are important virulence factors. Inhibition of bacterial virulence factors has emerged as a novel strategy for the development of new antibacterial agents [91]. Quadri and coworkers described the synthesis of a compound that inhibits the biosynthesis of the phenolic glycolipids [92].

5.1.5. Porins   The cell wall also contains a small number of porins that control access of hydrophilic solutes through the otherwise relatively impermeable cell wall to the plasma membrane. Porins allow passive passage of smaller solutes (<600 Da) through the cell wall. Due to the low number of porins in the mycobacterial cell wall, the identification and characterization of the porins has been difficult. Genome analysis has identified a porin with some homology to one of the *E. coli* porins (OmpA) but the porin is smaller than would be expected for the size of protein required to transverse the thick mycobacterial cell wall and knockout of this gene has indicated no major growth defects indicating that other porins clearly play a role in controlling access of nutrients [93]. While the porins are critical for obtaining nutrients, they likely are poor targets for drug discovery due to functional redundancy and lack of druggability due to the challenges of obtaining a small molecule capable of sterically occluding the pore.

5.2. Targeting DNA Synthesis and Repair

The fluoroquinolines are broad-spectrum antibacterial agents that have also found an important role in TB chemotherapy due to their potent antimycobacterial activity against replicating as well as nonreplicating bacilli [94]. The fluoroquinolines inhibit DNA gyrase in *M. tuberculosis*, which is a tetrameric A2B2 protein that is responsible for DNA replication, transcription, and recombination [95]. Each subunit is encoded by the genes *gyrA* and *gyrB*. Crystal structures of GyrA and GyrB have recently been published and provide the basis for further refining the antitubercular activity of fluoroquinolines [96,97]. Another target involved in DNA replication and repair includes the NAD-dependent DNA ligase encoded by the essential gene *ligA*. LigA is an attractive target since it varies functionally from it eukaryotic counterparts employing NAD as the cofactor instead of adenosine triphosphate (ATP) to catalyze formation of the phosphodiester linkage between adjacent double-stranded DNA termini. The three-dimensional structure has been solved and small molecule inhibitors were identified from high-throughput screening [98–101].

Potential targets involved in nucleotide synthesis include thymidine monophosphate kinase (TMPK), inosine monophosphate dehydrogenase (IMPDH), and ribonucleotide reductase (RNR), responsible respectively for the synthesis of deoxythymidine nucleotides, guanosine nucleotides, and 2′-deoxyribonucleotides. These are all established targets in other therapeutic areas and represent potential targets in *M. tuberculosis* due to their essentiality, lack of homology to their human counterparts, and availability of known inhibitors and/or crystal structures. Thus, the three-dimensional structure of thymidine monophosphate kinase has been determined and thymidine analogs have been reported that display potent enzyme inhibition and antimycobacterial activity [102,103]. The nucleoside Gemcitabine (2′-deoxy-2′,2′-difluorocytidine) is clinically used in cancer chemotherapy and is a mechanism-based inhibitor of RNR [104]. *M. tuberculosis* encodes for class Ib and class II RNRs; however only the class Ib RNR is essential [105]. Extensive biochemical and structural studies of mycobacterial class Ib RNR suggest large differences in the structure and enzyme mechanism, providing the rationale for the design of selective RNR inhibitors [106–108]. Inosine monophosphate dehydrogenase is the target of the anticancer agent mycophenolic acid and the antiviral agent ribavirin [109]. *M. tuberculosis* encodes three IMPDH homologs encoded by the genes *guaB1–B3*, but only *guaB2* has been shown as essential [48]. GuaB2 shares low homology to human IMPDH and may therefore represent a potential target if the pathogen is solely dependent on *de novo* synthesis of purine nucleotides.

5.3. Targeting Protein Synthesis and Degradation

5.3.1. Ribosome Protein synthesis in prokaryotes is performed by the 70S ribosome, which is comprised of two subunits, 50S and 30S, each of which is made up of RNA and protein. The mycobacterial ribosome machinery has been reconstituted *in vitro* providing the ability to biochemically decipher structure–activity relationships of ribosomal inhibitors [110]. The bacterial ribosome is a validated drug target and is the site of action of the second-line antitubercular injectable aminoglycosides (streptomycin, kanamycin, amikacin) and capreomycin. Interestingly, the bactericidal inhibitors of protein synthesis including the macrolides, tetracyclines, and streptogramins, which are widely used for treatment of Gram-positive and Gram-negative bacteria are largely ineffective against *M. tuberculosis*. The lack of activity of macrolides, which are the antibiotics of choice for many respiratory pathogens, has largely been attributed to intrinsic resistance mechanisms through ribosomal methylation (target modification) and drug efflux [111]. Franzblau and coworkers synthesized and evaluated over 300 macrolides and ketolides derivatives against *M. tuberculosis* [112,113]. Theses studies provided comprehensive structure–activity relationships and showed modification of the macrolide scaffold can provide substantial enhancement in antitubercular activity. Linezolid and its thiomorpholine analog U-100480 are synthetic oxazolidine antibacterial agent that bind the 50S ribosomal subunit and were initially shown to possess excellent antimycobacterial activity *in vitro* and *in vivo* [114]. The crystal cocrystal structure of linezolid and the 50S ribosomal subunit provide the basis for further modifying linezolid in order to decrease potential side effects caused by long-term therapy [115,116].

5.3.2. Aminoacyl-tRNA Synthetases *M. tuberculosis* encodes for all 20 aminoacyl-tRNA synthetases (aaRS), which are responsible for activating and loading each amino acid onto its cognate tRNA molecule. The aminoacyl-tRNA synthetases are essential and represent attractive targets for the development of new antitubercular agents [117]. The natural product mupirocin is an inhibitor of isoleucyl tRNA synthetase. This clinically used topical antibiotic is effective for many Gram-positive bacteria, but has no antimycobacterial activity [118]. The crystal structure of the methionyl tRNA synthetase has been solved in the presence of methionine and adenosine and simple bisubstrate inhibitors have been reported that possess potent enzyme inhibition, but no antitubercular activity [119,120].

5.3.3. Proteasome   An important component of the mycobacterial defense against nitrosative stress is the proteasome [121]. Proteasomes are uncommon amongst bacteria and have so far only been identified in actinomycetes and archaeobacteria [122]. The mycobacterial proteasome has similarities in structure with the eukaryotic proteasome consisting of two stacks of beta rings (encoded by *prcB*) capped on each side by an alpha ring (encoded by *prcA*) [123]. Similarity even extends to the requirement of a ubiquitin-like protein that tags proteins destined for proteasomal degradation [124,125]. The essentiality of the proteasome for *in vivo* pathogenesis of has been established [126]. Nathan and coworkers identified oxathiazol-2-one compounds as mechanism-based inhibitors using both biochemical and structural studies [127,128]. The oxathiazol-2-one were shown to carbonylate the catalytic active site threonine and displayed potent activity against nonreplicating *M. tuberculosis*, and remarkable selectivity toward the mycobacterial proteasome over the human homolog. This novel class of compounds shows great promise and serves to chemically validate the proteasome as an attractive target for further drug development.

5.4. Targeting Amino Acid Biosynthesis

The genome sequence revealed that *M. tuberculosis* has the full metabolic potential to synthesize all amino acids [41]. Some of these have been shown to be essential even in the presence of supplementation with their products, indicating that these might be attractive candidates for chemotherapeutic intervention [129]. Since *M. tuberculosis* can acquire many amino acids *in vivo*, the selection

of any of the biosynthetic pathways as drug targets relies on experimental evidence of their essentiality *in vivo*. In this respect, it has been shown for example that *M. tuberculosis* cannot acquire sufficient amounts of leucine, lysine, tryptophan, and proline *in vivo* [130–132]. Detailed structural, kinetic and mechanistic studies have been performed on LeuA, a 2-isopropyl malate synthase, that catalyzes the first step in leucine biosynthesis [133,134]. The lysine biosynthetic pathway is particularly attractive since this pathway also produces diaminopimelate, which is a key building block of the peptidoglycan. Nearly the entire lysine biosynthetic pathway, except for DapE, has been structurally and biochemically characterized from DapA, which catalyzes the first committed step in lysine biosynthesis, to LysA, a diaminopimelate decarboxylase, that catalyzes the final step in lysine biosynthesis [130,135]. Based on the attenuated virulence of the tryptophan auxotroph, the tryptohpan pathway is also appealing and the three-dimensional structure of TrpD, an anthranilate phosphoribosyltransferase, which catalyzes the second step in tryptophan biosynthesis, has been solved [136]. While definitive genetic confirmation is lacking for the other amino acid biosynthetic pathways, these all represent potential targets. In support of this latter suggestion, Sacchettini and coworkers solved the structure of HisG a phosphoribosyltransfer that catalyzes the first step in histidine biosynthesis and then employed virtual screening to identify low micromolar nitrobenzothiazole enzyme inhibitors with comparable antimycobacterial activity [137,138].

The shikimate pathway has long been considered an attractive target for development of antimicrobial agents and herbicides since this pathway is absent in mammals, but absolutely essential in most microorganisms including *M. tuberculosis* and the herbicide glyphosate inhibits the penultimate biosynthetic step thereby providing chemical validation of this pathway [139]. The shikimate pathway produces chorismate, a central intermediate in aromatic amino biosynthesis. Chorismate is also a key precursor for isochorismate, 4-hydroxybenzoic acid, and 4-aminobenzoic acid that are required for the synthesis of menaquinones, mycobactins, folates, ubiquinones, and phenolic glycolipids. The shikimate pathway is comprised of seven steps starting from D-erythrose-4-phosphate (E4P) and phosphoenolpyruvate (PEP) that is performed by AroG, AroB, AroD, AroE, AroK, AroA, and AroF. Detailed biochemical and structural studies have been performed for each step providing an excellent foundation for inhibitor development, which is thoroughly reviewed by Ducati et al. [139].

5.5. Targeting Cofactor Biosynthesis

The genome sequence also revealed that *M. tuberculosis* has the full metabolic potential to synthesize all vitamins and cofactors [41]. Cofactor biosynthesis is a rich source of potential drug targets because of the essential nature of these throughout metabolism [140]. In the following subsections, several of the most promising cofactors, from the perspective of drug discovery, are discussed including riboflavin, pantothenate, folic acid, biotin, menaquinone, NAD, and ATP. Other essential and promising cofactors that are not discussed include pyridoxal phosphate (vitamin B6), lipoic acid, S-adenosyl methionine (SAM), heme, and 3'-phosphoadenosine-5'-phosphosulfate (PAPS).

5.5.1. Riboflavin
Riboflavin (vitamin B2) is the direct precursor of flavin mononucleotide (FMN), flavin adenine dinucleotide (FAD), and coenzyme F_{420}, which are the redox cofactors of flavoenzymes that are involved in a numerous essential cellular processes. Riboflavin biosynthesis begins from guanosine triphosphate and proceeds in six steps catalyzed by the mycobacterial proteins RibA1/2, RibD, RibG, RibH, and RibC. The final two steps of the riboflavin biosynthetic pathway catalyzed by lumazine synthase (RibH) and riboflavin synthase (RibC) are attractive targets due to the availability of potent small molecule inhibitors and cocrystal structures with the corresponding mycobacterial proteins [141–143].

5.5.2. Pantothenate
Pantothenate also known as vitamin B5 is the core of coenzyme A, an essential cofactor in the central pathways of respiration and lipid metabolism. The phosphopantetheine moiety of coenzyme A is also the prosthetic group in more than 30 carrier proteins found in the fatty acid synthases, polyketide synthases, and nonribosomal peptide synthetases (NRPS) in *M. tuberculosis*. Pantothenate biosynthesis is accomplished in four steps employing the enzymes PanB and PanE to synthesize pantoic acid and PanD, an aspartate α-decarboxylase, to produce β-alanine. The adenylating enzyme PanC uses ATP to catalyze the condensation of pantoic acid and β-alanine to afford pantothenate. Detailed mechanistic and structural information is available for all enzymes in this pathway [144]. Furthermore, a *panC* gene knockout exhibited highly attenuated virulence in two immunocompetent mouse models [145]. PanC has been most extensively studied as a target and several inhibitors have been described, although none possess potent antimycobacterial activity [146–148].

5.5.3. Folic Acid
Folates (vitamin B9) in their fully reduced form (tetrahydrofolate) are essential cofactors for one-carbon transfer reactions in a myriad of metabolic processes ranging from *de novo* purine synthesis to the biosynthesis of serine, glycine, and methionine [149]. Folate biosynthesis is a validated pathway for drug development. The sulfonamide class of antibacterial agents inhibits the antipenultimate step catalyzed by dihydropteroate synthase (DHPS) while trimethoprim inhibits the final step catalyzed by dihydrofolate reductase (DHFR). The sulfonamides and trimethoprim have not been systematically used in TB chemotherapy as earlier reports showed these were ineffective and trimethoprim was to shown to possess weak micromolar inhibition of the mycobacterial DHFR [150]. However, a recent report demonstrated that combination therapy with sulfamethoxazole (a sulfonamide antibacterial agent) and trimethoprim was clinically effective [151]. Both DHPS and DHFR from *M. tuberculosis* have been biochemically and structurally characterized providing opportunities for development of more potent and selective compounds against these targets [152–154]. Additionally, the bisubstrate inhibitor INH-NAD, which results from bioactivation of isonizaid and subsequent condensation with

NAD, is a potent subnanomolar inhibitor of DHFR suggesting a new strategy for inhibitor design [155].

5.5.4. Biotin Biotin (vitamin H) is the cofactor responsible for activation of carbon dioxide in acyl-CoA carboxylases involved in fatty acid metabolism and pyruvate carboxylase in the Krebs cycle [156]. Biotin auxotrophs of other bacterial species have been shown to require micromolar levels of biotin, whereas biotin levels in human serum are in the low nanomolar range, which provides the motivation for targeting biotin biosynthesis in mycobacteria. The biotin pathway proceeds in four steps from pimeloyl-CoA and alanine catalyzed by BioF, BioA, BioD, and BioB, respectively, whose corresponding genes are clustered in an operon. In *E. coli*, the rate-limiting step appears to be upstream of pimeloyl-CoA provided from intermediary metabolism [157]. BioA, a 7,8-diaminopelargonic acid aminotransferase that utilizes a pyridoxal phosphate (PLP) cofactor, appears as the most attractive target in the pathway due to the availability of a mechanism-based inhibitor, deposition of its three-dimensional structure in the protein data bank, and the fact that BioA is the only biochemically characterized enzyme in the pathway [158,159]. By contrast, BioB or biotin synthase is the most interesting biochemical transformation in the pathway, but least biochemically tractable, since this uses an oxygen-sensitive $[4Fe-4S]^{2+}$ cluster for insertion of sulfur in the carbon backbone of desthiobiotin [160].

5.5.5. Menaquinone *M. tuberculosis* utilizes menaquinone (a napthoquinone) in the electron transport chain for ATP synthesis, which functions analogously to ubiquinone (a benzoquinone) used in humans. Menaquinone (vitamin K2) has been proposed as an attractive target since humans do not utilize menaquinone in their electron transport chain, menaquinone was shown to be critical for mycobacterial viability, and the transposon mutagenesis studies by Sassetti and coworkers demonstrated the essentiality of several genes in the pathway [48,161]. Menaquinone biosynthesis begins from chorismate and proceeds in eight steps catalyzed sequentially by MenF, MenD,

MenC, MenE, MenB, yfbB, MenA, and MenG. Small molecule inhibitors have been described against MenA, a 1,4-dihydroxy-2-napthoate prenyltransferase, which catalyzes a decarboxylative prenylation and MenE, an acyl-CoA synthetase [162,163]. Additionally, the structure of MenB, a 1,4-dihydroxynaphthoyl synthase has been reported [164]. MenF, an isochorimate mutase, represents a potentially attractive target since its structure was recently reported and small molecule inhibitors against the *E. coli* homolog EntC have been described [165,166].

5.5.6. NAD NAD is an essential cofactor that is required for redox balance, energy metabolism, protein deacetylation, activity for the NAD-dependent prokaryotic DNA ligase, and protein ADP-ribosylases. NAD can be synthesized *de novo* from aspartate and dihydroxyacetone phosphate or it can be recycled via the Preiss-Handler salvage pathway and both pathways are utilized *in vivo* by *M. tuberculosis* [167]. The NAD *de novo* and salvage pathways converge at nicotinate mononucleotide (NaMN), which is then converted to NAD in two steps by the sequential action of NadD, a nicotinic acid mononucleotide adenylyltransferase, and NadE, a NAD synthetase. Based on the redundancy of both NAD *de novo* synthesis and salvage pathways only the final two steps catalyzed by NadD and NadE are valid drug targets. NadD has not been biochemically characterized, although inhibitors of NadD from *E. coli* have been described [168]. NadE from *M. tuberculosis* has been functionally and structurally characterized and small molecule inhibitors have been described, although these are only tool compounds since they contain a quaternary ammonium ion [169–171].

5.5.7. ATP ATP synthesis is essential for all forms of life. The multimeric membrane-bound ATP synthase that couples ATP synthesis with proton motive force is highly conserved between prokaryotes and eukaryotes, which would strongly disfavor selection as a potential target. The discovery of the diarylquinoline TMC207, an extremely potent and selective inhibitor of subunit c of the mycobacterial ATP synthase, shattered this conventional wisdom [172,173]. ATP synthase has a transmembrane F_0 part (subunits a, b, and c) and a cytoplasmic F_1 part (subunits α, β, γ, δ, and ε) whose subunits are encoded by the genes *atpA–H*. The chemical validation provided by TMC207, which was found by high-throughput whole cell screening, suggests a more systematic approach could identify new inhibitors that bind to alternate subunits. More recently it has been shown that the *de novo* synthesis of ATP is essential for the viability of hypoxic nonreplicating *M. tuberculosis* confirming ATP synthesis as a prime target for the development of new antitubercular agents [174].

5.6. Targeting Cytochrome P450 Monooxygenases

M. tuberculosis is different from most bacteria by the fact that it encodes for approximately 20 cytochrome P450 monooxygenases that are involved in the oxidation of endogenous and host lipids [175,176]. The antifungal azoles inhibit P450s providing chemical validation and motivation for development of mycobacterial P450 inhibitors. The transponson-mutagenesis studies of Sassetti and coworkers failed to identify any of the P450s as essential for *in vitro* growth; however, CYP121 was subsequently confirmed as essential through targeted genetic disruption [177]. A recent analysis of 1500 candidate drug targets from *M. tuberculosis* identified six P450 enzymes among the top 10 targets [178]. A total of five P450s (CYP51, CYP121, CYP124, CYP125, and CYP130) have been biochemically and structurally characterized providing the basis for inhibitor development [175,179].

5.7. Targeting Intermediary Metabolism and Respiration

M. tuberculosis has all the key enzymes required for the function of glycolysis, the pentose-phosphate cycle, and the Krebs cycle. An unusual feature of its Krebs cycle is that mycobacteria do not encode a functional α-ketoglutarate dehydrogenase and instead have an α-ketoglutarate decarboxylase (Rv1248c, initially annotated as *sucA*—the E1 component of α-ketoglutarate dehydrogenase) [180]. The succinic semialdehyde produced by

α-ketoglutarate decarboxylase is then oxidized to succinate by the succinic semialdehyde dehydrogenase activity of GabD1 (Rv0234c) and GabD2 (Rv1731) [180]. The *sucB* gene (now reannotated as *dlaT*) does not encode the E2 component of α-ketoglutarate dehydrogenase although it does perform this function in the pyruvate dehydrogenase complex (PDC). The E1 component of PDC is performed by AceE whereas the E3 component is carried by Lpd. Lpd and DlaT also function as a peroxynitrite reductase–peroxidase complex that shuttles electrons from NADH through DlaT via the activity of Lpd, to the thioredoxin-like protein AhpD and to the peroxidase AhpC. AhpC reduces products of oxidative damage such as alkyl hydroperoxides [181]. Reduced cofactors produced in the Krebs cycle and by β-oxidation are reoxidized by membrane-associated dehydrogenases. Although *M. tuberculosis* encodes the genes for the proton-pumping bioenergetically more efficient type I NADH dehydrogenase, this dehydrogenase is not essential and may be inactive or poorly active whereas one of the two nonproton pumping type II respiratory NADH dehydrogenases encoded by the genome (*ndh*) appears to be essential [48,182]. The respiratory dehydrogenases reduce membrane-bound menaquinones that serve as membrane soluble electron carriers for the terminal oxidases such as the cytochrome bd oxidase, cytochrome c oxidase, and nitrate reductase systems [183–185]. *M. tuberculosis* is able to adapt to hypoxia and survive under anaerobic conditions and the genome encodes a variety of genes that play a role in anaerobic survival. Although the function of many of these genes remains unknown, it has been shown that the high-oxygen-affinity cytochrome bd-type menaquinol oxidase is upregulated during exposure to reduced oxygen [183,186] and that nitrate reductase activity, which would allow respiration on the alternative electron acceptor nitrate, is upregulated under hypoxia [187]. Maintenance of the proton motive force and low ATP levels generated by the transmembrane ATP synthase complex are essential for maintaining viability of anaerobically persisting *M. tuberculosis* [174]. The organism is extremely susceptible to inhibitors of these processes indicating that maintaining an energized membrane may be an Achilles' heel of hypoxic nonreplicating bacteria [174,188]. The study of metabolic processes required to maintain viability under nonreplicating conditions is very relevant to understanding the potential drug targets for treatment of latent disease. In this respect, it has for example been demonstrated that granulomas in primates and rabbits, are often hypoxic [189]. Hypoxia is a major signal that results in metabolic shiftdown to a state of nonreplicating persistence.

5.8. Lipid Metabolism

Mycobacteria have an unusual capacity to metabolize lipids. Besides a variety of lipases, esterases, and phospholipases, some of which are known to play a role in modulating host–pathogen interactions, M. tuberculosis encodes a vast number of proteins potentially involved in β-oxidation of fatty acids [190,191]. This includes 6 acetyl-CoA C-acetyltransferases, five 3-hydroxyacyl-CoA, 22 enoyl-CoA hydratase/isomerase superfamily members, 35 acyl-CoA synthases, and 35 acyl-CoA dehydrogenases. It is unlikely that this amount of evolutionary gene duplication has occurred to increase redundancy. More likely, there are as yet to be determined substrate-specific preferences for these enzymes allowing metabolism of a wide variety of fatty acid substrates. The majority of these β-oxidation substrates appear to be redundant for growth on synthetic media containing glucose and glycerol as carbon sources [192,193]. This is not surprising given that growth on specific carbon sources will be required to elucidate the role of many of these enzymes. The essential role of β-oxidation during growth in host tissues has been demonstrated by the essential requirement for isocitrate lyase, an enzyme required for assimilation of carbon substrates into Krebs cycle intermediates, during growth on fatty acids, and for growth and persistence in mouse tissues [194,195]. Despite intensive investigation into inhibitors of isocitrate lyase, no leads have been published to date that could be ascribed to the small charged substrate binding pocket for which druggable binders may be impossible to find [196]. Nevertheless, allosteric inhibitors of this enzyme could potentially provide future leads for drug devel-

opment. Drug development for targets such as isocitrate lyase is further complicated by the existence of two isocitrate lyases in M. tuberculosis although some strains possess only one functional equivalent of the enzyme [195]. There is some substrate specificity in the isocitrate lyases with one of the isocitrate lyases being capable of utilizing both methylisocitrate, a product formed during growth on fatty acids with uneven numbers of carbon units in their backbones that release propionyl-CoA in addition to acetyl-CoA, as well as isocitrate that is generated during metabolism of acetyl-CoA by the Krebs cycle [197].

5.9. Targeting Mycobactin Biosynthesis and Iron Acquisition

Polyketide synthases are also involved in synthesis of the mycobactins that are specific iron-chelating molecules produced by mycobacteria [198]. Mycobactins are able to scavenge host iron bound to ferritin, lactoferrin, or transferrin by virtue of their extremely high affinity for Fe^{3+} (K_{ass} 10^{30} M^{-1}) [199]. Mutants of the mycobactin biosynthetic pathway are severely attenuated for survival in host macrophages indicating that mycobactin biosynthesis may be an attractive drug target [200]. Mycobacteria synthesize two types of mycobactin, the carboxymycobactins and the more lipophilic mycobactins [201]. It was initially presumed that the carboxymycobactins functioned by scavenging iron from the extracellular environment, transferring the Fe^{3+} to cell wall-associated lipophilic mycobactins after which a reductase reduced the metal to Fe^{2+} which in turn is transported into the cell by molecules such as salicylate where it is bound by a variety of iron binding proteins [201]. Recently this hypothesis was revised by the demonstration that the lipophilic mycobactins distributed throughout lipid-containing regions of the host cell as well as bystander cells [202]. From here the mycobactins were able to bind iron and the ferri-mycobactins subsequently accumulated in lipid droplets that traffic to the phagosome [202]. The pks genes involved in mycobactin biosynthesis are clustered with other mycobactin biosynthetic genes on the chromosome. Inhibition of at least one of the enzymes responsible for mycobactin biosynthesis has been shown to abrogate growth of this pathogen [203,204]. *M. tuberculosis* encodes two bacterioferritin genes that probably serve as storage depots for iron. Iron acquisition and storage is tightly regulated by the iron-dependent repressor IdeR [205,206]. Under iron replete conditions, IdeR binds Fe^{2+} and represses genes involved in mycobactin biosynthesis and iron acquisition to ensure that toxic overload does not occur that would lead to oxidative damage via the Fenton reaction. Under iron-limited conditions such as during *in vivo* growth, gene repression by IdeR is relieved, leading to increased synthesis of mycobactins and other IdeR-controlled genes that include virulence genes and genes with no clear role in iron utilization or metabolism.

5.10. Targeting Mycothiol Biosynthesis

Mycobacteria and most members of the *Actinobacteria* use a low molecular weight thiol known as mycothiol (1-D-*myo*-inositol 2-deoxy-2-*N*-acetamido-L-cystein-amido-α-D-glucopyranoside) that functions analogously to glutathione in detoxification by forming *S*-conjugates with drugs [207]. Mycothiol biosynthesis is carried out in four steps from inositol-1-phosphate catalyzed by MshA, MshB, MshC, and MshD, whose corresponding genes are scattered throughout the genome. Targeted genetic disruption studies have shown that *mshA* and *mshC* are essential while *mshB* and *mshD* are dispensible for growth of *M. tuberculosis* [207]. MshA catalyzes the first biosynthetic step of mycothiol and is a glycosyltransferase that employs UDP-GlcNAc as substrate. MshA represents an attractive target as glycosyltransferases have been successfully targeted previously [208]. Although MshA from *M. tuberculosis* has proven difficult to express, the MshA homolog from *Corynebacterium glutamicum* has been functionally and structurally characterized [209]. MshC, a cysteine ligase is responsible for the third step in mycothiol biosynthesis and has been most extensively investigated as a potential target. Detailed kinetic analysis as well as the 1.6 Å crystal structure have been reported [210,211]. High-throughput screening of MshC led to the identification of diben-

zothiazepinones as modest enzyme inhibitors and a potent nanomolar bisubstrate inhibitor has also been described [210,212]. While mycothiol synthesis is essential for *M. tuberculosis* viability, mycothiol is also essential for bioactivation of ethionamide, thus inhibition of mycothiol synthesis could lead to decreased susceptibility to this important second-line antitubercular agent [213,214].

5.11. Targeting Terpenoid Biosynthesis

Mycobacterial-derived terpenes including decaprenyl phosphate (C_{50}-P), menaquinone and the diterpene edaxadiene play critical roles in cell wall synthesis, electron transport, and phagosomal maturation [215,216]. Mycobacteria utilize the 2*C*-methyl-D-erythritol 4-phosphate (MEP) pathway for synthesis of the hemiterpene building blocks isopentenyl diphosphate (IPP) and dimethylallyl diphosphate (DMAPP), which are used to construct all terpenoid metabolites in mycobacteria. The MEP pathway is an attractive pathway since this is biochemically distinct from the mevalonate pathway used by mammals. Furthermore, the MEP pathway has been confirmed as essential by Himar1-based transposon mutagenesis as well as targeted genetic disruption of *ispD* and *dxr*, whose gene products catalyze the second and third steps, respectively [48]. The MEP pathway proceeds in eight steps from glycerol-3-phosphate and pyruvate catalyzed sequentially by DXS, DXR (also IspC), IspD, IspE, IspF, IspG, IspH, and Idi. The first committed step catalyzed by DXR is the most attractive target in the pathway and DXR has been biochemically and structurally characterized [217,218]. Additionally, the highly polar antibiotic fosmidomycin, which is currently being evaluated for treatment of malaria, is a potent nanomolar inhibitor of DXR, but possesses no whole cell antimycobacterial activity due to lack of uptake [219]. The recent identification of lipophilic DXR inhibitors with broad-spectrum antibacterial activity is very promising, although these have not yet been evaluated against *M. tuberculosis* [220]. Crystal structures of the *E. coli* homologs of IspD, IspE, IspF, and Idi are available and high-throughput assays have been developed against the first three of these enzymes [215]. IspG and IspH are less tractable as these employ prosthetic $[4Fe-4S]^{2+}$ clusters [215]. The mechanistic insight and structural information gained from the study of the MEP pathway, since its discovery more than a decade ago, provide rich opportunities for inhibitor development.

5.12. Targeting Signal Transduction

M. tuberculosis senses its environment and regulates its metabolism by an array of different regulatory and signal transduction mechanisms. Among the 189 regulation and signal transduction mechanisms, there are 11 two-component systems, 5 unpaired response regulators, 2 unpaired histidine kinases, 11 protein kinases, 13 sigma (σ) factors, and 140 other transcription regulators [41] some of which regulate the response to adverse environmental stimuli such as cold shock [221], carbon starvation [222], heat shock [223,224], nitric oxide [31], hypoxia [225], iron or zinc starvation [205,226], and surface and oxidative stresses [227–229]. Several of these play a role in modulating gene expression during infection of animal models [230,231].

5.12.1. Sigma Factors
The σ factors control the choice of promoter during transcription and interact directly with RNA polymerase. Of the 13σ factors, one (encoded by *sigA*) is the essential principle σ factor. The *sigB* gene product belongs to the group 2σ factor group that generally respond to stationary phase conditions and the general stress response and *sigF* belongs to the group 3σ factor group that respond to stresses such as heat shock. Ten other transcription factors belong to the extracytoplasmic function σ factors that respond to a variety of stresses such as iron limitation, surface stress, and oxidative stress [232]. The 12 nonessential σ factors are responsible for regulating gene expression to a wide variety of largely overlapping conditions that regulate gene expression during infection of macrophages and in animal models [232]. In addition, anti-sigma and anti-anti-sigma factor regulatory networks control the activity of these sigma factors [233].

5.12.2. Two-Component Systems
MTB encodes 11 two-component systems of which 1 is deemed essential and 7 orphan components of these consisting of either a histidine kinase or response regulator that is not genetically linked to its cognate partner [234,235]. The two-component systems consist of a cytoplasmic or transmembrane sensor histidine kinase that phosphorylates an aspartate on its cognate response regulator. The best-studied two-component system is the DosT/DosS-DosR system, which regulates the transcriptional response to inhibition of respiration due to hypoxia or inhibition of the respiratory cytochromes by nitric oxide or carbon monoxide [236]. DosS and DosT contain heme that bind carbon monoxide, nitric oxide, or oxygen with different affinities such that DosS functions as a redox sensor and DosT as an hypoxia sensor [236]. Both the DosT and DosS sensor kinases phosphorylate DosR thereby regulating a set of genes that control adaptation to hypoxia and anaerobiasis. The PhoP-PhoR two-component regulator system controls the structure of LAM that is a potent immunomodulator also involved in phagosome maturation, the synthesis of pathogenic lipids such as sulfolipids, diacyltrehaloses, and polyacyltrehaloses, the secretion of the potent T-cell antigen ESAT-6, the stress response, the expression of isocitrate lyase, and the regulation of expression of the dormancy regulon by crosstalk with DosR [237–241]. A point mutation in *M. tuberculosis* has been identified as one of the primary genetic differences between a virulent and avirulent laboratory strain of *M. tuberculosis* [242]. Finally, consistent with its myriad roles, deletion of *phoP* causes attenuation of growth in mice [243].

5.12.3. Serine/Threonine Protein Kinases
The apparent paucity of two-component systems in *M. tuberculosis* compared to *E. coli* and *B. subtilis*, which each contain more than 30 two-component regulators, is offset by the existence of several eukaryotic-like serine/threonine protein kinases (STPKs) in this pathogen's genome [41]. The eukaryotic-like serine/threonine protein kinases are unusual in bacteria but 11 STPKs and 4 protein phosphatases are found in *M. tuberculosis*. Eight of the STPKs have a transmembrane domain

allowing these proteins to transmit signals to the cell from the extracellular environment. The protein phosphatases control aspects of bacterial metabolism such as cell elongation and division (PknA and PknB), phosphate uptake (PknD), membrane transport (PknE and PknF), amino acid transport including glutamine-glutamate metabolism (PknG), SigH-controlled stress responses (PknB), stationary phase adaptation (PknG), inhibition of phagosome–lysosome fusion and host cell signaling (PknG), arabinan synthesis (PknH), cell division (PknI), transcription (PknK and PknL) and production of secondary metabolites (PknK) [234,235]. Three of the STPKs are essential for growth of *M. tuberculosis* (PknA, PknB, and PknG) [48] although it is likely that the other kinases may play essential roles under certain conditions of mycobacterial growth or survival *in vivo*. The role of PknA and PknB in regulating cell shape and probably cell division is directly related to their regulation of the activity of several enzymes involved in cell wall synthesis including *N*-acetylglucosamine-1-phosphate uridyltransferase [244], UDP-*N*-acetylmuramoyl-L-alanine: D-glutamate ligase [245], penicillin binding protein A (PBPA) [246], as well as the mycobacterial FabH enzyme that links the FAS-I and FAS-II systems [247]. The essential role of PknA, PknB, and PknG has initiated several drug development programs against these targets with some initial successes where chemical inhibition of PknB has been shown to result in cell death [248] although current hits are not good leads for future drug development programs [249]. Nanomolar hits against PknG have shown some promise as leads and these have been shown to be effective against *M. tuberculosis* residing in macrophages [249].

6. MECHANISMS OF DRUG RESISTANCE

Plasmid-mediated drug resistance, a major determinant of resistance in other human bacterial pathogens does not occur naturally in *M. tuberculosis*. Resistance as a phenotype can be caused by tolerance or by genetic mutation. Tolerance is a conditional phenotype that is not inheritable and is reversible based on physiological state of the cells. Typically, nongrowing *M. tuberculosis* is tolerant to antitubercular drugs that target macromolecular biosynthetic processes such as cell wall synthesis or translation [250,251]. Thus, *M. tuberculosis* that transitions to a nonreplicating state as a result of hypoxia, starvation, or stationary phase, becomes insensitive or orders of magnitude less sensitive to the frontline drugs isoniazid, rifampin, and streptomycin [250,252–254]. In addition, even actively growing populations of bacteria contain a small fraction of cells that are tolerant to drugs that inhibit or kill the majority of the population. These cells have been termed persister cells and in *E. coli* have been shown to be nongrowing cells [255]. The mechanisms that lead to the formation of persisters are not understood although it has been postulated that the chromosomally encoded toxin–antitoxin systems found in most bacterial genomes account for the formation of persisters [255,256]. The toxin–antitoxin modules consist of a stable toxin and an unstable antitoxin, which form an inactive complex. In the absence of continued expression of the antitoxin, by for example transcriptional or translational inhibition [256–258], the previously synthesized antitoxin is degraded by cellular proteases thereby releasing the toxin. The toxins inhibit major metabolic processes of the cells, some of them for example inhibiting translation by acting as ribonucleases [259–261]. It has been postulated that stochastic overexpression of the toxins in subpopulations of cells leads to metabolic arrest, thereby generating drug tolerant cells [259–261]. *M. tuberculosis* encodes 38 toxin–antitoxin modules and it is possible that some of these could contribute to the existence of drug tolerant persisters *in vivo* [258,262]. Other mechanisms that give rise to persisters could include populations of cells that show stochastic increased expression of the global negative transcriptional regulators PhoY1 and PhoY2, which downregulate the expression of many genes required for key metabolic processes during normal growth.

Heritable acquired resistance is caused by mutations in genes that generally play a role in the processes targeted by the drugs by either overexpression or drug target modification.

Other mechanisms include drug inactivation mechanisms and upregulation of expression of drug efflux systems. Upregulation of drug efflux systems in *M. tuberculosis* generally gives rise to low levels of resistance and has been described for fluoroquinolones [263,264], tetracycline, and streptomycin [265]. Inactivation of β-lactams by β-lactamases to a large extent accounts for the insensitivity of *M. tuberculosis* to clinically achievable levels of β-lactam drugs although the combination of β-lactamase inhibitors with β-lactams that are poorer substrates for the major *M. tuberculosis* β-lactamase may provide some therapeutic possibilities [51]. The primary β-lactamase is BlaC that has recently been crystallized [266]. BlaC is irreversibly inhibited by clavulanate at high concentrations, but the other commercially available β-lactamase inhibitors, sulbactam and tazobactam, are slowly hydrolyzed by the enzyme. The relative insensitivity of *M. tuberculosis* to many aminoglycosides and macrolides has been ascribed to the 23S rRNA methyltransferase which methylates the nucleotide bases in the rRNA that are important for binding interactions with these drugs [267].

Several antitubercular drugs are prodrugs that require activation to their active metabolites. Examples include isoniazid, ethionamide, pyrazinamide, and PA-824. For all of these drugs, the activation mechanisms are not essential for normal growth processes and mutation in the activation mechanisms occur at a high frequency. Inactivation of *katG* that encodes a catalase/peroxidase results in inability to activate isoniazid but also may lead to a fitness loss for the organism in that complete loss of KatG activity leads to enhanced sensitivity to reactive oxygen intermediates and thus attenuation *in vivo* [268]. The most common mutation in *katG* however, Ser315Thr confers high-level INH resistance, but still carries sufficient catalase/peroxidase activity to protect the organism against oxidative stress encountered *in vivo*. Similarly, ethionamide resistance is conferred by mutations in a FAD-containing monooxygenase (encoded by *ethA*) required for activation of thioamides to an active *S*-oxide [269] whereas pyrazinamide is hydrolyzed to its corresponding cell-inhibitory acid by pyrazinamide/nicotinamidase (encoded by *pncA*) [270]. PA-824 is reduced by a novel nitroreductase mechanism that leads to the formation of nitrous acid and nitric oxide thereby mimicking aspects of immune defense against this pathogen [271].

The mutations that lead to resistance are often in genes that play key roles in metabolism of the organism. Thus, *rpoB* mutations associated with rifampin resistance could be expected to decrease the enzymatic efficiency of the RNA polymerase subunit that it encodes. However, the most common *rpoB* mutation (Ser531Leu) is associated with a very minimal loss in fitness compared to its parental counterpart strain [272]. Some of the *rpoB* mutations that occur at a lower frequency in *M. tuberculosis* are associated with a loss in fitness, but usually strains harboring these mutations evolve secondary mutations in the chromosome that compensate for the fitness defect conveyed by the first mutation. Mutations and even deletion of *pncA* involved in pyrazinamide resistance have not been found to confer any noticeable effect on virulence or transmission in patients [273]. The W-Beijing family of *M. tuberculosis* strains has been associated with a higher incidence of multidrug resistance but despite this, members of this family are seen as highly virulent and highly transmissible in human populations. The reason for this is not understood. Although this lineage of strains has mutations in some DNA repair genes that could conceivably lead to enhanced mutation frequencies [274–276], *in vitro* studies have shown that these strains do not have an increased mutation frequency to rifampin resistance [277]. It is possible that the pathology elicited by the W-Beijing strains by expression of phenolic glycolipid that leads to enhanced cavitary disease, could result in increased absolute numbers of bacilli in lesions, thereby increasing the probability for drug-resistant mutants [25,278].

The permeability barrier posed by the mycobacterial cell wall has historically been considering a determining factor in the intrinsic resistance of mycobacteria to antibacterial compounds. Indeed the permeability of *M. tuberculosis* is comparable to that of *Pseudomonas aeruginosa* and about 100-fold slower than that of *E. coli* to small molecules such as β-lactams [279]. However, many drugs including the polar aminoglycosides can penetrate the mycobacterial cell envelope, nonpolar drugs enter easily, and resistance to β-lactams is not to lack of permeability, but rather to a chromosomally broad-spectrum β-lactamase. While the mycobacterial cell envelope may not be as impenetrable as it is conventionally considered, it does shield the bacterium from environmental stress and plays a key role in TB-persistence and pathogenesis.

7. METHODS OF ANTITUBERCULAR DRUG DISCOVERY

Development of new drugs for the treatment of tuberculosis requires the identification of appropriate drug targets. The criteria for such a drug target include its essentiality for growth or survival in human disease and a sufficiently low homology to human enzymes and enzymes from gastrointestinal commensal organisms to allow specific inhibition of the mycobacterial target. The identification of targets that meet these criteria is hampered by our relative lack of knowledge of the metabolic pathways that play a role in vivo. The literature about the function of individual genes and pathways in the M. tuberculosis genome is accumulating and has generated a mass of information about individual genes that may play a role in parasitism of the human host. Targeted approaches based on available information about disease relevance of genes known to be required for growth and survival of other pathogens has similarly added to this knowledge database. Several strategies have attempted to identify genes that are predicted to be essential for aspects of survival in vivo. Whole genome transposon mutagenesis approaches have enabled to identification of gene functions that are predicted to be essential for growth in vitro [48,192]. These transposon mutagenesis approaches have been further developed to identify genes that are required for growth under certain in vitro conditions that mimic aspects of human disease [280,281] as well as during stages of parasitism of mouse tissues in vivo [48]. Genome analyses of clinical isolates have also indicated which genes are dispensable for human disease by identifying genomic dele-

tions that have occurred in various clinical isolates of M. tuberculosis worldwide [282–284]. Transcriptional analyses of M. tuberculosis exposed to a variety of in vivo relevant stresses have further helped to delineate metabolic pathways that are predicted to play a role at various stages of human disease [31,186,254,285]. In silico methods to identify drug targets have further taken into account factors such as the search for druggable protein domains based on the Interpro database (http://www.ebi.ac.uk/interpro/) that contains a list of domains that bind small molecules conforming to the Lipinski rule of 5, databases of inhibitors of known enzymes, the availability of crystal structures or predicted crystal structures, methods to identify ligand binding pockets on protein structures, metabolic pathway analyses to search for metabolic chokepoints, protein–protein interaction maps, genome comparison databases and tools for searching for close homologs in the human genome or genomes from other bacteria such as intestinal gut flora [286–288]. Currently crystal structures of about 6% of the M. tuberculosis proteome have been obtained although further structures can be modeled based on available structures from similar proteins from other organisms by using for example the ModBase database (http://modbase.compbio.ucsf.edu/modbase-cgi/search_form.cgi).

Agnostic approaches to identify drug targets include whole cell screening assays. In this approach small molecule libraries such as libraries of synthetic compounds or natural products are screened for inhibition of growth or cidal activity against M. tuberculosis cells in culture. Screening conditions include growth on synthetic media on a variety of carbon sources as well as nonreplicating persistence under in vivo relevant conditions such as hypoxia [289,290]. In whole cell screening, only molecules that are cell permeable are interrogated overcoming future obstacles required for target validation studies. The challenge of whole cell screening is the identification of the proteins inhibited by the hits. Microarray analyses of M. tuberculosis exposed to such inhibitors followed by comparison of the transcriptional profiles to published databases of expression profiles from drug exposed cells enables faster identification of molecules with mechanisms of action similar to other drug such as translational inhibitors and has also accelerated the identification of major metabolic processes affected by the molecules [186]. Macromolecular incorporation assays have also pinpointed major processes inhibited by drugs such as lipid biosynthesis, protein synthesis, RNA, or DNA synthesis as demonstrated in the discovery of the target of platensimycin [291,292]. The power of whole cell screening approaches is not necessarily in the individual compounds identified as hits in such screens. These may in themselves not necessarily be leads for future drug development but information about the processes that are susceptible to inhibition under different growth conditions allows prediction of pathways that are important for growth under certain restrictions. Moreover, high-throughput screening approaches followed by target identification can lead to a sufficient database of information that will allow metabolic pathways to be mapped for different environmental conditions.

Drug targets further need to be validated to verify that their inhibition *in vivo* will indeed lead to cell death. For many bacterial pathogens, bacteriostatic drugs are sufficient to clear disease since immunocompetent individuals are often able to clear the infection after it has been halted by these agents. However, in active cases of tuberculosis, the immune system is clearly not sufficient to eradicate the bacilli and the requirement for new drugs would be that they have a bactericidal action *in vivo*. Thus, initial studies are required to verify that inhibitors of the target under investigation not only inhibit growth *in vitro* but also result in loss of viability. In cases where inhibitors have not yet been identified, the requirement of the target can be interrogated by genetic means by using for example tetracycline-regulatable promoters to downregulate gene expression at a particular stage of growth or survival *in vitro* and even *in vivo* [293]. For drug targets where inhibitors are available, it is essential to establish that the effects of the inhibitor are on-target in whole cells. Ideally this would be done by directly measuring metabolites affected by the process under investigation. The next step of

target validation is establishing that the process is essential for survival in infected macrophages but especially infected animal models. The most popular animal model to date is the mouse. The mouse offers the advantage of the availability of immunological tools, small size enabling studies on larger groups of animals, and a large body of literature about *M. tuberculosis* infection and immunology of this animal. Mice represent certain aspects of human disease including the role of T_H-1 type immune response [294,295]. However, disease progression is quite different between mice and men in that the granulomas are distributed throughout all lobes of the mouse lung whereas in human disease hematogenous spread takes place from the initial site of injection (the Ghon complex) to the apical lobes with uneven distribution of granulomas in the lung. In addition lesions in granulomas are aggregates of lymphocytes and macrophages that are unlike human granulomas possessing a clear lymphocyte cuff and which progress to caseation and liquefaction. In addition, the onset of acquired immunity in mice leads to a chronic phase of the disease that is characterized by high bacterial numbers in the lungs and spleen. *M. tuberculosis* growth in the chronic stage is kept in check by immune-mediated release of reactive nitrogen intermediates (RNI) [296,297]. In contrast, guinea pig and rabbit models are more similar to human disease in the similarity of granuloma pathology, which are structurally relatively similar with a caseous center and can progress to liquefaction and cavity formation [39,295]. Spread from initial site of infections occurs hematogenously to other lobes. The guinea pig is highly susceptible to tuberculosis and does not develop latent tuberculosis but instead progressively develops extensive tissue destruction and ultimately death. The animal model that most closely mimics human disease in both disease pathology and disease progression is the nonhuman primate [294,298–300]. Cynomolgous macaques can be infected by the respiratory route by very low numbers of bacteria and disease progression is either by rapid mycobacterial growth leading to active disease within 3 months of infection or by a slower progression to clinical symptoms or by the development of latent disease characterized by the absence of clinical symptoms. Latent disease is, similarly to humans associated with granulomas some of which are caseous but can be reactivated by immunosuppression by for example blocking TNF-α.

The disadvantage of the rabbit and existing primate models for tuberculosis is that these models are more expensive with the result that powering a study with sufficient numbers of animals becomes costly. In addition, larger body size requires larger amounts of drug. Where this may not be a problem for commercially available compounds, new investigational compounds are often synthesized in small amounts with few labs having the capacity to upscale production to the levels required for larger animal models. Thus, smaller animal models that mimic human disease more closely than the mouse are urgently required for tuberculosis drug development. Animal studies on chemical inhibitors require knowledge about the nontoxic nature of the compounds under investigation against eukaryotic cells and are not mutagenic. Determination of preliminary pharmacokinetic properties is important to ensure that the inhibitors are bioavailable after oral administration, have a reasonable half-life in blood, display good lung penetration, and are tolerated by the animal.

Monitoring efficacy of treatment of infected animals by drugs under investigation is typically done by measuring organ burdens by plating of homogenates on solid mycobacterial growth media. Other methods of monitoring success of treatment include measurement of body weight as an indirect measure of animal health [301]. Success in animal studies may validate the essentiality of a target for mycobacterial survival *in vivo* but even with the availability of inhibitors for such targets, drug development may be years away from clinical trials. Many inhibitors are not particularly druggable and further high-throughput screening of the protein target in question may be required to develop more druggable scaffolds. Further lead optimization is an iterative process of medicinal chemistry to improve its drug-like properties while maintaining on-target potency. In addition, detailed pharmacokinetic, pharmacodynamic, and safety tests are required, such as developing an ADME profile that includes studies on permeability/absorption, oral bioavailability, mechanisms of tissue clearance, modification by cytochrome P450 enzymes, evaluation of drug interaction potential, and plasma protein binding. Initial safety profiles are established by *in vitro* micronucleus assays, tests to assess cardiovascular risk (e.g., hERG binding assays), profiling of broad ligands, development of biosafety markers, and maximum tolerated dose in various animal models. The coinfection of many tuberculosis patients with HIV requires compatibility with antiretroviral therapy. Moreover, tuberculosis chemotherapy cannot be given as monotherapy, thus new drugs must be compatible with components of modern front-line chemotherapy.

Establishing success in human studies require noninvasive means of measurement of chemotherapeutic efficacy. Clearance of bacilli from sputum is often measured to monitor treatment outcome. Measurement of sputum clearance directly samples the clearance of bacilli from cavities that have eroded into the airways. However, this clearly does not sample all lesions present in a tuberculosis patient and would not be expected to be a direct measure of bacillary loads in, for example, latent lesions. The long-term success of chemotherapy is measured by monitoring disease relapse but such studies require follow-up of patients for 2 years after termination of treatment. Currently studies are underway to develop newer noninvasive means of measuring treatment outcome in animal models. These studies include monitoring of mycobacterial antigens or immune products as biomarkers of treatment response and outcome, and bioimaging studies with CT-scans and PET imaging [302].

8. INTRODUCTION TO CHEMOTHERAPEUTIC AGENTS

TB drugs are divided into two classes: first-line and second-line agents. First-line antitubercular drugs are the most effective and best tolerated. Isoniazid and rifampin are the two most important first-line drugs and multidrug-resistant TB is defined as resistance to these two agents. Ethambutol and pyrazinamide represent the other two first-line agents. The second-line agents are used when a patient develops resistance or is unable to tolerate one of the first-line agents. In general, the second-line agents are less effective and have more substantial side effects. The fluoroquinolones have recently been introduced into TB chemotherapy based on their excellent bactericidal activity, compatibility with existing first-line agents, outstanding lung penetration, and oral bioavailability. The injectable drugs include the aminoglycosides kanamycin, amikacin, streptomycin, and the polypeptide capreomycin. These drugs are also very effective, but the lack of oral bioavailability and increased side effects relegates these compounds to second-line status. The other second-line agents that are still widely used today in order of increasing toxicity include *para*-aminosalicylic acid, ethionamide, cycloserine, and thiacetazone. Several new drugs in clinical development include the nitroimidazoles (PA-824 and OPC-67683), diamine compound SQ109, the diarylquinoline (TMC207). Additionally, linezolid and its thiomorpholine analog are being evaluated for use in TB chemotherpay. All of these drugs are described in some detail, together with general information about the chemical analogs, mechanism of action, pharmacokinetics, metabolism, clinical use, and adverse effects. The information, in summary form, is intended to cover the aspects that are useful for understanding the role of each product in current therapy, the limitations of use, and the need for improvement or for further studies (Fig. 3).

8.1. First-Line Agents

8.1.1. Isoniazid

History   The rationale leading to the discovery of isoniazid began with the antitubercular drug known as thiacetazone (**13**, *p*-acetamidobenzaldehyde thiosemicarbazone, see Fig. 4a), which was synthesized and evaluated by Domagk and coworkers at Bayer [303]. The findings that nicotinamide **14** was modestly tuberculostatic [304], prompted the preparation of the corresponding pyridyl analog **15** of thiacetazone that was in turn prepared from

isonicotinaldehyde **16**, and thiosemicarbazide **17** (Fig. 4b) [305]. The observation that **15** was slightly more potent than thiacetazone **13** led to the evaluation of the intermediates isonicotinic acid hydrazide **1** and isonicotinyl-2-benzenesulfonylhydrazine **19** [306]. Remarkably, isonicotinic acid hydrazide (isoniazid, **1**) was 10 times more potent than streptomycin, the best antitubercular agent at the time. The aforementioned line of reasoning derives from the series of papers published by H. Herbert Fox at Hoffmann-La Roche [307]. Bayer in Germany and Squibb in the United States also independently discovered the antitubercular activity of isoniazid. After the initial disclosure by Hoffmann-La Roche it was discovered that isonicotinic acid hydrazide (isoniazid) had first been synthesized in 1912, but never investigated as a potential antibacterial agent [308].

SAR   The outstanding antitubercular activity of isoniazid in experimental infections, confirmed by clinical trials, stimulated the study of chemical modifications of this simple molecule. Hundreds of derivatives of isoniazid were prepared, yet none had superior activity to the parent drug and isoniazid continues to be a mainstay of TB chemotherapy [309]. Among the modified forms that retained appreciable activity, the N2-alkyl derivatives are noteworthy [310]. In particular, the N2-isopropyl derivative (iproniazid), was found to be active *in vivo*. Extensive clinical trials proved the therapeutic effectiveness of iproniazid, but revealed that is also a psychomotor stimulant, which is caused by the inhibition of monoamine oxidase [311,312]. Use of iproniazid in the treatment of tuberculosis or of psychotic and neurotic depression was discontinued because of the hepatic toxicity of the drug. Although acetyl isoniazid is virtually inactive (MIC = 72 µg/mL) [313], its hydrazones constitute a group of isoniazid congeners that have activity of the same order of the parent compound [314]. The activity of these compounds generally is related to the rate of their hydrolysis to the parent compound. Some hydrazones were introduced into therapeutic use, such as the 3,4-dimethoxybenzilidene (verazide) and the 3-methoxy-4-hydroxy-benzilidene (phthivazid) derivatives; however, use of these derivatives has been discontinued [315–318].

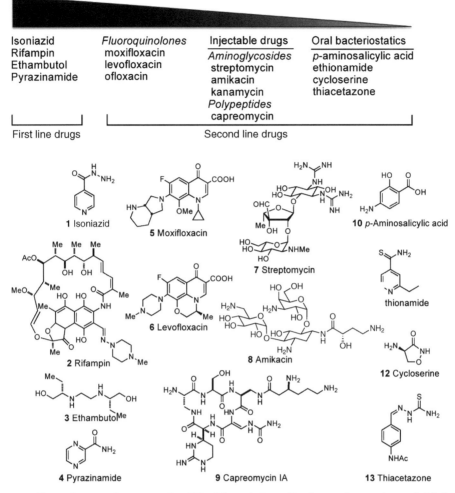

Figure 3. Chemotherapeutic agents for TB. Adapted from Bewley and coworkers, J Med Chem 2008;51:2606–2612.

Antibacterial Activity Isoniazid is bactericidal for rapidly growing *M. tuberculosis*, but bacteriostatic for nonreplicating bacilli. The minimum inhibitor concentration (MIC) of isoniazid for *M. tuberculosis* is 0.025–0.050 µg/mL and this drug exhibits exquisite selectivity for this organism. Isoniazid is not effective against nontuberculous (atypical) mycobacteria except for *M. kansasii*; however, susceptibility should be evaluated since MICs against this organism may be elevated. Additionally, isoniazid demonstrates excellent penetration and is effective against both intra- and extracellular organisms.

Mechanism of Action Isoniazid is now recognized as a prodrug, which is bioactivated by KatG, a catalase/peroxidase, to afford an isonicotinoyl radical **20** (Fig. 5a) [268]. This acyl radical reacts nonenzymatically with cellular pyridine nucleotides to afford a mixture of acyclic 4*R* and 4*S* diastereomeric isonicotinoyl-NAD(P) adducts that are in equilibrium with the cyclic hemiamidals (Fig. 5b) [319,320]. The resulting (4*S*)-acyclic INH-NAD adduct **21**

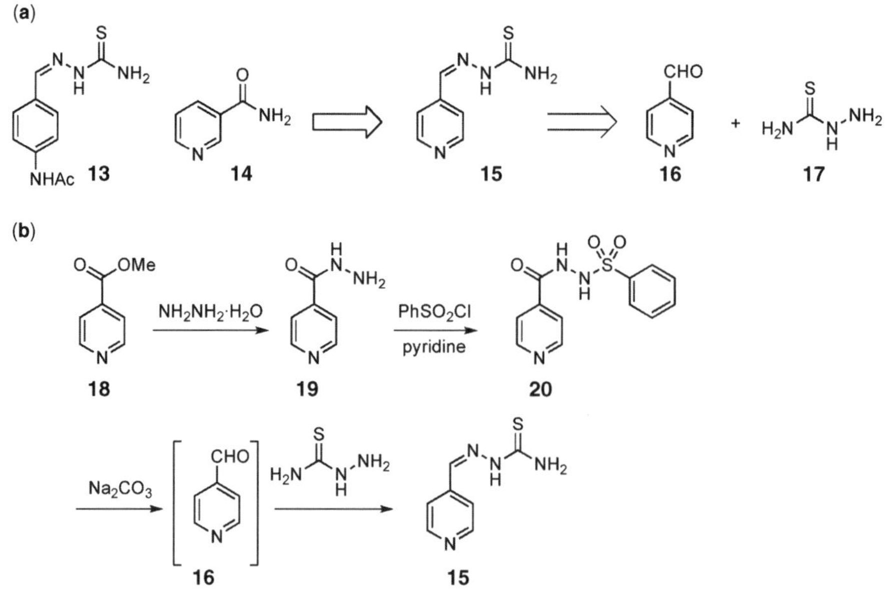

(a)

NHAc **13**   **14**   **15**   **16**   + **17**

(b)

18   NH₂NH₂·H₂O   **19**   PhSO₂Cl / pyridine   **20**

Na₂CO₃   **16**   **15**

Figure 4. (a) Thiacetazone **13** and nicotinamide **14** and hybrid molecule **15**, which is derived from fragments **16** and **17**. (b) Synthesis of isonicotinaldehyde thiosemicarbazone **15**. Isonicotinaldehyde **16** was prepared from the McFayden-Stevens reaction, which involved the base-catalyzed decomposition of benzenesulfonylhydrazine **19** to isonicotinaldehyde **16** in the presence of thiosemicarbazide **17**, provided an excellent route to isonicotinaldehyde thiosemicarbazone **15**.

is a potent slow tight binding reversible inhibitor of InhA ($K_i^* = 1$–5 nM), a NADH-dependent enoyl ACP reductase [321]. The primary action of isoniazid is due to inhibition of InhA, which blocks elongation of C_{26} fatty acids by the FAS-II system and consequently disrupts mycolic acid synthesis (Fig. 6). Additionally, the diastereomeric (4R)-acyclic INH-NAD adduct **22** has been biochemically shown to inhibit dihydrofolate reductase (DfrA, encoded by Rv2763c), which is essential for nucleic acid biosynthesis [155].

Although resistance to INH is primarily conferred by mutations to *katG* or *inhA*, approximately 15% of the INH-resistant clinical isolates have unknown genotypes. Consequently, the INH-NAD(P) adducts may inhibit other targets such as DfrA discussed above. Proteome-wide identification of additional isoniazid targets employing an INH-NAD–sepharaose affinity column identified 16 other INH-NAD(P) binding proteins in addition to InhA and DfrA [322]. The majority of these

proteins are expected to possess a pyridine nucleotide binding pocket and five of the corresponding genes are essential. These results suggest inhibition of additional targets by the INH-NAD(P) adduct may also partially contribute to INHs activity. The exquisite selectivity of INH for *M. tuberculosis* can be reconciled by the highly selective bioactivation of INH by katG.

Resistance Mutations occur spontaneously at the rate of approximately 3×10^{-6} in the genome of *M. tuberculosis* to confer resistance to isoniazid [323]. Thus, isoniazid monotherapy leads to the rapid selection of resistant mutants for infected individuals. However, isoniazid can be used alone in prophylactic treatment since the bacterial load is low. Chemoprophylaxis is used in households or situations where there is a documented TB patient, sensitive to isoniazid.

Several molecular mechanisms of resistance to isoniazid have been characterized. Resistance to isoniazid is most commonly

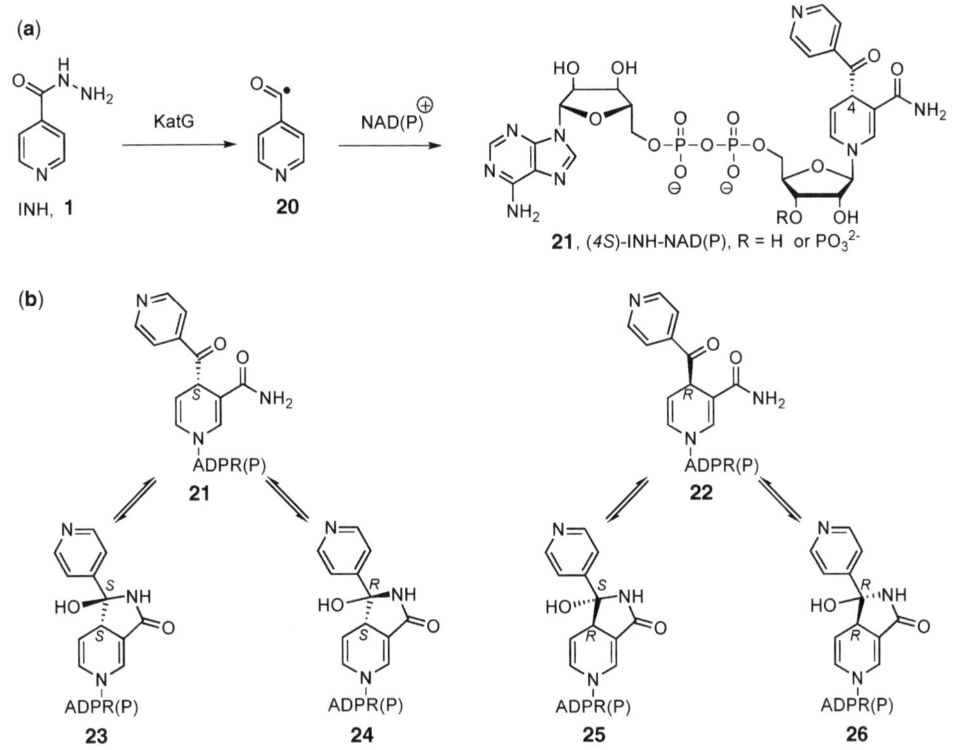

Figure 5. (a) Bioactivation of INH by KatG to afford INH-NAD(P) adducts. The (4S)-acyclic INH-NAD adduct **21** inhibits InhA. (b) Chemical structures of the acyclic diastereomeric adducts **21** and **22** along with the corresponding cyclic hemiamidals **23–26**.

caused by mutations to *katG*. Indeed over 130 *katG* mutations have been identified resulting in MICs ranging from 0.2 to 256 μg/mL [324–326]. The most frequent mutation to *katG* is KatG(S315T), whose activity is approximately 10- to 100-fold lower than wild-type KatG (depending on the oxidant used in the assay). This biochemical result correlates closely with the corresponding 20- to 200-fold higher MIC values for KatG (S315T) Mtb strains [327]. InhA overexpression caused by mutations to *inhA*'s promoter region are also clinically significant. Mutation to *inhA*'s structural region that reduce affinity of NADH have also been characterized. Biochemical studies showed that InhA (S94A), binds the INH-NAD adduct approximately 34-fold more weakly than the wild-type enzyme. Cocrystallization of the INH-NAD adduct with InhA(S94A) demonstrated that the position and orientation of the INH-NAD bisubstrate inhibitor was similar to the

wild-type enzyme. However, deletion of the serine hydroxyl group in the S94A mutant resulted in "movement of an ordered water molecule that disrupted the hydrogen bonding network" [328].

Mutation to *ndhII*, a NADH:menaquinone oxidoreductase involved in the electron transport chain, leads to an accumulation of NADH [182,329,330]. The resulting elevated NADH concentrations acts as a competitive inhibitor of the INH-NAD adduct [329]. Inactivation of isoniazid through acetylation catalyzed by the *M. tuberculosis* arylamine N-acetyltransferase (Mtb-NAT) has been proposed as another potential resistance mechanism. Overexpression of the Mtb-NAT encoded by Rv3556c in *M. smegmatis* led to reduced susceptibility to isoniazid. However, recent biochemical results using purified recombinant Mtb-NAT with isoniazid provided a specificity constant (k_{cat}/K_m) four-orders of magnitude lower than the best substrate

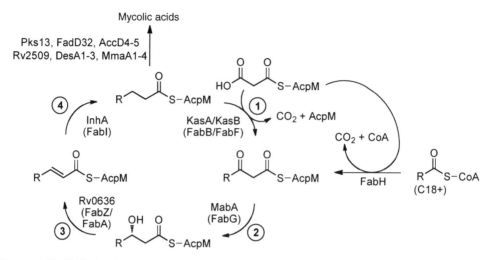

Figure 6. The FAS-II pathway and mycolic acid biosynthesis in *M. tuberculosis*. In *M. tuberculosis*, the FAS-II pathway elongates C_{18+} acyl-CoAs from FAS-I pathway to C_{54}–C_{56} acids by an iterative four-step process employing discrete proteins for each step. In the first step, a ketosynthase condenses a fatty acid with malonyl-AcpM to afford a β-ketoacyl-AcpM. The β-keto function is reduced by three sequential steps catalyzed by MabA (a ketoreductase), Rv0636 (a dehydratase), and InhA (a desaturase) to afford a two-carbon homologated fatty acid. Beginning from a C_{18} fatty acid, this cycle is repeated 17–18 times to afford the C_{54}–C_{56} meromycolates, which are converted to the mycolic acids by the mycobacterial enzymes Pks13, FadD32, AccD4-5, Rv2509, DesA1-3, and MmaA1-4. The ketosynthase FabH catalyzed the initial two-carbon extension of the C_{18} fatty acid derived from the FAS-I pathway to afford the β-ketoacyl-AcpM. Thereafter, KasA and KasB act to homologate the C_{20} acyl-AcpM wherein KasA is responsible for the early steps of elongation. The *E. coli* homlogs are shown in parentheses.

suggesting that this enzyme is unlikely to contribute to significant isoniazid resistance [331]. Finally, high-level resistance to INH is observed in mutants (*mshA*, *mshC*, and *mshD*) deficient in production of mycothiol, a glutathione equivalent in Mtb and other *Actinobacteria*, that is involved in detoxification of reactive xenobiotics [207]. Consequently, mycothiol is thought to play a role in bioactivation of INH [332]. Among the numerous strategies employed by *M. tuberculosis*, the dominant-resistant mechanisms involve reduced bioactivation of INH by KatG as well as InhA overexpression. Mutations in *inhA*, *ndhII*, *nat*, and the *msh* operon that respectively reduce affinity to INH-NAD adduct, lead to an accumulation of NADH levels, inactivation of INH by acetylation, and inhibition of mycothiol synthesis, play a comparatively minor role.

ADME Isoniazid (isonicotinic acid hydrazide, INH) has a MW of 137.1 with a log *P* of −0.8 and is highly soluble in water (140 mg/mL). INH is readily absorbed from the gastrointestinal tract in humans with a median time to maximum peak concentration of 1.0 h under fasting conditions. However, in AIDS patients that are coinfected with *M. avium* or have chronic diarrhea due to protozoal infections, a malabsorption syndrome may occur leading to lower than expected concentrations and resistance [333]. After absorption, isoniazid is well distributed in body fluids and tissues, including the cerebrospinal fluid, and penetrates into the macrophages. The CSF/plasma partition ratio was 1.17 in Korean patients with tuberculous meningitis [334]. Plasma protein binding is negligible (0–10%). The major pathway for isoniazid metabolism is by *N*-acetylation. Polymorphisms in NAT2, the enzyme responsible for isoniazid metabolism, are common and differ between various racial groups (see Table 2). NAT2*4 is considered to be the reference ("wild-type") allele and NAT2*5, *6, and *7 are the most common

Table 2. Percentage of NAT2 Slow Acetylators in Different Racial Populations

Race	% of Slow Acetylators	Major Slow Genotypes
Caucasians	50–60	*NAT2* 5B, NAT2* 6*
African-Americans	50–60	*NAT2* 5C* (6%), *NAT2* 14A* (9%)
Japanese	7 (homozygote slow)	*NAT2* 6A* (19.3%), *NAT2* 7B* (9.7%)
Han Chinese	16.7 (homozygote slow)	*NAT2* 6, NAT2* 7*
Turkish	57.4 (genotypes)	*NAT* 5* (41.7%), *NAT2* 6A* (30.5%) *NAT2* 7B* (4.5%)
Egyptians	80	*NAT2* 5, NAT2* 6*
Arabs (Emiratis)	63	*NAT2* 5* (0.53%), *NAT2* 6* (0.21%)

mutant alleles encoding for an inactive protein.

Based on their genetics, patients may be classified into rapid (extensive) metabolizers and slow (poor) metabolizer groups [335,336]. In some cases, a trimodal distribution may be observed. A population pharmacokinetic study was conducted in 24 males for a Phase I trial of two combination dosage forms of INH plus rifampin along with 1500 mg of pyrazinamide [337]. Mean peak concentrations (C_{max}) of $2.33 \pm 0.59 \mu g/mL$ were observed in serum of rapid acetylators versus 3.55 ± 0.78 g/mL in slow acetylators after a 250 mg oral dose. For comparison, the MIC is approximately $0.05 \mu g/mL$ [338] and the time above the MIC would be approximately 8 h in rapid acetylators versus 22 h in slow acetylators. Exposure based on the area under the concentration time curve (AUC) was approximately threefold lower in rapid acetylators. The median elimination half-lives were 1.2 and 3.3 h, respectively. The apparent volume of distribution (V/F) and apparent oral clearance (Cl/F) values were 0.97 ± 0.21 L and 26.8 ± 18.3 L/h, respectively for all subjects. The high variability in the Cl/F estimate is a function of the genetic differences. As described above, the primary metabolic route that determines isoniazids rate of elimination is acetylation in the liver to acetyl isoniazid. Isoniazid is excreted mainly in the urine in unchanged form, together with various inactive metabolites including N-acetylisoniazid, monoacetylhydrazine, diacetylhydrazine, ammonia, isonicotinic acid, isonicotinylglycine, and isoniazid hydrazones with pyruvic and ketoglutaric acid (see Fig. 7) [339].

Slow acetylators will have higher INH levels and thus potentially better efficacy, but may be at more risk for toxicity. The metabolites hydrazine and acetylhydrazine can be oxidized to hydroxylamines by CYP2E1 leading to liver damage or detoxified to diacetylhydrazine. Slow acetylators appear to be at a higher risk for hepatotoxicity based on a large number of studies in different racial groups [340]. Other risk factors for hepatotoxicity include advanced age, female sex, alcohol intake, viral hepatitis, and HIV infection.

Adverse Effects Isoniazid is usually well tolerated for a long period of treatment. Hepatic side effects consist of frequent subclinic asymptomatic enzyme abnormalities (increase of SGOT and bilirubin), which occasionally cause severe clinical hepatitis, especially in elderly patients with previous hepatobiliary diseases and in alcoholics. The risk of hepatitis is age-related, being very rare in children or young people. Neurological side effects, such as peripheral neuritis, are rare at the daily dose of 5 mg/kg, but more frequent at doses of 10 mg/kg. Administration of pyridoxine to patients receiving high doses of isoniazid generally prevents peripheral neuropathy. Other side effects are at the GI level and occasional hypersensitivity reactions.

Drug Interactions Isoniazid is a reversible, competitive inhibitor of CYP2C19 ($K_i = 25$–36 μM) and CYP3A ($K_i = 50$–75 μM) [341]. For comparison, peak concentrations of INH in plasma are 17–26 μM. INH is also an irreversible inhibitor (mechanism-based inhibitor of several other P450s in microsomal incubations (CYP1A2, CYP2A6, CYP2C19, CYP3A4) with K_i^{app} values ranging from 10 μM (2C19) to

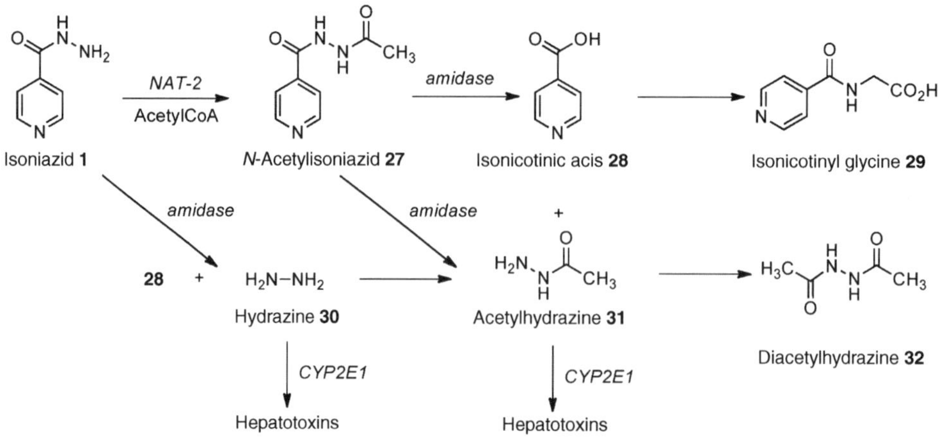

Figure 7. Metabolism of isoniazid (INH).

60 µM (1A2) [342]. Clinical interaction data indicates that CYP2C19 inhibition is most important. Consequently, isoniazid will slow the elimination of coadministered drugs including the HIV type 1 protease inhibitors (e. g., nelfinavir), benzodiazepines (diazepam, midazolam, triazolam), and phenytoin. Slow acetylators are likely to have more prominent drug interactions.

8.1.2. Rifamycin Antibacterials: Rifampin, Rifabutin, and Rifapentine

History The rifamycin antibacterials are semisynthetic derivatives of the ansamycin antibiotic rifamycin B (Fig. 8) [343]. The rifamycins were first isolated as a suite of five related compounds designated as rifamycin A–E from *Amycolatopsis mediterranei* (origin-

ally classified as *Streptomyces mediterranei*) in 1959 by Sensi and his coworkers at Lepetit SA in Milan, Italy [344]. The rifamycins are characterized by a naphthalene core that is bridged by a 19-atom polyketide chain. Extensive structure–activity relationships were performed on these structurally complex natural products and rifampin (RIF, also known as rifampicin) emerged as the first derivative with improved bioactivity and oral bioavailability [345,346]. Rifampin was first approved for clinical use in 1968 in Italy and received Food and Drug Administration (FDA) approval for use in the United States in 1971. Rifabutin (RFB, a semisynthetic derivative of rifamycin S) was discovered in 1975 at Archifar laboratories in Italy (since bought by Adria/FarmItalia). Rifabutin (approved as Mycobutin® in 1992 in the United States) was

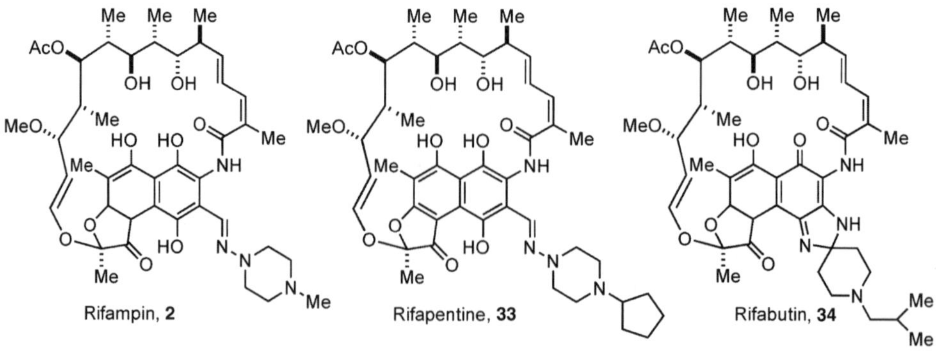

Figure 8. Structures of rifamycin derivatives in clinical use.

initially used for treatment of *M. avium* complex infections (in combination with clarithromycin and ethambutol), but has since become an important part of antitubercular therapy in HIV+ patients because it is a less potent inducer of drug metabolism than rifampin. Rifabutin is the recommended rifamycin in persons taking HIV protease inhibitors in the United States, but is significantly more expensive and is not widely used globally. Rifapentine (RFP) is a long-acting, once-weekly rifamycin first prepared in 1965 (at the same time as rifampin) that was approved in 1998 in the United States as Priftin®.

Rifampin and rifapentine are produced from rifamycin B, the most abundant rifamycin congener. Oxidation of rifamycin B **35** with sodium persulfate provides rifamycin O **36** that is hydrolyzed with concentrated sulfuric acid to yield rifamycin S **37** (Fig. 9) [347,348]. Treatment of **37** with piperidine and formaldehyde affords a Mannich adduct, which is reduced *in situ* with ascorbic acid to afford **38** [349]. Subsequent oxidation with lead tetraacetate as well as a variety of other oxidizing agents furnishes the key intermediate 3-formyl-rifamycin SV **39** that provides access to a wide range of analogs through reactions with amines, alkoxyamines, hydrazides, and hydrazones [350]. Rifampin **33** and rifapentine **43** are prepared by condensation with *N*-methyl-*N*-aminopiperazine and *N*-cyclopentyl-*N*-aminopiperazine, respectively.

SAR Extensive modifications of the rifamycin scaffold have provided comprehensive structure–activity relationships [351]. These studies have identified the minimal structural requirements to maintain activity and served to define positions amenable to modification for optimization of potency and modulation of physicochemical and drug disposition properties. The molecule can be divided into two domains (Fig. 10a): the furanonaphthohydroquinone and the ansa-bridge. The defining feature of the topologically novel rifamycins is the ansa-bridge that substantially reduces the overall conformational flexibility of this molecule and ideally positions the essential phenols at C-1 and C-8 as well as the C-21 and C-23 hydroxyl groups for interaction with an allosteric binding site of bacterial DNA-dependent RNA polymerase. Thus, acetylation at positions C-21 or C-23 or methylation at C-1 or C-8 leads to almost complete loss of activity. Similarly, stepwise hydrogenation of the olefins located in the ansa-bridge leads to incremental decreases in biological activity.

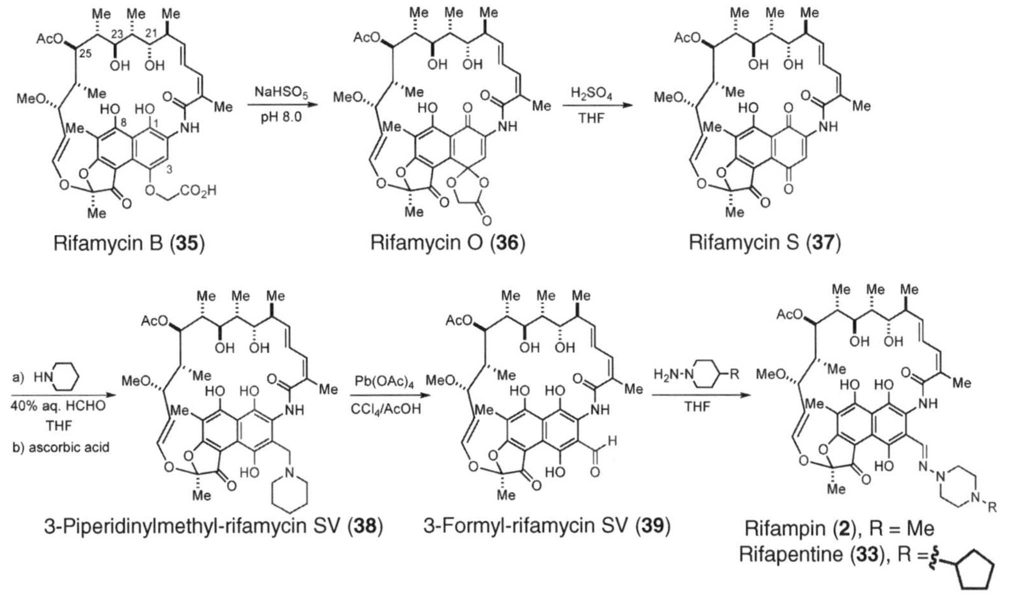

Figure 9. Synthesis of rifampin and rifapentine. (This figure is available in full color at http://mrw.interscience.wiley.com/emrw/9780471266945/home.)

(a)   (b)

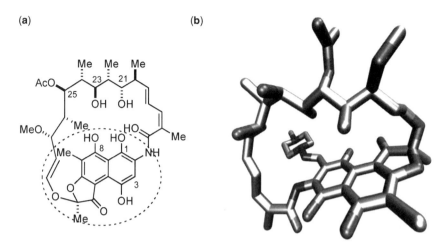

Figure 10. (a) Structure of rifamycin depicting the chromophore (circled) and ansa-bridge domains. (b) X-ray structure of rifampin. (This figure is available in full color at http://mrw.interscience.wiley.com/emrw/ 9780471266945/home.)

Virtually all discovery efforts have focused on modification of the C-3 and C-4 positions of the furanonaphthohydroquinone of rifamycin SV (see Table 3 for representative SAR) [351]. Modification of the C-11 keto group of the furanone moiety has also been reported [352]. The X-ray cocrystal structure of rifampin and RNAP reveals that groups appended to C-3 are directed away from the protein consistent with the observation that modifications at these positions are well tolerated [353]. The ansa-bridge is much less tolerant to modification, since this portion of the molecule makes extensive van der Waals contacts and hydrogen-bond interactions with RNAP. As mentioned previously, substitution of either the C-21 or C-23 results in almost complete loss in biological activity. However, replacement of the C-25 acetate with carbamates has provided a new series of biologically active compounds [354]. Several of the C-25 carbamate derivatives were less susceptible to ADP-ribosylation at C-23, an unusual bacterial resistance mechanism recently observed for the rifamycin class of antibiotics, which is discussed further below.

Antibacterial Activity Rifampin is bactericidal against *M. tuberculosis* and other mycobacteria of the *M. tuberculosis* complex including *M. bovis* and *M. africanum* with MICs in the range of 0.03–0.125 μg/mL [355]. Among the nontuberculosis mycobacteria, *M. kansasii*

(>90%) and all isolates of *M. marinum* are susceptible at 0.78 μg/mL [356]. *M. scrofulaceium*, *M. intracellulare*, and *M. avium* possess MICs on the order of 4 μg/mL, while *M. fortuitum* is resistant [357]. Rifampin is bactericidal against *M. leprae* with an MIC of less than 1 μg/mL and due to the high-level resistance to dapsone, the WHO now recommends combination therapy with rifampin [358]. Rifampin demonstrates excellent penetration and is effective against both intra- and extracellular organisms. Additionally, rifampin is very active against other Gram-positive organisms including *Staphylococcus aureus* (MIC 0.003–0.012 μg/mL), *Neisseria meningitidis*, *Haemophilus influenza*, and *Legionella* sp., and possesses modest activity against Gram-negative organisms, likely due to decreased permeability across the outer cell membrane [359]. In addition to its use in tuberculosis chemotherapy, rifampin is used as an alternative agent for *Staphylococcal* infections in combination with aminoglycosides, treatment of asymptomatic carriers of *Neisseria meningitidis*, and as an alternative agent for *Legionella* not responsive to macrolides.

The pharmacodynamic model of RIF-mediated killing of *M. tuberculosis* H37Ra has recently been studied in a hollow-fiber bioreactor [360]. In this system, the pharmacokinetics of rifampin dosing were duplicated for daily 600 mg regimen compared to intermittent

Table 3. Antimycobacterial Activity of 3-Formylrifamycin SV Derivatives

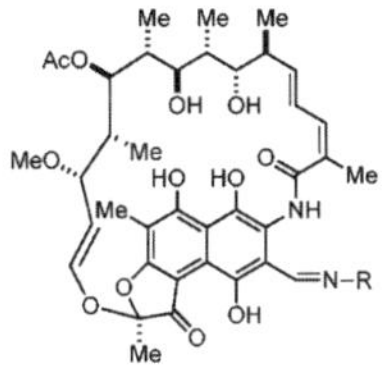

Compound	R =	MIC (μg/mL)
40	—NH$_2$	1
41	—NHMe	5
42	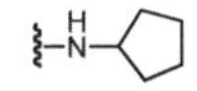 —N(H)-cyclopentyl	0.2
43	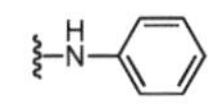 —N(H)-phenyl	2
44	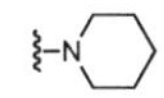 —N-piperidinyl	0.05
45	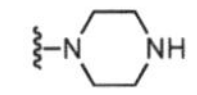 —N-piperazinyl-NH	2
2 (rifampin)	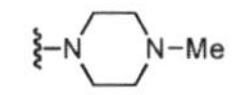 —N-piperazinyl-N—Me	0.5
46	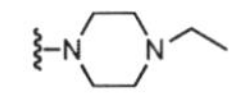 —N-piperazinyl-N-ethyl	0.2
47	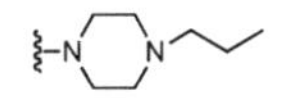 —N-piperazinyl-N-propyl	0.2
48	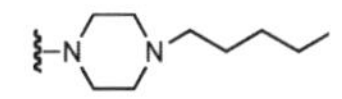 —N-piperazinyl-N-butyl	0.02
33 (rifapentine)	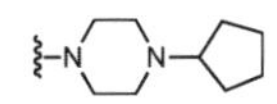 —N-piperazinyl-N-cyclopentyl	0.03

doses of 2100 mg twice weekly or 4200 mg once weekly (assumes linear pharmacokinetics). At subtherapeutic concentrations, *rpoB* mutations were observed at codons 526 His>Arg and 531 Ser>Leu (mutations commonly found clinically). Previous animal experiments conducted in preclinical testing had demonstrated that intermittent dosing was just as effective or more effective than daily dosing suggesting a concentration-dependent mechanism of killing [361,362]. In the bioreactor system, there was no difference in the rate of killing between the three dosing regimens, indicating that the time above the MIC or AUC/MIC ratio may be the most important phamacodynamic factor. However, a very long postantibiotic effect

(PAE) was observed in the once-weekly *in vitro* dosing experiment and short exposure time studies (0.5–7 h) revealed that the postantibiotic effect was clearly concentration-dependent. At 2 μg/mL the PAE was 5.2 days (C_{max}/MIC 64), at 7 μg/mL the PAE was 12–13 days (C_{max}/MIC = 224), and at 14 μg/mL the PAE was 19 days (C_{max}/MIC = 448). This data also correlates well with other *in vitro* studies of Chan, who observed a PAE of 2.8 days at a C_{max}/MIC ratio of 32 [363]. When used in combination with isoniazid (±ethambutol or streptomycin) PAEs were even longer with a mean of approximately 7 days. Collectively, these studies indicate that high intermittent doses (once or twice weekly) would be a viable strategy in most patients.

Rifampin plays the dominant role in sterilization of the DOTS treatment regimen and is unique among all currently employed antimycobacterial agents due to its ability kill bacilli that have a rapid burst in metabolism [364]. Mitchison and coworkers have hypothesized that dormant bacilli occasionally reawaken and are metabolically active for short periods of time [365]. Consequently, the effectiveness of rifampin may lie in its ability to rapidly kill these bacilli [366]. This hypothesis helps rationalize why rifampin, which is less bactericidal than other TB drugs in the conventional sense (that is, using *in vitro* activity or by early bactericidal activity (EBA) in patients with pulmonary TB), is the most effective in sterilization.

Mechanism of Action Rifamycins inhibit bacterial DNA-dependent RNA polymerase, thus preventing RNA transcription and are the only clinically used inhibitors of RNA transcription [367,368]. The essential catalytic core of RNAP is a 400 kDa heterotetramer comprised of four subunits (α2ββ′ω) [369,370]. Rifampin binds with a dissociation constant of approximately 1 nM to the β-subunit encoded by *rpoB* in the DNA/RNA channel, which is approximately 12 Å downstream of the Mg^{2+}-containing active site [353]. The resulting stable RNAP–rifampin complex blocks the nascent RNA transcript as it is extruded out of the active site, leading to premature truncation at two to three nucleotides. This mechanism has been termed a steric-occlusion mechanism. Artsimovitch et al. proposed an alternative mechanism involving allosteric modulation of Mg^{2+} binding to the RNA polymerase active center [371]. However, this model was shown to be incorrect and the steric-occlusion model is consistent with all biochemical, mutational, and structural studies of RNAP [372].

Resistance In *M. tuberculosis*, resistance to rifampin occurs through point mutations or short insertions or deletions to the RNA polymerase beta subunit gene (*rpoB*) that lowers the affinity for the drug. These mutations occur spontaneously with a mutation frequency of $10^{-6}-10^{-7}$. The majority (96%) of these mutations are found in a 81 bp core region of *rpoB*, panning codons 507–533 [272]. Remarkably, 86% of all rifampin-resistant isolates of *M. tuberculosis* contain point mutations at only one of three conserved positions corresponding to D396, H406, and S411 of the *Thermus aquaticus* RNAP. The cocrystal structure of rifampin and the *Thermus aquaticus* RNAP reconciles the observed mutants and reveals that H406 and D396 directly H-bond with the alcohol at C-21 of rifampin while S411 H-bonds with phenol at C-8; the hydroxy groups that constitute part of the rifampin pharmacophore [353]. Furthermore, the other clinically observed mutations at positions 387, 390–395, 398, 401–402, 405, 407, and 413 (numbered according to the *T. aquaticus* sequence) are all found in the rifampin binding pocket and most of the residues either directly interact with rifampin or substitution likely distort the binding pocket.

Another recently characterized mechanism of rifampin resistance in *M. smegmatis* is through ADP-ribosylation of the C-21 alcohol of rifampin catalyzed by a chromosomally encoded ADP-ribosyltransferase (Arr-ms) [373]. The ribosylated rifampin presumably can no longer bind RNAP. Although Arr-ms paralogs are not found in *M. tuberculosis*, several Arr-ms genes have been observed in other atypical mycobacteria and Gram-negative organisms including *Klebsiella pneumoniae*, *Acinetobacter baumannii*, and *Pseudomonas aeruginosa* [373].

ADME Rifampin is highly lipophilic (log *P* 3.72) and 85% plasma protein bound, primarily to alpha-1-acid glycoprotein [346,374]. At the typical 600 mg dose (recommended for adults, once a day) rifampin is well absorbed (oral bioavailability 68%) reaching peak levels of 8–20 μg/ml 1.5–2 h after ingestion. The initial half-life of rifampin is dose-dependent and is approximately 3 h for a 600 mg dose and 5 h for a 900 mg dose [375]. Rifampin primarily undergoes hepatic metabolism to afford biologically active compounds through deacetylation at C-25 and hydrolysis of the hydrazone to yield formyl derivatives [375]. 25-Desacetylrifampin and lesser amounts of the parent drug are excreted through the bile, but only rifampin is reabsorbed, thus hepatic deacetylation is the main clearance mechanism. The desacetyl metabolite is pharmacologically active, but is not a major contributor to the total activity in plasma (concentrations are less than 10% of rifampin). Biliary excretion is saturated with a dose of 300–450 mg [376]. Consequently, a single dose once a day versus multiple doses provides a substantial enhancement in half-life, peak plasma concentrations, and area under the concentration time curve values [376]. Induction of hepatic microsomal enzymes leads to 40% decrease in rifampin half-life and steady-state concentrations are reached after 6 days of treatment [346]. Approximately 13–24% of the dose is excreted in the urine as unchanged drug and the remainder of the drug and metabolites are excreted in the feces [375].

The rifamycin-derived antibiotics are potent inducers of cytochrome P450-3A family (CYP3A) by activation of the pregnane X receptor (PXR) [377]. The relative potency of the rifamycins as CYP3A inducers is rifampin > rifapentine > rifabutin [378]. Additionally, glucuronosyl transferases UGT1A9 and UGT2B7 are also induced [379,380]. Rifamycins have a significant effect on the metabolism of other drugs, most notably the antiretroviral drugs, which are often used in combination therapy for HIV-infected TB patients. For example, CYP3A induction by rifampin was shown to result in an 87% decrease in the median plasma concentration of the HIV protease inhibitor indinavir [381]. Rifabutin is the preferred rifamycin in HIV-infected patients, since it has the smallest CYP3A induction potential, but its use is limited by the high cost of the drug.

Adverse Effects The most common adverse effect of rifampin are mild influenza-like symptoms, which have been attributed to the development of an immune reaction [382]. The influenza-like syndrome is most often found in intermittent treatment regimens. These adverse immunoallergic reactions result in thrombocytopenia and less frequently in acute hemolytic anemia, respiratory disorders, acute renal failure, gastrointestinal reactions, and cutaneous reactions. Additionally, rifampin has been shown to have an immunosuppressive effect in animals [383]. Rifampin has been reported to result in hepatotoxicity in 2–5% and altered liver function (elevated transaminases) in 10–15% of patients [384]. The combination of rifampin plus pyrazinamide is no longer recommended for prophylaxis due to a high rate of hepatotoxicity compared to isoniazid. Additionally, rifampin has one superficial adverse effect, which is due to the furanonapthoquinone chromophore of rifampin that results in a distinctive orange-red color to all body fluids (tears, urine, sweat).

Drug Interactions Drug interactions between rifamycins and HIV protease inhibitors can be dramatic. For example, rifampin 600 mg daily reduced lopinavir (LPV) trough level (boosted by ritonavir, RTV) by more than 90% in a chronic healthy volunteer study [385]. Conversely, increasing the RTV dose had no significant effect on rifampin concentration. Table 4 summarizes the effects of the various rifamycins on commonly used antiretrovirals.

Rifabutin Rifabutin belongs to the group of spiroimidazorifamycins obtained by condensation of 3-amino-4-iminorifamycin SV with *N*-butyl-4-piperidone. Rifabutin has an antibacterial spectrum similar to rifampin, but seems to possess incomplete cross-resistance with rifampin *in vitro*. In fact some strains resistant to rifampin are still moderately sensitive to rifabutin. Another characteristic of rifabutin is that its activity against *M. avium* complex is higher than that of rifampin.

Table 4. Effect of Rifamycins on Common Antiretrovirals?[a]

Object Drug	RIF (600 mg daily)	RFB (300 mg 2× weekly)	RFP (1200 mg weekly)
Amprenavir	AUC decr 82%	AUC decr 14%	
Indinavir	AUC decr 89%	AUC decr 32%	AUC decr 70% C_{max} decr 55%
Nelfinavir	AUC decr 82%	AUC decr 32%	NA
Ritonavir	AUC decr 35%	AUC decr <10%	NA
Lopinavir (+RTV)	C_{min} decr 90–93%		NA
Fosamprenavir (+RTV)		AUC incr 35% C_{min} incr 17%	NA
Saquinavir	AUC decr 89%	AUC decr 40%	NA
Saquinavir (+RTV)	AUC decr 39.5% C_{min} decr 48.7% Not recommended 40% liver toxicity	NA[b]	NA
Atazanavir (+RTV)	AUC decr 72% C_{min} decr 97.5%	NA	NA
Tipranavir (+RTV)	Not recommended	NA	NA
Efavirenz	C_{min} decr 25% AUC decr 22%	NA	NA
Nevirapine	AUC decr 37% AUC decr 47%	AUC decr 16%	NA
Zidovudine	C_{max} 43% Cl/F incr 89%	$T_{1/2}$ decr 28%	NA
Etravirine	Not recommended	AUC decr 35% C_{min} decr 35%	NA

[a] Ref. [388].
[b] NA = no available information.

ADME Rifabutin is rapidly absorbed, but its oral bioavailability is only 20%, and there is considerable interpatient variation. Rifabutin has a long half-life of 45 h (range 16–69 h). As a result of a large volume of distribution, average unbound plasma concentrations remain relatively low after repeated administration of standard doses ($C_{max} = 0.13 \, \mu g/mL$ after 300 mg twice-weekly dose versus $1.5 \, \mu g/mL$ for a 600 mg twice-weekly dose of RIF). Rifabutin is slowly but extensively metabolized by CYP3A4 to predominantly the 31-OH metabolite. More than 20 metabolites have been identified in humans. The 25-*O*-desacetyl derivative is also a major non-P450-mediated, active metabolite formed by microsomal cholinesterase and β-esterase, but undergoes further CYP3A4-mediated hydroxylation [374]. RFB is a pregnane X receptor agonist, and induces CYP2B6, CYP3A4, CYP2C9, CYP2C19, UGT1A1, and UGT2B7. In HIV + patients on highly active antiretroviral therapy (HAART), numerous bidirectional drug interactions can take place. For patients taking ritonavir as a pharmacokinetic enhancer of protease inhibitors, the RFB dose should be reduced because of inhibition of CYP3A4 (Table 5).

Adverse Effects The adverse effects are similar to those observed for rifampin. In addition RFB can cause uveitis, an eye disorder that is an inflammation of the middle layer of the eye, characterized by pain, blurred vision, and photophobia.

Rifapentine Rifapentine (3-(4-cyclopentyl-1-piperazinyl-iminomethyl)-rifamycin SV) is an analog of rifampin wherein a cyclopentyl group substitutes for a methyl group on the piperazine ring. Its activity is similar to that of rifampin, but is slightly superior *in vitro* against mycobacteria, including the *M. avium* complex. In experimental tuberculous infections, rifapentine administered once a week has practically the same therapeutic efficacy as rifampin administered daily. Rifapentine is used for the therapy of tuberculosis and leprosy at a dose of 1200 mg once weekly. However, relapse with rifamycin monoresistant tuberculosis occurred among HIV-seropositive tuberculosis patients treated with a once-weekly isoniazid/rifapentine continuation phase regimen [386]. The CDC recommends that persons with HIV-TB and CD4 + cell counts $<100/mm^3$ should not be treated with intermittent (i.e., once or twice weekly) regimens. These patients should receive daily therapy during the intensive phase, and daily or three doses a week during the continuation phase. In this group of patients, CDC recommends directly observed therapy for both daily and three-doses-a-week regimens. The low relapse rate suggests that current recommendations concerning duration are sufficient (i. e., 6 months minimum, extended to 9 months in patients with delayed response to therapy).

ADME The bioavailability of rifapentine is unknown, but absorption is slow (T_{max} 5–6 h) and the AUC is increased 50% by a high fat meal [374]. Rifapentine is slightly more lipophilic than rifampin and has a serum half-life about five times longer than rifampin. This is due to its high affinity to serum proteins (97–98% bound) compared to rifampin (85%). At the recommended 1200 mg dose, total rifapentine concentrations ranged between 10 and $20 \, \mu g/mL$ for approximately 18 h. Rifapentine also induces its own metabolism and the half-life changes from 18.5 h initially to 14.5 h after repeated thrice-weekly dosing [387]. Although the half-life of rifapentine is long, and intermittent dosing is feasible, the high protein binding (98%) results in much lower free concentrations than rifampin or rifabutin [374]. Based on a free fraction of 0.02 (98% bound), the concentration of free drug would be $0.2–0.4 \, \mu g/mL$ (the reported MIC is $0.02 \, \mu g/mL$). Rifapentine is excreted primarily as intact drug in the feces; less than

Table 5. Dosage Adjustments of Antiretrovirals and Rifabutin for Patients Receiving Single-Interacting HAART, According to guidelines?[a]

Drug	Adjustment	Rifabutin Dosage[b]
NRTI[a]	None	300 mg q.d.
Indinavir	1000 mg q8h	150 mg q.d.
Ritonavir	None	150 mg twice per week
Nelfinavir	1000 mg t.i.d.	150 mg q.d.
Amprenavir	None	150 mg q.d.
Saquinavir	None	300 mg q.d.
Efavirenz	None	450 mg q.d.

[a] NRTI, nucleoside reverse-transcriptase inhibitor.
[b] Standard rifabutin dosage is 300 mg p.o. q.d.

5% of it and its metabolites are excreted in the urine. The primary metabolite in bile and feces is 25-desacetyl-rifapentine, with smaller amounts of the degradation by-products, 3-formyl-rifapentine and 3-formyl-desacetyl-rifapentine, formed in the gut.

8.1.3. Ethambutol

History Ethambutol was discovered at Lederle laboratories and its synthesis and biological activity were first reported in 1961 [389,390]. Random screening of compounds identified N,N'-diisopropyl ethylenediamine as a promising lead with good oral bioavailability and modest *in vivo* activity in an animal model. Several thousand analogs were prepared and ethambutol emerged as the optimal candidate due to its favorable and highly specific antitubercular activity, low toxicity, and excellent drug disposition properties [391]. Despite ethambutol's relatively modest antitubercular activity, it remains a first-line agent since it possesses excellent synergy with other antitubercular drugs and low toxicity. Ethambutol is a simple C-2 symmetrical diamine that is prepared from ethylene dichloride and neat (S)-2-amino-1-butanol [389] (Fig. 11).

SAR Wilkinson and coworkers at Lederle reported detailed structure–activity relationships of the lead compound N,N'-diisopropyl ethylenediamine that led to the discovery of ethambutol [391]. The SAR campaign was driven by *in vivo* activity in infected animals. Although clear SAR trends emerged from this analysis, it is important to note that the observed SAR is a composite of not only antimycobacterial activity, but also the drug disposition properties of these molecules. The reported SAR in Tables 6–8 below show activities relative to the lead compound N,N'-diisopropyl ethylenediamine.

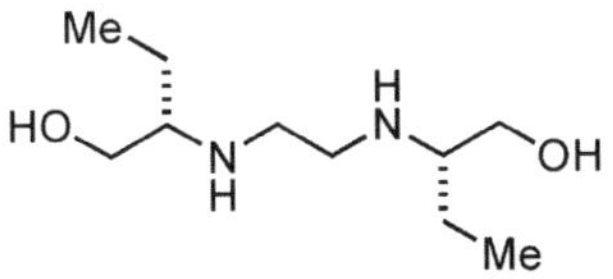

Figure 11. Structure of ethambutol.

Table 6. SAR of Ethambutol Alkyl Chain

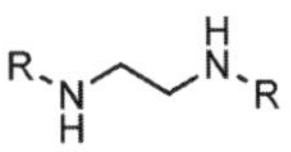

Compound	R =	Relative Activity In Vivo[a]
49		<1/16
50		<1/8
51	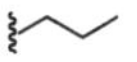	<1/8
52		1
53		≤1/8
54	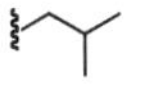	≤1/8
55	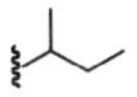	1
56	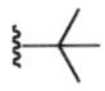	1
57	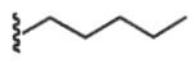	<1/8
58	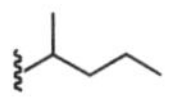	<1/30
3 (ethambutol)	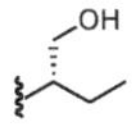	4
59	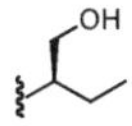	<1/110
60	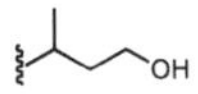	<1/32
61	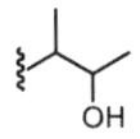	<1/32

[a] ED_{50}(compound)/ED_{50}(compound #52), where ED_{50} is the effective oral dose that results in 50% survival of mice infected with a lethal dose of *Mycobacterium tuberculosis* H37Rv produced by intravenous injection of the bacterial culture.

The general pharmacophore of ethambutol contains a central ethylenediamine scaffold with *N*-alkyl groups (Table 6). Initial optimization of the lead compound isopropyl **52** showed that *N*-substituted ethylenediamine compounds with C_1–C_5 linear alkyl chains were inactive (relative activities <1/8 of **52**). However, the C_4 derivatives, *sec*-butyl **55** and *tert*-butyl **56** that contained a branch on the alpha-carbon were equipotent to **52** whereas *iso*-butyl **54** containing a beta-branch was approximately one-eight as active as **52**. The alpha branched *sec*-pentyl derivative **58** was inactive, which served to define the maximum side-chain length at four carbons. Based on the working hypothesis that these compounds were potential chelating agents due to the presence of the ethylenediamine moiety, a hydroxy group was incorporated in the *sec*-butyl side chain of **55** resulting in compounds **3** and **59–61**. The *S*-configured 1-hydroxy-but-2-yl side chain in **3** was fourfold more active than the lead compound **52** whereas the *R*-configured side chain in **59** and the *meso*-diasteromers (not shown) were inactive. Remarkably, the (*S,S*)-isomer **3** (ethambutol) is more than 500-fold more active than its (*R,R*)-antipode. Introduction of the hydroxy group at the 3- and 4-positions of the 1-hydroxy-but-2-yl side chain resulted in inactive compounds **60** and **61** demonstrating the strict substrate requirements for activity. Importantly, introduction of the hydroxy group in **3** substantially reduced the toxicity providing a therapeutic index of 150–200, which represents a 37- to 50-fold improvement over compound **52**.

Variation of the chain length of the alkyldiamine pharmacophore of ethambutol from C_2 to C_4 in **3**, **62**, and **63** revealed that increasing the chain length beyond two carbon atoms results in complete loss of activity (Table 7). Amide derivatives **64** and **65** also resulted in significant loss of activity suggesting that basic nitrogen atoms are required, although simple steric or electrostatic arguments are also plausible. Further *N*-alkylation of the secondary alcohols of ethambutol provided methyl derivative **66** and ethyl derivative **67**. Interestingly, methyl analog **66** was equipotent to ethambutol **3** whereas ethyl analog **67** was approximately 164 as active as ethambutol **3**. However, the activity of **66** was due to rapid metabolism via demethylation to afford ethambutol **3**. The impact of substitution of the hydroxymethyl side chain of ethambutol **3** was examined with analogs **68–72** as shown in Table 8. Replacement of the hydroxymethyl group in ethambutol **3** with aminomethyl-, thiomethyl-, carboxy- or carboxamido groups in **69–72** resulted in complete loss of activity. Methoxymethyl **68** maintained activity, but

Table 7. SAR of Diaminoalkyl Scaffold

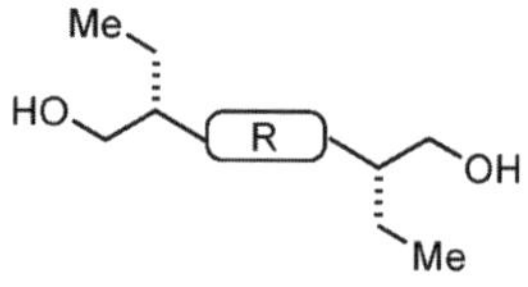

Compound	R =	Relative Activity *In Vivo*[a]
3	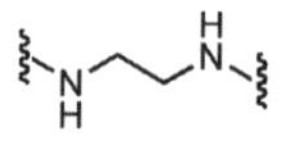 –NH–CH₂CH₂–NH–	4
62	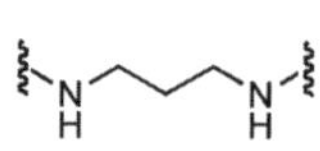 –NH–CH₂CH₂CH₂–NH–	<1/32
63	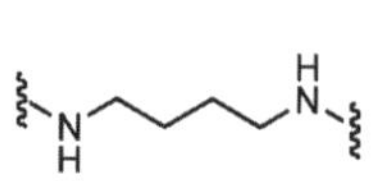 –NH–CH₂CH₂CH₂CH₂–NH–	<1/32
64	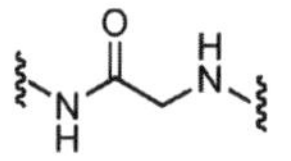 –NH–CH₂–C(=O)–NH–	<1/2
65	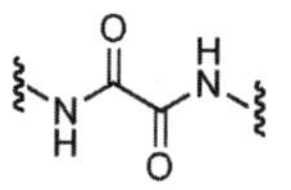 –NH–C(=O)–C(=O)–NH–	<1/16
66	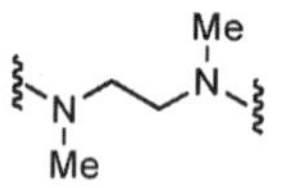 –N(Me)–CH₂CH₂–N(Me)–	4
67	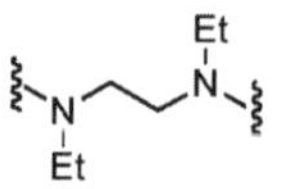 –N(Et)–CH₂CH₂–N(Et)–	1/16

[a] ED_{50}(compound)/ED_{50}(compound #**52**), where ED_{50} is the effective oral dose that results in 50% survival of mice infected with a lethal dose of *Mycobacterium tuberculosis* H37Rv produced by intravenous injection of the bacterial culture.

this may be due to metabolism via *O*-demethylation to provide ethambutol **3**.

Given the emergence of MDR-TB and desire to further reduce the duration of the current treatment regimen, several closely related novel ethambutol analogs have recently been disclosed [392–395]. However, none of the reported analogs exhibited activity superior to ethambutol. These studies further confirmed the highly specific structural requirements for activity. Inspired by the central ethylenedia-

Table 8. Impact of Hydroxymethyl Side Chain

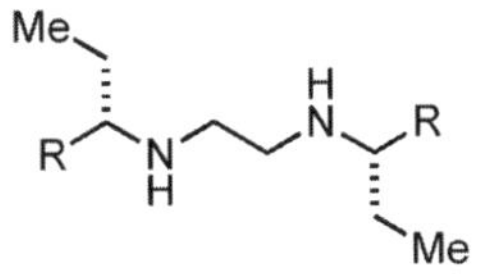

Compound	R =	Relative Activity In Vivo[a]
3	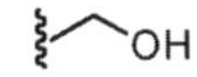 ⟨CH₂CH₂OH⟩ OH	4
68	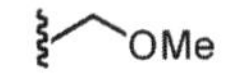 ⟨CH₂CH₂OMe⟩ OMe	2–4
69	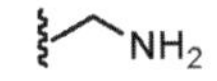 ⟨CH₂NH₂⟩ NH₂	<1/8
70	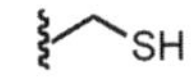 ⟨CH₂SH⟩ SH	<1/32
71	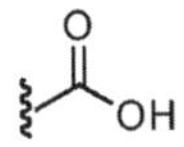 ⟨C(=O)OH⟩	<1/32
72	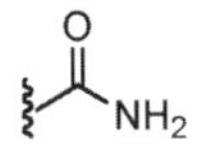 ⟨C(=O)NH₂⟩	<1/8

[a] ED_{50}(compound)/ED_{50}(compound #**52**), where ED_{50} is the effective oral dose that results in 50% survival of mice infected with a lethal dose of *Mycobacterium tuberculosis* H37Rv produced by intravenous injection of the bacterial culture.

mine pharmacophore, Lee and coworkers prepared a combinatorial solid-phase library of approximately 64,000 compounds from which *N*-(2-adamantyl)-*N*′-geranyl-ethane1,2-diamine (SQ109), which bears only a slight resemblance to ethambutol and does not possess the same mechanism of action, emerged as the most active compound and displayed a 14–35 improvement in activity *in vitro* against *M. tuberculosis* H37Rv [396]. This compound is currently in clinical development and is discussed further in Section 8.3.

Antibacterial Activity Ethambutol is only effective against mycobacteria and inhibits 90% of strains with an MIC equal to or less than $2\,\mu$M [397–399]. Strains of the *M. tuberculosis* complex and many nontuberculosis mycobacteria are susceptible; however, most strains of the *M. avium* complex and all isolates of *M. fortuitum* are resistant [356,400]. The effect of ethambutol on mycobacteria is primarily bacteriostatic, although bactericidal activity can be observed under certain growth condi-

tions [401]. The growth inhibition by ethambutol is more related to the time of exposure rather than drug concentration.

Mechanism of Action The mechanism of action of ethambutol is due to inhibition of arabinogalactan biosynthesis (Fig. 12) [402–404]. The synergistic effects of ethambutol with other drugs are readily understood since AG is an integral part of the mycobacterial cell wall and disruption of the cell envelope enhances permeability of other drugs. Arabinogalactan is attached to the inner peptidoglycan scaffold while the AG termini are esterified with mycolic acids. Inhibition of AG biosynthesis by ethambutol is extremely rapid and results in the accumulation of mycolic acids and their trehalose esters as well as decaprenolphospho-β-D-arabinofuranose, the key mycobacterial lipid carrier of arabinose [405,406]. These results from whole cell studies have been recapitulated with cell-free studies, which have definitively shown that ethambutol inhibits incorporation of decaprenolphospho-β-D-arabinofuranose into arabinan oligosaccharides [407]. Attempts to more precisely define the molecular targets via plasmid-mediated target overexpression of a *M. avium* genomic library identified *embA* and *embB* [408]. These genes are part of the *embCAB* operon and encode for putative membrane-associated arabinosyl transferases [409]. Although biochemical evidence is lacking, genetic studies suggest that *embAB* are involved in arabinan synthesis while *embC* is involved in synthesis of arabinan domains of lipoarabinomannan, an antigenic lipopolysaccharide noncovalently associated with the cell wall [410,411]. Ethambutol has also been shown to inhibit LAM synthesis and galactin components of AG, albeit more weakly [404,412]. The recent functional characterization of the two processive galactosyltransferases, GlfT1 and GlfT2, which are responsible for the complete biosynthesis of the mycobacterial galactan of AG, should enable direct biochemical confirmation of these additional targets [413,414]. Based on isolated resistance mutants, the primary molecular target of ethambutol is EmbB; however, other functionally related glycosyltransferases including EmbA, EmbC, and potentially the GlfTs likely contribute to ethambutol's overall mechanism of action.

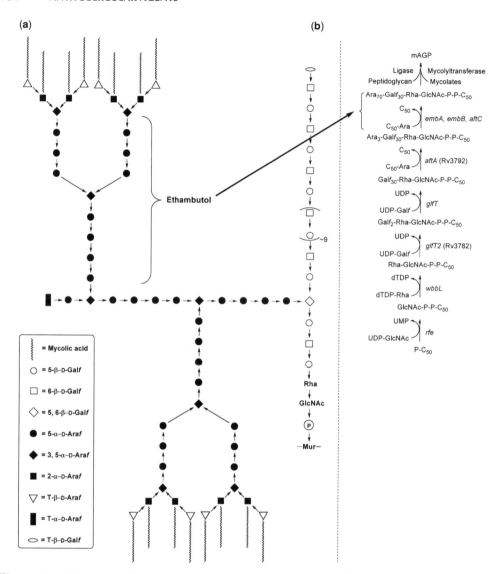

Figure 12. (a) Structure of the mycobacterial cell wall arabinogalactan (AG). The galactan and arabinan components are represented by the open and filled circles/squares, respectively. The reducing end is attached to the peptidoglycan via the disaccharide (Rha-GlcNAc). The peptidoglycan is represented by a single muramic acid (Mur) residue. On the other end are the mycolic acids. The figure is not meant to illustrate three-dimensional relationships. (b) Arbinogalactan biosynthetic pathway. Part (a) and legend adapted from Ref. [404].

Resistance Clinically, monoresistance to ethambutol is rare and resistance is most often associated with multiply drug-resistant TB strains. Approximately 70% of *M. tuberculosis* ethambutol-resistant clinical isolates contain a mutation in *embB*, a glycosyltransferase with 11 predicted membrane-spanning segments [415]. The most prevalent mutations occur at Met306 followed by Gly406. Mutations in Met306 are not sufficient to generate high-level ethambutol resistance [416]. Nevertheless, the *embB306* locus has been proposed as a candidate marker for multi- and extensively drug-resistant strains

[417]. Additionally, mutations were observed in *embA*, *embC*, and *embR* (the transcriptional regulator of the *embCAB* operon) along with seven other genes that are upregulated during exposure to ethambutol [415]. The origin of resistance for the remaining 30% of the ethambutol-resistance isolates is unknown. As mentioned in the preceding section, both *glfT1* and *glfT2* represent potential candidate genes. Overexpression of *embB in vitro* leads to higher levels of resistance, thus it is possible that unlinked mutations that lead to increase expression of the *embCAB* operon could provide low-level resistance [409]. A potential candidate locus is *embR*, which regulates *embCAB* expression, as well as *pknH*, a serine threonine protein kinase that positively regulates *embR* via phosphorylation [418]. Another potential mechanism involves decreased drug accumulation through efflux by one of the many mycobacterial multidrug efflux pumps [419–421].

ADME   In current therapeutic use, ethambutol is administered orally at daily doses of 15–25 mg/kg, in combination with other antitubercular agents during the intensive phase of treatment [422,423]. Intermittent dosing (twice or thrice weekly) at higher doses is also commonly employed. The drug is well absorbed from the gastrointestinal tract providing a peak serum concentration (C_{max}) of approximately 5 µg/mL 4 h (T_{max}) after ingestion [424]. Except for the cerebrospinal fluid, ethambutol is widely distributed to most tissues and fluids with an average volume of distribution (V/F) of 450 L. Approximately 50–60% of the ingested dose is excreted as unchanged drug in the urine, where there are also minor quantities (8–15% of the absorbed dose) of two inactive metabolites: the dialdehyde and the dicarboxylic acid derivatives [425,426].

In a recent study of rifampin and EMB pharmacokinetics in HIV+ adults (ACTG 309), Perlman et al. reported that daily EMB doses of 20 mg/kg resulted in subtherapeutic concentrations in 69% of patients [427]. With intermittent EMB dosing (50 mg/kg twice weekly or 30 mg/kg thrice weekly), 79% of patients had C_{max} less than 4 µg/mL and 28% had very low C_{max} concentrations (<2 µg/mL). In children, the current recommended EMB dosages also result in subtherapeutic levels. It appears to be more valid to calculate the EMB dosage on the basis of body surface rather than body weight (at a dose of 867 mg/m^2), leading to higher dosages especially in younger children [428]. Zhu et al. reported that the half-life was shorter in children with TB (2.5 h versus 4.0 h in adults) and the absorption was slower and more erratic than in adults [424]. The mean C_{max} in adults upon daily doses of 1300 mg was 2.1 µg/mL, a value close to the MIC resulting in C_{max}/MIC of less than two. Twice-weekly dosing of 3100 mg results in C_{max}/MIC values of 2–5 and may have a pharmacodynamic advantage for this bacteriostatic agent given the extended postantibiotic effects observed with combination therapy (see Section 8.1.2).

Adverse Reactions   Ethambutol is generally well tolerated. The main side effect of concern is ocular toxicity, consisting of retrobulbar neuritis with various symptoms, including reduced visual acuity, constriction of visual fields, and color blindness. Ocular toxicity seems to be dose-related [429]. At a daily dose of 25 mg/kg, visual impairment occurs in about 3% of patients, rising to 20% at doses higher than 30 mg/kg/day. Ocular complications are usually reversible, although defects in color vision may persist for a few months. If the drug is not discontinued, permanent visual impairment may occur. Patients should have visual testing done every 6 weeks while on therapy.

8.1.4. Pyrazinamide

History   Pyrazinamide is an important component in the intensive phase of short-course treatment of tuberculosis owing to its sterilizing activity, ability to work in acidic environments (in macrophages), and excellent synergy with rifampin [273]. The initial reports that nicotinamide (vitamin B3) possessed modest antitubercular activity stimulated the search for analogs with improved activity [304,430]. These efforts resulted in the independent discovery of pyrazinamide, whose antitubercular activity was first disclosed in 1952 by the Lederle and Merck laboratories [431–433]. However, the synthesis of the pyrazinamide had been described

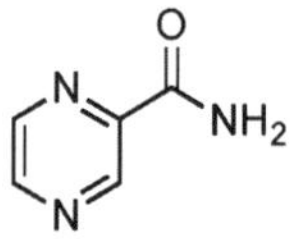

Figure 13. Structure of pyrazinamide.

almost two decades earlier by chemists at E. Merck in Germany [434]. Remarkably, pyrazinamide displayed no activity *in vitro*, yet was extremely potent *in vivo*, a paradox that was subsequently explained by the findings that pyrazinamide is only active under acidic conditions [431,435]. Despite over 50 years since its introduction, pyrazinamide remains among the least understood of the first- and second-line antitubercular agents [273] (Fig. 13).

SAR The early evaluation of pyrazinamide analog relied on *in vivo* evaluation in a murine model of TB infection, since the pH requirement for bioactivity was not discovered until 1954. Consequently, the *in vitro* antimycobacterial activity of many of the early analogs has never been reported. The available *in vitro* susceptibility data in Table 9 are reported as minimum inhibitory concentrations (MICs) measured at pH 5.5–6.0. Pyrazinamide exhibits remarkably stringent structure–activity relationships demonstrating an absolute requirement for the pyrazine heterocycle and carboxamide at C-2 for potent activity. Thus, substitution of the carboxamide group in thioamide **73**, *N*-methyl **74**, *N*-acetyl **75**, hydrazide **76**, nitrile **77**, tetrazole **78**, and carboxylic acid **79** provided compounds that were completely inactive *in vivo* [431]. The importance of the pyrazine nucleus was probed with pyrimidine **80** and pyridazine **81** and **82**, which were all either inactive or very weakly active [432]. Substitution of the pyrazine nucleus was also poorly tolerated as 3-hydroxy **83**, 3-amino **84**, and 6-methyl **86** were inactive *in vivo* [431]. 5-Chloropyrazinamide **85** has not been evaluated *in vivo*, but showed excellent activity *in vitro* against susceptible and PZA-resistant strains of *M. tuberculosis* [436]. However, chloropyrazinamide **85** has been shown to possess a different mechanism of action [437].

As discussed below, PZA is hydrolyzed intracellularly by a mycobacterial amidase to liberate pyrazinoic acid (POA) **79**, which is the presumed active compound. Although pyrazinoic acid is inactive *in vivo*, apparently due to poor pharmacokinetics, it was subsequently shown to possess *in vitro* activity commensurate with PZA and more importantly was active against PZA-resistant *M. tuberculosis* strains [438]. Attempts to improve on the drug disposition properties of pyrazinoic acid motivated the preparation of almost 50 esters as prodrugs from which *n*-propyl pyrazinoate **87** emerged as the most promising candidate [439,440]. However, efficacy studies in mice have failed to show any antitubercular activity likely due to poor stability of the esters in plasma [273]. Similarly, prodrug strategies enabled conversion of inactive tetrazole **78** to an active pivaloyloxymethyl ester **88** that exhibited *in vitro* activity similar to PZA [441]. Ethyl thioester **89** represents a potential prodrug of pyrazinoic acid and exhibited excellent *in vivo* activity; however, the activity is likely due to liberation of ethanethiol and not pyrazinoic acid [442]. Finally, several aminomethylene analogs of PZA have been reported including morphazinamide **90** and *N*,*N*-diethylaminomethylene **91** that liberate PZA and formaldehyde *in vivo* [443,444]. Morphazinamide was the only active analog that was further developed, but the lack of any demonstrable improvement over PZA *in vivo*, led to its abandonment [445].

Antibacterial Activity Pyrazinamide is active *in vitro* only under acidic conditions (pH 5–6) with reported minimum inhibitory concentrations in the range of 16–50 μg/mL for *M. tuberculosis* (Mtb) at pH 5.5, but possesses no activity under neutral or alkaline conditions [446,447]. PZA is also useful for treatment of other members of the Mtb complex (*M. africanum*, *M. microti*, and *M. canetti*) except for *M. bovis* [448]. Like isoniazid, PZA is a very selective antibacterial agent with no activity toward *E. coli* at concentrations of 2000 μg/mL and other nontuberculosis mycobacteria including *M. smegmatis*, *M. kansasii*, and *M. avium* [449,450].

Mechanism of Action The currently accepted mechanism of action for pyrazinamide proposes that PZA is passively taken up by Mtb and hydrolyzed by a promiscuous amidase encoded by the gene *pncA*, which is part of the

Table 9. Pyrazinamide SAR

Compound	R =	Activity[a] (µg/mL)	Compound	R =	Activity[a] (µg/mL)
4 (PZA)	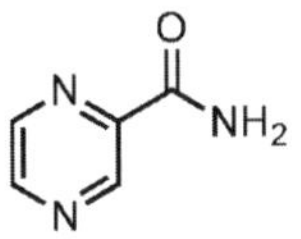	$16–50^{a,b,c}$	**80**	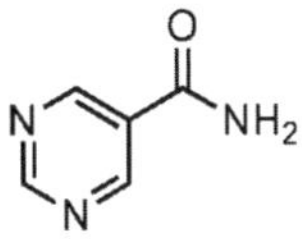	Inactive *in vivo*[f]
73	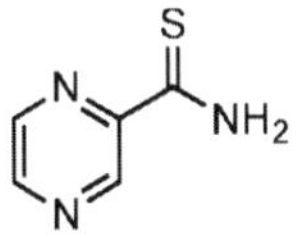	Inactive *in vivo*[d]	**81**	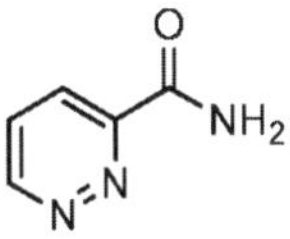	Weakly active *in vivo*[f]
75	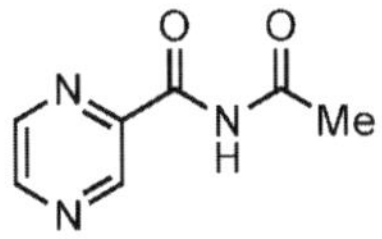	Inactive *in vivo*[d]	**82**	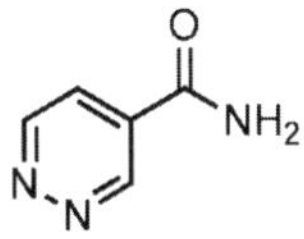	Inactive *in vivo*[f]
74	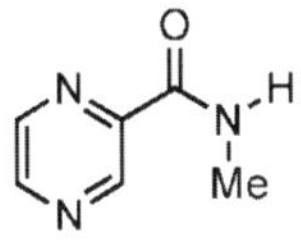	Inactive *in vivo*[d]	**83**	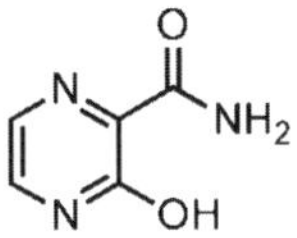	Inactive *in vivo*[f]
76	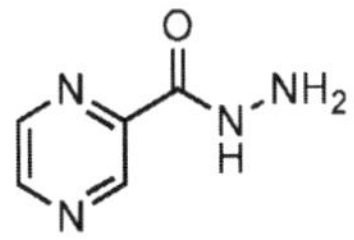	Inactive *in vivo*[d] (toxic)	**84**	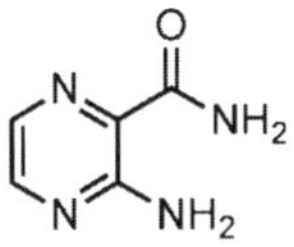	Inactive *in vivo*[f]
77	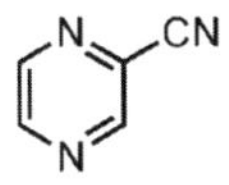	Inactive *in vivo*[d]	**85**	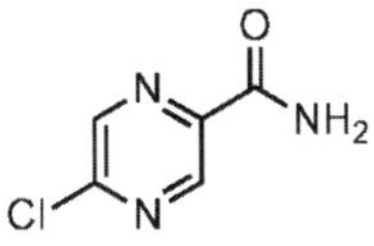	16^{g}
78	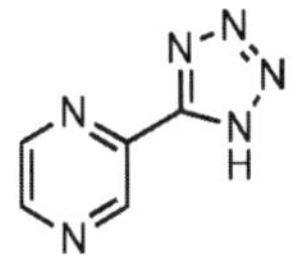	$>200^{h}$	**86**	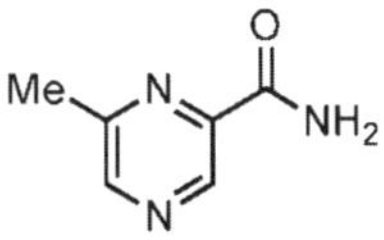	Inactive *in vivo*[d]
79	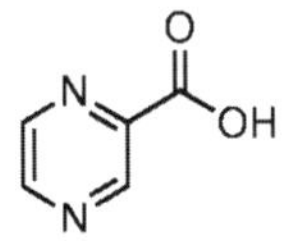	Inactive *in vivo* $32^{a,c}$	**87**	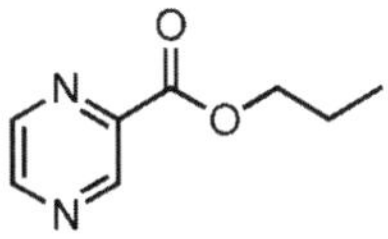	0.06^{a}

(continued)

Table 9. (*Continued*)

Compound	R =	Activity[a] (µg/mL)	Compound	R =	Activity[a] (µg/mL)
88	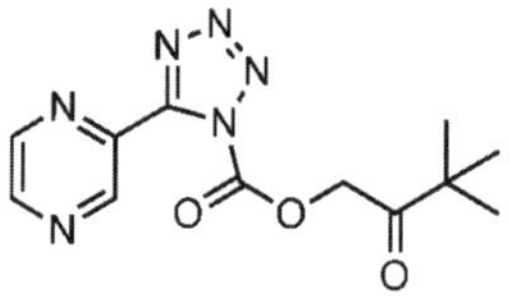	13^h	90	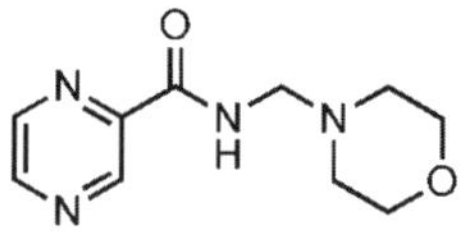	25^b
89	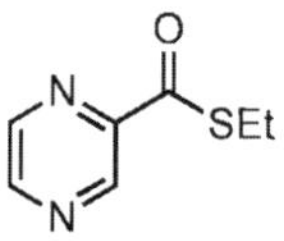	Active *in vivo*[e]	91	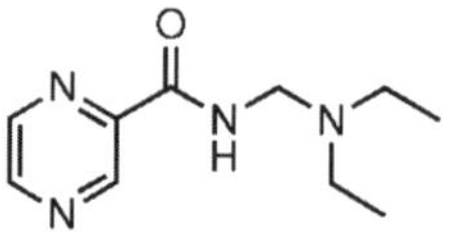	100^b

[a] Antitubercular activity assessed against strain H37Rv at pH 5.8 in 7H10 media [439].
[b] Antitubercular activity assessed against strain H37Rv at pH 6.0 in 7H12 media [444].
[c] Antitubercular activity assessed against strain H37Rv at pH 5.8 in 7H10 media [440].
[d] Inactive when administered orally at 0.2% of diet in a murine TB model [431].
[e] Activity assessed in a murine TB model. The authors used a qualitative criteria, where pyrazinamide was assigned as inactive (−) or from active (+), medium activity (+ +), strongly active (+ + +), and very active (+ + + +) [442].
[f] Activity assessed in a murine TB model. The authors used a qualitative criteria: inactive (−) or from weak activity (+), medium activity (+ +), strongly active (+ + +) [432].
[g] Antitubercular activity assessed against strain H37Rv at pH 5.8 in 7H10 media [436].
[h] Antitubercular activity assessed against strain H37Rv at pH 6.0 using the BACTEC 460 system [441].

NAD salvage pathway, to release pyrazinoic acid [270,451,452]. Accumulation of POA (pKa 2.9) leads to a lowering of intracellular pH that disrupts the transmembrane proton gradient and hence the proton motive force, required for ATP synthesis [453]. Consistent with this finding, PZA led to an upregulation of the *cyd* operon, which is highly responsive to alterations in transmembrane proton gradient [186]. POA undergoes both passive and active efflux, reducing the intracellular concentrations. Reuptake of the neutral acid form of POA, but not the negatively charged conjugate base of POA, explains the observed pH dependent activity of PZA. Thus, PZA acts by a nonspecific mechanism, which is supported by the inability to isolate any resistant mutants to POA. Additionally, given the structural similarity of PZA to nicotinamide and the findings that PZA is bioactivated to POA by PncA, the first enzyme in the NAD salvage pathway, it has been suggested that POA could potentially disrupt NAD biosynthesis. However, it has been shown that PZA neither inhibits NAD biosynthesis nor is converted to a NAD analog (H. Boshoff, unpublished results) [453]. PZA was shown to inhibit type I fatty acid

synthase [454,455]. In a subsequently more detailed metabolic and biochemical study, PZA had no effect on fatty acid synthesis; however, 5-chloro-PZA, was shown to irreversibly inhibit FAS-I [437].

Resistance   Consistent with the proposed mechanism of action, resistance to pyrazinamide is almost exclusively due to mutations in *pncA*, which encodes a 186 amino acid cytosolic metalloenzyme (containing Mn^{2+} or Fe^{2+}) [270,456]. The majority of *pncA* mutations are missense mutations leading to amino acid substitutions. Additionally, insertions, deletions, and mutations in the promoter region have been observed. The mutations are scattered throughout the gene, although some clustering is observed in regions involved in catalysis and or metal binding including 3–17, 61–85, and 132–142 (based on the crystal structure of the PncA homolog from *Pyrococcus horikoshii*, 37% amino acid identity to *M. tuberculosis* PncA) [456,457]. Functional characterization of a series of PncA variants demonstrated that Asp8, Lys96, and Cys138 were essential for catalytic activity while mutations to Asp49, His51, His57, and His71 that are putatively involved in metal coordination were severely compromised in enzymatic activity [270]. A similar study with recombinant PncA from 12 clinical isolates that were resistant to PZA demonstrated a direct linear correlation between the enzymatic k_{cat} values and PZA resistance [48]. The findings that no resistance hot spots were found in Mtb *pncA* is consistent with the nonessential role as determined by Himar-transposon mutagenesis studies [49]. Interestingly and in stark contrast to *M. tuberculosis*, intrinsic resistance of *M. bovis* to PZA is due to a single point mutation of His57 [452]. Complementation of *M. bovis* BCG with a functional *pncA* gene from *M. tuberculosis* restored drug susceptibility [452]. However, the intrinsic resistance of *M. smegmatis* and *M. avium* is not due to a defect in PncA activity, but rather the lack of accumulation of POA, which has been ascribed to either a highly active efflux pump or alternatively to a less active transporter of POA or PZA [449,453]. Neither of the putative efflux pumps or transporters of POA or PZA have yet been identified.

ADME The recommended daily dose of pyrazinamide is 20–30 mg/kg given orally [459]. The typical adult dose is 2 g for patients more than 50 kg and 1.5 g in patients less than 50 kg. Pyrazinamide is rapidly absorbed from the gastrointestinal tract and well behaved from a pharmacokinetic viewpoint. Following an oral dose peak concentrations of 53.4 ± 10.4 g/mL were observed under fasting conditions in healthy volunteers within 1–2 h ($T_{max} = 1.43 \pm 1.06$ h) [460]. Antacids had no significant effect on peak concentrations or area under the curve values, but a high fat meal reduced peak concentrations by 15% with slower absorption ($T_{max} = 3$ h), but no significant change in the AUC [337,461–463]. Pyrazinamide is widely distributed in body fluids, tissues, and cerebrospinal fluid. Population half-lives in children and adults with tuberculosis were 3.5 and 6 h, respectively [464]. Metabolism is primarily in the liver by hydrolysis to the major active metabolite pyrazinoic acid that accounts for approximately one-third of the ingested dose and is rapidly eliminated [463,465]. Additionally, both pyrazinamide and pyrazinoic acid are oxidized by xanthine oxidase or aldehyde oxidase to the 5-hydroxy congeners, which together account for another one-third of the ingested dose [465–468]. Renal clearance of the metabolites of PZA represents the major mechanism of elimination. Approximately 70% of an oral dose is excreted in the urine as POA, 5-hydroxy-POA, and 5-hydroxy-PZA while only 3% of PZA is excreted as the unchanged drug [463]. Significantly, pyrazinamide can be effectively removed by hemodialysis, unlike the other first-line agents isoniazid, rifampin, or ethambutol [469]. Allopurinol, a xanthine oxidase inhibitor, decreases the clearance of PZA [470].

Adverse Reactions Combination antitubercular therapy increases the risk of hepatotoxicity. In a recent cohort and case control analysis of more than 3000 patients in Hong Kong, patients receiving isoniazid (INH), RIF, and PZA had an estimated risk of hepatotoxicity of 2% versus 0.8% for INH + RIF. Furthermore, *in vitro* results have demonstrated that INH or its metabolite hydrazine, but not rifampin increased the sensitivity of HepG2 cells to PZA toxicity [471,472]. Unexpectedly high rates of hepatotoxicity were also observed in 2-month prophylactic regimens of RIF + PZA compared to INH alone, resulting in recommendations not to use this effective dual-agent prophylactic regimen [411,473]. The mechanism whereby PZA causes hepatotoxicity is unknown [340]. The other common side effect of PZA is nongouty arthralgia due to elevated serum uric acid concentrations [470,474,475]. In a recent study conducted in Japan, the average uric acid concentrations in serum were 4.78 ± 1.73 mg/dL before PZA and 10.6 ± 2.7 mg/dL after PZA. Hyperuricemia (>8 mg/dL) was observed in 85% of patients and arthralgia developed in 4% of these patients [476]. Although arthralgia has been reported in up to 40% of patients, it generally does not require drug withdrawal and can be treated with uricosuric agents [477]. Classic acute gout is much less frequent [474].

8.2. Second-Line Agents

8.2.1. Streptomycin The pharmacology, mechanism of action, and adverse effects of streptomycin are discussed elsewhere in this volume. Here features of the drug are discussed that pertain to its use in TB chemotherapy.

History Streptomycin was the first effective widely used antibiotic for treatment of tuberculosis in humans. Although its importance

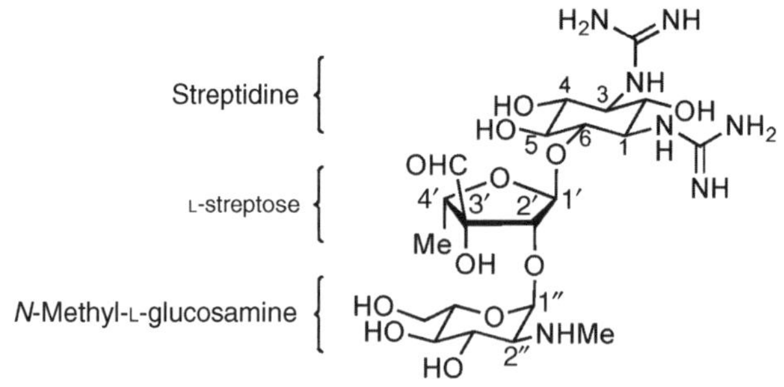

Figure 14. Structure of streptomycin.

declined after the introduction of other powerful antituberculous agents that are orally bioavailable, it is still widely used for the treatment of TB cases that cannot be treated with first-line agents. In 1944, Albert Schatz and Selman Waksman discovered streptomycin as a fermentation product of *Streptomyces griseus* [478,479]. Streptomycin belongs to the family of aminoglycoside antibiotics that includes kanamycin and amikacin, which are also used in tuberculosis chemotherapy. Streptomycins contain a central L-streptose core that is glycosylated at the *O*-2 position with *N*-methylglucosamine and contains a streptidine moiety (1,3-bis-guanylated streptamine) at the anomeric position (Fig. 14) [480–482]. The aminocyclitol (a cyclohexane with hydroxy and amino substituents) 2-deoxystreptamine is found in the vast majority of other aminoglycosides. Thus, streptomycin that contains a streptidine as the aminocyclitol is considered an atypical aminoglycoside, despite being the first member of this important class of antibiotics.

Antibacterial Activity   Streptomycin exhibits bacteriostatic activity against *M. tuberculosis* with a minimum inhibitory concentration of 0.5–2.0 µg/mL and possesses modest bactericidal activity [483]. Streptomycin has poor intracellular activity against *M. tuberculosis*-infected macrophages that could be due to poor membrane penetration as a result of its highly polar nature (log$P = -8.0$) [484,485]. Streptomycin is also effective against members of the *M. tuberculosis* complex, nontuberculosis mycobacteria [356], and a wide range of Gram-positive and -negative bacteria.

Mechanism of Action   Streptomycin binds to the 16S rRNA at the tRNA acceptor A (Aminoacyl site) of the 30S ribosomal subunit, thus inhibiting an early step in bacterial protein synthesis. Streptomycin also induces the production of aberrant and miscoded proteins [486–488]. The cocrystal structure of streptomycin and the intact 30S ribosome from *Thermus thermophilus* revealed a number of hydrogen bond and electrostatic interactions with the 16S RNA subunit in the A-site [489]. A particularly unique interaction, relative to the other aminoglycosides, are hydrogen bonds between the 4- and 5-hydroxyl groups of the streptidine ring and the ε-NH$_2$ group of Lys45 of the S12 ribosomal protein [489]. Streptomycin's bacteriostatic activity is likely due to inhibition of protein synthesis while the bactericidal activity correlates with formation of mistranslated proteins [490].

Resistance   Clinically, both high-level resistance (MIC > 500 µg/mL) and low-level resistance (MIC < 20 µg/mL) to streptomycin are observed. High-level streptomycin resistance is due to mutations in the 16S rRNA gene (*rrs*) and the *rpsL* gene encoding ribosomal protein S12 [491–496]. Mutations to *rpsL* are significantly more prevalent and account for close to 50% of clinically observed resistance while mutations to *rrs* only occur in 10% of clinical isolates [497]. The most common mutation in *rpsL* is due to a point mutation in codon 43 resulting in a Lys-Arg substitution while mutations in *rrs* are clustered around nucleotides 530 (referred to as the 530 loop) and 915 [492–494,496]. Low-level resistance is caused by mutation to *gidB*, which encodes a 7-methylguanosine methyl transferase that has been shown to methylate G527 located in the 530 loop [498]. Mutations to *gidB* occur at a frequency of 1×10^{-6}. However, once a *gidB* mutant emerges, the frequency of developing high-level streptomycin resistance in *M. tuberculosis* increases over 2000-fold from approximately 4×10^{-8} to 1.4×10^{-4} [498].

Other potential resistance mechanisms include drug efflux and inactivation. Aminoglycoside resistance in most organisms is due to drug inactivation by aminoglycoside modifying enzymes that catalyze *N*- and *O*-acetylation, *O*-adenylation, and *O*-phosphorylation [499]. *M. tuberculosis* encodes a single aminoglycoside *N*-acetyltransferase, which inactivates typical aminoglycosides, but not streptomycin, since it is a structurally atypical aminoglycoside [500]. The efflux pumps in *M. tuberculosis* are incompletely characterized. The gene Rv1258c encodes for an efflux pump of the major facilitator superfamily (MFS) of efflux systems. Overexpression of Rv1258c in *M. bovis* BCG resulted in a modest increase in the MIC for streptomycin [265,501].

Disposition Streptomycin is not orally bioavailable and must be given either intravenously (i.v.) or by intramuscular (i.m.) injection. Following parenteral administration, streptomycin reaches concentrations of 25–50 µg/mL in plasma after 1 h [502]. The initial pharmacokinetic study of streptomycin was done by Zintel et al. in 1945 [503]. A more recent population pharmacokinetic study was completed in patients receiving either intramuscular or intravenous dosing and served to confirm the earlier findings [504]. With a mean i.m. dose of 18 mg/kg, the mean C_{max} was 42.5 µg/mL with an estimated T_{max} of 1.5 h. The predicted half-life was 4.3 h (2.0–14.3 h). Concentrations increased linearly with increasing dose (500–1800 mg) after i.v. administration. With i.m. administration some nonlinearity was observed presumably due to incomplete or slow absorption from the injection site. Streptomycin is largely eliminated unchanged by the kidney and the dose should be adjusted based on the creatinine clearance. Since aminoglycosides are concentration-dependent killers of bacteria, high AUC/MIC ratios are desired. This can be achieved by administration of higher, but less frequent dosing (two to three times per week) in patients with good renal function [505].

Adverse Effects The major side effects of aminoglycosides in general and streptomycin in particular are ototoxicity and nephrotoxicity. A recent study evaluated the degree of toxicity at i.v. doses of 15 mg/kg daily or 25 mg/kg of streptomycin thrice weekly [505]. Ototoxicity (hearing loss ≥ 20 db) was observed in 37% of the patients with a median onset of 9 weeks. The risk was higher in elderly patients and correlated with larger cumulative doses. Vestibular toxicity (nystagmus, heal-to-toe walking changes) was observed in 8% of patients and usually resolved. Fifteen percent of patients developed mild nephrotoxicity that was reversible in all cases. Ototoxicity may be caused by metabolism of streptomycin to release streptidine [502,506].

8.2.2. Kanamycin and Amikacin The structure–activity relationships, pharmacology, mechanism of action, and adverse effects of kanamycin and amikacin are discussed elsewhere in this volume. Here, features of the drug are discussed that pertain to its use in TB chemotherapy.

History The aminoglycoside kanamycin was isolated in 1957 from the fermentation product of *Streptomyces kanamyceticus* as a suite of three-components kanamycin A, the major component comprising 98% of the mixture (hereafter designated as kanamycin), and kanamycins B and C [507]. Kanamycin contains a central deoxystreptamine aminocyclitol (instead of the streptidine present in the streptomycin molecule), which is glycosylated at the 6-position with 3-amino-3-deoxyglucose and at the 4-position with various aminodeoxyglucose derivatives that give rise to the kanamycins A–C (Fig. 15). Amikacin is a semisynthetic derivative of kanamycin A first reported in 1972, wherein the C-1 amino group of the central 2-deoxystreptamine aminocyclitol is acylated with (*S*)-2-hydroxy-4-aminobutyric acid (HABA) [508,509]. The HABA side chain was initially identified in the aminoglycoside antibiotic butirosins and was shown to provide enhanced spectrum of activity as well as activity against kanamycin-resistant strains [510]. Consequently, amikacin can be considered a hybrid semisynthetic antibiotic comprised of the core kanamycin and the butirosin-derived HABA side chain.

Antibacterial Activity In addition to kanamycin's broad-spectrum activity against

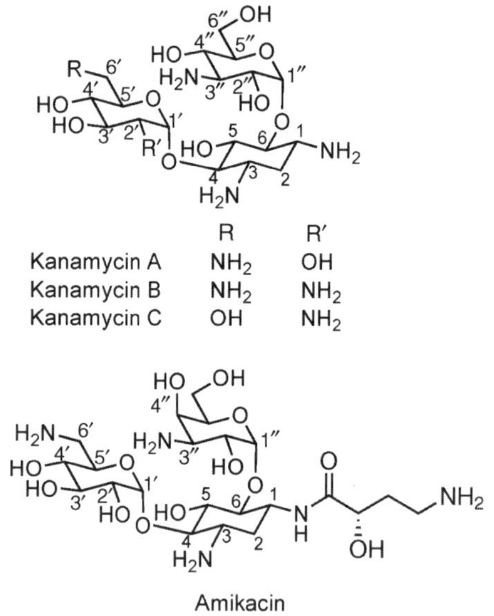

	R	R'
Kanamycin A	NH_2	OH
Kanamycin B	NH_2	NH_2
Kanamycin C	OH	NH_2

Amikacin

Figure 15. Structure of the kanamycins and amikacin.

most Gram-negative bacteria and Gram-positive cocci, kanamycin is also effective against *M. tuberculosis* strains with minimum inhibitory concentrations ranging from 2 to 4 µg/mL [483,511]. The corresponding minimum bactericidal concentrations (MBCs) against *M. tuberculosis* are approximately eightfold higher [511]. Kanamycin was also shown to be effective against *M. scrofulaceum* with MICs in the range of 4–16 µg/mL, but in general was poorly effective against nontuberculosis mycobacteria exhibiting MICs greater than 64 µg/mL against *M. kansasii*, *M. avium-intracellulare*, *M. fortuitum*, and *M. chelonae* [511,512].

Amikacin is the most active aminoglycoside antibiotic against *M. tuberculosis* and drug-resistant strains of *M. tuberculosis* with MICs ranging from 0.5 to 1.0 µg/mL [511]. Amikacin also displays slightly better activity than kanamycin against nontuberculosis mycobacteria with MICs ranging from 8 to 16 µg/mL against *M. fortuitum*, *M. kansasii* and *M. scrofulaceum* [511].

Mechanism of Action and Resistance Kanamycin and amikacin, like streptomycin lead to formation of mistranslated proteins and inhibition of protein synthesis [486–488]. These antibiotics bind adjacent to the strep-

tomycin binding site in the A-site of the 30S ribosome [489,513]. Consequently, cross-resistance between kanamycin/amikacin and streptomycin has generally not been observed [514,515]. However, a recent study based on limited set of only 17 streptomycin-resistant isolates demonstrated that 7 of these were also cross-resistant to amikacin and kanamycin [511]. On the other hand, cross-resistance between kanamycin and amikacin is usually observed [514].

High-level resistance to both kanamycin and amikacin in *M. tuberculosis* is due to target modification. The most prevalent mutation occurs in position 1401 followed by 1402 and 1484 of the *M. tuberculosis rrs* gene (this is the updated numbering based on the reannotated *M. tuberculosis* genome [516] and equivalent to position 1408 in *E. coli*), which is observed in 60–75% of kanamycin- and amikacin-resistant clinical isolates [517,518]. Resistance in other mycobacteria to these aminoglycosides is also conferred by mutation the *rrs* gene at the equivalent position 1401 [519]. The cause of low-level resistance is currently not known, but may be due to drug inactivation and/or decreased drug accumulation. The aminoglycoside *N*-acetyltransferase encoded by Rv0262c, has been shown to slowly *O*-acetylate the 2'-OH of kanamycin and amikacin [500].

ADME and Adverse Effects Kanamycin and amikacin are not orally bioavailable. The recommended dose is 15 mg/kg daily or 25 mg/kg thrice weekly while the maximum dose should not exceed 1 g. In a comparative study, median C_{max} values were 44 and 46 µg/mL after daily 15 mg/kg dosing, and 72 and 79 µg/mL after 25 mg/kg doses for kanamycin and amikacin, respectively [505]. Median half-lives for kanamycin and amikacin were 2.1 and 2.5 h, respectively (range 1.4–4.0 h). Like all aminoglycosides, the major side effects are ototoxicity and nephrotoxicity [520,521]. Ototoxicity is more likely with amikacin or kanamycin compared to streptomycin [505].

8.2.3. Capreomycin

History Capreomycin (Capastat®, Eli-Lilly) is a mixture of four related cyclic pentapeptides (capreomycins IA, IB, IIA, and IIB in relative ratios of 25:67:3:6) comprised mostly of nonproteinogenic amino acids that was first isolated from *Saccharothrix mutabilis* subsp. *capreolus* [522] (previously *Streptomyces capreolus*) by Herr et al. at Eli-Lilly in 1959 [523,524]. These highly basic peptides are biosynthesized by a nonribosomal peptide synthetase pathway and the corresponding genes, which encode for the biosynthetic enzymes have been identified [522,525]. The 16-membered pentapeptide core contains a single proteinogenic amino acid consisting of either L-serine or L-alanine at position 1 that gives rise to the capreomycin type A and B members, respectively, a (S)-2,3-diaminopropionic acid (DAP) at position 2, which is acylated with (S)-β-lysine in capreomycin derivatives IA and IB, a β-ureidodehydroalanine at position 3, a cyclic guanidine amino acid known as (2S,3R)-capreomycidine at position 4, and another DAP residue at position 5 (Fig. 16). Two total synthesis of capreomycin IA and IB have been reported serving to confirm the assigned structures [526,527].

SAR Variation of the side chain in position 1 from alanine to serine results in a mere two-fold decrease in MIC value indicating the hydroxyl side chain is not important for activity [528]. Deletion of the β-lysine side chain in position 2 found in capreomycins IA-B (see Fig. 15 for numbering) leads to a two- to

Capreomycin IA, R^1 = OH, R^2 = β-lysyl
Capreomycin IB, R^1 = H, R^2 = β-lysyl
Capreomycin IIA, R^1 = OH, R^2 = H
Capreomycin IIB, R^1 = H, R^2 = H

β-lysyl side-chain

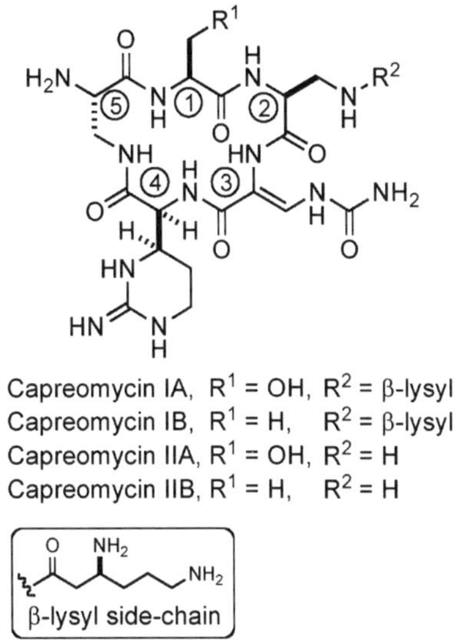

Figure 16. Structure of the capreomycins.

fourfold loss in antimycobacterial activity while substitution of the side-chain amino group for a hydroxy groups provides a further twofold loss in potency [528]. Modification of the ureido side chain at position 3 with small groups is tolerated based on the SAR results from the related tuberactinomycin-N analogs [529]. Thus, introduction of a *N*-methyl group onto the ureido function or replacement of the ureido carbonyl with a thiocarbonyl moiety does not impact activity while *N,N*-dimethylation results in complete loss of activity [529]. *N*-Arylation of the ureido group provides a great enhancement in broad-spectrum antibacterial activity [530]. Unfortunately, the antimycobacterial activity of the *N*-arylureido series of compounds has not been reported. The importance of the cyclic guanidine in the (2S,3R)-capreomycidine residue at position 4 has been probed with two tuberractinomycin-B analogs (formerly named viomycin) that are close structural congeners of the capreomycins [531]. Thus, hydroxylation at the δ-carbon of (2S,3R)-capreomycidine or ring opening of the guandine leads to two- and fourfold loss of potency, respectively [531]. Introduction of carbamate- but not aryl-substituents at the δ-carbon of (2S,3R)-capreomycidine provides a greater than 50-fold increase in antibacterial activity against *E. coli*; however, the antimycobacterial has not been reported [532]. Acylation of the amino side chain at position 5 with β-alanine affords a twofold increase in antitubercular activity while palmitoylation results in completed loss of activity [533].

Antibacterial Activity The minimum inhibitory concentration against susceptible *M. tuberculosis* isolates is 1.0–2.0 µg/mL while the minimum bactericidal concentration is 2.0–4.0 µg/mL [483,512,534]. Capreomycin is also effective against nontuberculosis mycobacteria including *M. avium intracellulare* [535,536], but poorly active against *M. kansasii* isolates [537]. Among the current first- and second-line antitubercular agents capreomycin is the most effective against latent nonreplicating bacilli *in vitro* under anaerobic conditions [538].

Mechanism of Action In contrast to the aminoglycosides, the current knowledge of capreomycins's mechanism of action is incompletely understood. Early studies showed that capreomycin inhibits protein synthesis by interfering with assembly of the 30S ribosomal subunit as well as blocking tRNA translocation [539,540]. Capreomycins shares a similar transcriptional profile to the aminoglycosides showing a general downregulation of macromolecular synthesis and an upregulation of genes implicated in ribosomal architecture and translation [186]. Based on more recent mutagenesis studies, capreomycin likely binds to the 16S rRNA within helix 44 adjacent to the aminoglycoside binding site and also binds to the 23S rRNA within helix 69 [541,542]. These independent binding sites come in close contact during assembly of the 70S ribosome [542].

Resistance Capreomycin exhibits cross-resistance with the aminoglycosides due to mutation in the 16S ribosomal RNA *rrs* gene [514,515]. The most prevalent mutations in *rrs* that confer resistance to amikacin and kanamycin are in position 1401, followed by 1402, and 1484. In laboratory-generated mutants, the molecular basis for cross-resistance between capreomycin and kanamycin and amikacin showed that the *rrs* A1401G mutant exhibited capreomycin MICs of 20–80 µg/mL and high-level resistance to both kanamycin and amikacin [541]. The *rrs* C1402T mutants exhibited high-level capreomycin resistance (MIC > 160 µg/mL), displayed low-level resistance to kanamycin (MICs 10–20 µg/mL), and was susceptible to amikacin [541]. Finally, the *rrs* G1484T mutants displayed high-level resistance to all three drugs [541]. Another mechanism of capreomycin resistance that often occurs in conjunction with mutations to *rrs* is due to mutation to the gene *tlyA*, which encodes a 2'-*O*-methyltransferase that methylates positions C1409 of the 16S rRNA and nucleotide C1920 of the 23S rRNA [541,542].

ADME Capreomycin is a highly polar weak base with pK_a values of 13.3 (cyclic guanidine) and 10.1 (for the primary amines) [543]. Capreomycin is not absorbed by the gastrointestinal tract and is administered parentally. The capreomycin dosage form (Capastat, Lilly) contains four components, consisting of two major components (IA and IB) and two minor components. Capacin (Cheiljedang Corp), a Korean preparation has less of the two minor components as well as other minor trace impurities and displays a significant 40-fold higher LD$_{50}$ in rats [544]. Peak concentrations of 30 µg/mL in serum are achieved 1–2 h after intramuscular administration of 1 g of the drug [545,546]. There was a high correlation between clearance of the drug and creatinine clearance in patients with renal impairment [546]. The drug can be removed by hemodialysis. The half-life is 3–6 h and the drug is eliminated unchanged in the urine [547].

Adverse Effects Capreomycin is ototoxic and nephrotoxic like its aminoglycoside counterparts [547–549]. Renal damage (36% of patients with BUN >20 mg/100 mL) is the most consistent and significant toxic effect of capreomycin (Capastat Package Insert, Lilly). Eighth cranial nerve damage can lead to either ototoxicity (11% subclinical auditory loss) or vestibular toxicity. Partial neuromuscular blockade has been observed after large i. v. doses. Additionally, pain and excessive bleeding at the site of injection have been observed.

8.2.4. para-Aminosalicylic Acid

History *para*-Aminosalicylic acid (PAS) was conceived by the Swedish physician Jörgen Lehmann and first synthesized by the Karl-Gustav Rosdahl at Ferrosan Research Laboratories in 1943 [550] (Fig. 17). The observation that benzoic- and salicylic acid have a stimulatory effect on the respiration of mycobacteria suggested that analogs of benzoic acid might interfere with the oxidative metabolism of the bacilli [551]. Based on the known structure–activity relationships of the sulfonamide antibacterial agents, which demonstrated a strict requirement for a *para*-amino substituent on the benzenesulfonamide core, Dr. Lehmann deductively reasoned that installation of *para*-amino group on salicylic acid would provide an antitubercular agent [552,553]. Although there was little biochemical rationale in the design of PAS and indeed the biochemical mechanism of action remains nebulous, PAS proved to be a remarkably effective antitubercular agent, which was demonstrated by two successful clinical trials [554,555]. The rapid development of resistance to monotherapy led

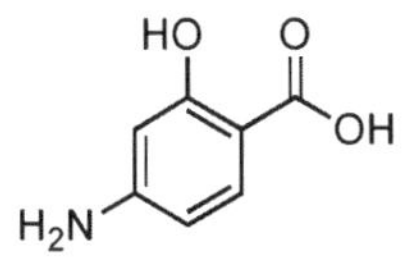

Figure 17. Structure of *p*-aminosalicylic acid.

to the advent of combination therapy with streptomycin, also discovered in 1943, and provided the first effective treatment for TB [556]. The subsequent discovery of isoniazid (INH) in 1953 led to the triple therapy regimen of streptomycin + PAS + INH, which became the standard effective treatment until the mid-1970s, when it was supplanted with a 6-month short-course therapy comprising isoniazid + rifampin + pyrazinamide [557]. Following several outbreaks of multidrug-resistant TB, PAS was reintroduced in 1992 in the United States [558]. Newer formulations of PAS have proven to have reduced gastrointestinal toxicity and enable twice-a-day dosing [559,560]. Several synthetic routes to PAS have been reported [561]. The most efficient is the Kolbe–Schmidt reaction of 3-aminophenol with K_2CO_3 under a CO_2 atmosphere at 170 °C to afford PAS in 90% yield [562].

SAR   Following the initial disclosure of PAS by Lehmann, numerous analogs were synthesized in order to improve on its activity. The antitubercular activity for the compounds listed in Table 10 was obtained under identical conditions. The SAR trends are apparent from the relative activities even though the absolute MIC value for PAS reported in Table 10 is substantially lower than the currently accepted value of around 1 µg/mL [563]. PAS 10 exhibits remarkably tight structure–activity relationships. Deletion of the *p*-amino group in 92 or replacement with a hydroxy and nitro substituent in 93 and 94 result in a 64- to 128-fold loss in antitubercular activity. Similarly, acetylation, carbamoylation, and allylation in 95–97 of the *p*-amino group are deleterious to activity resulting in a 128-fold loss in potency. Only the *N*-methyl substituted analog 98 maintains respectable biological activity; however, metabolism via *N*-demethylation, a generally facile process, would afford the parent compound PAS. The importance of the *ortho*- hydroxy group was examined by

substitution with a sulfhydryl analog 99 or *O*-methylation to provide 100, but both modifications are poorly tolerated. Several analogs were prepared to explore the impact of the carboxylic acid 101–108. Deletion of the carboxy group affords inactive *m*-aminophenol 101. The methyl and ethyl esters 102 and 103 are 8- and 32-fold less active than PAS. The observed activities likely reflect the ease of hydrolysis of these esters to the corresponding carboxylic acid. The glycine amide derivative 104 is only fourfold less active; however, the activity is abolished in the presence of 10% serum. Analogs 105–107 incorporating carboxamide, sulfonamide, and sulfonic acid isosteres as well as the amidine analog 108 are 128-fold less active than PAS demonstrating the requirement for the carboxylic acid function. Finally, the regioisomer 5-aminosalicylic acid 109 displays no antitubercular activity [564].

Antibacterial Activity   PAS is bacteriostatic *in vitro* against most strains of *M. tuberculosis* at 1 µg/mL, but displays no bactericidal activity [565]. The spectrum of activity is remarkably narrow with poor activity against other nontuberculosis mycobacterial strains and no activity against most other microorganisms [356].

Mechanism of Action   Based on the mechanism of the structurally related *p*-aminobenzenesulfonamide antibacterials, PAS has historically been considered an antimetabolite interfering with incorporation of *p*-aminobenzoic acid into folic acid [566–568]. The enzymatic target of the sulfonamide antibacterials is dihydropteroate synthase, which catalyzes the condensation of *p*-aminobenzoic acid with 6-hydroxymethyl-7,8-dihydropterin diphosphate to afford 7,8-dihydropteroate. PAS was shown to be an extremely poor inhibitor ($K_i = 1$ µM) of the mycobacterial DHPS encoded by the gene *folP1* in comparison to three sulfonamide antibiotics (K_i values ranging from 13 to 31 nM) [569]. Additionally, no mutations to *folP1* have been observed in PAS-resistant strains [570].

Screening a library of transposon mutants showed that PAS resistance is associated with mutations in the gene *thyA*, which encodes for thymidylate synthase A [571]. ThyA catalyzes reductive methylation of deoxyuridine mono-

Table 10. *para*-Aminosalicylic Acid SAR

Compound	R	MIC (µg/mL)
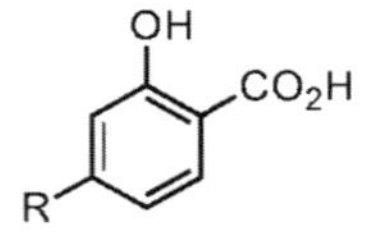 **10**	$-NH_2$	0.078 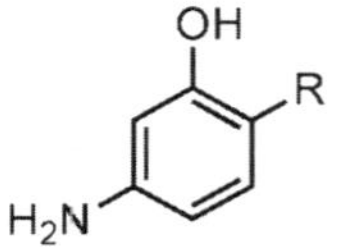
92	$-H$	10
93	$-OH$	10
94	$-NO_2$	5
95	$-NHAc$	10
96	$-NHCO_2Et$	10
97	$-NHallyl$	10
98	$-NHMe$	0.625
99	$-SH$	10
100	$-OMe$	10

Compound	R	MIC (µg/mL)
101	$-H$	>10
102	$-CO_2Me$	0.625
103	$-CO_2Et$	2.5
104	(glycine amide)	0.312
105	$-CONH_2$	10
106	$-SO_2NH_2$	10
107	$-SO_3H$	10
108	(amidine)	10
109		>10

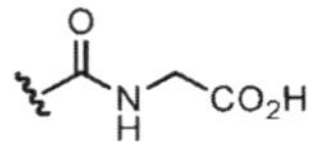

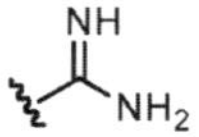

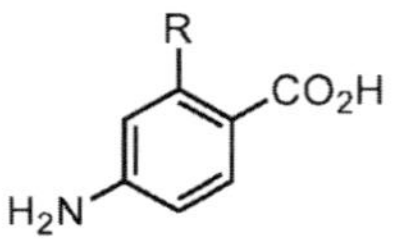

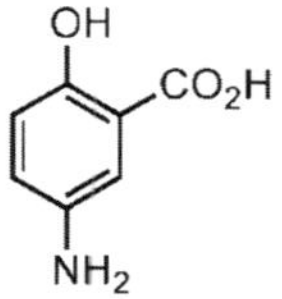

phosphate (dUMP) to yield deoxythymidine monophosphate (dTMP), required for *de novo*-deoxythymidine triphosphate (dTTP) synthesis. ThyA utilizes 5,10-methylenetetrahydrofolate as the carbon donor in the methylation reaction [572]. The authors suggested that ThyA may bioactivate PAS [571].

PAS has also been suggested to interfere with biosynthesis of the mycobactins, which are small-molecule iron chelators required for iron acquisition [200,573,574]. Mycobactin biosynthesis is carried out by a mixed nonribosomal peptide synthetase polyketide synthase (NRPS-PKS) pathway [575]. The first protein in this pathway known as MbtA, a salicyl-AMP ligase, activates salicylic acid with ATP to salicyl-AMP and transfers this intermediate onto the downstream protein MbtB [198]. Consequently, PAS could act as a competitive inhibitor of salicylic acid or alternatively as an antimetabolite if incorporation of PAS by MbtA during mycobactin biosynthesis were to block downstream biosynthetic steps. Indeed, treatment of *M. smegmatis* with $100\,\mu g/mL$ PAS led to a 40–80% decrease in mycobactin production and a concomitant accumulation of salicylic acid [576]. PAS has also been shown to have an immunomodulatory role in primary human macrophages by modulating the inflammatory response through inhibition of the p38 MAPK-prostaglandin signaling cascade, which suppresses matrix metalloprotease-1 activity [577]. In summary, PAS's mechanism of action remains incompletely understood and it may act through multiple pathways of both the bacteria and host.

Resistance Molecular genetic analysis of over 50 PAS-resistant strains from clinical isolates and spontaneous mutants generated *in vitro* showed that 37% of these PAS^r strains had mutations in the *thyA* gene [570]. Among these 50 strains, no mutations were observed in any of the five other genes examined in the folate metabolic pathway and biosynthesis of thymidine nucleotides including *dfrA*, *folC*, *folP1*, *folP2*, and *thyX* revealing that PAS resistance in 63% of PAS^r strains involves mechanisms independent of thymine nucleotide biosynthesis. A total of 24 different mutations to *thyA* were observed distributed throughout the gene [570]. The mutations all mapped to regions in ThyA were predicted to reside within essential functional or structural sites [570].

ADME PAS is readily absorbed by the gastrointestinal tract with an oral bioavailability around 60–65% and is well distributed throughout the body [559]. Peak serum levels of $155\,\mu g/mL$ (C_{max}) are reached 1–2 h (T_{max}) after oral administration of 40 mg/kg of the sodium salt of PAS. The half-life is very short (0.8 h) and PAS is primarily eliminated in the urine as the inactive N-acetyl-PAS (50–75%) and N-(p-aminosalicyl)glycine (25%), which together account for 90% of the metabolites found in urine [578–580]. N-Acetylation is efficiently catalyzed by both human N-acetyltranferase-I and N-acetyltranferase-II isozymes with the k_{cat} and K_M kinetic parameters for PAS acetylation by NAT1 equal to $97 \pm 11\,s^{-1}$ and $575 \pm 135\,\mu M$, respectively ($C_{max} = 1\,mM$) [581,582]. Additionally, both ester and ether glucuronides of PAS have been observed [578].

In 1995, the FDA approved a granule form of PAS designed to improve the gastrointestinal tolerance (Paser; Jacobius Pharmaceuticals Co., Princeton, MJ). This new sustained release PAS exhibited a delayed T_{max} at 4.4 h and a lower C_{max} of $21\,\mu g/mL$; however, the slow-release characteristics led to a much flatter serum concentration versus time curve [583]. Consequently, a 4 g dose of this new formulation provides serum concentrations above the MIC for 100% of a 12 h dosing interval and enables convenient twice-a-day dosing [560,583].

Adverse Effects Gastrointestinal irritation is a very common side effect, with manifestations of various degrees of intensity and severity, which may lead to discontinuation of treatment [565,584]. Hypersensitivity reactions occur in about 5–10% of patients, including rash, fever, and pruritus, rarely followed by exfoliative dermatitis or hepatitis of allergic nature. PAS should be used with caution in patients with renal impairment, since it is largely excreted in the urine.

8.2.5. D-Cycloserine

History D-Cycloserine (D-4-amino-3-isoxazolidinone, DCS) is a cyclic D-alanine analog that was independently discovered by several groups from the fermentation broths of

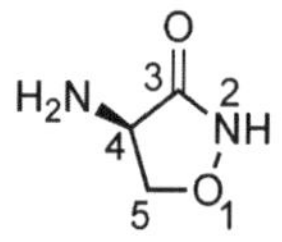

Figure 18. Structure of D-cycloserine.

Streptomyces sp. [585–588]. It was first marketed by Merck as Oxamycin and by Lilly as Seromycin. Cycloserine is a broad-spectrum antibiotic, but due to its toxicity, cycloserine's use is currently restricted to treat tuberculosis. Cycloserine is most efficiently produced synthetically from DL-serine and resolved as the D-enantiomer with tartaric acid [589,590].

SAR D-Cycloserine is simple molecule and all attempts to modify it molecule have either abolished activity or led to a sharp reduction in potency [591]. Thus, the L-antipode is inactive. The amino group is essential for activity and any attempt to modify this results in complete loss of activity. Similarly, substitution at N-2 leads to complete loss of activity [592]. These SAR results are readily understood since the amino group is required for the mechanism-based inactivation mechanism below, while substitution at N-2 would prevent aromatization to an isoxazole. Replacement of the isoxazolidinone oxygen or nitrogen atoms also results in sharp reductions in potency. The only site in the molecule that is marginally tolerant to modification is the C-5 position, which can be substituted with small nonheteroatom groups.

Antibacterial Activity Cycloserine displays broad-spectrum antibacterial activity. The minimum inhibitory concentration against *M. tuberculosis* was originally reported as 10–20 μg/mL while a more recent evaluation against the H37Rv strain yielded an MIC of 25 μg/mL [483,593]. Cycloserine is also used to treat atypical mycobacteria and most strains of *M. kansasii* are susceptible to 10 μg/mL [594].

Mechanism of Action Early studies demonstrated that D-cycloserine (DCS) prevents incorporation of D-alanine into the mycobacterial cell wall [595]. Thus, treatment of cells with cycloserine results a buildup of the bacterial cell wall precursor UDP-*N*-acetylmuramyl-tripeptide lacking the terminal D-Ala-D-Ala moiety and concomitant decrease in UDP-

N-acetylmuramyl-pentapeptide (Fig. 19). This effect is reversed by treatment with D-alanine, but not L-alanine. The D-Ala-D-Ala dipeptide is biosynthesized by two enzymes, D-alanine racemase (Alr, encoded by Rv3423c) a pyridoxal cofactor dependent enzyme that converts L-alanine to D-alanine and D-ala-D-ala ligase (DdlA, encoded by Rv2981c), which uses ATP to condense two molecules of D-Ala. Kinetic analysis of the D-ala-D-ala ligase from *S. faecalis* revealed cycloserine is a simple competitive reversible inhibitor with a K_i of approximately 100 μM [596]. For comparison the typical maximum serum concentrations of cycloserine achievable is approximately 300 μM.

Structural and biochemical analysis of the alanine racemase from *Bacillus stearothermophilus* have shown that cycloserine is a mechanism-based irreversible inhibitor that covalently modifies the pyridoxal (PLP) cofactor [597,598]. This mechanism involves initial Schiff base formation between the enzyme-bound PLP cofactor **110** and D-cycloserine **12** to afford aldimine **111** (Fig. 20) [599]. Subsequent 1,3-prototropic shift mediated by the conserved lysine residue provides **113** via **112** and double tautomerization results in aromatization to afford the crystallographically observed isoxazole-PLP adduct **114** that cannot undergo hydrolysis [597]. The reported kinetic parameters k_{inact} and K_i^{app} for inactivation of the *B. stearothermophilus* D-alanine racemase by D-cycloserine are $16 \times 10^{-3}\,\text{s}^{-1}$ and 0.13 mM, respectively, which yield a half-life for inactivation of only 17 s at 300 μM cycloserine [596].

Although cycloserine inhibits both alanine racemase and D-ala-D-ala ligase, initial molecular genetic and metabolomic studies of *alr* and *ddlA* mutants in *M. smegmatis* suggest that the lethal target of cycloserine was the D-ala-D-ala ligase DdlA [600–604]. The strongest evidence to support this hypothesis was the observation by Chacon et al. that their *alr*⁻ mutant strain generated by insertional inactivation of a kanamycin resistance gene (*alr::aphA-3*) remained viable, suggesting an alternate biosynthetic route to D-alanine [602]. However, a subsequent study performed by Krause and coworkers using a Δ*alr* deletion mutant definitively proved that Alr is essential for growth in the absence of

Peptidoglycan
UDP-MurNAc-L-Ala-D-Glu-*meso*-DAP-D-Ala-D-Ala
D-Ala-D-Ala
D-Ala-D-Ala ligase, DdlA
(Rv2981c)
UDP-MurNAc-L-Ala-D-Glu-*meso*-DAP
meso-DAP
D-Ala
D-Cycloserine
UDP-MurNAc-L-Ala-D-Glu
D-Glu
Alanine racemase, Alr
(Rv3423c)
UDP-MurNAc-L-Ala
L-Ala
UDP-MurNAc

Figure 19. Biosynthesis of UDP-*N*-acetylmuramyl-pentapeptide.

D-alanine [605]. Although the strain harboring the insertionally inactivated *alr::aphA-3* did not display any alanine racemase activity, the limit of detection was only 4% of the wild-type activity. Consistent with the minimally 25-fold lower alanine racemase activity, the *alr::aphA-3* mutant exhibited an altered morphological phenotype and displayed hypersusceptibility to D-cycloserine with an MIC of 2.56 μg/mL that is 30-fold lower than the

110
111
112
113
114
12
aromatization

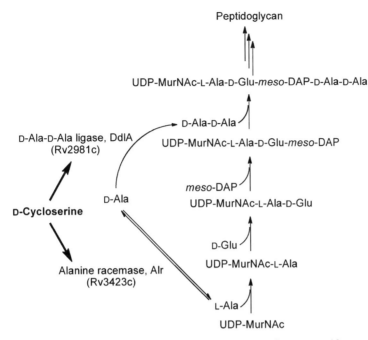

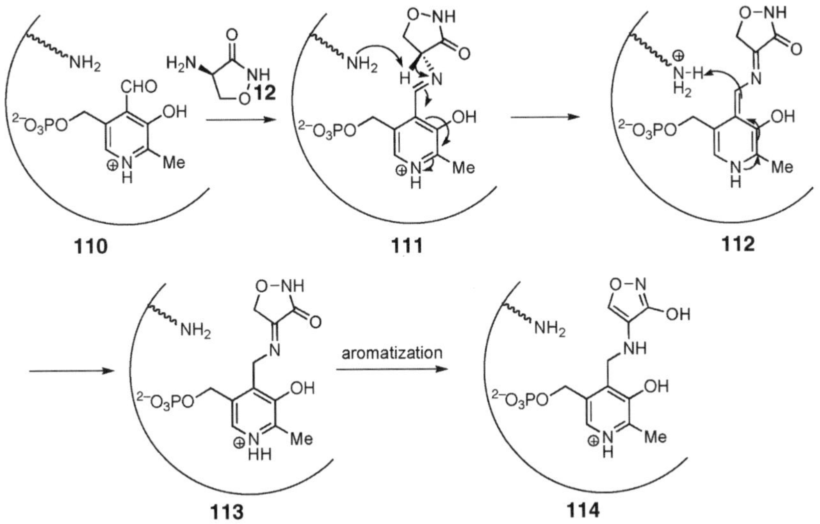

Figure 20. Mechanism of alanine racemase inactivation by cycloserine.

wild-type strain [602]. By contrast, the A365V DdlA mutant was 30-fold less active than the wild-type enzyme, yet the strain exhibited a mere 4-fold lower MIC value [601]. Thus, alanine racemase is the likely primary molecular target while D-ala-D-ala ligase DdlA appears to play an important secondary target based on (1) the rapid and irreversible nature of inhibition of alanine racemase Alr versus the modest reversible inhibition of D-ala-D-ala ligase DdlA, (2) the apparent greater susceptibility of *alr* versus *ddlA* mutants to D-cycloserine, and (3) the early observation that D-alanine alone is able to rescue cells treated with cycloserine.

Resistance Given that D-cycloserine is a second-line agent with moderate to high toxicity, relatively few retrospective molecular genetic studies have been performed. Laboratory generated mutants have helped define the importance of both *alr* and *ddlA* as resistant determinants. Thus, overexpression of Alr resulted in a fourfold increase in the MIC [602]. A strain of *M. smegmatis* that had a point mutation in the DdlA-coding region (A365V) was approximately 30-fold less active than the wild-type enzyme and displayed a corresponding 4-fold increase in MIC [601]. Feng and Barletta developed a *M. smegmatis* strain overproducing both wild-type DdlA and Alr that exhibited an MIC of 600 μg/mL. Cáceres et al. raised a spontaneously resistant mutant (GPM14) of *M. smegmatis* in 500–600 μg/mL of D-cycloserine that had a 20-fold increase in D-ala racemase activity and a 30-fold increase in *alrA* mRNA due to a point mutation at −13 in the promoter region [600]. Transformation of this *alrA* resistance gene into *M. intracellulare* conferred the D-cycloserine resistance phenotype [600]. One of the two spontaneously resistant mutants that Cáceres et al. raised to D-cycloserine did not show an altered sequence or expression of *alr* suggesting that alternate resistance mechanisms may occur in clinical isolates. In summary, resistance to D-cycloserine may occur by overproduction of Alr or point mutations in *ddlA*. Further examination of clinically resistant D-cycloserine strains may be helpful in understanding which of these mutations is more common in patients. Interestingly, self-resistance to D-cycloserine by the produ-

cing organism *Streptomyces lavendulae* is due the DdlA ortholog that has 40- to 100-fold lower affinity for D-cycloserine [606].

ADME D-Cycloserine is a cyclic amino acid with a MW of 102.1 and log P of −1.63 that is water soluble, but unstable at neutral or acidic solutions [607]. D-Cycloserine is given orally as a 250 mg tablet, and the usual daily dose is 500–750 mg. The initial ADME studies were done by a colorimetric method that may not have been selective for the parent compound versus other metabolites [608]. Careful pharmacokinetic studies were subsequently performed by Peloquin and coworkers using an HPLC method [609]. The pharmacokinetics of a single 500 mg cycloserine oral dose were evaluated under fasting conditions, with a high fat meal, orange juice, or simultaneous antacid administration. Pyridoxine (100 mg) was also given to prevent neuropathy. The highest C_{max} was observed with antacids (median = 19.2 μg/mL) with a T_{max} of 0.88 h. Under fasting conditions, the C_{max} was 14.8 μg/mL with a T_{max} of 0.75 h. A high fat meal caused a delay in the absorption (median T_{max} = 3.5 h, range 2–8 h), but there was not a significant difference in the median AUC values (214–225 μg/h/mL) between the four treatments. The urinary recovery was 26–29%. Based on the above data, a simulation of 16 doses (Q12 h) was conducted indicating an accumulation resulting in a C_{max} on day 3 that was 66% higher than the first dose (C_{max} = 24 μg/mL, trough concentration = 10.2 μg/mL). Cycloserine likely displays a time-dependent bactericidal effect like the β-lactams and vancomycin that also interfere with cell wall biosynthesis. The MIC for cycloserine is about 10 μg/mL, so a 500 mg dose of cycloserine given every 12 h would achieve concentrations above the MIC for the entire dosing interval. Due to CNS side effects, patients typically are started at lower doses (250 mg every 12–24 h), and these doses may barely reach the MIC, potentially leading to resistance. Cycloserine is readily removed by hemodialysis (56% of the dose), but it is renally excreted, so the recommended dose is 250–500 mg three times per week in these patients [469]. Penetration of D-cycloserine across the blood–brain barrier appears to be high based on a case report in a 21-month-old girl with tuberculous meningitis.

The concentrations in the cerebrospinal fluid ranged from 49% to 94% of the concentration in serum even though the sampling of the CSF was done 8 h after the serum concentration was taken [610].

Adverse Effects The primary side effects of cycloserine are neurotoxicity and hypersensitivity reactions. Central nervous system side effects are common with D-cycloserine most typically described as drowsiness, slurred speech, psychotic episodes, and seizures [611]. At daily doses of 1 g, side effects are more frequent occurring in up to 50% of patients. Reducing the dose and giving it more often, for example, 250 mg two to three times/day reduces the incidence. D-Cycloserine is a partial agonist at *N*-methyl-D-aspartate (NMDA) receptors and appears to bind at glycine modulatory site [612]. It may also inhibit enzymes that metabolize and synthesize the neurotransmitter γ-aminobutyric acid (GABA) [613,614]. D-Cycloserine has been evaluated for a number of neurologic disorders including schizophrenia [615], anxiety disorders [616], and Alzheimer's disease [617]. Suicide has also been reported in patients taking cycloserine [618]. Encephalopathy due to cycloserine was confirmed by a recent brain imaging study in a patient exhibiting hypersomnolence and asterixis [619]. Hypersensitivity reactions may be severe including Steven–Johnson's syndrome [620].

8.2.6. Ethionamide

History and SAR The discovery of the modest antitubercular activity of nicotinamide led to the synthesis of various series of analogs including the thioisonicotinamides, which had the intriguing property of *in vivo* efficacy superior to that expected from the *in vitro* activity [621–623]. The hypothesis that some metabolic product of the drug was responsible for the activity *in vivo* stimulated the synthesis and testing of a series of potential thioisonicotinamide metabolites and various derivatives. Among the latter, increased activity was observed for the 2-alkyl analogs [624]. 2-Ethyl-thioisonicotinamide (ethionamide) and the 2-*n*-propyl analog (prothionamide) were selected for clinical use. Of these two drugs, ethionamide has been more extensively stu-

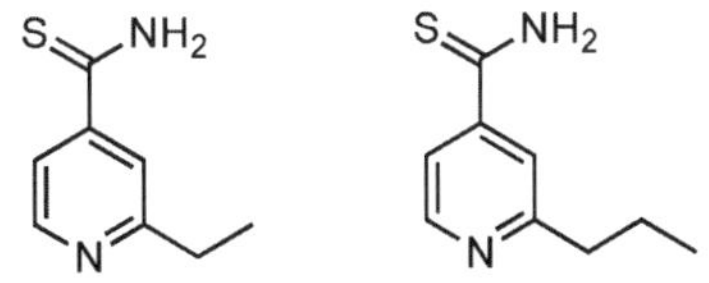

Figure 21. Structures of ethionamide and prothionamide.

died, although prothionamide seems to possess similar biological properties (Fig. 21).

Antibacterial Activity At concentrations around 0.6–2.5 μg/mL, ethionamide is active *in vitro* against *M. tuberculosis* strains, either sensitive or resistant to isoniazid, streptomycin, and *p*-aminosalicylic acid and is equally effective against intracellular or extracellular organisms [623]. It also shows activity against other mycobacteria, especially *M. kansasii*. Ethionamide is remarkably selective against mycobacteria and shows no activity against most other microorganisms.

Mechanism of Action Ethionamide (ETA) is a prodrug that is bioactivated to afford an ETA-NAD adduct, which is a potent inhibitor of InhA involved in mycolic acid synthesis in analogy to isoniazid [625,626]. While isoniazid utilizes the catalase-peroxidase KatG for bioactivation, ethionamide is activated by the monooxygenase EthA in a process that is dependent on the presence of mycothiol, the major thiol of *M. tuberculosis* [214,222,625]. A proposed mechanism is shown in Fig. 22. Sequential oxidation of ethionamide via the sulfenic acid **115** affords sulfinic acid **116**. Formal one-electron reduction and loss of neutral sulfur dioxide provides imidoyl radical **117** that could then add to NAD to afford the observed ETA-NAD adduct **118** in analogy to formation of the isoniazid-NAD adduct. The ETA-NAD adduct **118** is a potent tight binding inhibitor of InhA with a reported K_i of 7 nM [626]. The cocrystal structure of ETA-NAD bound to InhA is nearly identical to the isoniazid-NAD adduct discussed in Section 8.1 [626]. In analogy to the INH-NAD adduct, ETA-NAD is expected to inhibit other targets enzymes besides InhA that require NAD as a cofactor.

Resistance Resistance to the ethionamide is due to three primary mechanisms. The first mechanism involves mutations that affect the

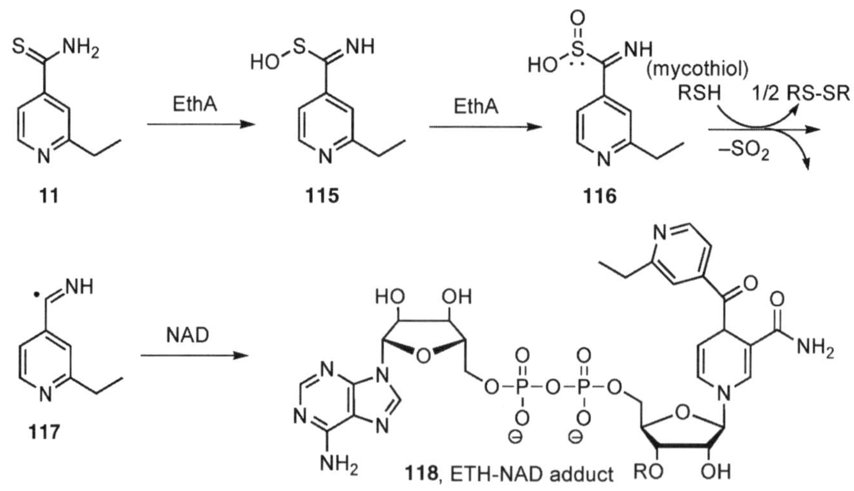

Figure 22. Proposed activation process ETA.

catalytic activity or expression of the bioactivating enzyme EthA. Thus, point and missense mutations to *ethA* have been clinically observed [627]. Resistance can also be observed by mutations to *ethR*, a transcriptional repressor of *ethA* that reduces *ethA* expression [628]. In a novel approach, inspired by the initial observation of Baulard and coworkers, inhibitors of EthR have been described that lead to increased expression of EthA and consequently increase the activity of ethionamide [629,630]. The second mechanism of ethionamide resistance involves mutation to the molecular target *inhA* as previously described in Section 8.1.1 [625]. Mutations in the *inhA* promoter and structural regions result in cross-resistance between isoniazid and ethionamide. The third known mechanism that can lead to ethionamide resistance is due to mutations to *mshA* that encodes for an enzyme that catalyzes the first step in biosynthesis of mycothiol [214]. Mycothiol is required along with EthA for bioactivation of ethionamide by an incompletely understood mechanism. Mycothiol is a glutathione equivalent in Mtb and other *Actinobacteria* that is involved in detoxification of reactive xenobiotics [207].

ADME Ethionamide (ETA) is a simple and inexpensive compound, with a molecular weight of 166.3 that is sparingly soluble in water. Ethionamide is almost completely metabolized, with less than 1% recovered in the urine and feces [631]. The major metabolite is the sulfoxide, which is also active against mycobacteria *in vitro*. Ethionamide is rapidly absorbed with a volume of distribution approximately 2–3 times total body water. It penetrates well into the CSF [632]. Peloquin and coworkers studied the pharmacokinetics of a 500 mg dose of ethionamide in 12 healthy volunteers in the fasted state, with orange juice or antacids, and with a high fat meal in a crossover design with HPLC quantitation [633]. The terminal half-life was 1.7–2.2 h, and the T_{max} under fasting conditions or with orange juice was 1.7–1.9 h and was slightly prolonged with antacids or a high fat meal. The C_{max} was not significantly different by treatment with median values from 2.2 to 2.5 µg/mL (range 0.47–6.11 µg/mL). The apparent oral clearance (Cl/F) was 56–72 L/h and the apparent volume of distribution (V/F) was 2.0–2.8 L/kg. Since ETA does not accumulate due to its short half-life, it is difficult to achieve concentrations greater than the MIC in patients [634]. A dose of 15–30 mg/kg/day up to 1.0 g day is used in treatment.

Adverse Effects ETA causes a variety of gastrointestinal symptoms such as nausea, metallic taste, vomiting, anorexia, and diarrhea that are very common and occur in the majority of patients [635,636]. Liver damage is relatively uncommon, but may be potentiated by rifampin. Neurotoxic effects such as depression, anxiety, and acute psychosis have been reported along with dizziness and rare visual disturbances. It has been suggested that nicotinamide be given with ETA to prevent some of these CNS side effects. ETA is teratogenic in animals and should not be administered in pregnancy.

8.2.7. Thiacetazone

History Thiacetazone (TB-I-698, Conteben, TAC) was initially prepared by the chemists Behnisch, Mietzsch, and Schmidt at Farbenfabriksen Bayer in Germany in 1941 and evaluated for antitubercular activity by Gerhard Domagk [303,637] (Figure 23). Thiacetazone was first used to treat patients in 1947 and by the end of 1949, more than 10,000 German TB patients had received this synthetic antimicrobial agent. After the introduction of isoniazid into TB chemotherapy, thiacetazone use declined due to its toxicity. As a result of its low cost, thiacetazone was reexamined in clinical trials by the British in East Africa beginning in 1960 in combination with INH and streptomycin as part of a short-course therapy [632]. It has been commonly used as a combination product with isoniazid known as Thiazina for two decades as first-line therapy in Asia and Africa prior to the rise of HIV. Currently, the drug is used much less often in Africa, due to a high rate of serious hypersensitivity reaction in HIV-infected patients [638].

SAR Behnisch et al. reviewed the early SAR of the thiosemicarbazones [637]. The sulfur atom of the thiosemicarbazone is essential as the corresponding semicarbazone and other close structural analogs were either inactive or substantially less active. Thiosemicarbazones of benzaldehyde derivatives had greater activity than derivatives of aryl alkyl ketones such as acetophenone or aliphatic aldehydes. Substitution of either of nitrogen atoms in the thiosemicarbazones led to proportionally reduced activity with increasing steric bulk. The trend in activity for substitution of the aromatic ring was *para* > *meta* > *ortho* and the acetamido substituent was optimal among a wide variety of other replacements including $-NO_2$, $-NH_2$, $-OH$, $-CO_2H$, $-NHCOR$

(where R = alkyl), $-O$-alkyl, and $-NH$-alkyl. Several additional analogs have been recently reported that demonstrated superior efficacy against *M. avium* [639].

Antibacterial Activity The minimum inhibitor concentration of thiacetazone against most strains of *M. tuberculosis* is 0.5–1 µg/mL [640]. Thiacetazone is generally considered bacteriostatic, which may be due to dose-limiting toxicity, as typical doses of 150 mg/day, typical peak concentrations are just above the MIC.

Mechanisms of Action and Resistance Thiacetazone is thought to inhibit synthesis of mycolic acids, which are essential components of the cell wall of mycobacteria [69,269]. Thiacetazone is bioactivated by the monooxygenase EthA through oxidation to generate a putative sulfinic acid and carbodiimide metabolite via a sulfenic acid intermediate (Fig. 24) [625,641,642]. Thiacetazone has been shown to inhibit mycolic acid cyclopropanation *in vivo*. Overexpression of the cyclopropylmethyltransferases *cmaA2*, *mmaA2*, or *pcaA* decreased susceptibility to thiacetazone suggesting that these are potential molecular targets [69]. Inactivation of the repressor EthR that regulates the transcription of *ethA* leads to a 10-fold increase in sensitivity to both thiacetazone and a rapid cessation of mycolic acid biosynthesis [269].

ADME Thiacetazone has MW of 236.3 and poorly soluble in water and most organic solvents except glycols. Peloquin et al. studied the pharmacokinetics of thiacetazone in a Phase I trial in 12 patients with *M. avium* complex infections who were HIV positive [643]. The maximum concentration in serum was 1.59 ± 0.47 µg/ml with a T_{max} of 3.30 ± 1.18 h after a dose of 150 mg. The half-life was 15–16 h and less than 25% of thiacetazone was recovered unchanged in the urine over 48 h. Rashes occurred in two subjects at the end of the 7-day dosing period and resolved without progression or sequelae. Thiacetazone is oxidatively metabolized by

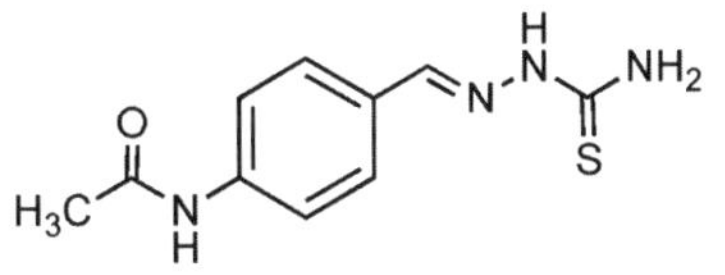

Figure 23. Structure of thiacetazone.

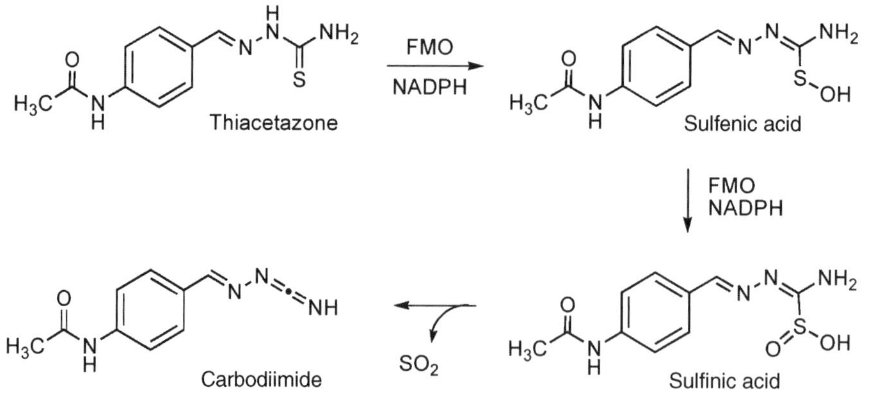

Figure 24. Metabolism of thiacetazone.

flavin monooxygenase (Fig. 24). FMO1 (present in intestine and kidney), FMO2 (present in the lung), and FMO3 (present in liver) metabolize the drug by sulfoxidation. In Sub-Saharan Africans, FMO2.1 is likely to play a major role in its disposition [644]. FMO2 is a polymorphic enzyme that is not expressed as an active protein in Caucasians and Asians (their genes encodes for FMO2.2) and thus there may be significant racial differences in the metabolism and toxicity.

Adverse Effects Early work from Germany showed the most common side effect was diarrhea along with nausea and vomiting, which declined with continuous use. Headache, anemia, and conjunctivitis were observed at higher doses (>300 mg/day). Agranulocytosis was rarely observed, occurring predominantly in female patients. Exanthema characterized by an itchy, maculopapular rash (hives) was observed, but was treated with antihistamines. Because of the thiacetazone's low cost, it is particularly attractive in third world countries. Unfortunately, in HIV-infected patients, thiacetazone did not appear to be well-tolerated with 25% of HIV-positive patients reporting cutaneous hypersensitivity reactions, which tended to be more severe [645]. Lawn et al. reported that 6.8% of HIV-positive patients in Ghana receiving thiacetazone had life-threatening skin reactions compared to only 0.62% of non-HIV patients [646]. Sulfonamide allergies are also well recognized to be more severe in HIV-positive patients, possibly due to lower glutathione concentrations in immune cells. Both the sulfenic acid inter-

mediate and the resulting carbodiimide can react with protein nucleophiles or DNA resulting in either the formation of hapten–protein complexes or cellular toxicity. This may explain why the drug frequently causes skin rashes and may be hepatotoxic. Alternatively, another mechanism analogous to sulfonamide metabolism may involve hydrolysis of the acetamide to *p*-amino-benzyl-semithiocarbazone. *N*-Hydroxylation by cytochrome P450 to hydroxyamino and nitroso compounds could also result in the formation of hapten–protein complexes similar to sulfonamides.

8.2.8. Fluoroquinolones The structure–activity relationships, pharmacology, mechanism of action, and adverse effects of the fluoroquinolines are discussed elsewhere in this volume. Here features of the drug are discussed that pertain to its use in TB chemotherapy.

History Fluoroquinolones, especially moxifloxacin (MXF), have recently been recommended by the WHO as part of second-line TB therapy in patients who have become resistant to first-line drugs, developed grade 3 or higher hepatotoxicity, or in patients with HIV as a rifampin replacement to reduce drug–drug interactions [647,648]. Initially, ofloxacin was evaluated for TB, but moxifloxacin has good lung and bone penetration and is available as a once-daily formulation and is now considered to be the preferred agent [649]. Smaller studies have also been conducted with levofloxacin, another respiratory fluoroquinolone that is the active isomer of ofloxacin [650] (Fig. 25).

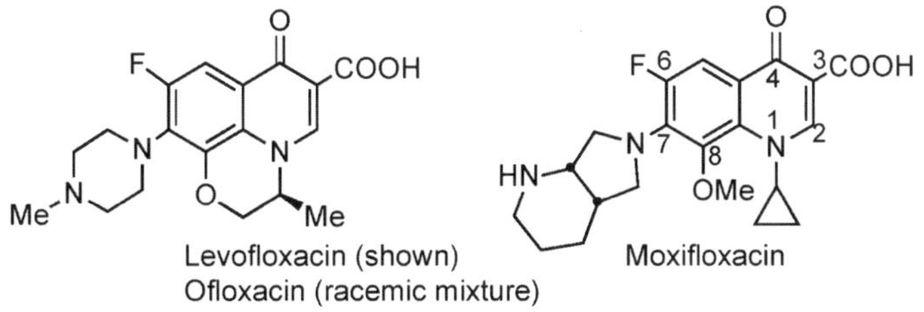

Figure 25. Fluoroquinolones.

Antibacterial Activity Moxifloxacin has an MIC of 0.2 µg/mL against most *M. tuberculosis* strains [651]. When added to a standard regimen of isoniazid/rifampin/pyrazinamide, moxifloxacin was shown to be more effective than ethambutol at 8 weeks with 80% of patients having negative sputum cultures compared to 63% in an EMB group in a double-blind Phase II trial [649].

Mechanism of Action Fluoroquinolones inhibit DNA gyrase and topoisomerase which are two essential enzymes involved in the supercoiling and uncoiling of bacterial DNA. DNA gyrase is a tetramer with two A and two B subunits encoded by *gyrA* and *gyrB*. Topoisomerase (encoded by *parC* and *parE*) are present in most bacteria, but homologs of these genes have not been identified in *M. tuberculosis* [94]. A homology model of *M. tuberculosis* DNA gyrase was recently developed based on the *E. coli* enzyme [652]. An A83S substitution in the mycobacterial enzyme confers intrinsic resistance and higher MIC values compared to *E. coli*.

Resistance Resistance testing prior to initiation of TB therapy will likely be essential. Fluoroquinolones are widely used for treatment of urinary tract infections and community acquired pneumonia and thus brief prior exposures can elicit resistance in *M. tuberculosis* [653]. A recent study from a tertiary care center in Mumbai, India found an alarming increase in fluoroquinolone-resistant TB from 3% in 1996 to 35% in 2004 [654]. Resistance to moxifloxacin has been observed in patient isolates from Taiwan [655]. Fourteen quinolone-resistant isolates (from 420 patients) were found with mutations of D94G ($n = 4$) or A90V ($n = 1$) in *gyrA* or N58D in *gyrB* ($n = 1$). MIC values for moxifloxacin ranged from 0.25 to 8.0 and 0.5 to 8.0 µg/mL

for levofloxacin. Overall resistance rates were 3.3% in clinical isolates and 19% in MDR isolates in this study. A functional analysis of DNA gyrase mutants identified from clinical isolates was conducted by Aubry et al., who showed that D94H and T80A in *gyrA* and D472H and N510D in *gyrB* cause resistance [656].

A novel mechanism of fluoroquinolone resistance in mycobacteria involves a "pentapeptide repeat" protein known as MfpA that mimics B-DNA and has been shown to bind to and inhibit DNA gyrase [657,658]. MfpA prevents fluoroquinolone binding to the requisite DNA–DNA gyrase complex, thus explaining the molecular mechanism of action of this novel protein. The MIC to ciprofloxacin is increased four- to eightfold when MfpA is overexpressed in *M. smegmatis*. Glutamate racemase (MurI) can also bind to DNA gyrase and overexpression of MurI led to ciprofloxacin resistance [659]. Another mechanism of resistance is the overexpression of efflux pumps. An operon, Rv2686c-Rv2687c-Rv2688c, encoding an ABC transporter in *M. tuberculosis* was shown to confer resistance to ciprofloxacin and to a lesser extent moxifloxacin when expressed in *M. smegmatis* [263]. Verapamil and reserpine, known P-glycoprotein inhibitors, inhibited the transporter and restored sensitivity to fluoroquinolones.

ADME Peloquin et al. conducted a population pharmacokinetic study comparing levofloxacin (1000 mg daily) to either gatifloxacin or moxifloxacin (400 mg daily) [660]. Levofloxacin at a high dose resulted in higher peak concentrations in serum (C_{max} of 15.5 µg/mL) than moxifloxacin (C_{max} of 6.1 µg/mL). Gatifloxacin was removed from the US market due to alterations of blood glucose, but is available in some countries as an oral and i.v. product. For tuberculosis, lung penetration is a key pharmacokinetic property. Breilh et al. measured the maximal lung concentrations of 16.2 µg/g lung tissue after an oral 400 mg dose of moxifloxacin [661]. Moxifloxacin is highly concentrated in bronchiolar macrophages with an intracellular/plasma ratio of 90:1 [662]. The tissue to plasma ratios of moxifloxacin were 7.2:1 in bronchial mucosa and 2:1 in epithelial lining fluid. In a similar study conducted with levofloxacin, the tissue to plasma ratios were 4:1 in alveolar macrophages and 1:1 in epithelial lining fluid [663]. Quinolones are concentration-dependent killers of bacteria and thus higher peak concentrations at the site of action will be more effective. Moxifloxacin is metabolized by glucuronidation to an acyl glucuronide by UGT1A1 and less than 20% of the dose is recovered unchanged in urine [664]. By contrast, 87% of levofloxacin is recovered as the parent compound in the urine. The combination of rifampin and isoniazid was shown to reduce moxifloxacin concentrations by 32%, presumably by rifampin-mediated induction of moxifloxacin glucuronidation [665]. High dose, intermittent rifapentine also reduced moxifloxacin concentrations [387].

Adverse Effects Respiratory quinolones are generally well tolerated in short-course anti-infective therapy [666]. Long-term use of quinolones may result in more frequent reports of tendon rupture. Quinolones are not approved for use in children or in pregnant women because they have shown to cause arthrotoxicity in dogs and degeneration of chrondrocytes and cartilage damage [667]. Moxifloxacin (400 mg) may mildly prolong the QTc interval (7.5–12.5 ms) and should be used with caution in patients with cardiac arrhythmias [668]. Levofloxacin at higher doses may cause some CNS disturbances such as dizziness.

8.3. New Drugs in Preclinical and Clinical Evaluation

8.3.1. Nitroimidazoles (PA-824 and OPC-67683)

History The nitroimidazoles represented by the prototypical agent metronidazole **121** are well-known antiprotozoal agents with activity against a variety of anaerobic bacteria. Through a random screening effort to identify new antimicrobial agents, bicyclic nitroimidazole **122** (CGI-17341) was reported that exhibited potent antitubercular activity (Fig. 26) [669,670]. Unfortunately, the appreciable mutagenicity discouraged further work on this compound. In general, the therapeutic activities and mutagenicity of nitroimidazoles have historically been closely linked. However, Walsh et al. at Merck Sharp and Dohme demonstrated that therapeutic activity and mutagenicities of nitroimidazoles could be separated [671]. Based on the original CGI-17341 lead **122**, Baker and coworkers synthesized over 300 analogs [672]. Imidazooxazine **122** (PA-824) emerged as the leading candidate due to its lack of mutagenicity and potent antitubercular activity [672]. Subsequently, Tsubouchi and coworkers at Otsuka Pharmaceuticals Co. reported the design of the related imidazooxazole **120** (OPC-67683) [673,674]. Both compounds are in Phase II clinical trials. Syntheses of the PA-824 [675] and OPC-67683 [673] have been described.

SAR The nitroimidazoles represented by the prototype PA-824 have attracted considerable interest due to their antitubercular activity against latent nonreplicating bacilli under anaerobic conditions (as measured by the minimum anaerobicidal concentration, MAC). PA-824 and derivatives are also effective against rapidly replicating bacilli as measured by the minimum inhibitory concentration. As discussed in more detail in Section "Mechanism of Action" below, PA-824 is bioactivated through reduction of the imidazole ring by the protein deazaflavin-dependent nitroreductase (Ddn). The specificity constant (k_{cat}/K_M) for reduction of PA-824 analogs by Ddn has reasonable correlation with the MIC activity and is thus a useful predictive parameter.

The nitro group in PA-824 is indispensable for activity and deletion of the nitro functional group in **127** (Table 11) results in complete loss of aerobic activity (MIC) and anaerobic bactericidal activity (MAC). The conformationally restricted bicyclic core of PA-824 is required for potent activity as demonstrated with acyclic PA-824 analog **130**, which exhibited an approximately 8-fold loss in the MIC

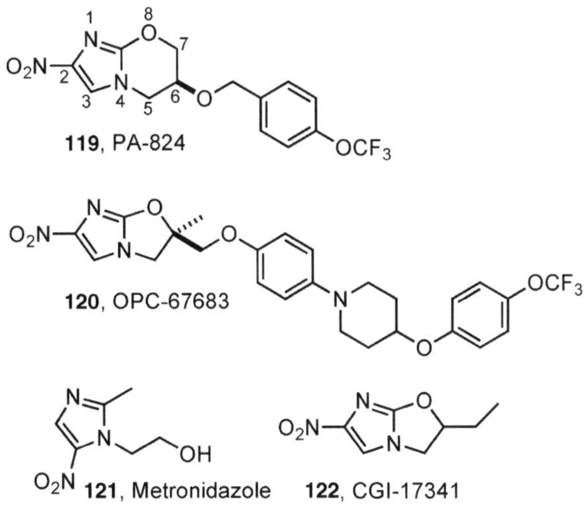

Figure 26. Antitubercular nitroimidazoles.

and more dramatic 32-fold decrease in the MAC. Modification of the bicyclic scaffold of PA-824 revealed that bulky hydrophobic substituents at C-6 are required. Thus, the *p*-(trifluoromethoxy)benzyloxy substituent of PA-824 **119** possessed potent antitubercular activity while the methoxy and hydroxy analogs **124** and **125** were inactive. The *S*-configuration of PA-824 at C-6 is approximately 1–2 orders of magnitude more potent than the *R*-antipode **123**.

PA-824 is poorly water-soluble (10.2 µg/mL) requiring the use of a complex formulation, which is not desirable. Consequently, modifications to improve its water solubility have been investigated. Significantly, the C-6 amino derivative **126** is substantially more water-soluble while retaining potent antitubercular activity. In efforts to rationally improve water solubility by decreasing the thermodynamic stability of the crystalline form, introduction of methyl substituents at C-7 was explored with 7*R*- and 7*S*-methyl analogs **128** and **129** that were expected to disrupt crystal packing. While these compounds failed to show improvements in aqueous solubility, they demonstrated that introduction of small substituents at C-7 is tolerated.

The nitro group of PA-824 is thought to be bioreductively activated by FGD1, a mycobacterial glucose-6-phosphate dehydrogenase (encoded by Rv0407 in MTB) that utilizes a

F_{420} cofactor (a 7,8-didemethyl-8-hydroxy-5-deazariboflavin electron transfer agent) [672]. Consequently, substitution of the 8-oxygen atom in PA-824 has been explored in order to modulate the reduction potential of the nitro group. The sulfur and amino analogs **131** and **133** exhibited biological activity commensurate with PA-824 and were equally efficient substrates for Ddn-catalyzed reduction as measured by the specificity constant (k_{cat}/K_M). Chemical reduction of the sulfur analog **131** also demonstrated a preference for two-electron reduction of the imidazole ring versus the nitro group. The corresponding sulfonyl analog **132** and sulfoxide analog (not shown) were inactive under aerobic conditions, yet retained partial anaerobic activity. Neither sulfonyl or sulfoxide derivatives were substrates for Ddn, consistent with the lack of aerobic activity and suggesting a different mechanism for bioactivation under anaerobic conditions. Indeed, chemical reduction of the sulfonyl analog suggested that the decreased reduction potential results in direct nitro reduction. The C-carba derivative **134** was a poor substrate for Ddn-catalyzed reduction, possessed a 30 mV lower one-electron reduction potential, and correspondingly resulted in a significant 32-fold loss in activity under both aerobic and anaerobic conditions.

Both PA-824 and OPC-67683 were initially optimized for aerobic activity. The recent find-

Table 11. PA-824 SAR

Compound	R or X	MIC^e (μg/mL)	MAC^f (μg/mL)	Ddn^h k_{cat}/K_M (min^{-1} μM^{-1})
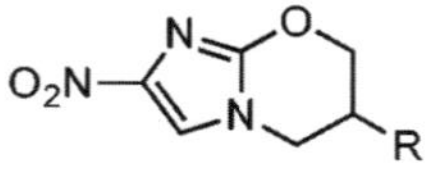 119^a	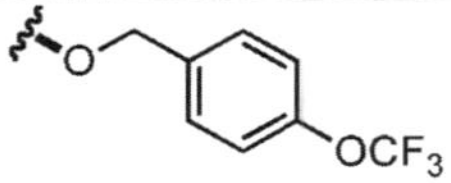 (OCF$_3$ benzyloxy)	0.8	8–16	0.145
123^j	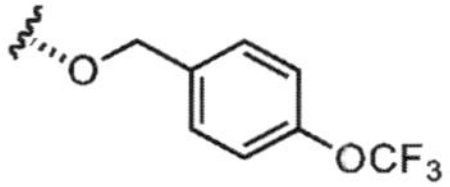 (OCF$_3$ benzyloxy)	110	250	0.016
124^a	 OMe	>125	250	0.0079
125^a	 OH	>100	250	0.005
126^b	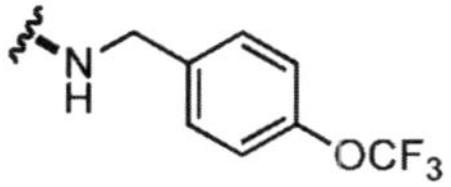 (OCF$_3$ benzylamino)	0.31	12.5	0.172
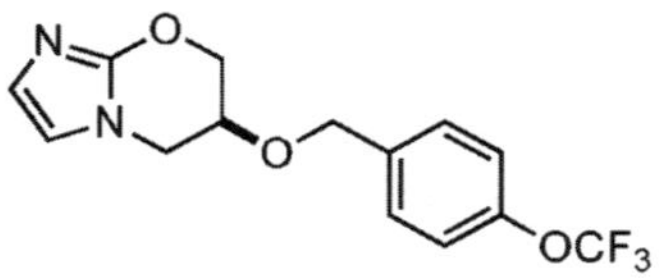 127^a	na^d	>160	>500	ns^j
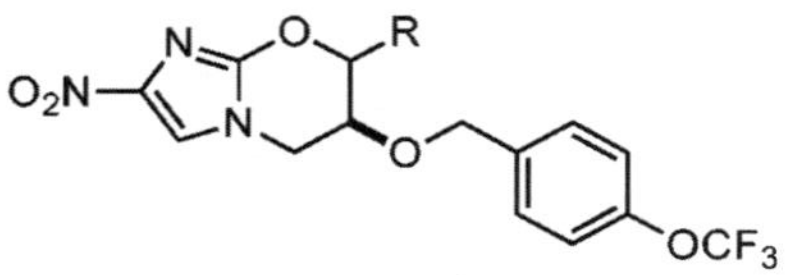 128^c	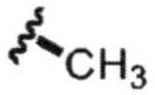 CH$_3$	0.2–0.4	16	nd^g
129^c	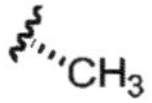 CH$_3$	0.2	8–16	nd^g

Compound	X	MIC	MAC	Specificity constant
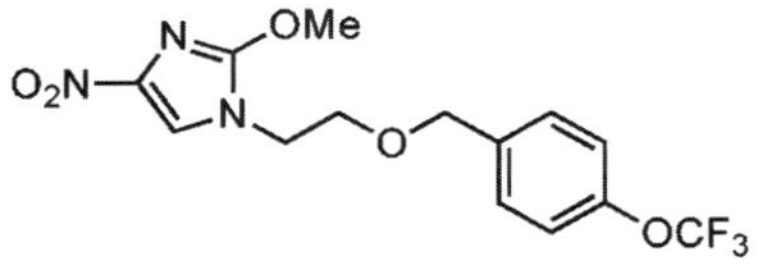 130[a]	na[e]	6.25	250–500	0.030
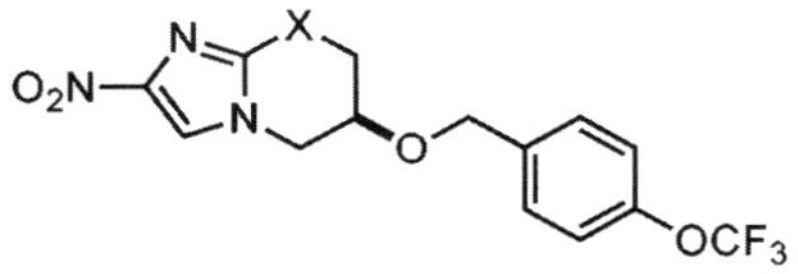 131[b]	S	0.8–1.6	25	0.146
137[b]	SO$_2$	>100	25	nd[g]
133[b]	NH	0.31	12.5	0.172
134[a]	CH$_2$	25	250	0.0235

[a] Ref. [676].
[b] Ref. [677].
[c] Ref. [678].
[d] Not applicable.
[e] Minimum inhibitory concentration against *M. tuberculosis* H37Rv.
[f] Minimum anaerobicidal concentration against *M. tuberculosis* H37Rv.
[g] Not determined.
[h] Specificity constant in nitroreductase assay using recombinant Ddn (Rv3547).
[i] Not a substrate.
[j] Ref. [271].

779

ings that anaerobic activity correlated with formation of a *des*-nitro metabolite of PA-824 and concomitant release of a reactive nitrogen species may enable design of analogs with improved anaerobicidal activity for treatment of latent tuberculosis. The current SAR suggests limited opportunities for modification of the central bicyclic nitroimidazole chromophore; however, alteration of the side chain at C-6 is tolerated leading to enhanced activity and improved drug disposition and physicochemical properties.

Antibacterial Activity PA-824 is effective against a wide variety of Mtb strains including ones individually resistant to the first-line agents as well as multidrug-resistant strains with minimum inhibitory concentrations of 0.015–0.375 µg/mL [672,679]. In murine and guinea pig models, PA-824 significantly reduced organism loads in lung and spleen by 4–5 log units [672]. PA-824 has been evaluated in combination therapy in murine models of tuberculosis [680,681]. In a recent study, PA-824 replaced isoniazid (INH) in a standard regimen that also included rifampin and pyrazinamide [681]. At a 100 mg/kg daily oral dose of PA-824, combination treatment for 2 months cured all mice and they remained culture negative at 4 months, whereas 15% of mice relapsed on the standard regimen of INH/RIF/PZA. PA-824 was not synergistic with RIF at lower doses of 12.5 and 25 mg/kg. In a second study, the combination of PA-824, MXF, and PZA for 2 months followed by PA-824 and MXF for 1 month was found to have impressive sterilizing activity in the mouse model [680]. The $\log_{10}$ CFU in lungs was reduced from 7.77 ± 0.09 before treatment to 1.46 ± 0.38 after 2 months with a cure rate of 26% at 3 months. This was significantly better than regimens of RIF/PA-824/PZA or RIF/MXF/PA-824. Survival rates were better for regimen of 2 months RIF/MXF/PZA followed by 1 month of RIF/MXF (56% cure rate), but CFUs in lung at 2 months were not significantly different compared to the PA-824.

OPC-67683 has excellent potency with a MIC values ranging from 0.006 to 0.012 µg/mL against *M. tuberculosis* strains that were sensitive or resistant to isoniazid, rifampin, ethambutol, or streptomycin [674]. It is a concentration-dependent killer of mycobacteria.

A 95% reduction in tissue CFU values was observed at a dose of 0.625 mg/kg. At a dose of 5 mg/kg daily, there was a 3 log drop in tissue CFU after 4 weeks.

Mechanism of Action Initially, PA-824 was shown to disrupt mycolic acid synthesis, but this mechanism of action seems indirect as remodeling of these essential cell wall components is unlikely under latent nonreplicating conditions [672]. Barry and coworkers recently demonstrated that PA-824 acts by release of nitric oxide (NO), a reactive nitrogen species that plays a major role in the mammalian defense system against mycobacterial infections [271]. These authors showed that PA-824 is bioactivated by the F_{420} Ddn encoded by Rv3547. The deazaflavin F_{420} cofactor acts as a hydride donar and is recycled back to a reduced state by glucose-6-phosphate dehydrogenase (FGD1) using glucose-5-phosphate as the terminal reductant (Fig. 27) [682]. Ddn-catalyzed hydride reduction of the bicyclic nitroimidazole occurs at the C-3 position to afford a dihydroimidazole intermediate. Evidence for this unusual reduction was independently supported by electrochemical studies of PA-824 that showed a preference for reduction of the imidazole moiety over the nitro group [683]. Loss of nitrous acid from the intermediate dihydroimidazole followed by protonation affords the observed des-nitro metabolite and disproportionation of nitrous acid yields nitric oxide (NO). Nitrous acid production *in vitro* was confirmed by reaction with Griess reagent while NO production in intact cells was identified using a fluorogenic probe for NO. A correlation with NO production and anaerobic killing was observed, but no correlation was observed with any metabolite and aerobic killing. NO can react with cytochrome oxidase, disrupting cellular respiration and leading to cell death. Proteosome mutants that are more sensitive to NO toxicity were sensitized to PA-824. Under aerobic conditions, PA-824 may act like conventional nitroimidazoles through one-electron reduction resulting in a nitro anion radical that can react with oxygen to produce superoxide radical, which can damage to DNA, proteins, and lipids. Thus, reactive nitrogen species are likely responsible for bactericidal activity under anaerobic (latent) conditions, whereas

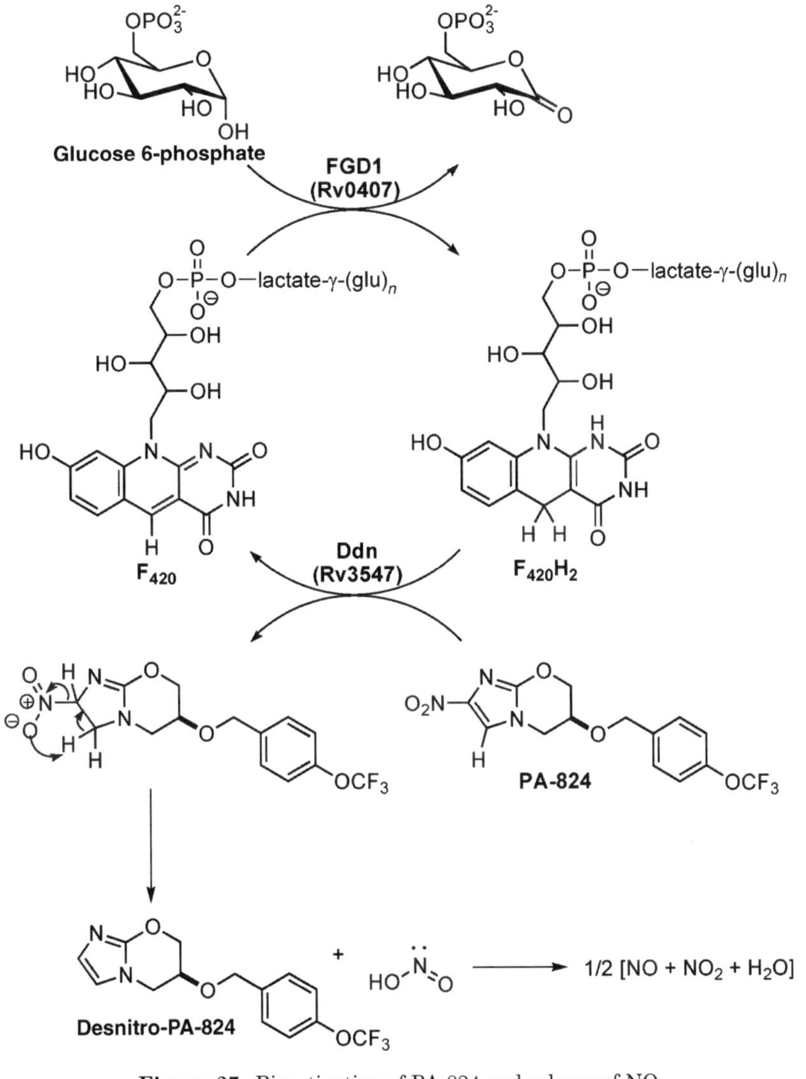

Figure 27. Bioactivation of PA-824 and release of NO.

reactive oxygen species may be responsible for killing under aerobic conditions.

Resistance Resistance to PA-824 has been studied using *in vitro* and *in vivo* generated spontaneous mutants, which arise at a frequency of approximately 6.5×10^{-7} [682]. These studies demonstrated three primary mechanisms of resistance involving mutations to the nitroreductase Ddn, genes involved in synthesis of the required F_{420} cofactor, and the glucose-6-phosphate dehydrogenase FDG1 that recycles the F_{420} cofactor [682]. Among the mutants examined, approximately 20% failed to produce the FGD1 protein while 60% failed to accumulate cofactor F_{420}. Mutants that could not make F_{420} contained transposons inserted into *fbiA* and *fbiB* that are responsible for F_{420} biosynthesis. Additionally, mutations to the nitroreductase Ddn were identified, but the frequency of these was not reported. *M. leprae* notably lacks a Ddn homolog and is naturally resistant to PA-824 [684]. **ADME** PA-824 has a log P of 3.39 and a MW of 359 [685]. Sung et al. recently developed a dry powder formulation of PA-824 for inhalation and compared the bioavailability of direct lung delivery to i.v. doses at 20 mg/kg and oral doses at 40 mg/kg [686]. Pharmacokinetic parameters of the i.v. dose were as follows: clearance (Cl) of 12.6 mL/min/kg, half-life of 1.91 ± 0.24 h and a maximum serum concentration (C_{max} at 0.11 min) of 9.2 μg/mL. The oral bioavailability was $56 \pm 12\%$ with a C_{max} of 4.14 ± 0.78 μg/mL after a 40 mg/kg dose. In the rat, Spigelman of the Global Alliance for TB Development reported that PA-824 had excellent distribution into the lung and spleen with AUC values that were three- to eightfold higher than in plasma [687]. The bioavailability in monkeys was reported as 40% (TB Alliance). PA-824 does not appear to interact with P450 enzymes and did not affect levels of isoniazid, rifampin, or pyrazinamide in animal models [685].

OPC-67683 (Otsuka Pharmaceutical) has been evaluated in single and multiple dose trials in normal volunteers for safely and pharmacokinetic analysis [674]. The compound is being tested in a Phase II trial for MDR-TB. Preclinical studies have been conducted at Otsuka and were reported in 2006 [674]. Pharmacokinetic studies conducted in mice at an oral dose of 2.5 mg/kg (suspended in 4% gum arabic) gave a C_{max} value of 0.297 μg/mL with a reported half-life of 7.5 h and an AUC of 4.33 μg h/mL [674]. The compound was slowly absorbed with a T_{max} of 6 h. OPC-67683 was not found to be an inhibitor of any of the major drug-metabolizing P450 enzymes at concentrations up to 30 μg/mL and was not metabolized by either P450s or in human or animal liver microsomes under aerobic conditions.

Adverse Effects   Unlike other nitroimidazoles and nitrofurans, OPC-67683 was only very weakly mutagenic in a bacterial reversion test [674]. In contrast, CGI-17341 was not further developed due to mutagenicity. Similarly, PA-824 is reported not to be mutagenic [672]. Six Phase I trials of PA-824 have been completed according to the TBA Alliance. These included single and multiple dose PK and safety studies and two studies with radiolabeld compound to evaluate the absorption, metabolism, and excretion. A mild, reversible elevation in serum creatinine has been observed and was further studied, but was deemed not to be clinically significant. In general, the compound was well tolerated with no dose-limiting adverse effects. Early bactericidal activity Phase II clinical trials began in late 2007 in South Africa (14-day study). PA-824 has been granted fast track status by the US FDA and is joint venture of Chiron and the TB Alliance.

Phase I trials of OPC-67683 with an older and new formulation (100–400 mg in multiple doses for 10 days to healthy volunteers) have been completed as well as a small single-center Phase II EBA clinical trial (Norbert Hittel, Otsuka Frankfurt Research Institute). An extended multicenter EBA trial is ongoing at doses ranging from 100 to 400 mg. In the latter trial, a 400 mg dose of OPC-67683 was administered for 7 days. Both PA-824 and OPC-67683 are in clinical trials, but there is no published information on adverse effects as of early 2009 [688].

8.3.2. SQ109—N-(2-Adamantyl)-N'-Geranyl-Ethane-1,2-Diamine

History and SAR   N-(2-Adamantyl)-N'-geranyl-ethane-1,2-diamine (SQ109, Sequella) was identified from a combinatorial library of compounds based on the diaminoethane scaffold of ethambutol [396,689]. A total of 63,238 EMB analogs with the 1,2-diamine were prepared by solid-phase synthesis. Adamantyl derivatives with a cyclooctyl or diaryl substituents on the other amine gave compounds with MIC values of approximately 1 μg/mL. A series of geranyl compounds with a variety of cycloalkyl, diaryl, or heterocyclic substituents also had MIC values in the range of 1 μg/mL. Combination of the geranyl and adamantine side chains on the 1,2-diamine scaffold produced the initial lead compound, designated as SQ109 with an MIC of 0.2 μg/mL (Fig. 28).

Antibacterial Activity   The minimum inhibitory concentration of SQ109 against H37Rv, Erdman and drug-resistant strains of *M. tuberculosis* ranges from 0.7 to 1.56 μg/mL [689,690]. SQ109 is also effective against other mycobacteria including *M. bovis* (0.25 μg/mL), *M. marinum* (8 μg/mL), but poorly active against *M. avium* and *M. smeg-*

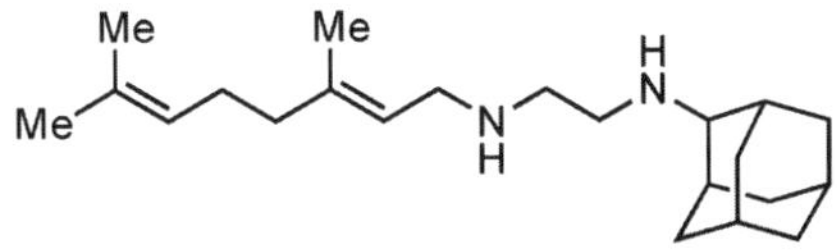

Figure 28. Structure of SQ109.

matis [691]. SQ109 also possesses an MIC of 1 µg/mL against intracellular *M. tuberculosis* H37Rv, indicating reasonable penetration [690]. In mice infected with *M. tuberculosis* H37Rv by inhalation, SQ109 is equivalent to 100 mg/g EMB at doses of 10 and 25 mg/kg. At these doses, a 1.5–2.0 log drop in lung and spleen CFU was observed [690]. SQ109 is synergistic *in vitro* with both isoniazid and rifampin and additive with streptomycin [692].

Mechanism of Action and Resistance   No published data are available on resistance of *M. tuberculosis* to SQ109. A single report on the mechanism of action using a proteomics approach has shown that SQ109 and ethambutol share similar proteomic profiles [693]. Both SQ109 and ethambutol upregulated the synthesis of several proteins including AphC, CFP-10, ESAT-6, FixA, Lppd, Rv3865, and Rv0207 in a dose-dependent fashion and downregulated TrpS and PE. AhpC is a subunit of the alkyl-hydroperoxide reductase that detoxifies cells by reducing reactive oxygen species while ESAT-6 and CFP-10 are secreted antigenic proteins. Differences in expression levels between ethambutol and SQ109 were noted for some proteins, but these results provided relatively limited insight into the mechanism of action.

ADME   SQ109 is a highly lipophilic molecule with a log *P* of 6.45 and a molecular weight of 330.6 [691]. Single dose pharmacokinetics studies of SQ109 have been conducted in mice, rats, and dogs providing C_{max} values of 0.135, 0.64, and 0.011 µg/mL after oral doses of 25, 13, and 3.75 mg/kg, respectively. Little unchanged drug was found in feces, suggesting that the compound is well absorbed but undergoes rapid first-pass metabolism. The clearance and volume of distribution in mice were respectively 3.79 L/h kg and 11.8 L/kg while the compound possessed a terminal half-life of 3.5 h after a short distribution

phase. The tissue distribution after an i.v. dose revealed the highest concentrations in lung followed by spleen, kidney, and heart while the concentrations were low in the liver. At 10 h, the lung concentration after i.v. dosing was approximately 10 µg/g and 4 µg/g after oral dosing, concentrations that were well above the MIC. Interspecies pharmacokinetic studies have also been reported to predict the initial dose that should be used in humans [694]. The bioavailability in mice, rats, and dogs was 2.4–5%, 12%, and 3.8%, respectively, with the highest clearance observed in dogs. The half-life was longer in this species due to a larger volume of distribution. Plasma protein binding was low (6–23%). Metabolic stability was conducted in human and animal liver microsomes. In human liver microsomes, 58% of the compound was metabolized in 10 min, indicating that rapid first-pass metabolism will likely occur in humans. Oxidative metabolism suggested that the major pathways of metabolism are aliphatic oxidation, epoxidation (rapidly rearranges to a ketone), and *N*-dealkylation (P450-mediated metabolites). Reaction phenotyping indicated that CYP2D6 and CYP2C19 were the principle enzymes involved, based on incubations with cloned, expressed enzymes and inhibition of metabolism in microsomes with quinidine and ticlopidine. Ticlopidine also inhibits CYP2B6, so this enzyme may also contribute. The *N*-dealkylation of the geranyl side chain was catalyzed by CYP2C19. However, both of these enzymes show significant polymorphisms that could affect clinical trial design.

Clinical Trials   Sequella, Inc. (Rockville, MD) received a fast track designation for SQ109 by the FDA in January 2007. A Phase I trial was begun in 2006 and Phase Ib trials (multiple dose studies) began in 2009 (Sequella May 5, 2009 Press release).

8.3.3. TMC207 (Diarylquinoline)

History   TMC207   (1-(6-bromo-2-methoxy-quinolin-3-yl)-4-dimethylamino-2-(*S*)-naphthalen-1-yl-1-(*R*)-phenyl-butan-2-ol, R207910) is a new diarylquinoline antitubercular compound (licensed to Tibotec BVBA) that was discovered at Johnson and Johnson in Bel-

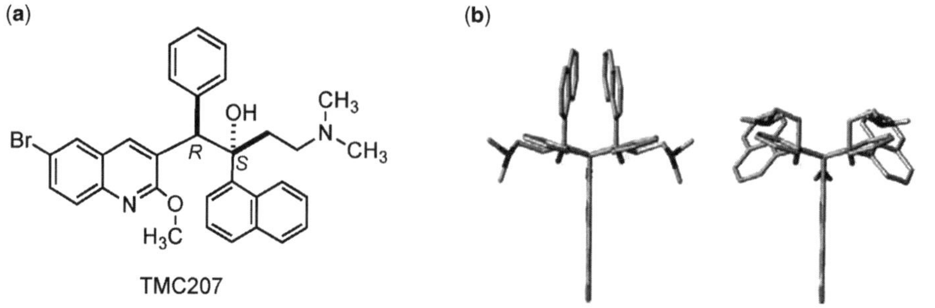

(a)

(b)

TMC207

Figure 29. (a) Structure of TMC207. (b) Conformation of the *R,S* or *S,R* diastereomers (left) compared to the *S,S*, or *R,R* diastereomers (right) [695].

gium and France from a whole cell phenotypic screen against *M. smegmatis* followed by chemical optimization [172] (Fig. 29).

SAR After initial screening at Johnson and Johnson in Belgium, 20 diarylquinoline were identified with MIC values of less than 0.5 µg/mL. The stereochemistry around the two chiral centers is critical for activity. The *R,S* configuration had an MIC against *M. tuberculosis* of 0.06 µg/mL compared to 8.8 µg/mL for the *S,R* configuration [173]. Gaurrand et al. determined the conformation of TMC207 in solution by 2D-NMR and by X-ray crystallography while the low energy conformation of the *R,S* diastereomer was determined by *ab initio* calculations [695]. Docking of the *R,S* diastereomer into a model of the active site of the c subunit of ATP synthase suggested key interactions with Glu61, Phe65 and Arg186 [696]. Upadhayaya et al. recently prepared a series of 3-benzyl-6-bromo-2-methoxy-quinolines and docked the compounds and TMC207 in a molecular model of the c subunit of ATP synthase [697]. The most potent analogs had MIC values of 6.25 µg/mL indicating that the naphthalene ring and dimethylamino side chain in TMC207 provide additional potency.

Antibacterial Activity TMC207 possesses MIC values ranging from 0.03 to 0.120 µg/mL against a variety of clinical *M. tuberculosis* isolates including isolates resistant to first-line agents and fluoroquinolones [172]. TMC207 was also active against other mycobacteria including *M. bovis*, *M. avium*, *M. intracellulare*, and *M. marinum* with similar MICs, but was inactive against most other bacteria including staphylococci and enterococci. A single 100 mg/kg dose reduced the

CFU in lung of infected mice by more than 2.5 logs that lasted for 8 days. Upon daily dosing at 12.5 and 25 mg/kg, TMC207 was more active than isoniazid. Furthermore, TMC207 was found to be synergistic with pyrazinamide in mice infected with MTb [698].

The initial report of the first Phase II trial of TMC207 was published in 2009 by Diacon et al. and demonstrated striking effectiveness for MDR-TB [699]. Patients ($n = 47$) with MDR-TB were randomly assigned to receive 400 mg of TMC207 daily for 2 weeks followed by 200 mg three times per week for another 6 weeks ($n = 23$) compared to patients on an MDR-TB regimen + placebo ($n = 24$). TMC207 significantly reduced the time to negative sputum culture and increased the proportion of patients with a negative sputum culture from 9% to 48%. The initial drop in log CFU counts was modest in the first week (−0.57 log), but accelerated rapidly thereafter compared to placebo.

Mechanism of Action and Resistance TMC207 has a novel mechanism of action due to inhibition of the c subunit of ATP synthase in mycobacteria, which leads to a reduction in intracellular ATP levels [173]. ATP synthesis is also essential for dormant mycobacteria and explains the exceptional activity of TMC207 against populations of actively replicating and dormant bacilli [188]. The target of TMC207 was initially identified in a resistant strains of *M. smegmatis* and *M. tuberculosis* by mutations in *atpE* (encoding for subunit c of ATP synthase) [172]. Spontaneous resistant Mtb mutants can be generated at a frequency of 5×10^{-7} to 5×10^{-8}. Two mutations in *atpE* (encoding for subunit c of ATP synthase) were identified at A63P or I66M through whole genome sequencing [700]. In these strains, treatment with TMC207 had no effect on intracellular ATP [173].

ADME Initial pharmacokinetic and pharmacodynamic studies were conducted in mice by Andries et al. [172]. After an oral dose of 6.25 mg/kg, a maximum serum concentration (C_{max}) of 0.5 µg/mL was achieved after 1 h (T_{max}). At a 6.25 mg/kg dose, the C_{max} of 1.2 µg/mL occurred at 2–4 h. The half-lives in plasma were unusually long (43–64 h in mice), suggesting a high volume of distribution for this very lipophilic, weakly basic compound (Clog P of 7.25). The lung to plasma ratio was 22:1 in mice. A Phase I dose ranging study from 10 to 700 mg was conducted and the PK was linear with dose [172]. The median T_{max} was 5 h with dose proportionality based on AUC values. After short-term dosing for 14 days, mean steady-state concentrations were 1.0 and 2.2 µg/mL after daily doses of 150 and 400 mg and the "effective half-life" was 24 h. In the Phase II study, a 200 mg thrice-weekly regimen provided peak, trough, and steady-state concentrations of 1.66, 0.62, and 0.90 ± 0.54 µg/mL at week 8 [699].

Adverse Effects Only one patient withdrew from the initial 14-day exposure study due to an unrelated urinary tract infection. Overall, TMC207 was well tolerated. In the Phase II trial, nausea was the most common adverse effect (26% versus 4% in the placebo group) and none of the 23 patients discontinued the drug [699]. The QTc interval increased in both groups and patients in the TMC207 had modestly higher increases (1–10 ms), however no patient had a QTC interval of more than 500 ms.

8.3.4. Linezolid

History Linezolid is a member of the oxazolidinone class of synthetic antimicrobial agents. The initial patent on oxazolidones was from Dupont in 1978 that described the synthesis of 5-(halomethyl)-3-aryl-2-oxazolidinones with activity against plant pathogens (DuP-721). Based on these initial finding, several more active analogs with improved pharmacokinetics were developed by DuPont and Ujohn. Linezolid was developed by Pharmacia and Upjohn (now part of Pfizer) and was initially approved in April 2000 for the treatment of Gram-positive cocci that are resistant to other agents, most notably methicillin-resistant *Staphyloccocus aureus*, vancomycin-resistant enterococci, and penicillin-resistant *Streptococcus pneumoniae*. Linezolid has been tested both *in vitro* and *in vivo* against *M. tuberculosis* and was found to have reasonable activity. Because of its limited use for drug-resistant Gram-positive infections, the drug is very expensive in the United States (~$50 per tablet) precluding its use for tuberculosis, except for rare cases of MDR-TB or XDR-TB (Fig. 30).

Antibacterial Activity The antibacterial activity of the oxazolidinones is discussed elsewhere in this volume. Linezolid is active versus many drug-resistant Gram-positive organisms and is primarily reserved for staphylococcal, streptococcal, and enterococcal infections that are resistant to β-lactams or vancomycin. The antituberculosis activity of oxazolidinones was first reported by Barbachyn et al. at the Upjohn Laboratories in 1996 [115]. Both the parent compound and the expected sulfone metabolite had impressive activity even against resistant strains with typical MICs ranging from 0.125 to 0.5 µg/mL.

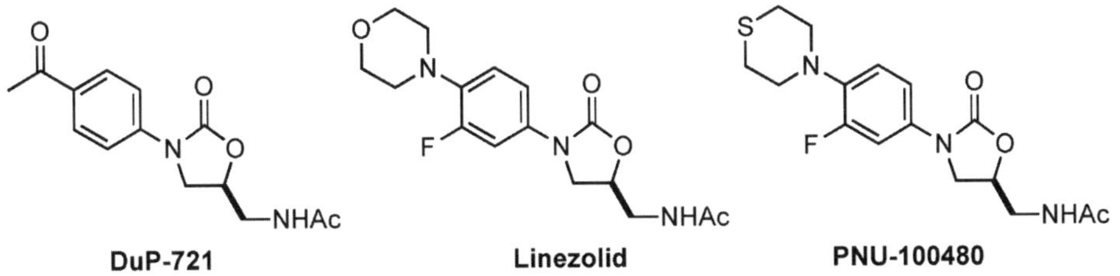

Figure 30. Structures of oxazolidinones.

Early studies conducted by Upjohn indicated that the thiomorpholine analog of linezolid PNU-100480 (PNU), had better activity than linezolid for *M. tuberculosis* H37Rv (<0.125 g/mL). PNU was also active in a mouse model with similar CFU reductions in lung and spleen at 100 mg/kg compared to 25 mg/kg of INH. In a murine model of tuberculosis, PNU (100 mg/kg/day) provided an additional $2.0\log_{10}$ unit reduction in lung CFU counts when added to a standard regimen of RIF, INH, and PZA [701]. Compared to a RIF/INH/PZA regimen, the combination of PNU-100480, moxifloxacin, and pyrazinamide (for MDR-TB) was also more active.

SAR The structure–activity relationships of the oxazolidinones against Gram-positive bacteria is discussed elsewhere in this volume. The initial chemistry and SAR of a small series of oxazolidinones was initially presented by Barbachyn et al. at Upjohn [114].

Mechanisms of Action and Resistance Linezolid inhibits initiation of protein synthesis by binding to the 50S ribosomal subunit. It binds near the 30S ribosomal interface and prevent the initiation complex from forming. Unlike other protein synthesis inhibitors oxazolidinones do not affect the binding of *N*-formyl Met-tRNA, elongation, or termination. Binding is inhibited weakly by chloramphenicol and clindamycin, but there does not appear to be cross-resistance with these agents. Resistance occurs due to mutations in the 23S subunit of the 50S ribosomal RNA.

ADME Linezolid has excellent oral bioavailability (>90%) and is also available in an intravenous formulation. The half-life is 5.5 h and protein binding is low (31%). After oral dosing of 400 or 625 mg three times daily, the mean plasma concentrations were 12.4 and 26.4 μg/mL, respectively with trough values of 4 μg/mL. Thirty percent of the drug is excreted unchanged in urine. The major metabolite is a ring-opened morphiline derivative that occurs via a hydroxylation on the carbon next to the oxygen in the morpholine ring. This reaction is not mediated by any known cytochrome P450 enzyme or flavin monooxygenase, but is formed by an NADPH-dependent enzyme.

Adverse Effects Linezolid has a good safety profile for short-term antibacterial regimens. In Phase III clinical trials, 60% of patients reported some "digestive event." Tongue discoloration was also reported by some patients. Headache and diarrhea that occurred in less than 10% of the patients were the other common adverse effects. Linezolid is a weak inhibitor of monoamine oxidase. Serotonin syndrome was reported in several postmarketing case reports with the following antidepressants, bupropion, citalopram, duloxetine, fluoxetine, mirtazapine, paroxetine, sertaline, and venlafaxine. Chronic use of linezolid (as would be necessary for treatment of MDR-TB) has not been well studied. The drug has been known to cause rare cases of thrombocytopenia, and periodic monitoring of platelets is recommended. In small clinical trials for MDR-TB, linezolid was not well tolerated with a number of cases of anemia/thrombocytopenia or peripheral neuropathy. Addition of 50–100 mg of vitamin B6 helps prevent the neuropathy. Half doses of linezolid have been used to lower the extent of side effects.

REFERENCES

1. World Health Organization. Global Tuberculosis Control: Surveillance, Planning, and Financing; WHO Report 2008; WHO Press: Geneva, Switzerland, 2008.

2. Donald PR, Diacon AH. The early bactericidal activity of anti-tuberculosis drugs: a literature review. Tuberculosis (Edinb) 2008;88(Suppl 1): S75–S83.

3. Matteelli A, et al. Multidrug-resistant and extensively drug-resistant *Mycobacterium tuberculosis*: epidemiology and control. Expert Rev Anti Infect Ther 2007:5(5): 857–871.

4. Chan ED, Iseman MD. Multidrug-resistant and extensively drug-resistant tuberculosis: a review. Curr Opin Infect Dis 2008;21(6): 587–595.

5. Kappelman J, et al. First Homo erectus from Turkey and implications for migrations into temperate Eurasia. Am J Phys Anthropol 2008;135(1): 110–116.

6. Hershkovitz I, et al. Detection and molecular characterization of 9,000-year-old Mycobacterium tuberculosis from a Neolithic settlement in the Eastern Mediterranean. PLoS One 2008;3 (10): pe3426.

7. Zink AR, et al. Characterization of *Mycobacterium tuberculosis* complex DNAs from Egyptian mummies by spoligotyping. J Clin Microbiol 2003;41(1): 359–367.

8. Zink AR, Grabner W, Nerlich AG.Molecular identification of human tuberculosis in recent and historic bone tissue samples: the role of molecular techniques for the study of historic tuberculosis. Am J Phys Anthropol 2005; 126(1): 32–47.

9. Sager P, Schalimtzer M, Moller-Christensen V. A case of spondylitis tuberculosa in the Danish Neolithic Age. Dan Med Bull 1972;19(5): 176–180.

10. Bryskier AC, Couturier C. Tuberculosis and its treatments over ages. Antibiotiques 2003;5(4): 233–239.

11. Salo, W.L., et al. Identification of *Mycobacterium tuberculosis* DNA in a pre-Columbian Peruvian mummy. Proc Natl Acad Sci USA 1994.91(6): 2091–2094.

12. Brosch, R., et al. A new evolutionary scenario for the *Mycobacterium tuberculosis* complex. Proc Natl Acad Sci USA 2002;99(6): 3684–3689.

13. Mostowy S, et al. Revisiting the evolution of *Mycobacterium bovis*. J Bacteriol 2005;187 (18): 6386–6395.

14. Minnikin DE, et al. Mycolic acid patterns of some species of *Mycobacterium*. Arch Microbiol 1984;139(2–3): 225–231.

15. Colombo RE, Olivier KN.Diagnosis and treatment of infections caused by rapidly growing mycobacteria. Semin Respir Crit Care Med 2008;29(5): 577–588.

16. Medical Section of the American Lung Association. Diagnosis and treatment of disease caused by nontuberculous mycobacteria. This official statement of the American Thoracic Society was approved by the Board of Directors, March 1997. Am J Respir Crit Care Med, 1997;156(2 Pt 2): S1–S25.

17. Hopewell PC, Pai M.Tuberculosis, vulnerability, and access to quality care. JAMA 2005;293 (22): 2790–2793.

18. Fenton MJ, Riley LW, Schlesinger LS. Receptor-mediated recognition of *Mycobacterium tuberculosis* by host cells. In: Cole ST, et al., editors. Tuberculosis and the Tubercle Bacillus. Washington, DC: ASM Press; 2005. p 405–426.

19. van Kooyk Y, Geijtenbeek TB.DC-SIGN: escape mechanism for pathogens. Nat Rev Immunol 2003;3(9): 697–709.

20. Russell DG. *Mycobacterium tuberculosis*: life and death in the phagosome. In: Kaufmann SH, Rubin E, editors. Handbook of Tuberculosis. Weinheim: Wiley; 2008. p. 307–322.

21. Davis JM, Ramakrishnan L.The role of the granuloma in expansion and dissemination of early tuberculous infection. Cell 2009;136(1): 37–49.

22. Dascher CC, Brenner MB.CD1 antigen presentation and infectious disease. Contrib Microbiol 2003;10:164–182.

23. Kursar M, et al. Cutting edge: regulatory T cells prevent efficient clearance of *Mycobacterium tuberculosis*. J Immunol 2007;178(5): 2661–2665.

24. Pan H, et al. *Ipr1* gene mediates innate immunity to tuberculosis. Nature 2005;434 (7034): 767–772.

25. Reed MB, et al. A glycolipid of hypervirulent tuberculosis strains that inhibits the innate immune response. Nature 2004;431(7004): 84–87.

26. Ottenhoff TH, et al. Control of human host immunity to mycobacteria. Tuberculosis (Edinb) 2005;85(1–2): 53–64.

27. Caws M, et al. The influence of host and bacterial genotype on the development of disseminated disease with *Mycobacterium tuberculosis*. PLoS Pathog 2008;4(3): pe1000034.

28. Tosh, K, et al. Variants in the *SP110* gene are associated with genetic susceptibility to tuberculosis in West Africa. Proc Natl Acad Sci USA, 2006.103(27): 10364–10368.

29. Li CM, et al. Association of a polymorphism in the *P2X7* gene with tuberculosis in a Gambian population. J Infect Dis 2002;186(10): 1458–1462.

30. Olesen R, et al. DC-SIGN (CD209), pentraxin 3 and vitamin D receptor gene variants associate with pulmonary tuberculosis risk in West Africans. Genes Immun 2007;8(6): 456–467.

31. Voskuil MI, et al. Inhibition of respiration by nitric oxide induces a *Mycobacterium tuberculosis* dormancy program. J Exp Med 2003;198 (5): 705–713.

32. Voskuil MI, Visconti KC, Schoolnik GK.*Mycobacterium tuberculosis* gene expression during adaptation to stationary phase and low-oxygen dormancy. Tuberculosis (Edinb) 2004;84(3–4): 218–227.

33. MacMicking JD, Taylor GA, McKinney JD.Immune control of tuberculosis by IFN-gamma-inducible LRG-47. Science 2003;302(5645): 654–659.

34. Gutierrez MG, et al. Autophagy is a defense mechanism inhibiting BCG and *Mycobacterium tuberculosis* survival in infected macrophages. Cell 2004;119(6): 753–766.

35. Alonso, S, et al. Lysosomal killing of Mycobacterium mediated by ubiquitin-derived peptides is enhanced by autophagy. Proc Natl Acad Sci USA 2007;104(14): 6031–6036.

36. Ulrichs T, et al. Differential organization of the local immune response in patients with active cavitary tuberculosis or with nonprogressive tuberculoma. J Infect Dis 2005;192 (1): 89–97.

37. Kaplan G, et al. *Mycobacterium tuberculosis* growth at the cavity surface: a microenvironment with failed immunity. Infect Immun 2003;71(12): 7099–7108.

38. Canetti G.Present aspects of bacterial resistance in tuberculosis. Am Rev Respir Dis 1965;92(5): 687–703.

39. Dannenberg AM Jr.Pathogenesis of pulmonary *Mycobacterium bovis* infection: basic principles established by the rabbit model. Tuberculosis (Edinb) 2001;81(1–2): 87–96.

40. Mitchison DA.The Garrod Lecture. Understanding the chemotherapy of tuberculosis—current problems. J Antimicrob Chemother 1992;29(5): 477–493.

41. Cole ST, et al. Deciphering the biology of *Mycobacterium tuberculosis* from the complete genome sequence. Nature 1998;393(6685): 537–544.

42. Bhowruth V, et al. Tuberculosis: a balanced diet of lipids and carbohydrates. Biochem Soc Trans 2008;36(Pt 4): 555–565.

43. Onwueme KC, et al. The dimycocerosate ester polyketide virulence factors of mycobacteria. Prog Lipid Res 2005;44(5): 259–302.

44. Gokhale RS, et al. Versatile polyketide enzymatic machinery for the biosynthesis of complex mycobacterial lipids. Nat Prod Rep 2007;24(2): 267–277.

45. Malaga W, et al. Deciphering the genetic bases of the structural diversity of phenolic glycolipids in strains of the *Mycobacterium tuberculosis* complex. J Biol Chem 2008;283(22): 15177–15184.

46. Goffin C, Ghuysen JM.Biochemistry and comparative genomics of SxxK superfamily acyltransferases offer a clue to the mycobacterial paradox: presence of penicillin-susceptible target proteins versus lack of efficiency of penicillin as therapeutic agent. Microbiol Mol Biol Rev 2002;66(4): 702–738.

47. Mainardi JL, et al. A novel peptidoglycan cross-linking enzyme for a beta-lactam-resistant transpeptidation pathway. J Biol Chem 2005;280 (46): 38146–36152.

48. Sassetti CM, Boyd DH, Rubin EJ.Genes required for mycobacterial growth defined by high density mutagenesis. Mol Microbiol 2003; 48(1): 77–84.

49. Lavollay M, et al. The peptidoglycan of stationary-phase *Mycobacterium tuberculosis* predominantly contains cross-links generated by L,D-transpeptidation. J Bacteriol 2008;190 (12): 4360–4366.

50. Jarlier V, Gutmann L, Nikaido H.Interplay of cell wall barrier and beta-lactamase activity determines high resistance to beta-lactam antibiotics in *Mycobacterium chelonae*. Antimicrob Agents Chemother 1991;35(9): 1937–1939.

51. Hugonnet JE, et al. Meropenem-clavulanate is effective against extensively drug-resistant *Mycobacterium tuberculosis*. Science 2009;323(5918): 1215–1218.

52. Alderwick LJ, et al. Identification of a novel arabinofuranosyltransferase (AftA) involved in cell wall arabinan biosynthesis in *Mycobacterium tuberculosis*. J Biol Chem 2006;281(23): 15653–15661.

53. Birch HL, et al. Biosynthesis of mycobacterial arabinogalactan: identification of a novel alpha(1 → 3)arabinofuranosyltransferase. Mol Microbiol 2008;69(5): 1191–1206.

54. Seidel M, et al. Identification of a novel arabinofuranosyltransferase AftB involved in a terminal step of cell wall arabinan biosynthesis in Corynebacteriaceae, such as *Corynebacterium glutamicum* and *Mycobacterium tuberculosis*. J Biol Chem 2007;282(20): 14729–14740.

55. Makarov V, et al. Benzothiazinones kill *Mycobacterium tuberculosis* by blocking arabinan synthesis. Science 2009;324(5928): 801–804.

56. Dykhuizen EC, et al. Inhibitors of UDP-galactopyranose mutase thwart mycobacterial growth. J Am Chem Soc 2008;130(21): 6706–6707.

57. Gruber TD, et al. X-ray crystallography reveals a reduced substrate complex of UDP-galactopyranose mutase poised for covalent catalysis by flavin. Biochemistry 2009;48(39): 9171–9173.

58. Li W, et al. *rmlB* and *rmlC* genes are essential for growth of mycobacteria. Biochem Biophys Res Commun 2006;342(1): 170–178.

59. Sivendran, S, et al. Identification of triazinoindol-benzimidazolones as nanomolar inhibitors of the *Mycobacterium tuberculosis* enzyme TDP-6-deoxy-d-xylo-4-hexopyranosid-4-ulose 3,5-epimerase (RmlC). Bioorg Med Chem Lett 2010:18(2): 896–908.

60. Brennan PJ, Nikaido H.The envelope of mycobacteria. Annu Rev Biochem 1995;64: 29–63.

61. Jarlier V, Nikaido H.Mycobacterial cell wall: structure and role in natural resistance to antibiotics. FEMS Microbiol Lett 1994;123 (1–2): 11–18.

62. Barry CE 3rd, Mdluli K.Drug sensitivity and environmental adaptation of mycobacterial cell wall components. Trends Microbiol 1996;4(7): 275–281.

63. Dubnau E, et al. Oxygenated mycolic acids are necessary for virulence of *Mycobacterium tuberculosis* in mice. Mol Microbiol 2000;36(3): 630–637.

64. Glickman MS, Cox JS, Jacobs WR Jr.A novel mycolic acid cyclopropane synthetase is required for cording, persistence, and virulence of *Mycobacterium tuberculosis*. Mol Cell 2000;5 (4): 717–727.

65. Daffe M, Draper P.The envelope layers of mycobacteria with reference to their pathogenicity. Adv Microb Physiol 1998;39:131–203.

66. Takayama K, Wang C, Besra GS.Pathway to synthesis and processing of mycolic acids in *Mycobacterium tuberculosis*. Clin Microbiol Rev 2005;18(1): 81–101.

67. Yuan Y, et al. The effect of oxygenated mycolic acid composition on cell wall function and macrophage growth in *Mycobacterium tuberculosis*. Mol Microbiol 1998;29(6): 1449–1458.

68. Barry CE, Crick DC, McNeil MR.Targeting the formation of the cell wall core of *M. tuberculosis*. Infect Disord Drug Targets 2007;7(2): 182–202.

69. Alahari A, et al. Thiacetazone, an antitubercular drug that inhibits cyclopropanation of cell wall mycolic acids in mycobacteria. PLoS One 2007;2(12): pe1343.

70. Barkan D, et al. Mycolic acid cyclopropanation is essential for viability, drug resistance, and cell wall integrity of *Mycobacterium tuberculosis*. Chem Biol 2009;16(5): 499–509.

71. Vaubourgeix J, et al. *S*-Adenosyl-*N*-decyl-aminoethyl, a potent bisubstrate inhibitor of *Mycobacterium tuberculosis* mycolic acid methyltransferases. J Biol Chem 2009;284 (29): 19321–19330.

72. Belisle JT, et al. Role of the major antigen of *Mycobacterium tuberculosis* in cell wall biogenesis. Science 1997;276(5317): 1420–1422.

73. Kovac, A, et al. New lipophilic phthalimido- and 3-phenoxybenzyl sulfonates: inhibition of antigen 85C mycolyltransferase activity and cytotoxicity. J Enzyme Inhib Med Chem, 2006,21(4): 391–397.

74. Bhatt, A, et al. The *Mycobacterium tuberculosis* FAS-II condensing enzymes: their role in mycolic acid biosynthesis, acid-fastness, pathogenesis and in future drug development. Mol Microbiol 2007;64(6): 1442–1454.

75. Brinster, S, et al. Type II fatty acid synthesis is not a suitable antibiotic target for Gram-positive pathogens. Nature, 2009;458(7234): 83–86.

76. Sullivan TJ, et al. High affinity InhA inhibitors with activity against drug-resistant strains of *Mycobacterium tuberculosis*. ACS Chem Biol 2006;1(1): 43–53.

77. Freundlich JS, et al. Triclosan derivatives: towards potent inhibitors of drug-sensitive and drug-resistant *Mycobacterium tuberculosis*. ChemMedChem 2009;4(2): 241–248.

78. Kim P, et al. Structure–activity relationships at the 5-position of thiolactomycin: an intact (5R)-isoprene unit is required for activity against the condensing enzymes from *Mycobacterium tuberculosis* and *Escherichia coli*. J Med Chem 2006;49(1): 159–171.

79. Luckner, SR, et al. Crystal structures of *Mycobacterium tuberculosis* KasA show mode of action within cell wall biosynthesis and its inhibition by thiolactomycin. Structure, 2009; 17(7): 1004–1013.

80. Machutta, CA, et al. Slow onset inhibition of bacterial {beta}-ketoacyl-ACP synthases by thiolactomycin. J Biol Chem 2010;285(9): 6161–6169.

81. Brown AK, et al. Platensimycin activity against mycobacterial beta-ketoacyl-ACP synthases. PLoS One 2009;4(7): pe6306.

82. Bhowruth V, Brown AK, Besra GS.Synthesis and biological evaluation of NAS-21 and NAS-91 analogues as potential inhibitors of the mycobacterial FAS-II dehydratase enzyme Rv0636. Microbiology 2008;154(Pt 7): 1866–1875.

83. Portevin D, et al. A polyketide synthase catalyzes the last condensation step of mycolic acid biosynthesis in mycobacteria and related organisms. Proc Natl Acad Sci USA 2004;101(1): 314–319.

84. Bhatt A, et al. Loss of a mycobacterial gene encoding a reductase leads to an altered cell wall containing beta-*oxo*-mycolic acid analogs and accumulation of ketones. Chem Biol 2008;15(9) 930–939.

85. Raman K, Rajagopalan P, Chandra N.Flux balance analysis of mycolic acid pathway: targets for anti-tubercular drugs. PLoS Comput Biol 2005;1(5): pe46.

86. Arora P, et al. Mechanistic and functional insights into fatty acid activation in *Mycobacterium tuberculosis*. Nat Chem Biol 2009;5(3): 166–173.

87. Leger M, et al. The dual function of the *Mycobacterium tuberculosis* FadD32 required for mycolic acid biosynthesis. Chem Biol 2009;16 (5): 510–519.

88. Lin TW, et al. Structure-based inhibitor design of AccD5, an essential acyl-CoA carboxylase carboxyltransferase domain of *Mycobacterium tuberculosis*. Proc Natl Acad Sci USA 2006;103 (9): 3072–3077.

89. Matsunaga I, et al. *Mycobacterium tuberculosis* pks12 produces a novel polyketide presented by CD1c to T cells. J Exp Med 2004;200(12): 1559–1569.

90. Constant P, et al. Role of the *pks15/1* gene in the biosynthesis of phenolglycolipids in the *Mycobacterium tuberculosis* complex. Evidence that all strains synthesize glycosylated *p*-hydroxybenzoic methyl esters and that strains devoid of phenolglycolipids harbor a frameshift mutation in the *pks15/1* gene. J Biol Chem 2002;277(41): 38148–38158.

91. Clatworthy AE, Pierson E, Hung DT. Targeting virulence: a new paradigm for antimicrobial therapy. Nat Chem Biol 2007;3(9): 541–548.

92. Ferreras JA, et al. Mycobacterial phenolic glycolipid virulence factor biosynthesis: mechanism and small-molecule inhibition of polyketide chain initiation. Chem Biol 2008;15(1): 51–61.

93. Song H, et al. Identification of outer membrane proteins of *Mycobacterium tuberculosis*. Tuberculosis (Edinb) 2008;88(6): 526–544.

94. Mdluli K, Ma Z. *Mycobacterium tuberculosis* DNA gyrase as a target for drug discovery. Infect Disord Drug Targets 2007;7(2): 159–168.

95. Aubry A, et al. *Mycobacterium tuberculosis* DNA gyrase: interaction with quinolones and correlation with antimycobacterial drug activity. Antimicrob Agents Chemother 2004;48(4): 1281–1288.

96. Tretter EM, et al. Crystal structure of the DNA gyrase GyrA N-terminal domain from *Mycobacterium tuberculosis*. Proteins 2010;78(2): 492–495.

97. Fu G, et al. Crystal structure of DNA gyrase B′ domain sheds lights on the mechanism for T-segment navigation. Nucleic Acids Res 2009;37(17): 5908–5916.

98. Gong C, et al. Biochemical and genetic analysis of the four DNA ligases of mycobacteria. J Biol Chem 2004;279(20): 20594–20606.

99. Srivastava SK, Tripathi RP, Ramachandran R. NAD+-dependent DNA Ligase (Rv3014c) from *Mycobacterium tuberculosis*. Crystal structure of the adenylation domain and identification of novel inhibitors. J Biol Chem 2005;280(34): 30273–30281.

100. Srivastava SK, et al. *Mycobacterium tuberculosis* NAD+-dependent DNA ligase is selectively inhibited by glycosylamines compared with human DNA ligase I. Nucleic Acids Res 2005;33(22): 7090–7101.

101. Srivastava SK, et al. NAD+-dependent DNA ligase (Rv3014c) from *Mycobacterium tuberculosis*: novel structure–function relationship and identification of a specific inhibitor. Proteins 2007;69(1): 97–111.

102. Fioravanti E, et al. The crystal structure of *Mycobacterium tuberculosis* thymidylate kinase in complex with 3′-azidodeoxythymidine monophosphate suggests a mechanism for competitive inhibition. Biochemistry 2005;44 (1): 130–137.

103. Van Daele I, et al. Rational design of 5′-thiourea-substituted alpha-thymidine analogues as thymidine monophosphate kinase inhibitors capable of inhibiting mycobacterial growth. J Med Chem 2007;50(22): 5281–5292.

104. Wnuk SF, Robins MJ. Ribonucleotide reductase inhibitors as anti-herpes agents. Antiviral Res 2006;71(2–3): 122–126.

105. Mowa MB, et al. Function and regulation of class I ribonucleotide reductase-encoding genes in mycobacteria. J Bacteriol 2009;191 (3): 985–995.

106. Liu A, et al. The tyrosyl free radical of recombinant ribonucleotide reductase from *Mycobacterium tuberculosis* is located in a rigid hydrophobic pocket. Biochemistry 1998;37 (46): 16369–16377.

107. Yang F, et al. Characterization of two genes encoding the *Mycobacterium tuberculosis* ribonucleotide reductase small subunit. J Bacteriol 1997;179(20): 6408–6415.

108. Uppsten M, et al. Crystal structure of the biologically active form of class Ib ribonucleotide reductase small subunit from *Mycobacterium tuberculosis*. FEBS Lett 2004;569(1–3): 117–122.

109. Hedstrom L. IMP dehydrogenase: structure, mechanism, and inhibition. Chem Rev 2009;109(7): 2903–2928.

110. Bruell CM, et al. Conservation of bacterial protein synthesis machinery: initiation and elongation in *Mycobacterium smegmatis*. Biochemistry 2008;47(34): 8828–8839.

111. Nakajima Y. Mechanisms of bacterial resistance to macrolide antibiotics. J Infect Chemother 1999;5(2): 61–74.

112. Zhu ZJ, et al. Structure–activity relationships of macrolides against *Mycobacterium tuberculosis*. Tuberculosis (Edinb) 2008;88(Suppl 1): S49–S63.

113. Falzari K, et al. *In vitro* and *in vivo* activities of macrolide derivatives against *Mycobacterium tuberculosis*. Antimicrob Agents Chemother 2005;49(4): 1447–1454.

114. Barbachyn MR, et al. Identification of a novel oxazolidinone (U-100480) with potent antimycobacterial activity. J Med Chem 1996;39(3): 680–685.

115. Wilson DN, et al. The oxazolidinone antibiotics perturb the ribosomal peptidyl-transferase center and effect tRNA positioning. Proc Natl Acad Sci USA 2008;105(36): 13339–13344.

116. Ippolito JA, et al. Crystal structure of the oxazolidinone antibiotic linezolid bound to the 50S ribosomal subunit. J Med Chem 2008;51 (12): 3353–3356.

117. Kim S, et al. Aminoacyl-tRNA synthetases and their inhibitors as a novel family of antibiotics. Appl Microbiol Biotechnol 2003;61(4): 278–288.

118. Sassanfar M, et al. A eubacterial *Mycobacterium tuberculosis* tRNA synthetase is eukaryote-like and resistant to a eubacterial-specific antisynthetase drug. Biochemistry 1996;35 (31): 9995–10003.

119. Ingvarsson H, Jones TA, Unge T. Crystallization of *Mycobacterium smegmatis* methionyl-tRNA synthetase in the presence of methionine and adenosine. Acta Crystallogr Sect F Struct Biol Cryst Commun 2009;65(Pt 6): 618–620.

120. Lee J, et al. Methionyl adenylate analogues as inhibitors of methionyl-tRNA synthetase. Bioorg Med Chem Lett 1999;9(10): 1365–1370.

121. Darwin KH, et al. The proteasome of *Mycobacterium tuberculosis* is required for resistance to nitric oxide. Science 2003;302(5652): 1963–1966.

122. Lupas A, Zwickl P, Baumeister W. Proteasome sequences in eubacteria. Trends Biochem Sci 1994;19(12): 533–534.

123. Lin G, et al. *Mycobacterium tuberculosis prcBA* genes encode a gated proteasome with broad oligopeptide specificity. Mol Microbiol 2006;59 (5): 1405–1416.

124. Pearce MJ, et al. Ubiquitin-like protein involved in the proteasome pathway of *Mycobacterium tuberculosis*. Science 2008;322(5904): 1104–1107.

125. Burns KE, et al. Proteasomal protein degradation in mycobacteria is dependent upon a prokaryotic ubiquitin-like protein. J Biol Chem 2009;284(5): 3069–3075.

126. Gandotra S, et al. *In vivo* gene silencing identifies the *Mycobacterium tuberculosis* proteasome as essential for the bacteria to persist in mice. Nat Med 2007;13(12): 1515–1520.

127. Lin G, et al. Distinct specificities of *Mycobacterium tuberculosis* and mammalian proteasomes for *N*-acetyl tripeptide substrates. J Biol Chem 2008;283(49): 34423–34431.

128. Lin G, et al. Inhibitors selective for mycobacterial versus human proteasomes. Nature 2009;461(7264): 621–626.

129. Parish, T, Stoker, NG. The common aromatic amino acid biosynthesis pathway is essential in *Mycobacterium tuberculosis*. Microbiology, 2002,148(Pt 10): 3069–3077.

130. Gokulan K, et al. Crystal structure of *Mycobacterium tuberculosis* diaminopimelate decarboxylase, an essential enzyme in bacterial lysine biosynthesis. J Biol Chem 2003;278(20): 18588–18596.

131. Hondalus MK, et al. Attenuation of and protection induced by a leucine auxotroph of *Mycobacterium tuberculosis*. Infect Immun 2000;68(5): 2888–2898.

132. Smith DA, et al. Characterization of auxotrophic mutants of *Mycobacterium tuberculosis* and their potential as vaccine candidates. Infect Immun 2001;69(2): 1142–1150.

133. de Carvalho LP, Blanchard JS. Kinetic and chemical mechanism of alpha-isopropylmalate synthase from *Mycobacterium tuberculosis*. Biochemistry 2006;45(29): 8988–8999.

134. Koon N, Squire CJ, Baker EN. Crystal structure of LeuA from *Mycobacterium tuberculosis*, a key enzyme in leucine biosynthesis. Proc Natl Acad Sci USA 2004;101(22): 8295–8300.

135. Kefala G, Perry LJ, Weiss MS. Cloning, expression, purificition, crystallization and preliminary X-ray diffraction analysis of LysA (Rv1293) from *Mycobacterium tuberculosis*. Acta Crystallogr Sect F Struct Biol Cryst Commun 2005;61(Pt 8): 782–784.

136. Lee CE, et al. The crystal structure of TrpD, a metabolic enzyme essential for lung colonization by *Mycobacterium tuberculosis*, in complex with its substrate phosphoribosyl-

pyrophosphate. J Mol Biol 2006;355(4): 784–797.

137. Cho Y, Sharma V, Sacchettini JC.Crystal structure of ATP phosphoribosyltransferase from *Mycobacterium tuberculosis*. J Biol Chem 2003;278(10): 8333–8339.

138. Cho Y, Ioerger TR, Sacchettini JC.Discovery of novel nitrobenzothiazole inhibitors for *Mycobacterium tuberculosis* ATP phosphoribosyl transferase (HisG) through virtual screening. J Med Chem 2008;51(19): 5984–5992.

139. Ducati RG, Basso LA, Santos DS.Mycobacterial shikimate pathway enzymes as targets for drug design. Curr Drug Targets 2007;8(3): 423–435.

140. Gerdes, SY et al. From genetic footprinting to antimicrobial drug targets: examples in cofactor biosynthetic pathways. J Bacteriol 2002;184(16): 4555–4572.

141. Morgunova E, et al. Crystal structure of lumazine synthase from *Mycobacterium tuberculosis* as a target for rational drug design: binding mode of a new class of purinetrione inhibitors. Biochemistry 2005;44(8): 2746–2758.

142. Zhao Y, et al. Discovery and development of the covalent hydrates of trifluoromethylated pyrazoles as riboflavin synthase inhibitors with antibiotic activity against *Mycobacterium tuberculosis*. J Org Chem 2009;74(15): 5297–5303.

143. Talukdar A, et al. Discovery and development of a small molecule library with lumazine synthase inhibitory activity. J Org Chem 2009;74(15): 5123–5134.

144. Webb ME, Smith AG, Abell C.Biosynthesis of pantothenate. Nat Prod Rep 2004;21(6): 695–721.

145. Sambandamurthy VK, et al. A pantothenate auxotroph of *Mycobacterium tuberculosis* is highly attenuated and protects mice against tuberculosis. Nat Med 2002;8(10): 1171–1174.

146. Velaparthi S, et al. 5-*tert*-Butyl-*N*-pyrazol-4-yl-4,5,6,7-tetrahydrobenzo[d]isoxazole-3-carboxamide derivatives as novel potent inhibitors of *Mycobacterium tuberculosis* pantothenate synthetase: initiating a quest for new antitubercular drugs. J Med Chem 2008;51 (7): 1999–2002.

147. Ciulli A, et al. Inhibition of *Mycobacterium tuberculosis* pantothenate synthetase by analogues of the reaction intermediate. Chembiochem 2008;9(16): 2606–2611.

148. White EL, et al. A novel inhibitor of *Mycobacterium tuberculosis* pantothenate synthetase. J Biomol Screen 2007;12(1): 100–105.

149. Shane B.Folylpolyglutamate synthesis and role in the regulation of one-carbon metabolism. Vitam Horm 1989;45:263–335.

150. White EL, et al. Cloning, expression, and characterization of *Mycobacterium tuberculosis* dihydrofolate reductase. FEMS Microbiol Lett 2004;232(1): 101–105.

151. Forgacs P, et al. Tuberculosis and trimethoprim-sulfamethoxazole. Antimicrob Agents Chemother 2009;53(11): 4789–4793.

152. Baca AM, et al. Crystal structure of *Mycobacterium tuberculosis* 7,8-dihydropteroate synthase in complex with pterin monophosphate: new insight into the enzymatic mechanism and sulfa-drug action. J Mol Biol 2000;302(5): 1193–1212.

153. Li R, et al. Three-dimensional structure of M.tuberculosis dihydrofolate reductase reveals opportunities for the design of novel tuberculosis drugs. J Mol Biol 2000;295(2): 307–323.

154. Gengenbacher M, et al. Biochemical and structural characterization of the putative dihydropteroate synthase ortholog Rv1207 of *Mycobacterium tuberculosis*. FEMS Microbiol Lett 2008;287(1): 128–135.

155. Argyrou A, et al. *Mycobacterium tuberculosis* dihydrofolate reductase is a target for isoniazid. Nat Struct Mol Biol 2006;13(5): 408–413.

156. Dakshinamurti K, Chauhan J.Biotin. Vitam Horm 1989;45:337–384.

157. Lévy-Schil S, et al. Biotin biosynthetic pathway in recombinant strains of *Escherichia coli* overexpressing bio genes: evidence for a limiting step upstream of KAPA. Appl Microbiol Biotechnol 1993;38:755–762.

158. Mann S, Ploux O.7,8-Diaminoperlargonic acid aminotransferase from *Mycobacterium tuberculosis*, a potential therapeutic target. Characterization and inhibition studies. FEBS J 2006;273(20): 4778–4789.

159. Sandmark J, et al. Structural basis for the inhibition of the biosynthesis of biotin by the antibiotic amiclenomycin. J Biol Chem 2002;277(45): 43352–43358.

160. Lotierzo M, et al. Biotin synthase mechanism: an overview. Biochem Soc Trans 2005;33(Pt 4): 820–823.

161. Dhiman RK, et al. Menaquinone synthesis is critical for maintaining mycobacterial viability during exponential growth and recovery from non-replicating persistence. Mol Microbiol 2009;72(1): 85–97.

162. Kurosu M, et al. Discovery of 1,4-dihydroxy-2-naphthoate prenyltransferase inhibitors: new

drug leads for multidrug-resistant gram-positive pathogens. J Med Chem 2007;50(17): 3973–3975.

163. Lu X, et al. Mechanism-based inhibitors of MenE, an acyl-CoA synthetase involved in bacterial menaquinone biosynthesis. Bioorg Med Chem Lett 2008;18(22): 5963–5966.

164. Truglio JJ, et al. Crystal structure of *Mycobacterium tuberculosis* MenB, a key enzyme in vitamin K2 biosynthesis. J Biol Chem 2003;278(43): 42352–42360.

165. Parsons JF, Shi KM, Ladner JE. Structure of isochorismate synthase in complex with magnesium. Acta Crystallogr D Biol Crystallogr 2008;64(Pt 5): 607–610.

166. Kozlowski MC, et al. Chorismate-utilizing enzymes isochorismate synthase, anthranilate synthase, and *p*-aminobenzoate synthase: mechanistic insight through inhibitor design. J Am Chem Soc 1995;117:2128–2140.

167. Boshoff HI, et al. Biosynthesis and recycling of nicotinamide cofactors in *Mycobacterium tuberculosis*. An essential role for NAD in nonreplicating bacilli. J Biol Chem 2008;283(28): 19329–19341.

168. Sorci L, et al. Targeting NAD biosynthesis in bacterial pathogens: structure-based development of inhibitors of nicotinate mononucleotide adenylyltransferase NadD. Chem Biol 2009;16(8): 849–861.

169. Bellinzoni M, et al. Heterologous expression, purification, and enzymatic activity of *Mycobacterium tuberculosis* NAD(+) synthetase. Protein Exp Purif 2002;25(3): 547–557.

170. LaRonde-LeBlanc N, Resto M, Gerratana B. Regulation of active site coupling in glutamine-dependent NAD(+) synthetase. Nat Struct Mol Biol 2009;16(4): 421–429.

171. Velu SE, et al. Tethered dimers as NAD synthetase inhibitors with antibacterial activity. J Med Chem 2003;46(15): 3371–3381.

172. Andries K, et al. A diarylquinoline drug active on the ATP synthase of *Mycobacterium tuberculosis*. Science 2005;307(5707): 223–227.

173. Koul A, et al. Diarylquinolines target subunit c of mycobacterial ATP synthase. Nat Chem Biol 2007;3(6): 323–324.

174. Rao SP, et al. The protonmotive force is required for maintaining ATP homeostasis and viability of hypoxic, nonreplicating *Mycobacterium tuberculosis*. Proc Natl Acad Sci USA 2008;105(33): 11945–11950.

175. Ouellet H, Johnston JB, Ortiz de Montellano PR. The *Mycobacterium tuberculosis* cytochrome P450 system. Arch Biochem Biophys 2010;493(1): 82–95.

176. Van der Geize R, et al. A gene cluster encoding cholesterol catabolism in a soil actinomycete provides insight into *Mycobacterium tuberculosis* survival in macrophages. Proc Natl Acad Sci USA 2007;104(6): 1947–1952.

177. McLean KJ, et al. Characterization of active site structure in CYP121. A cytochrome P450 essential for viability of *Mycobacterium tuberculosis* H37Rv. J Biol Chem 2008;283(48): 33406–33416.

178. Aguero F, et al. Genomic-scale prioritization of drug targets: the TDR Targets database. Nat Rev Drug Discov 2008;7(11): 900–907.

179. McLean KJ, et al. The structure of *Mycobacterium tuberculosis* CYP125: molecular basis for cholesterol binding in a P450 needed for host infection. J Biol Chem 2009;284(51): 35524–35533.

180. Tian J, et al. Variant tricarboxylic acid cycle in *Mycobacterium tuberculosis*: identification of alpha-ketoglutarate decarboxylase. Proc Natl Acad Sci USA 2005;102(30): 10670–10675.

181. Bryk R, et al. Metabolic enzymes of mycobacteria linked to antioxidant defense by a thioredoxin-like protein. Science 2002;295(5557): 1073–1077.

182. Miesel L, et al. NADH dehydrogenase defects confer isoniazid resistance and conditional lethality in *Mycobacterium smegmatis*. J Bacteriol 1998;180(9): 2459–2467.

183. Kana BD, et al. Characterization of the cydAB-encoded cytochrome bd oxidase from *Mycobacterium smegmatis*. J Bacteriol 2001;183(24): 7076–7086.

184. Matsoso LG, et al. Function of the cytochrome bc1-aa3 branch of the respiratory network in mycobacteria and network adaptation occurring in response to its disruption. J Bacteriol 2005;187(18): 6300–6308.

185. Sohaskey CD, Wayne LG. Role of narK2X and narGHJI in hypoxic upregulation of nitrate reduction by *Mycobacterium tuberculosis*. J Bacteriol 2003;185(24): 7247–7256.

186. Boshoff HI, et al. The transcriptional responses of *Mycobacterium tuberculosis* to inhibitors of metabolism: novel insights into drug mechanisms of action. J Biol Chem 2004;279(38): 40174–40184.

187. Wayne LG, Hayes LG. Nitrate reduction as a marker for hypoxic shiftdown of *Mycobacterium tuberculosis*. Tuberc Lung Dis 1998;79(2): 127–132.

188. Koul A, et al. Diarylquinolines are bactericidal for dormant mycobacteria as a result of disturbed ATP homeostasis. J Biol Chem 2008; 283(37): 25273–25280.

189. Via LE, et al. Tuberculous granulomas are hypoxic in guinea pigs, rabbits, and nonhuman primates. Infect Immun 2008;76(6): 2333–2340.

190. Raynaud C, et al. Phospholipases C are involved in the virulence of Mycobacterium tuberculosis. Mol Microbiol 2002;45(1): 203–217.

191. Viana-Niero C, et al. Analysis of genetic polymorphisms affecting the four phospholipase C (plc) genes in Mycobacterium tuberculosis complex clinical isolates. Microbiology 2004;150(Pt 4): 967–978.

192. Lamichhane G, et al. A postgenomic method for predicting essential genes at subsaturation levels of mutagenesis: application to Mycobacterium tuberculosis. Proc Natl Acad Sci USA 2003;100(12): 7213–7218.

193. Sassetti CM, Rubin EJ. Genetic requirements for mycobacterial survival during infection. Proc Natl Acad Sci USA 2003;100(22): 12989–12994.

194. McKinney JD, et al. Persistence of Mycobacterium tuberculosis in macrophages and mice requires the glyoxylate shunt enzyme isocitrate lyase. Nature 2000;406(6797): 735–738.

195. Munoz-Elias EJ, McKinney JD. Mycobacterium tuberculosis isocitrate lyases 1 and 2 are jointly required for in vivo growth and virulence. Nat Med 2005;11(6): 638–644.

196. Sharma V, et al. Structure of isocitrate lyase, a persistence factor of Mycobacterium tuberculosis. Nat Struct Biol 2000;7(8): 663–668.

197. Gould TA, et al. Dual role of isocitrate lyase 1 in the glyoxylate and methylcitrate cycles in Mycobacterium tuberculosis. Mol Microbiol 2006;61(4): 940–947.

198. Quadri LE, et al. Identification of a Mycobacterium tuberculosis gene cluster encoding the biosynthetic enzymes for assembly of the virulence-conferring siderophore mycobactin. Chem Biol 1998;5(11): 631–645.

199. Gobin J, Horwitz MA. Exochelins of Mycobacterium tuberculosis remove iron from human iron-binding proteins and donate iron to mycobactins in the M. tuberculosis cell wall. J Exp Med 1996;183(4): 1527–1532.

200. De Voss JJ, et al. The salicylate-derived mycobactin siderophores of Mycobacterium tuberculosis are essential for growth in macrophages. Proc Natl Acad Sci USA 2000;97(3): 1252–1257.

201. Ratledge C. Iron, mycobacteria and tuberculosis. Tuberculosis (Edinb) 2004;84(1–2): 110–130.

202. Luo M, Fadeev EA, Groves JT. Mycobactin-mediated iron acquisition within macrophages. Nat Chem Biol 2005;1(3): 149–153.

203. Ferreras JA, et al. Small-molecule inhibition of siderophore biosynthesis in Mycobacterium tuberculosis and Yersinia pestis. Nat Chem Biol 2005;1(1): 29–32.

204. Somu RV, et al. Rationally designed nucleoside antibiotics that inhibit siderophore biosynthesis of Mycobacterium tuberculosis. J Med Chem 2006;49(1): 31–34.

205. Rodriguez GM, Smith I. Mechanisms of iron regulation in mycobacteria: role in physiology and virulence. Mol Microbiol 2003;47(6): 1485–1494.

206. Rodriguez GM. Control of iron metabolism in Mycobacterium tuberculosis. Trends Microbiol 2006; 320–327.

207. Newton GL, Buchmeier N, Fahey RC. Biosynthesis and functions of mycothiol, the unique protective thiol of actinobacteria. Microbiol Mol Biol Rev 2008;72(3): 471–494.

208. Hu Y, et al. Identification of selective inhibitors for the glycosyltransferase MurG via high-throughput screening. Chem Biol 2004;11(5): 703–711.

209. Vetting MW, Frantom PA, Blanchard JS. Structural and enzymatic analysis of MshA from Corynebacterium glutamicum: substrate-assisted catalysis. J Biol Chem 2008;283(23): 15834–15844.

210. Fan F, et al. Steady-state and pre-steady-state kinetic analysis of Mycobacterium smegmatis cysteine ligase (MshC). Biochemistry 2007;46 (40): 11421–11429.

211. Tremblay LW, et al. The 1.6 A crystal structure of Mycobacterium smegmatis MshC: the penultimate enzyme in the mycothiol biosynthetic pathway. Biochemistry 2008;47(50): 13326–13335.

212. Fahey RC, et al. Inhibitors of MshC and homologs thereof, and methods of identifying same, WIPO. 2008. International Application Number PCT/US2007/013558. 2007 Jul 6.

213. Sareen D, et al. Mycothiol is essential for growth of Mycobacterium tuberculosis Erdman. J Bacteriol 2003;185(22): 6736–6740.

214. Vilcheze C, et al. Mycothiol biosynthesis is essential for ethionamide susceptibility in Mycobacterium tuberculosis. Mol Microbiol 2008;69(5): 1316–1329.

215. Eoh H, Brennan PJ, Crick DC.The *Mycobacterium tuberculosis* MEP (2*C*-methyl-d-erythritol 4-phosphate) pathway as a new drug target. Tuberculosis (Edinb) 2009;89(1): 1–11.

216. Mann FM, et al. Edaxadiene: a new bioactive diterpene from *Mycobacterium tuberculosis*. J Am Chem Soc 2009;131(48): 17526–17527.

217. Munos JW, et al. A secondary kinetic isotope effect study of the 1-deoxy-D-xylulose-5-phosphate reductoisomerase-catalyzed reaction: evidence for a retroaldol-aldol rearrangement. J Am Chem Soc 2009;131(6): 2048–2049.

218. Henriksson LM, et al. Structures of *Mycobacterium tuberculosis* 1-deoxy-D-xylulose-5-phosphate reductoisomerase provide new insights into catalysis. J Biol Chem 2007;282(27): 19905–19916.

219. Brown AC, Parish T.Dxr is essential in *Mycobacterium tuberculosis* and fosmidomycin resistance is due to a lack of uptake. BMC Microbiol 2008;8:78.

220. Deng L, et al. Coordination chemistry based approach to lipophilic inhibitors of 1-deoxy-D-xylulose-5-phosphate reductoisomerase. J Med Chem 2009;52(21): 6539–6542.

221. Shires K, Steyn L.The cold-shock stress response in *Mycobacterium smegmatis* induces the expression of a histone-like protein. Mol Microbiol 2001;39(4): 994–1009.

222. Vannelli TA, Dykman A, Ortiz de Montellano PR.The antituberculosis drug ethionamide is activated by a flavoprotein monooxygenase. J Biol Chem 2002;277(15): 12824–12829.

223. Manganelli R, et al. Differential expression of 10 sigma factor genes in *Mycobacterium tuberculosis*. Mol Microbiol 1999;31(2): 715–724.

224. Stewart GR, et al. Dissection of the heat-shock response in *Mycobacterium tuberculosis* using mutants and microarrays. Microbiology 2002;148(Pt 10): 3129–3138.

225. Park HD, et al. Rv3133c/dosR is a transcription factor that mediates the hypoxic response of *Mycobacterium tuberculosis*. Mol Microbiol 2003;48(3): 833–843.

226. Canneva F, et al. Rv2358 and FurB: two transcriptional regulators from *Mycobacterium tuberculosis* which respond to zinc. J Bacteriol 2005;187(16): 5837–5840.

227. Manganelli R, et al. Role of the extracytoplasmic-function sigma factor sigma(H) in *Mycobacterium tuberculosis* global gene expression. Mol Microbiol 2002;45(2): 365–374.

228. Manganelli R, et al. The *Mycobacterium tuberculosis* ECF sigma factor sigmaE: role in global gene expression and survival in macrophages. Mol Microbiol 2001;41(2): 423–437.

229. Sala C, et al. *Mycobacterium tuberculosis* FurA autoregulates its own expression. J Bacteriol 2003;185(18): 5357–5362.

230. Manganelli R, et al. The extra cytoplasmic function sigma factor sigma(E) is essential for *Mycobacterium tuberculosis* virulence in mice. Infect Immun 2004;72(5): 3038–3041.

231. Steyn AJ, et al. *Mycobacterium tuberculosis* WhiB3 interacts with RpoV to affect host survival but is dispensable for *in vivo* growth. Proc Natl Acad Sci USA 2002;99(5): 3147–3152.

232. Rodrigue S, et al. The sigma factors of *Mycobacterium tuberculosis*. FEMS Microbiol Rev 2006;30(6): 926–941.

233. Beaucher J, et al. Novel *Mycobacterium tuberculosis* anti-sigma factor antagonists control sigmaF activity by distinct mechanisms. Mol Microbiol 2002;45(6): 1527–1540.

234. Av-Gay Y, Everett M.The eukaryotic-like Ser/Thr protein kinases of *Mycobacterium tuberculosis*. Trends Microbiol 2000;8(5): 238–244.

235. Wehenkel A, et al. Mycobacterial Ser/Thr protein kinases and phosphatases: physiological roles and therapeutic potential. Biochim Biophys Acta 2008;1784(1): 193–202.

236. Kumar A, et al. *Mycobacterium tuberculosis* DosS is a redox sensor and DosT is a hypoxia sensor. Proc Natl Acad Sci USA 2007;104(28): 11568–11573.

237. Ludwiczak P, et al. *Mycobacterium tuberculosis* phoP mutant: lipoarabinomannan molecular structure. Microbiology 2002;148(Pt 10): 3029–3037.

238. Chesne-Seck ML, et al. A point mutation in the two-component regulator PhoP-PhoR accounts for the absence of polyketide-derived acyltrehaloses but not that of phthiocerol dimycocerosates in *Mycobacterium tuberculosis* H37Ra. J Bacteriol 2008;190(4): 1329–1334.

239. Frigui W, et al. Control of *M. tuberculosis* ESAT-6 secretion and specific T cell recognition by PhoP. PLoS Pathog 2008;4(2): p e33.

240. Gonzalo-Asensio J, et al. PhoP: a missing piece in the intricate puzzle of *Mycobacterium tuberculosis* virulence. PLoS One 2008;3(10): e3496.

241. Ryndak M, Wang S, Smith I.PhoP, a key player in *Mycobacterium tuberculosis* virulence. Trends Microbiol 2008;16(11): 528–534.

242. Lee JS, et al. Mutation in the transcriptional regulator PhoP contributes to avirulence of *Mycobacterium tuberculosis* H37Ra strain. Cell Host Microbe 2008;3(2): 97–103.

243. Perez E, et al. An essential role for phoP in *Mycobacterium tuberculosis* virulence. Mol Microbiol 2001;41(1): 179–187.

244. Parikh A, et al. PknB-mediated phosphorylation of a novel substrate, *N*-acetylglucosamine-1-phosphate uridyltransferase, modulates its acetyltransferase activity. J Mol Biol 2009;386 (2): 451–464.

245. Thakur M, Chakraborti PK.Ability of PknA, a mycobacterial eukaryotic-type serine/threonine kinase, to transphosphorylate MurD, a ligase involved in the process of peptidoglycan biosynthesis. Biochem J 2008;415(1): 27–33.

246. Dasgupta A, et al. The serine/threonine kinase PknB of *Mycobacterium tuberculosis* phosphorylates PBPA, a penicillin-binding protein required for cell division. Microbiology 2006;152(Pt 2): 493–504.

247. Veyron-Churlet R, et al. The *Mycobacterium tuberculosis* beta-ketoacyl-acyl carrier protein synthase III activity is inhibited by phosphorylation on a single threonine residue. J Biol Chem 2009;284(10): 6414–6424.

248. Drews SJ, Hung F, Av-Gay Y.A protein kinase inhibitor as an antimycobacterial agent. FEMS Microbiol Lett 2001;205(2): 369–374.

249. Szekely R, et al. A novel drug discovery concept for tuberculosis: inhibition of bacterial and host cell signalling. Immunol Lett 2008;116 (2): 225–231.

250. Zhang Y.Persistent and dormant tubercle bacilli and latent tuberculosis. Front Biosci 2004;9:1136–1156.

251. Zhang Y, Post-Martens K, Denkin S.New drug candidates and therapeutic targets for tuberculosis therapy. Drug Discov Today 2006;11 (1–2): 21–27.

252. Xie Z, Siddiqi N, Rubin EJ.Differential antibiotic susceptibilities of starved *Mycobacterium tuberculosis* isolates. Antimicrob Agents Chemother 2005;49(11): 4778–4780.

253. Bryk R, et al. Selective killing of nonreplicating mycobacteria. Cell Host Microbe 2008;3(3): 137–145.

254. Schnappinger D, et al. Transcriptional Adaptation of *Mycobacterium tuberculosis* within macrophages: insights into the phagosomal environment. J Exp Med 2003;198(5): 693–704.

255. Lewis K.Multidrug tolerance of biofilms and persister cells. Curr Top Microbiol Immunol 2008;322:107–131.

256. Hayes F.Toxins–antitoxins: plasmid maintenance, programmed cell death, and cell cycle arrest. Science 2003;301(5639): 1496–1499.

257. Gerdes K, Christensen SK, Lobner-Olesen A. Prokaryotic toxin–antitoxin stress response loci. Nat Rev Microbiol 2005;3(5): 371–382.

258. Pandey DP, Gerdes K.Toxin–antitoxin loci are highly abundant in free-living but lost from host-associated prokaryotes. Nucleic Acids Res 2005;33(3): 966–976.

259. Keren I, et al. Specialized persister cells and the mechanism of multidrug tolerance in *Escherichia coli*. J Bacteriol 2004;186(24): 8172–8180.

260. Shah D, et al. Persisters: a distinct physiological state of *E. coli*. BMC Microbiol 2006;6:53.

261. Smith PA, Romesberg FE.Combating bacteria and drug resistance by inhibiting mechanisms of persistence and adaptation. Nat Chem Biol 2007;3(9): 549–556.

262. Zhang Y, Jacobs WRJ. Mechanisms of drug action, drug resistance, and drug tolerance in *Mycobacterium tuberculosis*: expected phenotypes from evolutionary pressures from a highly successful pathogen. In: Kaufmann SH, Rubin E, editors. Handbook of Tuberculosis. Weinheim: Wiley-VCH; 2008. p. 323–378.

263. Pasca MR, et al. Rv2686c-Rv2687c-Rv2688c, an ABC fluoroquinolone efflux pump in *Mycobacterium tuberculosis*. Antimicrob Agents Chemother 2004;48(8): 3175–3178.

264. Takiff HE, et al. Efflux pump of the proton antiporter family confers low-level fluoroquinolone resistance in *Mycobacterium smegmatis*. Proc Natl Acad Sci USA 1996;93(1): 362–366.

265. Ainsa JA, et al. Molecular cloning and characterization of Tap, a putative multidrug efflux pump present in *Mycobacterium fortuitum* and *Mycobacterium tuberculosis*. J Bacteriol 1998;180(22): 5836–5843.

266. Wang F, Cassidy C, Sacchettini JC.Crystal structure and activity studies of the *Mycobacterium tuberculosis* beta-lactamase reveal its critical role in resistance to beta-lactam antibiotics. Antimicrob Agents Chemother 2006;50(8): 2762–2771.

267. Buriankova K, et al. Molecular basis of intrinsic macrolide resistance in the *Mycobacterium tuberculosis* complex. Antimicrob Agents Chemother 2004;48(1): 143–150.

268. Vilcheze C, Jacobs WR Jr.The mechanism of isoniazid killing: clarity through the scope of genetics. Annu Rev Microbiol 2007;61: 35–50.

269. Dover LG, et al. EthA, a common activator of thiocarbamide-containing drugs acting on different mycobacterial targets. Antimicrob Agents Chemother 2007;51(3): 1055–1063.

270. Zhang H, et al. Characterization of *Mycobacterium tuberculosis* nicotinamidase/pyrazinamidase. FEBS J 2008;275(4): 753–762.

271. Singh R, et al. PA-824 kills nonreplicating *Mycobacterium tuberculosis* by intracellular NO release. Science 2008;322(5906): 1392–1395.

272. Ramaswamy S, Musser JM.Molecular genetic basis of antimicrobial agent resistance in *Mycobacterium tuberculosis*: 1998 update. Tuberc Lung Dis 1998;79(1): 3–29.

273. Zhang Y, Mitchison D.The curious characteristics of pyrazinamide: a review. Int J Tuberc Lung Dis 2003;7(1): 6–21.

274. Ebrahimi-Rad M, et al. Mutations in putative mutator genes of *Mycobacterium tuberculosis* strains of the W-Beijing family. Emerg Infect Dis 2003;9(7): 838–845.

275. Lari N, et al. Mutations in *mutT* genes of *Mycobacterium tuberculosis* isolates of Beijing genotype. J Med Microbiol 2006;55(Pt 5): 599–603.

276. Olano J, et al. Mutations in DNA repair genes are associated with the Haarlem lineage of *Mycobacterium tuberculosis* independently of their antibiotic resistance. Tuberculosis (Edinb) 2007;87(6): 502–508.

277. Werngren J, Hoffner SE.Drug-susceptible *Mycobacterium tuberculosis* Beijing genotype does not develop mutation-conferred resistance to rifampin at an elevated rate. J Clin Microbiol 2003;41(4): 1520–1524.

278. Tsenova L, et al. Virulence of selected *Mycobacterium tuberculosis* clinical isolates in the rabbit model of meningitis is dependent on phenolic glycolipid produced by the bacilli. J Infect Dis 2005;192(1): 98–106.

279. Chambers HF, et al. Can penicillins and other beta-lactam antibiotics be used to treat tuberculosis? Antimicrob. Agents Chemother 1995;39(12): 2620–2624.

280. Joshi SM, et al. Characterization of mycobacterial virulence genes through genetic interaction mapping. Proc Natl Acad Sci USA 2006;103(31): 11760–11765.

281. Pandey AK, Sassetti CM.Mycobacterial persistence requires the utilization of host cholesterol. Proc Natl Acad Sci USA 2008;105(11): 4376–4380.

282. Hirsh AE, et al. Stable association between strains of *Mycobacterium tuberculosis* and their human host populations. Proc Natl Acad Sci USA 2004;101(14): 4871–4876.

283. Tsolaki AG, et al. Genomic deletions classify the Beijing/W strains as a distinct genetic lineage of *Mycobacterium tuberculosis*. J Clin Microbiol 2005;43(7): 3185–3191.

284. Tsolaki AG, et al. Functional and evolutionary genomics of *Mycobacterium tuberculosis*: insights from genomic deletions in 100 strains. Proc Natl Acad Sci USA 2004;101(14): 4865–4870.

285. Voskuil MI.*Mycobacterium tuberculosis* gene expression during environmental conditions associated with latency. Tuberculosis (Edinb) 2004;84(3–4): 138–143.

286. Hasan S, et al. Prioritizing genomic drug targets in pathogens: application to *Mycobacterium tuberculosis*. PLoS Comput Biol 2006;2(6): pe61.

287. Raman K, Chandra N.*Mycobacterium tuberculosis* interactome analysis unravels potential pathways to drug resistance. BMC Microbiol 2008;8:234.

288. Raman K, Yeturu K, Chandra N.TargetTB: a target identification pipeline for *Mycobacterium tuberculosis* through an interactome, reactome and genome-scale structural analysis. BMC Syst Biol 2008;2:109.

289. Khan A, Sarkar D.A simple whole cell based high throughput screening protocol using *Mycobacterium bovis* BCG for inhibitors against dormant and active tubercle bacilli. J Microbiol Methods 2008;73(1): 62–68.

290. Cho SH, et al. Low-oxygen-recovery assay for high-throughput screening of compounds against nonreplicating *Mycobacterium tuberculosis*. Antimicrob Agents Chemother 2007;51(4): 1380–1385.

291. Wang J, et al. Platensimycin is a selective FabF inhibitor with potent antibiotic properties. Nature 2006;441(7091): 358–361.

292. Wilkinson B, Micklefield J.Mining and engineering natural-product biosynthetic pathways. Nat Chem Biol 2007;3(7): 379–386.

293. Ehrt S, et al. Controlling gene expression in mycobacteria with anhydrotetracycline and Tet repressor. Nucleic Acids Res 2005;33(2): pe21.

294. Capuano SV 3rd, et al. Experimental *Mycobacterium tuberculosis* infection of cynomolgus

macaques closely resembles the various manifestations of human *M. tuberculosis* infection. Infect Immun 2003;71(10): 5831–5844.

295. McMurray DN, et al. Pathogenesis of experimental tuberculosis in animal models. Curr Top Microbiol Immunol 1996;215:157–179.

296. MacMicking JD, et al. Identification of nitric oxide synthase as a protective locus against tuberculosis. Proc Natl Acad Sci USA 1997;94 (10): 5243–5248.

297. Flynn JL, et al. Effects of aminoguanidine on latent murine tuberculosis. J Immunol 1998;160(4): 1796–1803.

298. Fuller CL, Flynn JL, Reinhart TA.*In situ* study of abundant expression of proinflammatory chemokines and cytokines in pulmonary granulomas that develop in cynomolgus macaques experimentally infected with *Mycobacterium tuberculosis*. Infect Immun 2003;71(12): 7023–7034.

299. Langermans JA, et al. Divergent effect of bacillus Calmette-Guerin (BCG) vaccination on *Mycobacterium tuberculosis* infection in highly related macaque species: implications for primate models in tuberculosis vaccine research. Proc Natl Acad Sci USA 2001;98(20): 11497–11502.

300. Walsh GP, et al. The Philippine cynomolgus monkey (*Macaca fasicularis*) provides a new nonhuman primate model of tuberculosis that resembles human disease. Nat Med 1996;2(4): 430–436.

301. Nikonenko BV, et al. Preclinical study of new TB drugs and drug combinations in mouse models. Recent Pat Antiinfect Drug Discov 2008;3(2): 102–116.

302. Walzl G, et al. Biomarkers for TB treatment response: challenges and future strategies. J Infect 2008;57(2): 103–109.

303. Domagk G, et al. Über eine neue, gegen Tuberkelbazillen *in vitro* wirksame Verbindungsklasse. Naturwissenschaften 1946;33:315.

304. Chorine V.Action of nicotinamide on bacilli of the species *Mycobacterium*. C R Acad Sci 1945;220:150–151.

305. Fox HH.Synthetic tuberculostats. III. Isonicotinaldehyde thiosemicarbazone and some related compounds. 1952;17:555–562.

306. Fox HH, Gibas JT.Synthetic tuberculostats. IV. Pyridine carboxylic acid hydrazides and benzoic acid hydrazides. J Org Chem 1952;17:1653–1660.

307. Fox HH.The chemical approach to the control of tuberculosis. Science 1952;116(3006): 129–134.

308. Meyer H, Mally J.Hydrazine derivatives of pyridine-carboxylic acids. Monatshefte für Chemie und verwandte teile anderer Wissenschaften 1912;33:393–414.

309. Fox HH.The chemical attack on tuberculosis. Trans N Y Acad Sci 1953;15:234–242.

310. Fox HH, Gibas JT.Synthetic tuberculostats. VII. Monoalkyl derivatives of isonicotinylhydrazine. J Org Chem 1953;18:994–1002.

311. Zeller EA, et al. Experientia 1952;8:349.

312. Zeller EA, Barsky J.*In vivo* inhibition of liver and brain monoamine oxidase by 1-Isonicotinyl-2-isopropyl hydrazine. Proc Soc Exp Biol Med 1952;81(2): 459–461.

313. Kakimoto S, Tone I.Antituberculous compounds. 23. Alkyl- and acylisonicotinic acid hydrazides. J Med Chem 1965;8(6): 868.

314. Fox HH, Gibas JT.Synthetic tuberculostats. VIII. Acyl derivatives of isonicotinyl hydrazine. J Org Chem 1952;18:1375–1379.

315. Rubbo SD, et al. Chemotherapy of tuberculosis. III. Verazide in the treatment of pulmonary tuberculosis. Am Rev Tuberc 1958;78(2): 251–258.

316. Rubbo SD, Vaughan G.Chemotherapy of tuberculosis. II. Some observations on the pharmacology of verazide. Am Rev Tuberc 1957;76 (3): 346–359.

317. Rubbo SD, Edgar J, Vaughan G.Chemotherapy of tuberculosis. I. Antituberculous activity of verazide and related hydrazones. Am Rev Tuberc 1957;76(3): 331–345.

318. Stepanian ES.Comparative data on the tolerance of phthivazid, methazid and tubazid in patients with pulmonary tuberculosis. Vrach Delo 1965;10:8–10.

319. Rozwarski DA, et al. Modification of the NADH of the isoniazid target (InhA) from *Mycobacterium tuberculosis*. Science 1998;279(5347): 98–102.

320. Nguyen M, et al. A fast and efficient metal-mediated oxidation of isoniazid and identification of isoniazid-NAD(H) adducts. Chembiochem 2001;2(12): 877–883.

321. Rawat R, Whitty A, Tonge PJ.The isoniazid-NAD adduct is a slow, tight-binding inhibitor of InhA, the *Mycobacterium tuberculosis* enoyl reductase: adduct affinity and drug resistance. Proc Natl Acad Sci USA 2003;100(24): 13881–13886.

322. Argyrou A, et al. Proteome-wide profiling of isoniazid targets in *Mycobacterium tuberculosis*. Biochemistry 2006;45(47): 13947–13953.

323. Johnson R, et al. Drug resistance in *Mycobacterium tuberculosis*. Curr Issues Mol Biol 2006;8(2): 97–111.

324. Zhang Y, et al. The catalase-peroxidase gene and isoniazid resistance of *Mycobacterium tuberculosis*. Nature 1992;358(6387): 591–593.

325. Heym B, Cole ST.Isolation and characterization of isoniazid-resistant mutants of *Mycobacterium smegmatis* and *M. aurum*. Res Microbiol 1992;143(7): 721–730.

326. Heym B, et al. Missense mutations in the catalase-peroxidase gene, *katG*, are associated with isoniazid resistance in *Mycobacterium tuberculosis*. Mol Microbiol 1995;15(2): 235–245.

327. Ghiladi RA, Cabelli DE, Ortiz de Montellano PR.Superoxide reactivity of KatG: insights into isoniazid resistance pathways in TB. J Am Chem Soc 2004;126(15): 4772–4773.

328. Vilcheze C, et al. Transfer of a point mutation in *Mycobacterium tuberculosis* inhA resolves the target of isoniazid. Nat Med 2006;12(9): 1027–1029.

329. Vilcheze C, et al. Altered NADH/NAD + ratio mediates coresistance to isoniazid and ethionamide in mycobacteria. Antimicrob Agents Chemother 2005;49(2): 708–720.

330. Weinstein EA, et al. Inhibitors of type II NADH:menaquinone oxidoreductase represent a class of antitubercular drugs. Proc Natl Acad Sci USA 2005;102(12): 4548–4553.

331. Sikora AL, Frankel BA, Blanchard JS.Kinetic and chemical mechanism of arylamine *N*-acetyltransferase from *Mycobacterium tuberculosis*. Biochemistry 2008;47(40): 10781–10789.

332. Rawat M, et al. Mycothiol-deficient *Mycobacterium smegmatis* mutants are hypersensitive to alkylating agents, free radicals, and antibiotics. Antimicrob Agents Chemother 2002;46(11): 3348–3355.

333. Peloquin CA, MacPhee AA, Berning SE.Malabsorption of antimycobacterial medications. N Engl J Med 1993;329(15): 1122–1123.

334. Shin SG, et al. Kinetics of isoniazid transfer into cerebrospinal fluid in patients with tuberculous meningitis. J Korean Med Sci 1990;5(1): 39–45.

335. Sunahara S, Urano M, Ogawa M.Genetical and geographic studies on isoniazid inactivation. Science 1961;134:1530–1531.

336. Mandel W, et al. Combined drug treatment of tuberculosis. II. Studies of antimicrobially active isoniazid and streptomycin serum levels in adult tuberculous patients. J Clin Invest 1959;38(8): 1356–1365.

337. Peloquin CA, et al. Population pharmacokinetic modeling of isoniazid, rifampin, and pyrazinamide. Antimicrob Agents Chemother 1997;41(12): 2670–2679.

338. Heifets LB, Lindholm-Levy PJ, Flory M.-Comparison of bacteriostatic and bactericidal activity of isoniazid and ethionamide against *Mycobacterium avium* and *Mycobacterium tuberculosis*. Am Rev Respir Dis 1991;143(2): 268–270.

339. Preziosi P.Isoniazid: metabolic aspects and toxicological correlates. Curr Drug Metab 2007;8(8): 839–851.

340. Tostmann A, et al. Antituberculosis drug-induced hepatotoxicity: concise up-to-date review. J Gastroenterol Hepatol 2008;23(2): 192–202.

341. Desta Z, Soukhova NV, Flockhart DA.Inhibition of cytochrome P450 (CYP450) isoforms by isoniazid: potent inhibition of CYP2C19 and CYP3A. Antimicrob Agents Chemother 2001; 45(2): 382–392.

342. Wen X, et al. Isoniazid is a mechanism-based inhibitor of cytochrome P450 1A2, 2A6, 2C19 and 3A4 isoforms in human liver microsomes. Eur J Clin Pharmacol 2002;57 (11): 799–804.

343. Floss HG, Yu TW.Rifamycin-mode of action, resistance, and biosynthesis. Chem Rev 2005;105(2): 621–632.

344. Sensi P.History of the development of rifampin. Rev Infect Dis 1983;5(Suppl 3): S402–S406.

345. Binda G, et al. Rifampicin, a general review. Arzneimittelforschung 1971;21(12): 1907–1977.

346. Rifampin Tuberculosis (Edinb) 2008;88(2): 151–154.

347. Timbal MT, Sensi P. Antibiotics prepared from rifamycin B. GB 924,472. 1963 April.

348. Maggi N, Sensi P. Mannich bases of rifamycin SV, US Patent 3,349,082. 1967 Oct 24.

349. Maggi N, Arioli V, Sensi P.Rifamycins. X.L.I. A new class of active semisynthetic rifamycins. N-substituted aminomethyl derivatives of rifamycin SV 2. J Med Chem 1965;8(6): 790–793.

350. Maggi N, Gallo GG, Sensi P.Synthesis of 3-formylrifamycin SV. Il Farmaco 1967;22(5): 316–325.

351. Lancini G, Zanichelli W. Structure–activity relationships in rifamycins In: Structure–Activity Relationships Among the Semisynthetic Antibiotics. New York: Academic Press; 1977. p. 531–600.

352. Jing L, Ding CZ, Ma Z. Rifamycin C-11 oxime derivatives effective against drug-resistant microbes. US patent 7,256,187. 2007 August 14.

353. Campbell EA, et al. Structural mechanism for rifampicin inhibition of bacterial RNA polymerase. Cell 2001;104(6): 901–912.

354. Combrink KD, et al. New C25 carbamate rifamycin derivatives are resistant to inactivation by ADP-ribosyl transferases. Bioorg Med Chem Lett 2007;17(2): 522–526.

355. Bemer-Melchior P, Bryskier A, Drugeon HB. Comparison of the *in vitro* activities of rifapentine and rifampicin against *Mycobacterium tuberculosis* complex. J Antimicrob Chemother 2000;46(4): 571–576.

356. Kuze F, et al. *In vitro* and *in vivo* susceptibility of atypical mycobacteria to various drugs. Rev Infect Dis 1981;3(5): 885–897.

357. Hobby GL, Lenert TF.Observations on the action of rifampin and ethambutol alone and in combination with other antituberculous drugs. Am Rev Respir Dis 1972;105(2): 292–295.

358. WHO Leprosy Document No Fact Sheet#101 Revised 2005.

359. Sande MA.The use of rifampin in the treatment of nontuberculous infections: an overview. Rev Infect Dis 1983;5(Suppl 3): S399–S401.

360. Gumbo T, et al. Concentration-dependent *Mycobacterium tuberculosis* killing and prevention of resistance by rifampin. Antimicrob Agents Chemother 2007;51(11): 3781–3788.

361. Verbist L.Rifampicin blood levels in man. Acta Tuberc Pneumol Belg 1969;60(3): 288–298.

362. Mitchison DA, Dickinson JM.Laboratory aspects of intermittent drug therapy. Postgrad Med J 1971;47(553): 737–741.

363. Chan CY, et al. Postantibiotic effects of anti-tuberculosis agents alone and in combination. Antimicrob Agents Chemother 2001;45(12): 3631–3634.

364. Dickinson JM, Jackett PS, Mitchison DA.The effect of pulsed exposures to rifampin on the uptake of uridine 14C by *Mycobacterium tuberculosis*. Am Rev Respir Dis 1972;105(4): 519–527.

365. Fox W, Mitchison DA.Short-course chemotherapy for pulmonary tuberculosis. Am Rev Respir Dis 1975;111(3): 325–353.

366. Dickinson JM, Mitchison DA.Experimental models to explain the high sterilizing activity of rifampin in the chemotherapy of tuberculosis. Am Rev Respir Dis 1981;123(4 Pt 1): 367–371.

367. Wehrli W, Knusel F, Staehelin M.Action of rifamycin on RNA-polymerase from sensitive and resistant bacteria. Biochem Biophys Res Commun 1968;32(2): 284–288.

368. Wehrli W, et al. Interaction of rifamycin with bacterial RNA polymerase. Proc Natl Acad Sci USA 1968;61(2): 667–673.

369. Sweetser D, Nonet M, Young RA.Prokaryotic and eukaryotic RNA polymerases have homologous core subunits. Proc Natl Acad Sci USA 1987;84(5): 1192–1196.

370. Mustaev A, et al. Modular organization of the catalytic center of RNA polymerase. Proc Natl Acad Sci USA 1997;94(13): 6641–6645.

371. Artsimovitch I, et al. Allosteric modulation of the RNA polymerase catalytic reaction is an essential component of transcription control by rifamycins. Cell 2005;122(3): 351–363.

372. Feklistov A, et al. Rifamycins do not function by allosteric modulation of binding of Mg^{2+} to the RNA polymerase active center. Proc Natl Acad Sci USA 2008;105(39): 14820–14825.

373. Baysarowich J, et al. Rifamycin antibiotic resistance by ADP-ribosylation: structure and diversity of Arr. Proc Natl Acad Sci USA 2008;105(12): 4886–4891.

374. Burman WJ, Gallicano K, Peloquin C.Comparative pharmacokinetics and pharmacodynamics of the rifamycin antibacterials. Clin Pharmacokinet 2001;40(5): 327–341.

375. Acocella G.Clinical pharmacokinetics of rifampicin. Clin Pharmacokinet 1978;3(2): 108–127.

376. Acocella G.Pharmacokinetics and metabolism of rifampin in humans. Rev Infect Dis 1983;5 (Suppl 3): S428–S432.

377. Chen J, Raymond K.Roles of rifampicin in drug-drug interactions: underlying molecular mechanisms involving the nuclear pregnane X receptor. Ann Clin Microbiol Antimicrob 2006;5. DOI: 10.1186/1476-0711-5-3.

378. Li AP, et al. Primary human hepatocytes as a tool for the evaluation of structure–activity relationship in cytochrome P450 induction potential of xenobiotics: evaluation of rifampin, rifapentine and rifabutin. Chem Biol Interact 1997;107(1–2): 17–30.

379. Rae JM, et al. Rifampin is a selective, pleiotropic inducer of drug metabolism genes in human hepatocytes: studies with cDNA and oligonucleotide expression arrays. J Pharmacol Exp Ther 2001;299(3): 849–857.

380. Soars MG, et al. An assessment of UDP-glucuronosyltransferase induction using primary

human hepatocytes. Drug Metab Dispos 2004;32(1): 140–148.

381. Justesen US, et al. Pharmacokinetic interaction between rifampin and the combination of indinavir and low-dose ritonavir in HIV-infected patients. Clin Infect Dis 2004;38(3): 426–429.

382. Girling DJ.Adverse reactions to rifampicin in antituberculosis regimens. J Antimicrob Chemother 1977;3(2): 115–132.

383. Grosset J, Leventis S.Adverse effects of rifampin. Rev Infect Dis 1983;5(Suppl 3): S440–S450.

384. Schaberg T.The dark side of antituberculosis therapy: adverse events involving liver function. Eur Respir J 1995;8(8): 1247–1249.

385. la Porte CJ, et al. Pharmacokinetics of adjusted-dose lopinavir-ritonavir combined with rifampin in healthy volunteers. Antimicrob Agents Chemother 2004;48(5): 1553–1560.

386. Vernon A, et al. Acquired rifamycin monoresistance in patients with HIV-related tuberculosis treated with once-weekly rifapentine and isoniazid. Tuberculosis Trials Consortium. Lancet 1999;353(9167): 1843–1847.

387. Dooley K, et al. Repeated administration of high-dose intermittent rifapentine reduces rifapentine and moxifloxacin plasma concentrations. Antimicrob Agents Chemother 2008;52 (11): 4037–4042.

388. Finch CK, et al. Rifampin and rifabutin drug interactions: an update. Arch Intern Med 2002;162(9): 985–992.

389. Wilkinson RG, et al. Stereospecificity in a new type of synthetic antituberculous agent. J Am Chem Soc 1961;83:2212–2213.

390. Thomas JP, et al. A new synthetic compound with antituberculous activity in mice: ethambutol (dextro-2,2′-(ethylenediimino)-di-1-butanol). Am Rev Respir Dis 1961;83:891–893.

391. Shepherd RG, et al. Structure–activity studies leading to ethambutol, a new type of antituberculous compound. Ann N Y Acad Sci 1966;135(2): 686–710.

392. Reynolds RC, et al. Ethambutol-sugar hybrids as potential inhibitors of mycobacterial cell-wall biosynthesis. Carbohydr Res 1999;317 (1–4): 164–179.

393. Häusler H, et al. Ethambutol analogues as potential antimycobacterial agents. Bioorg Med Chem Lett 2001;11(13): 1679–1681.

394. Faugeroux V, et al. Synthesis and biological evaluation of conformationally constrained analogues of the antitubercular agent ethambutol. Bioorg Med Chem 2007;15(17): 5866–5876.

395. Yendapally R, Lee RE.Design, synthesis, and evaluation of novel ethambutol analogues. Bioorg Med Chem Lett 2008;18(5): 1607–1611.

396. Lee RE, et al. Combinatorial lead optimization of [1,2]-diamines based on ethambutol as potential antituberculosis preclinical candidates. J Comb Chem 2003;5(2): 172–187.

397. Karlson AG.The *in vitro* activity of ethambutol (dextro-2,2′-[ethyl-ethylenediimino]-di-1-butanol against tubercle bacilli and other microorganisms. Am Rev Respir Dis 1961;84: 905–906.

398. Lucchesi M, Mancini P.The anti-mycobacterial activity of ethambutol (ETB). Antibiot Chemother 1970;16:230–238.

399. Beggs WH, Andrews FA.Nonspecific ionic inhibition of ethambutol binding by *Mycobacterium smegmatis*. Antimicrob Agents Chemother 1973;4(2): 115–119.

400. Yates MD, Collins CH.Sensitivity of opportunist mycobacteria to rifampicin and ethambutol. Tubercle 1981;62(2): 117–121.

401. Forbes M, Kuck NA, Peets EA.Mode of action of ethambutol. J Bacteriol 1962;84:1099–1103.

402. Takayama K, Kilburn JO.Inhibition of synthesis of arabinogalactan by ethambutol in *Mycobacterium smegmatis*. Antimicrob Agents Chemother 1989;33(9): 1493–1499.

403. Mikusova K, et al. Biogenesis of the mycobacterial cell wall and the site of action of ethambutol. Antimicrob Agents Chemother 1995;39 (11): 2484–2489.

404. Deng L, et al. Recognition of multiple effects of ethambutol on metabolism of mycobacterial cell envelope. Antimicrob Agents Chemother 1995;39(3): 694–701.

405. Kilburn JO, Takayama K.Effects of ethambutol on accumulation and secretion of trehalose mycolates and free mycolic acid in *Mycobacterium smegmatis*. Antimicrob Agents Chemother 1981;20(3): 401–404.

406. Wolucka BA, et al. Recognition of the lipid intermediate for arabinogalactan/arabinomannan biosynthesis and its relation to the mode of action of ethambutol on mycobacteria. J Biol Chem 1994;269(37): 23328–23335.

407. Lee RE, et al. Synthesis of the mycobacterial arabinose donor beta-D-arabinofuranosyl-1-monphosphoryldecaprenol, development of a basic arabinosyl-transferase assay, and iden-

tification of ethambutol as an arabinosyl transferase inhibitor. J Am Chem Soc
1995;117:11829–11832.

408. Belanger AE, et al. The embAB genes of *My-cobacterium avium* encode an arabinosyl
transferase involved in cell wall arabinan bio-
synthesis that is the target for the antimycobacterial drug ethambutol. Proc Natl Acad Sci
USA 1996;93(21): 11919–11924.

409. Telenti A, et al. The emb operon, a gene cluster
of *Mycobacterium tuberculosis* involved in
resistance to ethambutol. Nat Med 1997;3(5):
567–570.

410. Escuyer VE, et al. The role of the *embA*
and *embB* gene products in the biosynthesis
of the terminal hexaarabinofuranosyl motif
of *Mycobacterium smegmatis* arabinogalactan.
J Biol Chem 2001;276(52): 48854–48862.

411. Zhang N, et al. The Emb proteins of mycobacteria direct arabinosylation of lipoarabinomannan and arabinogalactan via an N-terminal recognition region and a C-terminal
synthetic region. Mol Microbiol 2003;50(1):
69–76.

412. Khoo KH, et al. Truncated structural variants
of lipoarabinomannan in ethambutol drug-resistant strains of *Mycobacterium smegmatis*.
Inhibition of arabinan biosynthesis by ethambutol. J Biol Chem 1996;271(45): 28682–
28690.

413. Mikusova K, et al. Identification of a novel
galactosyl transferase involved in biosynthesis
of the mycobacterial cell wall. J Bacteriol
2006;188(18): 6592–6598.

414. Belanova M, et al. Galactosyl transferases in
mycobacterial cell wall synthesis. J Bacteriol
2008;190(3): 1141–1145.

415. Ramaswamy SV, et al. Molecular genetic analysis of nucleotide polymorphisms associated
with ethambutol resistance in human isolates
of *Mycobacterium tuberculosis*. Antimicrob
Agents Chemother 2000;44(2): 326–336.

416. Safi H, et al. Transfer of embB codon 306
mutations into clinical *Mycobacterium tuber-culosis* strains alters susceptibility to ethambutol, isoniazid, and rifampin. Antimicrob
Agents Chemother 2008;52(6): 2027–2034.

417. Shen X, et al. Association between embB codon
306 mutations and drug resistance in *Myco-bacterium tuberculosis*. Antimicrob Agents
Chemother 2007;51(7): 2618–2620.

418. Sharma K, et al. Transcriptional control of the
mycobacterial embCAB operon by PknH
through a regulatory protein, EmbR, *in vivo*.
J Bacteriol 2006;188(8): 2936–2944.

419. De Rossi E, Ainsa JA, Riccardi G.Role of mycobacterial efflux transporters in drug resistance: an unresolved question. FEMS Microbiol Rev 2006;30(1): 36–52.

420. Rodrigues L, et al. Thioridazine and chlorpromazine inhibition of ethidium bromide efflux
in *Mycobacterium avium* and *Mycobacterium
smegmatis*. J Antimicrob Chemother 2008;61
(5): 1076–1082.

421. Danilchanka O, Mailaender C, Niederweis M.
Identification of a novel multidrug efflux pump
of *Mycobacterium tuberculosis*. Antimicrob
Agents Chemother 2008;52(7): 2503–2511.

422. Corpe RF, Blalock FA.Retreatment of drug
resistant tuberculosis at Battey State Hospital. Dis Chest 1965;48(3): 305–310.

423. Bobrowitz ID, Gokulanathan KS.Ethambutol
in the retreatment of pulmonary tuberculosis.
Dis Chest 1965;48(3): 239–250.

424. Zhu M, et al. Pharmacokinetics of ethambutol
in children and adults with tuberculosis. Int J
Tuberc Lung Dis 2004;8(11): 1360–1367.

425. Place VA, Thomas JP.Clinical pharmacology of
ethambutol. Am Rev Respir Dis
1963;87:901–904.

426. Peets EA, et al. The absorption, excretion, and
metabolic fate of ethambutol in man. Am Rev
Respir Dis 1965;91:51–58.

427. Perlman DC, et al. The clinical pharmacokinetics of rifampin and ethambutol in HIV-infected persons with tuberculosis. Clin Infect
Dis 2005;41(11): 1638–1647.

428. Thee S, et al. Ethambutol in paediatric tuberculosis: aspects of ethambutol serum concentration, efficacy and toxicity in children. Int J
Tuberc Lung Dis 2007;11(9): 965–971.

429. Leibold JE.The ocular toxicity of ethambutol
and its relation to dose. Ann N Y Acad Sci
1966;135(2): 904–909.

430. McKenzie D, et al. The effect of nicotinic acid
amide on experimental tuberculosis of white
mice. J Lab Clin Med 1948;33(10): 1249–1253.

431. Kushner S, et al. Experimental chemotherapy
of tuberculosis. II. The synthesis of pyrazina-
mides and related compounds. J Am Chem Soc
1952;74:3617–3621.

432. Rogers EF, et al. Antitubercular diazine carboxamides. Science 1952;116(3010): 253–254.

433. Solotorovsky M, et al. Pyrazinoic acid amide;
an agent active against experimental murine
tuberculosis. Proc Soc Exp Biol Med 1952;79
(4): 563–565.

434. Dalmer O, Eugen W. Pyrazine derivatives. DE
632257. 1936.

435. McDermott W, Tompsett R.Activation of pyrazinamide and nicotinamide in acidic environments *in vitro*. Am Rev Tuberc 1954;70(4): 748–754.

436. Cynamon MH, Speirs RJ, Welch JT.*In vitro* antimycobacterial activity of 5-chloropyrazinamide. Antimicrob Agents Chemother 1998;42 (2): 462–463.

437. Boshoff HI, Mizrahi V, Barry CE 3rd.Effects of pyrazinamide on fatty acid synthesis by whole mycobacterial cells and purified fatty acid synthase I.J Bacteriol 2002;184(8): 2167–2172.

438. Cynamon MH, et al. Antimycobacterial activity of a series of pyrazinoic acid esters. J Med Chem 1992;35(7): 1212–1215.

439. Cynamon MH, et al. Pyrazinoic acid esters with broad spectrum *in vitro* antimycobacterial activity. J Med Chem 1995;38(20): 3902–3907.

440. Speirs RJ, Welch JT, Cynamon MH.Activity of *n*-propyl pyrazinoate against pyrazinamide-resistant *Mycobacterium tuberculosis*: investigations into mechanism of action of and mechanism of resistance to pyrazinamide. Antimicrob Agents Chemother 1995;39(6): 1269– 1271.

441. Wächter GA, et al. Antimycobacterial activity of substituted isosteres of pyridine- and pyrazinecarboxylic acids. J Med Chem 1998;41 (13): 2436–2438.

442. Kushner S, et al. Experimental chemotherapy of tuberculosis. III. Ethyl mercaptan and related compounds in tuberculosis. J Am Chem Soc 1955;77:1152–1155.

443. Felder E, Pitre D, Tiepolo U.*N*-Morpholinomethyl-pyrazinamide: chemico-physical characteristics and determination in biological fluids. Minerva Med 1962;53:1699–1703.

444. Chung WJ, et al. Inhibition of M. tuberculosis *in vitro* in monocytes and in mice by aminomethylene pyrazinamide analogs. Tuberculosis (Edinb) 2008;88(5): 410–419.

445. Trnka L, Kuska J, Havel A.Comparison of the antituberculous activity of morphazinamide and pyrazinamide on chronic experimental tuberculosis. I. The antimycobacterial efficacy made *in vitro* and *in vivo*. Chemotherapia (Basel) 1965;9:158–167.

446. Stottmeier KD, Beam RE, Kubica GP.Determination of drug susceptibility of mycobacteria to pyrazinamide in 7H10 agar. Am Rev Respir Dis 1967;96(5): 1072–1075.

447. Heifets L.Susceptibility testing of *Mycobacterium tuberculosis* to pyrazinamide. J Med Microbiol 2002;51(1): 11–12.

448. Fuursted K.Comparison of growth and susceptibility testing of pyrazinamide in different Bactec media using strains of the *M. tuberculosis* complex. APMIS 1993;101(2): 154–159.

449. Sun Z, Scorpio A, Zhang Y.The *pncA* gene from naturally pyrazinamide-resistant *Mycobacterium avium* encodes pyrazinamidase and confers pyrazinamide susceptibility to resistant *M. tuberculosis* complex organisms. Microbiology 1997;143(Pt 10): 3367–3373.

450. Good RC, et al. Identification and drug susceptibility test results for *Mycobacterium* spp. Clin Microbiol Newslett 1985;7:133–136.

451. Konno K, Feldmann FM, McDermott W.Pyrazinamide susceptibility and amidase activity of tubercle bacilli. Am Rev Respir Dis 1967;95 (3): 461–469.

452. Scorpio A, Zhang Y.Mutations in *pncA*, a gene encoding pyrazinamidase/nicotinamidase, cause resistance to the antituberculous drug pyrazinamide in tubercle bacillus. Nat Med 1996;2(6): 662–667.

453. Zhang Y, et al. Role of acid pH and deficient efflux of pyrazinoic acid in unique susceptibility of *Mycobacterium tuberculosis* to pyrazinamide. J Bacteriol 1999;181(7): 2044–2049.

454. Zimhony O, et al. Pyrazinoic acid and its *n*-propyl ester inhibit fatty acid synthase type I in replicating tubercle bacilli. Antimicrob Agents Chemother 2007;51(2): 752–754.

455. Ngo SC, et al. Inhibition of isolated *Mycobacterium tuberculosis* fatty acid synthase I by pyrazinamide analogs. Antimicrob Agents Chemother 2007;51(7): 2430–2435.

456. Scorpio A, et al. Characterization of pncA mutations in pyrazinamide-resistant *Mycobacterium tuberculosis*. Antimicrob Agents Chemother 1997;41(3): 540–543.

457. Lemaitre N, et al. Characterization of new mutations in pyrazinamide-resistant strains of *Mycobacterium tuberculosis* and identification of conserved regions important for the catalytic activity of the pyrazinamidase PncA. Antimicrob Agents Chemother 1999;43(7): 1761–1763.

458. Sheen P, et al. Effect of pyrazinamidase activity on pyrazinamide resistance in *Mycobacterium tuberculosis*. Tuberculosis (Edinb) 2009; 89(2): 109–113.

459. WHO Treatment of tuberculosis. Guidelines for national programmes. WHO document no. WHO/CDS/2003.313. 2003. p. 28.

460. Peloquin CA, et al. Pharmacokinetics of pyrazinamide under fasting conditions, with food, and with antacids. Pharmacotherapy 1998;18 (6): 1205–1211.

461. Ellard GA.Absorption, metabolism and excretion of pyrazinamide in man. Tubercle 1969;50 (2): 144–158.

462. Acocella G, et al. Pharmacokinetic studies on antituberculosis regimens in humans. I. Absorption and metabolism of the compounds used in the initial intensive phase of the short-course regimens: single administration study. Am Rev Respir Dis 1985;132(3): 510–515.

463. Lacroix C, et al. Pharmacokinetics of pyrazinamide and its metabolites in healthy subjects. Eur J Clin Pharmacol 1989;36(4): 395–400.

464. Zhu M, et al. Population pharmacokinetic modeling of pyrazinamide in children and adults with tuberculosis. Pharmacotherapy 2002;22(6): 686–695.

465. Weiner IM, Tinker JP.Pharmacology of pyrazinamide: metabolic and renal function studies related to the mechanism of drug-induced urate retention. J Pharmacol Exp Ther 1972;180 (2): 411–434.

466. Auscher C, et al. Study of urinary pyrazinamide metabolites and their action on the renal excretion of xanthine and hypoxanthine in a xanthinuric patient. Biomedicine 1978;28(2): 129–133.

467. Pitre D, et al. *In vitro* biotransformation of pyrazinamide by rat liver: identification of a new metabolite. Pharmacol Res Commun 1981;13(4): 351–362.

468. Yamamoto T, et al. Rapid and simultaneous determination of pyrazinamide and its major metabolites in human plasma by high-performance liquid chromatography. J Chromatogr 1987;413:342–346.

469. Malone RS, et al. The effect of hemodialysis on isoniazid, rifampin, pyrazinamide, and ethambutol. Am J Respir Crit Care Med 1999;159(5 Pt 1): 1580–1584.

470. Lacroix C, et al. Interaction between allopurinol and pyrazinamide. Eur Respir J 1988;1(9): 807–811.

471. Chang KC, et al. Hepatotoxicity of pyrazinamide: cohort and case-control analyses. Am J Respir Crit Care Med 2008;177(12): 1391–1396.

472. Tostmann A, et al. Isoniazid and its toxic metabolite hydrazine induce *in vitro* pyrazinamide toxicity. Int J Antimicrob Agents 2008;31 (6): 577–580.

473. Tortajada C, et al. Is the combination of pyrazinamide plus rifampicin safe for treating latent tuberculosis infection in persons not infected by the human immunodeficiency virus? Int. J Tuberc Lung Dis 2005;9(3): 276–281.

474. Cullen JH, Early LJ, Fiore JM.The occurrence of hyperuricemia during pyrazinamide-isoniazid therapy. Am Rev Tuberc 1956;74(2 Part 1): 289–292.

475. Jenner PJ, et al. Serum uric acid concentrations and arthralgia among patients treated with pyrazinamide-containing regimens in Hong Kong and Singapore. Tubercle 1981;62 (3): 175–179.

476. Taki H, et al. Epidemiological survey of hyperuricemia as an adverse reaction to antituberculous therapy with pyrazinamide. Kekkaku 2008;83(7): 497–501.

477. Zierski M, Bek E.Side effects of drug regimens used in short-course chemotherapy for pulmonary tuberculosis. A controlled clinical study. Tubercle 1980;61(1): 41–49.

478. Schatz A, Bugie E, Waksman S.Streptomycin, a substance exhibiting antibiotic activity against Gram-positive and Gram-negative bacteria. Proc Soc Exp Biol Med 1944;55:66–69.

479. Comroe JH Jr.Pay dirt: the story of streptomycin. Part I. From Waksman to Waksman. Am Rev Respir Dis 1978;117(4): 773–781.

480. Brink NG, Kuehl FA Jr, Folkers K.Streptomyces antibiotics. III. Degradation of streptomycin to streptobiosamine derivatives. Science 1945;102(2655): 506–507.

481. Kuehl FA Jr, Peck RL, et al. Streptomyces antibiotics: structure of streptomycin. J Am Chem Soc 1948;70(7): 2325–2330.

482. Kuehl FA Jr, Clark RL, et al. Streptomyces antibiotics; configuration of streptose and streptobiosamine. J Am Chem Soc 1949;71 (4): 1445–1448.

483. Rastogi N, Labrousse V, Goh KS.*In vitro* activities of fourteen antimicrobial agents against drug susceptible and resistant clinical isolates of *Mycobacterium tuberculosis* and comparative intracellular activities against the virulent H37Rv strain in human macrophages. Curr Microbiol 1996;33(3): 167–175.

484. Suter E.Multiplication of tubercle bacilli within phagocytes cultivated *in vitro*, and effect of streptomycin and isonicotinic acid hydrazide. Am Rev Tuberc 1952;65(6): 775–776.

485. Crowle AJ, et al. Inhibition by streptomycin of tubercle bacilli within cultured human macrophages. Am Rev Respir Dis 1984;130(5): 839–844.

486. Shaila MS, Gopinathan KP, Ramakrishnan T. Protein synthesis in *Mycobacterium tuberculosis* H37Rv and the effect of streptomycin in streptomycin-susceptible and -resistant

strains. Antimicrob Agents Chemother 1973;4 (3): 205–213.

487. Noller HF.Structure of ribosomal RNA. Annu Rev Biochem 1984;53:119–162.

488. Wimberly BT, et al. Structure of the 30S ribosomal subunit. Nature 2000;407(6802): 327–339.

489. Carter AP, et al. Functional insights from the structure of the 30S ribosomal subunit and its interactions with antibiotics. Nature 2000;407 (6802): 340–348.

490. Busse HJ, Wostmann C, Bakker EP.The bactericidal action of streptomycin: membrane permeabilization caused by the insertion of mistranslated proteins into the cytoplasmic membrane of *Escherichia coli* and subsequent caging of the antibiotic inside the cells due to degradation of these proteins. J Gen Microbiol 1992;138(3): 551–561.

491. Douglass J, Steyn LM.A ribosomal gene mutation in streptomycin-resistant *Mycobacterium tuberculosis* isolates. J Infect Dis 1993;167(6): 1505–1506.

492. Finken M, et al. Molecular basis of streptomycin resistance in *Mycobacterium tuberculosis*: alterations of the ribosomal protein *S12* gene and point mutations within a functional 16S ribosomal RNA pseudoknot. Mol Microbiol 1993;9(6): 1239–1246.

493. Nair J, et al. The *rpsL* gene and streptomycin resistance in single and multiple drug-resistant strains of *Mycobacterium tuberculosis*. Mol Microbiol 1993;10(3): 521–527.

494. Honore N, Cole ST.Streptomycin resistance in mycobacteria. Antimicrob Agents Chemother 1994;38(2): 238–242.

495. Meier A, et al. Genetic alterations in streptomycin-resistant *Mycobacterium tuberculosis*: mapping of mutations conferring resistance. Antimicrob Agents Chemother 1994;38(2): 228–233.

496. Meier A, et al. Correlation of molecular resistance mechanisms and phenotypic resistance levels in streptomycin-resistant *Mycobacterium tuberculosis*. Antimicrob Agents Chemother 1996;40(11): 2452–2454.

497. Sreevatsan S, et al. Characterization of rpsL and rrs mutations in streptomycin-resistant *Mycobacterium tuberculosis* isolates from diverse geographic localities. Antimicrob Agents Chemother 1996;40(4): 1024–1026.

498. Okamoto S, et al. Loss of a conserved 7-methylguanosine modification in 16S rRNA confers low-level streptomycin resistance in bacteria. Mol Microbiol 2007;63(4): 1096–1106.

499. Magnet S, Blanchard JS.Molecular insights into aminoglycoside action and resistance. Chem Rev 2005;105(2): 477–498.

500. Hegde SS, Javid-Majd F, Blanchard JS.Overexpression and mechanistic analysis of chromosomally encoded aminoglycoside 2′-*N*-acetyltransferase (AAC(2′)-Ic) from *Mycobacterium tuberculosis*. J Biol Chem 2001;276(49): 45876–45881.

501. Ramon-Garcia S, et al. Contribution of the Rv2333c efflux pump (the Stp protein) from *Mycobacterium tuberculosis* to intrinsic antibiotic resistance in *Mycobacterium bovis* BCG. J Antimicrob Chemother 2007;59(3): 544–547.

502. Streptomycin. Tuberculosis (Edinb) 2008;88 (2): 162–163.

503. Zintel HA, et al. Studies on streptomycin in man, absorption, distribution, excretion and toxicity. Am J Med Sci 1945;210:421–430.

504. Zhu M, et al. Population pharmacokinetics of intravenous and intramuscular streptomycin in patients with tuberculosis. Pharmacotherapy 2001;21(9): 1037–1045.

505. Peloquin CA, et al. Aminoglycoside toxicity: daily versus thrice-weekly dosing for treatment of mycobacterial diseases. Clin Infect Dis 2004;38(11): 1538–1544.

506. Granados O, Meza G.Streptidine, a metabolic derivative produced after administration of streptomycin *in vivo*, is vestibulotoxic in rats. Histol Histopathol 2005;20(2): 357–364.

507. Umezawa H, et al. Production and isolation of a new antibiotic: kanamycin. J Antibiot 1957;10(5): 181–188.

508. Kawaguchi H, et al. BB-K 8, a new semisynthetic aminoglycoside antibiotic. J Antibiot 1972;25(12): 695–708.

509. Kawaguchi H.Discovery, chemistry, and activity of amikacin. J Infect Dis 1976;134(Suppl): S242–S248.

510. Woo PWK, Dion HW, Bartz QR.Butirosins A and B, aminoglycoside antibiotics. III. Structures. Tetrahedron Lett 1971;28: 2625–2628.

511. Ho YI, Chan CY, Cheng AF.*In vitro* activities of aminoglycoside-aminocyclitols against mycobacteria. J Antimicrob Chemother 1997;40(1): 27–32.

512. Heifets L, Lindholm-Levy P.Comparison of bactericidal activities of streptomycin, amikacin, kanamycin, and capreomycin against *Mycobacterium avium* and *M. tuberculosis*. Antimicrob Agents Chemother 1989;33(8): 1298–1301.

513. Vicens Q, Westhof E.Crystal structure of a complex between the aminoglycoside tobramycin and an oligonucleotide containing the ribosomal decoding a site. Chem Biol 2002;9(6): 747–755.

514. Tsukamura M, Mizuno S.Cross-resistant relationships among the aminoglucoside antibiotics in *Mycobacterium tuberculosis*. J Gen Microbiol 1975;88(2): 269–274.

515. McClatchy JK, et al. Cross-resistance in *M. tuberculosis* to kanamycin, capreomycin and viomycin. Tubercle 1977;58(1): 29–34.

516. Camus JC, et al. Re-annotation of the genome sequence of *Mycobacterium tuberculosis* H37Rv. Microbiology 2002;148(Pt 10): 2967– 2973.

517. Alangaden GJ, et al. Mechanism of resistance to amikacin and kanamycin in *Mycobacterium tuberculosis*. Antimicrob Agents Chemother 1998;42(5): 1295–1297.

518. Suzuki Y, et al. Detection of kanamycin-resistant *Mycobacterium tuberculosis* by identifying mutations in the 16S rRNA gene. J Clin Microbiol 1998;36(5): 1220–1225.

519. Prammananan T, et al. A single 16S ribosomal RNA substitution is responsible for resistance to amikacin and other 2-deoxystreptamine aminoglycosides in *Mycobacterium abscessus* and *Mycobacterium chelonae*. J Infect Dis 1998;177(6): 1573–1581.

520. Kanamycin. Tuberculosis (Edinb) 2008;88(2): 117–118.

521. Amikacin. Tuberculosis (Edinb) 2008;88(2): 87–88.

522. Felnagle EA, et al. Identification of the biosynthetic gene cluster and an additional gene for resistance to the antituberculosis drug capreomycin. Appl Environ Microbiol 2007,73(13): 4162–4170.

523. Herr EB, et al. Proc Ind Acad Sci 1960; 69:134.

524. Herr EB Jr, Hamill RL, McGuire JM. Capreomycin and its preparation. US patent 3,143,468. 1964 Aug 4.

525. Thomas MG, Chan YA, Ozanick SG.Deciphering tuberactinomycin biosynthesis: isolation, sequencing, and annotation of the viomycin biosynthetic gene cluster. Antimicrob Agents Chemother 2003;47(9): 2823–2830.

526. Shiba T, et al. Revised structure and total synthesis of capreomycin. Tetrahedron Lett 1976;17:3907–3910.

527. DeMong DE, Williams RM.Asymmetric synthesis of (2*S*,3*R*)-capreomycidine and the total

synthesis of capreomycin IB. J Am Chem Soc 2003;125(28): 8561–8565.

528. Teshima T, et al. Chemical studies on tuberactinomycin. XII. Syntheses and antimicrobial activities of [Ala^3, Ala^4]-, [Ala^3]-, and [Ala^4]-tuberactinomycin O. Bull Chem Soc Jpn 1977;50:3372–3380.

529. Nomoto S, Shiba T.Chemical studies on tuberactinomycin. XIII. Modification of beta-ureidodehydroalanine residue in tuberactinomycin. N J Antibiot 1977;30(11): 1008–1011.

530. Dirlam JP, et al. Cyclic homopentapeptides 1. Analogs of tuberactinomycins and capreomycin with activity against vancomycin-resistant enterococci and pasteurella. Bioorg Med Chem Lett 1997;7:1139–1144.

531. Kitagawa T, et al. Relationships between antimicrobial activities and chemical structures of reduced products of viomycin. J Antibiot 1973;26(9): 528–531.

532. Lyssikatos JP, et al. Cyclic homopentapeptides 2. Synthetic modifications of viomycin. Bioorg Med Chem Lett 1997;7:1145–1148.

533. Yamada T, Teshima T, Shiba T.Activity of di-beta-lysyl-capreomycin IIA and palmitoyl tuberactinamine N against drug-resistant mutants with altered ribosomes. Antimicrob Agents Chemother 1981;20(6): 834–836.

534. Oliva B, Comanducci A, Chopra I.Antibacterial spectra of drugs used for chemotherapy of mycobacterial infections. Tuberc Lung Dis 1998;79(2): 107–109.

535. Sutton WB, et al. *In vitro* and *in vivo* laboratory studies on the antituberculous activity of capreomycin. Ann N Y Acad Sci 1966;135(2): 947–959.

536. Gobels K, et al. Capreomycin in the treatment of atypical mycobacterial disease in HIV-positive patients. Eur J Clin Microbiol Infect Dis 2002;21(7): 563–565.

537. Shitrit D, et al. Pulmonary *Mycobacterium kansasii* infection in Israel, 1999–2004: clinical features, drug susceptibility, and outcome. Chest 2006;129(3): 771–776

538. Heifets L, Simon J, Pham V.Capreomycin is active against non-replicating *M. tuberculosis*. Ann Clin Microbiol Antimicrob 2005;4. DOI: 10.1186/1476-0711-4-6.

539. Liou YF, Tanaka N.Dual actions of viomycin on the ribosomal functions. Biochem Biophys Res Commun 1976;71(2): 477–483.

540. Modolell J, VazquezThe inhibition of ribosomal translocation by viomycin. Eur J Biochem 1977;81(3): 491–497.

541. Maus CE, Plikaytis BB, Shinnick TM.-Mutation of tlyA confers capreomycin resistance in *Mycobacterium tuberculosis*. Antimicrob Agents Chemother 2005;49(2): 571–577.

542. Johansen SK, et al. Capreomycin binds across the ribosomal subunit interface using tlyA-encoded 2′-*O*-methylations in 16S and 23S rRNAs. Mol Cell 2006;23(2): 173–182.

543. Rifabutin. Tuberculosis (Edinb) 2008;88(2): 145–147.

544. Lee SH, et al. The impurities of capreomycin make a difference in the safety and pharmacokinetic profiles. Int J Antimicrob Agents 2003;22(1): 81–83.

545. Morse WC, et al. *M. tuberculosis in vitro* susceptibility and serum level experiences with capreomycin. Ann N Y Acad Sci 1966;135(2): 983–988.

546. Lehmann CR, et al. Capreomycin kinetics in renal impairment and clearance by hemodialysis. Am Rev Respir Dis 1988;138(5): 1312–1313.

547. Capreomycin. Tuberculosis (Edinb) 2008;88 (2): 89–91.

548. Browning RH, Donnerberg RL.Capreomycin-experiences in patient acceptance and toxicity. Ann N Y Acad Sci 1966;135(2): 1057– 1064.

549. Miller JD, et al. Toxicology studies in patients on prolonged therapy with capreomycin. Ann N Y Acad Sci 1966;135(2): 1047–1056.

550. Lehmann J.Preliminary communication: *para*-aminosalicylic acid in the treatment of tuberculosis. Lancet 1946;1:15–16.

551. Bernheim F.The effect of various substances on the oxygen uptake of the tubercle bacillus. J Bacteriol 1941;41(3): 387–395.

552. Lehmann J.Twenty years afterward historical notes on the discovery of the antituberculosis effect of *para*-aminosalicylic acid (PAS) and the first clinical trials. Am Rev Respir Dis 1964;90:953–956.

553. Dubovsky H.Correspondence with a pioneer, Jurgen Lehmann (1898–1989), producer of the first effective antituberculosis specific. S Afr Med J 1991;79(1): 48–50

554. Lehmann J.The treatment of tuberculosis in Sweden with *para*-aminosalicylic acid; a review. Dis Chest 1949;16(6): 684–703.

555. Therapeutic Trials Committee of the Swedish National Association against Tuberculosis. *para*-Aminosalicylic acid treatment in pulmonary tuberculosis. Am Rev Tuberc 1950;61:597–612.

556. Council MR.Treatment of pulmonary tuberculosis with *para*-aminosalicylic acid and streptomycin. Br Med J 1949;2:1521.

557. Jindani A.Short-course (6-month) treatment of pulmonary tuberculosis (Second East African/British Medical Research Council Study). Bull Int Union Tuberc 1976;51(1): 53–56.

558. CDCUpdate: availability of streptomycin and *para*-aminosalicylic acid—United States. Morb Mortal Wkly Rep 1992;41:482.

559. Peloquin CA, et al. Pharmacokinetic evaluation of *para*-aminosalicylic acid granules. Pharmacotherapy 1994;14(1): 40–46.

560. Peloquin CA, et al. Once-daily and twice-daily dosing of *p*-aminosalicylic acid granules. Am J Respir Crit Care Med 1999;159(3): 932–934.

561. Hassan MMA, Jado AI, Zubair MU. Aminosalicylic acid. Florey K, editor. Analytical Profiles of Drug Substances. Academic Press, New York, NY. 1981. p. 1–27.

562. Parker RP, Smith JM. Process for producing 4-amino-2-hydroxybenzoic acid. US patent 2,644,011. 1953 June 30.

563. Doub L, et al. Some derivatives of 4-amino-2-hydroxybenzoic acid (*p*-aminosalicylic acid). J Am Chem Soc 1951;73:903–906.

564. Youmans GP, Raleigh GW, Youmans AS.The tuberculostatic action of *para*-aminosalicylic acid. J Bacteriol 1947;54(4): 409–416.

565. *Para*-aminosalicylic acid. Tuberculosis (Edinb) 2008;88(2): 137–138.

566. Mandell GL, Petri WA Jr. Chapter 48: Antimicrobial agents: drugs used in the chemotherapy of tuberculosis and leprosy. In: Hardman, JG, et al., editors. Goodman and Gilman's The Pharmacological Basis of Therapeutics. 9th ed. McGraw-Hill, New York, NY. 1996. p 1164.

567. Scholar EM, Pratt WB. Chapter 11: Drugs that act on mycobacteria. In: The Antimicrobial Drugs. 2nd ed. New York: Oxford University Press; 2000. p. 305–306.

568. Lemke TL. Chapter 37: Antimycobacterial agents. In: Foye's Principles of Medicinal Chemistry. 5th ed. Lippincott Williams & Wilkins, Philadelphia, PA. 2002. p 913.

569. Nopponpunth V, et al. Cloning and expression of *Mycobacterium tuberculosis* and *Mycobacterium leprae* dihydropteroate synthase in *Escherichia coli*. J Bacteriol 1999;181(21): 6814–6821.

570. Mathys V, et al. Molecular genetics of *para*-aminosalicylic acid resistance in clinical isolates and spontaneous mutants of *Mycobacter-*

ium tuberculosis. Antimicrob Agents Chemother 2009;53(5): 2100–2109.

571. Rengarajan J, et al. The folate pathway is a target for resistance to the drug *para*-aminosalicylic acid (PAS) in mycobacteria. Mol Microbiol 2004;53(1): 275–282.

572. Kunz BA, Kohalmi SE.Modulation of mutagenesis by deoxyribonucleotide levels. Annu Rev Genet 1991;25:339–359.

573. Ratledge C, Brown KA.Inhibition of mycobactin formation in *Mycobacterium smegmatis* by *p*-aminosalicylate. A new proposal for the mode of action of *p-aminosalicylate.* Am Rev Respir Dis 1972;106(5): 774–776.

574. Vergne AF, Walz AJ, Miller MJ.Iron chelators from mycobacteria (1954–1999) and potential therapeutic applications. Nat Prod Rep 2000;17(1): 99–116

575. De Voss JJ, et al. Iron acquisition and metabolism by mycobacteria. J Bacteriol 1999;181 (15): 4443–4451.

576. Adilakshmi T, Ayling PD, Ratledge C.Mutational analysis of a role for salicylic acid in iron metabolism of *Mycobacterium smegmatis.* J Bacteriol 2000;182(2): 264–271.

577. Rand L, et al. Matrix metalloproteinase-1 is regulated in tuberculosis by a p38 MAPK-dependent, *p*-aminosalicylic acid-sensitive signaling cascade. J Immunol 2009;182(9): 5865–5872.

578. Zini F.Metabolism of *para*-aminosalicylic acid and adaptation of protective synthesis as aspects of the chemical defense of the organism. Riv Crit Clin Med 1953;53(2–3): 308–313.

579. Way EL, et al. The metabolism of *p*-aminosalicylic acid (PAS) in man. J Am Pharm Assoc Am Pharm Assoc 1955;44(2): 65–69.

580. Wan SH, Pentikainen PJ, Azarnoff DL.Bioavailability of aminosalicylic acid and its various salts in humans. 3. Absorption from tablets. J Pharm Sci 1974;63(5): 708–711.

581. Grant DM, et al. Monomorphic and polymorphic human arylamine *N*-acetyltransferases: a comparison of liver isozymes and expressed products of two cloned genes. Mol Pharmacol 1991;39(2): 184–191.

582. Wang H, et al. Over-expression, purification, and characterization of recombinant human arylamine *N*-acetyltransferase 1. Protein J 2005;24(2): 65–77.

583. Peloquin CA, et al. Pharmacokinetics of *para*-aminosalicylic acid granules under four dosing conditions. Ann Pharmacother 2001;35(11): 1332–1338.

584. Berte SJ, Dewlett HJ.Isoniazid and para-aminosalicylic acid toxicity in 513 cases: a study including high doses of INH and gastrointestinal intolerance to PAS. Dis Chest 1959;36(2): 146–151.

585. Epstein IG, Nair KG, Boyd LJ.Cycloserine, a new antibiotic, in the treatment of human pulmonary tuberculosis: a preliminary report. Antibiot Med Clin Ther 1955;1(2): 80–93.

586. Boyd LJ, Epstein IG, Nair KG.The treatment of human tuberculosis with cycloserine: a year's progress. Antibiot Annu 1955;3: 141–147.

587. Kuehl FA Jr, et al. D-Amino-3-isoxazolidone, a new antibiotic. J Am Chem Soc 1955;77: 2344–2345.

588. Hidy PH, et al. Structure and reactions of cycloserine. J Am Chem Soc 1955;77: 2345–2346.

589. Stammer CH, et al. Synthesis of cycloserine and a methyl analog. J Am Chem Soc 1957;79:3236–3240.

590. Plattner PA, et al. Synthesen des 4-amino-3-isoxazolidinons (cycloserin) und einiger analoga. Helv Chim Acta 1957;40:1531–1552.

591. Neuhaus FC.D-Cycloserine and *O*-carbamoyl-D-serine. In: Gottlieb D, Shaw PD, editors. Antibiotics I (Mode of Action). New York: Springer-Verlag; 1967. p. 40–83.

592. Kim MG, et al. *N*(2)-substituted D,L-cycloserine derivatives: synthesis and evaluation as alanine racemase inhibitors. J Antibiot 2003;56(2): 160–168.

593. Storey PB, McLean RL.A current appraisal of cycloserine. Antibiot Med Clin Ther 1957;4(4): 223–232.

594. Gernez-Rieux C, Devulder B.Comparative investigation *in vitro* of the sensibility of atypical mycobacteria to cycloserine and to other antibacterial substances. Scand J Respir Dis Suppl 1970;71:22–34.

595. Strominger JL, Threnn RH, Scott SS.Oxamycin, a competitive antagonist of the incorporation of D-alanine into a uridine nucleotide in *Staphylococcus aureus.* J Am Chem Soc 1959;81:3803–3804.

596. Neuhaus FC, Lynch JL.The enzymatic synthesis of D-alanyl-D-alanine. 3. On the inhibition of D-alanyl-D-alanine synthetase by the antibiotic D-cycloserine. Biochemistry 1964;3: 471–480.

597. Peisach D, et al. D-Cycloserine inactivation of D-amino acid aminotransferase leads to a stable noncovalent protein complex with an

aromatic cycloserine-PLP derivative. J Am Chem Soc 1998;120:2268–2274.

598. Fenn TD, et al. A side reaction of alanine racemase: transamination of cycloserine. Biochemistry 2003;42(19): 5775–5783.

599. Olson GT, et al. An aromatization mechanism of inactivation of gamma-aminobutyric acid aminotransferases for the antibiotic L-cycloserine. J Am Chem Soc 1998;120:2256–2267.

600. Caceres NE, et al. Overexpression of the D-alanine racemase gene confers resistance to D-cycloserine in *Mycobacterium smegmatis*. J Bacteriol 1997;179(16): 5046–5055.

601. Belanger AE, Porter JC, Hatfull GF.Genetic analysis of peptidoglycan biosynthesis in mycobacteria: characterization of a ddlA mutant of *Mycobacterium smegmatis*. J Bacteriol 2000;182(23): 6854–6856.

602. Chacon O, et al. *Mycobacterium smegmatis*D-alanine racemase mutants are not dependent on D-alanine for growth. Antimicrob Agents Chemother 2002;46(1): 47–54.

603. Feng Z, Barletta RG.Roles of *Mycobacterium smegmatis*D-alanine:D-alanine ligase and D-alanine racemase in the mechanisms of action of and resistance to the peptidoglycan inhibitor D-cycloserine. Antimicrob Agents Chemother 2003;47(1): 283–291.

604. Halouska S, et al. Use of NMR metabolomics to analyze the targets of D-cycloserine in mycobacteria: role of D-alanine racemase. J Proteome Res 2007;6(12): 4608–4614.

605. Milligan DL, et al. The alanine racemase of *Mycobacterium smegmatis* is essential for growth in the absence of D-alanine. J Bacteriol 2007;189(22): 8381–8386.

606. Noda M, et al. Self-protection mechanism in D-cycloserine-producing *Streptomyces lavendulae*. Gene cloning, characterization, and kinetics of its alanine racemase and D-alanyl-D-alanine ligase, which are target enzymes of D-cycloserine. J Biol Chem 2004;279(44): 46143–46152.

607. Cycloserine Tuberculosis (Edinb) 2008;88(2): 100–101.

608. Zitkova L, Tousek J.Pharmacokinetics of cycloserine and terizidone. A comparative study. Chemotherapy 1974;20(1): 18–28.

609. Zhu M, et al. Pharmacokinetics of cycloserine under fasting conditions and with high-fat meal, orange juice, and antacids. Pharmacotherapy 2001;21(8): 891–897.

610. DeVincenzo JP, et al. Multidrug-resistant tuberculosis meningitis: clinical problems and concentrations of second-line antituberculous medications. Ann Pharmacother 1999;33(11): 1184–1188.

611. Di Perri G, Bonora S.Which agents should we use for the treatment of multidrug-resistant *Mycobacterium tuberculosis*? J Antimicrob Chemother 2004;54(3): 593–602.

612. Hood WF, Compton RP, Monahan JB.D-Cycloserine: a ligand for the *N*-methyl-D-aspartate coupled glycine receptor has partial agonist characteristics. Neurosci Lett 1989;98(1): 91–95.

613. Thompson LT, Moskal JR, Disterhoft JF. Hippocampus-dependent learning facilitated by a monoclonal antibody or D-cycloserine. Nature 1992;359(6396): 638–641.

614. Wood JD, et al. Effect of L-cycloserine on brain GABA metabolism. Can J Physiol Pharmacol 1978;56(1): 62–68.

615. van Berckel BN, et al. Efficacy and tolerance of D-cycloserine in drug-free schizophrenic patients. Biol Psychiatry 1996;40(12): 1298–1300.

616. Otto MW, et al. Clinical perspectives on the combination of D-cycloserine and cognitive-behavioral therapy for the treatment of anxiety disorders. CNS Spectr 2007;12(1): 51–56, 59–61.

617. Falk WE, et al. A case series of D-cycloserine added to donepezil in the treatment of Alzheimer's disease. J Neuropsychiatry Clin Neurosci 2002;14(4): 466–467.

618. Esteves Pinto E.Suicide of two patients during the postoperative course after pulmonary resection: possible effect of cycloserine. Scand J Resp Dis Suppl 1970;71:256–258.

619. Kwon HM, et al. Cycloserine-induced encephalopathy: evidence on brain MRI. Eur J Neurol 2008;15(7): e60–e61.

620. Akula SK, et al. Cycloserine-induced Stevens-Johnson syndrome in an AIDS patient with multidrug-resistant tuberculosis. Int J Tuberc Lung Dis 1997;1(2): 187–190.

621. Gardner TS, Wenis E, Lee J.The synthesis of compounds for the chemotherapy of tuberculosis. IV. The amide function. J Org Chem 1954;17:753–757.

622. Meltzer RI, Lewis AD, King JA.Antitubercular substances. IV. Thioamides. J Am Chem Soc 1955;77:4062–4066.

623. Rist N, Grumbach F, Libermann D.Experiments on the antituberculous activity of alpha-ethylthioisonicotinamide. Am Rev Tuberc 1959;79(1): 1–5.

624. Grumbach F, et al. Experimental antituberculous activity of certain isonicotinic thioamides substituted on the nucleus. Compt Rend Hebd Seances Acad Sci 1956;242(17): 2187– 2189.

625. DeBarber AE, et al. Ethionamide activation and sensitivity in multidrug-resistant *Mycobacterium tuberculosis*. Proc Natl Acad Sci USA 2000;97(17): 9677–9682.

626. Wang F, et al. Mechanism of thioamide drug action against tuberculosis and leprosy. J Exp Med 2007;204(1): 73–78.

627. Morlock GP, et al. ethA, inhA, and katG loci of ethionamide-resistant clinical *Mycobacterium tuberculosis* isolates. Antimicrob Agents Chemother 2003;47(12): 3799–3805.

628. Engohang-Ndong J, et al. EthR, a repressor of the TetR/CamR family implicated in ethionamide resistance in mycobacteria, octamerizes cooperatively on its operator. Mol Microbiol 2004;51(1): 175–188.

629. Baulard AR, et al. Activation of the pro-drug ethionamide is regulated in mycobacteria. J Biol Chem 2000;275(36): 28326–28331.

630. Willand N, et al. Synthetic EthR inhibitors boost antituberculous activity of ethionamide. Nat Med 2009;15(5): 537–544.

631. Jenner PJ, et al. A comparison of the blood levels and urinary excretion of ethionamide and prothionamide in man. J Antimicrob Chemother 1984;13(3): 267–277.

632. Kucers A. The use of antibiotics. Kucers A, et al., editors. A Clinical Review of Antibacterial, Antifungal, and Antiviral Drugs. 5th ed. Oxford, UK: Butterworth-Heinemann; 1997.

633. Auclair B, et al. Pharmacokinetics of ethionamide administered under fasting conditions or with orange juice, food, or antacids. Antimicrob Agents Chemother 2001;45(3): 810–814.

634. Zhu M, et al. Population pharmacokinetics of ethionamide in patients with tuberculosis. Tuberculosis (Edinb) 2002;82(2–3): 91–96.

635. Verbist L, et al. Tolerance to ethionamide and PAS in original treatment of tuberculosis patients. Scand J Resp Dis 1967;47:225–235.

636. Fox W, et al. A study of acute intolerance to ethionamide, including a comparison with prothionamide, and of the influence of a vitamin B-complex additive in prophylaxis. Tubercle 1969;50(2): 125–143.

637. Behnisch R, Mietzsch F, Schmidt H.Chemical studies on thiosemicarbazones with particular reference to antituberculous activity. Am Rev Tuberc 1950;61(1): 1–7.

638. Nunn P, et al. Cutaneous hypersensitivity reactions due to thiacetazone in HIV-1 seropositive patients treated for tuberculosis. Lancet 1991;337(8742): 627–630.

639. Bermudez LE, et al. Thiosemicarbazole (thiacetazone-like) compound with activity against *Mycobacterium avium* in mice. Antimicrob Agents Chemother 2003;47(8): 2685–2687.

640. Heifets LB, Lindholm-Levy PJ, Flory M.Thiacetazone: *in vitro* activity against *Mycobacterium avium* and *M. tuberculosis*. Tubercle 1990;71(4): 287–291.

641. Qian L, Ortiz de Montellano PR.Oxidative activation of thiacetazone by the *Mycobacterium tuberculosis* flavin monooxygenase EtaA and human FMO1 and FMO3. Chem Res Toxicol 2006;19(3): 443–449.

642. Alahari A, et al. Mycolic acid methyltransferase, MmaA4, is necessary for thiacetazone susceptibility in *Mycobacterium tuberculosis*. Mol Microbiol 2009;71(5): 1263–1277.

643. Peloquin CA, et al. Pharmacokinetic evaluation of thiacetazone. Pharmacotherapy 1996;16(5): 735–741.

644. Francois AA, et al. Human flavin-containing monooxygenase 2.1 catalyzes oxygenation of the antitubercular drugs thiacetazone and ethionamide. Drug Metab Dispos 2009;37(1): 178–186.

645. Pozniak AL, et al. The influence of HIV status on single and multiple drug reactions to antituberculous therapy in Africa. AIDS 1992;6(8): 809–814.

646. Lawn SD, Frimpong EH, Acheampong JW. Life-threatening cutaneous reactions to thiacetazone-containing antituberculosis treatment in Kumasi, Ghana. West Afr J Med 1999;18(4): 249–253.

647. Ziganshina, LE and SB Squire.Fluoroquinolones for treating tuberculosis. Cochrane Database Syst Rev, 2008; (1): p. CD004795.

648. Bonora S, et al. Moxifloxacin for the treatment of HIV-associated tuberculosis in patients with contraindications or intolerance to rifamycins. J Infect 2008;57(1): 78–81.

649. Conde MB, et al. Moxifloxacin versus ethambutol in the initial treatment of tuberculosis: a double-blind, randomised, controlled phase II trial. Lancet 2009;373 (9670): 1183–1189.

650. Yew WW, et al. Outcomes of patients with multidrug-resistant pulmonary tuberculosis treated with ofloxacin/levofloxacin-containing regimens. Chest 2000;117(3): 744–751.

651. Marcel N, Nahta A, Balganesh M.Evaluation of killing kinetics of anti-tuberculosis drugs on *Mycobacterium tuberculosis* using a bacter-

iophage-based assay. Chemotherapy 2008;54 (5): 404–411.

652. Matrat S, et al. Are all the DNA gyrase mutations found in *Mycobacterium leprae* clinical strains involved in resistance to fluoroquinolones? Antimicrob. Agents Chemother 2008;52 (2): 745–747.

653. Long R, et al. Empirical treatment of community-acquired pneumonia and the development of fluoroquinolone-resistant tuberculosis. Clin Infect Dis 2009;48(10): 1354–1360.

654. Agrawal D, et al. Increasing incidence of fluoroquinolone-resistant *Mycobacterium tuberculosis* in Mumbai. India Int J Tuberc Lung Dis 2009;13(1): 79–83.

655. Wang JY, et al. Fluoroquinolone resistance in *Mycobacterium tuberculosis* isolates: associated genetic mutations and relationship to antimicrobial exposure. J Antimicrob Chemother 2007;59(5): 860–865.

656. Aubry A, et al. First functional characterization of a singly expressed bacterial type II topoisomerase: the enzyme from Mycobacterium tuberculosis. Biochem Biophys Res Commun 2006;348(1): 158–165.

657. Montero C, et al. Intrinsic resistance of *Mycobacterium smegmatis* to fluoroquinolones may be influenced by new pentapeptide protein MfpA. Antimicrob Agents Chemother 2001; 45(12): 3387–3392.

658. Hegde SS, et al. A fluoroquinolone resistance protein from *Mycobacterium tuberculosis* that mimics DNA. Science 2005;308(5727): 1480–1483.

659. Sengupta S, Ghosh S, Nagaraja V.Moonlighting function of glutamate racemase from *Mycobacterium tuberculosis*: racemization and DNA gyrase inhibition are two independent activities of the enzyme. Microbiology 2008; 154(Pt 9): 2796–2803.

660. Peloquin CA, et al. Population pharmacokinetics of levofloxacin, gatifloxacin, and moxifloxacin in adults with pulmonary tuberculosis. Antimicrob Agents Chemother 2008;52(3): 852–857.

661. Breilh D, et al. Diffusion of oral and intravenous 400 mg once-daily moxifloxacin into lung tissue at pharmacokinetic steady-state. J Chemother 2003;15(6): 558–562.

662. Soman A, et al. Concentrations of moxifloxacin in serum and pulmonary compartments following a single 400 mg oral dose in patients undergoing fibre-optic bronchoscopy. J Antimicrob Chemother 1999;44(6): 835–838.

663. Andrews JM, et al. Concentrations of levofloxacin (HR 355) in the respiratory tract following

a single oral dose in patients undergoing fibre-optic bronchoscopy. J Antimicrob Chemother 1997;40(4): 573–577.

664. Tachibana M, et al. Acyl glucuronidation of fluoroquinolone antibiotics by the UDP-glucuronosyltransferase 1A subfamily in human liver microsomes. Drug Metab Dispos 2005;33 (6): 803–811.

665. Nijland HM, et al. Rifampicin reduces plasma concentrations of moxifloxacin in patients with tuberculosis. Clin Infect Dis 2007;45(8): 1001–1007.

666. Van Bambeke F, Tulkens PM.Safety profile of the respiratory fluoroquinolone moxifloxacin: comparison with other fluoroquinolones and other antibacterial classes. Drug Saf 2009;32 (5): 359–378.

667. von Keutz E, Schluter G.Preclinical safety evaluation of moxifloxacin, a novel fluoroquinolone. J Antimicrob Chemother 1999;43 (Suppl B): 91–100.

668. Bloomfield DM, et al. The effect of moxifloxacin on QTc and implications for the design of thorough QT studies. Clin Pharmacol Ther 2008;84 (4): 475–480.

669. Nagarajan K, et al. Nitroimidazoles XXI. 2,3-Dihydro-6-nitroimidazo[2,1-b]oxazoles with antitubercular activity. Eur J Med Chem 1989;24:631–633.

670. Ashtekar DR, et al. *In vitro* and *in vivo* activities of the nitroimidazole CGI 17341 against *Mycobacterium tuberculosis*. Antimicrob Agents Chemother 1993;37(2): 183–186.

671. Walsh JS, et al. Structural alterations that differentially affect the mutagenic and antitrichomonal activities of 5-nitroimidazoles. J Med Chem 1987;30(1): 150–156.

672. Stover CK, et al. A small-molecule nitroimidazopyran drug candidate for the treatment of tuberculosis. Nature 2000;405(6789): 962–966.

673. Sasaki H, et al. Synthesis and antituberculosis activity of a novel series of optically active 6-nitro-2,3-dihydroimidazo[2,1-b]oxazoles. J Med Chem 2006;49(26): 7854–7860.

674. Matsumoto M, et al. OPC-67683, a nitro-dihydro-imidazooxazole derivative with promising action against tuberculosis *in vitro* and in mice. PLoS Med 2006;3(11): e466.

675. Baker WR, Shaopei C, Keeler EL Nitro-[2,1-*b*] imidazopyran compounds and antibacterial uses thereof. US patent 6,087,358. 2000 July 11.

676. Kim P, et al. Structure–activity relationships of antitubercular nitroimidazoles. 1. Structural features associated with aerobic and anaerobic activities of 4- and 5-nitroimidazoles. J Med Chem 2009;52:1317–1328.

677. Kim P, et al. Structure–activity relationships of antitubercular nitroimidazoles. 2. Determinants of aerobic activity and quantitative structure–activity relationships. J Med Chem 2009;52:1329–1344.

678. Li X, et al. Synthesis and antitubercular activity of 7-(R)- and 7-(S)-methyl-2-nitro-6-(S)-(4-(trifluoromethoxy)benzyloxy)-6,7-dihydro-5H-imidazo[2,1-b][1,3]oxazines, analogues of PA-824. Bioorg Med Chem Lett 2008;18(7): 2256–2262.

679. Lenaerts AJ, et al. Preclinical testing of the nitroimidazopyran PA-824 for activity against Mycobacterium tuberculosis in a series of in vitro and in vivo models. Antimicrob Agents Chemother 2005;49(6): 2294–2301.

680. Nuermberger E, et al. Powerful bactericidal and sterilizing activity of a regimen containing PA-824, moxifloxacin, and pyrazinamide in a murine model of tuberculosis. Antimicrob Agents Chemother 2008;52(4): 1522–1524.

681. Tasneen R, et al. Enhanced bactericidal activity of rifampin and/or pyrazinamide when combined with PA-824 in a murine model of tuberculosis. Antimicrob Agents Chemother 2008;52(10): 3664–3668.

682. Manjunatha UH, et al. Identification of a nitroimidazo-oxazine-specific protein involved in PA-824 resistance in Mycobacterium tuberculosis. Proc Natl Acad Sci USA 2006;103(2): 431–436.

683. Anderson RF, et al. Intermediates in the reduction of the antituberculosis drug PA-824, (6S)-2-nitro-6-{[4-(trifluoromethoxy)benzyl]oxy}-6,7-dihydro-5H-imidazo[2,1-b][1,3]oxazine, in aqueous solution. Org Biomol Chem 2008;6(11): 1973–1980.

684. Manjunatha UH, et al. Mycobacterium leprae is naturally resistant to PA-824. Antimicrob Agents Chemother 2006;50(10): 3350–3354.

685. Pa-824 Tuberculosis (Edinb) 2008;88(2): 134–136.

686. Sung JC, et al. Dry powder nitroimidazopyran antibiotic PA-824 aerosol for inhalation. Antimicrob Agents Chemother 2009;53(4): 1338–1343.

687. Spigelman MK.New tuberculosis therapeutics: a growing pipeline. J Infect Dis 2007; 196(Suppl 1): S28–34.

688. Opc-67683 Tuberculosis (Edinb) 2008;88(2): 132–133.

689. Protopopova M, et al. Identification of a new antitubercular drug candidate, SQ109, from a combinatorial library of 1,2-ethylenediamines. J Antimicrob Chemother 2005;56(5): 968–974.

690. Jia L, et al. Pharmacodynamics and pharmacokinetics of SQ109, a new diamine-based antitubercular drug. Br J Pharmacol 2005;144(1): 80–87.

691. Sq109 Tuberculosis (Edinb) 2008;88(2): 159–161.

692. Chen P, et al. Synergistic interactions of SQ109, a new ethylene diamine, with frontline antitubercular drugs in vitro. J Antimicrob Chemother 2006;58(2): 332–337.

693. Jia L, et al. Pharmacoproteomic effects of isoniazid, ethambutol, and N-geranyl-N'-(2-adamantyl)ethane-1,2-diamine (SQ109) on Mycobacterium tuberculosis H37Rv. J Pharmacol Exp Ther 2005;315(2): 905–911.

694. Jia L, et al. Interspecies pharmacokinetics and in vitro metabolism of SQ109. Br J Pharmacol 2006;147(5): 476–485.

695. Gaurrand S, et al. Conformational analysis of r207910, a new drug candidate for the treatment of tuberculosis, by a combined NMR and molecular modeling approach. Chem Biol Drug Des 2006;68(2): 77–84.

696. de Jonge MR, et al. A computational model of the inhibition of Mycobacterium tuberculosis ATPase by a new drug candidate R207910. Proteins 2007;67(4): 971–980.

697. Upadhayaya RS, et al. Design, synthesis, biological evaluation and molecular modelling studies of novel quinoline derivatives against Mycobacterium tuberculosis. Bioorg Med Chem Lett 2009;17(7): 2830–2841.

698. Ibrahim M, et al. Synergistic activity of R207910 combined with pyrazinamide against murine tuberculosis. Antimicrob Agents Chemother 2007;51(3): 1011–1015.

699. Diacon AH, et al. The diarylquinoline TMC207 for multidrug-resistant tuberculosis. N Engl J Med 2009;360(23): 2397–2405.

700. Petrella S, et al. Genetic basis for natural and acquired resistance to the diarylquinoline R207910 in mycobacteria. Antimicrob Agents Chemother 2006;50(8): 2853–2856.

701. Williams KN, et al. Promising antituberculosis activity of the oxazolidinone PNU-100480 relative to that of linezolid in a murine model. Antimicrob Agents Chemother 2009;53(4): 1314–1319.

INDEX